Course	**Descriptive & Inferential Statistics**
Course Number	**BUS 203-204**
	CLARK COLLEGE

http://create.mheducation.com

ISBN-10: 1308201265   ISBN-13: 9781308201269

Contents

Credits

What Is Statistics?

1

BARNES & NOBLE recently began selling an electronic book reader called the Nook Color. With this device, you can download from a selection of over two million e-books, newspapers, and magazines. It displays downloaded materials in full color. Assume you know the number of Nook Color units sold each day for the last month at the Barnes & Noble store at the Market Commons Mall in Riverside, California. Describe a condition in which this information could be considered a sample. Illustrate a second situation in which the same data would be regarded as a population. (See Exercise 11 and **LO1-3**.)

LEARNING OBJECTIVES

When you have completed this chapter, you will be able to:

LO1-1 Explain why knowledge of statistics is important.

LO1-2 Define statistics and provide an example of how statistics is applied.

LO1-3 Differentiate between descriptive and inferential statistics.

LO1-4 Classify variables as qualitative or quantitative, and discrete or continuous.

LO1-5 Distinguish between nominal, ordinal, interval, and ratio levels of measurement.

LO1-6 List the values associated with the practice of statistics.

INTRODUCTION

Suppose you work for a large company and your supervisor asks you to decide if a new version of a smartphone should be produced and sold. You start by thinking about the product's innovations and new features. Then, you stop and realize the weight of the decision. The product will need to make a profit so the pricing and the costs of production and distribution are all very important. The decision to introduce the product is based on many alternatives. So how will you know? Where do you start?

Without a long experience in the industry, beginning to develop an intelligence that will make you an expert is essential. You select three other people to work with and meet with them. The conversation focuses on what you need to know and what information and data you need. In your meeting, many questions are asked. How many competitors are already in the market? How are smartphones priced? What design features do competitors' products have? What features does the market require? What do customers want in a smartphone? What do customers like about the existing products? The answers will be based on business intelligence consisting of data and information collected through customer surveys, engineering analysis, and market research. In the end, your presentation to support your decision regarding the introduction of a new smartphone is based on the statistics that you use to summarize and organize your data, the statistics that you use to compare the new product to existing products, and the statistics to estimate future sales, costs, and revenues. The statistics will be the focus of the conversation that you will have with your supervisor about this very important decision.

As a decision maker, you will need to acquire and analyze data to support your decisions. The purpose of this text is to develop your knowledge of basic statistical techniques and methods and how to apply them to develop the business and personal intelligence that will help you make decisions.

WHY STUDY STATISTICS?

LO1-1

Explain why knowledge of statistics is important.

If you look through your university catalogue, you will find that statistics is required for many college programs. As you investigate a future career in accounting, economics, human resources, finance, or other business area, you will also discover that statistics is required as part of these college programs. So why is an education in statistics a requirement in so many disciplines?

A major driver of the requirement for statistics knowledge is the technologies available for capturing data. Examples include the technology that Google uses to track how Internet users access websites. As people use Google to search the Internet, Google records every search and then uses these data to sort and prioritize the results for future Internet searches. One recent estimate indicates that Google processes 20,000 terabytes of information per day. Big-box retailers like Target, Walmart, Kroger, and others scan every purchase and use the data to manage the distribution of products, to make decisions about marketing and sales, and to track daily and even hourly sales. Police departments collect and use data to provide city residents with maps that communicate information about crimes committed and their location. Every organization is collecting and using data to develop knowledge and intelligence that will help people make informed decisions, and to track the implementation of their decisions. The graphic to the left shows the amount of data generated every minute (www.domo.com). A good working knowledge of statistics is useful for summarizing and organizing data to provide information that is useful and supportive of decision making. Statistics is used to make valid comparisons and to predict the outcomes of decisions.

In summary, there are at least three reasons for studying statistics: (1) data are collected everywhere and require statistical knowledge to make the information useful, (2) statistical techniques are used to make professional and personal decisions, and (3) no matter what your career, you will need a knowledge of statistics to understand the world and to be conversant in your career. An understanding of statistics and statistical method will help you make more effective personal and professional decisions.

WHAT IS MEANT BY STATISTICS?

LO1-2
Define statistics and provide an example of how statistics is applied.

This question can be rephrased in two, subtly different ways: what are statistics and what is statistics? To answer the first question, a statistic is a number used to communicate a piece of information. Examples of **statistics** are:

- The inflation rate is 2%.
- Your grade point average is 3.5.
- The price of a new Tesla premium electric sedan is $85,400.

Each of these statistics is a numerical fact and communicates a very limited piece of information that is not very useful by itself. However, if we recognize that each of these statistics is part of a larger discussion, then the question "what **is** statistics" is applicable. Statistics is the set of knowledge and skills used to organize, summarize, and analyze data. The results of statistical analysis will start interesting conversations in the search for knowledge and intelligence that will help us make decisions. For example:

- The inflation rate for the calendar year was 2%. By applying statistics we could compare this year's inflation rate to the past observations of inflation. Is it higher, lower, or about the same? Is there a trend of increasing or decreasing inflation? Is there a relationship between interest rates and government bonds?
- Your grade point average (GPA) is 3.5. By collecting data and applying statistics, you can determine the required GPA to be admitted to the Master of Business Administration program at the University of Chicago, Harvard, or the University of Michigan. You can determine the likelihood that you would be admitted to a particular program. You may be interested in interviewing for a management position with Procter & Gamble. What GPA does Procter & Gamble require for college graduates with a bachelor's degree? Is there a range of acceptable GPAs?
- You are budgeting for a new car. You would like to own an electric car with a small carbon footprint. The price for the Tesla premium electric sedan is $85,400. By collecting additional data and applying statistics, you can analyze the alternatives. For example, another choice is a hybrid car that runs on both gas and electricity such as a Toyota Prius. It can be purchased for about $27,000. Another hybrid, the Chevrolet Volt, costs about $32,000. What are the differences in the cars' specifications? What additional information can be collected and summarized so that you can make a good purchase decision?

Another example of using statistics to provide information to evaluate decisions is the distribution and market share of Frito-Lay products. Data are collected on each of the Frito-Lay product lines. These data include the market share and the pounds of product sold. Statistics is used to present this information in a bar chart in Chart 1–1. It clearly shows Frito-Lay's dominance in the potato, corn, and tortilla chip markets. It also shows the absolute measure of pounds of each product line consumed in the United States.

These examples show that statistics is more than the presentation of numerical information. Statistics is about collecting and processing information to create a conversation, to stimulate additional questions, and to provide a basis for making decisions. Specifically, we define statistics as:

> **STATISTICS** The science of collecting, organizing, presenting, analyzing, and interpreting data to assist in making more effective decisions.

STATISTICS IN ACTION

We call your attention to a feature of our textbook—*Statistics in Action*. Read each one carefully to get an appreciation of the wide application of statistics in management, economics, nursing, law enforcement, sports, and other disciplines.

- In 2013, *Forbes* published a list of the richest Americans. William Gates, founder of Microsoft Corporation, is the richest. His net worth is estimated at $66.0 billion. (www.forbes.com)
- In 2013, the four largest privately owned American companies, ranked by revenue, were Cargill, Koch Industries, Mars, and Bechtel. (www.forbes.com)
- In the United States, a typical high school graduate earns $652 per week, a typical college graduate with a bachelor's degree earns $1,066 per week, and a typical college graduate with a master's degree earns $1,300 per week. (www.bls.gov/emp/ ep_chart_001.htm)

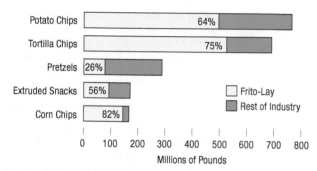

CHART 1–1 Frito-Lay Volume and Share of Major Snack Chip Categories in U.S. Supermarkets

In this book, you will learn the basic techniques and applications of statistics that you can use to support your decisions, both personal and professional. To start, we will differentiate between descriptive and inferential statistics.

LO1-3

Differentiate between descriptive and inferential statistics.

TYPES OF STATISTICS

When we use statistics to generate information for decision making from data, we use either descriptive statistics or inferential statistics. Their application depends on the questions asked and the type of data available.

Descriptive Statistics

Masses of unorganized data—such as the census of population, the weekly earnings of thousands of computer programmers, and the individual responses of 2,000 registered voters regarding their choice for president of the United States—are of little value as is. However, descriptive statistics can be used to organize data into a meaningful form. We define **descriptive statistics** as:

> **DESCRIPTIVE STATISTICS** Methods of organizing, summarizing, and presenting data in an informative way.

The following are examples that apply descriptive statistics to summarize a large amount of data and provide information that is easy to understand.

- There are a total of 46,837 miles of interstate highways in the United States. The interstate system represents only 1% of the nation's total roads but carries more than 20% of the traffic. The longest is I-90, which stretches from Boston to Seattle, a distance of 3,099 miles. The shortest is I-878 in New York City, which is 0.70 mile in length. Alaska does not have any interstate highways, Texas has the most interstate miles at 3,232, and New York has the most interstate routes with 28.
- The average person spent $103.00 on traditional Valentine's Day merchandise in 2013. This is an increase of $0.50 from 2012. As in previous years, men spent nearly twice the amount women spent on the holiday. The average man spent $135.35 to impress the people in his life while women only spent $72.28. Family pets also feel the love; the average person spent $3.27 on his or her furry friends, up from $2.17 last year.

Statistical methods and techniques to generate descriptive statistics are presented in Chapters 2 and 4. These include organizing and summarizing data with frequency distributions and presenting frequency distributions with charts and graphs.

WHAT IS STATISTICS?   5

In addition, statistical measures to summarize the characteristics of a distribution are discussed in Chapter 3.

Inferential Statistics

Sometimes we must make decisions based on a limited set of data. For example, we would like to know the operating characteristics, such as fuel efficiency measured by miles per gallon, of sport utility vehicles (SUVs) currently in use. If we spent a lot of time, money, and effort, all the owners of SUVs could be surveyed. In this case, our goal would be to survey the **population** of SUV owners.

> **POPULATION** The entire set of individuals or objects of interest or the measurements obtained from all individuals or objects of interest.

However, based on inferential statistics, we can survey a limited number of SUV owners and collect a **sample** from the population.

> **SAMPLE** A portion, or part, of the population of interest.

Samples are often used to obtain reliable estimates of population parameters. (Sampling is discussed in Chapter 8). In the process, we make trade-offs between the time, money, and effort to collect the data and the error of estimating a population parameter. The process of sampling SUVs is illustrated in the following graphic. In this example, we would like to know the mean or average SUV fuel efficiency. To estimate the mean of the population, six SUVs are sampled and the mean of their MPG is calculated.

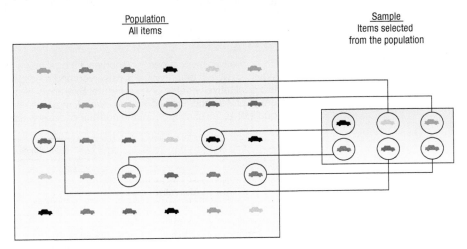

So, the sample of six SUVs represents evidence from the population that we use to reach an inference or conclusion about the average MPG for all SUVs. The process of sampling from a population with the objective of estimating properties of a population is called **inferential statistics.**

> **INFERENTIAL STATISTICS** The methods used to estimate a property of a population on the basis of a sample.

6 CHAPTER 1

Inferential statistics is widely applied to learn something about a population in business, agriculture, politics, and government, as shown in the following examples:

- Television networks constantly monitor the popularity of their programs by hiring Nielsen and other organizations to sample the preferences of TV viewers. For example, 10.5% of a sample of households with TVs watched *The Big Bang Theory* during the week of February 25, 2012 (www.nielsen.com). These program ratings are used to make decisions about advertising rates and whether to continue or cancel a program.
- In 2012, a sample of 40 U.S. Internal Revenue Service volunteer program sites was selected and the volunteer tax preparers were tested with three standard tax returns. The sample indicated that tax returns were completed with a 49% accuracy rate. In this example, the statistics are used to make decisions about how to improve the accuracy rate by correcting the most common errors and improving the training of volunteers. (www.treasury.gov/tigta/auditreports/2012reports/201240088fr.pdf)

A feature of our text is self-review problems. There are a number of them interspersed throughout each chapter. The first self-review follows. Each self-review tests your comprehension of preceding material. The answer and method of solution are given in Appendix E. You can find the answer to the following self-review in 1–1 in Appendix E. We recommend that you solve each one and then check your answer.

SELF-REVIEW

1–1

The answers are in Appendix E.

The Atlanta-based advertising firm Brandon and Associates asked a sample of 1,960 consumers to try a newly developed chicken dinner by Boston Market. Of the 1,960 sampled, 1,176 said they would purchase the dinner if it is marketed.
(a) What could Brandon and Associates report to Boston Market regarding acceptance of the chicken dinner in the population?
(b) Is this an example of descriptive statistics or inferential statistics? Explain.

LO1-4

Classify variables as qualitative or quantitative, and discrete or continuous.

TYPES OF VARIABLES

There are two basic types of variables: (1) qualitative and (2) quantitative (see Chart 1–2). When an object or individual is observed and recorded as a nonnumeric characteristic, it is a qualitative variable or an attribute. Examples of qualitative variables are gender, beverage preference, type of vehicle owned, state of birth, and eye color. When a variable is qualitative, we usually count the number of observations for each category and determine

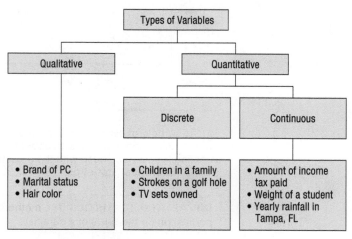

CHART 1–2 Summary of the Types of Variables

what percent are in each category. For example, if we observe the variable eye color, what percent of the population has blue eyes and what percent has brown eyes? If the variable is type of vehicle, what percent of the total number of cars sold last month were SUVs? Qualitative variables are often summarized in charts and bar graphs (Chapter 2).

When a variable can be reported numerically, the variable is called a quantitative variable. Examples of quantitative variables are the balance in your checking account, the ages of company presidents, the life of a car battery (such as 42 months), and the number of people employed by a company.

Quantitative variables are either discrete or continuous. Discrete variables can assume only certain values, and there are "gaps" between the values. Examples of discrete variables are the number of bedrooms in a house (1, 2, 3, 4, etc.), the number of cars arriving at Exit 25 on I-4 in Florida near Walt Disney World in an hour (326, 421, etc.), and the number of students in each section of a statistics course (25 in section A, 42 in section B, and 18 in section C). We count, for example, the number of cars arriving at Exit 25 on I-4, and we count the number of statistics students in each section. Notice that a home can have 3 or 4 bedrooms, but it cannot have 3.56 bedrooms. Thus, there is a "gap" between possible values. Typically, discrete variables are counted.

Observations of a continuous variable can assume any value within a specific range. Examples of continuous variables are the air pressure in a tire and the weight of a shipment of tomatoes. Other examples are the ounces of raisins in a box of raisin bran cereal and the duration of flights from Orlando to San Diego. Grade point average (GPA) is a continuous variable. We could report the GPA of a particular student as 3.2576952. The usual practice is to round to 3 places—3.258. Typically, continuous variables result from measuring.

LO1-5

Distinguish between nominal, ordinal, interval, and ratio levels of measurement.

LEVELS OF MEASUREMENT

Data can be classified according to levels of measurement. The level of measurement determines how data should be summarized and presented. It will also indicate the type of statistical analysis that can be performed. Here are two examples of the relationship between measurement and how we apply statistics. There are six colors of candies in a

bag of M&Ms. Suppose we assign brown a value of 1, yellow 2, blue 3, orange 4, green 5, and red 6. What kind of variable is the color of an M&M? It is a qualitative variable. Suppose someone summarizes M&M color by adding the assigned color values, divides the sum by the number of M&Ms, and reports that the mean color is 3.56. How do we interpret this statistic? You are correct in concluding that it has no meaning as a measure of M&M color. As a qualitative variable, we can only report the count and percentage of each color in a bag of M&Ms. As a second example, in a high school track meet there are eight competitors in the 400-meter run. We report the order of finish and that the mean finish is 4.5. What does the mean finish tell us? Nothing! In both of these instances, we have not used the appropriate statistics for the level of measurement.

There are four levels of measurement: nominal, ordinal, interval, and ratio. The lowest, or the most primitive, measurement is the nominal level. The highest is the ratio level of measurement.

Nominal-Level Data

For the **nominal level of measurement,** observations of a qualitative variable are measured and recorded as labels or names. The labels or names can only be classified and counted. There is no particular order to the labels.

> **NOMINAL LEVEL OF MEASUREMENT** Data recorded at the nominal level of measurement is represented as labels or names. They have no order. They can only be classified and counted.

8   CHAPTER 1

The classification of the six colors of M&M milk chocolate candies is an example of the nominal level of measurement. We simply classify the candies by color. There is no natural order. That is, we could report the brown candies first, the orange first, or any of the other colors first. Recording the variable gender is another example of the nominal level of measurement. Suppose we count the number of students entering a football game with a student ID and report how many are men and how many are women. We could report either the men or the women first. For the data measured at the nominal level, we are limited to counting the number in each category of the variable. Often, we convert these counts to percentages. For example, a study of the color of M&M candies reports the following results (www.sensationalcolor.com/color-trends/most-popular-colors-177/mam-colors.html):

Color	Percent in a bag
Blue	24%
Green	20
Orange	16
Yellow	14
Red	13
Brown	13

To process the data for a variable measured at the nominal level, we often numerically code the labels or names. For example, if we are interested in measuring the home state for students at East Carolina University, we would assign a student's home state of Alabama a code of 1, Alaska a code of 2, Arizona a 3, and so on. Using this procedure with an alphabetical listing of states, Wisconsin is coded 49 and Wyoming 50. Realize that the number assigned to each state is still a label or name. The reason we assign numerical codes is to facilitate counting the number of students from each state with statistical software. Note that assigning numbers to the states does not give us license to manipulate the codes as numerical information. Specifically, in this example, $1 + 2 = 3$ corresponds to Alabama + Alaska = Arizona. Clearly, the nominal level of measurement does not permit any mathematical operation that has any valid interpretation.

Ordinal-Level Data

The next higher level of measurement is the **ordinal level**. For this level of measurement a qualitative variable or attribute is either ranked or rated on a relative scale.

> **ORDINAL LEVEL OF MEASUREMENT** Data recorded at the ordinal level of measurement is based on a relative ranking or rating of items based on a defined attribute or qualitative variable. Variables based on this level of measurement are only ranked or counted.

Best Business Climate

1. Texas
2. Utah
3. Virginia
4. Florida
5. Louisiana
6. Indiana
7. South Carolina
8. Tennessee
9. Georgia
10. Nebraska

For example, many businesses make decisions about where to locate their facilities; in other words, where is the best place for their business? Business Facilities (www.businessfacilities.com) publishes a list of the top 10 states for the "best business climate." The 2012 rankings are shown to the left. They are based on the evaluation of 20 different factors, including the cost of labor, business tax climate, quality of life, transportation infrastructure, educated workforce, and economic growth potential to rank states based on the attribute "best business climate."

This is an example of an ordinal scale because the states are ranked in order of best to worst business climate. That is, we know the relative order of the states based on the attribute. For example, in 2012 Texas had the best business climate. Louisiana was fifth, and that was better than South Carolina but not as good as Virginia. Notice that we cannot say that Texas's business climate is five times better than Louisiana's business climate because the magnitude of the differences between the states is not known.

Another example of the ordinal level measure is based on a scale that measures an attribute. This type of scale is used when students rate instructors on a variety of attributes. One attribute may be: "Overall, how do you rate the quality of instruction in this class?" A student's response is recorded on a relative scale of inferior, poor, good, excellent, and superior. An important characteristic of using a relative measurement scale is that we cannot distinguish the magnitude of the differences between groups. We do not know if the difference between "Superior" and "Good" is the same as the difference between "Poor" and "Inferior."

Table 1–1 lists the frequencies of student ratings of instructional quality for Professor James Brunner in an Introduction to Finance course. The data are summarized based on the order of the scale used to rate the instructor. That is, they are summarized by the number of students who indicated a rating of superior (6), good (28), and so on. We can also convert the frequencies to percentages. About 37.8% of the students rated the instructor as good.

TABLE 1–1 Rating of a Finance Professor

Rating	Frequency
Superior	6
Good	28
Average	25
Poor	12
Inferior	3

Interval-Level Data

The **interval level of measurement** is the next highest level. It includes all the characteristics of the ordinal level, but, in addition, the difference or interval between values is meaningful.

> **INTERVAL LEVEL OF MEASUREMENT** For data recorded at the interval level of measurement, the interval or the distance between values is meaningful. The interval level of measurement is based on a scale with a known unit of measurement.

The Fahrenheit temperature scale is an example of the interval level of measurement. Suppose the high temperatures on three consecutive winter days in Boston are 28, 31, and 20 degrees Fahrenheit. These temperatures can be easily ranked, but we can also determine the interval or distance between temperatures. This is possible because 1 degree Fahrenheit represents a constant unit of measurement. That is, the distance between 10 and 15 degrees Fahrenheit is 5 degrees, and is the same as the 5-degree distance between 50 and 55 degrees Fahrenheit. It is also important to note that 0 is just a point on the scale. It does not represent the absence of the condition. The measurement of zero degrees Fahrenheit does not represent the absence of heat or cold. But by our own measurement scale, it is cold! A major limitation of a variable measured at the interval level is that we cannot make statements similar to 20 degrees Fahrenheit is twice as warm as 10 degrees Fahrenheit.

Another example of the interval scale of measurement is women's dress sizes. Listed below is information on several dimensions of a standard U.S. woman's dress.

Size	Bust (in)	Waist (in)	Hips (in)
8	32	24	35
10	34	26	37
12	36	28	39
14	38	30	41
16	40	32	43
18	42	34	45
20	44	36	47
22	46	38	49
24	48	40	51
26	50	42	53
28	52	44	55

Why is the "size" scale an interval measurement? Observe that as the size changes by two units (say from size 10 to size 12 or from size 24 to size 26), each of the measurements increases by 2 inches. To put it another way, the intervals are the same.

There is no natural zero point for dress size. A "size 0" dress does not have "zero" material. Instead, it would have a 24-inch bust, 16-inch waist, and 27-inch hips. Moreover, the ratios are not reasonable. If you divide a size 28 by a size 14, you do not get the same answer as dividing a size 20 by a size 10. Neither ratio is equal to two, as the "size" number would suggest. In short, if the distances between the numbers make sense, but the ratios do not, then you have an interval scale of measurement.

Ratio-Level Data

Almost all quantitative variables are recorded on the **ratio level of measurement.** The ratio level is the "highest" level of measurement. It has all the characteristics of the interval level, but, in addition, the 0 point and the ratio between two numbers are both meaningful.

> **RATIO LEVEL OF MEASUREMENT** Data recorded at the ratio level of measurement are based on a scale with a known unit of measurement and a meaningful interpretation of zero on the scale.

Examples of the ratio scale of measurement include wages, units of production, weight, changes in stock prices, distance between branch offices, and height. Money is also a good illustration. If you have zero dollars, then you have no money, and a wage of $50 per hour is two times the wage of $25 per hour. Weight is also measured at the ratio level of measurement. If a scale is correctly calibrated, then it will read 0 when nothing is on the scale. Further, something that weighs 1 pound is half as heavy as something that weighs 2 pounds.

Table 1–2 illustrates the ratio scale of measurement for the variable, annual income for four father-and-son combinations. Observe that the senior Lahey earns twice as much as his son. In the Rho family, the son makes twice as much as the father.

TABLE 1–2 Father–Son Income Combinations

Name	Father	Son
Lahey	$80,000	$ 40,000
Nale	90,000	30,000
Rho	60,000	120,000
Steele	75,000	130,000

WHAT IS STATISTICS?   11

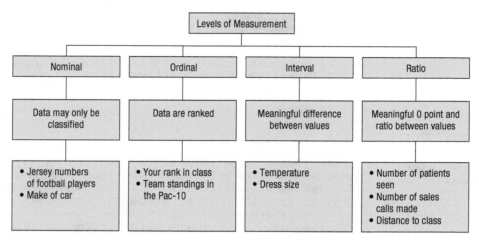

CHART 1–3 Summary and Examples of the Characteristics for Levels of Measurement

Chart 1–3 summarizes the major characteristics of the various levels of measurement. The level of measurement will determine the type of statistical methods that can be used to analyze a variable. Statistical methods to analyze variables measured on a nominal level are discussed in Chapter 15; methods for ordinal-level variables are discussed in Chapter 16. Statistical methods to analyze variables measured on an interval or ratio level are presented in Chapters 9 through 14.

SELF-REVIEW

1–2

What is the level of measurement reflected by the following data?
(a)   The age of each person in a sample of 50 adults who listen to one of the 1,230 talk radio stations in the United States is

35	29	41	34	44	46	42	42	37	47
30	36	41	39	44	39	43	43	44	40
47	37	41	27	33	33	39	38	43	22
44	39	35	35	41	42	37	42	38	43
35	37	38	43	40	48	42	31	51	34

(b)   In a survey of 200 luxury-car owners, 100 were from California, 50 from New York, 30 from Illinois, and 20 from Ohio.

EXERCISES

▼

The answers to the odd-numbered exercises are in Appendix D.

1.   What is the level of measurement for each of the following variables?
   a. Student IQ ratings.
   b. Distance students travel to class.
   c. The jersey numbers of a sorority soccer team.
   d. A student's state of birth.
   e. A student's academic class—that is, freshman, sophomore, junior, or senior.
   f. Number of hours students study per week.
2.   The *San Francisco Chronicle* is a large newspaper published daily. What is the level of measurement for each of the following variables?
   a. The number of papers sold each Sunday during 2014.
   b. The departments, such as editorial, advertising, sports, etc.
   c. The number of papers sold by county.
   d. The number of years with the paper for each employee.

12   CHAPTER 1

3. Look in the latest edition of *USA Today* or your local newspaper and find examples of each level of measurement. Write a brief memo summarizing your findings.
4. For each of the following, determine whether the group is a sample or a population.
   a. The participants in a study of a new cholesterol drug.
   b. The drivers who received a speeding ticket in Kansas City last month.
   c. Those on welfare in Cook County (Chicago), Illinois.
   d. The 30 stocks that make up the Dow Jones Industrial Average.

List the values associated with the practice of statistics.

ETHICS AND STATISTICS

Following events such as Wall Street money manager Bernie Madoff's Ponzi scheme, which swindled billions from investors, and financial misrepresentations by Enron and Tyco, business students need to understand that these events were based on the misrepresentation of business and financial information. In each case, people within each organization reported financial information to investors that indicated the companies were performing much better than the actual situation. When the true financial information was reported, the companies were worth much less than advertised. The result was many investors lost all or nearly all of the money that they had invested.

The article "Statistics and Ethics: Some Advice for Young Statisticians," in *The American Statistician* 57, no. 1 (2003), offers guidance. The authors advise us to practice statistics with integrity and honesty, and urge us to "do the right thing" when collecting, organizing, summarizing, analyzing, and interpreting numerical information. The real contribution of statistics to society is a moral one. Financial analysts need to provide information that truly reflects a company's performance so as not to mislead individual investors. Information regarding product defects that may be harmful to people must be analyzed and reported with integrity and honesty. The authors of *The American Statistician* article further indicate that when we practice statistics, we need to maintain "an independent and principled point-of-view" when analyzing and reporting findings and results.

As you progress through this text, we will highlight ethical issues in the collection, analysis, presentation, and interpretation of statistical information. We also hope that, as you learn about using statistics, you will become a more informed consumer of information. For example, you will question a report based on data that do not fairly represent the population, a report that does not include all relevant statistics, one that includes an incorrect choice of statistical measures, or a presentation that introduces bias in a deliberate attempt to mislead or misrepresent.

COMPUTER SOFTWARE APPLICATIONS

Using statistics to process and analyze data requires computer software. Throughout our text, we show the application of Microsoft Excel and, occasionally, Minitab. University and college computers usually have Microsoft Excel. Your computer may already be packaged with Microsoft Excel. If not, the Microsoft Office package with Excel is often sold at a reduced academic price through your university or college. In this text, we use Excel for the majority of the applications. We also use an Excel add-in called MegaStat. If your instructor requires this package, it is available at www .mhhe.com/megastat. This add-in gives Excel the capability to produce additional statistical reports. Occasionally, we use Minitab to illustrate an application. See www .minitab.com for further information. Minitab also offers discounted academic pricing. If you are using an Apple Mac computer with Excel, you should download the free, trial version of Stat Plus at www.analystsoft.com. It is a statistical software package that will integrate with Excel for Mac computers.

The following example shows the application of Excel to perform a statistical analysis. In Chapters 2, 3, and 4, we illustrate software methods for summarizing and describing data. An example used in these chapters refers to the Applewood Auto Group data set. These data and other data sets and files are available on the text's student website, www.mhhe.com/lind16e. The Applewood data set has several variables that were measured for 180 vehicles sold by the Applewood Auto Group. The following shows Excel's calculation of several statistics for the variable profit. The Excel output reveals, among other things, that there were 180 vehicles sold, the mean (average) profit per vehicle was $1,843.17, and the amount of profit ranged from $294 to $3,292. Throughout the text, the illustrations of Excel are supported by instructions so that you can learn how to apply Excel to do statistical analysis. The instructions are presented in Appendix C of this text.

	A	B	C	D	E	F	G	H
	Age	Profit	Location	Vehicle-Type	Previous		Profit	
1								
2	33	$1,889	Olean	SUV	1			
3	47	$1,461	Kane	Sedan	0		Mean	1843.17
4	44	$1,532	Tionesta	SUV	3		Standard Error	47.97
5	53	$1,220	Olean	Sedan	0		Median	1882.50
6	51	$1,674	Sheffield	Sedan	1		Mode	1915.00
7	41	$2,389	Kane	Truck	1		Standard Deviation	643.63
8	58	$2,058	Kane	SUV	1		Sample Variance	414256.61
9	35	$1,919	Tionesta	SUV	1		Kurtosis	-0.22
10	45	$1,266	Olean	Sedan	0		Skewness	-0.24
11	54	$2,991	Tionesta	Sedan	0		Range	2998
12	56	$2,695	Kane	Sedan	2		Minimum	294
13	41	$2,165	Tionesta	SUV	0		Maximum	3292
14	38	$1,766	Sheffield	SUV	0		Sum	331770
15	48	$1,952	Tionesta	Compact	1		Count	180

APPLEWOOD AUTO GROUP.xlsx

At the option of your instructor, and depending on the software system available, we urge you to apply a computer package to the exercises in the **Data Set Exercises** section in each chapter. It will relieve you of the tedious calculations and allow you to concentrate on the statistical analysis.

CHAPTER SUMMARY

I. Statistics is the science of collecting, organizing, presenting, analyzing, and interpreting data to assist in making more effective decisions.
II. There are two types of statistics.
  A. Descriptive statistics are procedures used to organize and summarize data.
  B. Inferential statistics involve taking a sample from a population and making estimates about a population based on the sample results.
    1. A population is an entire set of individuals or objects of interest or the measurements obtained from all individuals or objects of interest.
    2. A sample is a part of the population.
III. There are two types of variables.
  A. A qualitative variable is nonnumeric.
    1. Usually we are interested in the number or percent of the observations in each category.
    2. Qualitative data are usually summarized in graphs and bar charts.
  B. There are two types of quantitative variables and they are usually reported numerically.
    1. Discrete variables can assume only certain values, and there are usually gaps between values.
    2. A continuous variable can assume any value within a specified range.

IV. There are four levels of measurement.
  A. With the nominal level, the data are sorted into categories with no particular order to the categories.
  B. The ordinal level of measurement presumes that one classification is ranked higher than another.
  C. The interval level of measurement has the ranking characteristic of the ordinal level of measurement plus the characteristic that the distance between values is a constant size.
  D. The ratio level of measurement has all the characteristics of the interval level, plus there is a 0 point and the ratio of two values is meaningful.

C H A P T E R   E X E R C I S E S

5. Explain the difference between qualitative and quantitative variables. Give an example of qualitative and quantitative variables.
6. Explain the difference between a sample and a population.
7. Explain the difference between a discrete and a continuous variable. Give an example of each not included in the text.
8. For the following situations, would you collect information using a sample or a population? Why?
  a. Statistics 201 is a course taught at a university. Professor Rauch has taught nearly 1,500 students in the course over the past 5 years. You would like to know the average grade for the course.
  b. As part of a research project, you need to report the average profit as a percentage of revenue for the #1-ranked corporation in the Fortune 500 for each of the last 10 years.
  c. You are looking forward to graduation and your first job as a salesperson for one of five large pharmaceutical corporations. Planning for your interviews, you will need to know about each company's mission, profitability, products, and markets.
  d. You are shopping for a new MP3 music player such as the Apple iPod. The manufacturers advertise the number of music tracks that can be stored in the memory. Usually, the advertisers assume relatively short, popular songs to estimate the number of tracks that can be stored. You, however, like Broadway musical tunes and they are much longer. You would like to estimate how many Broadway tunes will fit on your MP3 player.
9. Exits along interstate highways were formerly numbered successively from the western or southern border of a state. However, the Department of Transportation has recently changed most of them to agree with the numbers on the mile markers along the highway.
  a. What level of measurement were data on the consecutive exit numbers?
  b. What level of measurement are data on the milepost numbers?
  c. Discuss the advantages of the newer system.
10. A poll solicits a large number of college undergraduates for information on the following variables: the name of their cell phone provider (AT&T, Verizon, and so on), the numbers of minutes used last month (200, 400, for example), and their satisfaction with the service (Terrible, Adequate, Excellent, and so forth). What is the level of measurement for each of these three variables?
11. Barnes & Noble recently began selling an electronic book reader called the Nook Color. With this device, you can download over two million e-books and newpapers and magazines. It displays downloaded materials in full color. Assume you know the number of Nook Color units sold each day for the last month at the Barnes & Noble store at the Market Commons Mall in Riverside, California. Describe a condition in which this information could be considered a sample. Illustrate a second situation in which the same data would be regarded as a population.
12. Utilize the concepts of sample and population to describe how a presidential election is unlike an "exit" poll of the electorate.
13. Place these variables in the following classification tables. For each table, summarize your observations and evaluate if the results are generally true. For example, salary is reported as a continuous quantitative variable. It is also a continuous ratio-scaled variable.
  a. Salary
  b. Gender
  c. Sales volume of MP3 players
  d. Soft drink preference
  e. Temperature
  f. SAT scores
  g. Student rank in class

WHAT IS STATISTICS?   15

h. Rating of a finance professor
i. Number of home computers

	Discrete Variable	**Continuous Variable**
Qualitative		
Quantitative		a. Salary

	Discrete	**Continuous**
Nominal		
Ordinal		
Interval		
Ratio		a. Salary

14. Using data from such publications as the *Statistical Abstract of the United States, The World Almanac, Forbes,* or your local newspaper, give examples of the nominal, ordinal, interval, and ratio levels of measurement.

15. The Struthers Wells Corporation employs more than 10,000 white-collar workers in its sales offices and manufacturing facilities in the United States, Europe, and Asia. A sample of 300 U.S. workers revealed 120 would accept a transfer to a location outside the United States. On the basis of these findings, write a brief memo to Ms. Wanda Carter, Vice President of Human Services, regarding all white-collar workers in the firm and their willingness to relocate.

16. AVX Stereo Equipment, Inc., recently began a "no-hassles" return policy. A sample of 500 customers who recently returned items showed 400 thought the policy was fair, 32 thought it took too long to complete the transaction, and the rest had no opinion. On the basis of this information, make an inference about customer reaction to the new policy.

17. *The Wall Street Journal's* website, www.wsj.com, reported the number of cars and light-duty trucks sold by the eight largest automakers in the first 2 months of 2013. Compare the 2013 data to the first 2 months of 2009 as reported below.

	Year-to-Date Sales	
Manufacturer	**Through February 2013**	**Through February 2009**
General Motors Corp.	419,013	252,701
Ford Motor Company	361,713	185,825
Toyota Motor Sales USA Inc.	324,102	226,870
Chrysler LLC	256,746	146,207
American Honda Motor Co. Inc.	201,613	142,606
Nissan North America Inc.	180,555	108,133
Hyundai Motor America	96,024	55,133
Mazda Motor of America Inc.	46,255	31,821

a. Compare the total sales for the eight automakers. Has there been an increase or a decrease in sales for 2013 compared to the same period in 2009?

b. The total number of cars and light-duty trucks sold in 2013 was 2.234 million while 1.346 million were sold in 2009. Compute the market share for each of the companies. Has there been a change in the market share for any of the companies?

c. Compute the percentage change in sales for each of the eight companies. Which companies had a significant change in sales?

18. The following chart depicts the average amounts spent by consumers on holiday gifts.

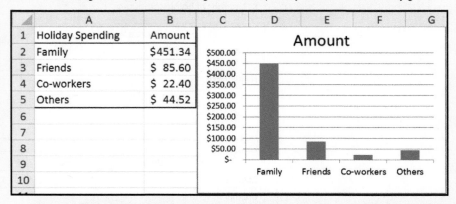

Write a brief report summarizing the amounts spent during the holidays. Be sure to include the total amount spent and the percent spent by each group.

19. The following chart depicts the earnings in billions of dollars for ExxonMobil for the period 2003 until 2012. Write a brief report discussing the earnings at ExxonMobil during the period. Was one year higher than the others? Did the earnings increase, decrease, or stay the same over the period?

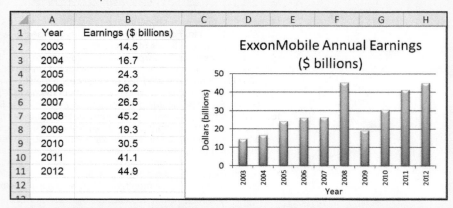

DATA SET EXERCISES

(The data for these exercises are available at the text website www.mhhe.com/lind16e.)

20. Refer to the Real Estate data, which report information on homes sold in the Goodyear, Arizona, area last year. Consider the following variables: selling price, number of bedrooms, township, and distance from the center of the city.
  a. Which of the variables are qualitative and which are quantitative?
  b. Determine the level of measurement for each of the variables.

21. Refer to the Baseball 2012 data, which report information on the 30 Major League Baseball teams for the 2012 season. Consider the following variables: number of wins, payroll, season attendance, whether the team is in the American or National League, and the number of home runs hit.
  a. Which of these variables are quantitative and which are qualitative?
  b. Determine the level of measurement for each of the variables.

22. Refer to the Buena School District bus data, which report information on the school district's bus fleet.
  a. Which of the variables are qualitative and which are quantitative?
  b. Determine the level of measurement for each variable.

Describing Data:

FREQUENCY TABLES, FREQUENCY DISTRIBUTIONS, AND GRAPHIC PRESENTATION

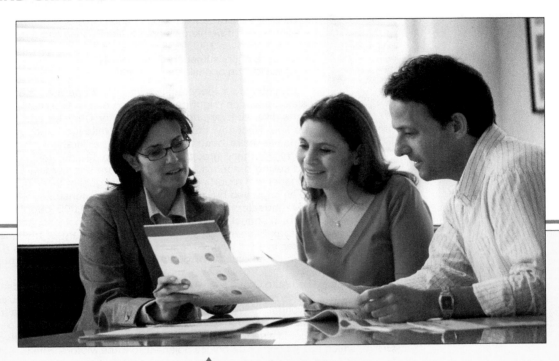

MERRILL LYNCH recently completed a study of online investment portfolios for a sample of clients. For the 70 participants in the study, organize these data into a frequency distribution. (See Exercise 43 and LO2-3.)

LEARNING OBJECTIVES

When you have completed this chapter, you will be able to:

LO2-1 Summarize qualitative variables with frequency and relative frequency tables.

LO2-2 Display a frequency table using a bar or pie chart.

LO2-3 Summarize quantitative variables with frequency and relative frequency distributions.

LO2-4 Display a frequency distribution using a histogram or frequency polygon.

18   CHAPTER 2

INTRODUCTION

The highly competitive automobile retailing industry in the United States has changed dramatically in recent years. These changes spurred events such as the

- bankruptcies of General Motors and Chrysler in 2009.
- elimination of well-known brands like Pontiac and Saturn.
- closing of over 1,500 local dealerships.
- collapse of consumer credit availability.
- consolidation of dealership groups.

Traditionally, a local family owned and operated the community dealership, which might have included one or two manufacturers or brands, like Pontiac and GMC Trucks or Chrysler and the popular Jeep line. Recently, however, skillfully managed and well-financed companies have been acquiring local dealerships throughout the country. As these groups acquire the local dealerships, they often bring standardized selling practices, common software and hardware technology platforms, and management reporting techniques. The goal of these new organizations is to provide an improved buying experience for the consumer, while increasing profitability. Megadealerships often employ over 10,000 people, generate several billion dollars in annual sales, own more than 50 franchises, and are traded on the New York Stock Exchange or NASDAQ. Today, the largest megadealership is AutoNation (ticker symbol AN). Others include Penske Auto Group (PAG and second largest), Asbury Automotive Group (ABG), and Hendrick Auto Group (which is privately held).

The Applewood Auto Group is an ownership group that includes four dealerships. The group sells a wide range of vehicles, including the inexpensive but popular Korean brands Kia and Hyundai, BMW and Volvo sedans and luxury SUVs, and a full line of Ford and Chevrolet cars and trucks.

Ms. Kathryn Ball is a member of the senior management team at Applewood Auto Group, which has its corporate offices adjacent to Kane Motors. She is responsible for tracking and analyzing vehicle sales and the profitability of those vehicles. Kathryn would like to summarize the profit earned on the vehicles sold with tables, charts, and graphs that she would review monthly. She wants to know the profit per vehicle sold, as well as the lowest and highest amount of profit. She is also interested in describing the demographics of the buyers. What are their ages? How many vehicles have they previously purchased from one of the Applewood dealerships? What type of vehicle did they purchase?

The Applewood Auto Group operates four dealerships:

- *Tionesta Ford Lincoln Mercury* sells the Ford, Lincoln, and Mercury cars and trucks.
- *Olean Automotive Inc.* has the Nissan franchise as well as the General Motors brands of Chevrolet, Cadillac, and GMC Trucks.
- *Sheffield Motors Inc.* sells Buick, GMC trucks, Hyundai, and Kia.
- *Kane Motors* offers the Chrysler, Dodge, and Jeep line as well as BMW and Volvo.

Every month, Ms. Ball collects data from each of the four dealerships and enters them into an Excel spreadsheet. Last month the Applewood Auto Group sold 180 vehicles at the four dealerships. A copy of the first few observations appears to the left. The variables collected include:

- *Age*—the age of the buyer at the time of the purchase.

APPLEWOOD AUTO GROUP

	A	B	C	D	E
	Age	Profit	Location	Vehicle-Type	Previous
1	Age	Profit	Location	Vehicle-Type	Previous
2	21	$1,387	Tionesta	Sedan	0
3	23	$1,754	Sheffield	SUV	1
4	24	$1,817	Sheffield	Hybrid	1
5	25	$1,040	Sheffield	Compact	0
6	26	$1,273	Kane	Sedan	1
7	27	$1,529	Sheffield	Sedan	1
8	27	$3,082	Kane	Truck	0
9	28	$1,951	Kane	SUV	1
10	28	$2,692	Tionesta	Compact	0
11	29	$1,206	Sheffield	Sedan	0
12	29	$1,342	Kane	Sedan	2
13	30	$443	Kane	Sedan	3
14	30	$754	Olean	Sedan	2
15	30	$1,621	Sheffield	Truck	1

- ***Profit***—the amount earned by the dealership on the sale of each vehicle.
- ***Location***—the dealership where the vehicle was purchased.
- ***Vehicle type***—SUV, sedan, compact, hybrid, or truck.
- ***Previous***—the number of vehicles previously purchased at any of the four Applewood dealerships by the consumer.

The entire data set is available at the McGraw-Hill website (**www.mhhe.com/lind16e**) and in Appendix A.4 at the end of the text.

LO2-1

Summarize qualitative variables with frequency and relative frequency tables.

CONSTRUCTING FREQUENCY TABLES

Recall from Chapter 1 that techniques used to describe a set of data are called descriptive statistics. Descriptive statistics organize data to show the general pattern of the data, to identify where values tend to concentrate, and to expose extreme or unusual data values. The first technique we discuss is a **frequency table.**

> **FREQUENCY TABLE** A grouping of qualitative data into mutually exclusive and collectively exhaustive classes showing the number of observations in each class.

In Chapter 1, we distinguished between qualitative and quantitative variables. To review, a qualitative variable is nonnumeric, that is, it can only be classified into distinct categories. Examples of qualitative data include political affiliation (Republican, Democrat, Independent), state of birth (Alabama, . . . , Wyoming), and method of payment for a purchase at Barnes & Noble (cash, check, debit, or credit). On the other hand, quantitative variables are numerical in nature. Examples of quantitative data relating to college students include the price of their textbooks, their age, and the number of credit hours they are registered for this semester.

In the Applewood Auto Group data set, there are five variables for each vehicle sale: age of the buyer, amount of profit, dealer that made the sale, type of vehicle sold, and number of previous purchases by the buyer. The dealer and the type of vehicle are *qualitative* variables. The amount of profit, the age of the buyer, and the number of previous purchases are *quantitative* variables.

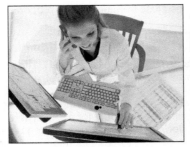

Suppose Ms. Ball wanted to summarize last month's sales by location. To summarize this qualitative data, we classify the vehicles sold last month according to their location: Tionesta, Olean, Sheffield, or Kane. We use location to develop a frequency table with four mutually exclusive (distinctive) classes. This means that a particular vehicle cannot belong to more than one class. Each vehicle is uniquely classified into one of the four mutually exclusive locations. In addition, the frequency table must be collectively exhaustive. This means that every vehicle is accounted for in the table. This frequency table is shown in Table 2–1. The number of observations, representing the sales at each location, is called the class frequency. So the class frequency for vehicles sold at the Kane location is 52.

TABLE 2–1 Frequency Table for Vehicles Sold Last Month at Applewood Auto Group by Location

Location	Number of Cars
Kane	52
Olean	40
Sheffield	45
Tionesta	43
Total	180

Relative Class Frequencies

You can convert class frequencies to relative class frequencies to show the fraction of the total number of observations in each class. A relative frequency captures the relationship between a class total and the total number of observations. In the vehicle sales example, we may want to know the percentage of total cars sold at each of the four locations. To convert a frequency distribution to a relative frequency distribution, each of the class frequencies is divided by the total number of observations. For example, the fraction of vehicles sold last month at the Kane location is 0.289, found by 52 divided by 180. The relative frequency for each location is shown in Table 2–2.

TABLE 2–2 Relative Frequency Table of Vehicles Sold by Type Last Month at Applewood Auto Group

Location	Number of Cars	Relative Frequency	Found by
Kane	52	.289	52/180
Olean	40	.222	40/180
Sheffield	45	.250	45/180
Tionesta	43	.239	43/180
Total	180	1.000	

LO2-2
Display a frequency table using a bar or pie chart.

GRAPHIC PRESENTATION OF QUALITATIVE DATA

The most common graphic form to present a qualitative variable is a **bar chart.** In most cases, the horizontal axis shows the variable of interest. The vertical axis shows the frequency or fraction of each of the possible outcomes. A distinguishing feature of a bar chart is there is distance or a gap between the bars. That is, because the variable of interest is qualitative, the bars are not adjacent to each other. Thus, a bar chart graphically describes a frequency table using a series of uniformly wide rectangles, where the height of each rectangle is the class frequency.

> **BAR CHART** A graph that shows qualitative classes on the horizontal axis and the class frequencies on the vertical axis. The class frequencies are proportional to the heights of the bars.

We use the Applewood Auto Group data as an example (Chart 2–1). The variable of interest is the location where the vehicle was sold and the number of vehicles sold at each location is the class frequency. We label the horizontal axis with the four locations and scale the vertical axis with the number sold. The height of the bars, or rectangles, corresponds to the number of vehicles at each location. There were 52 vehicles sold last month at the Kane location, so the height of the Kane bar is 52; the height of the bar for the Olean location is 40. The variable location is of nominal scale, so the order of the locations on the horizontal axis does not matter. Listing this variable alphabetically, as shown in Chart 2–1, or in order of decreasing frequencies is also appropriate.

Another useful type of chart for depicting qualitative information is a **pie chart.**

> **PIE CHART** A chart that shows the proportion or percentage that each class represents of the total number of frequencies.

DESCRIBING DATA: FREQUENCY TABLES, FREQUENCY DISTRIBUTIONS, AND GRAPHIC PRESENTATION   21

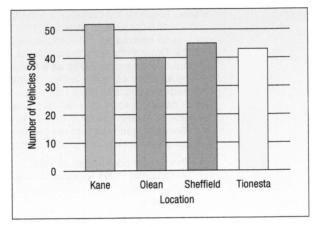

CHART 2–1 Number of Vehicles Sold by Location

We explain the details of constructing a pie chart using the information in Table 2–3, which shows the frequency and percent of cars sold by the Applewood Auto Group for each vehicle type.

TABLE 2–3 Vehicle Sales by Type at Applewood Auto Group

Vehicle Type	Number Sold	Percent Sold
Sedan	72	40
SUV	54	30
Compact	27	15
Truck	18	10
Hybrid	9	5
Total	180	100

The first step to develop a pie chart is to mark the percentages 0, 5, 10, 15, and so on evenly around the circumference of a circle (see Chart 2–2). To plot the 40% of total sales represented by sedans, draw a line from the center of the circle to 0 and

CHART 2–2 Pie Chart of Vehicles by Type

CHAPTER 2

another line from the center of the circle to 40%. The area in this "slice" represents the number of sedans sold as a percentage of the total sales. Next, add the SUV's percentage of total sales, 30%, to the sedan's percentage of total sales, 40%. The result is 70%. Draw a line from the center of the circle to 70%, so the area between 40 and 70 shows the sales of SUVs as a percentage of total sales. Continuing, add the 15% of total sales for compact vehicles, which gives us a total of 85%. Draw a line from the center of the circle to 85, so the "slice" between 70% and 85% represents the number of compact vehicles sold as a percentage of the total sales. The remaining 10% for truck sales and 5% for hybrid sales are added to the chart using the same method.

Because each slice of the pie represents the relative frequency of each vehicle type as a percentage of the total sales, we can easily compare them:

- The largest percentage of sales is for sedans.
- Sedans and SUVs together account for 70% of vehicle sales.
- Hybrids account for 5% of vehicle sales, in spite of being on the market for only a few years.

We can use Excel software to quickly count the number of cars for each vehicle type and create the frequency table, bar chart, and pie chart below. The Excel tool is called a Pivot Table. The instructions to produce these descriptive statistics and charts are given in Appendix C.

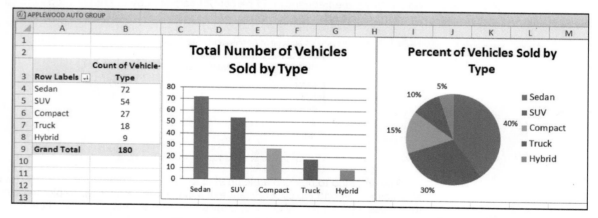

Pie and bar charts both serve to illustrate frequency and relative frequency tables. When is a pie chart preferred to a bar chart? In most cases, pie charts are used to show and compare the relative differences in the percentage of observations for each value or class of a qualitative variable. Bar charts are preferred when the goal is to compare the number or frequency of observations for each value or class of a qualitative variable. The following Example/Solution shows another application of bar and pie charts.

EXAMPLE

SkiLodges.com is test marketing its new website and is interested in how easy its website design is to navigate. It randomly selected 200 regular Internet users and asked them to perform a search task on the website. Each person was asked to rate the relative ease of navigation as poor, good, excellent, or awesome. The results are shown in the following table:

Awesome	102
Excellent	58
Good	30
Poor	10

DESCRIBING DATA: FREQUENCY TABLES, FREQUENCY DISTRIBUTIONS, AND GRAPHIC PRESENTATION   23

1. What type of measurement scale is used for ease of navigation?
2. Draw a bar chart for the survey results.
3. Draw a pie chart for the survey results.

SOLUTION

The data are measured on an ordinal scale. That is, the scale is ranked in relative ease when moving from "poor" to "awesome." Also, the interval between each rating is unknown so it is impossible, for example, to conclude that a rating of good is twice the value of a poor rating.

We can use a bar chart to graph the data. The vertical scale shows the relative frequency and the horizontal scale shows the values of the ease-of-navigation variable.

A pie chart can also be used to graph these data. The pie chart emphasizes that more than half of the respondents rate the relative ease of using the website awesome.

24   CHAPTER 2

SELF-REVIEW

2-1

The answers are in Appendix E.

DeCenzo Specialty Food and Beverage Company has been serving a cola drink with an additional flavoring, Cola-Plus, that is very popular among its customers. The company is interested in customer preferences for Cola-Plus versus Coca-Cola, Pepsi, and a lemon-lime beverage. They ask 100 randomly sampled customers to take a taste test and select the beverage they prefer most. The results are shown in the following table:

Beverage	Number
Cola-Plus	40
Coca-Cola	25
Pepsi	20
Lemon-Lime	15
Total	100

(a) Is the data qualitative or quantitative? Why?
(b) What is the table called? What does it show?
(c) Develop a bar chart to depict the information.
(d) Develop a pie chart using the relative frequencies.

EXERCISES

▼

The answers to the odd-numbered exercises are at the end of the book in Appendix D.

1. A pie chart shows the relative market share of cola products. The "slice" for Pepsi-Cola has a central angle of 90 degrees. What is its market share?

2. In a marketing study, 100 consumers were asked to select the best digital music player from the iPod, the iRiver, and the Magic Star MP3. To summarize the consumer responses with a frequency table, how many classes would the frequency table have?

3. A total of 1,000 residents in Minnesota were asked which season they preferred. One hundred liked winter best, 300 liked spring, 400 liked summer, and 200 liked fall. Develop a frequency table and a relative frequency table to summarize this information.

4. Two thousand frequent business travelers are asked which midwestern city they prefer: Indianapolis, Saint Louis, Chicago, or Milwaukee. One hundred liked Indianapolis best, 450 liked Saint Louis, 1,300 liked Chicago, and the remainder preferred Milwaukee. Develop a frequency table and a relative frequency table to summarize this information.

5. Wellstone Inc. produces and markets replacement covers for cell phones in five different colors: bright white, metallic black, magnetic lime, tangerine orange, and fusion red. To estimate the demand for each color, the company set up a kiosk in the Mall of America for several hours and asked randomly selected people which cover color was their favorite. The results follow:

Bright white	130
Metallic black	104
Magnetic lime	325
Tangerine orange	455
Fusion red	286

a. What is the table called?
b. Draw a bar chart for the table.
c. Draw a pie chart.
d. If Wellstone Inc. plans to produce 1 million cell phone covers, how many of each color should it produce?

DESCRIBING DATA: FREQUENCY TABLES, FREQUENCY DISTRIBUTIONS, AND GRAPHIC PRESENTATION   25

6. A small business consultant is investigating the performance of several companies. The fourth-quarter sales for last year (in thousands of dollars) for the selected companies were:

Company	Fourth-Quarter Sales ($ thousands)
Hoden Building Products	$ 1,645.2
J & R Printing Inc.	4,757.0
Long Bay Concrete Construction	8,913.0
Mancell Electric and Plumbing	627.1
Maxwell Heating and Air Conditioning	24,612.0
Mizelle Roofing & Sheet Metals	191.9

The consultant wants to include a chart in his report comparing the sales of the six companies. Use a bar chart to compare the fourth-quarter sales of these corporations and write a brief report summarizing the bar chart.

LO2-3
Summarize quantitative variables with frequency and relative frequency distributions.

CONSTRUCTING FREQUENCY DISTRIBUTIONS

In Chapter 1 and earlier in this chapter, we distinguished between qualitative and quantitative data. In the previous section, using the Applewood Automotive Group data, we summarized two qualitative variables: the location of the sale and the type of vehicle sold. We created frequency and relative frequency tables and depicted the results in bar and pie charts.

The Applewood Auto Group data also includes several quantitative variables: the age of the buyer, the profit earned on the sale of the vehicle, and the number of previous purchases. Suppose Ms. Ball wants to summarize last month's sales by profit earned. We can describe profit using a **frequency distribution.**

> **FREQUENCY DISTRIBUTION** A grouping of quantitative data into mutually exclusive and collectively exhaustive classes showing the number of observations in each class.

How do we develop a frequency distribution? The following example shows the steps to construct a frequency distribution. Remember, our goal is to construct tables, charts, and graphs that will quickly reveal the concentration, extreme values, and shape of the data.

EXAMPLE

We return to the situation where Ms. Kathryn Ball of the Applewood Auto Group wants to summarize the quantitative variable profit with a frequency distribution and display the distribution with charts and graphs. With this information, Ms. Ball can easily answer the following questions: What is the typical profit on each sale? What is the largest or maximum profit on any sale? What is the smallest or minimum profit on any sale? Around what value do the profits tend to cluster?

SOLUTION

To begin, we need the profits for each of the 180 vehicle sales, which are listed in Table 2–4. This information is called raw or ungrouped data because it is simply a listing of the individual, observed profits. It is possible to search the list and find the smallest or minimum profit ($294) and the largest or maximum profit ($3,292), but that is about all. It is difficult to determine a typical profit or to visualize where the profits tend to cluster. The raw data are more easily interpreted if we summarize the data with a frequency distribution as follows.

TABLE 2–4 Profit on Vehicles Sold Last Month by the Applewood Auto Group

Maximum

$1,387	$2,148	$2,201	$ 963	$ 820	$2,230	$3,043	$2,584	$2,370
1,754	2,207	996	1,298	1,266	2,341	1,059	2,666	2,637
1,817	2,252	2,813	1,410	1,741	3,292	1,674	2,991	1,426
1,040	1,428	323	1,553	1,772	1,108	1,807	934	2,944
1,273	1,889	352	1,648	1,932	1,295	2,056	2,063	2,147
1,529	1,166	482	2,071	2,350	1,344	2,236	2,083	1,973
3,082	1,320	1,144	2,116	2,422	1,906	2,928	2,856	2,502
1,951	2,265	1,485	1,500	2,446	1,952	1,269	2,989	783
2,692	1,323	1,509	1,549	369	2,070	1,717	910	1,538
1,206	1,760	1,638	2,348	978	2,454	1,797	1,536	2,339
1,342	1,919	1,961	2,498	1,238	1,606	1,955	1,957	2,700
443	2,357	2,127	294	1,818	1,680	2,199	2,240	2,222
754	2,866	2,430	1,115	1,824	1,827	2,482	2,695	2,597
1,621	732	1,704	1,124	1,907	1,915	2,701	1,325	2,742
870	1,464	1,876	1,532	1,938	2,084	3,210	2,250	1,837
1,174	1,626	2,010	1,688	1,940	2,639	377	2,279	2,842
1,412	1,762	2,165	1,822	2,197	842	1,220	2,626	2,434
1,809	1,915	2,231	1,897	2,646	1,963	1,401	1,501	1,640
2,415	2,119	2,389	2,445	1,461	2,059	2,175	1,752	1,821
1,546	1,766	335	2,886	1,731	2,338	1,118	2,058	2,487

Minimum

Step 1: **Decide on the number of classes.** A useful recipe to determine the number of classes (k) is the "2 to the k rule." This guide suggests you select the smallest number (k) for the number of classes such that 2^k (in words, 2 raised to the power of k) is greater than the number of observations (n). In the Applewood Auto Group example, there were 180 vehicles sold. So $n = 180$. If we try $k = 7$, which means we would use 7 classes, $2^7 = 128$, which is less than 180. Hence, 7 is too few classes. If we let $k = 8$, then $2^8 = 256$, which is greater than 180. So the recommended number of classes is 8.

Step 2: **Determine the class interval.** Generally, the **class interval** is the same for all classes. The classes all taken together must cover at least the distance from the minimum value in the data up to the maximum value. Expressing these words in a formula:

$$i \geq \frac{Maximum\ value - Minimum\ value}{k}$$

where i is the class interval, and k is the number of classes.

For the Applewood Auto Group, the minimum value is $294 and the maximum value is $3,292. If we need 8 classes, the interval should be:

$$i \geq \frac{Maximum\ value - Minimum\ value}{k} = \frac{\$3,292 - \$294}{8} = \$374.75$$

In practice, this interval size is usually rounded up to some convenient number, such as a multiple of 10 or 100. The value of $400 is a reasonable choice.

DESCRIBING DATA: FREQUENCY TABLES, FREQUENCY DISTRIBUTIONS, AND GRAPHIC PRESENTATION   27

Step 3: Set the individual class limits. State clear class limits so you can put each observation into only one category. This means you must avoid overlapping or unclear class limits. For example, classes such as "$1,300–$1,400" and "$1,400–$1,500" should not be used because it is not clear whether the value $1,400 is in the first or second class. In this text, we will generally use the format $1,300 **up to** $1,400 and $1,400 **up to** $1,500 and so on. With this format, it is clear that $1,399 goes into the first class and $1,400 in the second.

Because we always round the class interval up to get a convenient class size, we cover a larger than necessary range. For example, using 8 classes with an interval of $400 in the Applewood Auto Group example results in a range of 8($400) = $3,200. The actual range is $2,998, found by ($3,292 − $294). Comparing that value to $3,200, we have an excess of $202. Because we need to cover only the range (*Maximum* − *Minimum*), it is natural to put approximately equal amounts of the excess in each of the two tails. Of course, we should also select convenient class limits. A guideline is to make the lower limit of the first class a multiple of the class interval. Sometimes this is not possible, but the lower limit should at least be rounded. So here are the classes we could use for these data.

Classes
$ 200 up to $ 600
600 up to   1,000
1,000 up to   1,400
1,400 up to   1,800
1,800 up to   2,200
2,200 up to   2,600
2,600 up to   3,000
3,000 up to   3,400

Step 4: Tally the vehicle profit into the classes. To begin, the profit from the sale of the first vehicle in Table 2–4 is $1,387. It is tallied in the $1,000 up to $1,400 class. The second profit in the first row of Table 2–4 is $2,148. It is tallied in the $1,800 up to $2,200 class. The other profits are tallied in a similar manner. When all the profits are tallied, the table would appear as:

Profit	Frequency
$ 200 up to $ 600	JHT III
600 up to 1,000	JHT JHT I
1,000 up to 1,400	JHT JHT JHT JHT III
1,400 up to 1,800	JHT JHT JHT JHT JHT JHT JHT III
1,800 up to 2,200	JHT JHT JHT JHT JHT JHT JHT JHT JHT
2,200 up to 2,600	JHT JHT JHT JHT JHT II
2,600 up to 3,000	JHT JHT JHT IIII
3,000 up to 3,400	IIII

Step 5: Count the number of items in each class. The number of observations in each class is called the **class frequency.** In the $200 up to $600 class there are 8 observations, and in the $600 up to $1,000 class there are 11 observations. Therefore, the class frequency in

the first class is 8 and the class frequency in the second class is 11. There are a total of 180 observations in the entire set of data. So the sum of all the frequencies should be equal to 180.

TABLE 2–5 Frequency Distribution of Profit for Vehicles Sold Last Month at Applewood Auto Group

Profit	Frequency
$ 200 up to $ 600	8
600 up to 1,000	11
1,000 up to 1,400	23
1,400 up to 1,800	38
1,800 up to 2,200	45
2,200 up to 2,600	32
2,600 up to 3,000	19
3,000 up to 3,400	4
Total	180

Now that we have organized the data into a frequency distribution (see Table 2–5), we can summarize the profits of the vehicles for the Applewood Auto Group. Observe the following:

1. The profits from vehicle sales range between $200 and $3,400.
2. The vehicle profits are classified using a class interval of $400. The class interval is determined by subtracting consecutive lower or upper class limits. For example, the lower limit of the first class is $200, and the lower limit of the second class is $600. The difference is the class interval of $400.
3. The profits are concentrated between $1,000 and $3,000. The profit on 157 vehicles, or 87%, was within this range.
4. For each class, we can determine the typical profit or **class midpoint.** It is halfway between the lower or upper limits of two consecutive classes. It is computed by adding the lower or upper limits of consecutive classes and dividing by 2. Referring to Table 2–5, the lower class limit of the first class is $200, and the next class limit is $600. The class midpoint is $400, found by ($600 + $200)/2. The midpoint best represents, or is typical of, the profits of the vehicles in that class. Applewood sold 8 vehicles with a typical profit of $400.
5. The largest concentration, or highest frequency, of vehicles sold is in the $1,800 up to $2,200 class. There are 45 vehicles in this class. The class midpoint is $2,000. So we say that the typical profit in the class with the highest frequency is $2,000.

By presenting this information to Ms. Ball, we give her a clear picture of the distribution of the vehicle profits for last month.

We admit that arranging the information on profits into a frequency distribution does result in the loss of some detailed information. That is, by organizing the data into a frequency distribution, we cannot pinpoint the exact profit on any vehicle, such as $1,387, $2,148, or $2,201. Further, we cannot tell that the actual minimum profit for any vehicle sold is $294 or that the maximum profit was $3,292. However, the lower limit of the first class and the upper limit of the last class convey essentially the same meaning. Likely, Ms. Ball will make the same judgment if she knows the smallest profit is about $200 that she will if she knows the exact profit is $292. The advantages of summarizing the 180 profits into a more understandable and organized form more than offset this disadvantage.

When we summarize raw data with frequency distributions, equal class intervals are preferred. However, in certain situations unequal class intervals may be necessary to avoid a large number of classes with very small frequencies. Such is the case in Table 2–6. The U.S. Internal Revenue Service uses unequal-sized class intervals for adjusted gross income on individual tax returns to summarize the number of individual tax returns. If we use our method to find equal class intervals, the 2^k rule results in 25 classes, and a class interval of $400,000, assuming $0 and $10,000,000 as the minimum and maximum values for adjusted gross income. Using equal class intervals, the first 13 classes in Table 2–6 would be combined into one class of about 99.9% of all tax returns and 24 classes for the 0.1% of the returns with an adjusted gross income above $400,000. Using equal class intervals does not provide a good understanding of the raw data. In this case, good judgment in the use of unequal class intervals, as demonstrated in Table 2–6, is required to show the distribution of the number of tax returns filed, especially for incomes under $500,000.

TABLE 2–6 Adjusted Gross Income for Individuals Filing Income Tax Returns

Adjusted Gross Income	Number of Returns (in thousands)
No adjusted gross income	178.2
$ 1 up to 5,000	1,204.6
5,000 up to 10,000	2,595.5
10,000 up to 15,000	3,142.0
15,000 up to 20,000	3,191.7
20,000 up to 25,000	2,501.4
25,000 up to 30,000	1,901.6
30,000 up to 40,000	2,502.3
40,000 up to 50,000	1,426.8
50,000 up to 75,000	1,476.3
75,000 up to 100,000	338.8
100,000 up to 200,000	223.3
200,000 up to 500,000	55.2
500,000 up to 1,000,000	12.0
1,000,000 up to 2,000,000	5.1
2,000,000 up to 10,000,000	3.4
10,000,000 or more	0.6

SELF-REVIEW

2–2

The commissions earned for the first quarter of last year by the 11 members of the sales staff at Master Chemical Company are:

$1,650 $1,475 $1,510 $1,670 $1,595 $1,760 $1,540 $1,495 $1,590 $1,625 $1,510

(a) What are the values such as $1,650 and $1,475 called?
(b) Using $1,400 up to $1,500 as the first class, $1,500 up to $1,600 as the second class, and so forth, organize the quarterly commissions into a frequency distribution.
(c) What are the numbers in the right column of your frequency distribution called?
(d) Describe the distribution of quarterly commissions, based on the frequency distribution. What is the largest concentration of commissions earned? What is the smallest, and the largest? What is the typical amount earned?

30   CHAPTER 2

Relative Frequency Distribution

It may be desirable, as we did earlier with qualitative data, to convert class frequencies to relative class frequencies to show the proportion of the total number of observations in each class. In our vehicle profits, we may want to know what percentage of the vehicle profits are in the $1,000 up to $1,400 class. In another study, we may want to know what percentage of the employees used 5 up to 10 personal leave days last year. To convert a frequency distribution to a *relative* frequency distribution, each of the class frequencies is divided by the total number of observations. From the distribution of vehicle profits, Table 2–5, the relative frequency for the $1,000 up to $1,400 class is 0.128, found by dividing 23 by 180. That is, profit on 12.8% of the vehicles sold is between $1,000 and $1,400. The relative frequencies for the remaining classes are shown in Table 2–7.

TABLE 2–7 Relative Frequency Distribution of Profit for Vehicles Sold Last Month at Applewood Auto Group

Profit	Frequency	Relative Frequency	Found by
$ 200 up to $ 600	8	.044	8/180
600 up to 1,000	11	.061	11/180
1,000 up to 1,400	23	.128	23/180
1,400 up to 1,800	38	.211	38/180
1,800 up to 2,200	45	.250	45/180
2,200 up to 2,600	32	.178	32/180
2,600 up to 3,000	19	.106	19/180
3,000 up to 3,400	4	.022	4/180
Total	180	1.000	

As we mentioned in Chapter 1, there are many software packages that perform statistical calculations. Throughout this text, we will show the output from Microsoft Excel, MegaStat (a Microsoft Excel add-in), and Minitab (a statistical software package).

On page 22 of this chapter, we used the Pivot Table tool in Excel to create a frequency table. We use the same Excel tool to create frequency and relative frequency distributions for the profit variable in the Applewood Auto Group data. The necessary steps for the table to the left are given in the Software Commands section in Appendix C.

	A	B	C
	Profit Class	Frequency	Relative Frequency
2	200-600	8	4.44%
3	600-1000	11	6.11%
4	1000-1400	23	12.78%
5	1400-1800	38	21.11%
6	1800-2200	45	25.00%
7	2200-2600	32	17.78%
8	2600-3000	19	10.56%
9	3000-3400	4	2.22%
10	Grand Total	180	100.00%

SELF-REVIEW 2–3

Barry Bonds of the San Francisco Giants established a new single-season Major League Baseball home run record by hitting 73 home runs during the 2001 season. Listed below is the sorted distance of each of the 73 home runs.

320	320	347	350	360	360	360	361	365	370
370	375	375	375	375	380	380	380	380	380
380	390	390	391	394	396	400	400	400	400
405	410	410	410	410	410	410	410	410	410
410	410	411	415	415	416	417	417	420	420
420	420	420	420	420	420	429	430	430	430
430	430	435	435	436	440	440	440	440	440
450	480	488							

DESCRIBING DATA: FREQUENCY TABLES, FREQUENCY DISTRIBUTIONS, AND GRAPHIC PRESENTATION   31

(a) For this data, show that seven classes would be used to create a frequency distribution using the 2^k rule.
(b) Show that a class interval of 30 would summarize the data in seven classes.
(c) Construct frequency and relative frequency distributions for the data with seven classes and a class interval of 30. Start the first class with a lower limit of 300.
(d) How many home runs traveled a distance of 360 up to 390 feet?
(e) What percentage of the home runs traveled a distance of 360 up to 390 feet?
(f) What percentage of the home runs traveled a distance of 390 feet or more?

For **DATA FILE**, please visit www.mhhe.com/lind16e

7. A set of data consists of 38 observations. How many classes would you recommend for the frequency distribution?
8. A set of data consists of 45 observations between $0 and $29. What size would you recommend for the class interval?
9. A set of data consists of 230 observations between $235 and $567. What class interval would you recommend?
10. A set of data contains 53 observations. The minimum value is 42 and the maximum value is 129. The data are to be organized into a frequency distribution.
    a. How many classes would you suggest?
    b. What would you suggest as the lower limit of the first class?
11. Wachesaw Manufacturing Inc. produced the following number of units in the last 16 days.

27	27	27	28	27	25	25	28
26	28	26	28	31	30	26	26

The information is to be organized into a frequency distribution.
    a. How many classes would you recommend?
    b. What class interval would you suggest?
    c. What lower limit would you recommend for the first class?
    d. Organize the information into a frequency distribution and determine the relative frequency distribution.
    e. Comment on the shape of the distribution.

For **DATA FILE**, please visit www.mhhe.com/lind16e

12. The Quick Change Oil Company has a number of outlets in the metropolitan Seattle area. The daily number of oil changes at the Oak Street outlet in the past 20 days are:

65	98	55	62	79	59	51	90	72	56
70	62	66	80	94	79	63	73	71	85

The data are to be organized into a frequency distribution.
    a. How many classes would you recommend?
    b. What class interval would you suggest?
    c. What lower limit would you recommend for the first class?
    d. Organize the number of oil changes into a frequency distribution.
    e. Comment on the shape of the frequency distribution. Also determine the relative frequency distribution.

For **DATA FILE**, please visit www.mhhe.com/lind16e

13. The manager of the BiLo Supermarket in Mt. Pleasant, Rhode Island, gathered the following information on the number of times a customer visits the store during a month. The responses of 51 customers were:

5	3	3	1	4	4	5	6	4	2	6	6	6	7	1
1	14	1	2	4	4	4	5	6	3	5	3	4	5	6
8	4	7	6	5	9	11	3	12	4	7	6	5	15	1
1	10	8	9	2	12									

    a. Starting with 0 as the lower limit of the first class and using a class interval of 3, organize the data into a frequency distribution.
    b. Describe the distribution. Where do the data tend to cluster?
    c. Convert the distribution to a relative frequency distribution.

For **DATA FILE**, please visit
www.mhhe.com/lind16e

14. The food services division of Cedar River Amusement Park Inc. is studying the amount that families who visit the amusement park spend per day on food and drink. A sample of 40 families who visited the park yesterday revealed they spent the following amounts:

$77	$18	$63	$84	$38	$54	$50	$59	$54	$56	$36	$26	$50	$34	$44
41	58	58	53	51	62	43	52	53	63	62	62	65	61	52
60	60	45	66	83	71	63	58	61	71					

a. Organize the data into a frequency distribution, using seven classes and 15 as the lower limit of the first class. What class interval did you select?
b. Where do the data tend to cluster?
c. Describe the distribution.
d. Determine the relative frequency distribution.

LO2-4
Display a frequency distribution using a histogram or frequency polygon.

GRAPHIC PRESENTATION OF A FREQUENCY DISTRIBUTION

Sales managers, stock analysts, hospital administrators, and other busy executives often need a quick picture of the distributions of sales, stock prices, or hospital costs. These distributions can often be depicted by the use of charts and graphs. Three charts that will help portray a frequency distribution graphically are the histogram, the frequency polygon, and the cumulative frequency polygon.

Histogram

A **histogram** for a frequency distribution based on quantitative data is similar to the bar chart showing the distribution of qualitative data. The classes are marked on the horizontal axis and the class frequencies on the vertical axis. The class frequencies are represented by the heights of the bars. However, there is one important difference based on the nature of the data. Quantitative data are usually measured using scales that are continuous, not discrete. Therefore, the horizontal axis represents all possible values, and the bars are drawn adjacent to each other to show the continuous nature of the data.

> **HISTOGRAM** A graph in which the classes are marked on the horizontal axis and the class frequencies on the vertical axis. The class frequencies are represented by the heights of the bars, and the bars are drawn adjacent to each other.

E X A M P L E

Below is the frequency distribution of the profits on vehicle sales last month at the Applewood Auto Group.

Profit	Frequency
$ 200 up to $ 600	8
600 up to 1,000	11
1,000 up to 1,400	23
1,400 up to 1,800	38
1,800 up to 2,200	45
2,200 up to 2,600	32
2,600 up to 3,000	19
3,000 up to 3,400	4
Total	180

STATISTICS IN ACTION

Florence Nightingale is known as the founder of the nursing profession. However, she also saved many lives by using statistical analysis. When she encountered an unsanitary condition or an undersupplied hospital, she improved the conditions and then used statistical data to document the improvement. Thus, she was able to convince others of the need for medical reform, particularly in the area of sanitation. She developed original graphs to demonstrate that, during the Crimean War, more soldiers died from unsanitary conditions than were killed in combat.

Construct a histogram. What observations can you reach based on the information presented in the histogram?

S O L U T I O N

The class frequencies are scaled along the vertical axis (Y-axis) and either the class limits or the class midpoints along the horizontal axis. To illustrate the construction of the histogram, the first three classes are shown in Chart 2–3.

CHART 2–3 Construction of a Histogram

From Chart 2–3 we note the profit on eight vehicles was $200 up to $600. Therefore, the height of the column for that class is 8. There are 11 vehicle sales where the profit was $600 up to $1,000. So, logically, the height of that column is 11. The height of the bar represents the number of observations in the class.

This procedure is continued for all classes. The complete histogram is shown in Chart 2–4. Note that there is no space between the bars. This is a feature of the histogram. Why is this so? Because the variable plotted on the horizontal axis is a continuous variable. In a bar chart, the scale of measurement is often nominal and the vertical bars are separated. This is an important distinction between the histogram and the bar chart.

CHART 2–4 Histogram of the Profit on 180 Vehicles Sold at the Applewood Auto Group

We can make the following statements using Chart 2–4. They are the same as the observations based on Table 2–5 on page 28.

1. The profits from vehicle sales range between $200 and $3,400.
2. The vehicle profits are classified using a class interval of $400. The class interval is determined by subtracting consecutive lower or upper class limits. For example, the lower limit of the first class is $200, and the lower limit of the second class is $600. The difference is the class interval or $400.
3. The profits are concentrated between $1,000 and $3,000. The profit on 157 vehicles, or 87%, was within this range.
4. For each class, we can determine the typical profit or class midpoint. It is halfway between the lower or upper limits of two consecutive classes. It is computed by adding the lower or upper limits of consecutive classes and dividing by 2. Referring to Chart 2–4, the lower class limit of the first class is $200, and the next class limit is $600. The class midpoint is $400, found by ($600 + $200)/2. The midpoint best represents, or is typical of, the profits of the vehicles in that class. Applewood sold 8 vehicles with a typical profit of $400.
5. The largest concentration, or highest frequency of vehicles sold, is in the $1,800 up to $2,200 class. There are 45 vehicles in this class. The class midpoint is $2,000. So we say that the typical profit in the class with the highest frequency is $2,000.

Thus, the histogram provides an easily interpreted visual representation of a frequency distribution. We should also point out that we would have made the same observations and the shape of the histogram would have been the same had we used a relative frequency distribution instead of the actual frequencies. That is, if we had used the relative frequencies of Table 2–7, we would have had a histogram of the same shape as Chart 2–4. The only difference is that the vertical axis would have been reported in percentage of vehicles instead of the number of vehicles. The Excel commands to create Chart 2–4 are given in Appendix C.

Frequency Polygon

A **frequency polygon** also shows the shape of a distribution and is similar to a histogram. It consists of line segments connecting the points formed by the intersections of the class midpoints and the class frequencies. The construction of a frequency polygon is illustrated in Chart 2–5 on the next page. We use the profits from the cars sold last month at the Applewood Auto Group. The midpoint of each class is scaled on the X-axis and the class frequencies on the Y-axis. Recall that the class midpoint is the value at the center of a class and represents the typical values in that class. The class frequency is the number of observations in a particular class. The profit earned on the vehicles sold last month by the Applewood Auto Group is repeated below.

Profit	Midpoint	Frequency
$ 200 up to $ 600	$ 400	8
600 up to 1,000	800	11
1,000 up to 1,400	1,200	23
1,400 up to 1,800	1,600	38
1,800 up to 2,200	2,000	45
2,200 up to 2,600	2,400	32
2,600 up to 3,000	2,800	19
3,000 up to 3,400	3,200	4
Total		180

DESCRIBING DATA: FREQUENCY TABLES, FREQUENCY DISTRIBUTIONS, AND GRAPHIC PRESENTATION   35

CHART 2–5 Frequency Polygon of Profit on 180 Vehicles Sold at Applewood Auto Group

As noted previously, the $200 up to $600 class is represented by the midpoint $400. To construct a frequency polygon, move horizontally on the graph to the midpoint, $400, and then vertically to 8, the class frequency, and place a dot. The x and the y values of this point are called the *coordinates.* The coordinates of the next point are x = 800 and y = 11. The process is continued for all classes. Then the points are connected in order. That is, the point representing the lowest class is joined to the one representing the second class and so on. Note in Chart 2–5 that, to complete the frequency polygon, midpoints of $0 and $3,600 are added to the X-axis to "anchor" the polygon at zero frequencies. These two values, $0 and $3,600, were derived by subtracting the class interval of $400 from the lowest midpoint ($400) and by adding $400 to the highest midpoint ($3,200) in the frequency distribution.

Both the histogram and the frequency polygon allow us to get a quick picture of the main characteristics of the data (highs, lows, points of concentration, etc.). Although the two representations are similar in purpose, the histogram has the advantage of depicting each class as a rectangle, with the height of the rectangular bar representing the number in each class. The frequency polygon, in turn, has an advantage over the histogram. It allows us to compare directly two or more frequency distributions. Suppose Ms. Ball wants to compare the profit per vehicle sold at Applewood Auto Group with a similar auto group, Fowler Auto in Grayling, Michigan. To do this, two frequency polygons are constructed, one on top of the other, as in Chart 2–6. Two things are clear from the chart:

- The typical vehicle profit is larger at Fowler Motors—about $2,000 for Applewood and about $2,400 for Fowler.

CHART 2–6 Distribution of Profit at Applewood Auto Group and Fowler Motors

36   CHAPTER 2

• There is less dispersion in the profits at Fowler Motors than at Applewood. The lower limit of the first class for Applewood is $0 and the upper limit is $3,600. For Fowler Motors, the lower limit is $800 and the upper limit is the same: $3,600.

The total number of cars sold at the two dealerships is about the same, so a direct comparison is possible. If the difference in the total number of cars sold is large, then converting the frequencies to relative frequencies and then plotting the two distributions would allow a clearer comparison.

SELF-REVIEW

2–4

The annual imports of a selected group of electronic suppliers are shown in the following frequency distribution.

Imports ($ millions)	Number of Suppliers
2 up to 5	6
5 up to 8	13
8 up to 11	20
11 up to 14	10
14 up to 17	1

(a) Portray the imports as a histogram.
(b) Portray the imports as a relative frequency polygon.
(c) Summarize the important facets of the distribution (such as classes with the highest and lowest frequencies).

EXERCISES

15. Molly's Candle Shop has several retail stores in the coastal areas of North and South Carolina. Many of Molly's customers ask her to ship their purchases. The following chart shows the number of packages shipped per day for the last 100 days.

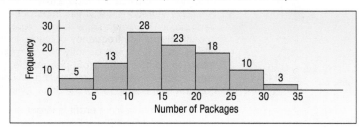

a. What is this chart called?
b. What is the total number of frequencies?
c. What is the class interval?
d. What is the class frequency of the 10 up to 15 class?
e. What is the relative frequency of the 10 up to 15 class?
f. What is the midpoint of the 10 up to 15 class?
g. On how many days were there 25 or more packages shipped?

16. The following chart shows the number of patients admitted daily to Memorial Hospital through the emergency room.

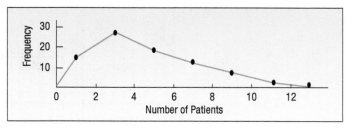

    a. What is the midpoint of the 2 up to 4 class?
    b. How many days were 2 up to 4 patients admitted?
    c. What is the class interval?
    d. What is this chart called?

17. The following frequency distribution reports the number of frequent flier miles, reported in thousands, for employees of Brumley Statistical Consulting Inc. during the most recent quarter.

Frequent Flier Miles (000)	Number of Employees
0 up to 3	5
3 up to 6	12
6 up to 9	23
9 up to 12	8
12 up to 15	2
Total	50

    a. How many employees were studied?
    b. What is the midpoint of the first class?
    c. Construct a histogram.
    d. A frequency polygon is to be drawn. What are the coordinates of the plot for the first class?
    e. Construct a frequency polygon.
    f. Interpret the frequent flier miles accumulated using the two charts.

18. Ecommerce.com, a large Internet retailer, is studying the lead time (elapsed time between when an order is placed and when it is filled) for a sample of recent orders. The lead times are reported in days.

Lead Time (days)	Frequency
0 up to 5	6
5 up to 10	7
10 up to 15	12
15 up to 20	8
20 up to 25	7
Total	40

    a. How many orders were studied?
    b. What is the midpoint of the first class?
    c. What are the coordinates of the first class for a frequency polygon?
    d. Draw a histogram.
    e. Draw a frequency polygon.
    f. Interpret the lead times using the two charts.

Cumulative Frequency Distributions

Consider once again the distribution of the profits on vehicles sold by the Applewood Auto Group. Suppose we were interested in the number of vehicles that sold for a profit of less than $1,400 or the profit earned on the lowest-selling 40% of the vehicles. These values can be approximated by developing a **cumulative frequency distribution** and portraying it graphically in a **cumulative frequency polygon.**

EXAMPLE

The frequency distribution of the profits earned at Applewood Auto Group is repeated from Table 2–5.

Profit	Frequency
$ 200 up to $ 600	8
600 up to 1,000	11
1,000 up to 1,400	23
1,400 up to 1,800	38
1,800 up to 2,200	45
2,200 up to 2,600	32
2,600 up to 3,000	19
3,000 up to 3,400	4
Total	180

Construct a cumulative frequency polygon to answer the following two questions. Seventy-five percent of the vehicles sold earned a profit of less than what amount? Sixty of the vehicles earned a profit of less than what amount?

SOLUTION

As the names imply, a cumulative frequency distribution and a cumulative frequency polygon require *cumulative frequencies.* To construct a cumulative frequency distribution, refer to the preceding table and note that there were eight vehicles in which the profit earned was less than $600. Those 8 vehicles, plus the 11 in the next higher class, for a total of 19, earned a profit of less than $1,000. The cumulative frequency for the next higher class is 42, found by 8 + 11 + 23. This process is continued for all the classes. All the vehicles earned a profit of less than $3,400. (See Table 2–8.)

TABLE 2–8 Cumulative Frequency Distribution for Profit on Vehicles Sold Last Month at Applewood Auto Group

Profit	Cumulative Frequency	Found by
Less than $ 600	8	8
Less than 1,000	19	8 + 11
Less than 1,400	42	8 + 11 + 23
Less than 1,800	80	8 + 11 + 23 + 38
Less than 2,200	125	8 + 11 + 23 + 38 + 45
Less than 2,600	157	8 + 11 + 23 + 38 + 45 + 32
Less than 3,000	176	8 + 11 + 23 + 38 + 45 + 32 + 19
Less than 3,400	180	8 + 11 + 23 + 38 + 45 + 32 + 19 + 4

To plot a cumulative frequency distribution, scale the upper limit of each class along the X-axis and the corresponding cumulative frequencies along the Y-axis. To provide additional information, you can label the vertical axis on the left in units and the vertical axis on the right in percent. In the Applewood Auto Group, the vertical axis on the left is labeled from 0 to 180 and on the right from 0 to 100%. The value of 50% corresponds to 90 vehicles.

To begin, the first plot is at $x = 200$ and $y = 0$. None of the vehicles sold for a profit of less than $200. The profit on 8 vehicles was less than $600, so the next plot is at $x = 600$ and $y = 8$. Continuing, the next plot is $x = 1,000$ and $y = 19$. There were 19 vehicles that sold for a profit of less than $1,000. The rest of the points are plotted and then the dots connected to form Chart 2–7.

CHART 2–7 Cumulative Frequency Polygon for Profit on Vehicles Sold Last Month at Applewood Auto Group

Using Chart 2–7 to find the amount of profit on 75% of the cars sold, draw a horizontal line from the 75% mark on the right-hand vertical axis over to the polygon, then drop down to the *X*-axis and read the amount of profit. The value on the *X*-axis is about $2,300, so we estimate that 75% of the vehicles sold earned a profit of $2,300 or less for the Applewood group.

To find the highest profit earned on 60 of the 180 vehicles, we use Chart 2–7 to locate the value of 60 on the left-hand vertical axis. Next, we draw a horizontal line from the value of 60 to the polygon and then drop down to the *X*-axis and read the profit. It is about $1,600, so we estimate that 60 of the vehicles sold for a profit of less than $1,600. We can also make estimates of the percentage of vehicles that sold for less than a particular amount. To explain, suppose we want to estimate the percentage of vehicles that sold for a profit of less than $2,000. We begin by locating the value of $2,000 on the *X*-axis, move vertically to the polygon, and then horizontally to the vertical axis on the right. The value is about 56%, so we conclude 56% of the vehicles sold for a profit of less than $2,000.

40   CHAPTER 2

SELF-REVIEW

2–5

A sample of the hourly wages of 15 employees at Home Depot in Brunswick, Georgia, was organized into the following table.

Hourly Wages	Number of Employees
$ 8 up to $10	3
10 up to 12	7
12 up to 14	4
14 up to 16	1

(a) What is the table called?
(b) Develop a cumulative frequency distribution and portray the distribution in a cumulative frequency polygon.
(c) On the basis of the cumulative frequency polygon, how many employees earn less than $11 per hour?

EXERCISES

▼

19. The following cumulative frequency polygon shows the hourly wages of a sample of certified welders in the Atlanta, Georgia, area.

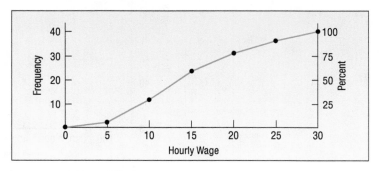

  a. How many welders were studied?
  b. What is the class interval?
  c. About how many welders earn less than $10.00 per hour?
  d. About 75% of the welders make less than what amount?
  e. Ten of the welders studied made less than what amount?
  f. What percent of the welders make less than $20.00 per hour?
20. The following cumulative frequency polygon shows the selling price ($000) of houses sold in the Billings, Montana, area.

  a. How many homes were studied?
  b. What is the class interval?

    c. One hundred homes sold for less than what amount?
    d. About 75% of the homes sold for less than what amount?
    e. Estimate the number of homes in the $150,000 up to $200,000 class.
    f. About how many homes sold for less than $225,000?

21. The frequency distribution representing the number of frequent flier miles accumulated by employees at Brumley Statistical Consulting Inc. is repeated from Exercise 17.

Frequent Flier Miles (000)	Frequency
0 up to 3	5
3 up to 6	12
6 up to 9	23
9 up to 12	8
12 up to 15	2
Total	50

    a. How many employees accumulated less than 3,000 miles?
    b. Convert the frequency distribution to a cumulative frequency distribution.
    c. Portray the cumulative distribution in the form of a cumulative frequency polygon.
    d. Based on the cumulative frequency polygon, about 75% of the employees accumulated how many miles or less?

22. The frequency distribution of order lead time at Ecommerce.com from Exercise 18 is repeated below.

Lead Time (days)	Frequency
0 up to 5	6
5 up to 10	7
10 up to 15	12
15 up to 20	8
20 up to 25	7
Total	40

    a. How many orders were filled in less than 10 days? In less than 15 days?
    b. Convert the frequency distribution to a cumulative frequency distribution.
    c. Develop a cumulative frequency polygon.
    d. About 60% of the orders were filled in less than how many days?

CHAPTER SUMMARY

  I. A frequency table is a grouping of qualitative data into mutually exclusive and collectively exhaustive classes showing the number of observations in each class.
  II. A relative frequency table shows the fraction of the number of frequencies in each class.
  III. A bar chart is a graphic representation of a frequency table.
  IV. A pie chart shows the proportion each distinct class represents of the total number of observations.
  V. A frequency distribution is a grouping of data into mutually exclusive and collectively exhaustive classes showing the number of observations in each class.
    A. The steps in constructing a frequency distribution are
      1. Decide on the number of classes.
      2. Determine the class interval.
      3. Set the individual class limits.
      4. Tally the raw data into classes.
      5. Count the number of tallies in each class.
    B. The class frequency is the number of observations in each class.
    C. The class interval is the difference between the limits of two consecutive classes.
    D. The class midpoint is halfway between the limits of consecutive classes.

42 CHAPTER 2

VI. A relative frequency distribution shows the percent of observations in each class.
VII. There are three methods for graphically portraying a frequency distribution.
    A. A histogram portrays the number of frequencies in each class in the form of a rectangle.
    B. A frequency polygon consists of line segments connecting the points formed by the intersection of the class midpoint and the class frequency.
    C. A cumulative frequency distribution shows the number or percent of observations less than a given value.

C H A P T E R   E X E R C I S E S

23. Describe the similarities and differences of qualitative and quantitative variables. Be sure to include the following:
    a. What level of measurement is required for each variable type?
    b. Can both types be used to describe both samples and populations?
24. Describe the similarities and differences between a frequency table and a frequency distribution. Be sure to include which requires qualitative data and which requires quantitative data.
25. Alexandra Damonte will be building a new resort in Myrtle Beach, South Carolina. She must decide how to design the resort based on the type of activities that the resort will offer to its customers. A recent poll of 300 potential customers showed the following results about customers' preferences for planned resort activities:

Like planned activities	63
Do not like planned activities	135
Not sure	78
No answer	24

    a. What is the table called?
    b. Draw a bar chart to portray the survey results.
    c. Draw a pie chart for the survey results.
    d. If you are preparing to present the results to Ms. Damonte as part of a report, which graph would you prefer to show? Why?

For **DATA FILE**, please visit
www.mhhe.com/lind16e

26. Speedy Swift is a package delivery service that serves the greater Atlanta, Georgia, metropolitan area. To maintain customer loyalty, one of Speedy Swift's performance objectives is on-time delivery. To monitor its performance, each delivery is measured on the following scale: early (package delivered before the promised time), on-time (package delivered within 5 minutes of the promised time), late (package delivered more than 5 minutes past the promised time), lost (package never delivered). Speedy Swift's objective is to deliver 99% of all packages either early or on-time. Another objective is to never lose a package.

Speedy collected the following data for last month's performance:

On-time	On-time	Early	Late	On-time	On-time	On-time	On-time	Late	On-time
Early	On-time	On-time	Early	On-time	On-time	On-time	On-time	On-time	On-time
Early	On-time	Early	On-time	On-time	On-time	Early	On-time	On-time	On-time
Early	On-time	On-time	Late	Early	Early	On-time	On-time	On-time	Early
On-time	Late	Late	On-time	On-time	On-time	On-time	On-time	On-time	On-time
On-time	Late	Early	On-time	Early	On-time	Lost	On-time	On-time	On-time
Early	Early	On-time	On-time	Late	Early	Lost	On-time	On-time	On-time
On-time	On-time	Early	On-time	Early	On-time	Early	On-time	Late	On-time
On-time	Early	On-time	On-time	On-time	Late	On-time	Early	On-time	On-time
On-time	On-time	On-time	On-time	On-time	Early	Early	On-time	On-time	On-time

    a. What scale is used to measure delivery performance? What kind of variable is delivery performance?
    b. Construct a frequency table for delivery performance for last month.

DESCRIBING DATA: FREQUENCY TABLES, FREQUENCY DISTRIBUTIONS, AND GRAPHIC PRESENTATION   43

    c. Construct a relative frequency table for delivery performance last month.
    d. Construct a bar chart of the frequency table for delivery performance for last month.
    e. Construct a pie chart of on-time delivery performance for last month.
    f. Analyze the data summaries and write an evaluation of last month's delivery performance as it relates to Speedy Swift's performance objectives. Write a general recommendation for further analysis.

27. A data set consists of 83 observations. How many classes would you recommend for a frequency distribution?

28. A data set consists of 145 observations that range from 56 to 490. What size class interval would you recommend?

29. The following is the number of minutes to commute from home to work for a group of 25 automobile executives.

For **DATA FILE**, please visit
www.mhhe.com/lind16e

| 28 | 25 | 48 | 37 | 41 | 19 | 32 | 26 | 16 | 23 | 23 | 29 | 36 |
| 31 | 26 | 21 | 32 | 25 | 31 | 43 | 35 | 42 | 38 | 33 | 28 | |

    a. How many classes would you recommend?
    b. What class interval would you suggest?
    c. What would you recommend as the lower limit of the first class?
    d. Organize the data into a frequency distribution.
    e. Comment on the shape of the frequency distribution.

30. The following data give the weekly amounts spent on groceries for a sample of 45 households.

For **DATA FILE**, please visit
www.mhhe.com/lind16e

$271	$363	$159	$ 76	$227	$337	$295	$319	$250
279	205	279	266	199	177	162	232	303
192	181	321	309	246	278	50	41	335
116	100	151	240	474	297	170	188	320
429	294	570	342	279	235	434	123	325

    a. How many classes would you recommend?
    b. What class interval would you suggest?
    c. What would you recommend as the lower limit of the first class?
    d. Organize the data into a frequency distribution.

31. A social scientist is studying the use of iPods by college students. A sample of 45 students revealed they played the following number of songs yesterday.

For **DATA FILE**, please visit
www.mhhe.com/lind16e

4	6	8	7	9	6	3	7	7	6	7	1	4	7	7
4	6	4	10	2	4	6	3	4	6	8	4	3	3	6
8	8	4	6	4	6	5	5	9	6	8	8	6	5	10

Organize the above information into a frequency distribution.
    a. How many classes would you suggest?
    b. What is the most suitable class interval?
    c. What is the lower limit of the initial class?
    d. Create the frequency distribution.
    e. Describe the profile of the distribution.

32. David Wise handles his own investment portfolio, and has done so for many years. Listed below is the holding time (recorded to the nearest whole year) between purchase and sale for his collection of 36 stocks.

For **DATA FILE**, please visit
www.mhhe.com/lind16e

| 8 | 8 | 6 | 11 | 11 | 9 | 8 | 5 | 11 | 4 | 8 | 5 | 14 | 7 | 12 | 8 | 6 | 11 | 9 | 7 |
| 9 | 15 | 8 | 8 | 12 | 5 | 9 | 8 | 5 | 9 | 10 | 11 | 3 | 9 | 8 | 6 | | | | |

    a. How many classes would you propose?
    b. What class interval would you suggest?
    c. What quantity would you use for the lower limit of the initial class?
    d. Using your responses to parts (a), (b), and (c), create a frequency distribution.
    e. Identify the appearance of the frequency distribution.

For **DATA FILE**, please visit
www.mhhe.com/lind16e

33. You are exploring the music in your iTunes library. The total play counts over the past year for the 27 songs on your "smart playlist" are shown below. Make a frequency distribution of the counts and describe its shape. It is often claimed that a small fraction of a person's songs will account for most of their total plays. Does this seem to be the case here?

128	56	54	91	190	23	160	298	445	50
578	494	37	677	18	74	70	868	108	71
466	23	84	38	26	814	17			

For **DATA FILE**, please visit
www.mhhe.com/lind16e

34. The monthly issues of the *Journal of Finance* are available on the Internet. The table below shows the number of times an issue was downloaded over the last 33 months. Suppose that you wish to summarize the number of downloads with a frequency distribution.

312	2,753	2,595	6,057	7,624	6,624	6,362	6,575	7,760	7,085	7,272
5,967	5,256	6,160	6,238	6,709	7,193	5,631	6,490	6,682	7,829	7,091
6,871	6,230	7,253	5,507	5,676	6,974	6,915	4,999	5,689	6,143	7,086

   a. How many classes would you propose?
   b. What class interval would you suggest?
   c. What quantity would you use for the lower limit of the initial class?
   d. Using your responses to parts (a), (b), and (c), create a frequency distribution.
   e. Identify the appearance of the frequency distribution.

35. The following histogram shows the scores on the first exam for a statistics class.

   a. How many students took the exam?
   b. What is the class interval?
   c. What is the class midpoint for the first class?
   d. How many students earned a score of less than 70?

36. The following chart summarizes the selling price of homes sold last month in the Sarasota, Florida, area.

   a. What is the chart called?
   b. How many homes were sold during the last month?
   c. What is the class interval?
   d. About 75% of the houses sold for less than what amount?
   e. One hundred seventy-five of the homes sold for less than what amount?

DESCRIBING DATA: FREQUENCY TABLES, FREQUENCY DISTRIBUTIONS, AND GRAPHIC PRESENTATION   45

For **DATA FILE**, please visit
www.mhhe.com/lind16e

37. A chain of sport shops catering to beginning skiers, headquartered in Aspen, Colorado, plans to conduct a study of how much a beginning skier spends on his or her initial purchase of equipment and supplies. Based on these figures, it wants to explore the possibility of offering combinations, such as a pair of boots and a pair of skis, to induce customers to buy more. A sample of 44 cash register receipts revealed these initial purchases:

$140	$ 82	$265	$168	$ 90	$114	$172	$230	$142
86	125	235	212	171	149	156	162	118
139	149	132	105	162	126	216	195	127
161	135	172	220	229	129	87	128	126
175	127	149	126	121	118	172	126	

a. Arrive at a suggested class interval.
b. Organize the data into a frequency distribution using a lower limit of $70.
c. Interpret your findings.

For **DATA FILE**, please visit
www.mhhe.com/lind16e

38. The numbers of outstanding shares for 24 publicly traded companies are listed in the following table.

Company	Number of Outstanding Shares (millions)	Company	Number of Outstanding Shares (millions)
Southwest Airlines	738	Costco	436
FIRSTENERGY	418	Home Depot	1,495
Harley Davidson	226	DTE Energy	172
Entergy	178	Dow Chemical	1,199
Chevron	1,957	Eastman Kodak	272
Pacific Gas and Electric	430	American Electric Power	485
DuPont	932	ITT Corporation	93
Westinghouse Solar	22	Ameren	243
Northeast Utilities	314	Virginia Electric and Power	575
Facebook	1,067	Public Service Electric & Gas	506
Google, Inc.	64	Consumers Energy	265
Apple	941	Starbucks	744

a. Using the number of outstanding shares, summarize the companies with a frequency distribution.
b. Display the frequency distribution with a frequency polygon.
c. Create a cumulative frequency distribution of the companies.
d. Display the cumulative frequency distribution with a cumulative frequency polygon.
e. Based on the cumulative frequency distribution, 75% of the companies have less than "what number" of outstanding shares?
f. Write a brief analysis of this group of companies based on your statistical summaries of "number of outstanding shares."

39. A recent survey showed that the typical American car owner spends $2,950 per year on operating expenses. Below is a breakdown of the various expenditure items. Draw an appropriate chart to portray the data and summarize your findings in a brief report.

Expenditure Item	Amount
Fuel	$ 603
Interest on car loan	279
Repairs	930
Insurance and license	646
Depreciation	492
Total	$2,950

46   CHAPTER 2

For **DATA FILE**, please visit
www.mhhe.com/lind16e

40. Midland National Bank selected a sample of 40 student checking accounts. Below are their end-of-the-month balances.

$404	$ 74	$234	$149	$279	$215	$123	$ 55	$ 43	$321
87	234	68	489	57	185	141	758	72	863
703	125	350	440	37	252	27	521	302	127
968	712	503	489	327	608	358	425	303	203

   a. Tally the data into a frequency distribution using $100 as a class interval and $0 as the starting point.
   b. Draw a cumulative frequency polygon.
   c. The bank considers any student with an ending balance of $400 or more a "preferred customer." Estimate the percentage of preferred customers.
   d. The bank is also considering a service charge to the lowest 10% of the ending balances. What would you recommend as the cutoff point between those who have to pay a service charge and those who do not?

41. Residents of the state of South Carolina earned a total of $69.5 billion in adjusted gross income. Seventy-three percent of the total was in wages and salaries; 11% in dividends, interest, and capital gains; 8% in IRAs and taxable pensions; 3% in business income pensions; 2% in Social Security; and the remaining 3% from other sources. Develop a pie chart depicting the breakdown of adjusted gross income. Write a paragraph summarizing the information.

42. A recent study of home technologies reported the number of hours of personal computer usage per week for a sample of 60 persons. Excluded from the study were people who worked out of their home and used the computer as a part of their work.

For **DATA FILE**, please visit
www.mhhe.com/lind16e

9.3	5.3	6.3	8.8	6.5	0.6	5.2	6.6	9.3	4.3
6.3	2.1	2.7	0.4	3.7	3.3	1.1	2.7	6.7	6.5
4.3	9.7	7.7	5.2	1.7	8.5	4.2	5.5	5.1	5.6
5.4	4.8	2.1	10.1	1.3	5.6	2.4	2.4	4.7	1.7
2.0	6.7	1.1	6.7	2.2	2.6	9.8	6.4	4.9	5.2
4.5	9.3	7.9	4.6	4.3	4.5	9.2	8.5	6.0	8.1

   a. Organize the data into a frequency distribution. How many classes would you suggest? What value would you suggest for a class interval?
   b. Draw a histogram. Interpret your result.

43. Merrill Lynch recently completed a study regarding the size of online investment portfolios (stocks, bonds, mutual funds, and certificates of deposit) for a sample of clients in the 40 up to 50 years old age group. Listed following is the value of all the investments in thousands of dollars for the 70 participants in the study.

For **DATA FILE**, please visit
www.mhhe.com/lind16e

$669.9	$ 7.5	$ 77.2	$ 7.5	$125.7	$516.9	$ 219.9	$645.2
301.9	235.4	716.4	145.3	26.6	187.2	315.5	89.2
136.4	616.9	440.6	408.2	34.4	296.1	185.4	526.3
380.7	3.3	363.2	51.9	52.2	107.5	82.9	63.0
228.6	308.7	126.7	430.3	82.0	227.0	321.1	403.4
39.5	124.3	118.1	23.9	352.8	156.7	276.3	23.5
31.3	301.2	35.7	154.9	174.3	100.6	236.7	171.9
221.1	43.4	212.3	243.3	315.4	5.9	1,002.2	171.7
295.7	437.0	87.8	302.1	268.1	899.5		

   a. Organize the data into a frequency distribution. How many classes would you suggest? What value would you suggest for a class interval?
   b. Draw a histogram. Interpret your result.

44. A total of 5.9% of the prime-time viewing audience watched shows on ABC, 7.6% watched shows on CBS, 5.5% on Fox, 6.0% on NBC, 2.0% on Warner Brothers, and 2.2% UPN. A total of 70.8% of the audience watched shows on other cable networks, such as CNN and ESPN. You can find the latest information on TV viewing from the following website: http://www.zap2it.com/tv/ratings/. Develop a pie chart or a bar chart to depict this information. Write a paragraph summarizing your findings.

45. Refer to the following chart:

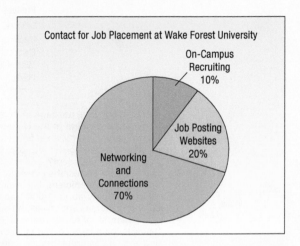

a. What is the name given to this type of chart?

b. Suppose that 1,000 graduates will start a new job shortly after graduation. Estimate the number of graduates whose first contact for employment occurred through networking and other connections.

c. Would it be reasonable to conclude that about 90% of job placements were made through networking, connections, and job posting websites? Cite evidence.

46. The following chart depicts the annual revenues, by type of tax, for the state of Georgia. The chart was developed using Kids Zone, an NCES project. Their website is nces.ed.gov/nceskids/createagraph/.

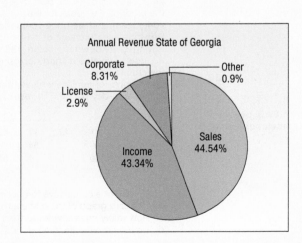

a. What percentage of the state revenue is accounted for by sales tax and individual income tax?
b. Which category will generate more revenue: corporate taxes or license fees?
c. The total annual revenue for the state of Georgia is $6.3 billion. Estimate the amount of revenue in billions of dollars for sales taxes and for individual taxes.

47. In 2011, the United States exported a total of $281 billion worth of products to Canada. The five largest categories were:

Product	Amount
Vehicles	$46.9
Machinery	44.2
Electrical machinery	27.1
Mineral fuel and oil	18.4
Plastic	12.6

a. Use a software package to develop a bar chart.
b. What percentage of the United States' total exports to Canada is represented by the two categories "Mineral fuel and oil" and "Vehicles"?
c. What percentage of the top five exported products do "Mineral fuel and oil" and "Vehicles" represent?

For **DATA FILE**, please visit www.mhhe.com/lind16e

48. In the United States, the industrial revolution of the early 20th century changed farming by making it more efficient. For example, in 1910 U.S. farms used 24.2 million horses and mules and only about 1,000 tractors. By 1960, 4.6 million tractors were used and only 3.2 million horses and mules. An outcome of making farming more efficient is the reduction of the number of farms from over 6 million in 1920 to about 2.2 million farms today. Listed below is the number of farms, in thousands, for each of the 50 states. Summarize the data and write a paragraph that describes your findings.

49	1	16	49	82	36	5	2	48	47
8	26	76	62	92	66	86	30	8	13
8	55	81	42	108	29	47	3	4	10
21	36	52	32	75	87	39	63	1	27
32	78	248	17	7	47	40	23	78	11

49. One of the most popular candies in the United States is M&M's, which are produced by the Mars Company. In the beginning M&M's were all brown; more recently they were produced in red, green, blue, orange, brown, and yellow. You can read about the history of the product, find ideas for baking, purchase the candies in the colors of your school or favorite team, and learn the percent of each color in the standard bags at www.m-ms.com. Recently, the purchase of a 14-ounce bag of M&M's Plain had 444 candies with the following breakdown by color: 130 brown, 98 yellow, 96 red, 35 orange, 52 blue, and 33 green. Develop a chart depicting this information and write a paragraph summarizing the results.

For **DATA FILE**, please visit www.mhhe.com/lind16e

50. The number of families who used the Minneapolis YWCA day care service was recorded during a 30-day period. The results are as follows:

31	49	19	62	24	45	23	51	55	60
40	35	54	26	57	37	43	65	18	41
50	56	4	54	39	52	35	51	63	42

a. Construct a cumulative frequency distribution.
b. Sketch a graph of the cumulative frequency polygon.
c. How many days saw fewer than 30 families utilize the day care center?
d. How busy were the highest 80% of the days?

DESCRIBING DATA: FREQUENCY TABLES, FREQUENCY DISTRIBUTIONS, AND GRAPHIC PRESENTATION   49

(The data for these exercises are available at the text website: www.mhhe.com/lind16e.)

51. Refer to the Real Estate data, which reports information on homes sold in the Goodyear, Arizona, area during the last year. Select an appropriate class interval and organize the selling prices into a frequency distribution. Write a brief report summarizing your findings. Be sure to answer the following questions in your report.

   a. Around what values do the data tend to cluster?

   b. Based on the frequency distribution, what is the typical selling price in the first class? What is the typical selling price in the last class?

   c. Draw a cumulative frequency distribution. How many homes sold for less than $200,000? Estimate the percent of the homes that sold for more than $220,000. What percent of the homes sold for less than $125,000?

   d. Refer to the variable regarding the townships. Draw a bar chart showing the number of homes sold in each township. Are there any differences or is the number of homes sold about the same in each township?

52. Refer to the Baseball 2012 data that report information on the 30 Major League Baseball teams for the 2012 season. Create a frequency distribution for the the team payroll variable and answer the following questions.

   a. What is the typical payroll for a team? What is the range of the payrolls?

   b. Comment on the shape of the distribution. Does it appear that any of the teams have a payroll that is out of line with the others?

   c. Draw a cumulative frequency distribution. Thirty percent of the teams have a payroll of less than what amount? About how many teams have total payroll of less than $100,000,000?

53. Refer to the Buena School District bus data. Select the variable referring to the number of miles traveled last month, and then organize these data into a frequency distribution.

   a. What is a typical amount of miles traveled? What is the range?

   b. Comment on the shape of the distribution. Are there any outliers in terms of miles driven?

   c. Draw a cumulative frequency distribution. Forty percent of the buses were driven fewer than how many miles? How many buses were driven less than 850 miles?

   d. Refer to the variables regarding the bus type and the number of seats in each bus. Draw a pie chart of each variable and comment on your findings.

3

Describing Data:
NUMERICAL MEASURES

THE KENTUCKY DERBY is held the first Saturday in May at Churchill Downs in Louisville, Kentucky. The race track is one and one-quarter miles. The table in Exercise 82 shows the winners since 1990, their margin of victory, the winning time, and the payoff on a $2 bet. Determine the mean and median for the variables winning time and payoff on a $2 bet. (See Exercise 82 and **LO3-1**.)

LEARNING OBJECTIVES

When you have completed this chapter, you will be able to:

LO3-1 Compute and interpret the mean, the median, and the mode.

LO3-2 Compute a weighted mean.

LO3-3 Compute and interpret the geometric mean.

LO3-4 Compute and interpret the range, variance, and standard deviation.

LO3-5 Explain and apply Chebyshev's theorem and the Empirical Rule.

LO3-6 Compute the mean and standard deviation of grouped data.

INTRODUCTION

Chapter 2 began our study of descriptive statistics. To summarize raw data into a meaningful form, we organized qualitative data into a frequency table and portrayed the results in a bar chart. In a similar fashion, we organized quantitative data into a frequency distribution and portrayed the results in a histogram. We also looked at other graphical techniques such as pie charts to portray qualitative data and frequency polygons to portray quantitative data.

This chapter is concerned with two numerical ways of describing quantitative variables, namely, **measures of location** and **measures of dispersion.** Measures of location are often referred to as averages. The purpose of a measure of location is to pinpoint the center of a distribution of data. An average is a measure of location that shows the central value of the data. Averages appear daily on TV, on various websites, in the newspaper, and in other journals. Here are some examples:

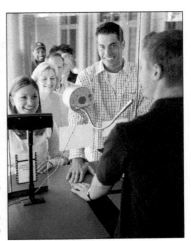

- The average U.S. home changes ownership every 11.8 years.
- An American receives an average of 568 pieces of mail per year.
- The average American home has more TV sets than people. There are 2.73 TV sets and 2.55 people in the typical home.
- The average American couple spends $20,398 for their wedding, while their budget is 50% less. This does not include the cost of a honeymoon or engagement ring.
- The average price of a theater ticket in the United States is $7.50, according to the National Association of Theatre Owners.

If we consider only measures of location in a set of data, or if we compare several sets of data using central values, we may draw an erroneous conclusion. In addition to measures of location, we should consider the **dispersion**—often called the *variation* or the *spread*—in the data. As an illustration, suppose the average annual income of executives for Internet-related companies is $80,000, and the average income for executives in pharmaceutical firms is also $80,000. If we looked only at the average incomes, we might wrongly conclude that the distributions of the two salaries are the same. However, we need to examine the dispersion or spread of the distributions of salary. A look at the salary ranges indicates that this conclusion of equal distributions is not correct. The salaries for the executives in the Internet firms range from $70,000 to $90,000, but salaries for the marketing executives in pharmaceuticals range from $40,000 to $120,000. Thus, we conclude that although the average salaries are the same for the two industries, there is much more spread or dispersion in salaries for the pharmaceutical executives. To describe the dispersion, we will consider the range, the variance, and the standard deviation.

MEASURES OF LOCATION

We begin by discussing measures of location. There is not just one measure of location; in fact, there are many. We will consider five: the arithmetic mean, the median, the mode, the weighted mean, and the geometric mean. The arithmetic mean is the most widely used and widely reported measure of location. We study the mean as both a population parameter and a sample statistic.

The Population Mean

Many studies involve all the values in a population. For example, there are 12 sales associates employed at the Reynolds Road Carpet Outlet. The mean amount of commission they earned last month was $1,345. This is a population value because we considered the commission of *all* the sales associates. Other examples of a population mean would be:

- The mean closing price for Johnson & Johnson stock for the last 5 days is $64.75.
- The mean number of hours of overtime worked last week by the six welders in the welding department of Butts Welding Inc. is 6.45 hours.
- Caryn Tirsch began a website last month devoted to organic gardening. The mean number of hits on her site for the 31 days in July was 84.36.

For raw data—that is, data that have not been grouped in a frequency distribution—the population mean is the sum of all the values in the population divided by the number of values in the population. To find the population mean, we use the following formula.

$$\text{Population mean} = \frac{\text{Sum of all the values in the population}}{\text{Number of values in the population}}$$

Instead of writing out in words the full directions for computing the population mean (or any other measure), it is more convenient to use the shorthand symbols of mathematics. The mean of the population using mathematical symbols is:

POPULATION MEAN	$\mu = \dfrac{\Sigma x}{N}$	[3–1]

where:

μ represents the population mean. It is the Greek lowercase letter "mu."
N is the number of values in the population.
x represents any particular value.
Σ is the Greek capital letter "sigma" and indicates the operation of adding.
Σx is the sum of the x values in the population.

Any measurable characteristic of a population is called a **parameter.** The mean of a population is an example of a parameter.

PARAMETER A characteristic of a population.

EXAMPLE

There are 42 exits on I-75 through the state of Kentucky. Listed below are the distances between exits (in miles).

11	4	10	4	9	3	8	10	3	14	1	10	3	5
2	2	5	6	1	2	2	3	7	1	3	7	8	10
1	4	7	5	2	2	5	1	1	3	3	1	2	1

Why is this information a population? What is the mean number of miles between exits?

> **SOLUTION**
>
> This is a population because we are considering all the exits on I-75 in Kentucky. We add the distances between each of the 42 exits. The total distance is 192 miles. To find the arithmetic mean, we divide this total by 42. So the arithmetic mean is 4.57 miles, found by 192/42. From formula (3–1):
>
> $$\mu = \frac{\Sigma x}{N} = \frac{11 + 4 + 10 + \cdots + 1}{42} = \frac{192}{42} = 4.57$$
>
> How do we interpret the value of 4.57? It is the typical number of miles between exits. Because we considered all the exits on I-75 in Kentucky, this value is a population parameter.

The Sample Mean

As explained in Chapter 1, we often select a sample from the population to estimate a specific characteristic of the population. Smucker's quality assurance department needs to be assured that the amount of orange marmalade in the jar labeled as containing 12 ounces actually contains that amount. It would be very expensive and time-consuming to check the weight of each jar. Therefore, a sample of 20 jars is selected, the mean of the sample is determined, and that value is used to estimate the amount in each jar.

For raw data—that is, ungrouped data—*the mean is the sum of all the sampled values divided by the total number of sampled values.* To find the mean for a sample:

$$\text{Sample mean} = \frac{\text{Sum of all the values in the sample}}{\text{Number of values in the sample}}$$

The mean of a sample and the mean of a population are computed in the same way, but the shorthand notation used is different. The formula for the mean of a *sample* is:

SAMPLE MEAN	$\bar{x} = \dfrac{\Sigma x}{n}$	[3–2]

where:

$\bar{x}$ represents the sample mean. It is read "x bar."
n is the number of values in the sample.
x represents any particular value.
Σ is the Greek capital letter "sigma" and indicates the operation of adding.
Σx is the sum of the x values in the sample.

The mean of a sample, or any other measure based on sample data, is called a **statistic.** If the mean weight of a sample of 10 jars of Smucker's orange marmalade is 11.5 ounces, this is an example of a statistic.

> **STATISTIC** A characteristic of a sample.

EXAMPLE

Verizon is studying the number of minutes used by clients in a particular cell phone rate plan. A random sample of 12 clients showed the following number of minutes used last month.

90	77	94	89	119	112
91	110	92	100	113	83

What is the arithmetic mean number of minutes used?

SOLUTION

Using formula (3–2), the sample mean is:

$$\text{Sample mean} = \frac{\text{Sum of all values in the sample}}{\text{Number of values in the sample}}$$

$$\bar{x} = \frac{\Sigma x}{n} = \frac{90 + 77 + \cdots + 83}{12} = \frac{1,170}{12} = 97.5$$

The arithmetic mean number of minutes used last month by the sample of cell phone users is 97.5 minutes.

Properties of the Arithmetic Mean

The arithmetic mean is a widely used measure of location. It has several important properties:

1. **To compute a mean, the data must be measured at the interval or ratio level.** Recall from Chapter 1 that ratio-level data include such data as ages, incomes, and weights, with the distance between numbers being constant.
2. **All the values are included in computing the mean.**
3. **The mean is unique.** That is, there is only one mean in a set of data. Later in the chapter, we will discover a measure of location that might appear twice, or more than twice, in a set of data.
4. **The sum of the deviations of each value from the mean is zero.** Expressed symbolically:

$$\Sigma(x - \bar{x}) = 0$$

As an example, the mean of 3, 8, and 4 is 5. Then:

$$\Sigma(x - \bar{x}) = (3 - 5) + (8 - 5) + (4 - 5)$$
$$= -2 + 3 - 1$$
$$= 0$$

Thus, we can consider the mean as a balance point for a set of data. To illustrate, we have a long board with the numbers 1, 2, 3, . . . , 9 evenly spaced on it. Suppose three bars of equal weight were placed on the board at numbers 3, 4, and 8, and the balance point was set at 5, the mean of the three numbers. We would find that the

DESCRIBING DATA: NUMERICAL MEASURES   55

board is balanced perfectly! The deviations below the mean (−3) are equal to the deviations above the mean (+3). Shown schematically:

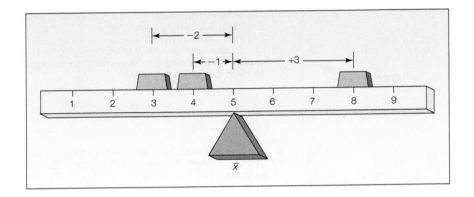

The mean does have a weakness. Recall that the mean uses the value of every item in a sample, or population, in its computation. If one or two of these values are either extremely large or extremely small compared to the majority of data, the mean might not be an appropriate average to represent the data. For example, suppose the annual incomes of a sample of financial planners at Merrill Lynch are $62,900, $61,600, $62,500, $60,800, and $1,200,000. The mean income is $289,560. Obviously, it is not representative of this group because all but one financial planner has an income in the $60,000 to $63,000 range. One income ($1.2 million) is unduly affecting the mean.

SELF-REVIEW

3–1

1. The annual incomes of a sample of middle-management employees at Westinghouse are $62,900, $69,100, $58,300, and $76,800.
   (a) Give the formula for the sample mean.
   (b) Find the sample mean.
   (c) Is the mean you computed in (b) a statistic or a parameter? Why?
   (d) What is your best estimate of the population mean?
2. All the students in advanced Computer Science 411 are a population. Their course grades are 92, 96, 61, 86, 79, and 84.
   (a) Give the formula for the population mean.
   (b) Compute the mean course grade.
   (c) Is the mean you computed in (b) a statistic or a parameter? Why?

EXERCISES

▼

The answers to the odd-numbered exercises are in Appendix D.

1. Compute the mean of the following population values: 6, 3, 5, 7, 6.
2. Compute the mean of the following population values: 7, 5, 7, 3, 7, 4.
3. **a.** Compute the mean of the following sample values: 5, 9, 4, 10.
   b. Show that $\Sigma(x - \bar{x}) = 0$.
4. **a.** Compute the mean of the following sample values: 1.3, 7.0, 3.6, 4.1, 5.0.
   b. Show that $\Sigma(x - \bar{x}) = 0$.
5. Compute the mean of the following sample values: 16.25, 12.91, 14.58.
6. Suppose you go to the grocery store and spend $61.85 for the purchase of 14 items. What is the mean price per item?

For Exercises 7–10, (a) compute the arithmetic mean and (b) indicate whether it is a statistic or a parameter.

7. There are 10 salespeople employed by Midtown Ford. The number of new cars sold last month by the respective salespeople were 15, 23, 4, 19, 18, 10, 10, 8, 28, 19.

8. The accounting department at a mail-order company counted the following numbers of incoming calls per day to the company's toll-free number during the first 7 days in May: 14, 24, 19, 31, 36, 26, 17.

9. The Cambridge Power and Light Company selected a random sample of 20 residential customers. Following are the amounts, to the nearest dollar, the customers were charged for electrical service last month:

For **DATA FILE**, please visit
www.mhhe.com/lind16e

| 54 | 48 | 58 | 50 | 25 | 47 | 75 | 46 | 60 | 70 |
| 67 | 68 | 39 | 35 | 56 | 66 | 33 | 62 | 65 | 67 |

10. The Human Relations Director at Ford began a study of the overtime hours in the Inspection Department. A sample of 15 workers showed they worked the following number of overtime hours last month.

For **DATA FILE**, please visit
www.mhhe.com/lind16e

| 13 | 13 | 12 | 15 | 7 | 15 | 5 | 12 |
| 6 | 7 | 12 | 10 | 9 | 13 | 12 | |

11. AAA Heating and Air Conditioning completed 30 jobs last month with a mean revenue of $5,430 per job. The president wants to know the total revenue for the month. Based on the limited information, can you compute the total revenue? What is it?

12. A large pharmaceutical company hires business administration graduates to sell its products. The company is growing rapidly and dedicates only 1 day of sales training for new salespeople. The company's goal for new salespeople is $10,000 per month. The goal is based on the current mean sales for the entire company, which is $10,000 per month. After reviewing the retention rates of new employees, the company finds that only 1 in 10 new employees stays longer than 3 months. Comment on using the current mean sales per month as a sales goal for new employees. Why do new employees leave the company?

The Median

We have stressed that, for data containing one or two very large or very small values, the arithmetic mean may not be representative. The center for such data can be better described by a measure of location called the **median.**

To illustrate the need for a measure of location other than the arithmetic mean, suppose you are seeking to buy a condominium in Palm Aire. Your real estate agent says that the typical price of the units currently available is $110,000. Would you still want to look? If you had budgeted your maximum purchase price at $75,000, you might think they are out of your price range. However, checking the prices of the individual units might change your mind. They are $60,000, $65,000, $70,000, and $80,000, and a superdeluxe penthouse costs $275,000. The arithmetic mean price is $110,000, as the real estate agent reported, but one price ($275,000) is pulling the arithmetic mean upward, causing it to be an unrepresentative average. It does seem that a price around $70,000 is a more typical or representative average, and it is. In cases such as this, the median provides a more valid measure of location.

> **MEDIAN** The midpoint of the values after they have been ordered from the minimum to the maximum values.

DESCRIBING DATA: NUMERICAL MEASURES   57

The median price of the units available is $70,000. To determine this, we order the prices from the minimum value ($60,000) to the maximum value ($275,000) and select the middle value ($70,000). For the median, the data must be at least an ordinal level of measurement.

Prices Ordered from Minimum to Maximum		Prices Ordered from Maximum to Minimum
$ 60,000		$275,000
65,000		80,000
70,000	← Median →	70,000
80,000		65,000
275,000		60,000

Note that there is the same number of prices below the median of $70,000 as above it. The median is, therefore, unaffected by extremely low or high prices. Had the highest price been $90,000, or $300,000, or even $1 million, the median price would still be $70,000. Likewise, had the lowest price been $20,000 or $50,000, the median price would still be $70,000.

In the previous illustration, there are an *odd* number of observations (five). How is the median determined for an *even* number of observations? As before, the observations are ordered. Then by convention to obtain a unique value we calculate the mean of the two middle observations. So for an even number of observations, the median may not be one of the given values.

E X A M P L E

Facebook is a popular social networking website. Users can add friends and send them messages, and update their personal profiles to notify friends about themselves and their activities. A sample of 10 adults revealed they spent the following number of hours last month using Facebook.

3	5	7	5	9	1	3	9	17	10

Find the median number of hours.

S O L U T I O N

Note that the number of adults sampled is even (10). The first step, as before, is to order the hours using Facebook from the minimum value to the maximum value. Then identify the two middle times. The arithmetic mean of the two middle observations gives us the median hours. Arranging the values from minimum to maximum:

1	3	3	5	5	7	9	9	10	17

The median is found by averaging the two middle values. The middle values are 5 hours and 7 hours, and the mean of these two values is 6. We conclude that the typical adult Facebook user spends 6 hours per month at the website. Notice that the median is not one of the values. Also, half of the times are below the median and half are above it.

58 CHAPTER 3

The major properties of the median are:

1. **It is not affected by extremely large or small values.** Therefore, the median is a valuable measure of location when such values do occur.
2. **It can be computed for ordinal-level data or higher.** Recall from Chapter 1 that ordinal-level data can be ranked from low to high.

The Mode

The **mode** is another measure of location.

> **MODE** The value of the observation that appears most frequently.

The mode is especially useful in summarizing nominal-level data. As an example of its use for nominal-level data, a company has developed five bath oils. The bar chart in Chart 3–1 shows the results of a marketing survey designed to find which bath oil consumers prefer. The largest number of respondents favored Lamoure, as evidenced by the highest bar. Thus, Lamoure is the mode.

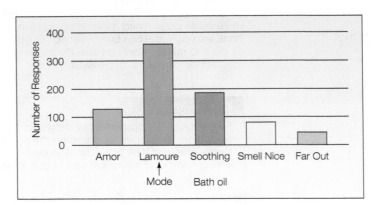

CHART 3–1 Number of Respondents Favoring Various Bath Oils

EXAMPLE

Recall the data regarding the distance in miles between exits on I-75 in Kentucky. The information is repeated below.

11	4	10	4	9	3	8	10	3	14	1	10	3	5
2	2	5	6	1	2	2	3	7	1	3	7	8	10
1	4	7	5	2	2	5	1	1	3	3	1	2	1

What is the modal distance?

SOLUTION

The first step is to organize the distances into a frequency table. This will help us determine the distance that occurs most frequently.

DESCRIBING DATA: NUMERICAL MEASURES 59

Distance in Miles between Exits	Frequency
1	8
2	7
3	7
4	3
5	4
6	1
7	3
8	2
9	1
10	4
11	1
14	1
Total	42

The distance that occurs most often is 1 mile. This happens eight times—that is, there are eight exits that are 1 mile apart. So the modal distance between exits is 1 mile.

Which of the three measures of location (mean, median, or mode) best represents the central location of these data? Is the mode the best measure of location to represent the Kentucky data? No. The mode assumes only the nominal scale of measurement and the variable miles is measured using the ratio scale. We calculated the mean to be 4.57 miles. See page 53. Is the mean the best measure of location to represent these data? Probably not. There are several cases in which the distance between exits is large. These values are affecting the mean, making it too large and not representative of the distances between exits. What about the median? The median distance is 3 miles. That is, half of the distances between exits are 3 miles or less. In this case, the median of 3 miles between exits is probably a more representative measure of the distance between exits.

In summary, we can determine the mode for all levels of data—nominal, ordinal, interval, and ratio. The mode also has the advantage of not being affected by extremely high or low values.

The mode does have disadvantages, however, that cause it to be used less frequently than the mean or median. For many sets of data, there is no mode because no value appears more than once. For example, there is no mode for this set of price data because every value occurs once: $19, $21, $23, $20, and $18. Conversely, for some data sets there is more than one mode. Suppose the ages of the individuals in a stock investment club are 22, 26, 27, 27, 31, 35, and 35. Both the ages 27 and 35 are modes. Thus, this grouping of ages is referred to as *bimodal* (having two modes). One would question the use of two modes to represent the location of this set of age data.

SELF-REVIEW
3–2

1. A sample of single persons in Towson, Texas, receiving Social Security payments revealed these monthly benefits: $852, $598, $580, $1,374, $960, $878, and $1,130.
   (a) What is the median monthly benefit?
   (b) How many observations are below the median? Above it?
2. The number of work stoppages in the automobile industry for selected months are 6, 0, 10, 14, 8, and 0.
   (a) What is the median number of stoppages?
   (b) How many observations are below the median? Above it?
   (c) What is the modal number of work stoppages?

13. What would you report as the modal value for a set of observations if there were a total of:
a. 10 observations and no two values were the same?
b. 6 observations and they were all the same?
c. 6 observations and the values were 1, 2, 3, 3, 4, and 4?

For Exercises 14–16, determine the (a) mean, (b) median, and (c) mode.

14. The following is the number of oil changes for the last 7 days at the Jiffy Lube located at the corner of Elm Street and Pennsylvania Avenue.

41	15	39	54	31	15	33

15. The following is the percent change in net income from last year to this year for a sample of 12 construction companies in Denver.

5	1	−10	−6	5	12	7	8	6	5	−1	11

16. The following are the ages of the 10 people in the video arcade at the Southwyck Shopping Mall at 10 a.m.

12	8	17	6	11	14	8	17	10	8

For **DATA FILE**, please visit
www.mhhe.com/lind16e

17. Several indicators of long-term economic growth in the United States and their annual percent change are listed below.

Economic Indicator	Percent Change	Economic Indicator	Percent Change
Inflation	4.5%	Real GNP	2.9%
Exports	4.7	Investment (residential)	3.6
Imports	2.3	Investment (nonresidential)	2.1
Real disposable income	2.9	Productivity (total)	1.4
Consumption	2.7	Productivity (manufacturing)	5.2

a. What is the median percent change?
b. What is the modal percent change?

For **DATA FILE**, please visit
www.mhhe.com/lind16e

18. Sally Reynolds sells real estate along the coastal area of Northern California. Below are her total annual commissions between 2002 and 2012. Find the mean, median, and mode of the commissions she earned for the 11 years.

Year	Amount (thousands)
2002	$237.51
2003	233.80
2004	206.97
2005	248.14
2006	164.69
2007	292.16
2008	269.11
2009	225.57
2010	255.33
2011	202.67
2012	206.53

For **DATA FILE**, please visit
www.mhhe.com/lind16e

19. The accounting firm of Rowatti and Koppel specializes in income tax returns for self-employed professionals, such as physicians, dentists, architects, and lawyers. The firm employs 11 accountants who prepare the returns. For last year, the number of returns prepared by each accountant was:

58	75	31	58	46	65	60	71	45	58	80

DESCRIBING DATA: NUMERICAL MEASURES   61

For **DATA FILE**, please visit
www.mhhe.com/lind16e

Find the mean, median, and mode for the number of returns prepared by each accountant. If you could report only one, which measure of location would you recommend reporting?

20. The demand for the video games provided by Mid-Tech Video Games Inc. has exploded in the last several years. Hence, the owner needs to hire several new technical people to keep up with the demand. Mid-Tech gives each applicant a special test that Dr. McGraw, the designer of the test, believes is closely related to the ability to create video games. For the general population, the mean on this test is 100. Below are the scores on this test for the applicants.

| 95 | 105 | 120 | 81 | 90 | 115 | 99 | 100 | 130 | 10 |

The president is interested in the overall quality of the job applicants based on this test. Compute the mean and the median scores for the 10 applicants. What would you report to the president? Does it seem that the applicants are better than the general population?

The Relative Positions of the Mean, Median, and Mode

Refer to the histogram in Chart 3–2. It is a symmetric distribution, which is also mound-shaped. This distribution *has the same shape on either side of the center*. If the histogram were folded in half, the two halves would be identical. For any symmetric distribution, the mode, median, and mean are located at the center and are always equal. They are all equal to 30 years in Chart 3–2. We should point out that there are symmetric distributions that are not mound-shaped.

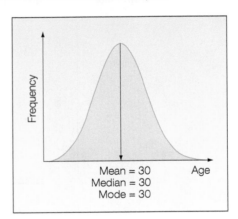

CHART 3–2 A Symmetric Distribution

The number of years corresponding to the highest point of the curve is the *mode* (30 years). Because the distribution is symmetrical, the *median* corresponds to the point where the distribution is cut in half (30 years). Also, because the arithmetic mean is the balance point of a distribution (as shown on page 55), and the distribution is symmetric, the arithmetic mean is 30. Logically, any of the three measures would be appropriate to represent the distribution's center.

If a distribution is nonsymmetrical, or **skewed,** the relationship among the three measures changes. In a **positively skewed distribution,** such as the distribution of weekly income in Chart 3–3, the arithmetic mean is the largest of the three measures. Why? Because the mean is influenced more than the median or mode by a few extremely high values. The median is generally the next largest measure in a positively skewed frequency distribution. The mode is the smallest of the three measures.

If the distribution is highly skewed, the mean would not be a good measure to use. The median and mode would be more representative.

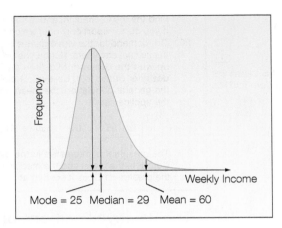

CHART 3–3 A Positively Skewed Distribution

Conversely, if a distribution is **negatively skewed,** such as the distribution of tensile strength in Chart 3–4, the mean is the lowest of the three measures. The mean is, of course, influenced by a few extremely low observations. The median is greater than the arithmetic mean, and the modal value is the largest of the three measures. Again, if the distribution is highly skewed, the mean should not be used to represent the data.

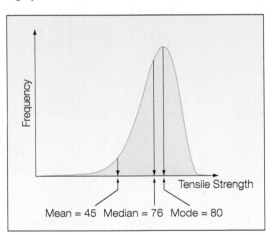

CHART 3–4 A Negatively Skewed Distribution

SELF-REVIEW

3–3

The weekly sales from a sample of Hi-Tec electronic supply stores were organized into a frequency distribution. The mean of weekly sales was computed to be $105,900, the median $105,000, and the mode $104,500.
(a) Sketch the sales in the form of a smoothed frequency polygon. Note the location of the mean, median, and mode on the *X*-axis.
(b) Is the distribution symmetrical, positively skewed, or negatively skewed? Explain.

EXERCISES

21. The unemployment rate in the state of Alaska by month is given in the table below:

Jan	Feb	Mar	Apr	May	Jun	Jul	Aug	Sep	Oct	Nov	Dec
8.7	8.8	8.7	7.8	7.3	7.8	6.6	6.5	6.5	6.8	7.3	7.6

DESCRIBING DATA: NUMERICAL MEASURES   63

For **DATA FILE**, please visit
www.mhhe.com/lind16e

For **DATA FILE**, please visit
www.mhhe.com/lind16e

   a. What is the arithmetic mean of the Alaska unemployment rates?
   b. Find the median and the mode for the unemployment rates.
   c. Compute the arithmetic mean and median for just the winter (Dec–Mar) months. Is it much different?

22. Big Orange Trucking is designing an information system for use in "in-cab" communications. It must summarize data from eight sites throughout a region to describe typical conditions. Compute an appropriate measure of central location for the variables wind direction, temperature, and pavement.

City	Wind Direction	Temperature	Pavement
Anniston, AL	West	89	Dry
Atlanta, GA	Northwest	86	Wet
Augusta, GA	Southwest	92	Wet
Birmingham, AL	South	91	Dry
Jackson, MS	Southwest	92	Dry
Meridian, MS	South	92	Trace
Monroe, LA	Southwest	93	Wet
Tuscaloosa, AL	Southwest	93	Trace

Software Solution

We can use a statistical software package to find many measures of location.

EXAMPLE

Table 2–4 on page 26 shows the profit on the sales of 180 vehicles at Applewood Auto Group. Determine the mean and the median selling price.

SOLUTION

The mean, median, and modal amounts of profit are reported in the following output (highlighted in the screen shot). (Reminder: The instructions to create the output appear in the **Software Commands** in Appendix C.) There are 180 vehicles in the study, so using a calculator would be tedious and prone to error.

APPLEWOOD AUTO GROUP

	A	B	C	D	E	F	G	H
1	Age	Profit	Location	Vehicle-Type	Previous		Profit	
2	21	$1,387	Tionesta	Sedan	0			
3	23	$1,754	Sheffield	SUV	1		Mean	1843.17
4	24	$1,817	Sheffield	Hybrid	1		Standard Error	47.97
5	25	$1,040	Sheffield	Compact	0		Median	1882.50
6	26	$1,273	Kane	Sedan	1		Mode	1915.00
7	27	$1,529	Sheffield	Sedan	1		Standard Deviation	643.63
8	27	$3,082	Kane	Truck	0		Sample Variance	414256.61
9	28	$1,951	Kane	SUV	1		Kurtosis	-0.22
10	28	$2,692	Tionesta	Compact	0		Skewness	-0.24
11	29	$1,342	Kane	Sedan	2		Range	2998
12	29	$1,206	Sheffield	Sedan	0		Minimum	294
13	30	$443	Kane	Sedan	3		Maximum	3292
14	30	$1,621	Sheffield	Truck	1		Sum	331770
15	30	$754	Olean	Sedan	2		Count	180

64   CHAPTER 3

> The mean profit is $1,843.17 and the median is $1,882.50. These two values are less than $40 apart, so either value is reasonable. We can also see from the Excel output that there were 180 vehicles sold and their total profit was $331,770.00. We will describe the meaning of standard error, standard deviation, and other measures reported on the output later in this chapter and in later chapters.
>
> What can we conclude? The typical profit on a vehicle is about $1,850. Management at Applewood might use this value for revenue projections. For example, if the dealership could increase the number sold in a month from 180 to 200, this would result in an additional estimated $37,000 of revenue, found by 20($1,850).

LO3-2

Compute a weighted mean.

THE WEIGHTED MEAN

The weighted mean is a convenient way to compute the arithmetic mean when there are several observations of the same value. To explain, suppose the nearby Wendy's Restaurant sold medium, large, and Biggie-sized soft drinks for $.90, $1.25, and $1.50, respectively. Of the last 10 drinks sold, 3 were medium, 4 were large, and 3 were Biggie-sized. To find the mean price of the last 10 drinks sold, we could use formula (3–2).

$$\bar{x} = \frac{\$.90 + \$.90 + \$.90 + \$1.25 + \$1.25 + \$1.25 + \$1.25 + \$1.50 + \$1.50 + \$1.50}{10}$$

$$\bar{x} = \frac{\$12.20}{10} = \$1.22$$

The mean selling price of the last 10 drinks is $1.22.

An easier way to find the mean selling price is to determine the weighted mean. That is, we multiply each observation by the number of times it happens. We will refer to the weighted mean as $\bar{x}_w$. This is read "x bar sub w."

$$\bar{x}_w = \frac{3(\$0.90) + 4(\$1.25) + 3(\$1.50)}{10} = \frac{\$12.20}{10} = \$1.22$$

In this case, the weights are frequency counts. However, any measure of importance could be used as a weight. In general, the weighted mean of a set of numbers designated $x_1, x_2, x_3, \ldots, x_n$ with the corresponding weights $w_1, w_2, w_3, \ldots, w_n$ is computed by:

WEIGHTED MEAN	$\bar{x}_w = \dfrac{w_1 x_1 + w_2 x_2 + w_3 x_3 + \cdots + w_n x_n}{w_1 + w_2 + w_3 + \cdots + w_n}$	**[3–3]**

This may be shortened to:

$$\bar{x}_w = \frac{\Sigma(wx)}{\Sigma w}$$

Note that the denominator of a weighted mean is always the sum of the weights.

E X A M P L E

The Carter Construction Company pays its hourly employees $16.50, $19.00, or $25.00 per hour. There are 26 hourly employees, 14 of whom are paid at the $16.50 rate, 10 at the $19.00 rate, and 2 at the $25.00 rate. What is the mean hourly rate paid the 26 employees?

S O L U T I O N

To find the mean hourly rate, we multiply each of the hourly rates by the number of employees earning that rate. From formula (3–3), the mean hourly rate is

$$\bar{x}_w = \frac{14(\$16.50) + 10(\$19.00) + 2(\$25.00)}{14 + 10 + 2} = \frac{\$471.00}{26} = \$18.1154$$

The weighted mean hourly wage is rounded to $18.12.

SELF-REVIEW

3–4

Springers sold 95 Antonelli men's suits for the regular price of $400. For the spring sale, the suits were reduced to $200 and 126 were sold. At the final clearance, the price was reduced to $100 and the remaining 79 suits were sold.
(a) What was the weighted mean price of an Antonelli suit?
(b) Springers paid $200 a suit for the 300 suits. Comment on the store's profit per suit if a salesperson receives a $25 commission for each one sold.

E X E R C I S E S

23. In June, an investor purchased 300 shares of Oracle (an information technology company) stock at $20 per share. In August, she purchased an additional 400 shares at $25 per share. In November, she purchased an additional 400 shares, but the stock declined to $23 per share. What is the weighted mean price per share?
24. The Bookstall Inc. is a specialty bookstore concentrating on used books sold via the Internet. Paperbacks are $1.00 each, and hardcover books are $3.50. Of the 50 books sold last Tuesday morning, 40 were paperback and the rest were hardcover. What was the weighted mean price of a book?
25. The Loris Healthcare System employs 200 persons on the nursing staff. Fifty are nurse's aides, 50 are practical nurses, and 100 are registered nurses. Nurse's aides receive $8 an hour, practical nurses $15 an hour, and registered nurses $24 an hour. What is the weighted mean hourly wage?
26. Andrews and Associates specialize in corporate law. They charge $100 an hour for researching a case, $75 an hour for consultations, and $200 an hour for writing a brief. Last week one of the associates spent 10 hours consulting with her client, 10 hours researching the case, and 20 hours writing the brief. What was the weighted mean hourly charge for her legal services?

LO3-3

Compute and interpret the geometric mean.

THE GEOMETRIC MEAN

The geometric mean is useful in finding the average change of percentages, ratios, indexes, or growth rates over time. It has a wide application in business and economics because we are often interested in finding the percentage changes in sales, salaries, or economic figures, such as the gross domestic product, which compound or build on each other. The geometric mean of a set of n positive numbers is defined as the nth root of the product of n values. The formula for the geometric mean is written:

GEOMETRIC MEAN	$GM = \sqrt[n]{(x_1)(x_2)\cdots(x_n)}$	[3–4]

The geometric mean will always be less than or equal to (never more than) the arithmetic mean. Also, all the data values must be positive.

As an example of the geometric mean, suppose you receive a 5% increase in salary this year and a 15% increase next year. The average annual percent increase is

66   CHAPTER 3

9.886, not 10.0. Why is this so? We begin by calculating the geometric mean. Recall, for example, that a 5% increase in salary is 105%. We will write it as 1.05.

$$GM = \sqrt{(1.05)(1.15)} = 1.09886$$

This can be verified by assuming that your monthly earning was $3,000 to start and you received two increases of 5% and 15%.

$$Raise\ 1 = \$3,000(.05) = \$150.00$$
$$Raise\ 2 = \$3,150(.15) = \underline{472.50}$$
$$Total \qquad\qquad\qquad \$622.50$$

Your total salary increase is $622.50. This is equivalent to:

$$\$3,000.00(.09886) = \$296.58$$
$$\$3,296.58(.09886) = \underline{325.90}$$
$$\$622.48\ \text{is about }\$622.50$$

The following example shows the geometric mean of several percentages.

EXAMPLE

The return on investment earned by Atkins Construction Company for four successive years was 30%, 20%, −40%, and 200%. What is the geometric mean rate of return on investment?

SOLUTION

The number 1.3 represents the 30% return on investment, which is the "original" investment of 1.0 plus the "return" of 0.3. The number 0.6 represents the loss of 40%, which is the original investment of 1.0 less the loss of 0.4. This calculation assumes the total return each period is reinvested or becomes the base for the next period. In other words, the base for the second period is 1.3 and the base for the third period is (1.3)(1.2) and so forth.
  Then the geometric mean rate of return is 29.4%, found by

$$GM = \sqrt[n]{(x_1)(x_2)\cdots(x_n)} = \sqrt[4]{(1.3)(1.2)(0.6)(3.0)} = \sqrt[4]{2.808} = 1.294$$

The geometric mean is the fourth root of 2.808. So, the average rate of return (compound annual growth rate) is 29.4%.
  Notice also that if you compute the arithmetic mean [(30 + 20 − 40 + 200)/4 = 52.5], you would have a much larger number, which would overstate the true rate of return!

A second application of the geometric mean is to find an average percentage change over a period of time. For example, if you earned $45,000 in 2000 and $100,000 in 2012, what is your annual rate of increase over the period? It is 6.88%. The rate of increase is determined from the following formula.

RATE OF INCREASE OVER TIME	$GM = \sqrt[n]{\dfrac{\text{Value at end of period}}{\text{Value at start of period}}} - 1$	[3–5]

In the above box, n is the number of periods. An example will show the details of finding the average annual percent increase.

EXAMPLE

During the decade of the 1990s, and into the 2000s, Las Vegas, Nevada, was the fastest-growing city in the United States. The population increased from 258,295 in 1990 to 584,539 in 2011. This is an increase of 326,244 people, or a 126.3% increase over the period. The population has more than doubled. What is the average *annual* percent increase?

SOLUTION

There are 21 years between 1990 and 2011, so $n = 21$. Then formula (3–5) for the geometric mean as applied to this problem is:

$$GM = \sqrt[21]{\frac{\text{Value at end of period}}{\text{Value at start of period}}} - 1.0 = \sqrt[21]{\frac{584,539}{258,295}} - 1.0 = 1.0397 - 1.0 = .0397$$

To summarize, the steps to compute the geometric mean are:

1. Divide the value at the end of the period by the value at the beginning of the period.
2. Find the nth root of the ratio, where n is the number of periods.
3. Subtract one.

The value of .0397 indicates that the average annual growth over the period was 3.97%. To put it another way, the population of Las Vegas increased at a rate of 3.97% per year from 1990 to 2011.

SELF-REVIEW

3–5

1. The percent increase in sales for the last 4 years at Combs Cosmetics were 4.91, 5.75, 8.12, and 21.60.
    (a) Find the geometric mean percent increase.
    (b) Find the arithmetic mean percent increase.
    (c) Is the arithmetic mean equal to or greater than the geometric mean?
2. Production of Cablos trucks increased from 23,000 units in 1993 to 120,520 in 2013. Find the geometric mean annual percent increase.

EXERCISES

27. Compute the geometric mean of the following percent increases: 8, 12, 14, 26, and 5.
28. Compute the geometric mean of the following percent increases: 2, 8, 6, 4, 10, 6, 8, and 4.
29. Listed below is the percent increase in sales for the MG Corporation over the last 5 years. Determine the geometric mean percent increase in sales over the period.

9.4	13.8	11.7	11.9	14.7

30. In 1996, a total of 14,968,000 taxpayers in the United States filed their individual tax returns electronically. By the year 2010, the number increased to 99,000,000. What is the geometric mean annual increase for the period?
31. The Consumer Price Index is reported monthly by the U.S. Bureau of Labor Statistics. It reports the change in prices for a market basket of goods from one period to another. The index for 2000 was 172.2. By 2012, it increased to 229.6. What was the geometric mean annual increase for the period?
32. JetBlue Airways is an American low-cost airline headquartered in New York City. Its main base is John F. Kennedy International Airport. JetBlue's revenue in 2002 was $635.2 million. By 2012, revenue had increased to $3,788.0 million. What was the geometric mean annual increase for the period?
33. In 1985, there were 340,213 cell phone subscribers in the United States. By 2012, the number of cell phone subscribers increased to 327,577,529. What is the geometric mean annual increase for the period?

68   CHAPTER 3

34. The information below shows the cost for a year of college in public and private colleges in 2002–03 and 2012–13. What is the geometric mean annual increase for the period for the two types of colleges? Compare the rates of increase.

Type of College	2002–03	2012–13
Public	$ 4,960	$ 8,655
Private	18,056	29,056

LO3-4

Compute and interpret the range, variance, and standard deviation.

STATISTICS IN ACTION

The U.S. Postal Service has tried to become more "user friendly" in the last several years. A recent survey showed that customers were interested in more *consistency* in the time it takes to make a delivery. Under the old conditions, a local letter might take only one day to deliver, or it might take several. "Just tell me how many days ahead I need to mail the birthday card to Mom so it gets there on her birthday, not early, not late," was a common complaint. The level of consistency is measured by the standard deviation of the delivery times.

WHY STUDY DISPERSION?

A measure of location, such as the mean, median, or mode, only describes the center of the data. It is valuable from that standpoint, but it does not tell us anything about the spread of the data. For example, if your nature guide told you that the river ahead averaged 3 feet in depth, would you want to wade across on foot without additional information? Probably not. You would want to know something about the variation in the depth. Is the maximum depth of the river 3.25 feet and the minimum 2.75 feet? If that is the case, you would probably agree to cross. What if you learned the river depth ranged from 0.50 foot to 5.5 feet? Your decision would probably be not to cross. Before making a decision about crossing the river, you want information on both the typical depth and the dispersion in the depth of the river.

A small value for a measure of dispersion indicates that the data are clustered closely, say, around the arithmetic mean. The mean is therefore considered representative of the data. Conversely, a large measure of dispersion indicates that the mean is not reliable. Refer to Chart 3–5. The 100 employees of Hammond Iron Works Inc., a steel fabricating company, are organized into a histogram based on the number of years of employment with the company. The mean is 4.9 years, but the spread of the data is from 6 months to 16.8 years. The mean of 4.9 years is not very representative of all the employees.

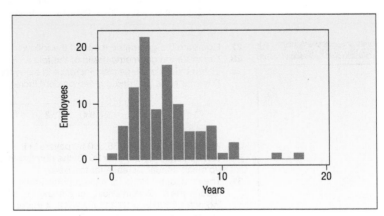

CHART 3–5 Histogram of Years of Employment at Hammond Iron Works Inc.

A second reason for studying the dispersion in a set of data is to compare the spread in two or more distributions. Suppose, for example, that the new Vision Quest LCD computer monitor is assembled in Baton Rouge and also in Tucson. The arithmetic mean hourly output in both the Baton Rouge plant and the Tucson plant is 50.

DESCRIBING DATA: NUMERICAL MEASURES   69

CHART 3–6 Hourly Production of Computer Monitors at the Baton Rouge and Tucson Plants

Based on the two means, you might conclude that the distributions of the hourly outputs are identical. Production records for 9 hours at the two plants, however, reveal that this conclusion is not correct (see Chart 3–6). Baton Rouge production varies from 48 to 52 assemblies per hour. Production at the Tucson plant is more erratic, ranging from 40 to 60 per hour. Therefore, the hourly output for Baton Rouge is clustered near the mean of 50; the hourly output for Tucson is more dispersed.

We will consider several measures of dispersion. The range is based on the maximum and minimum values in the data set; that is, only two values are considered. The variance and the standard deviation use all the values in a data set and are based on deviations from the arithmetic mean.

Range

The simplest measure of dispersion is the **range.** It is the difference between the maximum and minimum values in a data set. In the form of an equation:

RANGE	Range = Maximum value − Minimum value	[3–6]

The range is widely used in statistical process control (SPC) applications because it is very easy to calculate and understand.

EXAMPLE

Refer to Chart 3–6 above. Find the range in the number of computer monitors produced per hour for the Baton Rouge and the Tucson plants. Interpret the two ranges.

SOLUTION

The range of the hourly production of computer monitors at the Baton Rouge plant is 4, found by the difference between the maximum hourly production of

52 and the minimum of 48. The range in the hourly production for the Tucson plant is 20 computer monitors, found by 60 − 40. We therefore conclude that (1) there is less dispersion in the hourly production in the Baton Rouge plant than in the Tucson plant because the range of 4 computer monitors is less than a range of 20 computer monitors and (2) the production is clustered more closely around the mean of 50 at the Baton Rouge plant than at the Tucson plant (because a range of 4 is less than a range of 20). Thus, the mean production in the Baton Rouge plant (50 computer monitors) is a more representative measure of location than the mean of 50 computer monitors for the Tucson plant.

Variance

A defect of the range is that it is based on only two values, the maximum and the minimum; it does not take into consideration all of the values. The **variance** does. It measures the mean amount by which the values in a population, or sample, vary from their mean. In terms of a definition:

> **VARIANCE** The arithmetic mean of the squared deviations from the mean.

The following example illustrates how the variance is used to measure dispersion.

EXAMPLE

The chart below shows the number of cappuccinos sold at the Starbucks in the Orange County airport and the Ontario, California, airport between 4 and 5 p.m. for a sample of 5 days last month.

California Airports	
Orange County	Ontario
20	20
40	45
50	50
60	55
80	80

Determine the mean, median, range, and variance for each location. Comment on the similarities and differences in these measures.

SOLUTION

The mean, median, and range for each of the airport locations are reported below as part of an Excel spreadsheet.

DESCRIBING DATA: NUMERICAL MEASURES   71

	A	B	C
1		California Airports	
2		Orange County	Ontario
3		20	20
4		40	45
5		50	50
6		60	55
7		80	80
8			
9	Mean	50	50
10	Median	50	50
11	Range	60	60

Notice that all three of the measures are exactly the same. Does this indicate that there is no difference in the two sets of data? We get a clearer picture if we calculate the variance. First, for Orange County:

F	G	H
	Calculation of Variance for Orange County	
Number Sold	Each Value - Mean	Squared Deviation
20	20 - 50 = -30	900
40	40 - 50 = -10	100
50	50 - 50 = 0	0
60	60 - 50 = 10	100
80	80 - 50 = 30	900
	Total	2000

$$\text{Variance} = \frac{\Sigma(x - \mu)^2}{N} = \frac{(-30^2) + (-10^2) + 0^2 + 10^2 + 30^2}{5} = \frac{2,000}{5} = 400$$

The variance is 400. That is, the average squared deviation from the mean is 400.
The following shows the detail of determining the variance for the number of cappuccinos sold at the Ontario Airport.

Calculation of Variance for Ontario		
Number Sold	Each Value - Mean	Squared Deviation
20	20 - 50 = -30	900
45	45 - 50 = -5	25
50	50 - 50 = 0	0
55	55 - 50 = 5	25
80	80 - 50 = 30	900
	Total	1850

$$\text{Variance} = \frac{\Sigma(x - \mu)^2}{N} = \frac{(-30^2) + (-5^2) + 0^2 + 5^2 + 30^2}{5} = \frac{1,850}{5} = 370$$

So the mean, median, and range of the cappuccinos sold are the same at the two airports, but the variances are different. The variance at Orange County is 400, but it is 370 at Ontario.
Let's interpret and compare the results of our measures for the two Starbucks airport locations. The mean and median of the two locations are exactly the same,

72   CHAPTER 3

50 cappuccinos sold. These measures of location suggest the two distributions are the same. The range for both locations is also the same, 60. However, recall that the range provides limited information about the dispersion because it is based on only two of the observations.

The variances are not the same for the two airports. The variance is based on the differences between each observation and the arithmetic mean. It shows the closeness or clustering of the data relative to the mean or center of the distribution. Compare the variance for Orange County of 400 to the variance for Ontario of 370. Based on the variance, we conclude that the dispersion for the sales distribution of the Ontario Starbucks is more concentrated—that is, nearer the mean of 50—than for the Orange County location.

The variance has an important advantage over the range. It uses all the values in the computation. Recall that the range uses only the highest and the lowest values.

SELF-REVIEW

3–6

The weights of containers being shipped to Ireland are (in thousands of pounds):

95	103	105	110	104	105	112	90

(a) What is the range of the weights?
(b) Compute the arithmetic mean weight.
(c) Compute the variance of the weights.

EXERCISES

For Exercises 35–38, calculate the (a) range, (b) arithmetic mean, (c) variance, and (d) interpret the statistics.

35. There were five customer service representatives on duty at the Electronic Super Store during last weekend's sale. The numbers of HDTVs these representatives sold are 5, 8, 4, 10, and 3.
36. The Department of Statistics at Western State University offers eight sections of basic statistics. Following are the numbers of students enrolled in these sections: 34, 46, 52, 29, 41, 38, 36, and 28.
37. Dave's Automatic Door installs automatic garage door openers. The following list indicates the number of minutes needed to install 10 door openers: 28, 32, 24, 46, 44, 40, 54, 38, 32, and 42.
38. All eight companies in the aerospace industry were surveyed as to their return on investment last year. The results are (in percent) 10.6, 12.6, 14.8, 18.2, 12.0, 14.8, 12.2, and 15.6.
39. Ten young adults living in California rated the taste of a newly developed sushi pizza topped with tuna, rice, and kelp on a scale of 1 to 50, with 1 indicating they did not like the taste and 50 that they did. The ratings were:

34	39	40	46	33	31	34	14	15	45

In a parallel study, 10 young adults in Iowa rated the taste of the same pizza. The ratings were:

28	25	35	16	25	29	24	26	17	20

As a market researcher, compare the potential markets for sushi pizza.

For **DATA FILE**, please visit www.mhhe.com/lind16e

40. The personnel files of all eight employees at the Pawnee location of Acme Carpet Cleaners Inc. revealed that during the last 6-month period they lost the following number of days due to illness:

2	0	6	3	10	4	1	2

For **DATA FILE**, please visit www.mhhe.com/lind16e

All eight employees during the same period at the Chickpee location of Acme Carpets revealed they lost the following number of days due to illness:

2	0	1	0	5	0	1	0

As the director of human relations, compare the two locations. What would you recommend?

Population Variance

In the previous example, we developed the concept of variance as a measure of dispersion. Similar to the mean, we can calculate the variance of a population or the variance of a sample. The formula to compute the population variance is:

POPULATION VARIANCE	$\sigma^2 = \dfrac{\Sigma(x - \mu)^2}{N}$	**[3–7]**

where:
σ^2 is the population variance (σ is the lowercase Greek letter sigma). It is read as "sigma squared."
x is the value of a particular observation in the population.
μ is the arithmetic mean of the population.
N is the number of observations in the population.

The process for computing the variance is implied by the formula.

1. Begin by finding the mean.
2. Find the difference between each observation and the mean, and square that difference.
3. Sum all the squared differences.
4. Divide the sum of the squared differences by the number of items in the population.

So the population variance is the mean of the squared difference between each value and the mean. For populations whose values are near the mean, the variance will be small. For populations whose values are dispersed from the mean, the population variance will be large.

 The variance overcomes the weakness of the range by using all the values in the population, whereas the range uses only the maximum and minimum values. We overcome the issue where $\Sigma(x - \mu) = 0$ by squaring the differences. Squaring the differences will always result in nonnegative values. The following is a another example that illustrates the calculation and interpretation of the variance.

EXAMPLE

The number of traffic citations issued last year by month in Beaufort County, South Carolina, is reported below.

Citations by Month											
January	February	March	April	May	June	July	August	September	October	November	December
19	17	22	18	28	34	45	39	38	44	34	10

Determine the population variance.

SOLUTION

Because we are studying all the citations for a year, the data comprise a population. To determine the population variance, we use formula (3–7). The table below details the calculations.

Month	Citations (x)	x − μ	(x − μ)²
January	19	−10	100
February	17	−12	144
March	22	−7	49
April	18	−11	121
May	28	−1	1
June	34	5	25
July	45	16	256
August	39	10	100
September	38	9	81
October	44	15	225
November	34	5	25
December	10	−19	361
Total	348	0	1,488

1. We begin by determining the arithmetic mean of the population. The total number of citations issued for the year is 348, so the mean number issued per month is 29.

$$\mu = \frac{\Sigma x}{N} = \frac{19 + 17 + \cdots + 10}{12} = \frac{348}{12} = 29$$

2. Next we find the difference between each observation and the mean. This is shown in the third column of the table. Recall that earlier in the chapter (page 54) we indicated that the sum of the differences between each value and the mean is 0. In this example, the sum of the differences between the mean and the number of citations each month is 0.

3. The next step is to square the difference for each month. That is shown in the fourth column of the table. All the squared differences will be positive. Note that squaring a negative value, or multiplying a negative value by itself, always results in a positive value.

4. The squared differences are totaled. The total of the fourth column is 1,488. That is the term $\Sigma(x - \mu)^2$.

5. Finally, we divide the squared differences by N, the number of observations in the population.

$$\sigma^2 = \frac{\Sigma(x - \mu)^2}{N} = \frac{1,488}{12} = 124$$

So, the population variance for the number of citations is 124.

Like the range, the variance can be used to compare the dispersion in two or more sets of observations. For example, the variance for the number of citations issued in Beaufort County was just computed to be 124. If the variance in the number of citations issued in Marlboro County, South Carolina, is 342.9, we conclude that (1) there is less dispersion in the distribution of the number of citations issued in Beaufort County than in Marlboro County (because 124 is less than 342.9) and (2) the number of citations in Beaufort County is more closely clustered around the mean of 29 than for the number of citations issued in Marlboro County. Thus the mean number of citations issued in Beaufort County is a more representative measure of location than the mean number of citations in Marlboro County.

Population Standard Deviation

When we compute the variance, it is important to understand the unit of measure and what happens when the differences in the numerator are squared. That is, in the previous example, the number of monthly citations is the variable. When we calculate the variance, the unit of measure for the variance is citations squared. Using "squared citations" as a unit of measure is cumbersome.

There is a way out of this difficulty. By taking the square root of the population variance, we can transform it to the same unit of measurement used for the original data. The square root of 124 citations squared is 11.14 citations. The units are now simply citations. The square root of the population variance is the **population standard deviation.**

POPULATION STANDARD DEVIATION	$\sigma = \sqrt{\dfrac{\Sigma(x - \mu)^2}{N}}$	[3–8]

SELF-REVIEW

3–7

The Philadelphia office of Price Waterhouse Coopers LLP hired five accounting trainees this year. Their monthly starting salaries were $3,536; $3,173; $3,448; $3,121; and $3,622.
(a) Compute the population mean.
(b) Compute the population variance.
(c) Compute the population standard deviation.
(d) The Pittsburgh office hired six trainees. Their mean monthly salary was $3,550, and the standard deviation was $250. Compare the two groups.

EXERCISES

41. Consider these five values a population: 8, 3, 7, 3, and 4.
    a. Determine the mean of the population.
    b. Determine the variance.
42. Consider these six values a population: 13, 3, 8, 10, 8, and 6.
    a. Determine the mean of the population.
    b. Determine the variance.
43. The annual report of Dennis Industries cited these primary earnings per common share for the past 5 years: $2.68, $1.03, $2.26, $4.30, and $3.58. If we assume these are population values, what is:
    a. The arithmetic mean primary earnings per share of common stock?
    b. The variance?
44. Referring to Exercise 43, the annual report of Dennis Industries also gave these returns on stockholder equity for the same 5-year period (in percent): 13.2, 5.0, 10.2, 17.5, and 12.9.
    a. What is the arithmetic mean return?
    b. What is the variance?
45. Plywood Inc. reported these returns on stockholder equity for the past 5 years: 4.3, 4.9, 7.2, 6.7, and 11.6. Consider these as population values.
    a. Compute the range, the arithmetic mean, the variance, and the standard deviation.
    b. Compare the return on stockholder equity for Plywood Inc. with that for Dennis Industries cited in Exercise 44.
46. The annual incomes of the five vice presidents of TMV Industries are $125,000; $128,000; $122,000; $133,000; and $140,000. Consider this a population.
    a. What is the range?
    b. What is the arithmetic mean income?
    c. What is the population variance? The standard deviation?
    d. The annual incomes of officers of another firm similar to TMV Industries were also studied. The mean was $129,000 and the standard deviation $8,612. Compare the means and dispersions in the two firms.

76   CHAPTER 3

Sample Variance and Standard Deviation

The formula for the population mean is $\mu = \Sigma x/N$. We just changed the symbols for the sample mean; that is, $\bar{x} = \Sigma x/n$. Unfortunately, the conversion from the population variance to the sample variance is not as direct. It requires a change in the denominator. Instead of substituting n (number in the sample) for N (number in the population), the denominator is $n - 1$. Thus the formula for the **sample variance** is:

SAMPLE VARIANCE	$s^2 = \dfrac{\Sigma(x - \bar{x})^2}{n - 1}$	[3–9]

where:
  s^2 is the sample variance.
  x is the value of each observation in the sample.
  $\bar{x}$ is the mean of the sample.
  n is the number of observations in the sample.

Why is this change made in the denominator? Although the use of n is logical since $\bar{x}$ is used to estimate μ, it tends to underestimate the population variance, σ^2. The use of $(n - 1)$ in the denominator provides the appropriate correction for this tendency. Because the primary use of sample statistics like s^2 is to estimate population parameters like σ^2, $(n - 1)$ is preferred to n in defining the sample variance. We will also use this convention when computing the sample standard deviation.

EXAMPLE

The hourly wages for a sample of part-time employees at Home Depot are $12, $20, $16, $18, and $19. What is the sample variance?

SOLUTION

The sample variance is computed by using formula (3–9).

$$\bar{x} = \frac{\Sigma x}{n} = \frac{\$85}{5} = \$17$$

Hourly Wage (x)	$x - \bar{x}$	$(x - \bar{x})^2$
$12	−$5	25
20	3	9
16	−1	1
18	1	1
19	2	4
$85	0	40

$$s^2 = \frac{\Sigma(x - \bar{x})^2}{n - 1} = \frac{40}{5 - 1}$$

$$= 10 \text{ in dollars squared}$$

DESCRIBING DATA: NUMERICAL MEASURES   77

The sample standard deviation is used as an estimator of the population standard deviation. As noted previously, the population standard deviation is the square root of the population variance. Likewise, the *sample standard deviation is the square root of the sample variance*. The sample standard deviation is determined by:

SAMPLE STANDARD DEVIATION	$s = \sqrt{\dfrac{\Sigma(x - \bar{x})^2}{n - 1}}$	**[3–10]**

EXAMPLE

The sample variance in the previous example involving hourly wages was computed to be 10. What is the sample standard deviation?

SOLUTION

The sample standard deviation is $3.16, found by $\sqrt{10}$. Note again that the sample variance is in terms of dollars squared, but taking the square root of 10 gives us $3.16, which is in the same units (dollars) as the original data.

Software Solution

On page 63, we used Excel to determine the mean, median, and mode of profit for the Applewood Auto Group data. You will also note that it lists the sample variance and sample standard deviation. Excel, like most other statistical software, assumes the data are from a sample.

⊿	A	B	C	D	E	F	G	H
							Profit	
1	Age	Profit	Location	Vehicle-Type	Previous			
2	21	$1,387	Tionesta	Sedan	0			
3	23	$1,754	Sheffield	SUV	1		Mean	1843.17
4	24	$1,817	Sheffield	Hybrid	1		Standard Error	47.97
5	25	$1,040	Sheffield	Compact	0		Median	1882.50
6	26	$1,273	Kane	Sedan	1		Mode	1915.00
7	27	$1,529	Sheffield	Sedan	1		Standard Deviation	643.63
8	27	$3,082	Kane	Truck	0		Sample Variance	414256.61
9	28	$1,951	Kane	SUV	1		Kurtosis	-0.22
10	28	$2,692	Tionesta	Compact	0		Skewness	-0.24
11	29	$1,342	Kane	Sedan	2		Range	2998
12	29	$1,206	Sheffield	Sedan	0		Minimum	294
13	30	$443	Kane	Sedan	3		Maximum	3292
14	30	$1,621	Sheffield	Truck	1		Sum	331770
15	30	$754	Olean	Sedan	2		Count	180

APPLEWOOD AUTO GROUP

SELF-REVIEW

3–8

The years of service for a sample of seven employees at a State Farm Insurance claims office in Cleveland, Ohio, are 4, 2, 5, 4, 5, 2, and 6. What is the sample variance? Compute the sample standard deviation.

EXERCISES

For Exercises 47–52, do the following:

   a. Compute the sample variance.
   b. Determine the sample standard deviation.

47. Consider these values a sample: 7, 2, 6, 2, and 3.
48. The following five values are a sample: 11, 6, 10, 6, and 7.
49. Dave's Automatic Door, referred to in Exercise 37, installs automatic garage door openers. Based on a sample, following are the times, in minutes, required to install 10 door openers: 28, 32, 24, 46, 44, 40, 54, 38, 32, and 42.
50. The sample of eight companies in the aerospace industry, referred to in Exercise 38, was surveyed as to their return on investment last year. The results are 10.6, 12.6, 14.8, 18.2, 12.0, 14.8, 12.2, and 15.6.
51. The Houston, Texas, Motel Owner Association conducted a survey regarding weekday motel rates in the area. Listed below is the room rate for business-class guests for a sample of 10 motels.

For **DATA FILE**, please visit
www.mhhe.com/lind16e

| $101 | $97 | $103 | $110 | $78 | $87 | $101 | $80 | $106 | $88 |

For **DATA FILE**, please visit
www.mhhe.com/lind16e

52. A consumer watchdog organization is concerned about credit card debt. A survey of 10 young adults with credit card debt of more than $2,000 showed they paid an average of just over $100 per month against their balances. Listed below are the amounts each young adult paid last month.

| $110 | $126 | $103 | $93 | $99 | $113 | $87 | $101 | $109 | $100 |

LO3-5
Explain and apply Chebyshev's theorem and the Empirical Rule.

STATISTICS IN ACTION

Most colleges report the "average class size." This information can be misleading because average class size can be found in several ways. If we find the number of students *in each class* at a particular university, the result is the mean number of students per class. If we compile a list of the class sizes for each student and find the mean class size, we might find the mean to be quite different. One school found the mean number of students in each of its 747 classes to be 40. But when it found the mean from a list of the class sizes of each
(continued)

INTERPRETATION AND USES OF THE STANDARD DEVIATION

The standard deviation is commonly used as a measure to compare the spread in two or more sets of observations. For example, the standard deviation of the biweekly amounts invested in the Dupree Paint Company profit-sharing plan is computed to be $7.51. Suppose these employees are located in Georgia. If the standard deviation for a group of employees in Texas is $10.47, and the means are about the same, it indicates that the amounts invested by the Georgia employees are not dispersed as much as those in Texas (because $7.51 < $10.47). Since the amounts invested by the Georgia employees are clustered more closely about the mean, the mean for the Georgia employees is a more reliable measure than the mean for the Texas group.

Chebyshev's Theorem

We have stressed that a small standard deviation for a set of values indicates that these values are located close to the mean. Conversely, a large standard deviation reveals that the observations are widely scattered about the mean. The Russian mathematician P. L. Chebyshev (1821–1894) developed a theorem that allows us to determine the minimum proportion of the values that lie within a specified number of standard deviations of the mean. For example, according to **Chebyshev's theorem,** at least three out of every four, or 75%, of the values must lie between the mean plus two standard deviations and the mean minus two standard deviations. This relationship applies regardless of the shape of the distribution. Further, at least eight of nine values, or 88.9%, will lie between plus three standard deviations and minus three standard deviations of the mean. At least 24 of 25 values, or 96%, will lie between plus and minus five standard deviations of the mean.
   Chebyshev's theorem states:

CHEBYSHEV'S THEOREM For any set of observations (sample or population), the proportion of the values that lie within k standard deviations of the mean is at least $1 - 1/k^2$, where k is any value greater than 1.

E X A M P L E

The arithmetic mean biweekly amount contributed by the Dupree Paint employees to the company's profit-sharing plan is $51.54, and the standard deviation is $7.51. At least what percent of the contributions lie within plus 3.5 standard deviations and minus 3.5 standard deviations of the mean?

S O L U T I O N

About 92%, found by

$$1 - \frac{1}{k^2} = 1 - \frac{1}{(3.5)^2} = 1 - \frac{1}{12.25} = 0.92$$

(continued from p. 78)
student, it was 147. Why the disparity? Because there are few students in the small classes and a larger number of students in the larger classes, which has the effect of increasing the mean class size when it is calculated this way. A school could reduce this mean class size for each student by reducing the number of students in each class. That is, cut out the large freshman lecture classes.

The Empirical Rule

Chebyshev's theorem applies to any set of values; that is, the distribution of values can have any shape. However, for a symmetrical, bell-shaped distribution such as the one in Chart 3–7, we can be more precise in explaining the dispersion about the mean. These relationships involving the standard deviation and the mean are described by the **Empirical Rule,** sometimes called the **Normal Rule.**

> **EMPIRICAL RULE** For a symmetrical, bell-shaped frequency distribution, approximately 68% of the observations will lie within plus and minus one standard deviation of the mean; about 95% of the observations will lie within plus and minus two standard deviations of the mean; and practically all (99.7%) will lie within plus and minus three standard deviations of the mean.

These relationships are portrayed graphically in Chart 3–7 for a bell-shaped distribution with a mean of 100 and a standard deviation of 10.

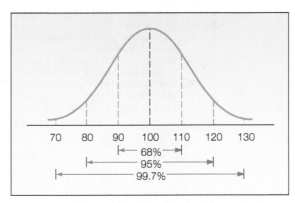

CHART 3–7 A Symmetrical, Bell-Shaped Curve Showing the Relationships between the Standard Deviation and the Percentage of Observations

Applying the Empirical Rule, if a distribution is symmetrical and bell-shaped, practically all of the observations lie between the mean plus and minus three standard deviations. Thus, if $\bar{x} = 100$ and $s = 10$, practically all the observations lie between $100 + 3(10)$ and $100 - 3(10)$, or 70 and 130. The estimated range is therefore 60, found by $130 - 70$.

Conversely, if we know that the range is 60 and the distribution is bell-shaped, we can approximate the standard deviation by dividing the range by 6. For this illustration: range ÷ 6 = 60 ÷ 6 = 10, the standard deviation.

EXAMPLE

A sample of the rental rates at University Park Apartments approximates a symmetrical, bell-shaped distribution. The sample mean is $500; the standard deviation is $20. Using the Empirical Rule, answer these questions:
1. About 68% of the monthly rentals are between what two amounts?
2. About 95% of the monthly rentals are between what two amounts?
3. Almost all of the monthly rentals are between what two amounts?

SOLUTION

1. About 68% are between $480 and $520, found by $\bar{x} \pm 1s = \$500 \pm 1(\$20)$.
2. About 95% are between $460 and $540, found by $\bar{x} \pm 2s = \$500 \pm 2(\$20)$.
3. Almost all (99.7%) are between $440 and $560, found by $\bar{x} \pm 3s = \$500 \pm 3(\$20)$.

SELF-REVIEW 3–9

The Pitney Pipe Company is one of several domestic manufacturers of PVC pipe. The quality control department sampled 600 10-foot lengths. At a point 1 foot from the end of the pipe, they measured the outside diameter. The mean was 14.0 inches and the standard deviation 0.1 inch.
(a) If the shape of the distribution is not known, at least what percent of the observations will be between 13.85 inches and 14.15 inches?
(b) If we assume that the distribution of diameters is symmetrical and bell-shaped, about 95% of the observations will be between what two values?

EXERCISES

53. According to Chebyshev's theorem, at least what percent of any set of observations will be within 1.8 standard deviations of the mean?
54. The mean income of a group of sample observations is $500; the standard deviation is $40. According to Chebyshev's theorem, at least what percent of the incomes will lie between $400 and $600?
55. The distribution of the weights of a sample of 1,400 cargo containers is symmetric and bell-shaped. According to the Empirical Rule, what percent of the weights will lie:
    a. Between $\bar{x} - 2s$ and $\bar{x} + 2s$?
    b. Between $\bar{x}$ and $\bar{x} + 2s$? Below $\bar{x} - 2s$?
56. The following graph portrays the distribution of the number of Biggie-sized soft drinks sold at a nearby Wendy's for the last 141 days. The mean number of drinks sold per day is 91.9 and the standard deviation is 4.67.

If we use the Empirical Rule, sales will be between what two values on 68% of the days? Sales will be between what two values on 95% of the days?

DESCRIBING DATA: NUMERICAL MEASURES   81

81

LO3-6

Compute the mean and standard deviation of grouped data.

STATISTICS IN ACTION

Buster Posey of the San Francisco Giants had the highest batting average, at .336, during the 2012 Major League Baseball season. Tony Gwynn hit .394 in the strike-shortened season of 1994, and Ted Williams hit .406 in 1941. No one has hit over .400 since 1941. The mean batting average has remained constant at about .260 for more than 100 years, but the standard deviation declined from .049 to .031. This indicates less dispersion in the batting averages today and helps explain the lack of any .400 hitters in recent times.

THE MEAN AND STANDARD DEVIATION OF GROUPED DATA

In most instances, measures of location, such as the mean, and measures of dispersion, such as the standard deviation, are determined by using the individual values. Statistical software packages make it easy to calculate these values, even for large data sets. However, sometimes we are given only the frequency distribution and wish to estimate the mean or standard deviation. In the following discussion, we show how we can estimate the mean and standard deviation from data organized into a frequency distribution. We should stress that a mean or a standard deviation from grouped data is an *estimate* of the corresponding actual values.

Arithmetic Mean of Grouped Data

To approximate the arithmetic mean of data organized into a frequency distribution, we begin by assuming the observations in each class are represented by the *midpoint* of the class. The mean of a sample of data organized in a frequency distribution is computed by:

ARITHMETIC MEAN OF GROUPED DATA	$\bar{x} = \dfrac{\Sigma fM}{n}$	**[3–11]**

where:

$\bar{x}$ is the designation for the sample mean.

M is the midpoint of each class.

f is the frequency in each class.

fM is the frequency in each class times the midpoint of the class.

ΣfM is the sum of these products.

n is the total number of frequencies.

E X A M P L E

The computations for the arithmetic mean of data grouped into a frequency distribution will be shown based on the Applewood Auto Group profit data. Recall in Chapter 2, in Table 2–7 on page 30, we constructed a frequency distribution for the vehicle profit. The information is repeated below. Determine the arithmetic mean profit per vehicle.

Profit	Frequency
$ 200 up to $ 600	8
600 up to 1,000	11
1,000 up to 1,400	23
1,400 up to 1,800	38
1,800 up to 2,200	45
2,200 up to 2,600	32
2,600 up to 3,000	19
3,000 up to 3,400	4
Total	180

S O L U T I O N

The mean vehicle selling price can be estimated from data grouped into a frequency distribution. To find the estimated mean, assume the midpoint of each class is representative of the data values in that class. Recall that the midpoint of a class is halfway between the lower class limits of two consecutive classes. To find the midpoint of a particular class, we add the lower limits of two consecutive classes and divide by 2. Hence, the midpoint of the first class is $400, found by ($200 + $600)/2. We assume the value of $400 is representative of the eight values in that class. To put it another way, we assume the sum of the eight values in this class is $3,200, found by 8($400). We continue the process of multiplying the class midpoint by the class frequency for each class and then sum these products. The results are summarized in Table 3–1.

TABLE 3–1 Profit on 180 Vehicles Sold Last Month at Applewood Auto Group

Profit	Frequency (f)	Midpoint (M)	fM
$ 200 up to $ 600	8	$ 400	$ 3,200
600 up to 1,000	11	800	8,800
1,000 up to 1,400	23	1,200	27,600
1,400 up to 1,800	38	1,600	60,800
1,800 up to 2,200	45	2,000	90,000
2,200 up to 2,600	32	2,400	76,800
2,600 up to 3,000	19	2,800	53,200
3,000 up to 3,400	4	3,200	12,800
Total	180		$333,200

Solving for the arithmetic mean using formula (3–11), we get:

$$\bar{x} = \frac{\Sigma fM}{n} = \frac{\$333,200}{180} = \$1,851.11$$

We conclude that the mean profit per vehicle is about $1,851.

Standard Deviation of Grouped Data

To calculate the standard deviation of data grouped into a frequency distribution, we need to adjust formula (3–10) slightly. We weight each of the squared differences by the number of frequencies in each class. The formula is:

STANDARD DEVIATION, GROUPED DATA $s = \sqrt{\dfrac{\Sigma f(M - \bar{x})^2}{n - 1}}$ **[3–12]**

where:

    s is the symbol for the sample standard deviation.
    M is the midpoint of the class.
    f is the class frequency.
    n is the number of observations in the sample.
    $\bar{x}$ is the designation for the sample mean.

EXAMPLE

Refer to the frequency distribution for the Applewood Auto Group profit data reported in Table 3–1. Compute the standard deviation of the vehicle selling prices.

SOLUTION

Following the same practice used earlier for computing the mean of data grouped into a frequency distribution, f is the class frequency, M the class midpoint, and n the number of observations.

Profit	Frequency (f)	Midpoint (M)	fM	$(M - \bar{x})$	$(M - \bar{x})^2$	$f(M - \bar{x})^2$
$ 200 up to $ 600	8	400	3,200	−1,451	2,105,401	16,843,208
600 up to 1,000	11	800	8,800	−1,051	1,104,601	12,150,611
1,000 up to 1,400	23	1,200	27,600	−651	423,801	9,747,423
1,400 up to 1,800	38	1,600	60,800	−251	63,001	2,394,038
1,800 up to 2,200	45	2,000	90,000	149	22,201	999,045
2,200 up to 2,600	32	2,400	76,800	549	301,401	9,644,832
2,600 up to 3,000	19	2,800	53,200	949	900,601	17,111,419
3,000 up to 3,400	4	3,200	12,800	1,349	1,819,801	7,279,204
Total	180		333,200			76,169,780

To find the standard deviation:

Step 1: Subtract the mean from the class midpoint. That is, find $(M - \bar{x})$ = ($400 − $1,851 = −$1,451) for the first class, for the second class ($800 − $1,851 = −$1,051), and so on.

Step 2: Square the difference between the class midpoint and the mean. For the first class, it would be ($400 − $1,851)² = 2,105,401, for the second class ($800 − $1,851)² = 1,104,601, and so on.

Step 3: Multiply the squared difference between the class midpoint and the mean by the class frequency. For the first class, the value is 8($400 − $1,851)² = 16,843,208; for the second, 11($800 − $1,851)² = 12,150,611, and so on.

Step 4: Sum the $f(M - \bar{x})^2$. The total is 76,169,920. To find the standard deviation, we insert these values in formula (3–12).

$$s = \sqrt{\frac{\Sigma f(M - \bar{x})^2}{n - 1}} = \sqrt{\frac{76,169,780}{180 - 1 -}} = 652.33$$

The mean and the standard deviation calculated from the data grouped into a frequency distribution are usually close to the values calculated from raw data. The grouped data result in some loss of information. For the vehicle profit example, the mean profit reported in the Excel output on page 63 is $1,843.17 and the standard deviation is $643.63. The respective values estimated from data grouped into a frequency distribution are $1,851.11 and $652.33. The difference in the means is $7.94, or about 0.4%. The standard deviations differ by $8.70, or 1.4%. Based on the percentage difference, the estimates are very close to the actual values.

SELF-REVIEW

3–10

The net incomes of a sample of large importers of antiques were organized into the following table:

Net Income ($ millions)	Number of Importers
2 up to 6	1
6 up to 10	4
10 up to 14	10
14 up to 18	3
18 up to 22	2

(a) What is the table called?
(b) Based on the distribution, what is the estimate of the arithmetic mean net income?
(c) Based on the distribution, what is the estimate of the standard deviation?

62. Advertising expenses are a significant component of the cost of goods sold. Listed below is a frequency distribution showing the advertising expenditures for 60 manufacturing companies located in the Southwest. Estimate the mean and the standard deviation of advertising expenses.

Advertising Expenditure ($ millions)	Number of Companies
25 up to 35	5
35 up to 45	10
45 up to 55	21
55 up to 65	16
65 up to 75	8
Total	60

ETHICS AND REPORTING RESULTS

In Chapter 1, we discussed the ethical and unbiased reporting of statistical results. While you are learning about how to organize, summarize, and interpret data using statistics, it is also important to understand statistics so that you can be an intelligent consumer of information.

In this chapter, we learned how to compute numerical descriptive statistics. Specifically, we showed how to compute and interpret measures of location for a data set: the mean, median, and mode. We also discussed the advantages and disadvantages for each statistic. For example, if a real estate developer tells a client that the average home in a particular subdivision sold for $150,000, we assume that $150,000 is a representative selling price for all the homes. But suppose that the client also asks what the median sales price is, and the median is $60,000. Why was the developer only reporting the mean price? This information is extremely important to a person's decision making when buying a home. Knowing the advantages and disadvantages of the mean, median, and mode is important as we report statistics and as we use statistical information to make decisions.

We also learned how to compute measures of dispersion: range, variance, and standard deviation. Each of these statistics also has advantages and disadvantages. Remember that the range provides information about the overall spread of a distribution. However, it does not provide any information about how the data are clustered or concentrated around the center of the distribution. As we learn more about statistics, we need to remember that when we use statistics we must maintain an independent and principled point of view. Any statistical report requires objective and honest communication of the results.

CHAPTER SUMMARY

I. A measure of location is a value used to describe the center of a set of data.
   A. The arithmetic mean is the most widely reported measure of location.
      1. It is calculated by adding the values of the observations and dividing by the total number of observations.
         a. The formula for a population mean of ungrouped or raw data is

$$\mu = \frac{\Sigma x}{N} \qquad\qquad\qquad\qquad \text{[3–1]}$$

         b. The formula for the mean of a sample is

$$\bar{x} = \frac{\Sigma x}{n} \qquad\qquad\qquad\qquad \text{[3–2]}$$

    c. The formula for the sample mean of data in a frequency distribution is

$$\bar{x} = \frac{\Sigma fM}{n}$$ **[3–11]**

  2. The major characteristics of the arithmetic mean are:
    a. At least the interval scale of measurement is required.
    b. All the data values are used in the calculation.
    c. A set of data has only one mean. That is, it is unique.
    d. The sum of the deviations from the mean equals 0.
B. The median is the value in the middle of a set of ordered data.
  1. To find the median, sort the observations from minimum to maximum and identify the middle value.
  2. The major characteristics of the median are:
    a. At least the ordinal scale of measurement is required.
    b. It is not influenced by extreme values.
    c. Fifty percent of the observations are larger than the median.
    d. It is unique to a set of data.
C. The mode is the value that occurs most often in a set of data.
  1. The mode can be found for nominal-level data.
  2. A set of data can have more than one mode.
D. The weighted mean is found by multiplying each observation by its corresponding weight.
  1. The formula for determining the weighted mean is

$$\bar{x}_w = \frac{w_1x_1 + w_2x_2 + w_3x_3 + \cdots + w_nx_n}{w_1 + w_2 + w_3 + \cdots + w_n}$$ **[3–3]**

E. The geometric mean is the *n*th root of the product of *n* positive values.
  1. The formula for the geometric mean is

$$GM = \sqrt[n]{(x_1)(x_2)(x_3) \cdots (x_n)}$$ **[3–4]**

  2. The geometric mean is also used to find the rate of change from one period to another.

$$GM = \sqrt[n]{\frac{\text{Value at end of period}}{\text{Value at beginning of period}}} - 1$$ **[3–5]**

  3. The geometric mean is always equal to or less than the arithmetic mean.
II. The dispersion is the variation or spread in a set of data.
A. The range is the difference between the maximum and minimum values in a set of data.
  1. The formula for the range is

$$\text{Range} = \text{Maximum value} - \text{Minimum value}$$ **[3–6]**

  2. The major characteristics of the range are:
    a. Only two values are used in its calculation.
    b. It is influenced by extreme values.
    c. It is easy to compute and to understand.
B. The variance is the mean of the squared deviations from the arithmetic mean.
  1. The formula for the population variance is

$$\sigma^2 = \frac{\Sigma(x - \mu)^2}{N}$$ **[3–7]**

  2. The formula for the sample variance is

$$s^2 = \frac{\Sigma(x - \bar{x})^2}{n - 1}$$ **[3–9]**

  3. The major characteristics of the variance are:
    a. All observations are used in the calculation.
    b. The units are somewhat difficult to work with; they are the original units squared.
C. The standard deviation is the square root of the variance.
  1. The major characteristics of the standard deviation are:
    a. It is in the same units as the original data.
    b. It is the square root of the average squared distance from the mean.
    c. It cannot be negative.
    d. It is the most widely reported measure of dispersion.

DESCRIBING DATA: NUMERICAL MEASURES   87

2. The formula for the sample standard deviation is

$$s = \sqrt{\frac{\Sigma(x - \bar{x})^2}{n - 1}}$$ **[3–10]**

3. The formula for the standard deviation of grouped data is

$$s = \sqrt{\frac{\Sigma f(M - \bar{x})^2}{n - 1}}$$ **[3–12]**

III. We use the standard deviation to describe a frequency distribution by applying Chebyshev's theorem or the Empirical Rule.
  A. Chebyshev's theorem states that regardless of the shape of the distribution, at least $1 - 1/k^2$ of the observations will be within k standard deviations of the mean, where k is greater than 1.
  B. The Empirical Rule states that for a bell-shaped distribution about 68% of the values will be within one standard deviation of the mean, 95% within two, and virtually all within three.

P R O N U N C I A T I O N   K E Y

SYMBOL	MEANING	PRONUNCIATION
μ	Population mean	*mu*
Σ	Operation of adding	*sigma*
Σx	Adding a group of values	*sigma x*
$\bar{x}$	Sample mean	*x bar*
$\bar{x}_w$	Weighted mean	*x bar sub w*
GM	Geometric mean	*G M*
ΣfM	Adding the product of the frequencies and the class midpoints	*sigma f M*
σ^2	Population variance	*sigma squared*
σ	Population standard deviation	*sigma*

C H A P T E R   E X E R C I S E S

63. The accounting firm of Crawford and Associates has five senior partners. Yesterday the senior partners saw six, four, three, seven, and five clients, respectively.
  a. Compute the mean and median number of clients seen by the partners.
  b. Is the mean a sample mean or a population mean?
  c. Verify that $\Sigma(x - \mu) = 0$.
64. Owens Orchards sells apples in a large bag by weight. A sample of seven bags contained the following numbers of apples: 23, 19, 26, 17, 21, 24, 22.
  a. Compute the mean and median number of apples in a bag.
  b. Verify that $\Sigma(x - \bar{x}) = 0$.
65. A sample of households that subscribe to United Bell Phone Company for landline phone service revealed the following number of calls received per household last week. Determine the mean and the median number of calls received.

52	43	30	38	30	42	12	46	39	37
34	46	32	18	41	5				

For **DATA FILE**, please visit
www.mhhe.com/lind16e

For **DATA FILE**, please visit
www.mhhe.com/lind16e

66. The Citizens Banking Company is studying the number of times the ATM located in a Lo-blaws Supermarket at the foot of Market Street is used per day. Following are the number of times the machine was used daily over each of the last 30 days. Determine the mean number of times the machine was used per day.

83	64	84	76	84	54	75	59	70	61
63	80	84	73	68	52	65	90	52	77
95	36	78	61	59	84	95	47	87	60

88   CHAPTER 3

For **DATA FILE**, please visit
www.mhhe.com/lind16e

67. A recent study of the laundry habits of Americans included the time in minutes of the wash cycle. A sample of 40 observations follows. Determine the mean and the median of a typical wash cycle.

35	37	28	37	33	38	37	32	28	29
39	33	32	37	33	35	36	44	36	34
40	38	46	39	37	39	34	39	31	33
37	35	39	38	37	32	43	31	31	35

For **DATA FILE**, please visit
www.mhhe.com/lind16e

68. Trudy Green works for the True-Green Lawn Company. Her job is to solicit lawn-care business via the telephone. Listed below is the number of appointments she made in each of the last 25 hours of calling. What is the arithmetic mean number of appointments she made per hour? What is the median number of appointments per hour? Write a brief report summarizing the findings.

9	5	2	6	5	6	4	4	7	2	3	6	3
4	4	7	8	4	4	5	5	4	8	3	3	

69. The Split-A-Rail Fence Company sells three types of fence to homeowners in suburban Seattle, Washington. Grade A costs $5.00 per running foot to install, Grade B costs $6.50 per running foot, and Grade C, the premium quality, costs $8.00 per running foot. Yesterday, Split-A-Rail installed 270 feet of Grade A, 300 feet of Grade B, and 100 feet of Grade C. What was the mean cost per foot of fence installed?

70. Rolland Poust is a sophomore in the College of Business at Scandia Tech. Last semester he took courses in statistics and accounting, 3 hours each, and earned an A in both. He earned a B in a 5-hour history course and a B in a 2-hour history of jazz course. In addition, he took a 1-hour course dealing with the rules of basketball so he could get his license to officiate high school basketball games. He got an A in this course. What was his GPA for the semester? Assume that he receives 4 points for an A, 3 for a B, and so on. What measure of location did you just calculate?

71. The table below shows the percent of the labor force that is unemployed and the size of the labor force for three counties in northwest Ohio. Jon Elsas is the Regional Director of Economic Development. He must present a report to several companies that are considering locating in northwest Ohio. What would be an appropriate unemployment rate to show for the entire region?

County	Percent Unemployed	Size of Workforce
Wood	4.5	15,300
Ottawa	3.0	10,400
Lucas	10.2	150,600

For **DATA FILE**, please visit
www.mhhe.com/lind16e

72. The American Diabetes Association recommends a blood glucose reading of less than 130 for those with Type 2 diabetes. Blood glucose measures the amount of sugar in the blood. Below are the readings for February for a person recently diagnosed with Type 2 diabetes.

112	122	116	103	112	96	115	98	106	111
106	124	116	127	116	108	112	112	121	115
124	116	107	118	123	109	109	106		

a. What is the arithmetic mean glucose reading?
b. What is the median glucose reading?
c. What is the modal glucose reading?

73. The metropolitan area of Los Angeles–Long Beach, California, showed the largest increase in the number of jobs between 1989 and 2010. The number of jobs increased from 5,164,900 to 6,286,800. What was the geometric mean expected yearly rate of increase?

DESCRIBING DATA: NUMERICAL MEASURES   89

74. A recent article suggested that, if you earn $25,000 a year today and the inflation rate continues at 3% per year, you'll need to make $33,598 in 10 years to have the same buying power. You would need to make $44,771 if the inflation rate jumped to 6%. Confirm that these statements are accurate by finding the geometric mean rate of increase.

75. The ages of a sample of Canadian tourists flying from Toronto to Hong Kong were 32, 21, 60, 47, 54, 17, 72, 55, 33, and 41.
   a. Compute the range.
   b. Compute the standard deviation.

76. The weights (in pounds) of a sample of five boxes being sent by UPS are 12, 6, 7, 3, and 10.
   a. Compute the range.
   b. Compute the standard deviation.

77. The enrollments of the 13 public universities in the state of Ohio are listed below.

For **DATA FILE**, please visit www.mhhe.com/lind16e

College	Enrollment
University of Akron	26,666
Bowling Green State University	17,298
Central State University	2,152
University of Cincinnati	33,347
Cleveland State University	17,529
Kent State University	27,706
Miami University	16,924
Ohio State University	56,387
Ohio University	25,223
Shawnee State University	4,630
University of Toledo	21,500
Wright State University	16,762
Youngstown State University	13,813

   a. Is this a sample or a population?
   b. What is the mean enrollment?
   c. What is the median enrollment?
   d. What is the range of the enrollments?
   e. Compute the standard deviation.

78. Health issues are a concern of managers, especially as they evaluate the cost of medical insurance. A recent survey of 150 executives at Elvers Industries, a large insurance and financial firm located in the Southwest, reported the number of pounds by which the executives were overweight. Compute the mean and the standard deviation.

Pounds Overweight	Frequency
0 up to 6	14
6 up to 12	42
12 up to 18	58
18 up to 24	28
24 up to 30	8

79. The Apollo space program lasted from 1967 until 1972 and included 13 missions. The missions lasted from as little as 7 hours to as long as 301 hours. The duration of each flight is listed below.

For **DATA FILE**, please visit www.mhhe.com/lind16e

9	195	241	301	216	260	7	244	192	147
10	295	142							

   a. Explain why the flight times are a population.
   b. Find the mean and median of the flight times.
   c. Find the range and the standard deviation of the flight times.

90   CHAPTER 3

For **DATA FILE**, please visit
www.mhhe.com/lind16e

80. Creek Ratz is a very popular restaurant located along the coast of northern Florida. They serve a variety of steak and seafood dinners. During the summer beach season, they do not take reservations or accept "call ahead" seating. Management of the restaurant is concerned with the time a patron must wait before being seated for dinner. Listed below is the wait time, in minutes, for the 25 tables seated last Saturday night.

28	39	23	67	37	28	56	40	28	50
51	45	44	65	61	27	24	61	34	44
64	25	24	27	29					

a. Explain why the times are a population.
b. Find the mean and median of the times.
c. Find the range and the standard deviation of the times.

81. A sample of 25 undergraduates reported the following dollar amounts of entertainment expenses last year:

For **DATA FILE**, please visit
www.mhhe.com/lind16e

684	710	688	711	722	698	723	743	738	722	696	721	685
763	681	731	736	771	693	701	737	717	752	710	697	

a. Find the mean, median, and mode of this information.
b. What are the range and standard deviation?
c. Use the Empirical Rule to establish an interval that includes about 95% of the observations.

82. The Kentucky Derby is held the first Saturday in May at Churchill Downs in Louisville, Kentucky. The race track is one and one-quarter miles. The following table shows the winners since 1990, their margin of victory, the winning time, and the payoff on a $2 bet.

For **DATA FILE**, please visit
www.mhhe.com/lind16e

Year	Winner	Winning Margin (lengths)	Winning Time (minutes)	Payoff on a $2 Win Bet
1990	Unbridled	3.5	2.03333	10.80
1991	Strike the Gold	1.75	2.05000	4.80
1992	Lil E. Tee	1	2.05000	16.80
1993	Sea Hero	2.5	2.04000	12.90
1994	Go For Gin	2	2.06000	9.10
1995	Thunder Gulch	2.25	2.02000	24.50
1996	Grindstone	nose	2.01667	5.90
1997	Silver Charm	head	2.04000	4.00
1998	Real Quiet	0.5	2.03667	8.40
1999	Charismatic	neck	2.05333	31.30
2000	Fusaichi Pegasus	1.5	2.02000	2.30
2001	Monarchos	4.75	1.99950	10.50
2002	War Emblem	4	2.01883	20.50
2003	Funny Cide	1.75	2.01983	12.80
2004	Smarty Jones	2.75	2.06767	4.10
2005	Giacomo	0.5	2.04583	50.30
2006	Barbaro	6.5	2.02267	6.10
2007	Street Sense	2.25	2.03617	4.90
2008	Big Brown	4.75	2.03033	6.80
2009	Mine That Bird	6.75	2.04433	103.20
2010	Super Saver	2.50	2.07417	18.00
2011	Animal Kingdom	2.75	2.034	43.80
2012	I'll Have Another	1.5	2.03050	32.60
2013	Orb	2.5	2.04817	12.80

a. Determine the mean and median for the variables winning time and payoff on a $2 bet.
b. Determine the range and standard deviation of the variables winning time and payoff on a $2 bet.

DESCRIBING DATA: NUMERICAL MEASURES   91

c. Refer to the variable winning margin. What is the level of measurement? What measure of location would be most appropriate?

83. The manager of the local Walmart Supercenter is studying the number of items purchased by customers in the evening hours. Listed below is the number of items for a sample of 30 customers.

For **DATA FILE**, please visit www.mhhe.com/lind16e

15	8	6	9	9	4	18	10	10	12
12	4	7	8	12	10	10	11	9	13
5	6	11	14	5	6	6	5	13	5

a. Find the mean and the median of the number of items.
b. Find the range and the standard deviation of the number of items.
c. Organize the number of items into a frequency distribution. You may want to review the guidelines in Chapter 2 for establishing the class interval and the number of classes.
d. Find the mean and the standard deviation of the data organized into a frequency distribution. Compare these values with those computed in part (a). Why are they different?

84. The following frequency distribution reports the electricity cost for a sample of 50 two-bedroom apartments in Albuquerque, New Mexico, during the month of May last year.

Electricity Cost	Frequency
$80 up to $100	3
100 up to 120	8
120 up to 140	12
140 up to 160	16
160 up to 180	7
180 up to 200	4
Total	50

a. Estimate the mean cost.
b. Estimate the standard deviation.
c. Use the Empirical Rule to estimate the proportion of costs within two standard deviations of the mean. What are these limits?

85. Bidwell Electronics Inc. recently surveyed a sample of employees to determine how far they lived from corporate headquarters. The results are shown below. Compute the mean and the standard deviation.

Distance (miles)	Frequency	M
0 up to 5	4	2.5
5 up to 10	15	7.5
10 up to 15	27	12.5
15 up to 20	18	17.5
20 up to 25	6	22.5

DATA SET EXERCISES

86. Refer to the Real Estate data, which reports information on homes sold in the Goodyear, Arizona, area during the last year. Prepare a report on the selling prices of the homes. Be sure to answer the following questions in your report.
a. Around what values do the data tend to cluster? What is the mean selling price? What is the median selling price? Is one measure more representative of the typical selling prices than the others?
b. What is the range of selling prices? What is the standard deviation? About 95% of the selling prices are between what two values?

CHAPTER 3

87. Refer to the Baseball 2012 data, which report information on the 30 Major League Baseball teams for the 2012 season. Refer to the variable team salary.
  a. Prepare a report on the team salaries. Be sure to answer the following questions in your report.
    1. Around what values do the data tend to cluster? Specifically what is the mean team salary? What is the median team salary? Is one measure more representative of the typical team salary than the others?
    2. What is the range of the team salaries? What is the standard deviation? About 95% of the salaries are between what two values?
  b. Refer to the information on the average salary for each year. In 1989 the average player salary was $512,930. By 2012 the average player salary had increased to $3,440,000. What was the rate of increase over the period?
88. Refer to the Buena School District bus data. Prepare a report on the maintenance cost for last month. Be sure to answer the following questions in your report.
  a. Around what values do the data tend to cluster? Specifically what was the mean maintenance cost last month? What is the median cost? Is one measure more representative of the typical cost than the others?
  b. What is the range of maintenance costs? What is the standard deviation? About 95% of the maintenance costs are between what two values?

Describing Data:

DISPLAYING AND EXPLORING DATA

4

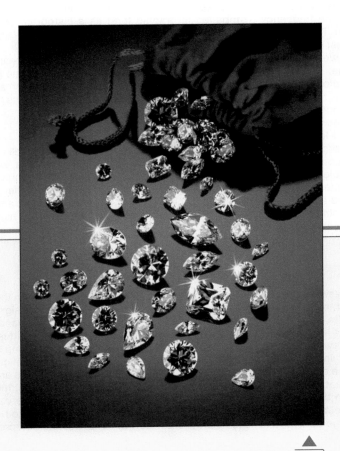

MCGIVERN JEWELERS recently ran an advertisement in the local newspaper reporting the shape, size, price, and cut grade for 33 of its diamonds in stock. Develop a box plot of the variable price and comment on the result. (See Exercise 37 and LO4-4.)

LEARNING OBJECTIVES

When you have completed this chapter, you will be able to:

LO4-1   Construct and interpret a dot plot.

LO4-2   Construct and describe a stem-and-leaf display.

LO4-3   Identify and compute measures of position.

LO4-4   Construct and analyze a box plot.

LO4-5   Compute and interpret the coefficient of skewness.

LO4-6   Create and interpret a scatter diagram.

LO4-7   Develop and explain a contingency table.

94   CHAPTER 4

INTRODUCTION

Chapter 2 began our study of descriptive statistics. In order to transform raw or un-grouped data into a meaningful form, we organize the data into a frequency distribution. We present the frequency distribution in graphic form as a histogram or a frequency polygon. This allows us to visualize where the data tend to cluster, the largest and the smallest values, and the general shape of the data.

In Chapter 3, we first computed several measures of location, such as the mean, median, and mode. These measures of location allow us to report a typical value in the set of observations. We also computed several measures of dispersion, such as the range, variance, and standard deviation. These measures of dispersion allow us to describe the variation or the spread in a set of observations.

We continue our study of descriptive statistics in this chapter. We study (1) dot plots, (2) stem-and-leaf displays, (3) percentiles, and (4) box plots. These charts and statistics give us additional insight into where the values are concentrated as well as the general shape of the data. Then we consider bivariate data. In bivariate data, we observe two variables for each individual or observation. Examples include the number of hours a student studied and the points earned on an examination; whether a sampled product is acceptable or not and the shift on which it is manufactured; and the amount of electricity used in a month by a homeowner and the mean daily high temperature in the region for the month.

LO4-1
Construct and interpret a dot plot.

DOT PLOTS

Recall for the Applewood Auto Group data, we summarized the profit earned on the 180 vehicles sold into eight classes. When we organized the data into the eight classes, we lost the exact value of the observations. A **dot plot,** on the other hand, groups the data as little as possible, and we do not lose the identity of an individual observation. To develop a dot plot, we display a dot for each observation along a horizontal number line indicating the possible values of the data. If there are identical observations or the observations are too close to be shown individually, the dots are "piled" on top of each other. This allows us to see the shape of the distribution, the value about which the data tend to cluster, and the largest and smallest observations. Dot plots are most useful for smaller data sets, whereas histograms tend to be most useful for large data sets. An example will show how to construct and interpret dot plots.

EXAMPLE

The service departments at Tionesta Ford Lincoln Mercury and Sheffield Motors Inc., two of the four Applewood Auto Group dealerships, were both open 24 days last month. Listed below is the number of vehicles serviced last month at the two dealerships. Construct dot plots and report summary statistics to compare the two dealerships.

Tionesta Ford Lincoln Mercury					
Monday	Tuesday	Wednesday	Thursday	Friday	Saturday
23	33	27	28	39	26
30	32	28	33	35	32
29	25	36	31	32	27
35	32	35	37	36	30

Sheffield Motors Inc.					
Monday	**Tuesday**	**Wednesday**	**Thursday**	**Friday**	**Saturday**
31	35	44	36	34	37
30	37	43	31	40	31
32	44	36	34	43	36
26	38	37	30	42	33

SOLUTION

The Minitab system provides a dot plot and outputs the mean, median, maximum, and minimum values, and the standard deviation for the number of cars serviced at each dealership over the last 24 working days.

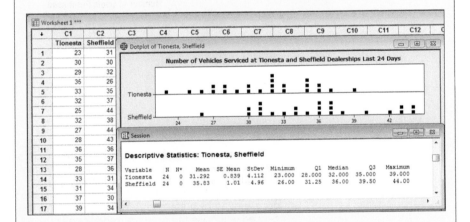

The dot plots, shown in the center of the output, graphically illustrate the distributions for each dealership. The plots show the difference in the location and dispersion of the observations. By looking at the dot plots, we can see that the number of vehicles serviced at the Sheffield dealership is more widely dispersed and has a larger mean than at the Tionesta dealership. Several other features of the number of vehicles serviced are:

- Tionesta serviced the fewest cars in any day, 23.
- Sheffield serviced 26 cars during their slowest day, which is 4 cars less than the next lowest day.
- Tionesta serviced exactly 32 cars on four different days.
- The numbers of cars serviced cluster around 36 for Sheffield and 32 for Tionesta.

From the descriptive statistics, we see Sheffield serviced a mean of 35.83 vehicles per day. Tionesta serviced a mean of 31.292 vehicles per day during the same period. So Sheffield typically services 4.54 more vehicles per day. There is also more dispersion, or variation, in the daily number of vehicles serviced at Sheffield than at Tionesta. How do we know this? The standard deviation is larger at Sheffield (4.96 vehicles per day) than at Tionesta (4.112 cars per day).

LO4-2
Construct and describe a stem-and-leaf display.

STEM-AND-LEAF DISPLAYS

In Chapter 2, we showed how to organize data into a frequency distribution so we could summarize the raw data into a meaningful form. The major advantage to organizing the data into a frequency distribution is we get a quick visual picture of the shape of the distribution without doing any further calculation. To put it another way, we can see where the data are concentrated and also determine whether there are any extremely large or small values. There are two disadvantages, however, to organizing the data into a frequency distribution: (1) we lose the exact identity of each value and (2) we are not sure how the values within each class are distributed. To explain, the following frequency distribution shows the number of advertising spots purchased by the 45 members of the Greater Buffalo Automobile Dealers Association in 2010. We observe that 7 of the 45 dealers purchased at least 90 but less than 100 spots. However, are the spots purchased within this class clustered about 90, spread evenly throughout the class, or clustered near 99? We cannot tell.

Number of Spots Purchased	Frequency
80 up to 90	2
90 up to 100	7
100 up to 110	6
110 up to 120	9
120 up to 130	8
130 up to 140	7
140 up to 150	3
150 up to 160	3
Total	45

One technique used to display quantitative information in a condensed form is the **stem-and-leaf display.** An advantage of the stem-and-leaf display over a frequency distribution is we do not lose the identity of each observation. In the above example, we would not know the identity of the values in the 90 up to 100 class. To illustrate the construction of a stem-and-leaf display using the number of advertising spots purchased, suppose the seven observations in the 90 up to 100 class are 96, 94, 93, 94, 95, 96, and 97. The **stem** value is the leading digit or digits, in this case 9. The **leaves** are the trailing digits. The stem is placed to the left of a vertical line and the leaf values to the right.

The values in the 90 up to 100 class would appear as follows:

9		6	4	3	4	5	6	7

It is also customary to sort the values within each stem from smallest to largest. Thus, the second row of the stem-and-leaf display would appear as follows:

9		3	4	4	5	6	6	7

With the stem-and-leaf display, we can quickly observe that two dealers purchased 94 spots and the number of spots purchased ranged from 93 to 97. A stem-and-leaf display is similar to a frequency distribution with more information, that is, the identity of the observations is preserved.

STEM-AND-LEAF DISPLAY A statistical technique to present a set of data. Each numerical value is divided into two parts. The leading digit(s) becomes the stem and the trailing digit the leaf. The stems are located along the vertical axis, and the leaf values are stacked against each other along the horizontal axis.

DESCRIBING DATA: DISPLAYING AND EXPLORING DATA   97

The following example explains the details of developing a stem-and-leaf display.

E X A M P L E

Listed in Table 4–1 is the number of 30-second radio advertising spots purchased by each of the 45 members of the Greater Buffalo Automobile Dealers Association last year. Organize the data into a stem-and-leaf display. Around what values do the number of advertising spots tend to cluster? What is the fewest number of spots purchased by a dealer? The largest number purchased?

TABLE 4–1 Number of Advertising Spots Purchased by Members of the Greater Buffalo Automobile Dealers Association

96	93	88	117	127	95	113	96	108	94	148	156
139	142	94	107	125	155	155	103	112	127	117	120
112	135	132	111	125	104	106	139	134	119	97	89
118	136	125	143	120	103	113	124	138			

S O L U T I O N

From the data in Table 4–1, we note that the smallest number of spots purchased is 88. So we will make the first stem value 8. The largest number is 156, so we will have the stem values begin at 8 and continue to 15. The first number in Table 4–1 is 96, which has a stem value of 9 and a leaf value of 6. Moving across the top row, the second value is 93 and the third is 88. After the first 3 data values are considered, your chart is as follows.

Stem	Leaf
8	8
9	6 3
10	
11	
12	
13	
14	
15	

Organizing all the data, the stem-and-leaf chart looks as follows.

Stem	Leaf
8	8 9
9	6 3 5 6 4 4 7
10	8 7 3 4 6 3
11	7 3 2 7 2 1 9 8 3
12	7 5 7 0 5 5 0 4
13	9 5 2 9 4 6 8
14	8 2 3
15	6 5 5

The usual procedure is to sort the leaf values from the smallest to largest. The last line, the row referring to the values in the 150s, would appear as:

15	5	5	6

The final table would appear as follows, where we have sorted all of the leaf values.

Stem	Leaf
8	8 9
9	3 4 4 5 6 6 7
10	3 3 4 6 7 8
11	1 2 2 3 3 7 7 8 9
12	0 0 4 5 5 5 7 7
13	2 4 5 6 8 9 9
14	2 3 8
15	5 5 6

You can draw several conclusions from the stem-and-leaf display. First, the minimum number of spots purchased is 88 and the maximum is 156. Two dealers purchased less than 90 spots, and three purchased 150 or more. You can observe, for example, that the three dealers who purchased more than 150 spots actually purchased 155, 155, and 156 spots. The concentration of the number of spots is between 110 and 130. There were nine dealers who purchased between 110 and 119 spots and eight who purchased between 120 and 129 spots. We can also tell that within the 120 to 129 group the actual number of spots purchased was spread evenly throughout. That is, two dealers purchased 120 spots, one dealer purchased 124 spots, three dealers purchased 125 spots, and two purchased 127 spots.

We can also generate this information on the Minitab software system. We have named the variable *Spots.* The Minitab output is below. You can find the Minitab commands that will produce this output in Appendix C.

The Minitab solution provides some additional information regarding cumulative totals. In the column to the left of the stem values are numbers such as 2, 9, 15, and so on. The number 9 indicates there are 9 observations that have occurred before the value of 100. The number 15 indicates that 15 observations have occurred prior to 110. About halfway down the column the number 9 appears in parentheses. The parentheses indicate that the middle value or median appears in that row and there are nine values in this group. In this case, we describe the middle value as the value below which half of the observations occur. There are a total of 45 observations, so the middle value, if the data were arranged from smallest to largest, would be the 23rd observation; its value is 118. After the median, the values begin to decline. These values represent the "more than" cumulative totals. There are 21 observations of 120 or more, 13 of 130 or more, and so on.

DESCRIBING DATA: DISPLAYING AND EXPLORING DATA   99

Which is the better choice, a dot plot or a stem-and-leaf chart? This is really a matter of personal choice and convenience. For presenting data, especially with a large number of observations, you will find dot plots are more frequently used. You will see dot plots in analytical literature, marketing reports, and occasionally in annual reports. If you are doing a quick analysis for yourself, stem-and-leaf tallies are handy and easy, particularly on a smaller set of data.

SELF-REVIEW 4–1

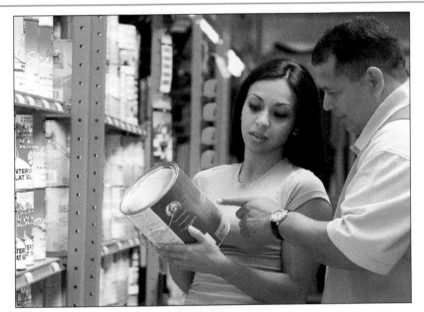

1. The number of employees at each of the 142 Home Depot stores in the Southeast region is shown in the following dot plot.

(a) What are the maximum and minimum numbers of employees per store?
(b) How many stores employ 91 people?
(c) Around what values does the number of employees per store tend to cluster?

2. The rate of return for 21 stocks is:

| 8.3 | 9.6 | 9.5 | 9.1 | 8.8 | 11.2 | 7.7 | 10.1 | 9.9 | 10.8 | |
| 10.2 | 8.0 | 8.4 | 8.1 | 11.6 | 9.6 | 8.8 | 8.0 | 10.4 | 9.8 | 9.2 |

Organize this information into a stem-and-leaf display.
(a) How many rates are less than 9.0?
(b) List the rates in the 10.0 up to 11.0 category.
(c) What is the median?
(d) What are the maximum and the minimum rates of return?

CHAPTER 4

1. Describe the differences between a histogram and a dot plot. When might a dot plot be better than a histogram?
2. Describe the differences between a histogram and a stem-and-leaf display.
3. Consider the following chart.

    a. What is this chart called?
    b. How many observations are in the study?
    c. What are the maximum and the minimum values?
    d. Around what values do the observations tend to cluster?

4. The following chart reports the number of cell phones sold at Radio Shack for the last 26 days.

    a. What are the maximum and the minimum numbers of cell phones sold in a day?
    b. What is a typical number of cell phones sold?

5. The first row of a stem-and-leaf chart appears as follows: 62 | 1 3 3 7 9. Assume whole number values.
    a. What is the "possible range" of the values in this row?
    b. How many data values are in this row?
    c. List the actual values in this row of data.

6. The third row of a stem-and-leaf chart appears as follows: 21 | 0 1 3 5 7 9. Assume whole number values.
    a. What is the "possible range" of the values in this row?
    b. How many data values are in this row?
    c. List the actual values in this row of data.

7. The following stem-and-leaf chart from the Minitab software shows the number of units produced per day in a factory.

1	3	8
1	4	
2	5	6
9	6	0133559
(7)	7	0236778
9	8	59
7	9	00156
2	10	36

    a. How many days were studied?
    b. How many observations are in the first class?
    c. What are the minimum value and the maximum value?

DESCRIBING DATA: DISPLAYING AND EXPLORING DATA   101

    d. List the actual values in the fourth row.
    e. List the actual values in the second row.
    f. How many values are less than 70?
    g. How many values are 80 or more?
    h. What is the median?
    i. How many values are between 60 and 89, inclusive?

8. The following stem-and-leaf chart reports the number of movies rented per day at Video Connection on the corner of Fourth and Main Streets.

3	12	689
6	13	123
10	14	6889
13	15	589
15	16	35
20	17	24568
23	18	268
(5)	19	13456
22	20	034679
16	21	2239
12	22	789
9	23	00179
4	24	8
3	25	13
1	26	
1	27	0

    a. How many days were studied?
    b. How many observations are in the last class?
    c. What are the maximum and the minimum values in the entire set of data?
    d. List the actual values in the fourth row.
    e. List the actual values in the next to the last row.
    f. On how many days were less than 160 movies rented?
    g. On how many days were 220 or more movies rented?
    h. What is the middle value?
    i. On how many days were between 170 and 210 movies rented?

9. A survey of the number of phone calls made by a sample of 16 Verizon subscribers last week revealed the following information. Develop a stem-and-leaf chart. How many calls did a typical subscriber make? What were the maximum and the minimum number of calls made?

For **DATA FILE**, please visit www.mhhe.com/lind16e

52	43	30	38	30	42	12	46	39
37	34	46	32	18	41	5		

10. Aloha Banking Co. is studying ATM use in suburban Honolulu. A sample of 30 ATMs showed they were used the following number of times yesterday. Develop a stem-and-leaf chart. Summarize the number of times each ATM was used. What were the typical, minimum, and maximum number of times each ATM was used?

For **DATA FILE**, please visit www.mhhe.com/lind16e

83	64	84	76	84	54	75	59	70	61
63	80	84	73	68	52	65	90	52	77
95	36	78	61	59	84	95	47	87	60

CHAPTER 4

LO4-3
Identify and compute measures of position.

MEASURES OF POSITION

The standard deviation is the most widely used measure of dispersion. However, there are other ways of describing the variation or spread in a set of data. One method is to determine the *location* of values that divide a set of observations into equal parts. These measures include **quartiles, deciles,** and **percentiles.**

Quartiles divide a set of observations into four equal parts. To explain further, think of any set of values arranged from the minimum to the maximum. In Chapter 3, we called the middle value of a set of data arranged from the minimum to the maximum the median. That is, 50% of the observations are larger than the median and 50% are smaller. The median is a measure of location because it pinpoints the center of the data. In a similar fashion, **quartiles** divide a set of observations into four equal parts. The first quartile, usually labeled Q_1, is the value below which 25% of the observations occur, and the third quartile, usually labeled Q_3, is the value below which 75% of the observations occur.

Similarly, **deciles** divide a set of observations into 10 equal parts and **percentiles** into 100 equal parts. So if you found that your GPA was in the 8th decile at your university, you could conclude that 80% of the students had a GPA lower than yours and 20% had a higher GPA. If your GPA was in the 92nd percentile, then 92% of students had a GPA less than your GPA and only 8% of students had a GPA greater than your GPA. Percentile scores are frequently used to report results on such national standardized tests as the SAT, ACT, GMAT (used to judge entry into many master of business administration programs), and LSAT (used to judge entry into law school).

Quartiles, Deciles, and Percentiles

To formalize the computational procedure, let L_p refer to the location of a desired percentile. So if we want to find the 92nd percentile we would use L_{92}, and if we wanted the median, the 50th percentile, then L_{50}. For a number of observations, n, the location of the *Pth* percentile, can be found using the formula:

LOCATION OF A PERCENTILE	$L_p = (n + 1)\dfrac{P}{100}$	[4–1]

An example will help to explain further.

E X A M P L E

Listed below are the commissions earned last month by a sample of 15 brokers at Morgan Stanley Smith Barney's Oakland, California, office. Morgan Stanley Smith Barney is an investment company with offices located throughout the United States.

$2,038	$1,758	$1,721	$1,637	$2,097	$2,047	$2,205	$1,787	$2,287
1,940	2,311	2,054	2,406	1,471	1,460			

Locate the median, the first quartile, and the third quartile for the commissions earned.

SOLUTION

The first step is to sort the data from the smallest commission to the largest.

$1,460	$1,471	$1,637	$1,721	$1,758	$1,787	$1,940	$2,038
2,047	2,054	2,097	2,205	2,287	2,311	2,406	

The median value is the observation in the center and is the same as the 50th percentile, so P equals 50. So the median or L_{50} is located at $(n + 1)(50/100)$, where n is the number of observations. In this case, that is position number 8, found by $(15 + 1)(50/100)$. The eighth-largest commission is $2,038. So we conclude this is the median and that half the brokers earned commissions more than $2,038 and half earned less than $2,038. The result using formula (4–1) to find the median is the same as the method presented in Chapter 3.

Recall the definition of a quartile. Quartiles divide a set of observations into four equal parts. Hence 25% of the observations will be less than the first quartile. Seventy-five percent of the observations will be less than the third quartile. To locate the first quartile, we use formula (4–1), where $n = 15$ and $P = 25$:

$$L_{25} = (n + 1)\frac{P}{100} = (15 + 1)\frac{25}{100} = 4$$

and to locate the third quartile, $n = 15$ and $P = 75$:

$$L_{75} = (n + 1)\frac{P}{100} = (15 + 1)\frac{75}{100} = 12$$

Therefore, the first and third quartile values are located at positions 4 and 12, respectively. The fourth value in the ordered array is $1,721 and the twelfth is $2,205. These are the first and third quartiles.

In the above example, the location formula yielded a whole number. That is, we wanted to find the first quartile and there were 15 observations, so the location formula indicated we should find the fourth ordered value. What if there were 20 observations in the sample, that is $n = 20$, and we wanted to locate the first quartile? From the location formula (4–1):

$$L_{25} = (n + 1)\frac{P}{100} = (20 + 1)\frac{25}{100} = 5.25$$

We would locate the fifth value in the ordered array and then move .25 of the distance between the fifth and sixth values and report that as the first quartile. Like the median, the quartile does not need to be one of the actual values in the data set.

To explain further, suppose a data set contained the six values 91, 75, 61, 101, 43, and 104. We want to locate the first quartile. We order the values from the minimum to the maximum: 43, 61, 75, 91, 101, and 104. The first quartile is located at

$$L_{25} = (n + 1)\frac{P}{100} = (6 + 1)\frac{25}{100} = 1.75$$

The position formula tells us that the first quartile is located between the first and the second values and it is .75 of the distance between the first and the second values.

STATISTICS IN ACTION

John W. Tukey (1915–2000) received a PhD in mathematics from Princeton in 1939. However, when he joined the Fire Control Research Office during World War II, his interest in abstract mathematics shifted to applied statistics. He developed effective numerical and graphical methods for studying patterns in data. Among the graphics he developed are the stem-and-leaf diagram and the box-and-whisker plot or box plot. From 1960 to 1980, Tukey headed the statistical division of NBC's election night vote projection team. He became renowned in 1960 for preventing an early call of victory for Richard Nixon in the presidential election won by John F. Kennedy.

The first value is 43 and the second is 61. So the distance between these two values is 18. To locate the first quartile, we need to move .75 of the distance between the first and second values, so .75(18) = 13.5. To complete the procedure, we add 13.5 to the first value, 43, and report that the first quartile is 56.5.

We can extend the idea to include both deciles and percentiles. To locate the 23rd percentile in a sample of 80 observations, we would look for the 18.63 position.

$$L_{23} = (n + 1)\frac{P}{100} = (80 + 1)\frac{23}{100} = 18.63$$

To find the value corresponding to the 23rd percentile, we would locate the 18th value and the 19th value and determine the distance between the two values. Next, we would multiply this difference by 0.63 and add the result to the smaller value. The result would be the 23rd percentile.

Statistical software is very helpful when describing and summarizing data. Excel, Minitab, and MegaStat, a statistical analysis Excel add-in, all provide summary statistics that include quartiles. For example, Minitab's summary of the Smith Barney commission data, shown below, includes the first and third quartiles, and other statistics. Based on the reported quartiles, 25% of the commissions earned were less than $1,721 and 75% were less than $2,205. These are the same values we calculated using formula (4–1).

Sheet1 ***		Session
↓	C1	**Descriptive Statistics: Commissions**
	Commissions	
1	1460	Variable N N* Mean SE Mean StDev Minimum Q1 Median Q3 Maximum
2	1471	Commissions 15 0 1947.9 77.1 298.8 1460.0 1721.0 2038.0 2205.0 2406.0
3	1637	
4	1721	

SmithBarney.xlsx				
	A	B	C	D
1	Commissions			
2	1460			
3	1471		Equation 4-1	
4	1637		Quartile 1	1721
5	1721			
6	1758		Quartile 3	2205
7	1787			
8	1940		Excel Method	
9	2038		Quartile 1	1739.5
10	2047			
11	2054		Quartile 3	2151
12	2097			
13	2205			
14	2287			
15	2311			
16	2406			

There are ways other than formula (4–1) to locate quartile values. For example, another method uses 0.25n + 0.75 to locate the position of the first quartile and 0.75n + 0.25 to locate the position of the third quartile. We will call this the *Excel Method*. In the Smith Barney data, this method would place the first quartile at position 4.5 (.25 × 15 + .75) and the third quartile at position 11.5 (.75 × 15 + .25). The first quartile would be interpolated as 0.5, or one-half the difference between the fourth- and the fifth-ranked values. Based on this method, the first quartile is $1739.5, found by ($1,721 + 0.5[$1,758 − $1,721]). The third quartile, at position 11.5, would be $2,151, or one-half the distance between the eleventh- and the twelfth-ranked values, found by ($2,097 + 0.5[$2,205 − $2,097]). Excel, as shown in the Smith Barney and Applewood examples, can compute quartiles using either of the two methods. **Please note the text uses formula (4–1) to calculate quartiles.**

Is the difference between the two methods important? No. Usually it is just a nuisance. In general, both methods calculate values that will support the statement that approximately 25% of the values are less than the value of the first quartile, and approximately 75% of the data values are less than the value of the third quartile. When the sample is large, the difference in the results from the two methods is small. For example, in the Applewood Auto Group data there are 180 vehicles. The

DESCRIBING DATA: DISPLAYING AND EXPLORING DATA   105

	A	B	C	D	E
1	**Age**	**Profit**			
2	44	$294			
3	40	$323		Equation 4-1	
4	42	$335		1st Quartile	1415.5
5	40	$352			
6	46	$369		3rd Quartile	2275.5
7	53	$377			
8	**30**	**$443**			
9	40	$482		Excel Method	
10	37	$732		1st Quartile	1422.5
11	**30**	**$754**			
12	62	$783		3rd Quartile	2268.5

quartiles computed using both methods are shown to the left. Based on the variable profit, 45 of the 180 values (25%) are less than both values of the first quartile, and 135 of the 180 values (75%) are less than both values of the third quartile.

When using Excel, be careful to understand the method used to calculate quartiles. In Excel 2007, quartiles are calculated using the *Excel Method*. Excel 2010 provides both methods to calculate quartiles. The Excel 2010 commands to compute the quartiles are shown in Appendix C.

SELF-REVIEW

4–2

The Quality Control department of Plainsville Peanut Company is responsible for checking the weight of the 8-ounce jar of peanut butter. The weights of a sample of nine jars produced last hour are:

7.69	7.72	7.8	7.86	7.90	7.94	7.97	8.06	8.09

(a) What is the median weight?
(b) Determine the weights corresponding to the first and third quartiles.

EXERCISES

For **DATA FILE**, please visit www.mhhe.com/lind16e

For **DATA FILE**, please visit www.mhhe.com/lind16e

For **DATA FILE**, please visit www.mhhe.com/lind16e

11. Determine the median and the first and third quartiles in the following data.

46	47	49	49	51	53	54	54	55	55	59

12. Determine the median and the first and third quartiles in the following data.

5.24	6.02	6.67	7.30	7.59	7.99	8.03	8.35	8.81	9.45
9.61	10.37	10.39	11.86	12.22	12.71	13.07	13.59	13.89	15.42

13. The Thomas Supply Company Inc. is a distributor of gas-powered generators. As with any business, the length of time customers take to pay their invoices is important. Listed below, arranged from smallest to largest, is the time, in days, for a sample of The Thomas Supply Company Inc. invoices.

13	13	13	20	26	27	31	34	34	34	35	35	36	37	38
41	41	41	45	47	47	47	50	51	53	54	56	62	67	82

a. Determine the first and third quartiles.
b. Determine the second decile and the eighth decile.
c. Determine the 67th percentile.

106   CHAPTER 4

For **DATA FILE**, please visit
www.mhhe.com/lind16e

14. Kevin Horn is the national sales manager for National Textbooks Inc. He has a sales staff of 40 who visit college professors all over the United States. Each Saturday morning he requires his sales staff to send him a report. This report includes, among other things, the number of professors visited during the previous week. Listed below, ordered from smallest to largest, are the number of visits last week.

38	40	41	45	48	48	50	50	51	51	52	52	53	54	55	55	55	56	56	57
59	59	59	62	62	62	63	64	65	66	66	67	67	69	69	71	77	78	79	79

a. Determine the median number of calls.
b. Determine the first and third quartiles.
c. Determine the first decile and the ninth decile.
d. Determine the 33rd percentile.

LO4-4
Construct and analyze a box plot.

BOX PLOTS

A **box plot** is a graphical display, based on quartiles, that helps us picture a set of data. To construct a box plot, we need only five statistics: the minimum value, Q_1 (the first quartile), the median, Q_3 (the third quartile), and the maximum value. An example will help to explain.

E X A M P L E

Alexander's Pizza offers free delivery of its pizza within 15 miles. Alex, the owner, wants some information on the time it takes for delivery. How long does a typical delivery take? Within what range of times will most deliveries be completed? For a sample of 20 deliveries, he determined the following information:

$$\text{Minimum value} = 13 \text{ minutes}$$

$$Q_1 = 15 \text{ minutes}$$

$$\text{Median} = 18 \text{ minutes}$$

$$Q_3 = 22 \text{ minutes}$$

$$\text{Maximum value} = 30 \text{ minutes}$$

Develop a box plot for the delivery times. What conclusions can you make about the delivery times?

S O L U T I O N

The first step in drawing a box plot is to create an appropriate scale along the horizontal axis. Next, we draw a box that starts at Q_1 (15 minutes) and ends at Q_3 (22 minutes). Inside the box we place a vertical line to represent the median (18 minutes). Finally, we extend horizontal lines from the box out to the minimum value (13 minutes) and the maximum value (30 minutes). These horizontal lines outside of the box are sometimes called "whiskers" because they look a bit like a cat's whiskers.

DESCRIBING DATA: DISPLAYING AND EXPLORING DATA   107

> The box plot also shows the interquartile range of delivery times between Q1 and Q3. The **interquartile range** is 7 minutes and indicates that 50% of the deliveries are between 15 and 22 minutes.

The box plot also reveals that the distribution of delivery times is positively skewed. In Chapter 3, we defined skewness as the lack of symmetry in a set of data. How do we know this distribution is positively skewed? In this case, there are actually two pieces of information that suggest this. First, the dashed line to the right of the box from 22 minutes (Q_3) to the maximum time of 30 minutes is longer than the dashed line from the left of 15 minutes (Q_1) to the minimum value of 13 minutes. To put it another way, the 25% of the data larger than the third quartile is more spread out than the 25% less than the first quartile. A second indication of positive skewness is that the median is not in the center of the box. The distance from the first quartile to the median is smaller than the distance from the median to the third quartile. We know that the number of delivery times between 15 minutes and 18 minutes is the same as the number of delivery times between 18 minutes and 22 minutes.

EXAMPLE

Refer to the Applewood Auto Group data. Develop a box plot for the variable age of the buyer. What can we conclude about the distribution of the age of the buyer?

SOLUTION

Minitab was used to develop the following chart and summary statistics.

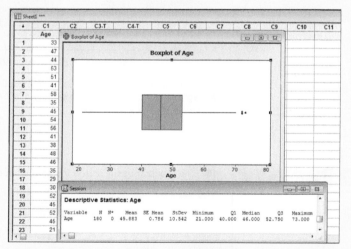

The median age of the purchaser is 46 years, 25% of the purchasers are less than 40 years of age, and 25% are more than 52.75 years of age. Based on the summary information and the box plot, we conclude:

- Fifty percent of the purchasers are between the ages of 40 and 52.75 years.
- The distribution of ages is symmetric. There are two reasons for this conclusion. The length of the whisker above 52.75 years (Q_3) is about the same

length as the whisker below 40 years (Q_1). Also, the area in the box between 40 years and the median of 46 years is about the same as the area between the median and 52.75.

There are three asterisks (*) above 70 years. What do they indicate? In a box plot, an asterisk identifies an **outlier.** An outlier is a value that is inconsistent with the rest of the data. It is defined as a value that is more than 1.5 times the interquartile range smaller than Q_1 or larger than Q_3. In this example, an outlier would be a value larger than 71.875 years, found by:

$$Outlier > Q_3 + 1.5(Q_3 - Q_1) = 52.75 + 1.5(52.75 - 40) = 71.875$$

An outlier would also be a value less than 20.875 years.

$$Outlier < Q_1 - 1.5(Q_3 - Q_1) = 40 - 1.5(52.75 - 40) = 20.875$$

From the box plot, we conclude there are three purchasers 72 years of age or older and none less than 21 years of age. Technical note: In some cases, a single asterisk may represent more than one observation because of the limitations of the software and space available. It is a good idea to check the actual data. In this instance, there are three purchasers 72 years old or older; two are 72 and one is 73.

SELF-REVIEW

4–3

The following box plot shows the assets in millions of dollars for credit unions in Seattle, Washington.

What are the smallest and largest values, the first and third quartiles, and the median? Would you agree that the distribution is symmetrical? Are there any outliers?

EXERCISES

15. The box plot below shows the amount spent for books and supplies per year by students at four-year public colleges.

   a. Estimate the median amount spent.
   b. Estimate the first and third quartiles for the amount spent.
   c. Estimate the interquartile range for the amount spent.
   d. Beyond what point is a value considered an outlier?
   e. Identify any outliers and estimate their value.
   f. Is the distribution symmetrical or positively or negatively skewed?

16. The box plot shows the undergraduate in-state charge per credit hour at four-year public colleges.

   a. Estimate the median.
   b. Estimate the first and third quartiles.
   c. Determine the interquartile range.
   d. Beyond what point is a value considered an outlier?
   e. Identify any outliers and estimate their value.
   f. Is the distribution symmetrical or positively or negatively skewed?

17. In a study of the gasoline mileage of model year 2013 automobiles, the mean miles per gallon was 27.5 and the median was 26.8. The smallest value in the study was 12.70 miles per gallon, and the largest was 50.20. The first and third quartiles were 17.95 and 35.45 miles per gallon, respectively. Develop a box plot and comment on the distribution. Is it a symmetric distribution?

18. A sample of 28 time shares in the Orlando, Florida, area revealed the following daily charges for a one-bedroom suite. For convenience, the data are ordered from smallest to largest. Construct a box plot to represent the data. Comment on the distribution. Be sure to identify the first and third quartiles and the median.

For **DATA FILE**, please visit
www.mhhe.com/lind16e

$116	$121	$157	$192	$207	$209	$209
229	232	236	236	239	243	246
260	264	276	281	283	289	296
307	309	312	317	324	341	353

LO4-5
Compute and interpret the coefficient of skewness.

SKEWNESS

In Chapter 3, we described measures of central location for a set of observations by reporting the mean, median, and mode. We also described measures that show the amount of spread or variation in a set of data, such as the range and the standard deviation.

    Another characteristic of a set of data is the shape. There are four shapes commonly observed: symmetric, positively skewed, negatively skewed, and bimodal. In a **symmetric** set of observations the mean and median are equal and the data values are evenly spread around these values. The data values below the mean and median are a mirror image of those above. A set of values is **skewed to the right** or **positively skewed** if there is a single peak, but the values extend much farther to the right of the peak than to the left of the peak. In this case, the mean is larger than the median. In a **negatively skewed** distribution there is a single peak, but the observations extend

CHAPTER 4

farther to the left, in the negative direction, than to the right. In a negatively skewed distribution, the mean is smaller than the median. Positively skewed distributions are more common. Salaries often follow this pattern. Think of the salaries of those employed in a small company of about 100 people. The president and a few top executives would have very large salaries relative to the other workers and hence the distribution of salaries would exhibit positive skewness. A **bimodal distribution** will have two or more peaks. This is often the case when the values are from two or more populations. This information is summarized in Chart 4–1.

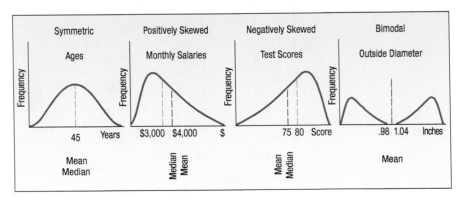

CHART 4–1 Shapes of Frequency Polygons

There are several formulas in the statistical literature used to calculate skewness. The simplest, developed by Professor Karl Pearson (1857–1936), is based on the difference between the mean and the median.

PEARSON'S COEFFICIENT OF SKEWNESS $$sk = \frac{3(\bar{x} - \text{Median})}{s}$$ **[4–2]**

Using this relationship, the coefficient of skewness can range from -3 up to 3. A value near -3, such as -2.57, indicates considerable negative skewness. A value such as 1.63 indicates moderate positive skewness. A value of 0, which will occur when the mean and median are equal, indicates the distribution is symmetrical and there is no skewness present.

In this text, we present output from Minitab and Excel. Both of these software packages compute a value for the coefficient of skewness based on the cubed deviations from the mean. The formula is:

SOFTWARE COEFFICIENT OF SKEWNESS $$sk = \frac{n}{(n-1)(n-2)}\left[\sum\left(\frac{x - \bar{x}}{s}\right)^3\right]$$ **[4–3]**

Formula (4–3) offers an insight into skewness. The right-hand side of the formula is the difference between each value and the mean, divided by the standard deviation. That is the portion $(x - \bar{x})/s$ of the formula. This idea is called **standardizing.** We will discuss the idea of standardizing a value in more detail in Chapter 7 when we describe the normal probability distribution. At this point, observe that the result is to report the difference between each value and the mean in units of the standard deviation. If this difference is positive, the particular value is larger than the mean; if the

DESCRIBING DATA: DISPLAYING AND EXPLORING DATA   111

value is negative, the standardized quantity is smaller than the mean. When we cube these values, we retain the information on the direction of the difference. Recall that in the formula for the standard deviation [see formula (3–10)] we squared the difference between each value and the mean, so that the result was all nonnegative values.

If the set of data values under consideration is symmetric, when we cube the standardized values and sum over all the values, the result would be near zero. If there are several large values, clearly separate from the others, the sum of the cubed differences would be a large positive value. If there are several small values clearly separate from the others, the sum of the cubed differences will be negative.

An example will illustrate the idea of skewness.

E X A M P L E

Following are the earnings per share for a sample of 15 software companies for the year 2013. The earnings per share are arranged from smallest to largest.

$0.09	$0.13	$0.41	$0.51	$ 1.12	$ 1.20	$ 1.49	$3.18
3.50	6.36	7.83	8.92	10.13	12.99	16.40	

Compute the mean, median, and standard deviation. Find the coefficient of skewness using Pearson's estimate and the software methods. What is your conclusion regarding the shape of the distribution?

S O L U T I O N

These are sample data, so we use formula (3–2) to determine the mean

$$\bar{x} = \frac{\Sigma x}{n} = \frac{\$74.26}{15} = \$4.95$$

The median is the middle value in a set of data, arranged from smallest to largest. In this case, the middle value is $3.18, so the median earnings per share is $3.18.

We use formula (3–10) on page 77 to determine the sample standard deviation.

$$s = \sqrt{\frac{\Sigma(x - \bar{x})^2}{n - 1}} = \sqrt{\frac{(\$0.09 - \$4.95)^2 + \cdots + (\$16.40 - \$4.95)^2}{15 - 1}} = \$5.22$$

Pearson's coefficient of skewness is 1.017, found by

$$sk = \frac{3(\bar{x} - \text{Median})}{s} = \frac{3(\$4.95 - \$3.18)}{\$5.22} = 1.017$$

This indicates there is moderate positive skewness in the earnings per share data.

We obtain a similar, but not exactly the same, value from the software method. The details of the calculations are shown in Table 4–2. To begin, we find the difference between each earnings per share value and the mean and divide this result by the standard deviation. We have referred to this as standardizing. Next, we cube, that is, raise to the third power, the result of the first step. Finally, we sum the cubed values. The details for the first company, that is, the company with an earnings per share of $0.09, are:

$$\left(\frac{x - \bar{x}}{s}\right)^3 = \left(\frac{0.09 - 4.95}{5.22}\right)^3 = (-0.9310)^3 = -0.8070$$

TABLE 4–2 Calculation of the Coefficient of Skewness

Earnings per Share	$\dfrac{(x - \bar{x})}{s}$	$\left(\dfrac{x - \bar{x}}{s}\right)^3$
0.09	−0.9310	−0.8070
0.13	−0.9234	−0.7873
0.41	−0.8697	−0.6579
0.51	−0.8506	−0.6154
1.12	−0.7337	−0.3950
1.20	−0.7184	−0.3708
1.49	−0.6628	−0.2912
3.18	−0.3391	−0.0390
3.50	−0.2778	−0.0214
6.36	0.2701	0.0197
7.83	0.5517	0.1679
8.92	0.7605	0.4399
10.13	0.9923	0.9772
12.99	1.5402	3.6539
16.40	2.1935	10.5537
		11.8274

When we sum the 15 cubed values, the result is 11.8274. That is, the term $\Sigma[(x - \bar{x})/s]^3 = 11.8274$. To find the coefficient of skewness, we use formula (4–3), with $n = 15$.

$$sk = \frac{n}{(n - 1)(n - 2)} \Sigma \left(\frac{x - \bar{x}}{s}\right)^3 = \frac{15}{(15 - 1)(15 - 2)} (11.8274) = 0.975$$

We conclude that the earnings per share values are somewhat positively skewed. The following Minitab summary reports the descriptive measures, such as the mean, median, and standard deviation of the earnings per share data. Also included are the coefficient of skewness and a histogram with a bell-shaped curve superimposed.

DESCRIBING DATA: DISPLAYING AND EXPLORING DATA   113

SELF-REVIEW

4–4

A sample of five data entry clerks employed in the Horry County Tax Office revised the following number of tax records last hour: 73, 98, 60, 92, and 84.
(a) Find the mean, median, and the standard deviation.
(b) Compute the coefficient of skewness using Pearson's method.
(c) Calculate the coefficient of skewness using the software method.
(d) What is your conclusion regarding the skewness of the data?

EXERCISES

For Exercises 19–22:

a. Determine the mean, median, and the standard deviation.
b. Determine the coefficient of skewness using Pearson's method.
c. Determine the coefficient of skewness using the software method.

For **DATA FILE**, please visit
www.mhhe.com/lind16e

19. The following values are the starting salaries, in $000, for a sample of five accounting graduates who accepted positions in public accounting last year.

36.0	26.0	33.0	28.0	31.0

For **DATA FILE**, please visit
www.mhhe.com/lind16e

20. Listed below are the salaries, in $000, for a sample of 15 chief financial officers in the electronics industry.

$516.0	$548.0	$566.0	$534.0	$586.0	$529.0
546.0	523.0	538.0	523.0	551.0	552.0
486.0	558.0	574.0			

For **DATA FILE**, please visit
www.mhhe.com/lind16e

21. Listed below are the commissions earned ($000) last year by the 15 sales representatives at Furniture Patch Inc.

$ 3.9	$ 5.7	$ 7.3	$10.6	$13.0	$13.6	$15.1	$15.8	$17.1
17.4	17.6	22.3	38.6	43.2	87.7			

For **DATA FILE**, please visit
www.mhhe.com/lind16e

22. Listed below are the salaries for the 2012 New York Yankees Major League Baseball team.

For **DATA FILE**, please visit
www.mhhe.com/lind16e

Player	Salary	Player	Salary
Alex Rodriguez	$30,000,000	Boone Logan	$1,875,000
Mark Teixeira	23,125,000	Joba Chamberlain	1,675,000
CC Sabathia	23,000,000	David Robertson	1,600,000
Derek Jeter	15,729,364	Raul Ibanez	1,100,000
Mariano Rivera	14,940,025	Eric Chavez	900,000
Robinson Cano	14,000,000	Michael Pineda	528,475
Rafael Soriano	11,000,000	Ivan Nova	527,200
Nick Swisher	10,250,000	Clay Rapada	525,000
Curtis Granderson	10,000,000	Eduardo Nunez	523,800
Hiroki Kuroda	10,000,000	Cory Wade	508,925
Russell Martin	7,500,000	David Aardsma	500,000
Freddy Garcia	4,000,000	Chris Stewart	482,500
Pedro Feliciano	3,750,000	Austin Romine	482,000
Phil Hughes	3,200,000	Cesar Cabral	480,000
Brett Gardner	2,800,000	Brad Meyers	480,000
Andruw Jones	2,000,000		

LO4-6
Create and interpret a
scatter diagram.

DESCRIBING THE RELATIONSHIP BETWEEN TWO VARIABLES

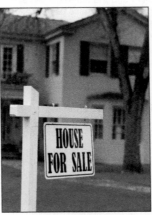

In Chapter 2 and the first section of this chapter, we presented graphical techniques to summarize the distribution of a single variable. We used a histogram in Chapter 2 to summarize the profit on vehicles sold by the Applewood Auto Group. Earlier in this chapter, we used dot plots and stem-and-leaf displays to visually summarize a set of data. Because we are studying a single variable, we refer to this as **univariate** data.

There are situations where we wish to study and visually portray the relationship between two variables. When we study the relationship between two variables, we refer to the data as **bivariate.** Data analysts frequently wish to understand the relationship between two variables. Here are some examples:

- Tybo and Associates is a law firm that advertises extensively on local TV. The partners are considering increasing their advertising budget. Before doing so, they would like to know the relationship between the amount spent per month on advertising and the total amount of billings for that month. To put it another way, will increasing the amount spent on advertising result in an increase in billings?
- Coastal Realty is studying the selling prices of homes. What variables seem to be related to the selling price of homes? For example, do larger homes sell for more than smaller ones? Probably. So Coastal might study the relationship between the area in square feet and the selling price.
- Dr. Stephen Givens is an expert in human development. He is studying the relationship between the height of fathers and the height of their sons. That is, do tall fathers tend to have tall children? Would you expect Dwight Howard, the 6' 11", 265-pound professional basketball player, to have relatively tall sons?

One graphical technique we use to show the relationship between variables is called a **scatter diagram.**

To draw a scatter diagram, we need two variables. We scale one variable along the horizontal axis (X-axis) of a graph and the other variable along the vertical axis (Y-axis). Usually one variable depends to some degree on the other. In the third example above, the height of the son *depends* on the height of the father. So we scale the height of the father on the horizontal axis and that of the son on the vertical axis.

We can use statistical software, such as Excel, to perform the plotting function for us. *Caution:* You should always be careful of the scale. By changing the scale of either the vertical or the horizontal axis, you can affect the apparent visual strength of the relationship.

Following are three scatter diagrams (Chart 4–2). The one on the left shows a rather strong positive relationship between the age in years and the maintenance cost last year for a sample of 10 buses owned by the city of Cleveland, Ohio. Note that as the age of the bus increases, the yearly maintenance cost also increases. The example in the center, for a sample of 20 vehicles, shows a rather strong indirect relationship between the odometer reading and the auction price. That is, as the number of miles driven increases, the auction price decreases. The example on the right depicts the relationship between the height and yearly salary for a sample of 15 shift supervisors. This graph indicates there is little relationship between their height and yearly salary.

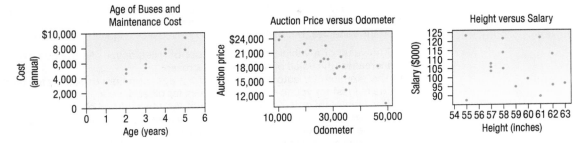

CHART 4–2 Three Examples of Scatter Diagrams.

EXAMPLE

In the introduction to Chapter 2, we presented data from the Applewood Auto Group. We gathered information concerning several variables, including the profit earned from the sale of 180 vehicles sold last month. In addition to the amount of profit on each sale, one of the other variables is the age of the purchaser. Is there a relationship between the profit earned on a vehicle sale and the age of the purchaser? Would it be reasonable to conclude that more profit is made on vehicles purchased by older buyers?

SOLUTION

We can investigate the relationship between vehicle profit and the age of the buyer with a scatter diagram. We scale age on the horizontal, or X-axis, and the profit on the vertical, or Y-axis. We assume profit depends on the age of the purchaser. As people age, they earn more income and purchase more expensive cars which, in turn, produce higher profits. We use Excel to develop the scatter diagram. The Excel commands are in Appendix C.

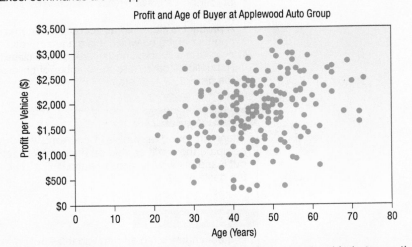

The scatter diagram shows a rather weak positive relationship between the two variables. It does not appear there is much relationship between the vehicle profit and the age of the buyer. In Chapter 13, we will study the relationship between variables more extensively, even calculating several numerical measures to express the relationship between variables.

116   CHAPTER 4

In the preceding example, there is a weak positive, or direct, relationship between the variables. There are, however, many instances where there is a relationship between the variables, but that relationship is inverse or negative. For example:

- The value of a vehicle and the number of miles driven. As the number of miles increases, the value of the vehicle decreases.
- The premium for auto insurance and the age of the driver. Auto rates tend to be the highest for younger drivers and less for older drivers.
- For many law enforcement personnel, as the number of years on the job increases, the number of traffic citations decreases. This may be because personnel become more liberal in their interpretations or they may be in supervisor positions and not in a position to issue as many citations. But in any event, as age increases, the number of citations decreases.

LO4-7
Develop and explain a contingency table.

CONTINGENCY TABLES

A scatter diagram requires that both of the variables be at least interval scale. In the Applewood Auto Group example, both age and vehicle profit are ratio scale variables. Height is also ratio scale as used in the discussion of the relationship between the height of fathers and the height of their sons. What if we wish to study the relationship between two variables when one or both are nominal or ordinal scale? In this case, we tally the results in a **contingency table.**

> **CONTINGENCY TABLE** A table used to classify observations according to two identifiable characteristics.

A contingency table is a cross-tabulation that simultaneously summarizes two variables of interest. For example:

- Students at a university are classified by gender and class (freshman, sophomore, junior, or senior).
- A product is classified as acceptable or unacceptable and by the shift (day, afternoon, or night) on which it is manufactured.
- A voter in a school bond referendum is classified as to party affiliation (Democrat, Republican, other) and the number of children that voter has attending school in the district (0, 1, 2, etc.).

E X A M P L E

There are four dealerships in the Applewood Auto Group. Suppose we want to compare the profit earned on each vehicle sold by the particular dealership. To put it another way, is there a relationship between the amount of profit earned and the dealership?

S O L U T I O N

In a contingency table, both variables only need to be nominal or ordinal. In this example, the variable dealership is a nominal variable and the variable profit is a ratio variable. To convert profit to an ordinal variable, we classify the variable profit into two categories, those cases where the profit earned is more than the median and those cases where it is less. On page 63 we calculated the median profit for all sales last month at Applewood Auto Group to be $1,882.50.

DESCRIBING DATA: DISPLAYING AND EXPLORING DATA   117

Contingency Table Showing the Relationship between Profit and Dealership					
Above/Below Median Profit	Kane	Olean	Sheffield	Tionesta	Total
Above	25	20	19	26	90
Below	27	20	26	17	90
Total	52	40	45	43	180

By organizing the information into a contingency table, we can compare the profit at the four dealerships. We observe the following:

- From the Total column on the right, 90 of the 180 cars sold had a profit above the median and half below. From the definition of the median, this is expected.
- For the Kane dealership, 25 out of the 52, or 48%, of the cars sold were sold for a profit more than the median.
- The percentage of profits above the median for the other dealerships are 50% for Olean, 42% for Sheffield, and 60% for Tionesta.

We will return to the study of contingency tables in Chapter 5 during the study of probability and in Chapter 15 during the study of nonparametric methods of analysis.

SELF-REVIEW

4–5

The rock group Blue String Beans is touring the United States. The following chart shows the relationship between concert seating capacity and revenue in $000 for a sample of concerts.

(a) What is the diagram called?
(b) How many concerts were studied?
(c) Estimate the revenue for the concert with the largest seating capacity.
(d) How would you characterize the relationship between revenue and seating capacity? Is it strong or weak, direct or inverse?

EXERCISES

For **DATA FILE**, please visit
www.mhhe.com/lind16e

23. Develop a scatter diagram for the following sample data. How would you describe the relationship between the values?

x-Value	y-Value	x-Value	y-Value
10	6	11	6
8	2	10	5
9	6	7	2
11	5	7	3
13	7	11	7

24. Silver Springs Moving and Storage Inc. is studying the relationship between the number of rooms in a move and the number of labor hours required for the move. As part of the analysis, the CFO of Silver Springs developed the following scatter diagram.

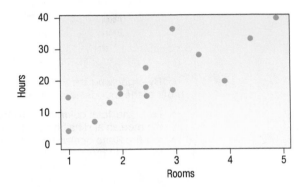

a. How many moves are in the sample?
b. Does it appear that more labor hours are required as the number of rooms increases, or do labor hours decrease as the number of rooms increases?

25. The Director of Planning for Devine Dining Inc. wishes to study the relationship between the gender of a guest and whether the guest orders dessert. To investigate the relationship, the manager collected the following information on 200 recent customers.

Dessert Ordered	Gender		Total
	Male	**Female**	
Yes	32	15	47
No	68	85	153
Total	100	100	200

a. What is the level of measurement of the two variables?
b. What is the above table called?
c. Does the evidence in the table suggest men are more likely to order dessert than women? Explain why.

26. Ski Resorts of Vermont Inc. is considering a merger with Gulf Shores Beach Resorts Inc. of Alabama. The board of directors surveyed 50 stockholders concerning their position on the merger. The results are reported below.

Number of Shares Held	Opinion			Total
	Favor	**Oppose**	**Undecided**	
Under 200	8	6	2	16
200 up to 1,000	6	8	1	15
Over 1,000	6	12	1	19
Total	20	26	4	50

a. What level of measurement is used in this table?
b. What is this table called?
c. What group seems most strongly opposed to the merger?

DESCRIBING DATA: DISPLAYING AND EXPLORING DATA   119

I. A dot plot shows the range of values on the horizontal axis and the number of observations for each value on the vertical axis.
  A. Dot plots report the details of each observation.
  B. They are useful for comparing two or more data sets.
II. A stem-and-leaf display is an alternative to a histogram.
  A. The leading digit is the stem and the trailing digit the leaf.
  B. The advantages of a stem-and-leaf display over a histogram include:
    1. The identity of each observation is not lost.
    2. The digits themselves give a picture of the distribution.
    3. The cumulative frequencies are also shown.
III. Measures of location also describe the shape of a set of observations.
  A. Quartiles divide a set of observations into four equal parts.
    1. Twenty-five percent of the observations are less than the first quartile, 50% are less than the second quartile, and 75% are less than the third quartile.
    2. The interquartile range is the difference between the third quartile and the first quartile.
  B. Deciles divide a set of observations into 10 equal parts and percentiles into 100 equal parts.
IV. A box plot is a graphic display of a set of data.
  A. A box is drawn enclosing the regions between the first quartile and the third quartile.
    1. A line is drawn inside the box at the median value.
    2. Dotted line segments are drawn from the third quartile to the largest value to show the highest 25% of the values and from the first quartile to the smallest value to show the lowest 25% of the values.
  B. A box plot is based on five statistics: the maximum and minimum values, the first and third quartiles, and the median.
V. The coefficient of skewness is a measure of the symmetry of a distribution.
  A. There are two formulas for the coefficient of skewness.
    1. The formula developed by Pearson is:

$$sk = \frac{3(\bar{x} - \text{Median})}{s} \qquad\qquad \textbf{[4–2]}$$

    2. The coefficient of skewness computed by statistical software is:

$$sk = \frac{n}{(n-1)(n-2)}\left[\sum\left(\frac{x - \bar{x}}{s}\right)^3\right] \qquad\qquad \textbf{[4–3]}$$

VI. A scatter diagram is a graphic tool to portray the relationship between two variables.
  A. Both variables are measured with interval or ratio scales.
  B. If the scatter of points moves from the lower left to the upper right, the variables under consideration are directly or positively related.
  C. If the scatter of points moves from the upper left to the lower right, the variables are inversely or negatively related.
VII. A contingency table is used to classify nominal-scale observations according to two characteristics.

SYMBOL	MEANING	PRONUNCIATION
L_p	Location of percentile	L sub p
Q_1	First quartile	Q sub 1
Q_3	Third quartile	Q sub 3

CHAPTER EXERCISES

27. A sample of students attending Southeast Florida University is asked the number of social activities in which they participated last week. The chart below was prepared from the sample data.

Activities

   a. What is the name given to this chart?
   b. How many students were in the study?
   c. How many students reported attending no social activities?

28. Doctor's Care is a walk-in clinic, with locations in Georgetown, Moncks Corner, and Aynor, at which patients may receive treatment for minor injuries, colds, and flu, as well as physical examinations. The following charts report the number of patients treated in each of the three locations last month.

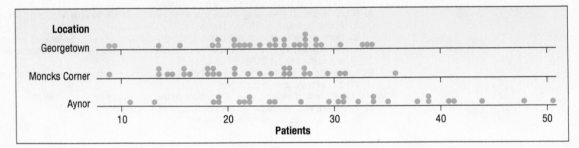

Describe the number of patients served at the three locations each day. What are the maximum and minimum numbers of patients served at each of the locations?

For **DATA FILE**, please visit www.mhhe.com/lind16e

29. The screen size for 23 LCD televisions is given below. Make a stem-and-leaf display of this variable.

| 46 | 52 | 46 | 40 | 42 | 46 | 40 | 37 | 46 | 40 | 52 | 32 | 37 | 32 | 52 |
| 40 | 32 | 52 | 40 | 52 | 46 | 46 | 52 | | | | | | | |

For **DATA FILE**, please visit www.mhhe.com/lind16e

30. The top 25 companies (by market capitalization) operating in the Washington, DC, area along with the year they were founded and the number of employees are given below. Make a stem-and-leaf display of each of these variables and write a short description of your findings.

Company Name	Year Founded	Employees
AES Corp.	1981	30,000
American Capital Strategies Ltd.	1986	484
AvalonBay Communities Inc.	1978	1,767
Capital One Financial Corp.	1995	31,800
Constellation Energy Group Inc.	1816	9,736
Coventry Health Care Inc.	1986	10,250
Danaher Corp.	1984	45,000
Dominion Resources Inc.	1909	17,500
Fannie Mae	1938	6,450
Freddie Mac	1970	5,533
		(*continued*)

DESCRIBING DATA: DISPLAYING AND EXPLORING DATA 121

Company Name	Year Founded	Employees
Gannett Co.	1906	49,675
General Dynamics Corp.	1952	81,000
Genworth Financial Inc.	2004	7,200
Harman International Industries Inc.	1980	11,246
Host Hotels & Resorts Inc.	1927	229
Legg Mason Inc.	1899	3,800
Lockheed Martin Corp.	1995	140,000
Marriott International Inc.	1927	151,000
MedImmune Inc.	1988	2,516
NII Holdings Inc.	1996	7,748
Norfolk Southern Corp.	1982	30,594
Pepco Holdings Inc.	1896	5,057
Sallie Mae	1972	11,456
Sprint Nextel Corp.	1899	64,000
T. Rowe Price Group Inc.	1937	4,605
The Washington Post Co.	1877	17,100

For **DATA FILE**, please visit www.mhhe.com/lind16e

31. In recent years, due to low interest rates, many homeowners refinanced their home mortgages. Linda Lahey is a mortgage officer at Down River Federal Savings and Loan. Below is the amount refinanced for 20 loans she processed last week. The data are reported in thousands of dollars and arranged from smallest to largest.

59.2	59.5	61.6	65.5	66.6	72.9	74.8	77.3	79.2
83.7	85.6	85.8	86.6	87.0	87.1	90.2	93.3	98.6
100.2	100.7							

a. Find the median, first quartile, and third quartile.
b. Find the 26th and 83rd percentiles.
c. Draw a box plot of the data.

32. A study is made by the recording industry in the United States of the number of music CDs owned by 25 senior citizens and 30 young adults. The information is reported below.

For **DATA FILE**, please visit www.mhhe.com/lind16e

Seniors									
28	35	41	48	52	81	97	98	98	99
118	132	133	140	145	147	153	158	162	174
177	180	180	187	188					

Young Adults									
81	107	113	147	147	175	183	192	202	209
233	251	254	266	283	284	284	316	372	401
417	423	490	500	507	518	550	557	590	594

a. Find the median and the first and third quartiles for the number of CDs owned by senior citizens. Develop a box plot for the information.
b. Find the median and the first and third quartiles for the number of CDs owned by young adults. Develop a box plot for the information.
c. Compare the number of CDs owned by the two groups.

For **DATA FILE**, please visit www.mhhe.com/lind16e

33. The corporate headquarters of *Bank.com*, a new Internet company that performs all banking transactions via the Internet, is located in downtown Philadelphia. The director of human resources is making a study of the time it takes employees to get to work. The city is planning to offer incentives to each downtown employer if they will encourage their

122   CHAPTER 4

employees to use public transportation. Below is a listing of the time to get to work this morning according to whether the employee used public transportation or drove a car.

Public Transportation									
23	25	25	30	31	31	32	33	35	36
37	42								

Private									
32	32	33	34	37	37	38	38	38	39
40	44								

a. Find the median and the first and third quartiles for the time it took employees using public transportation. Develop a box plot for the information.
b. Find the median and the first and third quartiles for the time it took employees who drove their own vehicle. Develop a box plot for the information.
c. Compare the times of the two groups.

34. The following box plot shows the number of daily newspapers published in each state and the District of Columbia. Write a brief report summarizing the number published. Be sure to include information on the values of the first and third quartiles, the median, and whether there is any skewness. If there are any outliers, estimate their value.

Number of Newspapers

35. Walter Gogel Company is an industrial supplier of fasteners, tools, and springs. The amounts of its invoices vary widely, from less than $20.00 to more than $400.00. During the month of January the company sent out 80 invoices. Here is a box plot of these invoices. Write a brief report summarizing the invoice amounts. Be sure to include information on the values of the first and third quartiles, the median, and whether there is any skewness. If there are any outliers, approximate the value of these invoices.

Invoice Amount

For **DATA FILE**, please visit www.mhhe.com/lind16e

36. The American Society of PeriAnesthesia Nurses (ASPAN; www.aspan.org) is a national organization serving nurses practicing in ambulatory surgery, preanesthesia, and postanesthesia care. The organization consists of the 40 components listed below.

State/Region	Membership	State/Region	Membership
Alabama	95	Illinois	562
Arizona	399	Indiana	270
Maryland, Delaware, DC	531	Iowa	117
Connecticut	239	Kentucky	197
Florida	631	Louisiana	258
Georgia	384	Michigan	411
Hawaii	73	Massachusetts	480
			(continued)

State/Region	Membership	State/Region	Membership
Maine	97	California	1,165
Minnesota, Dakotas	289	New Mexico	79
Missouri, Kansas	282	Pennsylvania	575
Mississippi	90	Rhode Island	53
Nebraska	115	Colorado	409
North Carolina	542	South Carolina	237
Nevada	106	Texas	1,026
New Jersey, Bermuda	517	Tennessee	167
Alaska, Idaho, Montana,		Utah	67
Oregon, Washington	708	Virginia	414
New York	891	Vermont,	
Ohio	708	New Hampshire	144
Oklahoma	171	Wisconsin	311
Arkansas	68	West Virginia	62

Use statistical software to answer the following questions.

a. Find the mean, median, and standard deviation of the number of members per component.

b. Find the coefficient of skewness, using the software. What do you conclude about the shape of the distribution of component size?

c. Compute the first and third quartiles using formula (4–1).

d. Develop a box plot. Are there any outliers? Which components are outliers? What are the limits for outliers?

For **DATA FILE**, please visit
www.mhhe.com/lind16e

37. McGivern Jewelers is located in the Levis Square Mall just south of Toledo, Ohio. Recently it ran an advertisement in the local newspaper reporting the shape, size, price, and cut grade for 33 of its diamonds currently in stock. The information is reported below.

Shape	Size (carats)	Price	Cut Grade	Shape	Size (carats)	Price	Cut Grade
Princess	5.03	$44,312	Ideal cut	Round	0.77	$2,828	Ultra ideal cut
Round	2.35	20,413	Premium cut	Oval	0.76	3,808	Premium cut
Round	2.03	13,080	Ideal cut	Princess	0.71	2,327	Premium cut
Round	1.56	13,925	Ideal cut	Marquise	0.71	2,732	Good cut
Round	1.21	7,382	Ultra ideal cut	Round	0.70	1,915	Premium cut
Round	1.21	5,154	Average cut	Round	0.66	1,885	Premium cut
Round	1.19	5,339	Premium cut	Round	0.62	1,397	Good cut
Emerald	1.16	5,161	Ideal cut	Round	0.52	2,555	Premium cut
Round	1.08	8,775	Ultra ideal cut	Princess	0.51	1,337	Ideal cut
Round	1.02	4,282	Premium cut	Round	0.51	1,558	Premium cut
Round	1.02	6,943	Ideal cut	Round	0.45	1,191	Premium cut
Marquise	1.01	7,038	Good cut	Princess	0.44	1,319	Average cut
Princess	1.00	4,868	Premium cut	Marquise	0.44	1,319	Premium cut
Round	0.91	5,106	Premium cut	Round	0.40	1,133	Premium cut
Round	0.90	3,921	Good cut	Round	0.35	1,354	Good cut
Round	0.90	3,733	Premium cut	Round	0.32	896	Premium cut
Round	0.84	2,621	Premium cut				

a. Develop a box plot of the variable price and comment on the result. Are there any outliers? What is the median price? What are the values of the first and the third quartiles?

b. Develop a box plot of the variable size and comment on the result. Are there any outliers? What is the median price? What are the values of the first and the third quartiles?

c. Develop a scatter diagram between the variables price and size. Be sure to put price on the vertical axis and size on the horizontal axis. Does there seem to be an association between the two variables? Is the association direct or indirect? Does any point seem to be different from the others?

d. Develop a contingency table for the variables shape and cut grade. What is the most common cut grade? What is the most common shape? What is the most common combination of cut grade and shape?

124   CHAPTER 4

For **DATA FILE**, please visit
www.mhhe.com/lind16e

38. Listed below is the amount of commissions earned last month for the eight members of the sales staff at Best Electronics. Calculate the coefficient of skewness using both methods. *Hint:* Use of a spreadsheet will expedite the calculations.

| 980.9 | 1,036.5 | 1,099.5 | 1,153.9 | 1,409.0 | 1,456.4 | 1,718.4 | 1,721.2 |

For **DATA FILE**, please visit
www.mhhe.com/lind16e

39. Listed below is the number of car thefts in a large city over the last week. Calculate the coefficient of skewness using both methods. *Hint:* Use of a spreadsheet will expedite the calculations.

| 3 | 12 | 13 | 7 | 8 | 3 | 8 |

40. The manager of Information Services at Wilkin Investigations, a private investigation firm, is studying the relationship between the age (in months) of a combination printer, copier, and fax machine and its monthly maintenance cost. For a sample of 15 machines, the manager developed the following chart. What can the manager conclude about the relationship between the variables?

41. An auto insurance company reported the following information regarding the age of a driver and the number of accidents reported last year. Develop a scatter diagram for the data and write a brief summary.

For **DATA FILE**, please visit
www.mhhe.com/lind16e

Age	Accidents	Age	Accidents
16	4	23	0
24	2	27	1
18	5	32	1
17	4	22	3

42. Wendy's offers eight different condiments (mustard, catsup, onion, mayonnaise, pickle, lettuce, tomato, and relish) on hamburgers. A store manager collected the following information on the number of condiments ordered and the age group of the customer. What can you conclude regarding the information? Who tends to order the most or least number of condiments?

Number of Condiments	Age			
	Under 18	18 up to 40	40 up to 60	60 or older
0	12	18	24	52
1	21	76	50	30
2	39	52	40	12
3 or more	71	87	47	28

43. Here is a table showing the number of employed and unemployed workers 20 years or older by gender in the United States.

Gender	Number of Workers (000)	
	Employed	Unemployed
Men	70,415	4,209
Women	61,402	3,314

    a. How many workers were studied?
    b. What percent of the workers were unemployed?
    c. Compare the percent unemployed for the men and the women.

DATA SET EXERCISES

(The data for these exercises is available at the text website: www.mhhe.com/lind16e.)

44. Refer to the Real Estate data, which reports information on homes sold in the Goodyear, Arizona, area during the last year. Prepare a report on the selling prices of the homes. Be sure to answer the following questions in your report.
    a. Develop a box plot. Estimate the first and the third quartiles. Are there any outliers?
    b. Develop a scatter diagram with price on the vertical axis and the size of the home on the horizontal. Does there seem to be a relationship between these variables? Is the relationship direct or inverse?
    c. Develop a scatter diagram with price on the vertical axis and distance from the center of the city on the horizontal axis. Does there seem to be a relationship between these variables? Is the relationship direct or inverse?
45. Refer to the Baseball 2012 data that report information on the 30 Major League Baseball teams for the 2012 season.
    a. In the data set, the variable, built, is the year that a stadium was constructed. Using this variable, create a new variable, age, by subtracting the value of the variable, built, from the current year for each team. Develop a box plot with the new variable, age. Are there any outliers? If so, which of the stadiums are outliers?
    b. Using the variable, payroll, create a box plot. Are there any outliers? Compute the quartiles using formula (4–1). How does the New York Yankees' payroll compare to other team payrolls? Write a brief summary of your analysis.
    c. Draw a scatter diagram with the variable, wins, on the vertical axis and payroll on the horizontal axis. What are your conclusions?
    d. Using the variable, wins, draw a dot plot. What can you conclude from this plot?
46. Refer to the Buena School District bus data.
    a. Refer to the maintenance cost variable. Develop a box plot. What are the first and third quartiles? Are there any outliers?
    b. Determine the median maintenance cost. Based on the median, develop a contingency table with bus manufacturer as one variable and whether the maintenance cost was above or below the median as the other variable. What are your conclusions?

A REVIEW OF CHAPTERS 1–4

This section is a review of the major concepts and terms introduced in Chapters 1–4. Chapter 1 began by describing the meaning and purpose of statistics. Next we described the different types of variables and the four levels of measurement. Chapter 2 was concerned with describing a set of observations by organizing it into a frequency distribution and then portraying the frequency distribution as a histogram or a frequency polygon. Chapter 3 began by describing measures of location, such as the mean, weighted mean, median, geometric mean, and mode. This chapter also included measures of dispersion, or spread. Discussed in this section were the range, variance, and standard deviation. Chapter 4 included several graphing techniques such as dot plots, box plots, and scatter diagrams. We also discussed the coefficient of skewness, which reports the lack of symmetry in a set of data.

126   A REVIEW OF CHAPTERS 1–4

Throughout this section we stressed the importance of statistical software, such as Excel and Minitab. Many computer outputs in these chapters demonstrated how quickly and effectively a large data set can be organized into a frequency distribution, several of the measures of location or measures of variation calculated, and the information presented in graphical form.

P R O B L E M S

For **DATA FILE**, please visit www.mhhe.com/lind16e

1. A sample of 50 funds deposited in First Federal Savings Bank's MCA (miniature checking account) revealed the following amounts.

$124	$ 14	$150	$289	$ 52	$156	$203	$ 82	$ 27	$248
39	52	103	58	136	249	110	298	251	157
186	107	142	185	75	202	119	219	156	78
116	152	206	117	52	299	58	153	219	148
145	187	165	147	158	146	185	186	149	140

Use a statistical software package such as Excel or Minitab to help answer the following questions.
a. Determine the mean, median, and standard deviation.
b. Determine the first and third quartiles.
c. Develop a box plot. Are there any outliers? Do the amounts follow a symmetric distribution or are they skewed? Justify your answer.
d. Organize the distribution of funds into a frequency distribution.
e. Write a brief summary of the results in parts a to d.

2. Listed below are the 44 U.S. presidents and their age as they began their terms in office.

For **DATA FILE**, please visit www.mhhe.com/lind16e

Number	Name	Age	Number	Name	Age
1	Washington	57	23	B. Harrison	55
2	J. Adams	61	24	Cleveland	55
3	Jefferson	57	25	McKinley	54
4	Madison	57	26	T. Roosevelt	42
5	Monroe	58	27	Taft	51
6	J. Q. Adams	57	28	Wilson	56
7	Jackson	61	29	Harding	55
8	Van Buren	54	30	Coolidge	51
9	W. H. Harrison	68	31	Hoover	54
10	Tyler	51	32	F. D. Roosevelt	51
11	Polk	49	33	Truman	60
12	Taylor	64	34	Eisenhower	62
13	Fillmore	50	35	Kennedy	43
14	Pierce	48	36	L. B. Johnson	55
15	Buchanan	65	37	Nixon	56
16	Lincoln	52	38	Ford	61
17	A. Johnson	56	39	Carter	52
18	Grant	46	40	Reagan	69
19	Hayes	54	41	G. H. W. Bush	64
20	Garfield	49	42	Clinton	46
21	Arthur	50	43	G. W. Bush	54
22	Cleveland	47	44	Obama	47

Use a statistical software package such as Excel or Minitab to help answer the following questions.
a. Determine the mean, median, and standard deviation.
b. Determine the first and third quartiles.

    c. Develop a box plot. Are there any outliers? Do the amounts follow a symmetric distribution or are they skewed? Justify your answer.

    d. Organize the distribution of ages into a frequency distribution.

    e. Write a brief summary of the results in parts a to d.

3. Listed below is the per capita income for the 50 states and the District of Columbia.

For **DATA FILE**, please visit
www.mhhe.com/lind16e

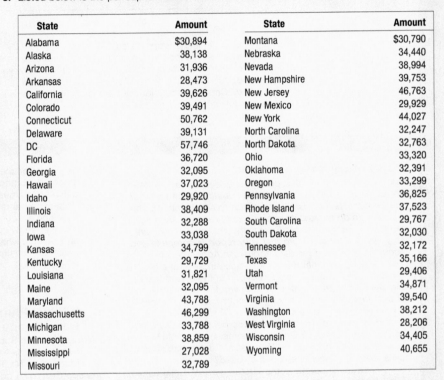

State	Amount	State	Amount
Alabama	$30,894	Montana	$30,790
Alaska	38,138	Nebraska	34,440
Arizona	31,936	Nevada	38,994
Arkansas	28,473	New Hampshire	39,753
California	39,626	New Jersey	46,763
Colorado	39,491	New Mexico	29,929
Connecticut	50,762	New York	44,027
Delaware	39,131	North Carolina	32,247
DC	57,746	North Dakota	32,763
Florida	36,720	Ohio	33,320
Georgia	32,095	Oklahoma	32,391
Hawaii	37,023	Oregon	33,299
Idaho	29,920	Pennsylvania	36,825
Illinois	38,409	Rhode Island	37,523
Indiana	32,288	South Carolina	29,767
Iowa	33,038	South Dakota	32,030
Kansas	34,799	Tennessee	32,172
Kentucky	29,729	Texas	35,166
Louisiana	31,821	Utah	29,406
Maine	32,095	Vermont	34,871
Maryland	43,788	Virginia	39,540
Massachusetts	46,299	Washington	38,212
Michigan	33,788	West Virginia	28,206
Minnesota	38,859	Wisconsin	34,405
Mississippi	27,028	Wyoming	40,655
Missouri	32,789		

Use a statistical software package such as Excel or Minitab to help answer the following questions.

    a. Determine the mean, median, and standard deviation.

    b. Determine the first and third quartiles.

    c. Develop a box plot. Are there any outliers? Do the amounts follow a symmetric distribution or are they skewed? Justify your answer.

    d. Organize the distribution of funds into a frequency distribution.

    e. Write a brief summary of the results in parts a to d.

4. A sample of 12 homes sold last week in St. Paul, Minnesota, revealed the following information. Draw a scatter diagram. Can we conclude that, as the size of the home (reported below in thousands of square feet) increases, the selling price (reported in $ thousands) also increases?

Home Size (thousands of square feet)	Selling Price ($ thousands)	Home Size (thousands of square feet)	Selling Price ($ thousands)
1.4	100	1.3	110
1.3	110	0.8	85
1.2	105	1.2	105
1.1	120	0.9	75
1.4	80	1.1	70
1.0	105	1.1	95

5. Refer to the following diagram.

    0   40   80   120   160   200

a. What is the graph called?
b. What are the median, and first and third quartile values?
c. Is the distribution positively skewed? Tell how you know.
d. Are there any outliers? If yes, estimate these values.
e. Can you determine the number of observations in the study?

C A S E S

A. Century National Bank

The following case will appear in subsequent review sections. Assume that you work in the Planning Department of the Century National Bank and report to Ms. Lamberg. You will need to do some data analysis and prepare a short written report. Remember, Mr. Selig is the president of the bank, so you will want to ensure that your report is complete and accurate. A copy of the data appears in Appendix A.6.

Century National Bank has offices in several cities in the Midwest and the southeastern part of the United States. Mr. Dan Selig, president and CEO, would like to know the characteristics of his checking account customers. What is the balance of a typical customer?

How many other bank services do the checking account customers use? Do the customers use the ATM service and, if so, how often? What about debit cards? Who uses them, and how often are they used?

To better understand the customers, Mr. Selig asked Ms. Wendy Lamberg, director of planning, to select a sample of customers and prepare a report. To begin, she has appointed a team from her staff. You are the head of the team and responsible for preparing the report. You select a random sample of 60 customers. In addition to the balance in each account at the end of last month, you determine (1) the number of ATM (automatic teller machine) transactions in the last month; (2) the number of other bank services (a savings account, a certificate of deposit, etc.) the customer uses; (3) whether the customer has a debit card (this is a bank service in which charges are made directly to the customer's account); and (4) whether or not interest is paid on the checking account. The sample includes customers from the branches in Cincinnati, Ohio; Atlanta, Georgia; Louisville, Kentucky; and Erie, Pennsylvania.

1. Develop a graph or table that portrays the checking balances. What is the balance of a typical customer? Do many customers have more than $2,000 in their accounts? Does it appear that there is a difference in the distribution of the accounts among the four branches? Around what value do the account balances tend to cluster?

2. Determine the mean and median of the checking account balances. Compare the mean and the median balances for the four branches. Is there a difference among the branches? Be sure to explain the difference between the mean and the median in your report.

3. Determine the range and the standard deviation of the checking account balances. What do the first and third quartiles show? Determine the coefficient of skewness and indicate what it shows. Because Mr. Selig does not deal with statistics daily, include a brief description and interpretation of the standard deviation and other measures.

B. Wildcat Plumbing Supply Inc.: Do We Have Gender Differences?

Wildcat Plumbing Supply has served the plumbing needs of Southwest Arizona for more than 40 years. The company was founded by Mr. Terrence St. Julian and is run today by his son Cory. The company has grown from a handful of employees to more than 500 today. Cory is concerned about several positions within the company where he has men and women doing essentially the same job but at different pay. To investigate, he collected the information below. Suppose you are a student intern in the Accounting Department and have been given the task to write a report summarizing the situation.

Yearly Salary ($000)	Women	Men
Less than 30	2	0
30 up to 40	3	1
40 up to 50	17	4
50 up to 60	17	24
60 up to 70	8	21
70 up to 80	3	7
80 or more	0	3

To kick off the project, Mr. Cory St. Julian held a meeting with his staff and you were invited. At this meeting, it was suggested that you calculate several measures of location, create charts or draw graphs such as a cumulative frequency distribution, and determine the quartiles for both men and women. Develop the charts and write the report summarizing the yearly salaries of employees at Wildcat Plumbing Supply. Does it appear that there are pay differences based on gender?

C. Kimble Products: Is There a Difference In the Commissions?

At the January national sales meeting, the CEO of Kimble Products was questioned extensively regarding the company policy for paying commissions to its sales representatives. The company sells sporting goods to two major markets. There are 40 sales representatives who call directly on large-volume customers, such as the athletic departments at major colleges and universities and professional sports franchises. There are 30 sales representatives who represent the company to retail stores located in shopping malls and large discounters such as Kmart and Target.

Upon his return to corporate headquarters, the CEO asked the sales manager for a report comparing the commissions earned last year by the two parts of the sales team. The information is reported below. Write a brief report. Would you conclude that there is a difference? Be sure to include information in the report on both the central tendency and dispersion of the two groups.

Commissions Earned by Sales Representatives Calling on Athletic Departments ($)

354	87	1,676	1,187	69	3,202	680	39	1,683	1,106
883	3,140	299	2,197	175	159	1,105	434	615	149
1,168	278	579	7	357	252	1,602	2,321	4	392
416	427	1,738	526	13	1,604	249	557	635	527

Commissions Earned by Sales Representatives Calling on Large Retailers ($)

1,116	681	1,294	12	754	1,206	1,448	870	944	1,255
1,213	1,291	719	934	1,313	1,083	899	850	886	1,556
886	1,315	1,858	1,262	1,338	1,066	807	1,244	758	918

P R A C T I C E   T E S T

There is a practice test at the end of each review section. The tests are in two parts. The first part contains several objective questions, usually in a fill-in-the-blank format. The second part is problems. In most cases, it should take 30 to 45 minutes to complete the test. The problems require a calculator. Check the answers in the Answer Section in the back of the book.

Part 1—Objective

1. The science of collecting, organizing, presenting, analyzing, and interpreting data to assist in making effective decisions is called _____.
2. Methods of organizing, summarizing, and presenting data in an informative way are called _____.
3. The entire set of individuals or objects of interest or the measurements obtained from all individuals or objects of interest are called the _____.
4. List the two types of variables.

5. The number of bedrooms in a house is an example of a _____. (discrete variable, continuous variable, qualitative variable—pick one)
6. The jersey numbers of Major League Baseball players are an example of what level of measurement?
7. The classification of students by eye color is an example of what level of measurement?
8. The sum of the differences between each value and the mean is always equal to what value?
9. A set of data contained 70 observations. How many classes would the 2^k method suggest to construct a frequency distribution?
10. What percent of the values in a data set are always larger than the median?
11. The square of the standard deviation is the _____.
12. The standard deviation assumes a negative value when _____. (all the values are negative, at least half the values are negative, or never—pick one.)
13. Which of the following is least affected by an outlier? (mean, median, or range—pick one)

1. _____
2. _____
3. _____
4. _____
   _____
5. _____
6. _____
7. _____
8. _____
9. _____
10. _____
11. _____
12. _____
13. _____

Part 2—Problems

1. The Russell 2000 index of stock prices increased by the following amounts over the last 3 years.

18%	4%	2%

What is the geometric mean increase for the 3 years?

_____

2. The information below refers to the selling prices ($000) of homes sold in Warren, Pennsylvania, during 2014.

Selling Price ($000)	Frequency
120.0 up to 150.0	4
150.0 up to 180.0	18
180.0 up to 210.0	30
210.0 up to 240.0	20
240.0 up to 270.0	17
270.0 up to 300.0	10
300.0 up to 330.0	6

   a. What is the class interval?
   b. How many homes were sold in 2014?
   c. How many homes sold for less than $210,000?
   d. What is the relative frequency of the 210 up to 240 class?
   e. What is the midpoint of the 150 up to 180 class?
   f. The selling prices range between what two amounts?

3. A sample of eight college students revealed they owned the following number of CDs.

52	76	64	79	80	74	66	69

   a. What is the mean number of CDs owned?
   b. What is the median number of CDs owned?
   c. What is the 40th percentile?
   d. What is the range of the number of CDs owned?
   e. What is the standard deviation of the number of CDs owned?

4. An investor purchased 200 shares of the Blair Company for $36 each in July of 2012, 300 shares at $40 each in September 2013, and 500 shares at $50 each in January 2014. What is the investor's weighted mean price per share?

5. During the 2014 Super Bowl, 30 million pounds of snack food were eaten. The chart below depicts this information.

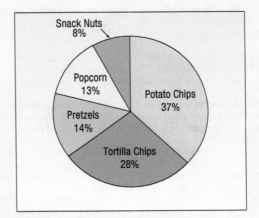

   a. What is the name given to this graph?
   b. Estimate, in millions of pounds, the amount of potato chips eaten during the game.
   c. Estimate the relationship of potato chips to popcorn. (twice as much, half as much, three times, none of these—pick one)
   d. What percent of the total do potato chips and tortilla chips comprise?

A Survey of Probability Concepts

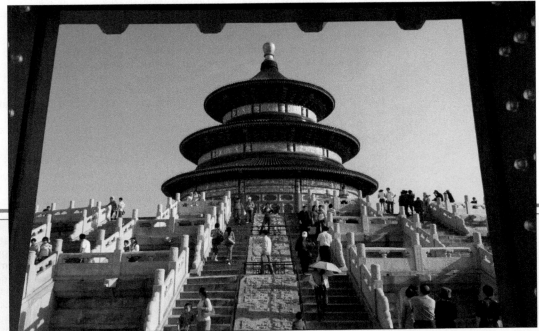

RECENT SURVEYS indicate 60% of tourists to China visited the Forbidden City, the Temple of Heaven, the Great Wall, and other historical sites in or near Beijing. Forty percent visited Xi'an and its magnificent terra-cotta soldiers, horses, and chariots, which lay buried for over 2,000 years. Thirty percent of the tourists went to both Beijing and Xi'an. What is the probability that a tourist visited at least one of these places? (See Exercise 76 and LO5-3.)

LEARNING OBJECTIVES

When you have completed this chapter, you will be able to:

LO5-1 Define the terms *probability, experiment, event,* and *outcome.*

LO5-2 Assign probabilities using a classical, empirical, or subjective approach.

LO5-3 Calculate probabilities using the rules of addition.

LO5-4 Calculate probabilities using the rules of multiplication.

LO5-5 Compute probabilities using a contingency table.

LO5-6 Calculate probabilities using Bayes' theorem.

LO5-7 Determine the number of outcomes using principles of counting.

132   CHAPTER 5

INTRODUCTION

The emphasis in Chapters 2, 3, and 4 is on descriptive statistics. In Chapter 2, we organize the profits on 180 vehicles sold by the Applewood Auto Group into a frequency distribution. This frequency distribution shows the smallest and the largest profits and where the largest concentration of data occurs. In Chapter 3, we use numerical measures of location and dispersion to locate a typical profit on vehicle sales and to examine the variation in the profit of a sale. We describe the variation in the profits with such measures of dispersion as the range and the standard deviation. In Chapter 4, we develop charts and graphs, such as a scatter diagram or a dot plot, to further describe the data graphically.

Descriptive statistics is concerned with summarizing data collected from past events. We now turn to the second facet of statistics, namely, *computing the chance that something will occur in the future*. This facet of statistics is called **statistical inference** or **inferential statistics.**

Seldom does a decision maker have complete information to make a decision. For example:

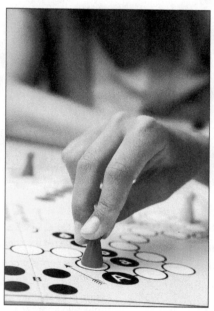

- Toys and Things, a toy and puzzle manufacturer, recently developed a new game based on sports trivia. It wants to know whether sports buffs will purchase the game. "Slam Dunk" and "Home Run" are two of the names under consideration. To investigate, the president of Toys and Things decided to hire a market research firm. The firm selected a sample of 800 consumers from the population and asked each respondent for a reaction to the new game and its proposed titles. Using the sample results, the company can estimate the proportion of the population that will purchase the game.
- The quality assurance department of a U.S. Steel mill must assure management that the quarter-inch wire being produced has an acceptable tensile strength. Clearly, not all the wire produced can be tested for tensile strength because testing requires the wire to bestretched until it breaks—thus destroying it. So a random sample of 10 pieces is selected and tested. Based on the test results, all the wire produced is deemed to be either acceptable or unacceptable.
- Other questions involving uncertainty are: Should the daytime drama *Days of Our Lives* be discontinued immediately? Will a newly developed mint-flavored cereal be profitable if marketed? Will Charles Linden be elected to county auditor in Batavia County?

Statistical inference deals with conclusions about a population based on a sample taken from that population. (The populations for the preceding illustrations are all consumers who like sports trivia games, all the quarter-inch steel wire produced, all television viewers who watch soaps, all who purchase breakfast cereal, and so on.)

Because there is uncertainty in decision making, it is important that all the known risks involved be scientifically evaluated. Helpful in this evaluation is *probability theory,* which has often been referred to as the science of uncertainty. The use of probability theory allows the decision maker with only limited information to analyze the risks and minimize the gamble inherent, for example, in marketing a new product or accepting an incoming shipment possibly containing defective parts.

Because probability concepts are so important in the field of statistical inference (to be discussed starting with Chapter 8), this chapter introduces the basic language of probability, including such terms as *experiment, event, subjective probability,* and *addition* and *multiplication rules.*

LO5-1

Define the terms *probability, experiment, event,* and *outcome.*

WHAT IS A PROBABILITY?

No doubt you are familiar with terms such as *probability, chance,* and *likelihood.* They are often used interchangeably. The weather forecaster announces that there is a 70% chance of rain for Super Bowl Sunday. Based on a survey of consumers who tested a newly developed toothpaste with a banana flavor, the probability is .03 that, if marketed, it will be a financial success. (This means that the chance of the banana-flavor toothpaste being accepted by the public is rather remote.) What is a probability? In general, it is a numerical value that describes the chance that something will happen.

> **PROBABILITY** A value between zero and one, inclusive, describing the relative possibility (chance or likelihood) an event will occur.

A probability is frequently expressed as a decimal, such as .70, .27, or .50. However, it may be given as a fraction such as 7/10, 27/100, or 1/2. It can assume any number from 0 to 1, inclusive. If a company has only five sales regions, and each region's name or number is written on a slip of paper and the slips put in a hat, the probability of selecting one of the five regions is 1. The probability of selecting from the hat a slip of paper that reads "Pittsburgh Steelers" is 0. Thus, the probability of 1 represents something that is certain to happen, and the probability of 0 represents something that cannot happen.

The closer a probability is to 0, the more improbable it is the event will happen. The closer the probability is to 1, the more sure we are it will happen. The relationship is shown in the following diagram along with a few of our personal beliefs. You might, however, select a different probability for Slo Poke's chances to win the Kentucky Derby or for an increase in federal taxes.

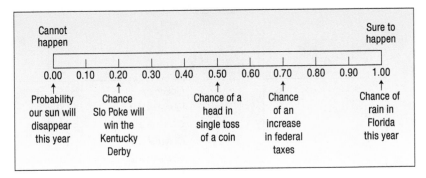

Sometimes, the likelihood of an event is expressed using the term *odds.* To explain, someone says the odds are "five to two" that an event will occur. This means that in a total of seven trials (5 + 2), the event will occur five times and not occur two times. Using odds, we can compute the probability that the event occurs as 5/(5 + 2) or 5/7. So, if the odds in favor of an event are x to y, the probability of the event is $x/(x + y)$.

Three key words are used in the study of probability: **experiment, outcome,** and **event.** These terms are used in our everyday language, but in statistics they have specific meanings.

     CHAPTER 5

> **EXPERIMENT** A process that leads to the occurrence of one and only one of several possible results.

This definition is more general than the one used in the physical sciences, where we picture someone manipulating test tubes or microscopes. In reference to probability, an experiment has two or more possible results, and it is uncertain which will occur.

> **OUTCOME** A particular result of an experiment.

For example, the tossing of a coin is an experiment. You are unsure of the outcome. When a coin is tossed, one particular outcome is a "head." The alternative outcome is a "tail." Similarly, asking 500 college students if they would travel more than 100 miles to attend a Mumford and Sons concert is an experiment. In this experiment, one possible outcome is that 273 students indicate they would travel more than 100 miles to attend the concert. Another outcome is that 317 students would attend the concert. Still another outcome is that 423 students indicate they would attend the concert. When one or more of the experiment's outcomes are observed, we call this an event.

> **EVENT** A collection of one or more outcomes of an experiment.

Examples to clarify the definitions of the terms *experiment, outcome,* and *event* are presented in the following figure.

In the die-rolling experiment, there are six possible outcomes, but there are many possible events. When counting the number of members of the board of directors for Fortune 500 companies over 60 years of age, the number of possible outcomes can be anywhere from zero to the total number of members. There are an even larger number of possible events in this experiment.

	Roll a die	Count the number of members of the board of directors for Fortune 500 companies who are over 60 years of age
Experiment	Roll a die	Count the number of members of the board of directors for Fortune 500 companies who are over 60 years of age
All possible outcomes	Observe a 1 Observe a 2 Observe a 3 Observe a 4 Observe a 5 Observe a 6	None is over 60 One is over 60 Two are over 60 ... 29 are over 60 ... ... 48 are over 60 ...
Some possible events	Observe an even number Observe a number greater than 4 Observe a number 3 or less	More than 13 are over 60 Fewer than 20 are over 60

SELF-REVIEW

5-1

Video Games Inc. recently developed a new video game. Its playability is to be tested by 80 veteran game players.
(a) What is the experiment?
(b) What is one possible outcome?
(c) Suppose 65 players tried the new game and said they liked it. Is 65 a probability?
(d) The probability that the new game will be a success is computed to be −1.0. Comment.
(e) Specify one possible event.

LO5-2

Assign probabilities using a classical, empirical, or subjective approach.

APPROACHES TO ASSIGNING PROBABILITIES

In this section, we describe three ways to assign a probability to an event: classical, empirical, and subjective. The classical and empirical methods are objective and are based on information and data. The subjective method is based on a person's belief or estimate of an event's likelihood.

Classical Probability

Classical probability is based on the assumption that the outcomes of an experiment are *equally likely*. Using the classical viewpoint, the probability of an event happening is computed by dividing the number of favorable outcomes by the number of possible outcomes:

CLASSICAL PROBABILITY	Probability of an event	$= \dfrac{\text{Number of favorable outcomes}}{\text{Total number of possible outcomes}}$	[5–1]

EXAMPLE

Consider an experiment of rolling a six-sided die. What is the probability of the event "an even number of spots appear face up"?

SOLUTION

The possible outcomes are:

a one-spot   a four-spot
a two-spot   a five-spot
a three-spot   a six-spot

There are three "favorable" outcomes (a two, a four, and a six) in the collection of six equally likely possible outcomes. Therefore:

$$\text{Probability of an even number} = \frac{3}{6} \leftarrow \begin{array}{l}\text{Number of favorable outcomes} \\ \hline \text{Total number of possible outcomes}\end{array}$$

$$= .5$$

The mutually exclusive concept appeared earlier in our study of frequency distributions in Chapter 2. Recall that we create classes so that a particular value is included in only one of the classes and there is no overlap between classes. Thus, only one of several events can occur at a particular time.

> **MUTUALLY EXCLUSIVE** The occurrence of one event means that none of the other events can occur at the same time.

The variable "gender" presents mutually exclusive outcomes, male and female. An employee selected at random is either male or female but cannot be both. A manufactured part is acceptable or unacceptable. The part cannot be both acceptable and unacceptable at the same time. In a sample of manufactured parts, the event of selecting an unacceptable part and the event of selecting an acceptable part are mutually exclusive.

If an experiment has a set of events that includes every possible outcome, such as the events "an even number" and "an odd number" in the die-tossing experiment, then the set of events is **collectively exhaustive.** For the die-tossing experiment, every outcome will be either even or odd. So the set is collectively exhaustive.

> **COLLECTIVELY EXHAUSTIVE** At least one of the events must occur when an experiment is conducted.

If the set of events is collectively exhaustive and the events are mutually exclusive, the sum of the probabilities is 1. Historically, the classical approach to probability was developed and applied in the 17th and 18th centuries to games of chance, such as cards and dice. It is unnecessary to do an experiment to determine the probability of an event occurring using the classical approach because the total number of outcomes is known before the experiment. The flip of a coin has two possible outcomes; the roll of a die has six possible outcomes. We can logically arrive at the probability of getting a tail on the toss of one coin or three heads on the toss of three coins.

The classical approach to probability can also be applied to lotteries. In South Carolina, one of the games of the Education Lottery is "Pick 3." A person buys a lottery ticket and selects three numbers between 0 and 9. Once per week, the three numbers are randomly selected from a machine that tumbles three containers each with balls numbered 0 through 9. One way to win is to match the numbers and the order of the numbers. Given that 1,000 possible outcomes exist (000 through 999), the probability of winning with any three-digit number is 0.001, or 1 in 1,000.

Empirical Probability

Empirical or **relative frequency** is the second type of objective probability. It is based on the number of times an event occurs as a proportion of a known number of trials.

> **EMPIRICAL PROBABILITY** The probability of an event happening is the fraction of the time similar events happened in the past.

The formula to determine an empirical probability is:

$$\text{Empirical probability} = \frac{\text{Number of times the event occurs}}{\text{Total number of observations}}$$

The empirical approach to probability is based on what is called the law of large numbers. The key to establishing probabilities empirically is that more observations will provide a more accurate estimate of the probability.

> **LAW OF LARGE NUMBERS** Over a large number of trials, the empirical probability of an event will approach its true probability.

A SURVEY OF PROBABILITY CONCEPTS   137

To explain the law of large numbers, suppose we toss a fair coin. The result of each toss is either a head or a tail. With just one toss of the coin the empirical probability for heads is either zero or one. If we toss the coin a great number of times, the probability of the outcome of heads will approach .5. The following table reports the results of seven different experiments of flipping a fair coin 1, 10, 50, 100, 500, 1,000, and 10,000 times and then computing the relative frequency of heads. Note as we increase the number of trials, the empirical probability of a head appearing approaches .5, which is its value based on the classical approach to probability.

Number of Trials	Number of Heads	Relative Frequency of Heads
1	0	.00
10	3	.30
50	26	.52
100	52	.52
500	236	.472
1,000	494	.494
10,000	5,027	.5027

What have we demonstrated? Based on the classical definition of probability, the likelihood of obtaining a head in a single toss of a fair coin is .5. Based on the empirical or relative frequency approach to probability, the probability of the event happening approaches the same value based on the classical definition of probability.

This reasoning allows us to use the empirical or relative frequency approach to finding a probability. Here are some examples.

- Last semester, 80 students registered for Business Statistics 101 at Scandia University. Twelve students earned an A. Based on this information and the empirical approach to assigning a probability, we estimate the likelihood a student will earn an A is .15.
- Kobe Bryant of the Los Angeles Lakers made 381 out of 451 free throw attempts during the 2011–12 NBA season. Based on the empirical rule of probability, the likelihood of him making his next free throw attempt is .845.

Life insurance companies rely on past data to determine the acceptability of an applicant as well as the premium to be charged. Mortality tables list the likelihood a person of a particular age will die within the upcoming year. For example, the likelihood a 20-year-old female will die within the next year is .00105.

The empirical concept is illustrated with the following example.

EXAMPLE

On February 1, 2003, the Space Shuttle *Columbia* exploded. This was the second disaster in 113 space missions for NASA. On the basis of this information, what is the probability that a future mission is successfully completed?

SOLUTION

We use letters or numbers to simplify the equations. P stands for probability and A represents the event of a successful mission. In this case, $P(A)$ stands for the probability a future mission is successfully completed.

$$\text{Probability of a successful flight} = \frac{\text{Number of successful flights}}{\text{Total number of flights}}$$

$$P(A) = \frac{111}{113} = .98$$

We can use this as an estimate of probability. In other words, based on past experience, the probability is .98 that a future space shuttle mission will be safely completed.

138   CHAPTER 5

Subjective Probability

If there is little or no experience or information on which to base a probability, it is estimated subjectively. Essentially, this means an individual evaluates the available opinions and information and then estimates or assigns the probability. This probability is called a **subjective probability.**

> **SUBJECTIVE CONCEPT OF PROBABILITY** The likelihood (probability) of a particular event happening that is assigned by an individual based on whatever information is available.

Illustrations of subjective probability are:

1. Estimating the likelihood the New England Patriots will play in the Super Bowl next year.
2. Estimating the likelihood you are involved in an automobile accident during the next 12 months.
3. Estimating the likelihood the U.S. budget deficit will be reduced by half in the next 10 years.

The types of probability are summarized in Chart 5–1. A probability statement always assigns a likelihood to an event that has not yet occurred. There is, of course, considerable latitude in the degree of uncertainty that surrounds this probability, based primarily on the knowledge possessed by the individual concerning the underlying process. The individual possesses a great deal of knowledge about the toss of a die and can state that the probability that a one-spot will appear face up on the toss of a true die is one-sixth. But we know very little concerning the acceptance in the marketplace of a new and untested product. For example, even though a market research director tests a newly developed product in 40 retail stores and states that there is a 70% chance that the product will have sales of more than 1 million units, she has limited knowledge of how consumers will react when it is marketed nationally. In both cases (the case of the person rolling a die and the testing of a new product), the individual is assigning a probability value to an event of interest, and a difference exists only in the predictor's confidence in the precision of the estimate. However, regardless of the viewpoint, the same laws of probability (presented in the following sections) will be applied.

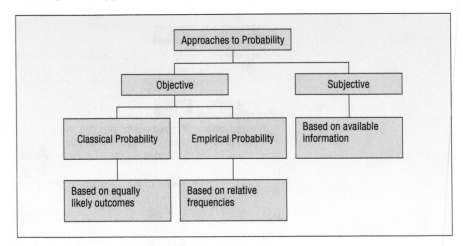

CHART 5–1 Summary of Approaches to Probability

SELF-REVIEW

5-2

1. One card will be randomly selected from a standard 52-card deck. What is the probability the card will be a queen? Which approach to probability did you use to answer this question?
2. The Center for Child Care reports on 539 children and the marital status of their parents. There are 333 married, 182 divorced, and 24 widowed parents. What is the probability a particular child chosen at random will have a parent who is divorced? Which approach did you use?
3. What is the probability you will save one million dollars by the time you retire? Which approach to probability did you use to answer this question?

EXERCISES

▼

For **DATA FILE**, please visit
www.mhhe.com/lind16e

1. Some people are in favor of reducing federal taxes to increase consumer spending and others are against it. Two persons are selected and their opinions are recorded. Assuming no one is undecided, list the possible outcomes.
2. A quality control inspector selects a part to be tested. The part is then declared acceptable, repairable, or scrapped. Then another part is tested. List the possible outcomes of this experiment regarding two parts.
3. A survey of 34 students at the Wall College of Business showed the following majors:

Accounting	10
Finance	5
Economics	3
Management	6
Marketing	10

   Suppose you select a student and observe his or her major.
   a. What is the probability he or she is a management major?
   b. Which concept of probability did you use to make this estimate?
4. A large company must hire a new president. The Board of Directors prepares a list of five candidates, all of whom are equally qualified. Two of these candidates are members of a minority group. To avoid bias in the selection of the candidate, the company decides to select the president by lottery.
   a. What is the probability one of the minority candidates is hired?
   b. Which concept of probability did you use to make this estimate?
5. In each of the following cases, indicate whether classical, empirical, or subjective probability is used.
   a. A baseball player gets a hit in 30 out of 100 times at bat. The probability is .3 that he gets a hit in his next at bat.
   b. A seven-member committee of students is formed to study environmental issues. What is the likelihood that any one of the seven is randomly chosen as the spokesperson?
   c. You purchase 1 of 5 million tickets sold for Lotto Canada. What is the likelihood you will win the $1 million jackpot?
   d. The probability of an earthquake in northern California in the next 10 years above 5.0 on the Richter Scale is .80.
6. A firm will promote two employees out of a group of six men and three women.
   a. List all possible outcomes.
   b. What probability concept would be used to assign probabilities to the outcomes?
7. A sample of 40 oil industry executives was selected to test a questionnaire. One question about environmental issues required a yes or no answer.
   a. What is the experiment?
   b. List one possible event.
   c. Ten of the 40 executives responded yes. Based on these sample responses, what is the probability that an oil industry executive will respond yes?
   d. What concept of probability does this illustrate?
   e. Are each of the possible outcomes equally likely and mutually exclusive?

140   CHAPTER 5

For **DATA FILE**, please visit www.mhhe.com/lind16e

8. A sample of 2,000 licensed drivers revealed the following number of speeding violations.

Number of Violations	Number of Drivers
0	1,910
1	46
2	18
3	12
4	9
5 or more	5
Total	2,000

     a. What is the experiment?
     b. List one possible event.
     c. What is the probability that a particular driver had exactly two speeding violations?
     d. What concept of probability does this illustrate?
  9. Bank of America customers select their own three-digit personal identification number (PIN) for use at ATMs.
     a. Think of this as an experiment and list four possible outcomes.
     b. What is the probability Mr. Jones and Mrs. Smith select the same PIN?
     c. Which concept of probability did you use to answer (b)?
 10. An investor buys 100 shares of AT&T stock and records its price change daily.
     a. List several possible events for this experiment.
     b. Which concept of probability did you use in (a)?

LO5-3

Calculate probabilities using the rules of addition.

RULES OF ADDITION FOR COMPUTING PROBABILITIES

There are two rules of addition, the special rule of addition and the general rule of addition. We begin with the special rule of addition.

Special Rule of Addition

When we use the **special rule of addition,** the events must be *mutually exclusive.* Recall that mutually exclusive means that when one event occurs, none of the other events can occur at the same time. An illustration of mutually exclusive events in the die-tossing experiment is the events "a number 4 or larger" and "a number 2 or smaller." If the outcome is in the first group {4, 5, and 6}, then it cannot also be in the second group {1 and 2}. Another illustration is a product coming off the assembly line cannot be defective and satisfactory at the same time.

If two events A and B are mutually exclusive, the special rule of addition states that the probability of one *or* the other event's occurring equals the sum of their probabilities. This rule is expressed in the following formula:

SPECIAL RULE OF ADDITION	$P(A \text{ or } B) = P(A) + P(B)$	**[5–2]**

For three mutually exclusive events designated A, B, and C, the rule is written:

$$P(A \text{ or } B \text{ or } C) = P(A) + P(B) + P(C)$$

A SURVEY OF PROBABILITY CONCEPTS   141

An example will show the details.

EXAMPLE

A machine fills plastic bags with a mixture of beans, broccoli, and other vegetables. Most of the bags contain the correct weight, but because of the variation in the size of the beans and other vegetables, a package might be underweight or overweight. A check of 4,000 packages filled in the past month revealed:

Weight	Event	Number of Packages	Probability of Occurrence	
Underweight	A	100	.025	← $\frac{100}{4,000}$
Satisfactory	B	3,600	.900	
Overweight	C	300	.075	
		4,000	1.000	

What is the probability that a particular package will be either underweight or overweight?

SOLUTION

The outcome "underweight" is the event A. The outcome "overweight" is the event C. Applying the special rule of addition:

$$P(A \text{ or } C) = P(A) + P(C) = .025 + .075 = .10$$

Note that the events are mutually exclusive, meaning that a package of mixed vegetables cannot be underweight, satisfactory, and overweight at the same time. They are also collectively exhaustive; that is, a selected package must be either underweight, satisfactory, or overweight.

English logician J. Venn (1834–1923) developed a diagram to portray graphically the outcome of an experiment. The *mutually exclusive* concept and various other rules for combining probabilities can be illustrated using this device. To construct a Venn diagram, a space is first enclosed representing the total of all possible outcomes. This space is usually in the form of a rectangle. An event is then represented by a circular area that is drawn inside the rectangle proportional to the probability of the event. The following Venn diagram represents the *mutually exclusive* concept. There is no overlapping of events, meaning that the events are mutually exclusive. In the following Venn diagram, assume the events A, B, and C are about equally likely.

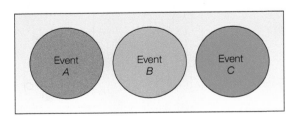

142   CHAPTER 5

Complement Rule

The probability that a bag of mixed vegetables selected is underweight, $P(A)$, plus the probability that it is not an underweight bag, written $P(\sim A)$ and read "not A," must logically equal 1. This is written:

$$P(A) + P(\sim A) = 1$$

This can be revised to read:

COMPLEMENT RULE	$P(A) = 1 - P(\sim A)$	[5–3]

This is the **complement rule.** It is used to determine the probability of an event occurring by subtracting the probability of the event not occurring from 1. This rule is useful because sometimes it is easier to calculate the probability of an event happening by determining the probability of it not happening and subtracting the result from 1. Notice that the events A and $\sim A$ are mutually exclusive and collectively exhaustive. Therefore, the probabilities of A and $\sim A$ sum to 1. A Venn diagram illustrating the complement rule is shown as:

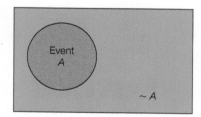

EXAMPLE

Referring to the previous example/solution, the probability a bag of mixed vegetables is underweight is .025 and the probability of an overweight bag is .075. Use the complement rule to show the probability of a satisfactory bag is .900. Show the solution using a Venn diagram.

SOLUTION

The probability the bag is unsatisfactory equals the probability the bag is overweight plus the probability it is underweight. That is, $P(A \text{ or } C) = P(A) + P(C) = .025 + .075 = .100$. The bag is satisfactory if it is not underweight or overweight, so $P(B) = 1 - [P(A) + P(C)] = 1 - [.025 + .075] = 0.900$. The Venn diagram portraying this situation is:

SELF-REVIEW

5–3

A sample of employees of Worldwide Enterprises is to be surveyed about a new health care plan. The employees are classified as follows:

Classification	Event	Number of Employees
Supervisors	A	120
Maintenance	B	50
Production	C	1,460
Management	D	302
Secretarial	E	68

(a) What is the probability that the first person selected is:
   (i)   either in maintenance or a secretary?
   (ii) not in management?
(b) Draw a Venn diagram illustrating your answers to part (a).
(c) Are the events in part (a)(i) complementary or mutually exclusive or both?

The General Rule of Addition

STATISTICS IN ACTION

If you wish to get some attention at the next gathering you attend, announce that you believe that at least two people present were born on the same date—that is, the same day of the year but not necessarily the same year. If there are 30 people in the room, the probability of a duplicate is .706. If there are 60 people in the room, the probability is .994 that at least two people share the same birthday. With as few as 23 people the chances are even, that is .50, that at least two people share the same birthday. Hint: To compute this, find the probability everyone was born on a different day and use the complement rule. Try this in your class.

The outcomes of an experiment may not be mutually exclusive. For example, the Florida Tourist Commission selected a sample of 200 tourists who visited the state during the year. The survey revealed that 120 tourists went to Disney World and 100 went to Busch Gardens near Tampa. What is the probability that a person selected visited either Disney World or Busch Gardens? If the special rule of addition is used, the probability of selecting a tourist who went to Disney World is .60, found by 120/200. Similarly, the probability of a tourist going to Busch Gardens is .50. The sum of these probabilities is 1.10. We know, however, that this probability cannot be greater than 1. The explanation is that many tourists visited both attractions and are being counted twice! A check of the survey responses revealed that 60 out of 200 sampled did, in fact, visit both attractions.

To answer our question, "What is the probability a selected person visited either Disney World or Busch Gardens?" (1) add the probability that a tourist visited Disney World and the probability he or she visited Busch Gardens, and (2) subtract the probability of visiting both. Thus:

$$P(\text{Disney or Busch}) = P(\text{Disney}) + P(\text{Busch}) - P(\text{both Disney and Busch})$$

$$= .60 + .50 - .30 = .80$$

When two events both occur, the probability is called a **joint probability.** The probability that a tourist visits both attractions (.30) is an example of a joint probability.

The following Venn diagram shows two events that are not mutually exclusive. The two events overlap to illustrate the joint event that some people have visited both attractions.

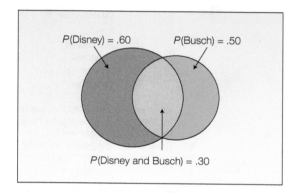

P(Disney) = .60   P(Busch) = .50

P(Disney and Busch) = .30

> **JOINT PROBABILITY** A probability that measures the likelihood two or more events will happen concurrently.

So the general rule of addition, which is used to compute the probability of two events that are not mutually exclusive, is:

> **GENERAL RULE OF ADDITION** $P(A \text{ or } B) = P(A) + P(B) - P(A \text{ and } B)$ **[5–4]**

For the expression $P(A \text{ or } B)$, the word *or* suggests that A may occur or B may occur. This also includes the possibility that A and B may occur. This use of *or* is sometimes called an **inclusive.** You could also write $P(A \text{ or } B \text{ or both})$ to emphasize that the union of the events includes the intersection of A and B.

If we compare the general and special rules of addition, the important difference is determining if the events are mutually exclusive. If the events *are* mutually exclusive, then the joint probability $P(A \text{ and } B)$ is 0 and we could use the special rule of addition. Otherwise, we must account for the joint probability and use the general rule of addition.

E X A M P L E

What is the probability that a card chosen at random from a standard deck of cards will be either a king or a heart?

S O L U T I O N

We may be inclined to add the probability of a king and the probability of a heart. But this creates a problem. If we do that, the king of hearts is counted with the kings and also with the hearts. So, if we simply add the probability of a king (there are 4 in a deck of 52 cards) to the probability of a heart (there are 13 in a deck of 52 cards) and report that 17 out of 52 cards meet the requirement, we have counted the king of hearts twice. We need to subtract 1 card from the 17 so the king of hearts is counted only once. Thus, there are 16 cards that are either hearts or kings. So the probability is 16/52 = .3077.

Card	Probability		Explanation
King	$P(A)$	$= 4/52$	4 kings in a deck of 52 cards
Heart	$P(B)$	$= 13/52$	13 hearts in a deck of 52 cards
King of Hearts	$P(A \text{ and } B)$	$= 1/52$	1 king of hearts in a deck of 52 cards

From formula (5–4):

$$P(A \text{ or } B) = P(A) + P(B) - P(A \text{ and } B)$$

$$= 4/52 + 13/52 - 1/52$$

$$= 16/52, \text{ or } .3077$$

A Venn diagram portrays these outcomes, which are not mutually exclusive.

SELF-REVIEW

5-4

Routine physical examinations are conducted annually as part of a health service program for General Concrete Inc. employees. It was discovered that 8% of the employees need corrective shoes, 15% need major dental work, and 3% need both corrective shoes and major dental work.
(a) What is the probability that an employee selected at random will need either corrective shoes or major dental work?
(b) Show this situation in the form of a Venn diagram.

EXERCISES

For **DATA FILE**, please visit www.mhhe.com/lind16e

11. The events A and B are mutually exclusive. Suppose $P(A) = .30$ and $P(B) = .20$. What is the probability of either A or B occurring? What is the probability that neither A nor B will happen?

12. The events X and Y are mutually exclusive. Suppose $P(X) = .05$ and $P(Y) = .02$. What is the probability of either X or Y occurring? What is the probability that neither X nor Y will happen?

13. A study of 200 advertising firms revealed their income after taxes:

Income after Taxes	Number of Firms
Under $1 million	102
$1 million to $20 million	61
$20 million or more	37

a. What is the probability an advertising firm selected at random has under $1 million in income after taxes?
b. What is the probability an advertising firm selected at random has either an income between $1 million and $20 million, or an income of $20 million or more? What rule of probability was applied?

14. The chair of the board of directors says, "There is a 50% chance this company will earn a profit, a 30% chance it will break even, and a 20% chance it will lose money next quarter."
a. Use an addition rule to find the probability the company will not lose money next quarter.
b. Use the complement rule to find the probability it will not lose money next quarter.

15. Suppose the probability you will get an A in this class is .25 and the probability you will get a B is .50. What is the probability your grade will be above a C?

16. Two coins are tossed. If A is the event "two heads" and B is the event "two tails," are A and B mutually exclusive? Are they complements?

Descriptive & Inferential Statistics

17. The probabilities of the events A and B are .20 and .30, respectively. The probability that both A and B occur is .15. What is the probability of either A or B occurring?
18. Let $P(X) = .55$ and $P(Y) = .35$. Assume the probability that they both occur is .20. What is the probability of either X or Y occurring?
19. Suppose the two events A and B are mutually exclusive. What is the probability of their joint occurrence?
20. A student is taking two courses, history and math. The probability the student will pass the history course is .60, and the probability of passing the math course is .70. The probability of passing both is .50. What is the probability of passing at least one?
21. The aquarium at Sea Critters Depot contains 140 fish. Eighty of these fish are green swordtails (44 female and 36 male) and 60 are orange swordtails (36 female and 24 males.). A fish is randomly captured from the aquarium:
    a. What is the probability the selected fish is a green swordtail?
    b. What is the probability the selected fish is male?
    c. What is the probability the selected fish is a male green swordtail?
    d. What is the probability the selected fish is either a male or a green swordtail?
22. A National Park Service survey of visitors to the Rocky Mountain region revealed that 50% visit Yellowstone Park, 40% visit the Tetons, and 35% visit both.
    a. What is the probability a vacationer will visit at least one of these attractions?
    b. What is the probability .35 called?
    c. Are the events mutually exclusive? Explain.

LO5-4
Calculate probabilities using the rules of multiplication.

RULES OF MULTIPLICATION TO CALCULATE PROBABILITY

In this section, we discuss the rules for computing the likelihood that two events both happen, or their joint probability. For example, 16% of the 2012 tax returns were prepared by H&R Block and 75% of those returns showed a refund. What is the likelihood a person's tax form was prepared by H&R Block and the person received a refund? Venn diagrams illustrate this as the intersection of two events. To find the likelihood of two events happening, we use the rules of multiplication. There are two rules of multiplication: the special rule and the general rule.

Special Rule of Multiplication

The special rule of multiplication requires that two events A and B are independent. Two events are independent if the occurrence of one event does not alter the probability of the occurrence of the other event.

> **INDEPENDENCE** The occurrence of one event has no effect on the probability of the occurrence of another event.

One way to think about independence is to assume that events A and B occur at different times. For example, when event B occurs after event A occurs, does A have any effect on the likelihood that event B occurs? If the answer is no, then A and B are independent events. To illustrate independence, suppose two coins are tossed. The outcome of a coin toss (head or tail) is unaffected by the outcome of any other prior coin toss (head or tail).

For two independent events A and B, the probability that A and B will both occur is found by multiplying the two probabilities. This is the **special rule of multiplication** and is written symbolically as:

SPECIAL RULE OF MULTIPLICATION	$P(A \text{ and } B) = P(A)P(B)$	[5–5]

A SURVEY OF PROBABILITY CONCEPTS   147

For three independent events, A, B, and C, the special rule of multiplication used to determine the probability that all three events will occur is:

$$P(A \text{ and } B \text{ and } C) = P(A)P(B)P(C)$$

EXAMPLE

A survey by the American Automobile Association (AAA) revealed 60% of its members made airline reservations last year. Two members are selected at random. What is the probability both made airline reservations last year?

SOLUTION

The probability the first member made an airline reservation last year is .60, written $P(R_1) = .60$, where R_1 refers to the fact that the first member made a reservation. The probability that the second member selected made a reservation is also .60, so $P(R_2) = .60$. Because the number of AAA members is very large, you may assume that R_1 and R_2 are independent. Consequently, using formula (5–5), the probability they both make a reservation is .36, found by:

$$P(R_1 \text{ and } R_2) = P(R_1)P(R_2) = (.60)(.60) = .36$$

All possible outcomes can be shown as follows. R means a reservation is made, and $\sim R$ means no reservation is made.

With the probabilities and the complement rule, we can compute the joint probability of each outcome. For example, the probability that neither member makes a reservation is .16. Further, the probability of the first or the second member (special addition rule) making a reservation is .48 (.24 + .24). You can also observe that the outcomes are mutually exclusive and collectively exhaustive. Therefore, the probabilities sum to 1.00.

Outcomes		Joint Probability	
R_1	R_2	(.60)(.60) =	.36
R_1	$\sim R_2$	(.60)(.40) =	.24
$\sim R_1$	R_2	(.40)(.60) =	.24
$\sim R_1$	$\sim R_2$	(.40)(.40) =	.16
Total			1.00

SELF-REVIEW

5–5

From experience, Teton Tire knows the probability is .95 that a particular XB-70 tire will last 60,000 miles before it becomes bald or fails. An adjustment is made on any tire that does not last 60,000 miles. You purchase four XB-70s. What is the probability all four tires will last at least 60,000 miles?

General Rule of Multiplication

If two events are not independent, they are referred to as **dependent.** To illustrate dependency, suppose there are 10 cans of soda in a cooler; 7 are regular and 3 are diet. A can is selected from the cooler. The probability of selecting a can of diet soda is 3/10, and the probability of selecting a can of regular soda is 7/10. Then a second can is selected from the cooler, without returning the first. The probability the second is diet depends on whether the first one selected was diet or not. The probability that the second is diet is:

2/9, if the first can is diet. (Only two cans of diet soda remain in the cooler.)
3/9, if the first can selected is regular. (All three diet sodas are still in the cooler.)

The fraction 2/9 (or 3/9) is called a **conditional probability** because its value is conditional on (dependent on) whether a diet or regular soda was the first selection from the cooler.

> **CONDITIONAL PROBABILITY** The probability of a particular event occurring, given that another event has occurred.

In the general rule of multiplication, the conditional probability is required to compute the joint probability of two events that are not independent. For two events, A and B, that are not independent, the conditional probability is represented as $P(B|A)$, and expressed as the probability of B given A. Or the probability of B is conditional on the occurrence and effect of event A. Symbolically, the general rule of multiplication for two events that are not independent is:

> **GENERAL RULE OF MULTIPLICATION** $P(A \text{ and } B) = P(A)P(B|A)$ **[5–6]**

> ### E X A M P L E
>
>
> A golfer has 12 golf shirts in his closet. Suppose 9 of these shirts are white and the others blue. He gets dressed in the dark, so he just grabs a shirt and puts it on. He plays golf two days in a row and does not launder and return the used shirts to the closet. What is the likelihood both shirts selected are white?
>
>
>
> ### S O L U T I O N
>
> The event that the first shirt selected is white is W_1. The probability is $P(W_1) = 9/12$ because 9 of the 12 shirts are white. The event that the second shirt selected is also white is identified as W_2. The conditional probability that the second shirt selected is white, given that the first shirt selected is also white, is $P(W_2|W_1) = 8/11$. Why is this so? Because after the first shirt is selected, there are only 11 shirts remaining in the closet and 8 of these are white. To determine the probability of 2 white shirts being selected, we use formula (5–6).
>
> $$P(W_1 \text{ and } W_2) = P(W_1)P(W_2|W_1) = \left(\frac{9}{12}\right)\left(\frac{8}{11}\right) = .55$$
>
> So the likelihood of selecting two shirts and finding them both to be white is .55.

We can extend the general rule of multiplication to more than two events. For three events A, B, and C, the formula is:

$$P(A \text{ and } B \text{ and } C) = P(A)P(B|A)P(C|A \text{ and } B)$$

A SURVEY OF PROBABILITY CONCEPTS   149

In the case of the golf shirt example, the probability of selecting three white shirts without replacement is:

$$P(W_1 \text{ and } W_2 \text{ and } W_3) = P(W_1)P(W_2|W_1)P(W_3|W_1 \text{ and } W_2) = \left(\frac{9}{12}\right)\left(\frac{8}{11}\right)\left(\frac{7}{10}\right) = .38$$

So the likelihood of selecting three shirts without replacement and all being white is .38.

SELF-REVIEW 5–6

The board of directors of Tarbell Industries consists of eight men and four women. A four-member search committee is to be chosen at random to conduct a nationwide search for a new company president.
(a)   What is the probability all four members of the search committee will be women?
(b)   What is the probability all four members will be men?
(c)   Does the sum of the probabilities for the events described in parts (a) and (b) equal 1? Explain.

LO5-5
Compute probabilities using a contingency table.

CONTINGENCY TABLES

Often we tally the results of a survey in a two-way table and use the results of this tally to determine various probabilities. We described this idea beginning on page 116 in Chapter 4. To review, we refer to a two-way table as a contingency table.

> **CONTINGENCY TABLE** A table used to classify sample observations according to two or more identifiable categories or classes.

A contingency table is a cross-tabulation that simultaneously summarizes two variables of interest and their relationship. The level of measurement can be nominal. Below are several examples.

- One hundred fifty adults were asked their gender and the number of Facebook accounts they used. The following table summarizes the results.

Facebook Accounts	Gender		Total
	Men	Women	
0	20	40	60
1	40	30	70
2 or more	10	10	20
Total	70	80	150

- The American Coffee Producers Association reports the following information on age and the amount of coffee consumed in a month.

Age (Years)	Coffee Consumption			Total
	Low	Moderate	High	
Under 30	36	32	24	92
30 up to 40	18	30	27	75
40 up to 50	10	24	20	54
50 and over	26	24	29	79
Total	90	110	100	300

According to this table, each of the 300 respondents is classified according to two criteria: (1) age and (2) the amount of coffee consumed.

STATISTICS IN ACTION

In 2000 George W. Bush won the U.S. presidency by the slimmest of margins. Many election stories resulted, some involving voting irregularities, others raising interesting election questions. In a local Michigan election, there was a tie between two candidates for an elected position. To break the tie, the candidates drew a slip of paper from a box that contained two slips of paper, one marked "Winner" and the other unmarked. To determine which candidate drew first, election officials flipped a coin. The winner of the coin flip also drew the winning slip of paper. But was the coin flip really necessary? No, because the two events are independent. Winning the coin flip did not alter the probability of either candidate drawing the winning slip of paper.

The following example shows how the rules of addition and multiplication are used when we employ contingency tables.

EXAMPLE

Last month, the National Association of Theater Managers conducted a survey of 500 randomly selected adults. The survey asked respondents their age and the number of times they saw a movie in a theater. The results are summarized in Table 5–1.

TABLE 5–1 Number of Movies Attended per Month by Age

Movies per Month		Age Less than 30 B_1	30 up to 60 B_2	60 or Older B_3	Total
0	A_1	15	50	10	75
1 or 2	A_2	25	100	75	200
3, 4, or 5	A_3	55	60	60	175
6 or more	A_4	5	15	30	50
Total		100	225	175	500

The association is interested in understanding the probabilities that an adult will see a movie in a theater, especially for adults 60 and older. This information is useful for making decisions regarding discounts on tickets and concessions for seniors. Determine the probability of:

1.   Selecting an adult who attended 6 or more movies per month.
2.   Selecting an adult who attended 2 or fewer movies per month.
3.   Selecting an adult who attended 6 or more movies per month **or** is 60 years of age or older.
4.   Selecting an adult who attended 6 or more movies per month **given** the person is 60 years of age or older.
5.   Selecting an adult who attended 6 or more movies per month **and** is 60 years of age or older.

and we will determine the

6.   Independence of the number of movies per month attended and the age of the adult.

SOLUTION

Table 5–1 is called a contingency table. In a contingency table, an individual or an object is classified according to two criteria. In this example, a sampled adult is classified by age and by the number of movies attended per month. The rules of addition [formulas (5–2) and (5–4)] and the rules of multiplication [formulas (5–5) and (5–6)] allow us to answer the various probability questions based on the contingency table.

1.   To find the probability that a randomly selected adult attended 6 or more movies per month, focus on the row labeled "6 or more" (also labeled A_4) in Table 5–1. The table shows that 50 of the total of 500 adults are in this class. Using the empirical approach, the probability is computed:

$$P(6 \text{ or more}) = P(A_4) = \frac{50}{500} = .10$$

A SURVEY OF PROBABILITY CONCEPTS   151

This probability indicates 10% of the 500 adults attend 6 or more movies per month.

2. To determine the probability of randomly selecting an adult who went to 2 or fewer movies per month, two outcomes must be combined: attending 0 movies per month and attending 1 or 2 movies per month. These two outcomes are mutually exclusive. That is, a person can only be classified as attending 0 movies per month, or 1 or 2 movies per month, not both. Because the two outcomes are mutually exclusive, we use the special rule of addition [formula (5–2)] by adding the probabilities of attending no movies and attending 1 or 2 movies:

$$P[\text{(attending 0) or (attending 1 or 2)}] = P(A_1) + P(A_2) = \left(\frac{75}{500} + \frac{200}{500}\right) = .55$$

So 55% of the adults in the sample attended 2 or fewer movies a month.

3. To determine the probability of randomly selecting an adult who went to "6 or more" movies per month or whose age is "60 or older," we again use the rules of addition. However, in this case the outcomes are **not** mutually exclusive. Why is this? Because a person can attend more than 6 movies per month, be 60 or older, or be both. So the two groups are not mutually exclusive because it is possible that a person would be counted in both groups. To determine this probability, the general rule of addition [formula (5–4)] is used.

$$P[\text{(6 or more) or (60 or older)}] = P(A_4) + P(B_3) - P(A_4 \text{ and } B_3)$$

$$= \left(\frac{50}{500} + \frac{175}{500} - \frac{30}{500}\right) = .39$$

So 39% of the adults are either 60 or older, attend 6 or more movies per month, or both.

4. To determine the probability of selecting a person who attends 6 or more movies per month given that the person is 60 or older, focus only on the column labeled B_3 in Table 5–1. That is, we are only interested in the 175 adults who are 60 or older. Of these 175 adults, 30 attended 6 or more movies. Using the general rule of multiplication [formula (5–6)]:

$$P[\text{(6 or more) given (60 or older)}] = P(A_4|B_3) = \frac{30}{175} = .17$$

Of the 500 adults, 17% of adults who are 60 or older attend 6 or more movies per month. This is called a conditional probability because the probability is based on the "condition" of being the age of 60 or older. Recall that in part (1), 10% of all adults attend 6 or more movies per month; here we see that 17% of adults who are 60 or older attend movies. This is valuable information for theater managers regarding the characteristics of their customers.

5. The probability a person attended 6 or more movies and is 60 or older is based on two conditions and they must both happen. That is, the two outcomes "6 or more movies" (A_4) and "60 or older" (B_3) must occur jointly. To find this joint probability we use the special rule of multiplication [formula (5–6)].

$$P[\text{(6 or more) and (60 or older)}] = P(A_4 \text{ and } B_3) = P(A_4)\,P(B_3|A_4)$$

To compute the joint probability, first compute the simple probability of the first outcome, A_4, randomly selecting a person who attends 6 or more movies. To find the probability, refer to row A_4 in Table 5–1. There are 50 of 500 adults that attended 6 or more movies. So $P(A_4) = 50/500$.

152   CHAPTER 5

Next, compute the conditional probability $P(B_3|A_4)$. This is the probability of selecting an adult who is 60 or older given that the person attended 6 or more movies. The conditional probability is:

$$P[(60 \text{ or older) given (60 or more)}] = P(B_3|A_4) = 30/50$$

Using these two probabilities, the joint probability that an adult attends 6 or more movies and is 60 or older is:

$$P[(6 \text{ or more) and (60 or older)}] = P(A_4 \text{ and } B_3) = P(A_4)\, P(B_3|A_4)$$
$$= (50/500)(30/50) = .06$$

Based on the sample information from Table 5–1, the probability that an adult is both over 60 and attended 6 or more movies is 6%. It is important to know that the 6% is relative to all 500 adults.

Is there another way to determine this joint probability without using the special rule of multiplication formula? Yes. Look directly at the cell where row A_4, attends 6 or more movies, and column B_3, 60 or older, intersect. There are 30 adults in this cell that meet both criteria, so $P(A_4 \text{ and } B_3) = 30/500 = .06$. This is the same as computed with the formula.

6. Are the events independent? We can answer this question with the help of the results in part 4. In part 4 we found the probability of selecting an adult who was 60 or older given that the adult attended 6 or more movies was .17. If age is not a factor in movie attendance then we would expect the probability of a person who is 30 or less that attended 6 or more movies to also be 17%. That is, the two conditional probabilities would be the same. The probability that an adult attends 6 or more movies per month given the adult is less than 30 years old is:

$$P[(6 \text{ or more) given (less than 30)}] = \frac{5}{100} = .05$$

Because these two probabilities are not the same, the number of movies attended and age are not independent. To put it another way, for the 500 adults, age is related to the number of movies attended. In Chapter 15, we investigate this concept of independence in greater detail.

SELF-REVIEW
5–7

Refer to Table 5–1 on page 150 to find the following probabilities.
(a) What is the probability of selecting an adult that is 30 up to 60 years old?
(b) What is the probability of selecting an adult who is under 60 years of age?
(c) What is the probability of selecting an adult who is less than 30 years old or attended no movies?
(d) What is the probability of selecting an adult who is less than 30 years old and went to no movies?

Tree Diagrams

A **tree diagram** is a visual that is helpful in organizing and calculating probabilities for problems similar to the previous example/solution. This type of problem involves several stages and each stage is illustrated with a branch of the tree. The branches of a tree diagram are labeled with probabilities. We will use the information in Table 5–1 to show the construction of a tree diagram.

1. We begin the construction by drawing a box with the variable, age, on the left to represent the root of the tree (see Chart 5–2).

A SURVEY OF PROBABILITY CONCEPTS 153

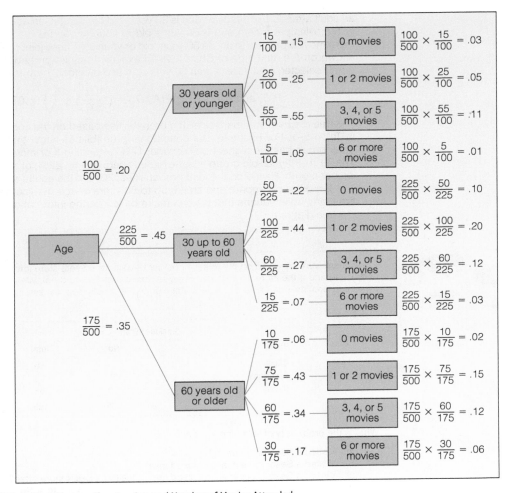

CHART 5–2 Tree Diagram Showing Age and Number of Movies Attended

2. There are three main branches going out from the root. The upper branch represents the outcome that an adult is less than 30 years old. The branch is labeled with the probability, $P(B_1) = 100/500$. The next branch represents the outcome that adults are 30 up to 60 years old. This branch is labeled with the probability $P(B_2) = 225/500$. The remaining branch is labeled $P(B_3) = 175/500$.

3. Four branches "grow" out of each of the four main branches. These branches represent the four categories of movies attended per month—0; 1 or 2; 3, 4, or 5; and 6 or more. The upper branches of the tree represent the conditional probabilities that an adult did not attend any movies given they are less than 30 years old. These are written $P(A_1|B_1)$, $P(A_2|B_1)$, $P(A_3|B_1)$, and $P(A_4|B_1)$ where A_1 refers to attending no movies; A_2 attending 1 or 2 movies per month; A_3 attending 3, 4, or 5 movies per month; and A_4 attending 6 or more movies per month. For the upper branch of the tree, these probabilities are 15/100, 25/100, 55/100, and 5/100. We write the conditional probabilities in a similar fashion on the other branches.

4. Finally we determine the various joint probabilities. For the top branches, the events are an adult attends no movies per month and is 30 years old or younger;

an adult attends 1 or 2 movies and is 30 years old or younger; an adult attends 3, 4, or 5 movies per month and is 30 years old or younger; and an adult attends 6 or more movies per month and is 30 years old or younger. These joint probabilities are shown on the right side of Chart 5–2. To explain, the joint probability that a randomly selected adult is less than 30 years old and attends 0 movies per month is:

$$P(B_1 \text{ and } A_1) = P(B_1)P(A_1|B_1) = \left(\frac{100}{500}\right)\left(\frac{15}{100}\right) = .03$$

The tree diagram summarizes all the probabilities based on the contingency table in Table 5–1. For example, the conditional probabilities show that the 60-and-older group has the highest percentage, 17%, attending 6 or movies per month. The 30-to-60-year-old group has the highest percentage, 22%, of seeing no movies per month. Based on the joint probabilities, 20% of the adults sampled attend 1 or 2 movies per month and are 30 up to 60 years of age. As you can see, there are many observations that we can make based on the information presented in the tree diagram.

SELF-REVIEW

5–8

Consumers were surveyed on the relative number of visits to a Sears store (often, occasional, and never) and if the store was located in an enclosed mall (yes and no). When variables are measured nominally, such as these data, the results are usually summarized in a contingency table.

Visits	Enclosed Mall		Total
	Yes	No	
Often	60	20	80
Occasional	25	35	60
Never	5	50	55
	90	105	195

What is the probability of selecting a shopper who:

 (a) Visited a Sears store often?
 (b) Visited a Sears store in an enclosed mall?
 (c) Visited a Sears store in an enclosed mall or visited a Sears store often?
 (d) Visited a Sears store often, given that the shopper went to a Sears store in an enclosed mall?

In addition:

 (e) Are the number of visits and the enclosed mall variables independent?
 (f) What is the probability of selecting a shopper who visited a Sears store often and it was in an enclosed mall?
 (g) Draw a tree diagram and determine the various joint probabilities.

EXERCISES

23. Suppose $P(A) = .40$ and $P(B|A) = .30$. What is the joint probability of A and B?
24. Suppose $P(X_1) = .75$ and $P(Y_2|X_1) = .40$. What is the joint probability of X_1 and Y_2?
25. A local bank reports that 80% of its customers maintain a checking account, 60% have a savings account, and 50% have both. If a customer is chosen at random, what is the probability the customer has either a checking or a savings account? What is the probability the customer does not have either a checking or a savings account?
26. All Seasons Plumbing has two service trucks that frequently need repair. If the probability the first truck is available is .75, the probability the second truck is available is .50, and the probability that both trucks are available is .30, what is the probability neither truck is available?

A SURVEY OF PROBABILITY CONCEPTS　　　　　　　　　155

For **DATA FILE**, please visit
www.mhhe.com/lind16e

27. Refer to the following table.

Second Event	First Event A_1	A_2	A_3	Total
B_1	2	1	3	6
B_2	1	2	1	4
Total	3	3	4	10

  a. Determine $P(A_1)$.
  b. Determine $P(B_1|A_2)$.
  c. Determine $P(B_2 \text{ and } A_3)$.

28. Three defective electric toothbrushes were accidentally shipped to a drugstore by Clean-brush Products along with 17 nondefective ones.
  a. What is the probability the first two electric toothbrushes sold will be returned to the drugstore because they are defective?
  b. What is the probability the first two electric toothbrushes sold will not be defective?

29. Each salesperson at Puchett, Sheets, and Hogan Insurance Agency is rated either below average, average, or above average with respect to sales ability. Each salesperson is also rated with respect to his or her potential for advancement—either fair, good, or excellent. These traits for the 500 salespeople were cross-classified into the following table.

For **DATA FILE**, please visit
www.mhhe.com/lind16e

Sales Ability	Potential for Advancement Fair	Good	Excellent
Below average	16	12	22
Average	45	60	45
Above average	93	72	135

  a. What is this table called?
  b. What is the probability a salesperson selected at random will have above average sales ability and excellent potential for advancement?
  c. Construct a tree diagram showing all the probabilities, conditional probabilities, and joint probabilities.

30. An investor owns three common stocks. Each stock, independent of the others, has equally likely chances of (1) increasing in value, (2) decreasing in value, or (3) remaining the same value. List the possible outcomes of this experiment. Estimate the probability at least two of the stocks increase in value.

31. A survey of 545 college students asked: What is your favorite winter sport? And, what type of college do you attend? The results are summarized below:

College Type	Favorite Winter Sport Snowboarding	Skiing	Ice Skating	Total
Junior College	68	41	46	155
Four-Year College	84	56	70	210
Graduate School	59	74	47	180
Total	211	171	163	545

  Using these 545 students as the sample, a student from this study is randomly selected.
  a. What is the probability of selecting a student whose favorite sport is skiing?
  b. What is the probability of selecting a junior-college student?
  c. If the student selected is a four-year-college student, what is the probability that the student prefers ice skating?
  d. If the student selected prefers snowboarding, what is the probability that the student is in junior college?
  e. If a graduate student is selected, what is the probability that the student prefers skiing or ice skating?

32. If you ask three strangers about their birthdays, what is the probability (a) All were born on Wednesday? (b) All were born on different days of the week? (c) None was born on Saturday?

156   CHAPTER 5

BAYES' THEOREM

In the 18th century, Reverend Thomas Bayes, an English Presbyterian minister, pon-
dered this question: Does God really exist? Being interested in mathematics, he attempted to develop a formula to arrive at the probability God does exist based on
evidence available to him on earth. Later Pierre-Simon Laplace refined Bayes' work
and gave it the name "Bayes' theorem." In a workable form, **Bayes' theorem** is:

BAYES' THEOREM $\quad P(A_i\|B) = \dfrac{P(A_i)P(B\|A_i)}{P(A_1)P(B\|A_1) + P(A_2)P(B\|A_2)}$	**[5–7]**

Assume in formula (5–7) that the events A_1 and A_2 are mutually exclusive and collectively
exhaustive, and A_i refers to either event A_1 or A_2. Hence A_1 and A_2 are in this case complements. The meaning of the symbols used is illustrated by the following example.

   Suppose 5% of the population of Umen, a fictional Third World country, have a
disease that is peculiar to that country. We will let A_1 refer to the event "has the disease" and A_2 refer to the event "does not have the disease." Thus, we know that if we
select a person from Umen at random, the probability the individual chosen has the
disease is .05, or $P(A_1) = .05$. This probability, $P(A_1) = P(\text{has the disease}) = .05$, is
called the **prior probability.** It is given this name because the probability is assigned
before any empirical data are obtained.

> **PRIOR PROBABILITY** The initial probability based on the present level of
> information.

The prior probability a person is not afflicted with the disease is therefore .95, or
$P(A_2) = .95$, found by $1 - .05$.
   There is a diagnostic technique to detect the disease, but it is not very accurate.
Let B denote the event "test shows the disease is present." Assume that historical
evidence shows that if a person actually has the disease, the probability that the test
will indicate the presence of the disease is .90. Using the conditional probability definitions developed earlier in this chapter, this statement is written as:

$$P(B\|A_1) = .90$$

Assume the probability is .15 that for a person who actually does not have the disease
the test will indicate the disease is present.

$$P(B\|A_2) = .15$$

   Let's randomly select a person from Umen and perform the test. The test results indicate the disease is present. What is the probability the person actually has the disease? In
symbolic form, we want to know $P(A_1\|B)$, which is interpreted as: $P(\text{has the disease} \mid \text{the}$
test results are positive). The probability $P(A_1\|B)$ is called a **posterior probability.**

> **POSTERIOR PROBABILITY** A revised probability based on additional information.

   With the help of Bayes' theorem, formula (5–7), we can determine the posterior
probability.

$$P(A_1\|B) = \frac{P(A_1)P(B\|A_1)}{P(A_1)P(B\|A_1) + P(A_2)P(B\|A_2)}$$

$$= \frac{(.05)(.90)}{(.05)(.90) + (.95)(.15)} = \frac{.0450}{.1875} = .24$$

A SURVEY OF PROBABILITY CONCEPTS   157

So the probability that a person has the disease, given that he or she tested positive, is .24. How is the result interpreted? If a person is selected at random from the population, the probability that he or she has the disease is .05. If the person is tested and the test result is positive, the probability that the person actually has the disease is increased about fivefold, from .05 to .24.

In the preceding problem, we had only two mutually exclusive and collectively exhaustive events, A_1 and A_2. If there are n such events, $A_1, A_2, \cdots, A_n$, Bayes' theorem, formula (5–7), becomes

$$P(A_i|B) = \frac{P(A_i)P(B|A_i)}{P(A_1)P(B|A_1) + P(A_2)P(B|A_2) + \cdots + P(A_n)P(B|A_n)}$$

With the preceding notation, the calculations for the Umen problem are summarized in the following table.

Event, A_i	Prior Probability, $P(A_i)$	Conditional Probability, $P(B\|A_i)$	Joint Probability, $P(A_i$ and $B)$	Posterior Probability, $P(A_i\|B)$
Disease, A_1	.05	.90	.0450	.0450/.1875 = .24
No disease, A_2	.95	.15	.1425	.1425/.1875 = .76
			$P(B) = .1875$	1.00

Another illustration of Bayes' theorem follows.

EXAMPLE

A manufacturer of cell phones purchases a particular microchip, called the LS-24, from three suppliers: Hall Electronics, Schuller Sales, and Crawford Components. Thirty percent of the LS-24 chips are purchased from Hall Electronics, 20% from Schuller Sales, and the remaining 50% from Crawford Components. The manufacturer has extensive histories on the three suppliers and knows that 3% of the LS-24 chips from Hall Electronics are defective, 5% of chips from Schuller Sales are defective, and 4% of the chips purchased from Crawford Components are defective.

When the LS-24 chips arrive from the three suppliers, they are placed directly in a bin and not inspected or otherwise identified by supplier. A worker selects a chip for installation and finds it defective. What is the probability that it was manufactured by Schuller Sales?

SOLUTION

As a first step, let's summarize some of the information given in the problem statement.

- There are three mutually exclusive and collectively exhaustive events, that is, three suppliers.

  A_1 The LS-24 was purchased from Hall Electronics.
  A_2 The LS-24 was purchased from Schuller Sales.
  A_3 The LS-24 was purchased from Crawford Components.

- The prior probabilities are:

    $P(A_1) = .30$ The probability the LS-24 was manufactured by Hall Electronics.

    $P(A_2) = .20$ The probability the LS-24 was manufactured by Schuller Sales.

    $P(A_3) = .50$ The probability the LS-24 was manufactured by Crawford Components.

- The additional information can be either:

    B_1 The LS-24 is defective, or

    B_2 The LS-24 is not defective.

- The following conditional probabilities are given.

    $P(B_1|A_1) = .03$ The probability that an LS-24 chip produced by Hall Electronics is defective.

    $P(B_1|A_2) = .05$ The probability that an LS-24 chip produced by Schuller Sales is defective.

    $P(B_1|A_3) = .04$ The probability that an LS-24 chip produced by Crawford Components is defective.

- A chip is selected from the bin. Because the chips are not identified by supplier, we are not certain which supplier manufactured the chip. We want to determine the probability that the defective chip was purchased from Schuller Sales. The probability is written $P(A_2|B_1)$.

    Look at Schuller's quality record. It is the worst of the three suppliers. Now that we have found a defective LS-24 chip, we suspect that $P(A_2|B_1)$ is greater than $P(A_2)$. That is, we expect the revised probability to be greater than .20. But how much greater? Bayes' theorem can give us the answer. As a first step, consider the tree diagram in Chart 5–3.

    The events are dependent, so the prior probability in the first branch is multiplied by the conditional probability in the second branch to obtain the joint probability. The joint probability is reported in the last column of Chart 5–3. To

CHART 5–3 Tree Diagram of the Cell Phone Manufacturing Problem

A SURVEY OF PROBABILITY CONCEPTS 159

construct the tree diagram of Chart 5–3, we used a time sequence that moved from the supplier to the determination of whether the chip was defective.

What we need to do is reverse the time process. That is, instead of moving from left to right in Chart 5–3, we need to move from right to left. We have a defective chip, and we want to determine the likelihood that it was purchased from Schuller Sales. How is that accomplished? We first look at the joint probabilities as relative frequencies out of 1,000 cases. For example, the likelihood of a defective LS-24 chip that was produced by Hall Electronics is .009. So of 1,000 cases, we would expect to find 9 defective chips produced by Hall Electronics. We observe that in 39 of 1,000 cases the LS-24 chip selected for assembly will be defective, found by 9 + 10 + 20. Of these 39 defective chips, 10 were produced by Schuller Sales. Thus, the probability that the defective LS-24 chip was purchased from Schuller Sales is 10/39 = .2564. We have now determined the revised probability of $P(A_2|B_1)$. Before we found the defective chip, the likelihood that it was purchased from Schuller Sales was .20. This likelihood has been increased to .2564.

This information is summarized in the following table.

Event, A_i	Prior Probability, $P(A_i)$	Conditional Probability, $P(B_1|A_i)$	Joint Probability, $P(A_i$ and $B_1)$	Posterior Probability, $P(A_i|B_1)$
Hall	.30	.03	.009	.009/.039 = .2308
Schuller	.20	.05	.010	.010/.039 = .2564
Crawford	.50	.04	.020	.020/.039 = .5128
			$P(B_1) = .039$	1.0000

The probability the defective LS-24 chip came from Schuller Sales can be formally found by using Bayes' theorem. We compute $P(A_2|B_1)$, where A_2 refers to Schuller Sales and B_1 to the fact that the selected LS-24 chip was defective.

$$P(A_2|B_1) = \frac{P(A_2)P(B_1|A_2)}{P(A_1)P(B_1|A_1) + P(A_2)P(B_1|A_2) + P(A_3)(B_1|A_3)}$$

$$= \frac{(.20)(.05)}{(.30)(.03) + (.20)(.05) + (.50)(.04)} = \frac{.010}{.039} = .2564$$

This is the same result obtained from Chart 5–3 and from the conditional probability table.

SELF-REVIEW

5–9

Refer to the preceding example and solution.
(a) Design a formula to find the probability the part selected came from Crawford Components, given that it was a good chip.
(b) Compute the probability using Bayes' theorem.

EXERCISES

33. $P(A_1) = .60$, $P(A_2) = .40$, $P(B_1|A_1) = .05$, and $P(B_1|A_2) = .10$. Use Bayes' theorem to determine $P(A_1|B_1)$.
34. $P(A_1) = .20$, $P(A_2) = .40$, $P(A_3) = .40$, $P(B_1|A_1) = .25$, $P(B_1|A_2) = .05$, and $P(B_1|A_3) = .10$. Use Bayes' theorem to determine $P(A_3|B_1)$.
35. The Ludlow Wildcats baseball team, a minor league team in the Cleveland Indians organization, plays 70% of their games at night and 30% during the day. The team wins 50% of their night games and 90% of their day games. According to today's newspaper, they won yesterday. What is the probability the game was played at night?
36. Dr. Stallter has been teaching basic statistics for many years. She knows that 80% of the students will complete the assigned problems. She has also determined that among those who do their assignments, 90% will pass the course. Among those students who do not do

their homework, 60% will pass. Mike Fishbaugh took statistics last semester from Dr. Stallter and received a passing grade. What is the probability that he completed the assignments?

37. The credit department of Lion's Department Store in Anaheim, California, reported that 30% of their sales are cash, 30% are paid with a credit card, and 40% with a debit card. Twenty percent of the cash purchases, 90% of the credit card purchases, and 60% of the debit card purchases are for more than $50. Ms. Tina Stevens just purchased a new dress that cost $120. What is the probability that she paid cash?

38. One-fourth of the residents of the Burning Ridge Estates leave their garage doors open when they are away from home. The local chief of police estimates that 5% of the garages with open doors will have something stolen, but only 1% of those closed will have something stolen. If a garage is robbed, what is the probability the doors were left open?

LO5-7
Determine the number of outcomes using principles of counting.

PRINCIPLES OF COUNTING

If the number of possible outcomes in an experiment is small, it is relatively easy to count them. There are six possible outcomes, for example, resulting from the roll of a die, namely:

If, however, there are a large number of possible outcomes, such as the number of heads and tails for an experiment with 10 tosses, it would be tedious to count all the possibilities. They could have all heads, one head and nine tails, two heads and eight tails, and so on. To facilitate counting, we describe three formulas: the **multiplication formula** (not to be confused with the multiplication *rule* described earlier in the chapter), the **permutation formula,** and the **combination formula.**

The Multiplication Formula

We begin with the multiplication formula.

MULTIPLICATION FORMULA If there are *m* ways of doing one thing and *n* ways of doing another thing, there are *m* × *n* ways of doing both.

In terms of a formula:

MULTIPLICATION FORMULA   Total number of arrangements = $(m)(n)$ **[5–8]**

This can be extended to more than two events. For three events *m*, *n*, and *o*:

Total number of arrangements = $(m)(n)(o)$

EXAMPLE

An automobile dealer wants to advertise that for $29,999 you can buy a convertible, a two-door sedan, or a four-door model with your choice of either wire wheel covers or solid wheel covers. Based on the number of models and wheel covers, how many different vehicles can the dealer offer?

SOLUTION

Of course, the dealer could determine the total number of different cars by picturing and counting them. There are six.

Convertible with wire wheel covers

Convertible with solid wheel covers

Two-door with wire wheel covers

Two-door with solid wheel covers

Four-door with wire wheel covers

Four-door with solid wheel covers

We can employ the multiplication formula as a check (where m is the number of models and n the wheel cover type). From formula (5–8):

$$\text{Total possible arrangements} = (m)(n) = (3)(2) = 6$$

It was not difficult to count all the possible model and wheel cover combinations in this example. Suppose, however, that the dealer decided to offer eight models and six types of wheel covers. It would be tedious to picture and count all the possible alternatives. Instead, the multiplication formula can be used. In this case, there are $(m)(n) = (8)(6) = 48$ possible arrangements.

Note in the preceding applications of the multiplication formula that there were *two or more groupings from which you made selections*. The automobile dealer, for example, offered a choice of models and a choice of wheel covers. If a home builder offered you four different exterior styles of a home to choose from and three interior floor plans, the multiplication formula would be used to find how many different arrangements were possible. There are 12 possibilities.

SELF-REVIEW

5–10

1. The Women's Shopping Network on cable TV offers sweaters and slacks for women. The sweaters and slacks are offered in coordinating colors. If sweaters are available in five colors and the slacks are available in four colors, how many different outfits can be advertised?
2. Pioneer manufactures three models of stereo receivers, two MP3 docking stations, four speakers, and three CD carousels. When the four types of components are sold together, they form a "system." How many different systems can the electronics firm offer?

The Permutation Formula

The multiplication formula is applied to find the number of possible arrangements for two or more groups. In contrast, we use the **permutation formula** to find the number of possible arrangements when there is a single group of objects. Illustrations of this type of problem are:

- Three electronic parts, a transistor, an LED, and a synthesizer, are assembled into a plug-in unit for a television. The parts can be assembled in any order. How many different ways can the three parts be assembled?
- A machine operator must make four safety checks before starting his machine. It does not matter in which order the checks are made. In how many different ways can the operator make the checks?

One order for the first illustration might be the transistor first, the LED second, and the synthesizer third. This arrangement is called a **permutation.**

> **PERMUTATION** Any arrangement of r objects selected from a single group of n possible objects.

Note that the arrangements $a\ b\ c$ and $b\ a\ c$ are different permutations. The formula to count the total number of different permutations is:

PERMUTATION FORMULA	$${}_nP_r = \frac{n!}{(n-r)!}$$	**[5–9]**

where:
    n is the total number of objects.
    r is the number of objects selected.

    Before we solve the two problems illustrated, the permutations and combinations (to be discussed shortly) use a notation called *n factorial*. It is written $n!$ and means the product of $n(n-1)(n-2)(n-3)\cdots(1)$. For instance, $5! = 5 \cdot 4 \cdot 3 \cdot 2 \cdot 1 = 120$.

    Many of your calculators have a button with $x!$ that will perform this calculation for you. It will save you a great deal of time. For example the Texas Instrument TI-36X calculator has the following key: $x!$

It is the "third function," so check your users' manual or the Internet for instructions.

    The factorial notation can also be canceled when the same number appears in both the numerator and the denominator, as shown below.

$$\frac{6!3!}{4!} = \frac{6 \cdot 5 \cdot \cancel{4} \cdot \cancel{3} \cdot \cancel{2} \cdot \cancel{1}(3 \cdot 2 \cdot 1)}{\cancel{4} \cdot \cancel{3} \cdot \cancel{2} \cdot \cancel{1}} = 180$$

By definition, zero factorial, written $0!$, is 1. That is, $0! = 1$.

E X A M P L E

▼ Referring to the group of three electronic parts that are to be assembled in any order, in how many different ways can they be assembled?

S O L U T I O N

There are three electronic parts to be assembled, so $n = 3$. Because all three are to be inserted in the plug-in unit, $r = 3$. Solving using formula (5–9) gives:

$$_nP_r = \frac{n!}{(n-r)!} = \frac{3!}{(3-3)!} = \frac{3!}{0!} = \frac{3!}{1} = 6$$

    We can check the number of permutations arrived at by using the permutation formula. We determine how many "spaces" have to be filled and the possibilities for each "space." In the problem involving three electronic parts, there are three locations in the plug-in unit for the three parts. There are three possibilities for the first place, two for the second (one has been used up), and one for the third, as follows:

$$(3)(2)(1) = 6 \text{ permutations}$$

The six ways in which the three electronic parts, lettered A, B, C, can be arranged are:

ABC	BAC	CAB	ACB	BCA	CBA

In the previous example, we selected and arranged all the objects, that is $n = r$. In many cases, only some objects are selected and arranged from the n possible objects. We explain the details of this application in the following example.

E X A M P L E

Betts Machine Shop Inc. has eight screw machines but only three spaces available in the production area for the machines. In how many different ways can the eight machines be arranged in the three spaces available?

S O L U T I O N

There are eight possibilities for the first available space in the production area, seven for the second space (one has been used up), and six for the third space. Thus:

$$(8)(7)(6) = 336,$$

that is, there are a total of 336 different possible arrangements. This could also be found by using formula (5–9). If $n = 8$ machines and $r = 3$ spaces available, the formula leads to

$$_nP_r = \frac{n!}{(n-r)!} = \frac{8!}{(8-3)!} = \frac{8!}{5!} = \frac{(8)(7)(6)\cancel{5!}}{\cancel{5!}} = 336$$

The Combination Formula

If the order of the selected objects is *not* important, any selection is called a **combination.** Logically, the number of combinations is always less than the number of permutations. The formula to count the number of r object combinations from a set of n objects is:

COMBINATION FORMULA $$_nC_r = \frac{n!}{r!(n-r)!}$$ **[5–10]**

For example, if executives Able, Baker, and Chauncy are to be chosen as a committee to negotiate a merger, there is only one possible combination of these three; the committee of Able, Baker, and Chauncy is the same as the committee of Baker, Chauncy, and Able. Using the combination formula:

$$_nC_r = \frac{n!}{r!(n-r)!} = \frac{3 \cdot 2 \cdot 1}{3 \cdot 2 \cdot 1(1)} = 1$$

E X A M P L E

The Grand 16 movie theater uses teams of three employees to work the concession stand each evening. There are seven employees available to work each evening. How many different teams can be scheduled to staff the concession stand?

S O L U T I O N

According to formula (5–10), there are 35 combinations, found by

$$_7C_3 = \frac{n!}{r!(n-r)!} = \frac{7!}{3!(7-3)!} = \frac{7!}{3!4!} = 35$$

The seven employees taken three at a time would create the possibility of 35 different teams.

When the number of permutations or combinations is large, the calculations are tedious. Computer software and handheld calculators have "functions" to compute these numbers. The Excel output for the location of the eight screw machines in the production area of Betts Machine Shop Inc. is shown below. There are a total of 336 arrangements.

Below is the output for the number of teams at the Grand 16 movie theater. Three employees are chosen from seven possible employees.

SELF-REVIEW

5–11

1. A musician wants to write a score based on only five chords: B-flat, C, D, E, and G. However, only three chords out of the five will be used in succession, such as C, B-flat, and E. Repetitions, such as B-flat, B-flat, and E, will not be permitted.
   (a) How many permutations of the five chords, taken three at a time, are possible?
   (b) Using formula (5–9), how many permutations are possible?
2. The 10 numbers 0 through 9 are to be used in code groups of four to identify an item of clothing. Code 1083 might identify a blue blouse, size medium; the code group 2031 might identify a pair of pants, size 18; and so on. Repetitions of numbers are not permitted. That is, the same number cannot be used twice (or more) in a total sequence. For example, 2256, 2562, or 5559 would not be permitted. How many different code groups can be designed?
3. In the preceding example/solution involving the Grand 16 movie theater, there were 35 possible teams of three taken from seven employees.
   (a) Use formula (5–10) to show this is true.
   (b) The manager of the theater wants to plan for staffing the concession stand with teams of five employees on the weekends to serve the larger crowds. From the seven employees, how many teams of five employees are possible?

A SURVEY OF PROBABILITY CONCEPTS   165

4. In a lottery game, three numbers are randomly selected from a tumbler of balls numbered 1 through 50.
    (a) How many permutations are possible?
    (b) How many combinations are possible?

E X E R C I S E S
▼

39. Solve the following:
    a. 40!/35!
    b. $_7P_4$
    c. $_5C_2$
40. Solve the following:
    a. 20!/17!
    b. $_9P_3$
    c. $_7C_2$
41. A pollster randomly selected 4 of 10 available people. How many different groups of 4 are possible?
42. A telephone number consists of seven digits, the first three representing the exchange. How many different telephone numbers are possible within the 537 exchange?
43. An overnight express company must include five cities on its route. How many different routes are possible, assuming that it does not matter in which order the cities are included in the routing?
44. A representative of the Environmental Protection Agency (EPA) wants to select samples from 10 landfills. The director has 15 landfills from which she can collect samples. How many different samples are possible?
45. A national pollster has developed 15 questions designed to rate the performance of the president of the United States. The pollster will select 10 of these questions. How many different arrangements are there for the order of the 10 selected questions?
46. A company is creating three new divisions and seven managers are eligible to be appointed head of a division. How many different ways could the three new heads be appointed? Hint: Assume the division assignment makes a difference.

C H A P T E R   S U M M A R Y

I. A probability is a value between 0 and 1 inclusive that represents the likelihood a particular event will happen.
  A. An experiment is the observation of some activity or the act of taking some measurement.
  B. An outcome is a particular result of an experiment.
  C. An event is the collection of one or more outcomes of an experiment.
II. There are three definitions of probability.
  A. The classical definition applies when there are n equally likely outcomes to an experiment.
  B. The empirical definition occurs when the number of times an event happens is divided by the number of observations.
  C. A subjective probability is based on whatever information is available.
III. Two events are mutually exclusive if by virtue of one event happening the other cannot happen.
IV. Events are independent if the occurrence of one event does not affect the occurrence of another event.
V. The rules of addition refer to the probability that any of two or more events can occur.
  A. The special rule of addition is used when events are mutually exclusive.

$$P(A \text{ or } B) = P(A) + P(B) \qquad \text{[5–2]}$$

  B. The general rule of addition is used when the events are not mutually exclusive.

$$P(A \text{ or } B) = P(A) + P(B) - P(A \text{ and } B) \qquad \text{[5–4]}$$

166   CHAPTER 5

STATISTICS IN ACTION

Government statistics show there are about 1.7 automobile-caused fatalities for every 100,000,000 vehicle-miles. If you drive 1 mile to the store to buy your lottery ticket and then return home, you have driven 2 miles. Thus the probability that you will join this statistical group on your next 2-mile round trip is $2 \times 1.7/100{,}000{,}000 = 0.000000034$. This can also be stated as "One in 29,411,765." Thus, if you drive to the store to buy your Powerball ticket, your chance of being killed (or killing someone else) is more than 4 times greater than the chance that you will win the Powerball Jackpot, one chance in 120,526,770. http://www.durangobill .com/Powerball Odds .html

C. The complement rule is used to determine the probability of an event happening by subtracting the probability of the event not happening from 1.

$$P(A) = 1 - P(\sim A) \tag{5-3}$$

VI. The rules of multiplication are applied when two or more events occur simultaneously.
   A. The special rule of multiplication refers to events that are independent.

$$P(A \text{ and } B) = P(A)P(B) \tag{5-5}$$

   B. The general rule of multiplication refers to events that are not independent.

$$P(A \text{ and } B) = P(A)P(B|A) \tag{5-6}$$

   C. A joint probability is the likelihood that two or more events will happen at the same time.
   D. A conditional probability is the likelihood that an event will happen, given that another event has already happened.
   E. Bayes' theorem is a method of revising a probability, given that additional information is obtained. For two mutually exclusive and collectively exhaustive events:

$$P(A_1|B) = \frac{P(A_1)P(B|A_1)}{P(A_1)P(B|A_1) + P(A_2)P(B|A_2)} \tag{5-7}$$

VII. There are three counting rules that are useful in determining the number of outcomes in an experiment.
   A. The multiplication rule states that if there are m ways one event can happen and n ways another event can happen, then there are mn ways the two events can happen.

$$\text{Number of arrangements} = (m)(n) \tag{5-8}$$

   B. A permutation is an arrangement in which the order of the objects selected from a specific pool of objects is important.

$$_nP_r = \frac{n!}{(n-r)!} \tag{5-9}$$

   C. A combination is an arrangement where the order of the objects selected from a specific pool of objects is not important.

$$_nC_r = \frac{n!}{r!(n-r)!} \tag{5-10}$$

P R O N U N C I A T I O N   K E Y

SYMBOL	MEANING	PRONUNCIATION
$P(A)$	Probability of A	P of A
$P(\sim A)$	Probability of not A	P of not A
$P(A \text{ and } B)$	Probability of A and B	P of A and B
$P(A \text{ or } B)$	Probability of A or B	P of A or B
$P(A|B)$	Probability of A given B has happened	P of A given B
$_nP_r$	Permutation of n items selected r at a time	Pnr
$_nC_r$	Combination of n items selected r at a time	Cnr

C H A P T E R   E X E R C I S E S

47. The marketing research department at Pepsico plans to survey teenagers about a newly developed soft drink. Each will be asked to compare it with his or her favorite soft drink.
   a. What is the experiment?
   b. What is one possible event?
48. The number of times a particular event occurred in the past is divided by the number of occurrences. What is this approach to probability called?

A SURVEY OF PROBABILITY CONCEPTS   167

49. The probability that the cause and the cure for all cancers will be discovered before the year 2020 is .20. What viewpoint of probability does this statement illustrate?

For **DATA FILE**, please visit www.mhhe.com/lind16e

50. Berdine's Chicken Factory has several stores in the Hilton Head, South Carolina, area. When interviewing applicants for server positions, the owner would like to include information on the amount of tip a server can expect to earn per check (or bill). A study of 500 recent checks indicated the server earned the following amounts in tips per 8-hour shift.

Amount of Tip	Number
$0 up to $ 20	200
20 up to 50	100
50 up to 100	75
100 up to 200	75
200 or more	50
Total	500

a. What is the probability of a tip of $200 or more?
b. Are the categories "$0 up to $20," "$20 up to $50," and so on considered mutually exclusive?
c. If the probabilities associated with each outcome were totaled, what would that total be?
d. What is the probability of a tip of up to $50?
e. What is the probability of a tip of less than $200?

51. Winning all three "Triple Crown" races is considered the greatest feat of a pedigree racehorse. After a successful Kentucky Derby, Corn on the Cob is a heavy favorite at 2 to 1 odds to win the Preakness Stakes.
a. If he is a 2 to 1 favorite to win the Belmont Stakes as well, what is his probability of winning the Triple Crown?
b. What do his chances for the Preakness Stakes have to be in order for him to be "even money" to earn the Triple Crown?

52. The first card selected from a standard 52-card deck is a king.
a. If it is returned to the deck, what is the probability that a king will be drawn on the second selection?
b. If the king is not replaced, what is the probability that a king will be drawn on the second selection?
c. What is the probability that a king will be selected on the first draw from the deck and another king on the second draw (assuming that the first king was not replaced)?

53. Armco, a manufacturer of traffic light systems, found that under accelerated-life tests, 95% of the newly developed systems lasted 3 years before failing to change signals properly.
a. If a city purchased four of these systems, what is the probability all four systems would operate properly for at least 3 years?
b. Which rule of probability does this illustrate?
c. Using letters to represent the four systems, write an equation to show how you arrived at the answer to part (a).

54. Refer to the following picture.

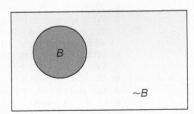

a. What is the picture called?
b. What rule of probability is illustrated?
c. B represents the event of choosing a family that receives welfare payments. What does $P(B) + P(\sim B)$ equal?

55. In a management trainee program at Claremont Enterprises, 80% of the trainees are female and 20% male. Ninety percent of the females attended college, and 78% of the males attended college.

  a. A management trainee is selected at random. What is the probability that the person selected is a female who did not attend college?

  b. Are gender and attending college independent? Why?

  c. Construct a tree diagram showing all the probabilities, conditional probabilities, and joint probabilities.

  d. Do the joint probabilities total 1.00? Why?

56. Assume the likelihood that any flight on Delta Airlines arrives within 15 minutes of the scheduled time is .90. We randomly selected a Delta flight on four different days.

  a. What is the likelihood all four of the selected flights arrived within 15 minutes of the scheduled time?

  b. What is the likelihood that none of the selected flights arrived within 15 minutes of the scheduled time?

  c. What is the likelihood at least one of the selected flights did not arrive within 15 minutes of the scheduled time?

57. There are 100 employees at Kiddie Carts International. Fifty-seven of the employees are hourly workers, 40 are supervisors, 2 are secretaries, and the remaining employee is the president. Suppose an employee is selected:

  a. What is the probability the selected employee is an hourly worker?

  b. What is the probability the selected employee is either an hourly worker or a supervisor?

  c. Refer to part (b). Are these events mutually exclusive?

  d. What is the probability the selected employee is neither an hourly worker nor a supervisor?

58. Buster Posey of the San Francisco Giants had the highest batting average in the 2012 Major League Baseball season. His average was .336. So assume the probability of getting a hit is .336 for each time he batted. In a particular game, assume he batted three times.

  a. This is an example of what type of probability?

  b. What is the probability of getting three hits in a particular game?

  c. What is the probability of not getting any hits in a game?

  d. What is the probability of getting at least one hit?

59. Four women's college basketball teams are participating in a single-elimination holiday basketball tournament. If one team is favored in its semifinal match by odds of 2 to 1 and another squad is favored in its contest by odds of 3 to 1, what is the probability that:

  a. Both favored teams win their games?

  b. Neither favored team wins its game?

  c. At least one of the favored teams wins its game?

60. There are three clues labeled "daily double" on the game show *Jeopardy*. If three equally matched contenders play, what is the probability that:

  a. A single contestant finds all three "daily doubles"?

  b. The returning champion gets all three of the "daily doubles"?

  c. Each of the players selects precisely one of the "daily doubles"?

61. Brooks Insurance Inc. wishes to offer life insurance to men age 60 via the Internet. Mortality tables indicate the likelihood of a 60-year-old man surviving another year is .98. If the policy is offered to five men age 60:

  a. What is the probability all five men survive the year?

  b. What is the probability at least one does not survive?

62. Forty percent of the homes constructed in the Quail Creek area include a security system. Three homes are selected at random:

  a. What is the probability all three of the selected homes have a security system?

  b. What is the probability none of the three selected homes has a security system?

  c. What is the probability at least one of the selected homes has a security system?

  d. Did you assume the events to be dependent or independent?

63. Refer to Exercise 62, but assume there are 10 homes in the Quail Creek area and 4 of them have a security system. Three homes are selected at random:

  a. What is the probability all three of the selected homes have a security system?

  b. What is the probability none of the three selected homes has a security system?

  c. What is the probability at least one of the selected homes has a security system?

  d. Did you assume the events to be dependent or independent?

A SURVEY OF PROBABILITY CONCEPTS   169

64. There are 20 families living in the Willbrook Farms Development. Of these families, 10 prepared their own federal income taxes for last year, 7 had their taxes prepared by a local professional, and the remaining 3 by H&R Block.
    a. What is the probability of selecting a family that prepared their own taxes?
    b. What is the probability of selecting two families, both of which prepared their own taxes?
    c. What is the probability of selecting three families, all of which prepared their own taxes?
    d. What is the probability of selecting two families, neither of which had their taxes prepared by H&R Block?

65. The board of directors of Saner Automatic Door Company consists of 12 members, 3 of whom are women. A new policy and procedures manual is to be written for the company. A committee of three is randomly selected from the board to do the writing.
    a. What is the probability that all members of the committee are men?
    b. What is the probability that at least one member of the committee is a woman?

66. A recent survey reported in *BloombergBusinessweek* dealt with the salaries of CEOs at large corporations and whether company shareholders made money or lost money.

	CEO Paid More Than $1 Million	CEO Paid Less Than $1 Million	Total
Shareholders made money	2	11	13
Shareholders lost money	4	3	7
Total	6	14	20

If a company is randomly selected from the list of 20 studied, what is the probability:
    a. The CEO made more than $1 million?
    b. The CEO made more than $1 million or the shareholders lost money?
    c. The CEO made more than $1 million given the shareholders lost money?
    d. Of selecting two CEOs and finding they both made more than $1 million?

67. Althoff and Roll, an investment firm in Augusta, Georgia, advertises extensively in the *Augusta Morning Gazette,* the newspaper serving the region. The *Gazette* marketing staff estimates that 60% of Althoff and Roll's potential market read the newspaper. It is further estimated that 85% of those who read the *Gazette* remember the Althoff and Roll advertisement.
    a. What percent of the investment firm's potential market sees and remembers the advertisement?
    b. What percent of the investment firm's potential market sees, but does not remember, the advertisement?

68. An Internet company located in Southern California has season tickets to the Los Angeles Lakers basketball games. The company president always invites one of the four vice presidents to attend games with him, and claims he selects the person to attend at random. One of the four vice presidents has not been invited to attend any of the last five Lakers home games. What is the likelihood this could be due to chance?

69. A computer-supply retailer purchased a batch of 1,000 CD-R disks and attempted to format them for a particular application. There were 857 perfect CDs, 112 CDs were usable but had bad sectors, and the remainder could not be used at all.
    a. What is the probability a randomly chosen CD is not perfect?
    b. If the disk is not perfect, what is the probability it cannot be used at all?

70. An investor purchased 100 shares of Fifth Third Bank stock and 100 shares of Santee Electric Cooperative stock. The probability the bank stock will appreciate over a year is .70. The probability the electric utility will increase over the same period is .60. Assume the two events are independent.
    a. What is the probability both stocks appreciate during the period?
    b. What is the probability the bank stock appreciates but the utility does not?
    c. What is the probability at least one of the stocks appreciates?

71. Flashner Marketing Research Inc. specializes in providing assessments of the prospects for women's apparel shops in shopping malls. Al Flashner, president, reports that he assesses the prospects as good, fair, or poor. Records from previous assessments show that 60% of the time the prospects were rated as good, 30% of the time fair, and 10% of the time poor. Of those rated good, 80% made a profit the first year; of those rated fair, 60% made a profit the first year; and of those rated poor, 20% made a profit the first year. Connie's Apparel was one of Flashner's clients. Connie's Apparel made a profit last year. What is the probability that it was given an original rating of poor?

72. Two boxes of men's Old Navy shirts were received from the factory. Box 1 contained 25 mesh polo shirts and 15 Super-T shirts. Box 2 contained 30 mesh polo shirts and 10 Super-T shirts. One of the boxes was selected at random, and a shirt was chosen at random from that box to be inspected. The shirt was a mesh polo shirt. Given this information, what is the probability that the mesh polo shirt came from box 1?

73. With each purchase of a large pizza at Tony's Pizza, the customer receives a coupon that can be scratched to see if a prize will be awarded. The probability of winning a free soft drink is 0.10, and the probability of winning a free large pizza is 0.02. You plan to eat lunch tomorrow at Tony's. What is the probability:
   a. That you will win either a large pizza or a soft drink?
   b. That you will not win a prize?
   c. That you will not win a prize on three consecutive visits to Tony's?
   d. That you will win at least one prize on one of your next three visits to Tony's?

74. For the daily lottery game in Illinois, participants select three numbers between 0 and 9. A number cannot be selected more than once, so a winning ticket could be, say, 307 but not 337. Purchasing one ticket allows you to select one set of numbers. The winning numbers are announced on TV each night.
   a. How many different outcomes (three-digit numbers) are possible?
   b. If you purchase a ticket for the game tonight, what is the likelihood you will win?
   c. Suppose you purchase three tickets for tonight's drawing and select a different number for each ticket. What is the probability that you will not win with any of the tickets?

75. Several years ago, Wendy's Hamburgers advertised that there are 256 different ways to order your hamburger. You may choose to have, or omit, any combination of the following on your hamburger: mustard, ketchup, onion, pickle, tomato, relish, mayonnaise, and lettuce. Is the advertisement correct? Show how you arrive at your answer.

76. Recent surveys indicate 60% of tourists to China visited the Forbidden City, the Temple of Heaven, the Great Wall, and other historical sites in or near Beijing. Forty percent visited Xi'an with its magnificent terra-cotta soldiers, horses, and chariots, which lay buried for over 2,000 years. Thirty percent of the tourists went to both Beijing and Xi'an. What is the probability that a tourist visited at least one of these places?

77. A new chewing gum has been developed that is helpful to those who want to stop smoking. If 60% of those people chewing the gum are successful in stopping smoking, what is the probability that in a group of four smokers using the gum at least one quits smoking?

78. Reynolds Construction Company has agreed not to erect all "look-alike" homes in a new subdivision. Five exterior designs are offered to potential home buyers. The builder has standardized three interior plans that can be incorporated in any of the five exteriors. How many different ways can the exterior and interior plans be offered to potential home buyers?

79. A new sports car model has defective brakes 15% of the time and a defective steering mechanism 5% of the time. Let's assume (and hope) that these problems occur independently. If one or the other of these problems is present, the car is called a "lemon." If both of these problems are present, the car is a "hazard." Your instructor purchased one of these cars yesterday. What is the probability it is:
   a. A lemon?
   b. A hazard?

80. The state of Maryland has license plates with three numbers followed by three letters. How many different license plates are possible?

81. There are four people being considered for the position of chief executive officer of Dalton Enterprises. Three of the applicants are over 60 years of age. Two are female, of which only one is over 60.
   a. What is the probability that a candidate is over 60 and female?
   b. Given that the candidate is male, what is the probability he is less than 60?
   c. Given that the person is over 60, what is the probability the person is female?

82. Tim Bleckie is the owner of Bleckie Investment and Real Estate Company. The company recently purchased four tracts of land in Holly Farms Estates and six tracts in Newburg Woods. The tracts are all equally desirable and sell for about the same amount.
   a. What is the probability that the next two tracts sold will be in Newburg Woods?
   b. What is the probability that of the next four sold at least one will be in Holly Farms?
   c. Are these events independent or dependent?

83. A computer password consists of four characters. The characters can be one of the 26 letters of the alphabet. Each character may be used more than once. How many different passwords are possible?

A SURVEY OF PROBABILITY CONCEPTS   171

84. A case of 24 cans contains 1 can that is contaminated. Three cans are to be chosen randomly for testing.
   a. How many different combinations of three cans could be selected?
   b. What is the probability that the contaminated can is selected for testing?

85. A puzzle in the newspaper presents a matching problem. The names of 10 U.S. presidents are listed in one column, and their vice presidents are listed in random order in the second column. The puzzle asks the reader to match each president with his vice president. If you make the matches randomly, how many matches are possible? What is the probability all 10 of your matches are correct?

86. Two components, A and B, operate in series. Being in series means that for the system to operate, both components A and B must work. Assume the two components are independent. What is the probability the system works under these conditions? The probability A works is .90 and the probability B functions is also .90.

87. Horwege Electronics Inc. purchases TV picture tubes from four different suppliers. Tyson Wholesale supplies 20% of the tubes, Fuji Importers 30%, Kirkpatricks 25%, and Parts Inc. 25%. Tyson Wholesale tends to have the best quality, as only 3% of its tubes arrive defective. Fuji Importers' tubes are 4% defective, Kirkpatricks' 7%, and Parts Inc.'s are 6.5% defective.
   a. What is the overall percent defective?
   b. A defective picture tube was discovered in the latest shipment. What is the probability that it came from Tyson Wholesale?

88. ABC Auto Insurance classifies drivers as good, medium, or poor risks. Drivers who apply to them for insurance fall into these three groups in the proportions 30%, 50%, and 20%, respectively. The probability a "good" driver will have an accident is .01, the probability a "medium" risk driver will have an accident is .03, and the probability a "poor" driver will have an accident is .10. The company sells Mr. Brophy an insurance policy and he has an accident. What is the probability Mr. Brophy is:
   a. A "good" driver?
   b. A "medium" risk driver?
   c. A "poor" driver?

89. You take a trip by air that involves three independent flights. If there is an 80% chance each specific leg of the trip is on time, what is the probability all three flights arrive on time?

90. The probability a D-Link network server is down is .05. If you have three independent servers, what is the probability that at least one of them is operational?

91. Twenty-two percent of all liquid crystal displays (LCDs) are manufactured by Samsung. What is the probability that in a collection of three independent LCD purchases, at least one is a Samsung?

DATA SET EXERCISES

(The data for these exercises are available at the text website: www.mhhe.com/lind16e.)

92. Refer to the Real Estate data, which report information on homes sold in the Goodyear, Arizona, area during the last year.
   a. Sort the data into a table that shows the number of homes that have a pool versus the number that don't have a pool in each of the five townships. If a home is selected at random, compute the following probabilities.
      1. The home is in Township 1 or has a pool.
      2. Given that it is in Township 3, that it has a pool.
      3. The home has a pool and is in Township 3.
   b. Sort the data into a table that shows the number of homes that have a garage attached versus those that don't in each of the five townships. If a home is selected at random, compute the following probabilities:
      1. The home has a garage attached.
      2. The home does not have a garage attached, given that it is in Township 5.
      3. The home has a garage attached and is in Township 3.
      4. The home does not have a garage attached or is in Township 2.

93. Refer to the Baseball 2012 data, which reports information on the 30 Major League Baseball teams for the 2012 season. Set up three variables:
   • Divide the teams into two groups, those that had a winning season and those that did not. That is, create a variable to count the teams that won 81 games or more, and those that won 80 or less.

- Create a new variable for attendance, using three categories: attendance less than 2.0 million, attendance of 2.0 million up to 3.0 million, and attendance of 3.0 million or more.
- Create a variable that shows the teams that play in a stadium less than 15 years old versus one that is 15 years old or more.

Answer the following questions.

a. Create a table that shows the number of teams with a winning season versus those with a losing season by the three categories of attendance. If a team is selected at random, compute the following probabilities:

    1. The team had a winning season.

    2. The team had a winning season or attendance of more than 3.0 million.

    3. The team had a winning season given attendance was more than 3.0 million.

    4. The team has a winning season and attracted fewer than 2.0 million fans.

b. Create a table that shows the number of teams with a winning season versus those that play in new or old stadiums. If a team is selected at random, compute the following probabilities:

    1. Selecting a team with a winning season.

    2. The likelihood of selecting a team with a winning record and playing in a new stadium.

    3. The team had a winning record or played in a new stadium.

94. Refer to the data on the school buses in the Buena School District. Set up a variable that divides the age of the buses into three groups: new (less than 5 years old), medium (5 but less than 10 years), and old (10 or more years). The median maintenance cost is $456. Based on this value, create a variable for those less than or equal to the median (low maintenance) and those more than the median (high maintenance). Finally, develop a table to show the relationship between maintenance cost and age of the bus.

a. What percentage of the buses are new?

b. What percentage of the new buses have low maintenance?

c. What percentage of the old buses have high maintenance?

d. Does maintenance cost seem to be related to the age of the bus? Hint: Compare the maintenance cost of the old buses with the cost of the new buses? Would you conclude maintenance cost is independent of the age?

Discrete Probability Distributions

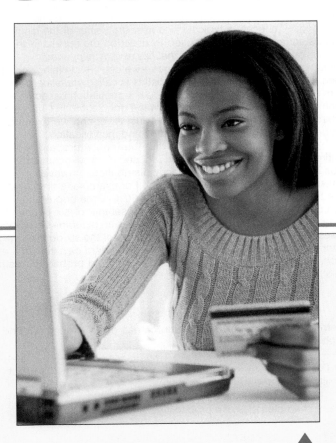

RECENT STATISTICS SUGGEST that 15% of those who visit a retail site on the Web make a purchase. A retailer wished to verify this claim. To do so, she selected a sample of 16 "hits" to her site and found that 4 had actually made a purchase. What is the likelihood of exactly four purchases? How many purchases should she expect? What is the likelihood that four or more "hits" result in a purchase? (See Exercise 49 and LO6-4.)

LEARNING OBJECTIVES

When you have completed this chapter, you will be able to:

LO6-1 Identify the characteristics of a probability distribution.

LO6-2 Distinguish between discrete and continuous random variables.

LO6-3 Compute the mean, variance, and standard deviation of a discrete probability distribution.

LO6-4 Explain the assumptions of the binomial distribution and apply it to calculate probabilities.

LO6-5 Explain the assumptions of the hypergeometric distribution and apply it to calculate probabilities.

LO6-6 Explain the assumptions of the Poisson distribution and apply it to calculate probabilities.

INTRODUCTION

Chapters 2 through 4 are devoted to descriptive statistics. We describe raw data by organizing the data into a frequency distribution and portraying the distribution in tables, graphs, and charts. Also, we compute a measure of location—such as the arithmetic mean, median, or mode—to locate a typical value near the center of the distribution. The range and the standard deviation are used to describe the spread in the data. These chapters focus on describing *something that has already happened.*

Starting with Chapter 5, the emphasis changes—we begin examining *something that could happen.* We note that this facet of statistics is called *statistical inference.* The objective is to make inferences (statements) about a population based on a number of observations, called a sample, selected from the population. In Chapter 5, we state that a probability is a value between 0 and 1 inclusive, and we examine how probabilities can be combined using rules of addition and multiplication.

This chapter begins the study of **probability distributions.** A probability distribution gives the entire range of values that can occur based on an experiment. A probability distribution is similar to a relative frequency distribution. However, instead of describing the past, it describes a likely future event. For example, a drug manufacturer may claim a treatment will cause weight loss for 80% of the population. A consumer protection agency may test the treatment on a sample of six people. If the manufacturer's claim is true, it is *almost impossible* to have an outcome where no one in the sample loses weight and it is *most likely* that five out of the six do lose weight.

In this chapter, we discuss the mean, variance, and standard deviation of a probability distribution. We also discuss three frequently occurring probability distributions: the binomial, hypergeometric, and Poisson.

LO6-1

Identify the characteristics of a probability distribution.

WHAT IS A PROBABILITY DISTRIBUTION?

A probability distribution shows the possible outcomes of an experiment and the probability of each of these outcomes.

> **PROBABILITY DISTRIBUTION** A listing of all the outcomes of an experiment and the probability associated with each outcome.

Below are the major characteristics of a probability distribution.

> **CHARACTERISTICS OF A PROBABILITY DISTRIBUTION**
>
> 1. The probability of a particular outcome is between 0 and 1 inclusive.
> 2. The outcomes are mutually exclusive.
> 3. The list of outcomes is exhaustive. So the sum of the probabilities of the outcomes is equal to 1.

How can we generate a probability distribution? The following example will explain.

EXAMPLE

Suppose we are interested in the number of heads showing face up on three tosses of a coin. This is the experiment. The possible results are zero heads, one head, two heads, and three heads. What is the probability distribution for the number of heads?

SOLUTION

There are eight possible outcomes. A tail might appear face up on the first toss, another tail on the second toss, and another tail on the third toss of the coin. Or we might get a tail, tail, and head, in that order. We use the multiplication formula for counting outcomes (5–8). There are (2)(2)(2) or 8 possible results. These results are shown on the next page.

| Possible | Coin Toss | | | Number of |
Result	First	Second	Third	Heads
1	T	T	T	0
2	T	T	H	1
3	T	H	T	1
4	T	H	H	2
5	H	T	T	1
6	H	T	H	2
7	H	H	T	2
8	H	H	H	3

Note that the outcome "zero heads" occurred only once, "one head" occurred three times, "two heads" occurred three times, and the outcome "three heads" occurred only once. That is, "zero heads" happened one out of eight times. Thus, the probability of zero heads is one-eighth, the probability of one head is three-eighths, and so on. The probability distribution is shown in Table 6–1. Because one of these outcomes must happen, the total of the probabilities of all possible events is 1.000. This is always true. The same information is shown in Chart 6–1.

TABLE 6–1 Probability Distribution for the Events of Zero, One, Two, and Three Heads Showing Face Up on Three Tosses of a Coin

Number of Heads, x	Probability of Outcome, $P(x)$
0	$\frac{1}{8} = .125$
1	$\frac{3}{8} = .375$
2	$\frac{3}{8} = .375$
3	$\frac{1}{8} = .125$
Total	$\frac{8}{8} = 1.000$

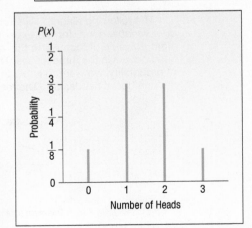

CHART 6–1 Graphical Presentation of the Number of Heads Resulting from Three Tosses of a Coin and the Corresponding Probability

176   CHAPTER 6

Refer to the coin-tossing example in Table 6–1. We write the probability of x as P(x). So the probability of zero heads is P(0 heads) = .125, and the probability of one head is P(1 head) = .375, and so forth. The sum of these mutually exclusive probabilities is 1; that is, from Table 6–1, .125 + .375 + .375 + .125 = 1.00.

SELF-REVIEW

6–1

The possible outcomes of an experiment involving the roll of a six-sided die are a one-spot, a two-spot, a three-spot, a four-spot, a five-spot, and a six-spot.
(a) Develop a probability distribution for the number of possible spots.
(b) Portray the probability distribution graphically.
(c) What is the sum of the probabilities?

LO6-2

Distinguish between discrete and continuous random variables.

RANDOM VARIABLES

In any experiment of chance, the outcomes occur randomly. So it is often called a *random variable.* For example, rolling a single die is an experiment: Any one of six possible outcomes can occur. Some experiments result in outcomes that are quantitative (such as dollars, weight, or number of children), and others result in qualitative outcomes (such as color or religious preference). Each value of the random variable is associated with a probability to indicate the chance of a particular outcome. A few examples will further illustrate what is meant by a **random variable.**

- If we count the number of employees absent from the day shift on Monday, the number might be 0, 1, 2, 3, . . . The number absent is the random variable.
- If we weigh four steel bars, the weights might be 2,492 pounds, 2,497 pounds, 2,506 pounds, and so on. The weight is the random variable.
- Other random variables might be the number of defective lightbulbs produced in an hour at the Cleveland Company Inc., the grade level (9, 10, 11, or 12) of the members of the St. James High School girls' basketball team, the number of runners in the 2013 New York City Marathon, and the daily number of drivers charged with driving under the influence of alcohol in Brazoria County, Texas, last month.

RANDOM VARIABLE A quantity resulting from an experiment that, by chance, can assume different values.

The following diagram illustrates the terms *experiment, outcome, event,* and *random variable.* First, for the experiment where a coin is tossed three times, there are eight possible outcomes. In this experiment, we are interested in the event that one head occurs in the three tosses. The random variable is the number of heads. In terms of probability, we want to know the probability of the event that the random variable, the number of heads, is 1. The result is P(1 head in 3 tosses) = .375.

Possible *outcomes* for three coin tosses

The *event* {one head} occurs and the *random variable* x = 1.

A random variable may be either *discrete* or *continuous.*

Discrete Random Variable

A discrete random variable can assume only a certain number of separated values. For example, the Bank of the Carolinas counts the number of credit cards carried for a group of customers. The data are summarized with the following frequency table.

Number of Credit Cards	Percent
0	3%
1	10%
2	18%
3	21%
4 or more	48%
Total	100%

In this frequency table, the number of cards carried is the discrete random variable.

> **DISCRETE RANDOM VARIABLE** A random variable that can assume only certain clearly separated values.

A discrete random variable can, in some cases, assume fractional or decimal values. These values must be separated—that is, have distance between them. As an example, the scores awarded by judges for technical competence and artistic form in figure skating are decimal values, such as 7.2, 8.9, and 9.7. Such values are discrete because there is distance between scores of, say, 8.3 and 8.4. A score cannot be 8.34 or 8.347, for example.

Continuous Random Variable

On the other hand, a random variable can be continuous. If we measure something such as the width of a room, the height of a person, or the pressure in an automobile tire, the variable is a *continuous random variable*. It can assume one of an infinitely large number of values, within certain limitations. As examples:

- The times of commercial flights between Atlanta and Los Angeles are 4.67 hours, 5.13 hours, and so on. The random variable is the time in hours.
- Tire pressure, measured in pounds per square inch (psi), for a new Chevy Trailblazer might be 32.78 psi, 31.62 psi, 33.07 psi, and so on. In other words, any values between 28 and 35 could reasonably occur. The random variable is the tire pressure.

As with discrete random variables, the likelihood of a continuous random variable can be summarized with a **probability distribution.** So what is the difference between a probability distribution and a random variable? A random variable reports the particular outcome of an experiment. A probability distribution reports all the possible outcomes as well as the corresponding probability.

The tools used, as well as the probability interpretations, are different for discrete and continuous probability distributions. This chapter is limited to the discussion and interpretation of discrete distributions. In the next chapter, we discuss continuous distributions. How do you tell the difference between the two types of distributions? Usually a discrete distribution is the result of counting something, such as:

- The number of heads appearing when a coin is tossed 3 times.
- The number of students earning an A in this class.
- The number of production employees absent from the second shift today.
- The number of 30-second commercials on NBC from 8 to 11 p.m. tonight.

178   CHAPTER 6

Continuous distributions are usually the result of some type of measurement, such as:

- The length of each song on the latest Linkin Park CD.
- The weight of each student in this class.
- The temperature outside as you are reading this book.
- The age in years of each of the 161,000 Ford Motor Company employees.

LO6-3

Compute the mean, variance, and standard deviation of a probability distribution.

THE MEAN, VARIANCE, AND STANDARD DEVIATION OF A DISCRETE PROBABILITY DISTRIBUTION

In Chapter 3, we discussed measures of location and variation for a frequency distribution. The mean reports the central location of the data, and the variance describes the spread in the data. In a similar fashion, a probability distribution is summarized by its mean and variance. We identify the mean of a probability distribution by the lowercase Greek letter mu (μ) and the standard deviation by the lowercase Greek letter sigma (σ).

Mean

The mean is a typical value used to represent the central location of a probability distribution. It also is the long-run average value of the random variable. The mean of a probability distribution is also referred to as its **expected value.** It is a weighted average where the possible values of a random variable are weighted by their corresponding probabilities of occurrence.

The mean of a discrete probability distribution is computed by the formula:

MEAN OF A PROBABILITY DISTRIBUTION	$\mu = \Sigma\,[xP(x)]$	**[6–1]**

where $P(x)$ is the probability of a particular value x. In other words, multiply each x value by its probability of occurrence, and then add these products.

Variance and Standard Deviation

The mean is a typical value used to summarize a discrete probability distribution. However, it does not describe the amount of spread (variation) in a distribution. The variance does this. The formula for the variance of a probability distribution is:

VARIANCE OF A PROBABILITY DISTRIBUTION	$\sigma^2 = \Sigma\,[(x - \mu)^2 P(x)]$	**[6–2]**

The computational steps are:

1. Subtract the mean from each value of the random variable, and square this difference.
2. Multiply each squared difference by its probability.
3. Sum the resulting products to arrive at the variance.

The standard deviation, σ, is found by taking the positive square root of σ^2; that is, $\sigma = \sqrt{\sigma^2}$.

An example will help explain the details of the calculation and interpretation of the mean and standard deviation of a probability distribution.

EXAMPLE

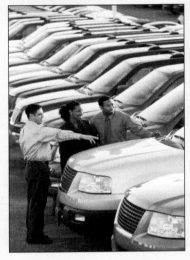

John Ragsdale sells new cars for Pelican Ford. John usually sells the largest number of cars on Saturday. He has developed the following probability distribution for the number of cars he expects to sell on a particular Saturday.

Number of Cars Sold, x	Probability, P(x)
0	.1
1	.2
2	.3
3	.3
4	.1
Total	1.0

1. What type of distribution is this?
2. On a typical Saturday, how many cars does John expect to sell?
3. What is the variance of the distribution?

SOLUTION

1. This is a discrete probability distribution for the random variable called "number of cars sold." Note that John expects to sell only within a certain range of cars; he does not expect to sell 5 cars or 50 cars. Further, he cannot sell half a car. He can sell only 0, 1, 2, 3, or 4 cars. Also, the outcomes are mutually exclusive—he cannot sell a total of both 3 and 4 cars on the same Saturday. The sum of the possible outcomes total 1. Hence, these circumstance qualify as a probability distribution.

2. The mean number of cars sold is computed by weighting the number of cars sold by the probability of selling that number and adding or summing the products, using formula (6–1):

$$\mu = \Sigma[xP(x)]$$

$$= 0(.1) + 1(.2) + 2(.3) + 3(.3) + 4(.1)$$

$$= 2.1$$

These calculations are summarized in the following table.

Number of Cars Sold, x	Probability, P(x)	x · P(x)
0	.1	0.0
1	.2	0.2
2	.3	0.6
3	.3	0.9
4	.1	0.4
Total	1.0	$\mu = 2.1$

How do we interpret a mean of 2.1? This value indicates that, over a large number of Saturdays, John Ragsdale expects to sell a mean of 2.1 cars a day. Of course, it is not possible for him to sell *exactly* 2.1 cars on any particular Saturday. However, the expected value can be used to predict the arithmetic mean number of cars sold on Saturdays in the long run. For example, if John works 50 Saturdays during a year, he can expect to sell (50) (2.1) or 105 cars just on Saturdays. Thus, the mean is sometimes called the expected value.

3. The following table illustrates the steps to calculate the variance using formula (6–2). The first two columns repeat the probability distribution. In column three, the mean is subtracted from each value of the random variable. In column four, the differences from column three are squared. In the fifth column, each squared difference in column four is multiplied by the corresponding probability. The variance is the sum of the values in column five.

Number of Cars Sold, x	Probability, $P(x)$	$(x - \mu)$	$(x - \mu)^2$	$(x - \mu)^2 P(x)$
0	.1	0 − 2.1	4.41	0.441
1	.2	1 − 2.1	1.21	0.242
2	.3	2 − 2.1	0.01	0.003
3	.3	3 − 2.1	0.81	0.243
4	.1	4 − 2.1	3.61	0.361
				$\sigma^2 = 1.290$

Recall that the standard deviation, σ, is the positive square root of the variance. In this example, $\sqrt{\sigma^2} = \sqrt{1.290} = 1.136$ cars. How do we apply a standard deviation of 1.136 cars? If salesperson Rita Kirsch also sold a mean of 2.1 cars on Saturdays, and the standard deviation in her sales was 1.91 cars, we would conclude that there is more variability in the Saturday sales of Ms. Kirsch than in those of Mr. Ragsdale (because 1.91 > 1.136).

SELF-REVIEW

6–2

The Pizza Palace offers three sizes of cola. The smallest size sells for $0.80, the medium for $0.90, and the large for $1.20. Thirty percent of the drinks sold are small, 50% are medium, and 20% are large. Create a probability distribution for the random variable price and answer the following questions.

(a) Is this a discrete probability distribution? Indicate why or why not.
(b) Compute the mean amount charged for a cola.
(c) What is the variance in the amount charged for a cola? The standard deviation?

EXERCISES

For **DATA FILE**, please visit www.mhhe.com/lind16e

1. Compute the mean and variance of the following discrete probability distribution.

x	$P(x)$
0	.2
1	.4
2	.3
3	.1

For **DATA FILE**, please visit www.mhhe.com/lind16e

2. Compute the mean and variance of the following discrete probability distribution.

x	$P(x)$
2	.5
8	.3
10	.2

DISCRETE PROBABILITY DISTRIBUTIONS   181

3. Compute the mean and variance of the following probability distribution.

x	P(x)
5	.1
10	.3
15	.2
20	.4

4. Which of these variables are discrete and which are continuous random variables?
   a. The number of new accounts established by a salesperson in a year.
   b. The time between customer arrivals to a bank ATM.
   c. The number of customers in Big Nick's barber shop.
   d. The amount of fuel in your car's gas tank.
   e. The number of minorities on a jury.
   f. The outside temperature today.

For **DATA FILE**, please visit www.mhhe.com/lind16e

5. The information below is the number of daily emergency service calls made by the volunteer ambulance service of Walterboro, South Carolina, for the last 50 days. To explain, there were 22 days on which there were two emergency calls, and 9 days on which there were three emergency calls.

Number of Calls	Frequency
0	8
1	10
2	22
3	9
4	1
Total	50

   a. Convert this information on the number of calls to a probability distribution.
   b. Is this an example of a discrete or continuous probability distribution?
   c. What is the mean number of emergency calls per day?
   d. What is the standard deviation of the number of calls made daily?

For **DATA FILE**, please visit www.mhhe.com/lind16e

6. The director of admissions at Kinzua University in Nova Scotia estimated the distribution of student admissions for the fall semester on the basis of past experience. What is the expected number of admissions for the fall semester? Compute the variance and the standard deviation of the number of admissions.

Admissions	Probability
1,000	.6
1,200	.3
1,500	.1

For **DATA FILE**, please visit www.mhhe.com/lind16e

7. Belk Department Store is having a special sale this weekend. Customers charging purchases of more than $50 to their Belk credit card will be given a special Belk Lottery card. The customer will scratch off the card, which will indicate the amount to be taken off the total amount of the purchase. Listed below are the amount of the prize and the percent of the time that amount will be deducted from the total amount of the purchase.

Prize Amount	Probability
$ 10	.50
25	.40
50	.08
100	.02

   a. What is the mean amount deducted from the total purchase amount?
   b. What is the standard deviation of the amount deducted from the total purchase?

182   CHAPTER 6

For **DATA FILE**, please visit
www.mhhe.com/lind16e

8. The Downtown Parking Authority of Tampa, Florida, reported the following information for a sample of 250 customers on the number of hours cars are parked and the amount they are charged.

Number of Hours	Frequency	Amount Charged
1	20	$ 3.00
2	38	6.00
3	53	9.00
4	45	12.00
5	40	14.00
6	13	16.00
7	5	18.00
8	36	20.00
	250	

a. Convert the information on the number of hours parked to a probability distribution. Is this a discrete or a continuous probability distribution?
b. Find the mean and the standard deviation of the number of hours parked. How would you answer the question: How long is a typical customer parked?
c. Find the mean and the standard deviation of the amount charged.

LO6-4
Explain the assumptions of the binomial distribution and apply it to calculate probabilities.

BINOMIAL PROBABILITY DISTRIBUTION

The **binomial probability distribution** is a widely occurring discrete probability distribution. To describe experimental outcomes with a binomial distribution, there are four requirements. The first requirement is there are only two possible outcomes on a particular experimental trial. For example, on a test, a true/false question is either true or false. In a resort, a housekeeping supervisor reviews an employee's work and evaluates it as acceptable or unacceptable. A key characteristic of the two outcomes is that they must be mutually exclusive. This means that the answer to a true/false question must be either true or false but cannot be both true and false at the same time. Another example is the outcome of a sales call. Either a customer purchases or does not purchase the product, but the sale cannot result in both outcomes. Frequently, we refer to the two possible outcomes of a binomial experiment as a "success" and a "failure." However, this distinction does not imply that one outcome is good and the other is bad, only that there are two mutually exclusive outcomes.

The second binomial requirement is that the random variable is the number of successes for a fixed and known number of trials. For example, we flip a coin five times and count the number of times a head appears in the five flips, we randomly select 10 employees and count the number who are older than 50 years of age, or we randomly select 20 boxes of Kellogg's Raisin Bran and count the number that weigh more than the amount indicated on the package. In each example, we count the number of successes from the fixed number of trials.

A third requirement is that we know the probability of a success and it is the same for each trial. Three examples are:

- For a test with 10 true/false questions, we know there are 10 trials and the probability of correctly guessing the answer for any of the 10 trials is 0.5. Or, for a test with 20 multiple-choice questions with four options and only one correct answer, we know that there are 20 trials and the probability of randomly guessing the correct answer for each of the 20 trials is 0.25.

- Bones Albaugh is a Division I college basketball player who makes 70% of his foul shots. If he has five opportunities in tonight's game, the likelihood he will be successful on each of the five attempts is 0.70.
- In a recent poll, 18% of adults indicated a Snickers bar was their favorite candy bar. We select a sample of 15 adults and ask each for his or her favorite candy bar. The likelihood a Snickers bar is the answer for each adult is 0.18.

The final requirement of a binomial probability distribution is that each trial is *independent* of any other trial. Independent means there is no pattern to the trials. The outcome of a particular trial does not affect the outcome of any other trial. Two examples are:

- A young family has two children, both boys. The probability of a third birth being a boy is still .50. That is, the gender of the third child is independent of the gender of the other two.
- Suppose 20% of the patients served in the emergency room at Waccamaw Hospital do not have insurance. If the second patient served on the afternoon shift today did not have insurance, that does not affect the probability the third, the tenth, or any of the other patients will or will not have insurance.

BINOMIAL PROBABILITY EXPERIMENT
1. An outcome on each trial of an experiment is classified into one of two mutually exclusive categories—a success or a failure.
2. The random variable is the number of successes in a fixed number of trials.
3. The probability of success is the same for each trial.
4. The trials are independent, meaning that the outcome of one trial does not affect the outcome of any other trial.

How Is a Binomial Probability Computed?

To construct a particular binomial probability, we use (1) the number of trials and (2) the probability of success on each trial. For example, if the Hannah Landscaping Company plants 10 Norfolk pine trees today knowing that 90% of these trees survive, we can compute the binomial probability that exactly 8 trees survive. In this case the number of trials is the 10 trees, the probability of success is .90, and the number of successes is eight. In fact, we can compute a binomial probability for any number of successes from 0 to 10 surviving trees.

A binomial probability is computed by the formula:

BINOMIAL PROBABILITY FORMULA $P(x) = {}_nC_x \pi^x(1 - \pi)^{n-x}$ **[6–3]**

---

where:
    C denotes a combination.
    n is the number of trials.
    x is the random variable defined as the number of successes.
    π is the probability of a success on each trial.

We use the Greek letter π (pi) to denote a binomial population parameter. Do not confuse it with the mathematical constant 3.1416.

EXAMPLE

There are five flights daily from Pittsburgh via US Airways into the Bradford Regional Airport in Bradford, Pennsylvania. Suppose the probability that any flight arrives late is .20. What is the probability that none of the flights are late today? What is the probability that exactly one of the flights is late today?

SOLUTION

We can use formula (6–3). The probability that a particular flight is late is .20, so let $\pi = .20$. There are five flights, so $n = 5$, and X, the random variable, refers to the number of successes. In this case, a "success" is a flight that arrives late. Because there are no late arrivals, $x = 0$.

$$P(0) = {}_nC_x(\pi)^x(1 - \pi)^{n-x}$$
$$= {}_5C_0(.20)^0(1 - .20)^{5-0} = (1)(1)(.3277) = .3277$$

The probability that exactly one of the five flights will arrive late today is .4096, found by

$$P(1) = {}_nC_x(\pi)^x(1 - \pi)^{n-x}$$
$$= {}_5C_1(.20)^1(1 - .20)^{5-1} = (5)(.20)(.4096) = .4096$$

The entire binomial probability distribution with $\pi = .20$ and $n = 5$ is shown in the following bar chart. We observe that the probability of exactly three late flights is .0512 and from the bar chart that the distribution of the number of late arrivals is positively skewed.

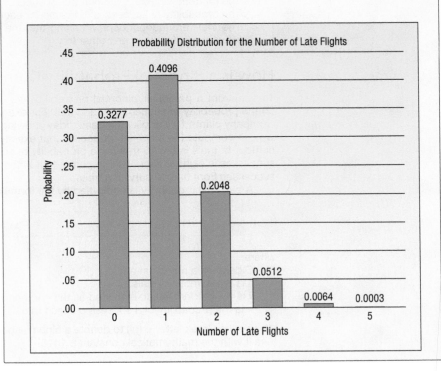

DISCRETE PROBABILITY DISTRIBUTIONS 185

The mean (μ) and the variance (σ^2) of a binomial distribution are computed in a "shortcut" fashion by:

MEAN OF A BINOMIAL DISTRIBUTION	$\mu = n\pi$	[6–4]

VARIANCE OF A BINOMIAL DISTRIBUTION	$\sigma^2 = n\pi(1 - \pi)$	[6–5]

For the example regarding the number of late flights, recall that $\pi = .20$ and $n = 5$. Hence:

$$\mu = n\pi = (5)(.20) = 1.0$$
$$\sigma^2 = n\pi(1 - \pi) = 5(.20)(1 - .20) = .80$$

The mean of 1.0 and the variance of .80 can be verified from formulas (6–1) and (6–2). The probability distribution from the bar chart on the previous page and the details of the calculations are shown below.

Number of Late Flights, x	$P(x)$	$xP(x)$	$x - \mu$	$(x - \mu)^2$	$(x - \mu)^2 P(x)$
0	0.3277	0.0000	−1	1	0.3277
1	0.4096	0.4096	0	0	0
2	0.2048	0.4096	1	1	0.2048
3	0.0512	0.1536	2	4	0.2048
4	0.0064	0.0256	3	9	0.0576
5	0.0003	0.0015	4	16	0.0048
		$\mu = 1.0000$			$\sigma^2 = 0.7997$

Binomial Probability Tables

Formula (6–3) can be used to build a binomial probability distribution for any value of n and π. However, for a larger n, the calculations take more time. For convenience, the tables in Appendix B.1 show the result of using the formula for various values of n and π. Table 6–2 shows part of Appendix B.1 for $n = 6$ and various values of π.

TABLE 6–2 Binomial Probabilities for $n = 6$ and Selected Values of π

	\multicolumn{11}{c}{$n = 6$ Probability}
$x\backslash\pi$	.05	.1	.2	.3	.4	.5	.6	.7	.8	.9	.95
---	---	---	---	---	---	---	---	---	---	---	---
0	.735	.531	.262	.118	.047	.016	.004	.001	.000	.000	.000
1	.232	.354	.393	.303	.187	.094	.037	.010	.002	.000	.000
2	.031	.098	.246	.324	.311	.234	.138	.060	.015	.001	.000
3	.002	.015	.082	.185	.276	.313	.276	.185	.082	.015	.002
4	.000	.001	.015	.060	.138	.234	.311	.324	.246	.098	.031
5	.000	.000	.002	.010	.037	.094	.187	.303	.393	.354	.232
6	.000	.000	.000	.001	.004	.016	.047	.118	.262	.531	.735

E X A M P L E

In the Southwest, 5% of all cell phone calls are dropped. What is the probability that out of six randomly selected calls, none was dropped? Exactly one? Exactly two? Exactly three? Exactly four? Exactly five? Exactly six out of six?

186   CHAPTER 6

SOLUTION

The binomial conditions are met: (a) there are only two possible outcomes (a particular call is either dropped or not dropped), (b) there are a fixed number of trials (6), (c) there is a constant probability of success (.05), and (d) the trials are independent.

Refer to Table 6–2 on the previous page for the probability of exactly zero dropped calls. Go down the left margin to an x of 0. Now move horizontally to the column headed by a π of .05 to find the probability. It is .735. The values in Table 6–2 are rounded to three decimal places.

The probability of exactly one dropped call in a sample of six calls is .232. The complete binomial probability distribution for $n = 6$ and $\pi = .05$ is:

Number of Dropped Calls, x	Probability of Occurrence, $P(x)$	Number of Dropped Calls, x	Probability of Occurrence, $P(x)$
0	.735	4	.000
1	.232	5	.000
2	.031	6	.000
3	.002		

Of course, there is a slight chance of getting exactly five dropped calls out of six random selections. It is .00000178, found by inserting the appropriate values in the binomial formula:

$$P(5) = {}_6C_5(.05)^5(.95)^1 = (6)(.05)^5(.95) = .00000178$$

For six out of the six, the exact probability is .000000016. Thus, the probability is very small that five or six calls will be dropped in six trials.

We can compute the mean or expected value of the distribution of the number defective:

$$\mu = n\pi = (6)(.05) = 0.30$$
$$\sigma^2 = n\pi(1 - \pi) = 6(.05)(.95) = 0.285$$

SELF-REVIEW

6–3

Ninety-five percent of the employees at the J. M. Smucker Company plant on Laskey Road have their bimonthly wages sent directly to their bank by electronic funds transfer. This is also called direct deposit. Suppose we select a random sample of seven employees.
(a)   Does this situation fit the assumptions of the binomial distribution?
(b)   What is the probability that all seven employees use direct deposit?
(c)   Use formula (6–3) to determine the exact probability that four of the seven sampled employees use direct deposit.
(d)   Use Excel to verify your answers to parts (b) and (c).

Appendix B.1 is limited. It gives probabilities for n values from 1 to 15 and π values of .05, .10, . . . , .90, and .95. A software program can generate the probabilities for a specified number of successes, given n and π. The Excel output on the next page shows the probability when $n = 40$ and $\pi = .09$. Note that the number of successes stops at 15 because the probabilities for 16 to 40 are very close to 0. The instructions are detailed in the Software Commands in Appendix C.

DISCRETE PROBABILITY DISTRIBUTIONS 187

	A	B
1	Success	Probability
2	0	0.0230
3	1	0.0910
4	2	0.1754
5	3	0.2198
6	4	0.2011
7	5	0.1432
8	6	0.0826
9	7	0.0397
10	8	0.0162
11	9	0.0057
12	10	0.0017
13	11	0.0005
14	12	0.0001
15	13	0.0000
16	14	0.0000
17	15	0.0000

Several additional points should be made regarding the binomial probability distribution.

1. If *n* remains the same but π increases from .05 to .95, the shape of the distribution changes. Look at Table 6–3 and Chart 6–2. The distribution for a π of .05 is positively skewed. As π approaches .50, the distribution becomes symmetrical. As π goes beyond .50 and moves toward .95, the probability distribution becomes negatively skewed. Table 6–3 highlights probabilities for *n* = 10 and a π of .05, .10, .20, .50, and .70. The graphs of these probability distributions are shown in Chart 6–2.

TABLE 6–3 Probability of 0, 1, 2, . . . Successes for a π of .05, .10, .20, .50, and .70, and an *n* of 10

$x\backslash\pi$	.05	.1	.2	.3	.4	.5	.6	.7	.8	.9	.95
0	.599	.349	.107	.028	.006	.001	.000	.000	.000	.000	.000
1	.315	.387	.268	.121	.040	.010	.002	.000	.000	.000	.000
2	.075	.194	.302	.233	.121	.044	.011	.001	.000	.000	.000
3	.010	.057	.201	.267	.215	.117	.042	.009	.001	.000	.000
4	.001	.011	.088	.200	.251	.205	.111	.037	.006	.000	.000
5	.000	.001	.026	.103	.201	.246	.201	.103	.026	.011	.001
6	.000	.000	.006	.037	.111	.205	.251	.200	.088	.011	.001
7	.000	.000	.001	.009	.042	.117	.215	.267	.201	.057	.010
8	.000	.000	.000	.001	.011	.044	.121	.233	.302	.194	.075
9	.000	.000	.000	.000	.002	.010	.040	.121	.268	.387	.315
10	.000	.000	.000	.000	.000	.001	.006	.028	.107	.349	.599

CHART 6–2 Graphing the Binomial Probability Distribution for a π of .05, .10, .20, .50, and .70, and an *n* of 10

2. If π, the probability of success, remains the same but *n* becomes larger, the shape of the binomial distribution becomes more symmetrical. Chart 6–3 shows a situation where π remains constant at .10 but *n* increases from 7 to 40.

CHART 6–3 Chart Representing the Binomial Probability Distribution for a π of .10 and an n of 7, 12, 20, and 40

EXERCISES ▼

9. In a binomial situation, $n = 4$ and $\pi = .25$. Determine the probabilities of the following events using the binomial formula.
   a. $x = 2$
   b. $x = 3$

10. In a binomial situation, $n = 5$ and $\pi = .40$. Determine the probabilities of the following events using the binomial formula.
    a. $x = 1$
    b. $x = 2$

11. Assume a binomial distribution where $n = 3$ and $\pi = .60$.
    a. Refer to Appendix B.1, and list the probabilities for values of x from 0 to 3.
    b. Determine the mean and standard deviation of the distribution from the general definitions given in formulas (6–1) and (6–2).

12. Assume a binomial distribution where $n = 5$ and $\pi = .30$.
    a. Refer to Appendix B.1 and list the probabilities for values of x from 0 to 5.
    b. Determine the mean and standard deviation of the distribution from the general definitions given in formulas (6–1) and (6–2).

13. An American Society of Investors survey found 30% of individual investors have used a discount broker. In a random sample of nine individuals, what is the probability:
    a. Exactly two of the sampled individuals have used a discount broker?
    b. Exactly four of them have used a discount broker?
    c. None of them has used a discount broker?

14. The U.S. Postal Service reports 95% of first-class mail within the same city is delivered within 2 days of the time of mailing. Six letters are randomly sent to different locations.
    a. What is the probability that all six arrive within 2 days?
    b. What is the probability that exactly five arrive within 2 days?
    c. Find the mean number of letters that will arrive within 2 days.
    d. Compute the variance and standard deviation of the number that will arrive within 2 days.

For **DATA FILE**, please visit www.mhhe.com/lind16e

15. Industry standards suggest that 10% of new vehicles require warranty service within the first year. Jones Nissan in Sumter, South Carolina, sold 12 Nissans yesterday.
    a. What is the probability that none of these vehicles requires warranty service?
    b. What is the probability exactly one of these vehicles requires warranty service?
    c. Determine the probability that exactly two of these vehicles require warranty service.
    d. Compute the mean and standard deviation of this probability distribution.

For **DATA FILE**, please visit www.mhhe.com/lind16e

For **DATA FILE**, please visit
www.mhhe.com/lind16e

16. A telemarketer makes six phone calls per hour and is able to make a sale on 30% of these contacts. During the next 2 hours, find:
 a. The probability of making exactly four sales.
 b. The probability of making no sales.
 c. The probability of making exactly two sales.
 d. The mean number of sales in the 2-hour period.

For **DATA FILE**, please visit
www.mhhe.com/lind16e

17. A recent survey by the American Accounting Association revealed 23% of students graduating with a major in accounting select public accounting. Suppose we select a sample of 15 recent graduates.
 a. What is the probability two select public accounting?
 b. What is the probability five select public accounting?
 c. How many graduates would you expect to select public accounting?

For **DATA FILE**, please visit
www.mhhe.com/lind16e

18. It is reported that 16% of American households use a cell phone exclusively for their telephone service. In a sample of eight households,
 a. Find the probability that no household uses a cell phone as their exclusive telephone service.
 b. Find the probability that exactly 5 households exclusively use a cell phone for telephone service.
 c. Find the mean number of households exclusively using cell phones.

Cumulative Binomial Probability Distributions

We may wish to know the probability of correctly guessing the answers to 6 *or more* true/false questions out of 10. Or we may be interested in the probability of *selecting less than two* defectives at random from production during the previous hour. In these cases, we need cumulative frequency distributions similar to the ones developed in Chapter 2. See page 37. The following example will illustrate.

EXAMPLE

A study by the Illinois Department of Transportation concluded that 76.2% of front seat occupants used seat belts. That is, both occupants of the front seat were using their seat belts. Suppose we decide to compare that information with current usage. We select a sample of 12 vehicles.

1. What is the probability the front seat occupants in exactly 7 of the 12 vehicles selected are wearing seat belts?
2. What is the probability the front seat occupants in at least 7 of the 12 vehicles are wearing seat belts?

SOLUTION

This situation meets the binomial requirements.

- In a particular vehicle, both the front seat occupants are either wearing seat belts or they are not. There are only two possible outcomes.
- There are a fixed number of trials, 12 in this case, because 12 vehicles are checked.
- The probability of a "success" (occupants wearing seat belts) is the same from one vehicle to the next: 76.2%.
- The trials are independent. If the fourth vehicle selected in the sample has all the occupants wearing their seat belts, this does not have any effect on the results for the fifth or tenth vehicle.

To find the likelihood the occupants of *exactly* 7 of the sampled vehicles are wearing seat belts, we use formula (6–3). In this case, $n = 12$ and $\pi = .762$.

$$P(x = 7) = {}_{12}C_7(.762)^7(1 - .762)^{12-7} = 792(.149171)(.000764) = .0902$$

So we conclude the likelihood that the occupants of exactly 7 of the 12 sampled vehicles will be wearing their seat belts is about 9%. We often use, as we did in this equation, a bar "|" to mean "given that." So in this equation we want to know the probability that x is equal to 7 "given that the number of trials is 12 and the probability of a success is .762."

To find the probability that the occupants in seven or more of the vehicles will be wearing seat belts, we use formula (6–3) from this chapter as well as the special rule of addition from the previous chapter. See formula (5–2) on page 140.

Because the events are mutually exclusive (meaning that a particular sample of 12 vehicles cannot have both a *total* of 7 and a *total* of 8 vehicles where the occupants are wearing seat belts), we find the probability of 7 vehicles where the occupants are wearing seat belts, the probability of 8, and so on up to the probability that occupants of all 12 sample vehicles are wearing seat belts. The probability of each of these outcomes is then totaled.

$$P(x \geq 7) = P(x = 7) + P(x = 8) + P(x = 9) + P(x = 10) + P(x = 11) + P(x = 12)$$

$$= .0902 + .1805 + .2569 + .2467 + .1436 + .0383$$

$$= .9562$$

So the probability of selecting 12 cars and finding that the occupants of 7 or more vehicles were wearing seat belts is .9562. This information is shown on the following Excel spreadsheet. There is a slight difference in the software answer due to rounding. The Excel commands are similar to those detailed in the Software Commands in Appendix C.

Cumulative Binomial.xlsx			
	A	B	C	D
1	Success	Probability		
2	0	0.0000		
3	1	0.0000		
4	2	0.0000		
5	3	0.0002		
6	4	0.0017		
7	5	0.0088		
8	6	0.0329		
9	7	0.0902		
10	8	0.1805		
11	9	0.2569	Sum of	
12	10	0.2467	Probabilities	
13	11	0.1436	for 7 or more	
14	12	0.0383	successes	
15		0.9563		

SELF-REVIEW

6–4

A recent study revealed that 40% of women in the San Diego metropolitan area who work full time also volunteer in the community. Suppose we randomly select eight women in the San Diego area.
(a)   What are the values for n and π?
(b)   What is the probability exactly three of the women volunteer in the community?
(c)   What is the probability at least one of the women volunteers in the community?

EXERCISES

▼

19. In a binomial distribution, $n = 8$ and $\pi = .30$. Find the probabilities of the following events.
   a. $x = 2$.
   b. $x \leq 2$ (the probability that x is equal to or less than 2).
   c. $x \geq 3$ (the probability that x is equal to or greater than 3).
20. In a binomial distribution, $n = 12$ and $\pi = .60$. Find the following probabilities.
   a. $x = 5$.
   b. $x \leq 5$.
   c. $x \geq 6$.

For **DATA FILE**, please visit www.mhhe.com/lind16e

For **DATA FILE**, please visit www.mhhe.com/lind16e

For **DATA FILE**, please visit www.mhhe.com/lind16e

For **DATA FILE**, please visit www.mhhe.com/lind16e

21. In a recent study, 90% of the homes in the United States were found to have large-screen TVs. In a sample of nine homes, what is the probability that:
    a. All nine have large-screen TVs?
    b. Less than five have large-screen TVs?
    c. More than five have large-screen TVs?
    d. At least seven homes have large-screen TVs?
22. A manufacturer of window frames knows from long experience that 5% of the production will have some type of minor defect that will require an adjustment. What is the probability that in a sample of 20 window frames:
    a. None will need adjustment?
    b. At least one will need adjustment?
    c. More than two will need adjustment?
23. The speed with which utility companies can resolve problems is very important. GTC, the Georgetown Telephone Company, reports it can resolve customer problems the same day they are reported in 70% of the cases. Suppose the 15 cases reported today are representative of all complaints.
    a. How many of the problems would you expect to be resolved today? What is the standard deviation?
    b. What is the probability 10 of the problems can be resolved today?
    c. What is the probability 10 or 11 of the problems can be resolved today?
    d. What is the probability more than 10 of the problems can be resolved today?
24. It is asserted that 80% of the cars approaching an individual toll booth in New Jersey are equipped with an E-ZPass transponder. Find the probability that in a sample of six cars:
    a. All six will have the transponder.
    b. At least three will have the transponder.
    c. None will have a transponder.

LO6-5
Explain the assumptions of the hypergeometric distribution and apply it to calculate probabilities.

HYPERGEOMETRIC PROBABILITY DISTRIBUTION

For the binomial distribution to be applied, the probability of a success must stay the same for each trial. For example, the probability of guessing the correct answer to a true/false question is .50. This probability remains the same for each question on an examination. Likewise, suppose that 40% of the registered voters in a precinct are Republicans. If 27 registered voters are selected at random, the probability of choosing a Republican on the first selection is .40. The chance of choosing a Republican on the next selection is also .40, assuming that the sampling is done *with replacement,* meaning that the person selected is put back in the population before the next person is selected.

Most sampling, however, is done *without replacement.* Thus, if the population is small, the probability of a success will change for each observation. For example, if the population consists of 20 items, the probability of selecting a particular item from that population is 1/20. If the sampling is done without replacement, after the first selection there are only 19 items remaining; the probability of selecting a particular item on the second selection is only 1/19. For the third selection, the probability is 1/18, and so on. This assumes that the population is **finite**—that is, the number in the population is known and relatively small in number. Examples of a finite population are 2,842 Republicans in the precinct, 9,241 applications for medical school, and the 18 2014 Dakota 4x4 Crew Cabs at Helfman Dodge Chrysler Jeep in Houston, TX.

Recall that one of the criteria for the binomial distribution is that the probability of success remains the same from trial to trial. Because the probability of success does not remain the same from trial to trial when sampling is from a relatively small population without replacement, the binomial distribution should not be used. Instead, the **hypergeometric distribution** is applied. Therefore, (1) if a sample is selected from a finite population without replacement and (2) if the size of the sample *n* is more than

192

CHAPTER 6

5% of the size of the population *N*, then the hypergeometric distribution is used to determine the probability of a specified number of successes or failures. It is especially appropriate when the size of the population is small.

The formula for the hypergeometric distribution is:

HYPERGEOMETRIC DISTRIBUTION	$P(x) = \dfrac{(_SC_x)(_{N-S}C_{n-x})}{_NC_n}$	[6–6]

where:
  N is the size of the population.
  S is the number of successes in the population.
  x is the number of successes in the sample. It may be 0, 1, 2, 3, ...
  n is the size of the sample or the number of trials.
  C is the symbol for a combination.

In summary, a hypergeometric probability distribution has these characteristics:

HYPERGEOMETRIC PROBABILITY EXPERIMENT
1. An outcome on each trial of an experiment is classified into one of two mutually exclusive categories—a success or a failure.
2. The random variable is the number of successes in a fixed number of trials.
3. The trials are *not independent*.
4. We assume that we sample from a finite population without replacement and $n/N > 0.05$. So, the probability of a success *changes* for each trial.

The following example illustrates the details of determining a probability using the hypergeometric distribution.

EXAMPLE

PlayTime Toys Inc. employs 50 people in the Assembly Department. Forty of the employees belong to a union and 10 do not. Five employees are selected at random to form a committee to meet with management regarding shift starting times. What is the probability that four of the five selected for the committee belong to a union?

SOLUTION

The population in this case is the 50 Assembly Department employees. An employee can be selected for the committee only once. Hence, the sampling is done without replacement. Thus, the probability of selecting a union employee, for example, changes from one trial to the next. The hypergeometric distribution is appropriate for determining the probability. In this problem,

  N is 50, the number of employees.
  S is 40, the number of union employees.
  x is 4, the number of union employees selected.
  n is 5, the number of employees selected.

DISCRETE PROBABILITY DISTRIBUTIONS

> We wish to find the probability 4 of the 5 committee members belong to a union. Inserting these values into formula (6–6):
>
> $$P(4) = \frac{(_{40}C_4)(_{50-40}C_{5-4})}{_{50}C_5} = \frac{(91,390)(10)}{2,118,760} = .431$$
>
> Thus, the probability of selecting 5 assembly workers at random from the 50 workers and finding 4 of the 5 are union members is .431.

Table 6–4 shows the hypergeometric probabilities of finding 0, 1, 2, 3, 4, and 5 union members on the committee.

TABLE 6–4 Hypergeometric Probabilities ($n = 5$, $N = 50$, and $S = 40$) for the Number of Union Members on the Committee

Union Members	Probability
0	.000
1	.004
2	.044
3	.210
4	.431
5	.311
	1.000

In order for you to compare the two probability distributions, Table 6–5 shows the hypergeometric and binomial probabilities for the PlayTime Toys Inc. example. Because 40 of the 50 Assembly Department employees belong to the union, we let $\pi = .80$ for the binomial distribution. The binomial probabilities for Table 6–5 come from the binomial distribution with $n = 5$ and $\pi = .80$.

TABLE 6–5 Hypergeometric and Binomial Probabilities for PlayTime Toys Inc. Assembly Department

Number of Union Members on Committee	Hypergeometric Probability, $P(x)$	Binomial Probability ($n = 5$ and $\pi = .80$)
0	.000	.000
1	.004	.006
2	.044	.051
3	.210	.205
4	.431	.410
5	.311	.328
	1.000	1.000

When the binomial requirement of a constant probability of success cannot be met, the hypergeometric distribution should be used. However, as Table 6–5 shows, under certain conditions the results of the binomial distribution can be used to approximate the hypergeometric. This leads to a rule of thumb:

> If selected items are not returned to the population, the binomial distribution can be used to closely approximate the hypergeometric distribution when $n < .05N$. In words, the binomial will suffice if the sample is less than 5% of the population.

	A	B
1	Union Members	Probability
2	0	0.000
3	1	0.004
4	2	0.044
5	3	0.210
6	4	0.431
7	5	0.311

A hypergeometric distribution can be created using Excel. See the output on the left. The necessary steps are given in Appendix C in the back of the text.

194   CHAPTER 6

SELF-REVIEW

6–5

Horwege Discount Brokers plans to hire five new financial analysts this year. There is a pool of 12 approved applicants, and George Horwege, the owner, decides to randomly select those who will be hired. There are eight men and four women among the approved applicants. What is the probability that three of the five hired are men?

EXERCISES

25. A CD contains 10 songs; 6 are classical and 4 are rock and roll. In a sample of three songs, what is the probability that exactly two are classical? Assume the samples are drawn without replacement.

26. A population consists of 15 items, 10 of which are acceptable. In a sample of four items, what is the probability that exactly three are acceptable? Assume the samples are drawn without replacement.

27. The Riverton Branch of the National Bank of Wyoming has 10 real estate loans over $1,000,000. Of these 10 loans, 3 are "underwater." A loan is underwater if the amount of the loan is greater than the value of the property. The chief loan officer decided to randomly select two of these loans to determine if they met all banking standards. What is the probability that neither of the selected loans is underwater?

28. The Computer Systems Department has eight faculty, six of whom are tenured. Dr. Vonder, the chairman, wants to establish a committee of three department faculty members to review the curriculum. If she selects the committee at random:
    a. What is the probability all members of the committee are tenured?
    b. What is the probability that at least one member is not tenured? (Hint: For this question, use the complement rule.)

29. Keith's Florists has 15 delivery trucks, used mainly to deliver flowers and flower arrangements in the Greenville, South Carolina, area. Of these 15 trucks, 6 have brake problems. A sample of five trucks is randomly selected. What is the probability that two of those tested have defective brakes?

30. The game called Lotto sponsored by the Louisiana Lottery Commission pays its largest prize when a contestant matches all 6 of the 40 possible numbers. Assume there are 40 ping-pong balls each with a single number between 1 and 40. Any number appears only once, and the winning balls are selected without replacement.
    a. The commission reports that the probability of matching all the numbers are 1 in 3,838,380. What is this in terms of probability?
    b. Use the hypergeometric formula to find this probability.
    The lottery commission also pays if a contestant matches four or five of the six winning numbers. Hint: Divide the 40 numbers into two groups, winning numbers and nonwinning numbers.
    c. Find the probability, again using the hypergeometric formula, for matching 4 of the 6 winning numbers.
    d. Find the probability of matching 5 of the 6 winning numbers.

LO6-6

Explain the assumptions of the Poisson distribution and apply it to calculate probabilities.

POISSON PROBABILITY DISTRIBUTION

The **Poisson probability distribution** describes the number of times some event occurs during a specified interval. The interval may be time, distance, area, or volume.

The distribution is based on two assumptions. The first assumption is that the probability is proportional to the length of the interval. The second assumption is that the intervals are independent. To put it another way, the longer the interval, the larger the probability, and the number of occurrences in one interval does not affect the other intervals. This distribution is also a limiting form of the binomial distribution when the probability of a success is very small and n is large. It is often referred to as the "law of improbable events," meaning that the probability, π, of a particular event's happening is quite small. The Poisson distribution is a discrete probability distribution because it is formed by counting.

The Poisson probability distribution has these characteristics:

POISSON PROBABILITY EXPERIMENT
1. The random variable is the number of times some event occurs during a defined interval.
2. The probability of the event is proportional to the size of the interval.
3. The intervals do not overlap and are independent.

Near the end of World War II, the Germans developed rocket bombs, which were fired at the city of London. The Allied military command didn't know whether these bombs were fired at random or whether they had an aiming device. To investigate, the city of London was divided into 586 square regions. The distribution of hits in each square was recorded as follows:

Hits					
0	1	2	3	4	5
Regions					
229	221	93	35	7	1

To interpret, the above chart indicates that 229 regions were not hit with one of the bombs. Seven regions were hit four times. Using the Poisson distribution, with a mean of 0.93 hits per region, the expected number of hits is as follows:

Hits					
0	1	2	3	4	5 or more
Regions					
231.2	215.0	100.0	31.0	7.2	1.6

Because the actual number of hits was close to the expected number of hits, the military command concluded that the bombs were falling at random. The Germans had not developed a bomb with an aiming device.

This probability distribution has many applications. It is used as a model to describe the distribution of errors in data entry, the number of scratches and other imperfections in newly painted car panels, the number of defective parts in outgoing shipments, the number of customers waiting to be served at a restaurant or waiting to get into an attraction at Disney World, and the number of accidents on I–75 during a three-month period.

The Poisson distribution is described mathematically by the formula:

POISSON DISTRIBUTION $$P(x) = \frac{\mu^{x}e^{-\mu}}{x!}$$ **[6–7]**

where:
  μ (mu) is the mean number of occurrences (successes) in a particular interval.
  e is the constant 2.71828 (base of the Napierian logarithmic system).
  x is the number of occurrences (successes).
  $P(x)$ is the probability for a specified value of x.

The mean number of successes, μ, is found by $n\pi$, where n is the total number of trials and π the probability of success.

MEAN OF A POISSON DISTRIBUTION $$\mu = n\pi$$ **[6–8]**

The variance of the Poisson is equal to its mean. If, for example, the probability that a check cashed by a bank will bounce is .0003, and 10,000 checks are cashed, the mean and the variance for the number of bad checks is 3.0, found by $\mu = n\pi = 10,000(.0003) = 3.0$.

Recall that for a binomial distribution there are a fixed number of trials. For example, for a four-question multiple-choice test there can only be zero, one, two, three, or four successes (correct answers). The random variable, x, for a Poisson distribution, however, can assume an *infinite number of values*—that is, 0, 1, 2, 3, 4, 5, . . . However, *the probabilities become very small after the first few occurrences* (successes).

To illustrate the Poisson probability computation, assume baggage is rarely lost by Northeast Airlines. Most flights do not experience any mishandled bags; some have one bag lost; a few have two bags lost; rarely a flight will have three lost bags; and so on. Suppose a random sample of 1,000 flights shows a total of 300 bags were lost. Thus, the arithmetic mean number of lost bags per flight is 0.3, found by 300/1,000. If the number of lost bags per flight follows a Poisson distribution with $\mu = 0.3$, we can compute the various probabilities using formula (6–7):

$$P(x) = \frac{\mu^{x}e^{-\mu}}{x!}$$

For example, the probability of not losing any bags is:

$$P(0) = \frac{(0.3)^{0}(e^{-0.3})}{0!} = 0.7408$$

196   CHAPTER 6

In other words, 74% of the flights will have no lost baggage. The probability of exactly one lost bag is:

$$P(1) = \frac{(0.3)^1(e^{-0.3})}{1!} = 0.2222$$

Thus, we would expect to find exactly one lost bag on 22% of the flights.
   Poisson probabilities can also be found in the table in Appendix B.2.

E X A M P L E

Recall from the previous illustration that the number of lost bags follows a Poisson distribution with a mean of 0.3. Use Appendix B.2 to find the probability that no bags will be lost on a particular flight. What is the probability exactly one bag will be lost on a particular flight? When should the supervisor become suspicious that a flight is having too many lost bags?

S O L U T I O N

Part of Appendix B.2 is repeated as Table 6–6. To find the probability of no lost bags, locate the column headed "0.3" and read down that column to the row labeled "0." The probability is .7408. That is the probability of no lost bags. The probability of one lost bag is .2222, which is in the next row of the table, in the same column. The probability of two lost bags is .0333, in the row below; for three lost bags, it is .0033; and for four lost bags, it is .0003. Thus, a supervisor should not be surprised to find one lost bag but should expect to see more than one lost bag infrequently.

TABLE 6–6 Poisson Table for Various Values of μ (from Appendix B.2)

					μ				
x	0.1	0.2	0.3	0.4	0.5	0.6	0.7	0.8	0.9
0	0.9048	0.8187	0.7408	0.6703	0.6065	0.5488	0.4966	0.4493	0.4066
1	0.0905	0.1637	0.2222	0.2681	0.3033	0.3293	0.3476	0.3595	0.3659
2	0.0045	0.0164	0.0333	0.0536	0.0758	0.0988	0.1217	0.1438	0.1647
3	0.0002	0.0011	0.0033	0.0072	0.0126	0.0198	0.0284	0.0383	0.0494
4	0.0000	0.0001	0.0003	0.0007	0.0016	0.0030	0.0050	0.0077	0.0111
5	0.0000	0.0000	0.0000	0.0001	0.0002	0.0004	0.0007	0.0012	0.0020
6	0.0000	0.0000	0.0000	0.0000	0.0000	0.0000	0.0001	0.0002	0.0003
7	0.0000	0.0000	0.0000	0.0000	0.0000	0.0000	0.0000	0.0000	0.0000

   These probabilities can also be found using Excel. The commands to compute Poisson probabilities are in Appendix C.

	A	B
	Success	Probability
2	0	0.7408
3	1	0.2222
4	2	0.0333
5	3	0.0033
6	4	0.0003
7	5	0.0000
8	6	0.0000
9	7	0.0000

Poisson Probability Distribution.xlsx

DISCRETE PROBABILITY DISTRIBUTIONS   197

Earlier in this section, we mentioned that the Poisson probability distribution is a limiting form of the binomial. That is, we could estimate a binomial probability using the Poisson.

The Poisson probability distribution is characterized by the number of times an event happens during some interval or continuum. Examples include:

- The number of misspelled words per page in a newspaper.
- The number of calls per hour received by Dyson Vacuum Cleaner Company.
- The number of vehicles sold per day at Hyatt Buick GMC in Durham, North Carolina.
- The number of goals scored in a college soccer game.

In each of these examples, there is some type of continuum—misspelled words per page, calls per hour, vehicles per day, or goals per game.

In the previous example, we investigated the number of bags lost per flight, so the continuum was a "flight." We knew the mean number of bags of luggage lost per flight, but we did not know the number of passengers or the probability of a bag being lost. We suspected the number of passengers was fairly large and the probability of a passenger losing his or her bag of luggage was small. In the following example, we use the Poisson distribution to estimate a binomial probability when n, the number of trials, is large and π, the probability of a success, small.

EXAMPLE

 Coastal Insurance Company underwrites insurance for beachfront properties along the Virginia, North and South Carolina, and Georgia coasts. It uses the estimate that the probability of a named Category III hurricane (sustained winds of more than 110 miles per hour) or higher striking a particular region of the coast (for example, St. Simons Island, Georgia) in any one year is .05. If a homeowner takes a 30-year mortgage on a recently purchased property in St. Simons, what is the likelihood that the owner will experience at least one hurricane during the mortgage period?

SOLUTION

To use the Poisson probability distribution, we begin by determining the mean or expected number of storms meeting the criterion hitting St. Simons during the 30-year period. That is:

$$\mu = n\pi = 30(.05) = 1.5$$

where:

n is the number of years, 30 in this case.
π is the probability a hurricane meeting the strength criteria comes ashore.
μ is the mean or expected number of storms in a 30-year period.

To find the probability of at least one storm hitting St. Simons Island, Georgia, we first find the probability of no storms hitting the coast and subtract that value from 1.

$$P(x \geq 1) = 1 - P(x = 0) = 1 - \frac{\mu^0 e^{-1.5}}{0!} = 1 - .2231 = .7769$$

We conclude that the likelihood a hurricane meeting the strength criteria will strike the beachfront property at St. Simons during the 30-year period when the mortgage is in effect is .7769. To put it another way, the probability St. Simons will be hit by a Category III or higher hurricane during the 30-year period is a little more than 75%.

We should emphasize that the continuum, as previously described, still exists. That is, there are expected to be 1.5 storms hitting the coast per 30-year period. The continuum is the 30-year period.

In the preceding case, we are actually using the Poisson distribution as an estimate of the binomial. Note that we've met the binomial conditions outlined on page 183.

- There are only two possible outcomes: a hurricane hits the St. Simons area or it does not.
- There are a fixed number of trials, in this case 30 years.
- There is a constant probability of success; that is, the probability of a hurricane hitting the area is .05 each year.
- The years are independent. That means if a named storm strikes in the fifth year, that has no effect on any other year.

To find the probability of at least one storm striking the area in a 30-year period using the binomial distribution:

$$P(x \geq 1) = 1 - P(x = 0) = 1 - [_{30}C_0(.05)^0(.95)^{30}] = 1 - [(1)(1)(.2146)] = .7854$$

The probability of at least one hurricane hitting the St. Simons area during the 30-year period using the binomial distribution is .7854.

Which answer is correct? Why should we look at the problem both ways? The binomial is the more "technically correct" solution. The Poisson can be thought of as an approximation for the binomial, when n, the number of trials is large, and π, the probability of a success, is small. We look at the problem using both distributions to emphasize the convergence of the two discrete distributions. In some instances, using the Poisson may be the quicker solution, and as you see there is little practical difference in the answers. In fact, as n gets larger and π smaller, the difference between the two distributions gets smaller.

The Poisson probability distribution is always positively skewed and the random variable has no specific upper limit. The Poisson distribution for the lost bags example/solution where $\mu = 0.3$, is highly skewed. As μ becomes larger, the Poisson distribution becomes more symmetrical. For example, Chart 6–4 shows the distributions of

CHART 6–4 Poisson Probability Distributions for Means of 0.7, 2.0, and 6.0

DISCRETE PROBABILITY DISTRIBUTIONS   199

the number of transmission services, muffler replacements, and oil changes per day at Avellino's Auto Shop. They follow Poisson distributions with means of 0.7, 2.0, and 6.0, respectively.

In summary, the Poisson distribution is a family of discrete distributions. All that is needed to construct a Poisson probability distribution is the mean number of defects, errors, and so on—designated as μ.

SELF-REVIEW

6–6

From actuary tables, Washington Insurance Company determined the likelihood that a man age 25 will die within the next year is .0002. If Washington Insurance sells 4,000 policies to 25-year-old men this year, what is the probability they will pay on exactly one policy?

EXERCISES

31. In a Poisson distribution $\mu = 0.4$.
   a. What is the probability that $x = 0$?
   b. What is the probability that $x > 0$?
32. In a Poisson distribution $\mu = 4$.
   a. What is the probability that $x = 2$?
   b. What is the probability that $x \leq 2$?
   c. What is the probability that $x > 2$?
33. Ms. Bergen is a loan officer at Coast Bank and Trust. From her years of experience, she estimates that the probability is .025 that an applicant will not be able to repay his or her installment loan. Last month she made 40 loans.
   a. What is the probability that three loans will be defaulted?
   b. What is the probability that at least three loans will be defaulted?
34. Automobiles arrive at the Elkhart exit of the Indiana Toll Road at the rate of two per minute. The distribution of arrivals approximates a Poisson distribution.
   a. What is the probability that no automobiles arrive in a particular minute?
   b. What is the probability that at least one automobile arrives during a particular minute?
35. It is estimated that 0.5% of the callers to the Customer Service department of Dell Inc. will receive a busy signal. What is the probability that of today's 1,200 callers at least 5 received a busy signal?
36. In the past, schools in Los Angeles County have closed an average of 3 days each year for weather emergencies. What is the probability that schools in Los Angeles County will close for 4 days next year?

CHAPTER SUMMARY

   I. A random variable is a numerical value determined by the outcome of an experiment.
  II. A probability distribution is a listing of all possible outcomes of an experiment and the probability associated with each outcome.
    A. A discrete probability distribution can assume only certain values. The main features are:
      1. The sum of the probabilities is 1.00.
      2. The probability of a particular outcome is between 0.00 and 1.00.
      3. The outcomes are mutually exclusive.
    B. A continuous distribution can assume an infinite number of values within a specific range.
 III. The mean and variance of a probability distribution are computed as follows.
    A. The mean is equal to:

$$\mu = \Sigma\,[xP(x)] \qquad\qquad\qquad\qquad \textbf{[6–1]}$$

    B. The variance is equal to:

$$\sigma^2 = \Sigma\,[(x - \mu)^2 P(x)] \qquad\qquad\qquad \textbf{[6–2]}$$

IV. The binomial distribution has the following characteristics.
  A. Each outcome is classified into one of two mutually exclusive categories.
  B. The distribution results from a count of the number of successes in a fixed number of trials.
  C. The probability of a success remains the same from trial to trial.
  D. Each trial is independent.
  E. A binomial probability is determined as follows:

$$P(x) = {}_nC_x\, \pi^x (1 - \pi)^{n-x} \qquad\qquad \text{[6–3]}$$

  F. The mean is computed as:

$$\mu = n\pi \qquad\qquad \text{[6–4]}$$

  G. The variance is

$$\sigma^2 = n\pi(1 - \pi) \qquad\qquad \text{[6–5]}$$

V. The hypergeometric distribution has the following characteristics.
  A. There are only two possible outcomes.
  B. The probability of a success is not the same on each trial.
  C. The distribution results from a count of the number of successes in a fixed number of trials.
  D. It is used when sampling without replacement from a finite population.
  E. A hypergeometric probability is computed from the following equation:

$$P(x) = \frac{({}_SC_x)({}_{N-S}C_{n-x})}{({}_NC_n)} \qquad\qquad \text{[6–6]}$$

VI. The Poisson distribution has the following characteristics.
  A. It describes the number of times some event occurs during a specified interval.
  B. The probability of a "success" is proportional to the length of the interval.
  C. Nonoverlapping intervals are independent.
  D. It is a limiting form of the binomial distribution when n is large and π is small.
  E. A Poisson probability is determined from the following equation:

$$P(x) = \frac{\mu^x e^{-\mu}}{x!} \qquad\qquad \text{[6–7]}$$

  F. The mean and the variance are:

$$\mu = n\pi \qquad\qquad \text{[6–8]}$$
$$\sigma^2 = n\pi$$

CHAPTER EXERCISES

37. What is the difference between a random variable and a probability distribution?
38. For each of the following indicate whether the random variable is discrete or continuous.
  a. The length of time to get a haircut.
  b. The number of cars a jogger passes each morning while running.
  c. The number of hits for a team in a high school girls' softball game.
  d. The number of patients treated at the South Strand Medical Center between 6 and 10 p.m. each night.
  e. The distance your car traveled on the last fill-up.
  f. The number of customers at the Oak Street Wendy's who used the drive-through facility.
  g. The distance between Gainesville, Florida, and all Florida cities with a population of at least 50,000.
39. An investment will be worth $1,000, $2,000, or $5,000 at the end of the year. The probabilities of these values are .25, .60, and .15, respectively. Determine the mean and variance of the worth of the investment.

For **DATA FILE**, please visit
www.mhhe.com/lind16e

DISCRETE PROBABILITY DISTRIBUTIONS   201

40. The following notice appeared in the golf shop at a Myrtle Beach, South Carolina, golf course.

> **Blackmoor Golf Club Members**
>
> The golf shop is holding a raffle to win a
> TaylorMade R9 10.5° Regular Flex Driver ($300 value).
> Tickets are $5.00 each.
> Only 80 tickets will be sold.
> Please see the golf shop to get your tickets!

John Underpar buys a ticket.
a. What are Mr. Underpar's possible monetary outcomes?
b. What are the probabilities of the possible outcomes?
c. Summarize Mr. Underpar's "experiment" as a probability distribution.
d. What is the mean or expected value of the probability distribution? Explain your result.
e. If all 80 tickets are sold, what is the expected return to the Club?

For **DATA FILE**, please visit www.mhhe.com/lind16e

41. Croissant Bakery Inc. offers special decorated cakes for birthdays, weddings, and other occasions. It also has regular cakes available in its bakery. The following table gives the total number of cakes sold per day and the corresponding probability. Compute the mean, variance, and standard deviation of the number of cakes sold per day.

Number of Cakes Sold in a Day	Probability
12	.25
13	.40
14	.25
15	.10

For **DATA FILE**, please visit www.mhhe.com/lind16e

42. The payouts for the Powerball lottery and their corresponding odds and probabilities of occurrence are shown below. The price of a ticket is $1.00. Find the mean and standard deviation of the payout. Hint: Don't forget to include the cost of the ticket and its corresponding probability.

Divisions	Payout	Odds	Probability
Five plus Powerball	$50,000,000	146,107,962	0.000000006844
Match 5	200,000	3,563,609	0.000000280614
Four plus Powerball	10,000	584,432	0.000001711060
Match 4	100	14,255	0.000070145903
Three plus Powerball	100	11,927	0.000083836351
Match 3	7	291	0.003424657534
Two plus Powerball	7	745	0.001340482574
One plus Powerball	4	127	0.007812500000
Zero plus Powerball	3	69	0.014285714286

43. In a recent survey, 35% indicated chocolate was their favorite flavor of ice cream. Suppose we select a sample of 10 people and ask them to name their favorite flavor of ice cream.
a. How many of those in the sample would you expect to name chocolate?
b. What is the probability exactly four of those in the sample name chocolate?
c. What is the probability four or more name chocolate?

For **DATA FILE**, please visit
www.mhhe.com/lind16e

44. Thirty percent of the population in a southwestern community are Spanish-speaking Americans. A Spanish-speaking person is accused of killing a non-Spanish-speaking American and goes to trial. Of the first 12 potential jurors, only 2 are Spanish-speaking Americans, and 10 are not. The defendant's lawyer challenges the jury selection, claiming bias against her client. The government lawyer disagrees, saying that the probability of this particular jury composition is common. Compute the probability and discuss the assumptions.

45. An auditor for Health Maintenance Services of Georgia reports 40% of policyholders 55 years or older submit a claim during the year. Fifteen policyholders are randomly selected for company records.
   a. How many of the policyholders would you expect to have filed a claim within the last year?
   b. What is the probability that 10 of the selected policyholders submitted a claim last year?
   c. What is the probability that 10 or more of the selected policyholders submitted a claim last year?
   d. What is the probability that more than 10 of the selected policyholders submitted a claim last year?

46. Tire and Auto Supply is considering a 2-for-1 stock split. Before the transaction is finalized, at least two-thirds of the 1,200 company stockholders must approve the proposal. To evaluate the likelihood the proposal will be approved, the CFO selected a sample of 18 stockholders. He contacted each and found 14 approved of the proposed split. What is the likelihood of this event, assuming two-thirds of the stockholders approve?

47. A federal study reported that 7.5% of the U.S. workforce has a drug problem. A drug enforcement official for the state of Indiana wished to investigate this statement. In her sample of 20 employed workers:
   a. How many would you expect to have a drug problem? What is the standard deviation?
   b. What is the likelihood that *none* of the workers sampled has a drug problem?
   c. What is the likelihood *at least one* has a drug problem?

48. The Bank of Hawaii reports that 7% of its credit card holders will default at some time in their life. The Hilo branch just mailed out 12 new cards today.
   a. How many of these new cardholders would you expect to default? What is the standard deviation?
   b. What is the likelihood that *none* of the cardholders will default?
   c. What is the likelihood *at least one* will default?

49. Recent statistics suggest that 15% of those who visit a retail site on the World Wide Web make a purchase. A retailer wished to verify this claim. To do so, she selected a sample of 16 "hits" to her site and found that 4 had actually made a purchase.
   a. What is the likelihood of exactly four purchases?
   b. How many purchases should she expect?
   c. What is the likelihood that four or more "hits" result in a purchase?

50. In Chapter 19, we discuss *acceptance sampling*. Acceptance sampling is a statistical method used to monitor the quality of purchased parts and components. To ensure the quality of incoming parts, a purchaser or manufacturer normally samples 20 parts and allows one defect.
   a. What is the likelihood of accepting a lot that is 1% defective?
   b. If the quality of the incoming lot was actually 2%, what is the likelihood of accepting it?
   c. If the quality of the incoming lot was actually 5%, what is the likelihood of accepting it?

51. Unilever Inc. recently developed a new body wash with a scent of ginger. Their research indicates that 30% of men like the new scent. To further investigate, Unilever's marketing research group randomly selected 15 men and asked them if they liked the scent. What is the probability that six or more men like the ginger scent in the body wash?

52. Dr. Richmond, a psychologist, is studying the daytime television viewing habits of college students. She believes 45% of college students watch soap operas during the afternoon. To further investigate, she selects a sample of 10.
   a. Develop a probability distribution for the number of students in the sample who watch soap operas.
   b. Find the mean and the standard deviation of this distribution.
   c. What is the probability of finding exactly four students who watch soap operas?
   d. What is the probability less than half of the students selected watch soap operas?

DISCRETE PROBABILITY DISTRIBUTIONS   203

For **DATA FILE**, please visit
www.mhhe.com/lind16e

53. A recent study conducted by Penn, Shone, and Borland, on behalf of LastMinute.com, revealed that 52% of business travelers plan their trips less than two weeks before departure. The study is to be replicated in the tri-state area with a sample of 12 frequent business travelers.
   a. Develop a probability distribution for the number of travelers who plan their trips within two weeks of departure.
   b. Find the mean and the standard deviation of this distribution.
   c. What is the probability exactly 5 of the 12 selected business travelers plan their trips within two weeks of departure?
   d. What is the probability 5 or fewer of the 12 selected business travelers plan their trips within two weeks of departure?

54. The Internal Revenue Service is studying the category of charitable contributions. A sample of 25 returns is selected from young couples between the ages of 20 and 35 who had an adjusted gross income of more than $100,000. Of these 25 returns, five had charitable contributions of more than $1,000. Four of these returns are selected for a comprehensive audit.
   a. Explain why the hypergeometric distribution is appropriate.
   b. What is the probability exactly one of the four audited had a charitable deduction of more than $1,000?
   c. What is the probability at least one of the audited returns had a charitable contribution of more than $1,000?

55. The law firm of Hagel and Hagel is located in downtown Cincinnati. There are 10 partners in the firm; 7 live in Ohio and 3 in northern Kentucky. Ms. Wendy Hagel, the managing partner, wants to appoint a committee of 3 partners to look into moving the firm to northern Kentucky. If the committee is selected at random from the 10 partners, what is the probability that:
   a. One member of the committee lives in northern Kentucky and the others live in Ohio?
   b. At least one member of the committee lives in northern Kentucky?

56. Topten is a leading source on energy-efficient products. Their list of the top seven vehicles in terms of fuel efficiency for 2014 includes three Hondas.
   a. Determine the probability distribution for the number of Hondas in a sample of two cars chosen from the top seven.
   b. What is the likelihood that in the sample of two at least one Honda is included?

57. The position of chief of police in the city of Corry, Pennsylvania, is vacant. A search committee of Corry residents is charged with the responsibility of recommending a new chief to the city council. There are 12 applicants, 4 of whom are either female or members of a minority. The search committee decides to interview all 12 of the applicants. To begin, they randomly select four applicants to be interviewed on the first day, and none of the four is female or a member of a minority. The local newspaper, the *Corry Press,* suggests discrimination in an editorial. What is the likelihood of this occurrence?

58. Listed below is the population by state for the 15 states with the largest population. Also included is whether that state's border touches the Gulf of Mexico, the Atlantic Ocean, or the Pacific Ocean (coastline).

For **DATA FILE**, please visit
www.mhhe.com/lind16e

Rank	State	Population	Coastline
1	California	36,553,215	Yes
2	Texas	23,904,380	Yes
3	New York	19,297,729	Yes
4	Florida	18,251,243	Yes
5	Illinois	12,852,548	No
6	Pennsylvania	12,432,792	No
7	Ohio	11,466,917	No
8	Michigan	10,071,822	No
9	Georgia	9,544,750	Yes
10	North Carolina	9,061,032	Yes
11	New Jersey	8,685,920	Yes
12	Virginia	7,712,091	Yes
13	Washington	6,468,424	Yes
14	Massachusetts	6,449,755	Yes
15	Indiana	6,345,289	No

Note that 5 of the 15 states do not have any coastline. Suppose three states are selected at random. What is the probability that:
  a. None of the states selected has any coastline?
  b. Exactly one of the selected states has a coastline?
  c. At least one of the selected states has a coastline?
59. The sales of Lexus automobiles in the Detroit area follow a Poisson distribution with a mean of 3 per day.
  a. What is the probability that no Lexus is sold on a particular day?
  b. What is the probability that for 5 consecutive days at least one Lexus is sold?
60. Suppose 1.5% of the antennas on new Nokia cell phones are defective. For a random sample of 200 antennas, find the probability that:
  a. None of the antennas is defective.
  b. Three or more of the antennas are defective.
61. A study of the checkout lines at the Safeway Supermarket in the South Strand area revealed that between 4 and 7 p.m. on weekdays there is an average of four customers waiting in line. What is the probability that you visit Safeway today during this period and find:
  a. No customers are waiting?
  b. Four customers are waiting?
  c. Four or fewer are waiting?
  d. Four or more are waiting?
62. An internal study by the Technology Services department at Lahey Electronics revealed company employees receive an average of two non-work-related e-mails per hour. Assume the arrival of these e-mails is approximated by the Poisson distribution.
  a. What is the probability Linda Lahey, company president, received exactly one non-work-related e-mail between 4 p.m. and 5 p.m. yesterday?
  b. What is the probability she received five or more non-work-related e-mails during the same period?
  c. What is the probability she did not receive any non-work-related e-mails during the period?
63. Recent crime reports indicate that 3.1 motor vehicle thefts occur each minute in the United States. Assume that the distribution of thefts per minute can be approximated by the Poisson probability distribution.
  a. Calculate the probability exactly *four* thefts occur in a minute.
  b. What is the probability there are *no* thefts in a minute?
  c. What is the probability there is *at least one* theft in a minute?
64. Recent difficult economic times have caused an increase in the foreclosure rate of home mortgages. Statistics from the Penn Bank and Trust Company show their monthly foreclosure rate is now 1 loan out of every 136 loans. Last month the bank approved 300 loans.
  a. How many foreclosures would you expect the bank to have last month?
  b. What is the probability of exactly two foreclosures?
  c. What is the probability of at least one foreclosure?
65. The National Aeronautics and Space Administration (NASA) has experienced two disasters. The *Challenger* exploded over the Atlantic Ocean in 1986, and the *Columbia* disintegrated on reentry over East Texas in 2003. Based on the first 113 missions, and assuming failures occur at the same rate, consider the next 23 missions. What is the probability of exactly two failures? What is the probability of no failures?
66. According to the "January theory," if the stock market is up for the month of January, it will be up for the year. If it is down in January, it will be down for the year. According to an article in *The Wall Street Journal,* this theory held for 29 out of the last 34 years. Suppose there is no truth to this theory; that is, the probability it is either up or down is .50. What is the probability this could occur by chance? You will probably need a software package such as Excel or Minitab.
67. During the second round of the 1989 U.S. Open golf tournament, four golfers scored a hole in one on the sixth hole. The odds of a professional golfer making a hole in one are estimated to be 3,708 to 1, so the probability is 1/3,709. There were 155 golfers participating in the second round that day. Estimate the probability that four golfers would score a hole in one on the sixth hole.
68. Suppose the National Hurricane Center forecasts that hurricanes will hit the strike area with a .95 probability.
  a. What probability distribution does this follow?
  b. If there are 10 hurricanes this season, what is the probability that all reach the strike area?
  c. What is the probability at least one of 10 hurricanes reaches land outside the strike area?

DISCRETE PROBABILITY DISTRIBUTIONS

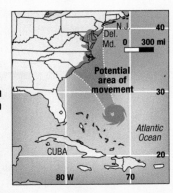

**STORM CONTINUES
NORTHWEST**
Position : **27.8 N, 71.4 W**
Movement: **NNW at 8 mph**
Sustained winds: **105 mph**
As of 11 p.m. EDT Tuesday

Hurricane watch
Tropical storm watch

69. A recent CBS News survey reported that 67% of adults felt the U.S. Treasury should continue making pennies.

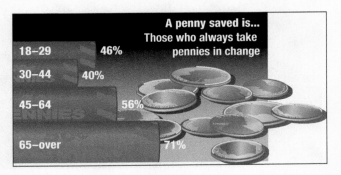

Suppose we select a sample of 15 adults.
a. How many of the 15 would we expect to indicate that the Treasury should continue making pennies? What is the standard deviation?
b. What is the likelihood that exactly eight adults would indicate the Treasury should continue making pennies?
c. What is the likelihood at least eight adults would indicate the Treasury should continue making pennies?

DATA SET EXERCISES

(The data for these exercises are available at the text website: **www.mhhe.com/lind16e.**)

70. Refer to the Real Estate data, which report information on homes sold in the Goodyear, Arizona, area last year.
a. Create a probability distribution for the number of bedrooms. Compute the mean and the standard deviation of this distribution.
b. Create a probability distribution for the number of bathrooms. Compute the mean and the standard deviation of this distribution.
71. Refer to the Baseball 2012 data. Compute the mean number of home runs per game. To do this, first find the mean number of home runs per team for 2012. Next, divide this value by 162 (a season comprises 162 games). Then multiply by 2 because there are two teams in each game. Use the Poisson distribution to estimate the number of home runs that will be hit in a game. Find the probability that:
a. There are no home runs in a game.
b. There are two home runs in a game.
c. There are at least four home runs in a game.

7 Continuous Probability Distributions

CRUISE SHIPS of the Royal Viking line report that 80% of their rooms are occupied during September. For a cruise ship having 800 rooms, what is the probability that 665 or more are occupied in September? (See Exercise 60 and LO7-4.)

LEARNING OBJECTIVES

When you have completed this chapter, you will be able to:

LO7-1   Describe the uniform probability distribution and use it to calculate probabilities.

LO7-2   Describe the characteristics of a normal probability distribution.

LO7-3   Describe the standard normal probability distribution and use it to calculate probabilities.

LO7-4   Approximate the binomial probability distribution using the standard normal probability distribution to calculate probabilities.

LO7-5   Describe the exponential probability distribution and use it to calculate probabilities.

INTRODUCTION

Chapter 6 began our study of probability distributions. We consider three *discrete* probability distributions: binomial, hypergeometric, and Poisson. These distributions are based on discrete random variables, which can assume only clearly separated values. For example, we select for study 10 small businesses that began operations during the year 2010. The number still operating in 2013 can be 0, 1, 2, . . . , 10. There cannot be 3.7, 12, or −7 still operating in 2013. In this example, only certain outcomes are possible and these outcomes are represented by clearly separated values. In addition, the result is usually found by counting the number of successes. We count the number of the businesses in the study that are still in operation in 2013.

We continue our study of probability distributions by examining *continuous* probability distributions. A continuous probability distribution usually results from measuring something, such as the distance from the dormitory to the classroom, the weight of an individual, or the amount of bonus earned by CEOs. As an example, at Dave's Inlet Fish Shack flounder is the featured, fresh-fish menu item. The distribution of the amount of flounder sold per day has a mean of 10.0 pounds per day and a standard deviation of 3.0 pounds per day. This distribution is continuous because Dave, the owner, "measures" the amount of flounder sold each day. It is important to realize that a continuous random variable has an infinite number of values within a particular range. So, for a continuous random variable, probability is for a range of values. The probability for a specific value of a continuous random variable is 0.

This chapter shows how to use three continuous probability distributions: the uniform probability distribution, the normal probability distribution, and the exponential probability distribution.

LO7-1

Describe the uniform probability distribution and use it to calculate probabilities.

THE FAMILY OF UNIFORM PROBABILITY DISTRIBUTIONS

The uniform probability distribution is the simplest distribution for a continuous random variable. This distribution is rectangular in shape and is completely defined by its minimum and maximum values. Here are some examples that follow a uniform distribution.

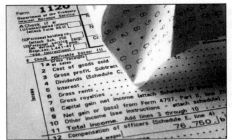

- The sales of gasoline at the Kwik Fill in Medina, New York, follow a uniform distribution that varies between 2,000 and 5,000 gallons per day. The random variable is the number of gallons sold per day and is continuous within the interval between 2,000 gallons and 5,000 gallons.
- Volunteers at the Grand Strand Public Library prepare federal income tax forms. The time to prepare form 1040-EZ follows a uniform distribution over the interval between 10 minutes and 30 minutes. The random variable is the number of minutes to complete the form, and it can assume any value between 10 and 30.

A uniform distribution is shown in Chart 7–1. The distribution's shape is rectangular and has a minimum value of *a* and a maximum of *b*. Also notice in Chart 7–1 the height of the distribution is constant or uniform for all values between *a* and *b*.

The mean of a uniform distribution is located in the middle of the interval between the minimum and maximum values. It is computed as:

MEAN OF THE UNIFORM DISTRIBUTION	$\mu = \dfrac{a + b}{2}$	**[7–1]**

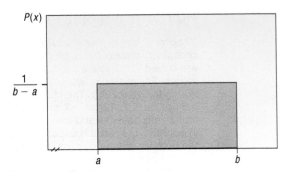

CHART 7–1 A Continuous Uniform Distribution

The standard deviation describes the dispersion of a distribution. In the uniform distribution, the standard deviation is also related to the interval between the maximum and minimum values.

STANDARD DEVIATION OF THE UNIFORM DISTRIBUTION	$\sigma = \sqrt{\dfrac{(b-a)^2}{12}}$	**[7–2]**

The equation for the uniform probability distribution is:

UNIFORM DISTRIBUTION	$P(x) = \dfrac{1}{b-a}$ if $a \leq x \leq b$ and 0 elsewhere	**[7–3]**

As we described in Chapter 6, probability distributions are useful for making probability statements concerning the values of a random variable. For distributions describing a continuous random variable, areas within the distribution represent probabilities. In the uniform distribution, its rectangular shape allows us to apply the area formula for a rectangle. Recall that we find the area of a rectangle by multiplying its length by its height. For the uniform distribution, the height of the rectangle is $P(x)$, which is $1/(b-a)$. The length or base of the distribution is $b-a$. So if we multiply the height of the distribution by its entire range to find the area, the result is always 1.00. To put it another way, the total area within a continuous probability distribution is equal to 1.00. In general

$$\text{Area} = (\text{height})(\text{base}) = \frac{1}{(b-a)}(b-a) = 1.00$$

So if a uniform distribution ranges from 10 to 15, the height is 0.20, found by $1/(15-10)$. The base is 5, found by $15-10$. The total area is:

$$\text{Area} = (\text{height})(\text{base}) = \frac{1}{(15-10)}(15-10) = 1.00$$

An example will illustrate the features of a uniform distribution and how we calculate probabilities using it.

EXAMPLE

Southwest Arizona State University provides bus service to students while they are on campus. A bus arrives at the North Main Street and College Drive stop every 30 minutes between 6 a.m. and 11 p.m. during weekdays. Students arrive

CONTINUOUS PROBABILITY DISTRIBUTIONS   209

at the bus stop at random times. The time that a student waits is uniformly distributed from 0 to 30 minutes.

1. Draw a graph of this distribution.
2. Show that the area of this uniform distribution is 1.00.
3. How long will a student "typically" have to wait for a bus? In other words, what is the mean waiting time? What is the standard deviation of the waiting times?
4. What is the probability a student will wait more than 25 minutes?
5. What is the probability a student will wait between 10 and 20 minutes?

SOLUTION

In this case, the random variable is the length of time a student must wait. Time is measured on a continuous scale, and the wait times may range from 0 minutes up to 30 minutes.

1. The graph of the uniform distribution is shown in Chart 7–2. The horizontal line is drawn at a height of .0333, found by 1/(30 − 0). The range of this distribution is 30 minutes.

CHART 7–2 Uniform Probability Distribution of Student Waiting Times

2. The times students must wait for the bus are uniform over the interval from 0 minutes to 30 minutes, so in this case a is 0 and b is 30.

$$\text{Area} = (\text{height})(\text{base}) = \frac{1}{(30 - 0)}(30 - 0) = 1.00$$

3. To find the mean, we use formula (7–1).

$$\mu = \frac{a + b}{2} = \frac{0 + 30}{2} = 15$$

The mean of the distribution is 15 minutes, so the typical wait time for bus service is 15 minutes.
   To find the standard deviation of the wait times, we use formula (7–2).

$$\sigma = \sqrt{\frac{(b - a)^2}{12}} = \sqrt{\frac{(30 - 0)^2}{12}} = 8.66$$

The standard deviation of the distribution is 8.66 minutes. This measures the variation in the student wait times.

4. The area within the distribution for the interval 25 to 30 represents this particular probability. From the area formula:

$$P(25 < \text{wait time} < 30) = (\text{height})(\text{base}) = \frac{1}{(30 - 0)}(5) = .1667$$

CHAPTER 7

So the probability a student waits between 25 and 30 minutes is .1667. This conclusion is illustrated by the following graph.

5. The area within the distribution for the interval 10 to 20 represents the probability.

$$P(10 < \text{wait time} < 20) = (\text{height})(\text{base}) = \frac{1}{(30 - 0)}(10) = .3333$$

We can illustrate this probability as follows.

SELF-REVIEW

7–1

Australian sheepdogs have a relatively short life. The length of their life follows a uniform distribution between 8 and 14 years.
(a) Draw this uniform distribution. What are the height and base values?
(b) Show the total area under the curve is 1.00.
(c) Calculate the mean and the standard deviation of this distribution.
(d) What is the probability a particular dog lives between 10 and 14 years?
(e) What is the probability a dog will live less than 9 years?

EXERCISES

1. A uniform distribution is defined over the interval from 6 to 10.
    a. What are the values for a and b?
    b. What is the mean of this uniform distribution?
    c. What is the standard deviation?
    d. Show that the total area is 1.00.
    e. Find the probability of a value more than 7.
    f. Find the probability of a value between 7 and 9.
2. A uniform distribution is defined over the interval from 2 to 5.
    a. What are the values for a and b?
    b. What is the mean of this uniform distribution?
    c. What is the standard deviation?

   d. Show that the total area is 1.00.
   e. Find the probability of a value more than 2.6.
   f. Find the probability of a value between 2.9 and 3.7.
3. The closing price of Schnur Sporting Goods Inc. common stock is uniformly distributed between $20 and $30 per share. What is the probability that the stock price will be:
   a. More than $27?
   b. Less than or equal to $24?
4. According to the Insurance Institute of America, a family of four spends between $400 and $3,800 per year on all types of insurance. Suppose the money spent is uniformly distributed between these amounts.
   a. What is the mean amount spent on insurance?
   b. What is the standard deviation of the amount spent?
   c. If we select a family at random, what is the probability they spend less than $2,000 per year on insurance per year?
   d. What is the probability a family spends more than $3,000 per year?
5. The April rainfall in Flagstaff, Arizona, follows a uniform distribution between 0.5 and 3.00 inches.
   a. What are the values for *a* and *b*?
   b. What is the mean amount of rainfall for the month? What is the standard deviation?
   c. What is the probability of less than an inch of rain for the month?
   d. What is the probability of *exactly* 1.00 inch of rain?
   e. What is the probability of more than 1.50 inches of rain for the month?
6. Customers experiencing technical difficulty with their Internet cable hookup may call an 800 number for technical support. It takes the technician between 30 seconds and 10 minutes to resolve the problem. The distribution of this support time follows the uniform distribution.
   a. What are the values for *a* and *b* in minutes?
   b. What is the mean time to resolve the problem? What is the standard deviation of the time?
   c. What percent of the problems take more than 5 minutes to resolve?
   d. Suppose we wish to find the middle 50% of the problem-solving times. What are the end points of these two times?

LO7-2

Describe the characteristics of a normal probability distribution.

THE FAMILY OF NORMAL PROBABILITY DISTRIBUTIONS

Next we consider the normal probability distribution. Unlike the uniform distribution [see formula (7–3)] the normal probability distribution has a very complex formula.

NORMAL PROBABILITY DISTRIBUTION	$P(x) = \dfrac{1}{\sigma\sqrt{2\pi}}\, e^{-\left[\frac{(x-\mu)^2}{2\sigma^2}\right]}$	**[7–4]**

However, do not be bothered by how complex this formula looks. You are already familiar with many of the values. The symbols μ and σ refer to the mean and the standard deviation, as usual. The Greek symbol π is a constant and its value is approximately 22/7 or 3.1416. The letter *e* is also a constant. It is the base of the natural log system and is approximately equal to 2.718. *x* is the value of a continuous random variable. So a normal distribution is based on—that is, it is defined by—its mean and standard deviation.

   You will not need to make calculations using formula (7–4). Instead you will use a table, given in Appendix B.3, to find various probabilities. These probabilities can also be calculated using Excel functions as well as other statistical software.

The normal probability distribution has the following characteristics:

- It is **bell-shaped** and has a single peak at the center of the distribution. The arithmetic mean, median, and mode are equal and located in the center of the distribution. The total area under the curve is 1.00. Half the area under the normal curve is to the right of this center point and the other half, to the left of it.
- It is **symmetrical** about the mean. If we cut the normal curve vertically at the center value, the two halves will be mirror images.
- It falls off smoothly in either direction from the central value. That is, the distribution is **asymptotic:** The curve gets closer and closer to the X-axis but never actually touches it. To put it another way, the tails of the curve extend indefinitely in both directions.
- The location of a normal distribution is determined by the mean, μ. The dispersion or spread of the distribution is determined by the standard deviation, σ.

These characteristics are shown graphically in Chart 7–3.

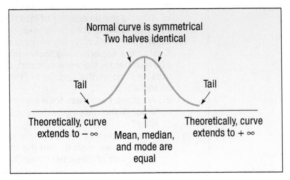

CHART 7–3 Characteristics of a Normal Distribution

There is not just one normal probability distribution, but rather a "family" of them. For example, in Chart 7–4 the probability distributions of length of employee service in three different plants are compared. In the Camden plant, the mean is 20 years and the standard deviation is 3.1 years. There is another normal probability distribution for the length of service in the Dunkirk plant, where μ = 20 years and σ = 3.9 years. In the Elmira plant, μ = 20 years and σ = 5.0 years. Note that the means are the same but the standard deviations are different. As the standard deviation gets smaller, the distribution becomes more narrow and "peaked."

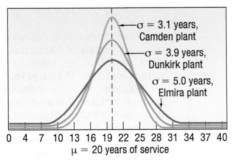

CHART 7–4 Normal Probability Distributions with Equal Means but Different Standard Deviations

CONTINUOUS PROBABILITY DISTRIBUTIONS   213

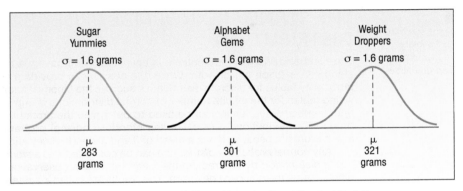

CHART 7–5 Normal Probability Distributions Having Different Means but Equal Standard Deviations

Chart 7–5 shows the distribution of box weights of three different cereals. The weights follow a normal distribution with different means but identical standard deviations.

Finally, Chart 7–6 shows three normal distributions having different means and standard deviations. They show the distribution of tensile strengths, measured in pounds per square inch (psi), for three types of cables.

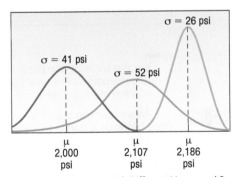

CHART 7–6 Normal Probability Distributions with Different Means and Standard Deviations

In Chapter 6, recall that discrete probability distributions show the specific likelihood a discrete value will occur. For example, on page 184, the binomial distribution is used to calculate the probability that none of the five flights arriving at the Bradford Pennsylvania Regional Airport would be late.

With a continuous probability distribution, areas below the curve define probabilities. The total area under the normal curve is 1.0. This accounts for all possible outcomes. Because a normal probability distribution is symmetric, the area under the curve to the left of the mean is 0.5, and the area under the curve to the right of the mean is 0.5. Apply this to the distribution of Sugar Yummies in Chart 7–5. It is normally distributed with a mean of 283 grams. Therefore, the probability of filling a box with more than 283 grams is 0.5 and the probability of filling a box with less than 283 grams is 0.5. We can also determine the probability that a box weighs between 280 and 286 grams. However, to determine this probability we need to know about the standard normal probability distribution.

214   CHAPTER 7

LO7-3
Describe the standard normal probability distribution and use it to calculate probabilities.

THE STANDARD NORMAL PROBABILITY DISTRIBUTION

The number of normal distributions is unlimited, each having a different mean (μ), standard deviation (σ), or both. While it is possible to provide a limited number of probability tables for discrete distributions such as the binomial and the Poisson, providing tables for the infinite number of normal distributions is impractial. Fortunately, one member of the family can be used to determine the probabilities for all normal probability distributions. It is called the **standard normal probability distribution,** and it is unique because it has a mean of 0 and a standard deviation of 1.

Any *normal probability distribution* can be converted into a *standard normal probability distribution* by subtracting the mean from each observation and dividing this difference by the standard deviation. The results are called **z values** or **z scores.**

> **z VALUE** The signed distance between a selected value, designated x, and the mean, μ, divided by the standard deviation, σ.

So, a z value is the distance from the mean, measured in units of the standard deviation. The formula for this conversion is:

> **STANDARD NORMAL VALUE** $$z = \frac{x - \mu}{\sigma}$$ **[7–5]**

where:

    x is the value of any particular observation or measurement.
    μ is the mean of the distribution.
    σ is the standard deviation of the distribution.

STATISTICS IN ACTION

An individual's skills depend on a combination of many hereditary and environmental factors, each having about the same amount of weight or influence on the skills. Thus, much like a binomial distribution with a large number of trials, many skills and attributes follow the normal distribution. For example, the SAT Reasoning Test is the most widely used standardized test for college admissions in the United States. Scores are based on a normal distribution with a mean of 1,500 and a standard deviation of 300.

As we noted in the preceding definition, a z value expresses the distance or difference between a particular value of x and the arithmetic mean in units of the standard deviation. Once the normally distributed observations are standardized, the z values are normally distributed with a mean of 0 and a standard deviation of 1. Therefore, the z distribution has all the characteristics of any normal probability distribution. These characteristics are listed on page 212. The table in Appendix B.3 (also on the inside back cover) lists the probabilities for the standard normal probability distribution. A small portion of this table follows.

TABLE 7–1 Areas under the Normal Curve

z	0.00	0.01	0.02	0.03	0.04	0.05	...
1.3	0.4032	0.4049	0.4066	0.4082	0.4099	0.4115	
1.4	0.4192	0.4207	0.4222	0.4236	0.4251	0.4265	
1.5	0.4332	0.4345	0.4357	0.4370	0.4382	0.4394	
1.6	0.4452	0.4463	0.4474	0.4484	0.4495	0.4505	
1.7	0.4554	0.4564	0.4573	0.4582	0.4591	0.4599	
1.8	0.4641	0.4649	0.4656	0.4664	0.4671	0.4678	
1.9	0.4713	0.4719	0.4726	0.4732	0.4738	0.4744	
.							
.							

Applications of the Standard Normal Distribution

The standard normal distribution is very useful for determining probabilities for any normally distributed random variable. The basic procedure is to find the *z* value for a particular value of the random variable based on the mean and standard deviation of its distribution. Then, using the *z* value, we can use the standard normal distribution to find various probabilities. The following example/solution describes the details of the application.

EXAMPLE

The weekly incomes of shift foremen in the glass industry follow the normal probability distribution with a mean of $1,000 and a standard deviation of $100. What is the *z* value for the income, let's call it *x*, of a foreman who earns $1,100 per week? For a foreman who earns $900 per week?

SOLUTION

Using formula (7–5), the *z* values corresponding to the two *x* values ($1,100 and $900) are:

For *x* = $1,100:

$$z = \frac{x - \mu}{\sigma}$$

$$= \frac{\$1,100 - \$1,000}{\$100}$$

$$= 1.00$$

For *x* = $900:

$$z = \frac{x - \mu}{\sigma}$$

$$= \frac{\$900 - \$1,000}{\$100}$$

$$= -1.00$$

The *z* of 1.00 indicates that a weekly income of $1,100 is one standard deviation above the mean, and a *z* of −1.00 shows that a $900 income is one standard deviation below the mean. Note that both incomes ($1,100 and $900) are the same distance ($100) from the mean.

SELF-REVIEW

7–2

A recent national survey concluded that the typical person consumes 48 ounces of water per day. Assume daily water consumption follows a normal probability distribution with a standard deviation of 12.8 ounces.

(a) What is the *z* value for a person who consumes 64 ounces of water per day? Based on this *z* value, how does this person compare to the national average?

(b) What is the *z* value for a person who consumes 32 ounces of water per day? Based on this *z* value, how does this person compare to the national average?

The Empirical Rule

The Empirical Rule is introduced in Chapter 3 on page 79. It states that if a random variable is normally distributed, then:

1. Approximately 68% of the observations will lie within plus and minus one standard deviation of the mean.
2. About 95% of the observations will lie within plus and minus two standard deviations of the mean.
3. Practically all, or 99.7% of the observations, will lie within plus and minus three standard deviations of the mean.

Now, knowing how to apply the standard normal probability distribution, we can verify the Empirical Rule. For example, one standard deviation from the mean is the same as a z value of 1.00. When we refer to the standard normal probability table, a z value of 1.00 corresponds to a probability of 0.3413. So what percent of the observations will lie within plus and minus one standard deviation of the mean? We multiply (2)(0.3413), which equals 0.6826, or approximately 68% of the observations are within plus and minus one standard deviation of the mean.

The Empirical Rule is summarized in the following graph.

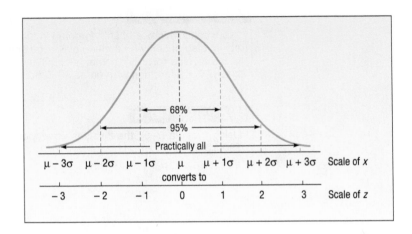

Transforming measurements to standard normal deviates changes the scale. The conversions are also shown in the graph. For example, $\mu + 1\sigma$ is converted to a z value of 1.00. Likewise, $\mu - 2\sigma$ is transformed to a z value of -2.00. Note that the center of the z distribution is zero, indicating no deviation from the mean, μ.

EXAMPLE

As part of its quality assurance program, the Autolite Battery Company conducts tests on battery life. For a particular D-cell alkaline battery, the mean life is 19 hours. The useful life of the battery follows a normal distribution with a standard deviation of 1.2 hours. Answer the following questions.

1. About 68% of the batteries failed between what two values?
2. About 95% of the batteries failed between what two values?
3. Virtually all of the batteries failed between what two values?

SOLUTION

We can use the Empirical Rule to answer these questions.

1. About 68% of the batteries will fail between 17.8 and 20.2 hours, found by $19.0 \pm 1(1.2)$ hours.
2. About 95% of the batteries will fail between 16.6 and 21.4 hours, found by $19.0 \pm 2(1.2)$ hours.
3. Practically all failed between 15.4 and 22.6 hours, found by $19.0 \pm 3(1.2)$ hours.

This information is summarized on the following chart.

SELF-REVIEW

7–3

The distribution of the annual incomes of a group of middle-management employees at Compton Plastics approximates a normal distribution with a mean of $47,200 and a standard deviation of $800.
(a)   About 68% of the incomes lie between what two amounts?
(b)   About 95% of the incomes lie between what two amounts?
(c)   Virtually all of the incomes lie between what two amounts?
(d)   What are the median and the modal incomes?
(e)   Is the distribution of incomes symmetrical?

EXERCISES

▼

7. Explain what is meant by this statement: "There is not just one normal probability distribution but a 'family' of them."
8. List the major characteristics of a normal probability distribution.
9. The mean of a normal probability distribution is 500; the standard deviation is 10.
    a. About 68% of the observations lie between what two values?
    b. About 95% of the observations lie between what two values?
    c. Practically all of the observations lie between what two values?
10. The mean of a normal probability distribution is 60; the standard deviation is 5.
    a. About what percent of the observations lie between 55 and 65?
    b. About what percent of the observations lie between 50 and 70?
    c. About what percent of the observations lie between 45 and 75?
11. The Kamp family has twins, Rob and Rachel. Both Rob and Rachel graduated from college 2 years ago, and each is now earning $50,000 per year. Rachel works in the retail industry, where the mean salary for executives with less than 5 years' experience is $35,000 with a standard deviation of $8,000. Rob is an engineer. The mean salary for engineers with less than 5 years' experience is $60,000 with a standard deviation of $5,000. Compute the z values for both Rob and Rachel and comment on your findings.
12. A recent article in the *Cincinnati Enquirer* reported that the mean labor cost to repair a heat pump is $90 with a standard deviation of $22. Monte's Plumbing and Heating Service completed repairs on two heat pumps this morning. The labor cost for the first was $75 and it was $100 for the second. Assume the distribution of labor costs follows the normal probability distribution. Compute z values for each and comment on your findings.

Finding Areas under the Normal Curve

The next application of the standard normal distribution involves finding the area in a normal distribution between the mean and a selected value, which we identify as *x*. The following example/solution will illustrate the details.

E X A M P L E

In the example/solution first described on page 215, we reported that the weekly income of shift foreman in the glass industry followed the normal distribution with a mean of $1,000 and a standard deviation of $100. That is, $\mu = \$1,000$ and $\sigma = \$100$. What is the likelihood of selecting a foreman whose weekly income is between $1,000 and $1,100?

S O L U T I O N

We have already converted $1,100 to a z value of 1.00 using formula (7–5). To repeat:

$$z = \frac{x - \mu}{\sigma} = \frac{\$1,100 - \$1,000}{\$100} = 1.00$$

The probability associated with a z of 1.00 is available in Appendix B.3. A portion of Appendix B.3 follows. To locate the probability, go down the left column to 1.0, and then move horizontally to the column headed .00. The value is .3413.

z	0.00	0.01	0.02
⋮	⋮	⋮	⋮
0.7	.2580	.2611	.2642
0.8	.2881	.2910	.2939
0.9	.3159	.3186	.3212
1.0	.3413	.3438	.3461
1.1	.3643	.3665	.3686
⋮	⋮	⋮	⋮

The area under the normal curve between $1,000 and $1,100 is .3413. We could also say 34.13% of the shift foremen in the glass industry earn between $1,000 and $1,100 weekly, or the likelihood of selecting a foreman and finding his or her income is between $1,000 and $1,100 is .3413.

This information is summarized in the following diagram.

CONTINUOUS PROBABILITY DISTRIBUTIONS   219

STATISTICS IN ACTION

Many processes, such as filling soda bottles and canning fruit, are normally distributed. Manufacturers must guard against both over- and underfilling. If they put too much in the can or bottle, they are giving away their product. If they put too little in, the customer may feel cheated and the government may question the label description. "Control charts," with limits drawn three standard deviations above and below the mean, are routinely used to monitor this type of production process.

In the example/solution just completed, we are interested in the probability between the mean and a given value. Let's change the question. Instead of wanting to know the probability of selecting at random a foreman who earned between $1,000 and $1,100, suppose we wanted the probability of selecting a foreman who earned less than $1,100. In probability notation, we write this statement as P(weekly income < $1,100). The method of solution is the same. We find the probability of selecting a foreman who earns between $1,000, the mean, and $1,100. This probability is .3413. Next, recall that half the area, or probability, is above the mean and half is below. So the probability of selecting a foreman earning less than $1,000 is .5000. Finally, we add the two probabilities, so .3413 + .5000 = .8413. About 84% of the foremen in the glass industry earn less than $1,100 per week. See the following diagram.

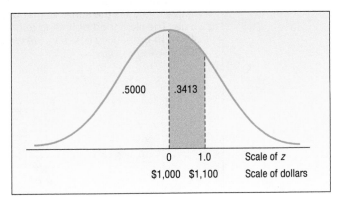

Excel will calculate this probability. The necessary commands are in the **Software Commands** in Appendix C. The answer is .8413, the same as we calculated.

E X A M P L E

Refer to the example/solution first discussed on page 215 regarding the weekly income of shift foremen in the glass industry. The distribution of weekly incomes follows the normal probability distribution, with a mean of $1,000 and a standard deviation of $100. What is the probability of selecting a shift foreman in the glass industry whose income is:

1. Between $790 and $1,000?
2. Less than $790?

SOLUTION

We begin by finding the z value corresponding to a weekly income of $790. From formula (7–5):

$$z = \frac{x - \mu}{s} = \frac{\$790 - \$1,000}{\$100} = -2.10$$

See Appendix B.3. Move down the left margin to the row 2.1 and across that row to the column headed 0.00. The value is .4821. So the area under the standard normal curve corresponding to a z value of 2.10 is .4821. However, because the normal distribution is symmetric, the area between 0 and a negative z value is the same as that between 0 and the corresponding positive z value. The likelihood of finding a foreman earning between $790 and $1,000 is .4821. In probability notation, we write $P(\$790 < \text{weekly income} < \$1,000) = .4821$.

z	0.00	0.01	0.02
⋮	⋮	⋮	⋮
2.0	.4772	.4778	.4783
2.1	.4821	.4826	.4830
2.2	.4861	.4864	.4868
2.3	.4893	.4896	.4898
⋮	⋮	⋮	⋮

The mean divides the normal curve into two identical halves. The area under the half to the left of the mean is .5000, and the area to the right is also .5000. Because the area under the curve between $790 and $1,000 is .4821, the area below $790 is .0179, found by .5000 − .4821. In probability notation, we write $P(\text{weekly income} < \$790) = .0179$.

So we conclude that 48.21% of the foremen have weekly incomes between $790 and $1,000. Further, we can anticipate that 1.79% earn less than $790 per week. This information is summarized in the following diagram.

CONTINUOUS PROBABILITY DISTRIBUTIONS   221

SELF-REVIEW

7–4

The temperature of coffee sold at the Coffee Bean Cafe follows the normal probability distribution, with a mean of 150 degrees. The standard deviation of this distribution is 5 degrees.
(a) What is the probability that the coffee temperature is between 150 degrees and 154 degrees?
(b) What is the probability that the coffee temperature is more than 164 degrees?

EXERCISES

13. A normal population has a mean of 20.0 and a standard deviation of 4.0.
    a. Compute the z value associated with 25.0.
    b. What proportion of the population is between 20.0 and 25.0?
    c. What proportion of the population is less than 18.0?
14. A normal population has a mean of 12.2 and a standard deviation of 2.5.
    a. Compute the z value associated with 14.3.
    b. What proportion of the population is between 12.2 and 14.3?
    c. What proportion of the population is less than 10.0?
15. A recent study of the hourly wages of maintenance crew members for major airlines showed that the mean hourly salary was $20.50, with a standard deviation of $3.50. Assume the distribution of hourly wages follows the normal probability distribution. If we select a crew member at random, what is the probability the crew member earns:
    a. Between $20.50 and $24.00 per hour?
    b. More than $24.00 per hour?
    c. Less than $19.00 per hour?
16. The mean of a normal probability distribution is 400 pounds. The standard deviation is 10 pounds.
    a. What is the area between 415 pounds and the mean of 400 pounds?
    b. What is the area between the mean and 395 pounds?
    c. What is the probability of selecting a value at random and discovering that it has a value of less than 395 pounds?

Another application of the normal distribution involves combining two areas, or probabilities. One of the areas is to the right of the mean and the other to the left.

EXAMPLE

Continuing the example/solution first discussed on page 215 using the weekly income of shift foremen in the glass industry, weekly income follows the normal probability distribution, with a mean of $1,000 and a standard deviation of $100. What is the area under this normal curve between $840 and $1,200?

SOLUTION

The problem can be divided into two parts. For the area between $840 and the mean of $1,000:

$$z = \frac{\$840 - \$1,000}{\$100} = \frac{-\$160}{\$100} = -1.60$$

For the area between the mean of $1,000 and $1,200:

$$z = \frac{\$1,200 - \$1,000}{\$100} = \frac{\$200}{\$100} = 2.00$$

The area under the curve for a z of −1.60 is .4452 (from Appendix B.3). The area under the curve for a z of 2.00 is .4772. Adding the two areas: .4452 + .4772 = .9224. Thus, the probability of selecting an income between $840 and $1,200 is .9224. In probability notation, we write P($840 < weekly income < $1,200) = .4452 + .4772 = .9224. To summarize, 92.24% of the foremen have weekly incomes between $840 and $1,200. This is shown in a diagram:

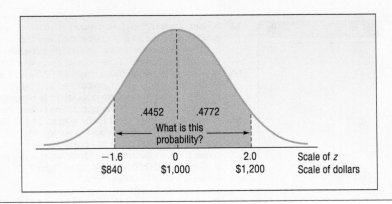

Another application of the normal distribution involves determining the area between values on the *same* side of the mean.

EXAMPLE

Returning to the weekly income distribution of shift foremen in the glass industry (μ = $1,000, σ = $100), what is the area under the normal curve between $1,150 and $1,250?

SOLUTION

The situation is again separated into two parts, and formula (7–5) is used. First, we find the z value associated with a weekly salary of $1,250:

$$z = \frac{\$1,250 - \$1,000}{\$100} = 2.50$$

Next we find the z value for a weekly salary of $1,150:

$$z = \frac{\$1,150 - \$1,000}{\$100} = 1.50$$

From Appendix B.3, the area associated with a z value of 2.50 is .4938. So the probability of a weekly salary between $1,000 and $1,250 is .4938. Similarly, the area associated with a z value of 1.50 is .4332, so the probability of a weekly salary between $1,000 and $1,150 is .4332. The probability of a weekly salary between $1,150 and $1,250 is found by subtracting the area associated with a z value of 1.50 (.4332) from that associated with a z of 2.50 (.4938). Thus, the probability of a weekly salary between $1,150 and $1,250 is .0606. In probability notation, we write P($1,150 < weekly income < $1,250) = .4938 − .4332 = .0606.

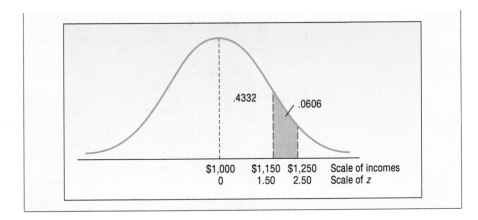

To summarize, there are four situations for finding the area under the standard normal probability distribution.

1. To find the area between 0 and z or $(-z)$, look up the probability directly in the table.
2. To find the area beyond z or $(-z)$, locate the probability of z in the table and subtract that probability from .5000.
3. To find the area between two points on different sides of the mean, determine the z values and add the corresponding probabilities.
4. To find the area between two points on the same side of the mean, determine the z values and subtract the smaller probability from the larger.

SELF-REVIEW

7–5

Refer to Self-Review 7–4. The temperature of coffee sold at the Coffee Bean Cafe follows the normal probability distribution with a mean of 150 degrees. The standard deviation of this distribution is 5 degrees.
(a) What is the probability the coffee temperature is between 146 degrees and 156 degrees?
(b) What is the probability the coffee temperature is more than 156 but less than 162 degrees?

EXERCISES

▼

17. A normal distribution has a mean of 50 and a standard deviation of 4.
    a. Compute the probability of a value between 44.0 and 55.0.
    b. Compute the probability of a value greater than 55.0.
    c. Compute the probability of a value between 52.0 and 55.0.
18. A normal population has a mean of 80.0 and a standard deviation of 14.0.
    a. Compute the probability of a value between 75.0 and 90.0.
    b. Compute the probability of a value of 75.0 or less.
    c. Compute the probability of a value between 55.0 and 70.0.
19. According to the Internal Revenue Service, the mean tax refund for the year 2013 was $3,000. Assume the standard deviation is $450 and that the amounts refunded follow a normal probability distribution.
    a. What percent of the refunds are more than $3,100?
    b. What percent of the refunds are more than $3,100 but less than $3,500?
    c. What percent of the refunds are more than $2,250 but less than $3,500?
20. The distribution of the number of viewers for the *American Idol* television show follows a normal distribution with a mean of 29 million and a standard deviation of 5 million. What is the probability next week's show will:
    a. Have between 30 and 34 million viewers?
    b. Have at least 23 million viewers?
    c. Exceed 40 million viewers?

224

CHAPTER 7

21. WNAE, an all-news AM station, finds that the distribution of the lengths of time listeners are tuned to the station follows the normal distribution. The mean of the distribution is 15.0 minutes and the standard deviation is 3.5 minutes. What is the probability that a particular listener will tune in for:
   a. More than 20 minutes?
   b. 20 minutes or less?
   c. Between 10 and 12 minutes?
22. Among U.S. cities with a population of more than 250,000, the mean one-way commute time to work is 24.3 minutes. The longest one-way travel time is in New York City, where the mean time is 38.3 minutes. Assume the distribution of travel times in New York City follows the normal probability distribution and the standard deviation is 7.5 minutes.
   a. What percent of the New York City commutes are for less than 30 minutes?
   b. What percent are between 30 and 35 minutes?
   c. What percent are between 30 and 40 minutes?

The previous example/solutions require finding the percent of the observations located between two observations or the percent of the observations above, or below, a particular observation x. A further application of the normal distribution involves finding the value of the observation x when the percent above or below the observation is given.

E X A M P L E

Layton Tire and Rubber Company wishes to set a minimum mileage guarantee on its new MX100 tire. Tests reveal the mean mileage is 67,900 with a standard deviation of 2,050 miles and that the distribution of miles follows the normal probability distribution. Layton wants to set the minimum guaranteed mileage so that no more than 4% of the tires will have to be replaced. What minimum guaranteed mileage should Layton announce?

S O L U T I O N

The facets of this case are shown in the following diagram, where x represents the minimum guaranteed mileage.

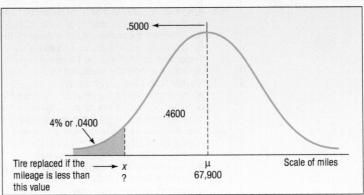

.5000

.4600

4% or .0400

Tire replaced if the ⟶ x
mileage is less than   ?
this value

μ
67,900

Scale of miles

Inserting these values in formula (7–5) for z gives:

$$z = \frac{x - \mu}{\sigma} = \frac{x - 67,900}{2,050}$$

There are two unknowns in this equation, z and x. To find x, we first find z, and then solve for x. Recall from the characteristics of a normal curve that the area to the left of μ is .5000. The area between μ and x is .4600, found by .5000 − .0400. Now refer to Appendix B.3. Search the body of the table for the area closest to .4600. The closest area is .4599. Move to the margins from this value and read the z value of 1.75. Because the value is to the left of the mean, it is actually −1.75. These steps are illustrated in Table 7–2.

TABLE 7–2 Selected Areas under the Normal Curve

z ...	.03	.04	.05	.06
⋮	⋮	⋮	⋮	⋮
1.5	.4370	.4382	.4394	.4406
1.6	.4484	.4495	.4505	.4515
1.7	.4582	.4591	.4599	.4608
1.8	.4664	.4671	.4678	.4686

Knowing that the distance between μ and x is -1.75σ or $z = -1.75$, we can now solve for x (the minimum guaranteed mileage):

$$z = \frac{x - 67,900}{2,050}$$

$$-1.75 = \frac{x - 67,900}{2,050}$$

$$-1.75(2,050) = x - 67,900$$

$$x = 67,900 - 1.75(2,050) = 64,312$$

So Layton can advertise that it will replace for free any tire that wears out before it reaches 64,312 miles, and the company will know that only 4% of the tires will be replaced under this plan.

Excel will also find the mileage value. See the following output. The necessary commands are given in the **Software Commands** in Appendix C.

226   CHAPTER 7

SELF-REVIEW

7–6

An analysis of the final test scores for Introduction to Business reveals the scores follow the normal probability distribution. The mean of the distribution is 75 and the standard deviation is 8. The professor wants to award an A to students whose score is in the highest 10%. What is the dividing point for those students who earn an A and those earning a B?

EXERCISES

23. A normal distribution has a mean of 50 and a standard deviation of 4. Determine the value below which 95% of the observations will occur.

24. A normal distribution has a mean of 80 and a standard deviation of 14. Determine the value above which 80% of the values will occur.

25. Assume that the hourly cost to operate a commercial airplane follows the normal distribution with a mean of $2,100 per hour and a standard deviation of $250. What is the operating cost for the lowest 3% of the airplanes?

26. The SAT Reasoning Test is perhaps the most widely used standardized test for college admissions in the United States. Scores are based on a normal distribution with a mean of 1500 and a standard deviation of 300. Clinton College would like to offer an honors scholarship to students who score in the top 10% of this test. What is the minimum score that qualifies for the scholarship?

27. According to media research, the typical American listened to 195 hours of music in the last year. This is down from 290 hours 4 years earlier. Dick Trythall is a big country and western music fan. He listens to music while working around the house, reading, and riding in his truck. Assume the number of hours spent listening to music follows a normal probability distribution with a standard deviation of 8.5 hours.
    a. If Dick is in the top 1% in terms of listening time, how many hours did he listen last year?
    b. Assume that the distribution of times 4 years earlier also follows the normal probability distribution with a standard deviation of 8.5 hours. How many hours did the 1% who listen to the *least* music actually listen?

28. For the most recent year available, the mean annual cost to attend a private university in the United States was $26,889. Assume the distribution of annual costs follows the normal probability distribution and the standard deviation is $4,500. Ninety-five percent of all students at private universities pay less than what amount?

29. In economic theory, a "hurdle rate" is the minimum return that a person requires before he or she will make an investment. A research report says that annual returns from a specific class of common equities are distributed according to a normal distribution with a mean of 12% and a standard deviation of 18%. A stock screener would like to identify a hurdle rate such that only 1 in 20 equities is above that value. Where should the hurdle rate be set?

30. The manufacturer of a laser printer reports the mean number of pages a cartridge will print before it needs replacing is 12,200. The distribution of pages printed per cartridge closely follows the normal probability distribution and the standard deviation is 820 pages. The manufacturer wants to provide guidelines to potential customers as to how long they can expect a cartridge to last. How many pages should the manufacturer advertise for each cartridge if it wants to be correct 99% of the time?

LO7-4

Approximate the binomial probability distribution using the standard normal probability distribution to calculate probabilities.

THE NORMAL APPROXIMATION TO THE BINOMIAL

Chapter 6 describes the binomial probability distribution, which is a discrete distribution. The table of binomial probabilities in Appendix B.1 goes successively from an *n* of 1 to an *n* of 15. If a problem involved taking a sample of 60, generating a binomial distribution for that large a number would be very time-consuming. A more efficient approach is to apply the *normal approximation to the binomial*.

We can use the normal distribution (a continuous distribution) as a substitute for a binomial distribution (a discrete distribution) for large values of *n* because, as *n* increases, a binomial distribution gets closer and closer to a normal distribution.

CHART 7–7 Binomial Distributions for an n of 1, 3, and 20, Where $\pi = .50$

Chart 7–7 depicts the change in the shape of a binomial distribution with $\pi = .50$ from an n of 1, to an n of 3, to an n of 20. Notice how the case where $n = 20$ approximates the shape of the normal distribution. That is, compare the case where $n = 20$ to the normal curve in Chart 7–3 on page 212.

When can we use the normal approximation to the binomial? The normal probability distribution is a good approximation to the binomial probability distribution when $n\pi$ and $n(1 - \pi)$ are both at least 5. However, before we apply the normal approximation, we must make sure that our distribution of interest is in fact a binomial distribution. Recall from Chapter 6 that four criteria must be met:

1. There are only two mutually exclusive outcomes to an experiment: a "success" and a "failure."
2. The distribution results from counting the number of successes in a fixed number of trials.
3. The probability of a success, π, remains the same from trial to trial.
4. Each trial is independent.

Continuity Correction Factor

To show the application of the normal approximation to the binomial and the need for a correction factor, suppose the management of the Santoni Pizza Restaurant found that 70% of its new customers return for another meal. For a week in which 80 new (first-time) customers dined at Santoni's, what is the probability that 60 or more will return for another meal?

Notice the binomial conditions are met: (1) There are only two possible outcomes—a customer either returns for another meal or does not return. (2) We can count the number of successes, meaning, for example, that 57 of the 80 customers return. (3) The trials are independent, meaning that if the 34th person returns for a second meal, that does not affect whether the 58th person returns. (4) The probability of a customer returning remains at .70 for all 80 customers.

Therefore, we could use the binomial formula (6–3) described on page 183.

$$P(x) = {}_nC_x\,(\pi)^x\,(1 - \pi)^{n-x}$$

To find the probability 60 or more customers return for another pizza, we need to first find the probability exactly 60 customers return. That is:

$$P(x = 60) = {}_{80}C_{60}\,(.70)^{60}\,(1 - .70)^{20} = .063$$

Next we find the probability that exactly 61 customers return. It is:

$$P(x = 61) = {}_{80}C_{61}\,(.70)^{61}\,(1 - .70)^{19} = .048$$

We continue this process until we have the probability that all 80 customers return. Finally, we add the probabilities from 60 to 80. Solving the preceding problem in this manner is tedious. We can also use statistical software packages to find the various probabilities. Listed below are the binomial probabilities for $n = 80$, $\pi = .70$, and x, the number of customers returning, ranging from 43 to 68. The probability of any number of customers less than 43 or more than 68 returning is less than .001. We can assume these probabilities are 0.000.

Many variables are approximately, normally distributed, such as IQ scores, life expectancies, and adult height. This implies that nearly all observations occur within 3 standard deviations of the mean. On the other hand, observations that occur beyond 3 standard deviations from the mean are extremely rare. For example, the mean adult male height is 68.2 inches (about 5 feet 8 inches) with a standard deviation of 2.74. This means that almost all males are between 60.0 inches (5 feet) and 76.4 inches (6 feet 4 inches). LeBron James, a professional basketball player with the Miami Heat, is 80 inches, or 6 feet 8 inches, which is clearly beyond 3 standard deviations from the mean. The height of a standard doorway is 6 feet 8 inches, and should be high enough for almost all adult males, except for a rare person like LeBron James.

As another example, the driver's seat in most vehicles is set to comfortably fit a person who is at least 159 cm (62.5 inches) tall. The distribution of heights of adult women is approximately a normal distribution with a mean of 161.5 cm and a standard deviation of 6.3 cm. Thus about 35% of adult women will not fit comfortably in the driver's seat.

Number Returning	Probability	Number Returning	Probability
43	.001	56	.097
44	.002	57	.095
45	.003	58	.088
46	.006	59	.077
47	.009	60	.063
48	.015	61	.048
49	.023	62	.034
50	.033	63	.023
51	.045	64	.014
52	.059	65	.008
53	.072	66	.004
54	.084	67	.002
55	.093	68	.001

We can find the probability of 60 or more returning by summing .063 + .048 + ⋯ + .001, which is .197. However, a look at the plot below shows the similarity of this distribution to a normal distribution. All we need do is "smooth out" the discrete probabilities into a continuous distribution. Furthermore, working with a normal distribution will involve far fewer calculations than working with the binomial.

The trick is to let the discrete probability for 56 customers be represented by an area under the continuous curve between 55.5 and 56.5. Then let the probability for 57 customers be represented by an area between 56.5 and 57.5, and so on. This is just the opposite of rounding off the numbers to a whole number.

Because we use the normal distribution to determine the binomial probability of 60 or more successes, we must subtract, in this case, .5 from 60. The value .5 is called the **continuity correction factor.** This small adjustment is made because a continuous distribution (the normal distribution) is being used to approximate a discrete distribution (the binomial distribution). Subtracting, $60 - .5 = 59.5$.

> **CONTINUITY CORRECTION FACTOR** The value .5 subtracted or added, depending on the question, to a selected value when a discrete probability distribution is approximated by a continuous probability distribution.

How to Apply the Correction Factor

Only four cases may arise. These cases are:

1. For the probability *at least* x occur, use the area *above* (x − .5).
2. For the probability that *more than* x occur, use the area *above* (x + .5).
3. For the probability that *x or fewer* occur, use the area *below* (x + .5).
4. For the probability that *fewer than* x occur, use the area *below* (x − .5).

To use the normal distribution to approximate the probability that 60 or more first-time Santoni customers out of 80 will return, follow the procedure shown below.

Step 1: Find the z value corresponding to an x of 59.5 using formula (7–5), and formulas (6–4) and (6–5) for the mean and the variance of a binomial distribution:

$$\mu = n\pi = 80(.70) = 56$$
$$\sigma^2 = n\pi(1 - \pi) = 80(.70)(1 - .70) = 16.8$$
$$\sigma = \sqrt{16.8} = 4.10$$
$$z = \frac{x - \mu}{\sigma} = \frac{59.5 - 56}{4.10} = 0.85$$

Step 2: Determine the area under the normal curve between a μ of 56 and an x of 59.5. From step 1, we know that the z value corresponding to 59.5 is 0.85. So we go to Appendix B.3 and read down the left margin to 0.8, and then we go horizontally to the area under the column headed by .05. That area is .3023.

Step 3: Calculate the area beyond 59.5 by subtracting .3023 from .5000 (.5000 − .3023 = .1977). Thus, .1977 is the probability that 60 or more first-time Santoni customers out of 80 will return for another meal. In probability notation, P(customers > 59.5) = .5000 − .3023 = .1977. The facets of this problem are shown graphically:

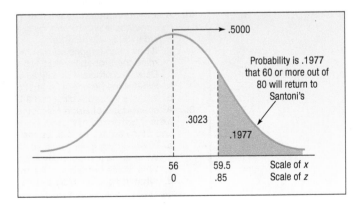

230   CHAPTER 7

No doubt you will agree that using the normal approximation to the binomial is a more efficient method of estimating the probability of 60 or more first-time customers returning. The result compares favorably with that computed on page 228, using the binomial distribution. The probability using the binomial distribution is .197, whereas the probability using the normal approximation is .1977.

SELF-REVIEW

7–7

A study by Great Southern Home Insurance revealed that none of the stolen goods were recovered by the homeowners in 80% of reported thefts.
(a) During a period in which 200 thefts occurred, what is the probability that no stolen goods were recovered in 170 or more of the robberies?
(b) During a period in which 200 thefts occurred, what is the probability that no stolen goods were recovered in 150 or more robberies?

EXERCISES

▼

31. Assume a binomial probability distribution with $n = 50$ and $\pi = .25$. Compute the following:
   a. The mean and standard deviation of the random variable.
   b. The probability that x is 15 or more.
   c. The probability that x is 10 or less.
32. Assume a binomial probability distribution with $n = 40$ and $\pi = .55$. Compute the following:
   a. The mean and standard deviation of the random variable.
   b. The probability that x is 25 or greater.
   c. The probability that x is 15 or less.
   d. The probability that x is between 15 and 25, inclusive.
33. Dottie's Tax Service specializes in federal tax returns for professional clients, such as physicians, dentists, accountants, and lawyers. A recent audit by the IRS of the returns she prepared indicated that an error was made on 7% of the returns she prepared last year. Assuming this rate continues into this year and she prepares 80 returns, what is the probability that she makes errors on:
   a. More than six returns?
   b. At least six returns?
   c. Exactly six returns?
34. Shorty's Muffler advertises it can install a new muffler in 30 minutes or less. However, the work standards department at corporate headquarters recently conducted a study and found that 20% of the mufflers were not installed in 30 minutes or less. The Maumee branch installed 50 mufflers last month. If the corporate report is correct:
   a. How many of the installations at the Maumee branch would you expect to take more than 30 minutes?
   b. What is the likelihood that fewer than eight installations took more than 30 minutes?
   c. What is the likelihood that eight or fewer installations took more than 30 minutes?
   d. What is the likelihood that exactly 8 of the 50 installations took more than 30 minutes?
35. A study conducted by the nationally known Taurus Health Club revealed that 30% of its new members are 15 pounds overweight. A membership drive in a metropolitan area resulted in 500 new members.
   a. It has been suggested that the normal approximation to the binomial be used to determine the probability that 175 or more of the new members are 15 pounds overweight. Does this problem qualify as a binomial problem? Explain.
   b. What is the probability that 175 or more of the new members are 15 pounds overweight?
   c. What is the probability that 140 or more new members are 15 pounds overweight?
36. A recent issue of *Bride Magazine* suggested that couples planning their wedding should expect two-thirds of those who are sent an invitation to respond that they will attend. Rich and Stacy are planning to be married later this year. They plan to send 197 invitations.
   a. How many guests would you expect to accept the invitation?
   b. What is the standard deviation?
   c. What is the probability 140 or more will accept the invitation?
   d. What is the probability exactly 140 will accept the invitation?

LO7-5
Describe the exponential probability distribution and use it to calculate probabilities.

THE FAMILY OF EXPONENTIAL DISTRIBUTIONS

So far in this chapter, we have considered two continuous probability distributions, the uniform and the normal. The next continuous distribution we consider is the exponential distribution. This continuous probability distribution usually describes times between events in a sequence. The actions occur independently at a constant rate per unit of time or length. Because time is never negative, an exponential random variable is always positive. The exponential distribution usually describes situations such as:

- The service time for customers at the information desk of the Dallas Public Library.
- The time between "hits" on a website.
- The lifetime of an electrical component.
- The time until the next phone call arrives in a customer service center.

The exponential probability distribution is positively skewed. That differs from the uniform and normal distributions, which were both symmetric. Moreover, the distribution is described by only one parameter, which we will identify as λ (pronounced "lambda"). λ is often referred to as the "rate" parameter. The following chart shows the change in the shape of the exponential distribution as we vary the value of λ from 1/3 to 1 to 2. Observe that as we decrease λ, the shape of the distribution changes to become "less skewed."

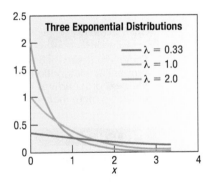

Another feature of the exponential distribution is its close relationship to the Poisson distribution. The Poisson is a discrete probability distribution and also has a single parameter, μ. We described the Poisson distribution starting on page 194 in Chapter 6. It too is a positively skewed distribution. To explain the relationship between the Poisson and the exponential distributions, suppose the rate customers arrive at a family restaurant during the dinner hour is six per hour. We use the Poisson distribution to find the probability in any particular dinner hour that two customers arrive, or that seven arrive, and so on. So we have a Poisson distribution with a mean of 6. But suppose instead of studying the number of customers *arriving in an hour,* we wished to study the time *between their arrivals.* The time between arrivals is a continuous distribution because time is measured as a continuous random variable. If customers arrive at a rate of six per hour, then logically the typical or mean time between arrivals is 1/6 of an hour, or 10 minutes. We need to be careful here to be consistent with our units, so let's stay with 1/6 of an hour. So in general, if we know customers arrive at a certain rate per hour, which we call μ, then we can expect the mean time between arrivals to be $1/\mu$. The rate parameter λ is equal to $1/\mu$. So in our restaurant arrival example, $\lambda = 1/6$.

The graph of the exponential distribution starts at the value of λ when the random variable's (x) value is 0. The distribution declines steadily as we move to the right with increasing values of x. Formula (7–6) describes the exponential probability distribution with λ as rate parameter. As we described with the Poisson distribution on page 194, e is a mathematical constant equal to 2.71828. It is the basis of the Napierian logarithmic system. It is a pleasant surprise that both the mean and the standard deviation of the exponential probability distribution are equal to $1/\lambda$.

EXPONENTIAL DISTRIBUTION	$P(x) = \lambda e^{-\lambda x}$	[7–6]

With continuous distributions, we do not address the probability that a distinct value will occur. Instead, areas or regions below the graph of the probability distribution between two specified values give the probability the random variable is in that interval. A table, such as Appendix B.3 for the normal distribution, is not necessary for the exponential distribution. The area under the exponential density function is found by a formula and the necessary calculations can be accomplished with a handheld calculator that has an e^x key. Most statistical software packages will also calculate exponential probabilities by inputting the rate parameter, λ, only. The probability of obtaining an arrival value less than a particular value of x is:

FINDING A PROBABILITY USING THE EXPONENTIAL DISTRIBUTION	$P(\text{Arrival time} < x) = 1 - e^{-\lambda x}$	[7–7]

EXAMPLE

Orders for prescriptions arrive at a pharmacy website according to an exponential probability distribution at a mean of one every 20 seconds. Find the probability the next order arrives in less than 5 seconds. Find the probability the next order arrives in more than 40 seconds.

SOLUTION

To begin, we determine the rate parameter λ, which in this case is 1/20. To find the probability, we insert 1/20 for λ and 5 for x in formula (7–7).

$$P(\text{Arrival time} < 5) = 1 - e^{-\frac{1}{20}(5)} = 1 - e^{-0.25} = 1 - .7788 = .2212$$

So we conclude there is a 22% chance the next order will arrive in less than 5 seconds. The region is identified as the rust-colored area under the curve.

CONTINUOUS PROBABILITY DISTRIBUTIONS   233

The preceding computations addressed the area in the left-tail area of the exponential distribution with $\lambda = 1/20$ and the area between 0 and 5—that is, the area that is below 5 seconds. What if you are interested in the right-tail area? It is found using the complement rule. See formula (5–3) on page 142 in Chapter 5. To put it another way, to find the probability the next order will arrive in more than 40 seconds, we find the probability the order arrives in less than 40 seconds and subtract the result from 1.00. We show this in two steps.

1. Find the probability an order is received *in less than* 40 seconds.

$$P(\text{Arrival} < 40) = 1 - e^{-\frac{1}{20}(40)} = 1 - .1353 = .8647$$

2. Find the probability an order is received *in more than* 40 seconds.

$$P(\text{Arrival} > 40) = 1 - P(\text{Arrival} < 40) = 1 - .8647 = .1353$$

We conclude that the likelihood that it will be 40 seconds or more before the next order is received at the pharmacy is 13.5%.

In the preceding example/solution, when we apply the exponential probability distribution to compute the probability that the arrival time is greater than 40 seconds, you probably observed that there is some redundancy. In general, if we wish to find the likelihood of a time greater than some value x, such as 40, the complement rule is applied as follows:

$$P(\text{Arrival} > x) = 1 - P(\text{Arrival} < x) = 1 - (1 - e^{-\lambda x}) = e^{-\lambda x}$$

In other words, when we subtract formula (7–7) from 1 to find the area in the right tail, the result is $e^{-\lambda x}$. Thus, the probability that more than 40 seconds go by before the next order arrives is computed without the aid of the complement rule as follows:

$$P(\text{Arrival} > 40) = e^{-\frac{1}{20}(40)} = .1353$$

The result is shown in the following graph.

What if you wish to determine the probability that it will take more than 5 seconds but less than 40 seconds for the next order to arrive? Use formula (7–7) with an x value of 40 and then subtract the value of formula (7–7) when x is 5.

In symbols, you can write this as:

$$P(5 \leq x \leq 40) = P(\text{Arrival} \leq 40) - P(\text{Arrival} \leq 5)$$

$$= (1 - e^{-\frac{1}{20}(40)}) - (1 - e^{-\frac{1}{20}(5)}) = .8647 - .2212 = .6435$$

We conclude that 64% of the time, the time between orders will be between 5 seconds and 40 seconds.

Previous examples require finding the percentage of the observations located between two values or the percentage of the observations above or below a particular value, *x*. We can also use formula (7–7) in "reverse" to find the value of the observation *x* when the percentage above or below the observation is given. The following example/solution illustrates this situation.

E X A M P L E

Compton Computers wishes to set a minimum lifetime guarantee on its new power supply unit. Quality testing shows the time to failure follows an exponential distribution with a mean of 4,000 hours. Compton wants a warranty period such that only 5% of the power supply units fail during that period. What value should they set for the warranty period?

S O L U T I O N

Note that 4,000 hours is a mean and not a rate. Therefore, we must compute λ as 1/4,000, or 0.00025 failure per hour. A diagram of the situation is shown below, where *x* represents the minimum guaranteed lifetime.

CONTINUOUS PROBABILITY DISTRIBUTIONS 235

We use formula (7–7) and essentially work backward for the solution. In this case, the rate parameter is 4,000 hours and we want the area, as shown in the diagram, to be .05.

$$P(\text{Arrival time} < x) = 1 - e^{(-\lambda x)}$$

$$.05 = 1 - e^{-\frac{1}{4,000}(x)}$$

Next, we solve this equation for x. So, we subtract 1 from both sides of the equation and multiply by -1 to simplify the signs. The result is:

$$.95 = e^{-\frac{1}{4,000}(x)}$$

Next, we take the natural log of both sides and solve for x:

$$\ln(.95) = -\frac{1}{4,000}x$$

$$-(.051293294) = -\frac{1}{4,000}x$$

$$x = 205.17$$

In this case, $x = 205.17$. Hence, Compton can set the warranty period at 205 hours and expect about 5% of the power supply units to be returned.

SELF-REVIEW

7–8

The time between ambulance arrivals at the Methodist Hospital emergency room follows an exponential distribution with a mean of 10 minutes.
(a) What is the likelihood the next ambulance will arrive in 15 minutes or less?
(b) What is the likelihood the next ambulance will arrive in more than 25 minutes?
(c) What is the likelihood the next ambulance will arrive in more than 15 minutes but less than 25?
(d) Find the 80th percentile for the time between ambulance arrivals. (This means only 20% of the runs are longer than this time.)

EXERCISES

37. Waiting times to receive food after placing an order at the local Subway sandwich shop follow an exponential distribution with a mean of 60 seconds. Calculate the probability a customer waits:
  a. Less than 30 seconds.
  b. More than 120 seconds.
  c. Between 45 and 75 seconds.
  d. Fifty percent of the patrons wait less than how many seconds? What is the median?
38. The lifetime of plasma and LCD TV sets follows an exponential distribution with a mean of 100,000 hours. Compute the probability a television set:
  a. Fails in less than 10,000 hours.
  b. Lasts more than 120,000 hours.
  c. Fails between 60,000 and 100,000 hours of use.
  d. Find the 90th percentile. So 10% of the TV sets last more than what length of time?
39. The Bureau of Labor Statistics' *American Time Use Survey* showed that the amount of time spent using a computer for leisure varied greatly by age. Individuals age 75 and over averaged 0.3 hour (18 minutes) per day using a computer for leisure. Individuals ages 15 to 19 spend 1.0 hour per day using a computer for leisure. If these times follow an exponential distribution, find the proportion of each group that spends:
  a. Less than 15 minutes per day using a computer for leisure.
  b. More than 2 hours.
  c. Between 30 minutes and 90 minutes using a computer for leisure.
  d. Find the 20th percentile. Eighty percent spend more than what amount of time?

236   CHAPTER 7

40. The cost per item at a supermarket follows an exponential distribution. There are many inexpensive items and a few relatively expensive ones. The mean cost per item is $3.50. What is the percentage of items that cost:
  a. Less than $1?
  b. More than $4?
  c. Between $2 and $3?
  d. Find the 40th percentile. Sixty percent of the supermarket items cost more than what amount?

C H A P T E R   S U M M A R Y

I. The uniform distribution is a continuous probability distribution with the following characteristics.
  A. It is rectangular in shape.
  B. The mean and the median are equal.
  C. It is completely described by its minimum value a and its maximum value b.
  D. It is described by the following equation for the region from a to b:

$$P(x) = \frac{1}{b - a}$$ [7–3]

  E. The mean and standard deviation of a uniform distribution are computed as follows:

$$\mu = \frac{(a + b)}{2}$$ [7–1]

$$\sigma = \sqrt{\frac{(b - a)^2}{12}}$$ [7–2]

II. The normal probability distribution is a continuous distribution with the following characteristics.
  A. It is bell-shaped and has a single peak at the center of the distribution.
  B. The distribution is symmetric.
  C. It is asymptotic, meaning the curve approaches but never touches the X-axis.
  D. It is completely described by its mean and standard deviation.
  E. There is a family of normal probability distributions.
    1. Another normal probability distribution is created when either the mean or the standard deviation changes.
    2. The normal probability distribution is described by the following formula:

$$P(x) = \frac{1}{\sigma\sqrt{2\pi}} e^{-\left[\frac{(x - \mu)^2}{2\sigma^2}\right]}$$ [7–4]

III. The standard normal probability distribution is a particular normal distribution.
  A. It has a mean of 0 and a standard deviation of 1.
  B. Any normal probability distribution can be converted to the standard normal probability distribution by the following formula.

$$z = \frac{x - \mu}{\sigma}$$ [7–5]

  C. By standardizing a normal probability distribution, we can report the distance of a value from the mean in units of the standard deviation.
IV. The normal probability distribution can approximate a binomial distribution under certain conditions.
  A. $n\pi$ and $n(1 - \pi)$ must both be at least 5.
    1. n is the number of observations.
    2. π is the probability of a success.
  B. The four conditions for a binomial probability distribution are:
    1. There are only two possible outcomes.
    2. π remains the same from trial to trial.

CONTINUOUS PROBABILITY DISTRIBUTIONS   237

    3. The trials are independent.

    4. The distribution results from a count of the number of successes in a fixed number of trials.

  C. The mean and variance of a binomial distribution are computed as follows:

$$\mu = n\pi$$

$$\sigma^2 = n\pi(1 - \pi)$$

  D. The continuity correction factor of .5 is used to extend the continuous value of x one-half unit in either direction. This correction compensates for approximating a discrete distribution by a continuous distribution.

V. The exponential probability distribution describes times between events in a sequence.

  A. The actions occur independently at a constant rate per unit of time or length.

  B. The probability density is given by the formula:

$$P(x) = \lambda e^{-\lambda x} \qquad \text{[7–6]}$$

  C. It is nonnegative, is positively skewed, declines steadily to the right, and is asymptotic.

  D. The area under the curve is given by the formula

$$P(\text{Arrival time} < x) = 1 - e^{-\lambda x} \qquad \text{[7–7]}$$

  E. Both the mean and standard deviation are $1/\lambda$.

C H A P T E R   E X E R C I S E S

41. The amount of cola in a 12-ounce can is uniformly distributed between 11.96 ounces and 12.05 ounces.
  a. What is the mean amount per can?
  b. What is the standard deviation amount per can?
  c. What is the probability of selecting a can of cola and finding it has less than 12 ounces?
  d. What is the probability of selecting a can of cola and finding it has more than 11.98 ounces?
  e. What is the probability of selecting a can of cola and finding it has more than 11.00 ounces?

42. A tube of Listerine Tartar Control toothpaste contains 4.2 ounces. As people use the toothpaste, the amount remaining in any tube is random. Assume the amount of toothpaste remaining in the tube follows a uniform distribution. From this information, we can determine the following information about the amount remaining in a toothpaste tube without invading anyone's privacy.
  a. How much toothpaste would you expect to be remaining in the tube?
  b. What is the standard deviation of the amount remaining in the tube?
  c. What is the likelihood there is less than 3.0 ounces remaining in the tube?
  d. What is the probability there is more than 1.5 ounces remaining in the tube?

43. Many retail stores offer their own credit cards. At the time of the credit application, the customer is given a 10% discount on the purchase. The time required for the credit application process follows a uniform distribution with the times ranging from 4 minutes to 10 minutes.
  a. What is the mean time for the application process?
  b. What is the standard deviation of the process time?
  c. What is the likelihood a particular application will take less than 6 minutes?
  d. What is the likelihood an application will take more than 5 minutes?

44. The time patrons at the Grande Dunes Hotel in the Bahamas spend waiting for an elevator follows a uniform distribution between 0 and 3.5 minutes.
  a. Show that the area under the curve is 1.00.
  b. How long does the typical patron wait for elevator service?
  c. What is the standard deviation of the waiting time?
  d. What percent of the patrons wait for less than a minute?
  e. What percent of the patrons wait more than 2 minutes?

45. The net sales and the number of employees for aluminum fabricators with similar characteristics are organized into frequency distributions. Both are normally distributed. For the net sales, the mean is $180 million and the standard deviation is $25 million. For the number of employees, the mean is 1,500 and the standard deviation is 120. Clarion Fabricators had sales of $170 million and 1,850 employees.
   a. Convert Clarion's sales and number of employees to z values.
   b. Locate the two z values.
   c. Compare Clarion's sales and number of employees with those of the other fabricators.

46. The accounting department at Weston Materials Inc., a national manufacturer of unattached garages, reports that it takes two construction workers a mean of 32 hours and a standard deviation of 2 hours to erect the Red Barn model. Assume the assembly times follow the normal distribution.
   a. Determine the z values for 29 and 34 hours. What percent of the garages take between 32 hours and 34 hours to erect?
   b. What percent of the garages take between 29 hours and 34 hours to erect?
   c. What percent of the garages take 28.7 hours or less to erect?
   d. Of the garages, 5% take how many hours or more to erect?

47. A recent report indicated a typical family of four spends $490 per month on food. Assume the distribution of food expenditures for a family of four follows the normal distribution, with a standard deviation of $90 per month.
   a. What percent of the families spend more than $30 but less than $490 per month on food?
   b. What percent of the families spend less than $430 per month on food?
   c. What percent spend between $430 and $600 per month on food?
   d. What percent spend between $500 and $600 per month on food?

48. A study of long-distance phone calls made from General Electric Corporate Headquarters in Fairfield, Connecticut, revealed the length of the calls, in minutes, follows the normal probability distribution. The mean length of time per call was 4.2 minutes and the standard deviation was 0.60 minute.
   a. What fraction of the calls lasts between 4.2 and 5 minutes?
   b. What fraction of the calls lasts more than 5 minutes?
   c. What fraction of the calls lasts between 5 and 6 minutes?
   d. What fraction of the calls lasts between 4 and 6 minutes?
   e. As part of her report to the president, the director of communications would like to report the length of the longest (in duration) 4% of the calls. What is this time?

49. Shaver Manufacturing Inc. offers dental insurance to its employees. A recent study by the human resource director shows the annual cost per employee per year followed the normal probability distribution, with a mean of $1,280 and a standard deviation of $420 per year.
   a. What fraction of the employees costs more than $1,500 per year for dental expenses?
   b. What fraction of the employees costs between $1,500 and $2,000 per year?
   c. Estimate the percent that did not have any dental expense.
   d. What was the cost for the 10% of employees who incurred the highest dental expense?

50. The annual commissions earned by sales representatives of Machine Products Inc., a manufacturer of light machinery, follow the normal probability distribution. The mean yearly amount earned is $40,000 and the standard deviation is $5,000.
   a. What percent of the sales representatives earn more than $42,000 per year?
   b. What percent of the sales representatives earn between $32,000 and $42,000?
   c. What percent of the sales representatives earn between $32,000 and $35,000?
   d. The sales manager wants to award the sales representatives who earn the largest commissions a bonus of $1,000. He can award a bonus to 20% of the representatives. What is the cutoff point between those who earn a bonus and those who do not?

51. According to the South Dakota Department of Health, the number of hours of TV viewing per week is higher among adult women than adult men. A recent study showed women spent an average of 34 hours per week watching TV, and men, 29 hours per week. Assume that the distribution of hours watched follows the normal distribution for both groups, and that the standard deviation among the women is 4.5 hours and is 5.1 hours for the men.
   a. What percent of the women watch TV less than 40 hours per week?
   b. What percent of the men watch TV more than 25 hours per week?
   c. How many hours of TV do the 1% of women who watch the most TV per week watch? Find the comparable value for the men.

CONTINUOUS PROBABILITY DISTRIBUTIONS   239

52. According to a government study among adults in the 25- to 34-year age group, the mean amount spent per year on reading and entertainment is $1,994. Assume that the distribution of the amounts spent follows the normal distribution with a standard deviation of $450.
   a. What percent of the adults spend more than $2,500 per year on reading and entertainment?
   b. What percent spend between $2,500 and $3,000 per year on reading and entertainment?
   c. What percent spend less than $1,000 per year on reading and entertainment?

53. Management at Gordon Electronics is considering adopting a bonus system to increase production. One suggestion is to pay a bonus on the highest 5% of production based on past experience. Past records indicate weekly production follows the normal distribution. The mean of this distribution is 4,000 units per week and the standard deviation is 60 units per week. If the bonus is paid on the upper 5% of production, the bonus will be paid on how many units or more?

54. Fast Service Truck Lines uses the Ford Super Duty F-750 exclusively. Management made a study of the maintenance costs and determined the number of miles traveled during the year followed the normal distribution. The mean of the distribution was 60,000 miles and the standard deviation 2,000 miles.
   a. What percent of the Ford Super Duty F-750s logged 65,200 miles or more?
   b. What percent of the trucks logged more than 57,060 but less than 58,280 miles?
   c. What percent of the Fords traveled 62,000 miles or less during the year?
   d. Is it reasonable to conclude that any of the trucks were driven more than 70,000 miles? Explain.

55. Best Electronics Inc. offers a "no hassle" returns policy. The number of items returned per day follows the normal distribution. The mean number of customer returns is 10.3 per day and the standard deviation is 2.25 per day.
   a. In what percent of the days are there eight or fewer customers returning items?
   b. In what percent of the days are between 12 and 14 customers returning items?
   c. Is there any chance of a day with no returns?

56. A recent news report indicated that 20% of all employees steal from their company each year. If a company employs 50 people, what is the probability that:
   a. Fewer than five employees steal?
   b. More than five employees steal?
   c. Exactly five employees steal?
   d. More than 5 but fewer than 15 employees steal?

57. The *Orange County Register,* as part of its Sunday health supplement, reported that 64% of American men over the age of 18 consider nutrition a top priority in their lives. Suppose we select a sample of 60 men. What is the likelihood that:
   a. 32 or more consider nutrition important?
   b. 44 or more consider nutrition important?
   c. More than 32 but fewer than 43 consider nutrition important?
   d. Exactly 44 consider diet important?

58. It is estimated that 10% of those taking the quantitative methods portion of the CPA examination fail that section. Sixty students are taking the exam this Saturday.
   a. How many would you expect to fail? What is the standard deviation?
   b. What is the probability that exactly two students will fail?
   c. What is the probability at least two students will fail?

59. The Georgetown, South Carolina, Traffic Division reported 40% of high-speed chases involving automobiles result in a minor or major accident. During a month in which 50 high-speed chases occur, what is the probability that 25 or more will result in a minor or major accident?

60. Cruise ships of the Royal Viking line report that 80% of their rooms are occupied during September. For a cruise ship having 800 rooms, what is the probability that 665 or more are occupied in September?

61. The goal at U.S. airports handling international flights is to clear these flights within 45 minutes. Let's interpret this to mean that 95% of the flights are cleared in 45 minutes, so 5% of the flights take longer to clear. Let's also assume that the distribution is approximately normal.
   a. If the standard deviation of the time to clear an international flight is 5 minutes, what is the mean time to clear a flight?
   b. Suppose the standard deviation is 10 minutes, not the 5 minutes suggested in part (a). What is the new mean?
   c. A customer has 30 minutes from the time her flight lands to catch her limousine. Assuming a standard deviation of 10 minutes, what is the likelihood that she will be cleared in time?

62. The funds dispensed at the ATM machine located near the checkout line at the Kroger's in Union, Kentucky, follows a normal probability distribution with a mean of $4,200 per day and a standard deviation of $720 per day. The machine is programmed to notify the nearby bank if the amount dispensed is very low (less than $2,500) or very high (more than $6,000).
   a. What percent of the days will the bank be notified because the amount dispensed is very low?
   b. What percent of the time will the bank be notified because the amount dispensed is high?
   c. What percent of the time will the bank not be notified regarding the amount of funds dispersed?

63. The weights of canned hams processed at Henline Ham Company follow the normal distribution, with a mean of 9.20 pounds and a standard deviation of 0.25 pound. The label weight is given as 9.00 pounds.
   a. What proportion of the hams actually weigh less than the amount claimed on the label?
   b. The owner, Glen Henline, is considering two proposals to reduce the proportion of hams below label weight. He can increase the mean weight to 9.25 and leave the standard deviation the same, or he can leave the mean weight at 9.20 and reduce the standard deviation from 0.25 pound to 0.15. Which change would you recommend?

64. The *Cincinnati Enquirer*, in its Sunday business supplement, reported that full-time employees in the region work an average of 43.9 hours per week. The article further indicated that about one-third of those employed full time work less than 40 hours per week.
   a. Given this information and assuming that number of hours worked follows the normal distribution, what is the standard deviation of the number of hours worked?
   b. The article also indicated that 20% of those working full time work more than 49 hours per week. Determine the standard deviation with this information. Are the two estimates of the standard deviation similar? What would you conclude?

65. Most four-year automobile leases allow up to 60,000 miles. If the lessee goes beyond this amount, a penalty of 20 cents per mile is added to the lease cost. Suppose the distribution of miles driven on four-year leases follows the normal distribution. The mean is 52,000 miles and the standard deviation is 5,000 miles.
   a. What percent of the leases will yield a penalty because of excess mileage?
   b. If the automobile company wanted to change the terms of the lease so that 25% of the leases went over the limit, where should the new upper limit be set?
   c. One definition of a low-mileage car is one that is 4 years old and has been driven less than 45,000 miles. What percent of the cars returned are considered low-mileage?

66. The price of shares of Bank of Florida at the end of trading each day for the last year followed the normal distribution. Assume there were 240 trading days in the year. The mean price was $42.00 per share and the standard deviation was $2.25 per share.
   a. What percent of the days was the price over $45.00? How many days would you estimate?
   b. What percent of the days was the price between $38.00 and $40.00?
   c. What was the stock's price on the *highest* 15% of days?

67. The annual sales of romance novels follow the normal distribution. However, the mean and the standard deviation are unknown. Forty percent of the time sales are more than 470,000, and 10% of the time sales are more than 500,000. What are the mean and the standard deviation?

68. In establishing warranties on HDTVs, the manufacturer wants to set the limits so that few will need repair at the manufacturer's expense. On the other hand, the warranty period must be long enough to make the purchase attractive to the buyer. For a new HDTV, the mean number of months until repairs are needed is 36.84 with a standard deviation of 3.34 months. Where should the warranty limits be set so that only 10% of the HDTVs need repairs at the manufacturer's expense?

69. DeKorte Tele-Marketing Inc. is considering purchasing a machine that randomly selects and automatically dials telephone numbers. DeKorte Tele-Marketing makes most of its calls during the evening, so calls to business phones are wasted. The manufacturer of the machine claims that its programming reduces the calling to business phones to 15% of all calls. To test this claim, the director of purchasing at DeKorte programmed the machine to select a sample of 150 phone numbers. What is the likelihood that more than 30 of the phone numbers selected are those of businesses, assuming the manufacturer's claim is correct?

CONTINUOUS PROBABILITY DISTRIBUTIONS   241

70. A carbon monoxide detector in the Wheelock household activates once every 200 days on average. Assume this activation follows the exponential distribution. What is the probability that:
  a. There will be an alarm within the next 60 days?
  b. At least 400 days will pass before the next alarm?
  c. It will be between 150 and 250 days until the next warning?
  d. Find the median time until the next activation.

71. "Boot time" (the time between the appearance of the Bios screen to the first file that is loaded in Windows) on Eric Mouser's personal computer follows an exponential distribution with a mean of 27 seconds. What is the probability his "boot" will require:
  a. Less than 15 seconds?
  b. More than 60 seconds?
  c. Between 30 and 45 seconds?
  d. What is the point below which only 10% of the boots occur?

72. The time between visits to a U.S. emergency room for a member of the general population follows an exponential distribution with a mean of 2.5 years. What proportion of the population:
  a. Will visit an emergency room within the next 6 months?
  b. Will not visit the ER over the next 6 years?
  c. Will visit an ER next year, but not this year?
  d. Find the first and third quartiles of this distribution.

73. The times between failures on a personal computer follow an exponential distribution with a mean of 300,000 hours. What is the probability of:
  a. A failure in less than 100,000 hours?
  b. No failure in the next 500,000 hours?
  c. The next failure occurring between 200,000 and 350,000 hours?
  d. What are the mean and standard deviation of the time between failures?

DATA SET EXERCISES

(The data for these exercises are available at the text website: www.mhhe.com/lind16e.)

74. Refer to the Real Estate data, which report information on homes sold in the Goodyear, Arizona, area during the last year.
  a. The mean selling price (in $ thousands) of the homes was computed earlier to be $221.10, with a standard deviation of $47.11. Use the normal distribution to estimate the percentage of homes selling for more than $280.0. Compare this to the actual results. Does the normal distribution yield a good approximation of the actual results?
  b. The mean distance from the center of the city is 14.629 miles, with a standard deviation of 4.874 miles. Use the normal distribution to estimate the number of homes 18 or more miles but less than 22 miles from the center of the city. Compare this to the actual results. Does the normal distribution yield a good approximation of the actual results?

75. Refer to the Baseball 2012 data, which report information on the 30 Major League Baseball teams for the 2012 season.
  a. The mean attendance per team for the season was 2.495 million, with a standard deviation of 0.6421 million. Use the normal distribution to estimate the number of teams with attendance of more than 3.5 million. Compare that estimate with the actual number. Comment on the accuracy of your estimate.
  b. The mean team salary was $98.023 million, with a standard deviation of $36.832 million. Use the normal distribution to estimate the number of teams with a team salary of more than $50 million. Compare that estimate with the actual number. Comment on the accuracy of the estimate.

76. Refer to the Buena School District bus data.
  a. Refer to the maintenance cost variable. The mean maintenance cost for last year is $450.29, with a standard deviation of $53.69. Estimate the number of buses with a cost of more than $500. Compare that with the actual number.
  b. Refer to the variable on the number of miles driven. The mean is 830.11 and the standard deviation is 42.19 miles. Estimate the number of buses traveling more than 900 miles. Compare that number with the actual value.

A REVIEW OF CHAPTERS 5–7

The chapters in this section consider methods of dealing with uncertainty. In Chapter 5, we describe the concept of probability. A *probability* is a value between 0 and 1 that expresses the likelihood a particular event will occur. We also looked at methods to calculate probabilities using rules of addition and multiplication; presented principles of counting, including permutations and combinations; and described situations for using Bayes' theorem.

Chapter 6 describes *discrete* probability distributions. Discrete probability distributions list all possible outcomes of an experiment and the probability associated with each outcome. We describe three discrete probability distributions: the *binomial distribution,* the *hypergeometric distribution,* and the *Poisson distribution.* The requirements for the binomial distribution are there are only two possible outcomes for each trial, there is a constant probability of success, there are a fixed number of trials, and the trials are independent. The binomial distribution lists the probabilities for the number of successes in a fixed number of trials. The hypergeometric distribution is similar to the binomial, but the probability of success is not constant, so the trials are not independent. The Poisson distribution is characterized by a small probability of success in a large number of trials. It has the following characteristics: the random variable is the number of times some event occurs in a fixed interval, the probability of a success is proportional to the size of the interval, and the intervals are independent and do not overlap.

Chapter 7 describes three continuous probability distributions: the *uniform distribution,* the *normal distribution,* and the *exponential distribution.* The uniform probability distribution is rectangular in shape and is defined by minimum and maximum values. The mean and the median of a uniform probability distribution are equal, and it does not have a mode.

A normal probability distribution is the most widely used and widely reported distribution. Its major characteristics are that it is bell-shaped and symmetrical, completely described by its mean and standard deviation, and asymptotic, that is, it falls smoothly in each direction from its peak but never touches the horizontal axis. There is a family of normal probability distributions—each with its own mean and standard deviation. There are an unlimited number of normal probability distributions.

To find the probabilities for any normal probability distribution, we convert a normal distribution to a *standard normal probability distribution* by computing z values. A z value is the distance between x and the mean in units of the standard deviation. The standard normal probability distribution has a mean of 0 and a standard deviation of 1. It is useful because the probability for any event from a normal probability distribution can be computed using standard normal probability tables (see Appendix B.3).

The exponential probability distribution describes the time between events in a sequence. These events occur independently at a constant rate per unit of time or length. The exponential probability distribution is positively skewed, with λ as the "rate" parameter. The mean and standard deviation are equal and are the reciprocal of λ.

P R O B L E M S

1. Proactine, a new medicine for acne, is claimed by the manufacturer to be 80% effective. It is applied to the affected area of a sample of 15 people. What is the probability that:
   a. All 15 will show significant improvement?
   b. Fewer than 9 of 15 will show significant improvement?
   c. 12 or more people will show significant improvement?
2. Customers at the Bank of Commerce of Idaho Falls, Idaho, default at a rate of .005 on small home-improvement loans. The bank has approved 400 small home-improvement loans. Assuming the Poisson probability distribution applies to this problem:
   a. What is the probability that no homeowners out of the 400 will default?
   b. How many of the 400 are expected not to default?
   c. What is the probability that three or more homeowners will default on their small home-improvement loans?
3. A study of the attendance at the University of Alabama's basketball games revealed that the distribution of attendance is normally distributed with a mean of 10,000 and a standard deviation of 2,000.
   a. What is the probability a particular game has an attendance of 13,500 or more?
   b. What percent of the games have an attendance between 8,000 and 11,500?
   c. Ten percent of the games have an attendance of how many or less?
4. Daniel-James Insurance Company will insure an offshore Mobil Oil production platform against weather losses for one year. The president of Daniel-James estimates the following losses for that platform (in millions of dollars) with the accompanying probabilities:

Amount of Loss ($ millions)	Probability of Loss
0	.98
40	.016
300	.004

a. What is the expected amount Daniel-James will have to pay to Mobil in claims?
b. What is the likelihood that Daniel-James will actually lose less than the expected amount?
c. Given that Daniel-James suffers a loss, what is the likelihood that it is for $300 million?
d. Daniel-James has set the annual premium at $2.0 million. Does that seem like a fair premium? Will it cover its risk?

5. The distribution of the number of school-age children per family in the Whitehall Estates area of Grand Junction, Colorado, is:

Number of children	0	1	2	3	4
Percent of families	40	30	15	10	5

a. Determine the mean and standard deviation of the number of school-age children per family in Whitehall Estates.
b. A new school is planned in Whitehall Estates. An estimate of the number of school-age children is needed. There are 500 family units. How many children would you estimate?
c. Some additional information is needed about only the families having children. Convert the preceding distribution to one for families with children. What is the mean number of children among families that have children?

6. The following table shows a breakdown of the 113th U.S. Congress by party affiliation.

	Party		
	Democrats	Republicans	Total
House	234	201	435
Senate	46	54	100
Total	280	255	535

a. A member of Congress is selected at random. What is the probability of selecting a Republican?
b. Given that the person selected is a member of the House of Representatives, what is the probability he or she is a Republican?
c. What is the probability of selecting a member of the House of Representatives or a Democrat?

CASES

A. Century National Bank

Refer to the Century National Bank data. Is it reasonable that the distribution of checking account balances approximates a normal probability distribution? Determine the mean and the standard deviation for the sample of 60 customers. Compare the actual distribution with the theoretical distribution. Cite some specific examples and comment on your findings.

Divide the account balances into three groups, of about 20 each, with the smallest third of the balances in the first group, the middle third in the second group, and those with the largest balances in the third group. Next, develop a table that shows the number in each of the categories of the account balances by branch. Does it appear that account balances are related to the branch? Cite some examples and comment on your findings.

B. Elections Auditor

An item such as an increase in taxes, recall of elected officials, or an expansion of public services can be placed on the ballot if a required number of valid signatures are collected on the petition. Unfortunately, many people will sign the petition even though they are not registered to vote in that particular district, or they will sign the petition more than once.

Sara Ferguson, the elections auditor in Venango County, must certify the validity of these signatures after the petition is officially presented. Not surprisingly, her staff is overloaded, so she is considering using statistical methods to validate the pages of 200 signatures, instead of validating each individual signature. At a recent professional meeting, she found that, in some communities in the state, election officials were checking only five signatures on each page and rejecting the entire page if two or more signatures were invalid. Some people are concerned that five may not be enough to make a good decision. They suggest that you should check 10 signatures and reject the page if 3 or more are invalid.

In order to investigate these methods, Sara asks her staff to pull the results from the last election and sample

30 pages. It happens that the staff selected 14 pages from the Avondale district, 9 pages from the Midway district, and 7 pages from the Kingston district. Each page had 200 signatures, and the data below show the number of invalid signatures on each.

Use the data to evaluate Sara's two proposals. Calculate the probability of rejecting a page under each of the approaches. Would you get about the same results by examining every single signature? Offer a plan of your own, and discuss how it might be better or worse than the two plans proposed by Sara.

Avondale	Midway	Kingston
9	19	38
14	22	39
11	23	41
8	14	39
14	22	41
6	17	39
10	15	39
13	20	
8	18	
8		
9		
12		
7		
13		

C. Geoff "Applies" His Education

Geoff Brown is the manager for a small telemarketing firm and is evaluating the sales rate of experienced workers in order to set minimum standards for new hires. During the past few weeks, he has recorded the number of successful calls per hour for the staff. These data appear next along with some summary statistics he worked out with a statistical software package. Geoff has been a student at the local community college and has heard of many different kinds of probability distributions (binomial, normal, hypergeometric, Poisson, etc.). Could you give Geoff some advice on which distribution to use to fit these data as well as possible and how to decide when a probationary employee should be accepted as having reached full production status? This is important because it means a pay raise for the employee, and there have been some probationary employees in the past who have quit because of discouragement that they would never meet the standard.

Successful sales calls per hour during the week of August 14:

4	2	3	1	4	5	5	2	3	2	2	4	5	2	5	3	3	0
1	3	2	8	4	5	2	2	4	1	5	5	4	5	1	2	4	

Descriptive statistics:

N	MEAN	MEDIAN	TRMEAN	STDEV	SEMEAN
35	3.229	3.000	3.194	1.682	0.284
MIN	MAX	Q1	Q3		
0.0	8.000	2.000	5.000		

Which distribution do you think Geoff should use for his analysis?

D. CNP Bank Card

Before banks issue a credit card, they usually rate or score the customer in terms of his or her projected probability of being a profitable customer. A typical scoring table appears below.

Age	Under 25 (12 pts.)	25–29 (5 pts.)	30–34 (0 pts.)	35+ (18 pts.)
Time at same address	<1 yr. (9 pts.)	1–2 yrs. (0 pts.)	3–4 yrs. (13 pts.)	5+ yrs. (20 pts.)
Auto age	None (18 pts.)	0–1 yr. (12 pts.)	2–4 yrs. (13 pts.)	5+ yrs. (3 pts.)
Monthly car payment	None (15 pts.)	$1–$99 (6 pts.)	$100–$299 (4 pts.)	$300+ (0 pts.)
Housing cost	$1–$199 (0 pts.)	$200–$399 (10 pts.)	Owns (12 pts.)	Lives with relatives (24 pts.)
Checking/savings accounts	Both (15 pts.)	Checking only (3 pts.)	Savings only (2 pts.)	Neither (0 pts.)

The score is the sum of the points on the six items. For example, Sushi Brown is under 25 years old (12 pts.), has lived at the same address for 2 years (0 pts.), owns a 4-year-old car (13 pts.), with car payments of $75 (6 pts.), housing cost of $200 (10 pts.), and a checking account (3 pts.). She would score 44.

A second chart is then used to convert scores into the probability of being a profitable customer. A sample chart of this type appears below.

Score	30	40	50	60	70	80	90
Probability	.70	.78	.85	.90	.94	.95	.96

Sushi's score of 44 would translate into a probability of being profitable of approximately .81. In other words, 81% of customers like Sushi will make money for the bank card operations.

Here are the interview results for three potential customers.

Name	David Born	Edward Brendan	Ann McLaughlin
Age	42	23	33
Time at same address	9	2	5
Auto age	2	3	7
Monthly car payment	$140	$99	$175
Housing cost	$300	$200	Owns clear
Checking/savings accounts	Both	Checking only	Neither

A REVIEW OF CHAPTERS 5–7   245

1. Score each of these customers and estimate their probability of being profitable.
2. What is the probability that all three are profitable?
3. What is the probability that none of them are profitable?
4. Find the entire probability distribution for the number of profitable customers among this group of three.
5. Write a brief summary of your findings.

P R A C T I C E   T E S T

Part 1—Objective

1. Under what conditions will a probability be greater than 1 or 100%?
2. An _____ is the observation of some activity or the act of taking some type of measurement.
3. An _____ is the collection of one or more outcomes to an experiment.
4. A _____ probability is the likelihood that two or more events will happen at the same time.
5. In a (5a) _____, the order in which the events are counted is important, but in a (5b) _____, it is not important.
6. In a discrete probability distribution, the sum of the possible outcomes is equal to _____.
7. Which of the following is *NOT* a requirement of the binomial distribution? (constant probability of success, three or more outcomes, the result of counts)
8. How many normal distributions are there? (1, 10, 30, 1,000, or infinite—pick one)
9. How many standard normal distributions are there? (1, 10, 30, 1,000, or infinite—pick one)
10. What is the probability of finding a z value between 0 and −0.76?
11. What is the probability of finding a z value greater than 1.67?
12. Two events are _____ if the occurrence of one event does not affect the occurrence of another event.
13. Two events are _____ if by virtue of one event happening the other cannot happen.
14. Which of the following is not true regarding the normal probability distribution? (asymptotic, family of distributions, only two outcomes, 50% of the observations greater than the mean)
15. Which of the following statements best describes the shape of a normal probability distribution? (bell-shaped, uniform, V-shaped, no constant shape)

1. _____
2. _____
3. _____
4. _____

5. a. _____
5. b. _____
6. _____

7. _____
8. _____
9. _____
10. _____
11. _____

12. _____
13. _____

14. _____

15. _____

Part 2—Problems

1. Fred Friendly, CPA, has 20 tax returns to prepare before the April 15th deadline. It is late at night so he decides to do two more before going home. In his stack of accounts, 12 are personal, 5 are businesses, and 3 are for charitable organizations. If he selects the two returns at random, what is the probability:
   a. Both are businesses?
   b. At least one is a business?
2. The IRS reports that 15% of returns where the adjusted gross income is more than $1,000,000 will be subject to a computer audit. For the year 2013, Fred Friendly, CPA, completed 16 returns where the adjusted gross income was more than $1,000,000.
   a. What is the probability exactly one of these returns will be audited?
   b. What is the probability at least one will be audited?
3. Fred works in a tax office with five other CPAs. There are five parking spots beside the office. In how many different ways can the cars belonging to the CPAs be arranged in the five spots? Assume they all drive to work.
4. Fred decided to study the number of exemptions claimed on personal tax returns he prepared in 2012. The data are summarized in the following table.

Exemptions	Percent
1	20
2	50
3	20
4	10

   a. What is the mean number of exemptions per return?
   b. What is the variance of the number of exemptions per return?

5. In a memo to all those involved in tax preparation, the IRS indicated that the mean amount of refund was $1,600 with a standard deviation of $850. Assume the distribution of the amounts returned follows the normal distribution.
   a. What percent of the refunds were between $1,600 and $2,000?
   b. What percent of the refunds were between $900 and $2,000?
   c. According to the above information, what percent of the refunds were less than $0; that is, the taxpayer owed the IRS.

6. For the year 2013, Fred Friendly completed a total of 80 returns. He developed the following table summarizing the relationship between number of dependents and whether or not the client received a refund.

| Refund | Dependents | | | Total |
	1	2	3 or more	
Yes	20	20	10	50
No	10	20	0	30
Total	30	40	10	80

   a. What is the name given to this table?
   b. What is the probability of selecting a client who received a refund?
   c. What is the probability of selecting a client who received a refund or had one dependent?
   d. Given that the client received a refund, what is the probability he or she had one dependent?
   e. What is the probability of selecting a client who did *not* receive a refund and had one dependent?

7. The IRS offers taxpayers the choice of allowing the IRS to compute the amount of their tax refund. During the busy filing season, the number of returns received at the Springfield Service Center that request this service follows a Poisson distribution with a mean of three per day. What is the probability that on a particular day:
   a. There are no requests?
   b. Exactly three requests appear?
   c. Five or more requests take place?
   d. There are no requests on two consecutive days?

Sampling Methods and the Central Limit Theorem

THE NIKE annual report says that the average American buys 6.5 pairs of sports shoes per year. Suppose the population standard deviation is 2.1 and that a sample of 81 customers will be examined next year. What is the standard error of the mean in this experiment? (See Exercise 45 and LO8-4.)

LEARNING OBJECTIVES

When you have completed this chapter, you will be able to:

LO8-1 Explain why populations are sampled and describe four methods to sample a population.

LO8-2 Define sampling error.

LO8-3 Demonstrate the construction of a sampling distribution of the sample mean.

LO8-4 Recite the central limit theorem and define the mean and standard error of the sampling distribution of the sample mean.

LO8-5 Apply the central limit theorem to calculate probabilities.

LO8-1

Explain why populations are sampled and describe four methods to sample a population.

INTRODUCTION

Chapters 2 through 4 emphasize techniques to describe data. To illustrate these techniques, we organize the profits for the sale of 180 vehicles by the four dealers included in the Applewood Auto Group into a frequency distribution and compute various measures of location and dispersion. Such measures as the mean and the standard deviation describe the typical profit and the spread in the profits. In these chapters, the emphasis is on describing the condition of the data. That is, we describe something that has already happened.

In Chapter 5, we begin to lay the foundation for statistical inference with the study of probability. Recall that in statistical inference our goal is to determine something about a *population* based only on the *sample*. The population is the entire group of individuals or objects under consideration, and the sample is a part or subset of that population. Chapter 6 extends the probability concepts by describing three discrete probability distributions: the binomial, the hypergeometric, and the Poisson. Chapter 7 describes three continuous probability distributions: the uniform, normal, and exponential. Probability distributions encompass all possible outcomes of an experiment and the probability associated with each outcome. We use probability distributions to evaluate the likelihood something occurs in the future.

This chapter begins our study of sampling. Sampling is a process of selecting items from a population so we can use this information to make judgments or inferences about the population. We begin this chapter by discussing methods of selecting a sample from a population. Next, we construct a distribution of the sample mean to understand how the sample means tend to cluster around the population mean. Finally, we show that for any population the shape of this sampling distribution tends to follow the normal probability distribution.

SAMPLING METHODS

In Chapter 1, we said the purpose of inferential statistics is to find something about a population based on a sample. A sample is a portion or part of the population of interest. In many cases, sampling is more feasible than studying the entire population. In this section, we discuss the major reasons for sampling, and then several methods for selecting a sample.

Reasons to Sample

When studying characteristics of a population, there are many practical reasons why we prefer to select portions or samples of a population to observe and measure. Here are some of the reasons for sampling:

1. **To contact the whole population would be time-consuming.** A candidate for a national office may wish to determine her chances for election. A sample poll using the regular staff and field interviews of a professional polling firm would take only 1 or 2 days. Using the same staff and interviewers and working 7 days a week, it would take nearly 200 years to contact all the voting population! Even if a large staff of interviewers could be assembled, the benefit of contacting all of the voters would probably not be worth the time.

2. **The cost of studying all the items in a population may be prohibitive.** Public opinion polls and consumer testing organizations, such as Harris International, CBS News Polls, and Zogby International, usually contact fewer than 2,000 of the nearly 60 million families in the United States. One consumer panel–type organization charges $40,000 to mail samples and tabulate responses to test a product (such as breakfast cereal, cat food, or perfume). The same product test using all 60 million families would be too expensive to be worthwhile.

3. **The physical impossibility of checking all items in the population.** Some populations are infinite. It would be impossible to check all the water in Lake Erie for bacterial levels, so we select samples at various locations. The populations of

fish, birds, snakes, deer, and the like are large and are constantly moving, being born, and dying. Instead of even attempting to count all the ducks in Canada or all the fish in Lake Pontchartrain, we make estimates using various techniques — such as counting all the ducks on a pond selected at random, tracking fish catches, or netting fish at predetermined places in the lake.

4. **The destructive nature of some tests.** If the wine tasters at the Sutter Home Winery in California drank all the wine to evaluate the vintage, they would consume the entire crop, and none would be available for sale. In the area of industrial production, steel plates, wires, and similar products must have a certain minimum tensile strength. To ensure that the product meets the minimum standard, the Quality Assurance Department selects a sample from the current production. Each piece is stretched until it breaks and the breaking point (usually measured in pounds per square inch) recorded. Obviously, if all the wire or all the plates were tested for tensile strength, none would be available for sale or use. For the same reason, only a few seeds are tested for germination by Burpee Seeds Inc. prior to the planting season.

5. **The sample results are adequate.** Even if funds were available, it is doubtful the additional accuracy of a 100% sample — that is, studying the entire population — is essential in most problems. For example, the federal government uses a sample of grocery stores scattered throughout the United States to determine the monthly index of food prices. The prices of bread, beans, milk, and other major food items are included in the index. It is unlikely that the inclusion of all grocery stores in the United States would significantly affect the index because the prices of milk, bread, and other major foods usually do not vary by more than a few cents from one chain store to another.

Simple Random Sampling

The most widely used type of sampling is a **simple random sample.**

> **SIMPLE RANDOM SAMPLE** A sample selected so that each item or person in the population has the same chance of being included.

To illustrate the selection process for a simple random sample, suppose the population of interest is the 750 Major League Baseball players on the active rosters of the 30 teams at the end of the 2012 season. The president of the players' union wishes to form a committee of 10 players to study the issue of concussions. One way of ensuring that every player in the population has the same chance of being chosen to serve on the Concussion Committee is to write each name of the 750 players on a slip of paper and place all the slips of paper in a box. After the slips of paper have been thoroughly mixed, the first selection is made by drawing a slip of paper from the box identifying the first player. The slip of paper is not returned to the box. (Note that the probability of each selection does increase because the slip is not replaced. However, the differences are very small. The probability of each selection is about 0.0013, rounded to four decimal places). This process is repeated nine more times to form the committee.

Of course, the process of writing all the players' names on a slip of paper is very time-consuming. A more convenient method of selecting a random sample is to use a **table of random numbers** such as the one in Appendix B.4. In this case the union president would prepare a list of all 750 players and number each of the players from 1 to 750 with a computer application. Using a table of random numbers, we would randomly pick a starting place in the table, and then select 10 three-digit numbers between 001 and 750. A computer can also be used to generate random numbers. These numbers would correspond with the 10 players in the list that will be asked to participate on the committee. As the name simple random sampling implies, the probability of selecting any number between 001 and 750 is the same. Thus, the probability of selecting the player assigned the number 131 is the same as the probability of selecting player 722 or player 382. Using random numbers to select players for the committee removes any bias from the selection process.

The following example shows how to select random numbers using a portion of a random number table illustrated below. First, we choose a starting point in the table. One way of selecting the starting point is to close your eyes and point at a number in the table. Any starting point will do. Another way is to randomly pick a column and row. Suppose the time is 3:04. Using the hour, three o'clock, pick the third column and then, using the minutes, four, move down to the fourth row of numbers. The number is 03759. Because there are only 750 players, we will use the first three digits of a five-digit random number. Thus, 037 is the number of the first player to be a member of the sample. To continue selecting players, we could move in any direction. Suppose we move right. The first three digits of the number to the right of 03759 are 447. Player number 447 is the second player selected to be on the committee. The next three-digit number to the right is 961. You skip 961 as well as the next number 784 because there are only 750 players. The third player selected is number 189. We continue this process until we have 10 players.

50525	57454	28455	68226	34656	38884	39018
72507	53380	53827	42486	54465	71819	91199
34986	74297	00144	38676	89967	98869	39744
68851	27305	03759	44723	96108	78489	18910
06738	62879	03910	17350	49169	03850	18910
11448	10734	05837	24397	10420	16712	94496
		Starting point	Second player			Third player

Statistical packages such as Minitab and spreadsheet packages such as Excel have software that will select a simple random sample. The following example/solution uses Excel to select a random sample from a list of the data.

EXAMPLE

Jane and Joe Miley operate the Foxtrot Inn, a bed and breakfast in Tryon, North Carolina. There are eight rooms available for rent at this B&B. Listed below is the number of these eight rooms rented each day during June 2013. Use Excel to select a sample of five nights during the month of June.

June	Rentals	June	Rentals	June	Rentals
1	0	11	3	21	3
2	2	12	4	22	2
3	3	13	4	23	3
4	2	14	4	24	6
5	3	15	7	25	0
6	4	16	0	26	4
7	2	17	5	27	1
8	3	18	3	28	1
9	4	19	6	29	3
10	7	20	2	30	3

SOLUTION

Excel will select the random sample and report the results. On the first sampled date, four of the eight rooms were rented. On the second sampled date in June, seven of the eight rooms were rented. The information is reported in column D of the Excel spreadsheet. The Excel steps are listed in the **Software Commands** in

Appendix C. The Excel system performs the sampling *with* replacement. This means it is possible for the same day to appear more than once in a sample.

	A	B	C	D
1	Day of June	Rentals		Sample
2	1	0		4
3	2	2		7
4	3	3		4
5	4	2		3
6	5	3		1
7	6	4		
8	7	2		
9	8	3		
10	9	4		
11	10	7		
12	11	3		
13	12	4		
14	13	4		
15	14	4		

SELF-REVIEW

8–1

The following class roster lists the students enrolling in an introductory course in business statistics. Three students are to be randomly selected and asked various questions regarding course content and method of instruction.
(a) The numbers 00 through 45 are handwritten on slips of paper and placed in a bowl. The three numbers selected are 31, 7, and 25. Which students would be included in the sample?
(b) Now use the table of random digits, Appendix B.4, to select your own sample.
(c) What would you do if you encountered the number 59 in the table of random digits?

```
                    CSPM 264 01 BUSINESS & ECONOMIC STAT
                      8:00 AM 9:40 AM MW ST 118 LIND D
```

RANDOM NUMBER	NAME	CLASS RANK	RANDOM NUMBER	NAME	CLASS RANK
00	ANDERSON, RAYMOND	SO	23	MEDLEY, CHERYL ANN	SO
01	ANGER, CHERYL RENEE	SO	24	MITCHELL, GREG R	FR
02	BALL, CLAIRE JEANETTE	FR	25	MOLTER, KRISTI MARIE	SO
03	BERRY, CHRISTOPHER G	FR	26	MULCAHY, STEPHEN ROBERT	SO
04	BOBAK, JAMES PATRICK	SO	27	NICHOLAS, ROBERT CHARLES	JR
05	BRIGHT, M. STARR	JR	28	NICKENS, VIRGINIA	SO
06	CHONTOS, PAUL JOSEPH	SO	29	PENNYWITT, SEAN PATRICK	SO
07	DETLEY, BRIAN HANS	JR	30	POTEAU, KRIS E	JR
08	DUDAS, VIOLA	SO	31	PRICE, MARY LYNETTE	SO
09	DULBS, RICHARD ZALFA	JR	32	RISTAS, JAMES	SR
10	EDINGER, SUSAN KEE	SR	33	SAGER, ANNE MARIE	SO
11	FINK, FRANK JAMES	SR	34	SMILLIE, HEATHER MICHELLE	SO
12	FRANCIS, JAMES P	JR	35	SNYDER, LEISHA KAY	SR
13	GAGHEN, PAMELA LYNN	JR	36	STAHL, MARIA TASHERY	SO
14	GOULD, ROBYN KAY	SO	37	ST. JOHN, AMY J	SO
15	GROSENBACHER, SCOTT ALAN	SO	38	STURDEVANT, RICHARD K	SO
16	HEETFIELD, DIANE MARIE	SO	39	SWETYE, LYNN MICHELE	SO
17	KABAT, JAMES DAVID	JR	40	WALASINSKI, MICHAEL	SO
18	KEMP, LISA ADRIANE	FR	41	WALKER, DIANE ELAINE	SO
19	KILLION, MICHELLE A	SO	42	WARNOCK, JENNIFER MARY	SO
20	KOPERSKI, MARY ELLEN	SO	43	WILLIAMS, WENDY A	SO
21	KOPP, BRIDGETTE ANN	SO	44	YAP, HOCK BAN	SO
22	LEHMANN, KRISTINA MARIE	JR	45	YODER, ARLAN JAY	JR

252   CHAPTER 8

Systematic Random Sampling

The simple random sampling procedure is awkward in some research situations. For example, Stood's Grocery Market needs to sample their customers to study the length of time customers spend in the store. Simple random sampling is not an effective method. Practically, we do not have a list of customers, so assigning random numbers to customers is impossible. Instead, we can use **systematic random sampling** to select a representative sample. Using this method for Stood's Grocery Market, we decide to select 100 customers over 4 days, Monday through Thursday. We will select 25 customers a day and begin the sampling at different times each day: 8 a.m., 11 a.m., 4 p.m., and 7 p.m. We write the 4 times and 4 days on slips of paper and put them in two hats—one hat for the days and the other hat for the times. We select one slip from each hat. This ensures that the time of day is randomly assigned for each day. Suppose we selected 4 p.m. for the starting time on Monday. Next we select a random number between 1 and 10; it is 6. Our selection process begins on Monday at 4 p.m. by selecting the sixth customer to enter the store. Then, we select every 10th (16th, 26th, 36th) customer until we reach the goal of 25 customers. For each of these sampled customers, we measure the length of time the customer spends in the store.

> **SYSTEMATIC RANDOM SAMPLE** A random starting point is selected, and then every kth member of the population is selected.

Simple random sampling is used in the selection of the days, the times, and the starting point. But the systematic procedure is used to select the actual customer.

Before using systematic random sampling, we should carefully observe the physical order of the population. When the physical order is related to the population characteristic, then systematic random sampling should not be used because the sample could be biased. For example, if we wanted to audit the invoices in a file drawer that were ordered in increasing dollar amounts, systematic random sampling would not guarantee an unbiased random sample. Other sampling methods should be used.

Stratified Random Sampling

When a population can be clearly divided into groups based on some characteristic, we may use **stratified random sampling.** It guarantees each group is represented in the sample. The groups are called **strata.** For example, college students can be grouped as full time or part time; as male or female; or as freshman, sophomore, junior, or senior. Usually the strata are formed based on members' shared attributes or characteristics. A random sample from each stratum is taken in a number proportional to the stratum's size when compared to the population. Once the strata are defined, we apply simple random sampling within each group or stratum to collect the sample.

> **STRATIFIED RANDOM SAMPLE** A population is divided into subgroups, called strata, and a sample is randomly selected from each stratum.

For instance, we might study the advertising expenditures for the 352 largest companies in the United States. The objective of the study is to determine whether firms with high returns on equity (a measure of profitability) spend more on advertising than firms with low returns on equity. To make sure the sample is a fair representation of the 352 companies, the companies are grouped on percent return on equity. Table 8–1 shows the strata and the relative frequencies. If simple random sampling is used, observe that firms in the 3rd and 4th strata have a high chance of selection (probability of 0.87) while firms in the other strata have a small chance of selection (probability of 0.13). We might not select any firms in stratum 1 or 5 *simply by chance*. However, stratified random sampling will guarantee that at least one firm in each of strata 1 and 5 is represented in the sample.

TABLE 8–1 Number Selected for a Proportional Stratified Random Sample

Stratum	Profitability (return on equity)	Number of Firms	Relative Frequency	Number Sampled
1	30% and over	8	0.02	1*
2	20 up to 30%	35	0.10	5*
3	10 up to 20%	189	0.54	27
4	0 up to 10%	115	0.33	16
5	Deficit	5	0.01	1
Total		352	1.00	50

*0.02 of 50 = 1, 0.10 of 50 = 5, etc.

Let's say that 50 firms are selected for intensive study. Then based on probability, 1 firm, or (0.02)(50), should be randomly selected from stratum 1. We would randomly select 5, or (0.10)(50), firms from stratum 2. In this case, the number of firms sampled from each stratum is proportional to the stratum's relative frequency in the population. Stratified sampling has the advantage, in some cases, of more accurately reflecting the characteristics of the population than does simple random or systematic random sampling.

Cluster Sampling

Another common type of sampling is **cluster sampling.** It is often employed to reduce the cost of sampling a population scattered over a large geographic area.

> **CLUSTER SAMPLING** A population is divided into clusters using naturally occurring geographic or other boundaries. Then, clusters are randomly selected and a sample is collected by randomly selecting from each cluster.

Suppose you want to determine the views of residents in the greater Chicago, Illinois, metropolitan area about state and federal environmental protection policies. Selecting a random sample of residents in this region and personally contacting each one would be time-consuming and very expensive. Instead, you could employ cluster sampling by subdividing the region into small units, perhaps by counties. These are often called *primary units.*

There are 12 counties in the greater Chicago metropolitan area. Suppose you randomly select 3 counties. The 3 chosen are La Porte, Cook, and Kenosha (see Chart 8–1 below). Next, you select a random sample of the residents in each of these counties and interview them. This is also referred to as sampling through an *intermediate unit.* In this case, the intermediate unit is the county. (Note that this is a combination of cluster sampling and simple random sampling.)

The discussion of sampling methods in the preceding sections did not include all the sampling methods available to a researcher. Should you become involved in a

CHART 8–1 The counties of the greater Chicago, Illinois, metropolitan area.

major research project in marketing, finance, accounting, or other areas, you would need to consult books devoted solely to sample theory and sample design.

SELF-REVIEW

8–2

Refer to Self-Review 8–1 and the class roster on page 251. Suppose a systematic random sample will select every ninth student enrolled in the class. Initially, the fourth student on the list was selected at random. That student is numbered 03. Remembering that the random numbers start with 00, which students will be chosen to be members of the sample?

EXERCISES

1. The following is a list of 24 Marco's Pizza stores in Lucas County. The stores are identified by numbering them 00 through 23. Also noted is whether the store is corporate-owned (C) or manager-owned (M). A sample of four locations is to be selected and inspected for customer convenience, safety, cleanliness, and other features.

ID No.	Address	Type	ID No.	Address	Type
00	2607 Starr Av	C	12	2040 Ottawa River Rd	C
01	309 W Alexis Rd	C	13	2116 N Reynolds Rd	C
02	2652 W Central Av	C	14	3678 Rugby Dr	C
03	630 Dixie Hwy	M	15	1419 South Av	C
04	3510 Dorr St	C	16	1234 W Sylvania Av	C
05	5055 Glendale Av	C	17	4624 Woodville Rd	M
06	3382 Lagrange St	M	18	5155 S Main	M
07	2525 W Laskey Rd	C	19	106 E Airport Hwy	C
08	303 Louisiana Av	C	20	6725 W Central	M
09	149 Main St	C	21	4252 Monroe	C
10	835 S McCord Rd	M	22	2036 Woodville Rd	C
11	3501 Monroe St	M	23	1316 Michigan Av	M

   a. The random numbers selected are 08, 18, 11, 54, 02, 41, and 54. Which stores are selected?
   b. Use the table of random numbers to select your own sample of locations.
   c. A sample is to consist of every seventh location. The number 03 is the starting point. Which locations will be included in the sample?
   d. Suppose a sample is to consist of three locations, of which two are corporate-owned and one is manager-owned. Select a sample accordingly.

2. The following is a list of 29 hospitals in the Cincinnati (Ohio) and Northern Kentucky region. The hospitals are identified by numbering them 00 through 28. Also included is whether the hospital is a general medical/surgical hospital (M/S) or a specialty hospital (S). We are interested in estimating the average number of full- and part-time nurses employed in the area hospitals.
   a. A sample of five hospitals is to be randomly selected. The random numbers are 09, 16, 00, 49, 54, 12, and 04. Which hospitals are included in the sample?
   b. Use a table of random numbers to develop your own sample of five hospitals.

ID Number	Name	Address	Type	ID Number	Name	Address	Type
00	Bethesda North	10500 Montgomery Cincinnati, Ohio 45242	M/S	05	Middletown Regional	105 McKnight Drive Middletown, Ohio 45044	M/S
01	Ft. Hamilton–Hughes	630 Eaton Avenue Hamilton, Ohio 45013	M/S	06	Clermont Mercy Hospital	3000 Hospital Drive Batavia, Ohio 45103	M/S
02	Jewish Hospital–Kenwood	4700 East Galbraith Rd. Cincinnati, Ohio 45236	M/S	07	Mercy Hospital–Anderson	7500 State Road Cincinnati, Ohio 45255	M/S
03	Mercy Hospital–Fairfield	3000 Mack Road Fairfield, Ohio 45014	M/S	08	Bethesda Oak Hospital	619 Oak Street Cincinnati, Ohio 45206	M/S
04	Mercy Hospital–Hamilton	100 Riverfront Plaza Hamilton, Ohio 45011	M/S	09	Children's Hospital Medical Center	3333 Burnet Avenue Cincinnati, Ohio 45229	M/S

SAMPLING METHODS AND THE CENTRAL LIMIT THEOREM   255

ID Number	Name	Address	Type	ID Number	Name	Address	Type
10	Christ Hospital	2139 Auburn Avenue Cincinnati, Ohio 45219	M/S	20	St. Luke's Hospital East	85 North Grand Avenue Ft. Thomas, Kentucky 41042	M/S
11	Deaconess Hospital	311 Straight Street Cincinnati, Ohio 45219	M/S	21	Care Unit Hospital	3156 Glenmore Avenue Cincinnati, Ohio 45211	S
12	Good Samaritan Hospital	375 Dixmyth Avenue Cincinnati, Ohio 45220	M/S	22	Emerson Behavioral Science	2446 Kipling Avenue Cincinnati, Ohio 45239	S
13	Jewish Hospital	3200 Burnet Avenue Cincinnati, Ohio 45229	M/S	23	Pauline Warfield Lewis Center for Psychiatric Treat.	1101 Summit Road Cincinnati, Ohio 45237	S
14	University Hospital	234 Goodman Street Cincinnati, Ohio 45267	M/S	24	Children's Psychiatric No. Kentucky	502 Farrell Drive Covington, Kentucky 41011	S
15	Providence Hospital	2446 Kipling Avenue Cincinnati, Ohio 45239	M/S	25	Drake Center Rehab— Long Term	151 W. Galbraith Road Cincinnati, Ohio 45216	S
16	St. Francis– St. George Hospital	3131 Queen City Avenue Cincinnati, Ohio 45238	M/S	26	No. Kentucky Rehab Hospital—Short Term	201 Medical Village Edgewood, Kentucky	S
17	St. Elizabeth Medical Center, North Unit	401 E. 20th Street Covington, Kentucky 41014	M/S	27	Shriners Burns Institute	3229 Burnet Avenue Cincinnati, Ohio 45229	S
18	St. Elizabeth Medical Center, South Unit	One Medical Village Edgewood, Kentucky 41017	M/S	28	VA Medical Center	3200 Vine Cincinnati, Ohio 45220	S
19	St. Luke's Hospital West	7380 Turfway Drive Florence, Kentucky 41075	M/S				

   c. A sample is to consist of every fifth location. We select 02 as the starting point. Which hospitals will be included in the sample?
   d. A sample is to consist of four medical and surgical hospitals and one specialty hospital. Select an appropriate sample.

3. Listed below are the 35 members of the Metro Toledo Automobile Dealers Association. We would like to estimate the mean revenue from dealer service departments. The members are identified by numbering them 00 through 34.

ID Number	Dealer	ID Number	Dealer	ID Number	Dealer
00	Dave White Acura	11	Thayer Chevrolet/Toyota	23	Kistler Ford, Inc.
01	Autofair Nissan	12	Spurgeon Chevrolet Motor Sales, Inc.	24	Lexus of Toledo
02	Autofair Toyota-Suzuki	13	Dunn Chevrolet	25	Mathews Ford Oregon, Inc.
03	George Ball's Buick GMC Truck	14	Don Scott Chevrolet	26	Northtowne Chevrolet
04	Yark Automotive Group	15	Dave White Chevrolet Co.	27	Quality Ford Sales, Inc.
05	Bob Schmidt Chevrolet	16	Dick Wilson Infinity	28	Rouen Chrysler Jeep Eagle
06	Bowling Green Lincoln Mercury Jeep Eagle	17	Doyle Buick	29	Saturn of Toledo
07	Brondes Ford	18	Franklin Park Lincoln Mercury	30	Ed Schmidt Jeep Eagle
08	Brown Honda	19	Genoa Motors	31	Southside Lincoln Mercury
09	Brown Mazda	20	Great Lakes Ford Nissan	32	Valiton Chrysler
10	Charlie's Dodge	21	Grogan Towne Chrysler	33	Vin Divers
		22	Hatfield Motor Sales	34	Whitman Ford

   a. We want to select a random sample of five dealers. The random numbers are 05, 20, 59, 21, 31, 28, 49, 38, 66, 08, 29, and 02. Which dealers would be included in the sample?
   b. Use the table of random numbers to select your own sample of five dealers.
   c. A sample is to consist of every seventh dealer. The number 04 is selected as the starting point. Which dealers are included in the sample?

4. Listed next are the 27 Nationwide Insurance agents in the Toledo, Ohio, metropolitan area. The agents are identified by numbering them 00 through 26. We would like to estimate the mean number of years employed with Nationwide.

ID Number	Agent	ID Number	Agent	ID Number	Agent
00	**Bly Scott** 3332 W Laskey Rd	10	**Heini Bernie** 7110 W Centra	19	**Riker Craig** 2621 N Reynolds Rd
01	**Coyle Mike** 5432 W Central Av	11	**Hinckley Dave**	20	**Schwab Dave** 572 W Dussel Dr
02	**Denker Brett** 7445 Airport Hwy		14 N Holland Sylvania Rd	21	**Seibert John H** 201 S Main
03	**Denker Rollie** 7445 Airport Hwy	12	**Joehlin Bob** 3358 Navarre Av	22	**Smithers Bob** 229 Superior St
04	**Farley Ron** 1837 W Alexis Rd	13	**Keisser David** 3030 W Sylvania Av	23	**Smithers Jerry** 229 Superior St
05	**George Mark** 7247 W Central Av	14	**Keisser Keith** 5902 Sylvania Av	24	**Wright Steve** 105 S Third St
06	**Gibellato Carlo** 6616 Monroe St	15	**Lawrence Grant** 342 W Dussel Dr	25	**Wood Tom** 112 Louisiana Av
07	**Glemser Cathy** 5602 Woodville Rd	16	**Miller Ken** 2427 Woodville Rd	26	**Yoder Scott** 6 Willoughby Av
08	**Green Mike** 4149 Holland Sylvania Rd	17	**O'Donnell Jim** 7247 W Central Av		
09	**Harris Ev** 2026 Albon Rd	18	**Priest Harvey** 5113 N Summit St		

a. We want to select a random sample of four agents. The random numbers are 02, 59, 51, 25, 14, 29, 77, 69, and 18. Which dealers would be included in the sample?

b. Use the table of random numbers to select your own sample of four agents.

c. A sample is to consist of every seventh dealer. The number 04 is selected as the starting point. Which agents will be included in the sample?

LO8-2

Define sampling error.

SAMPLING "ERROR"

In the previous section, we discussed sampling methods that are used to select a sample that is an unbiased representation of the population. In each method, the selection of every possible sample of a specified size from a population has a known chance or probability. This is another way to describe an unbiased sampling method.

Samples are used to estimate population characteristics. For example, the mean of a sample is used to estimate the population mean. However, since the sample is a part or portion of the population, it is unlikely that the sample mean would be *exactly equal* to the population mean. Similarly, it is unlikely that the sample standard deviation would be *exactly equal* to the population standard deviation. We can therefore expect a difference between a *sample statistic* and its corresponding *population parameter*. This difference is called **sampling error.**

> **SAMPLING ERROR** The difference between a sample statistic and its corresponding population parameter.

The following example/solution clarifies the idea of sampling error.

E X A M P L E

Refer to the example/solution on page 250, where we studied the number of rooms rented at the Foxtrot Inn bed and breakfast in Tryon, North Carolina. The population is the number of rooms rented each of the 30 days in June 2013. Find the mean of the population. Use Excel or other statistical software to select three random samples of 5 days. Calculate the mean of each sample and compare it to the population mean. What is the sampling error in each case?

S O L U T I O N

During the month, there were a total of 94 rentals. So the mean number of units rented per night is 3.13. This is the population mean. Hence we designate this value with the Greek letter μ.

$$\mu = \frac{\Sigma x}{N} = \frac{0 + 2 + 3 + \cdots + 3}{30} = \frac{94}{30} = 3.13$$

The first random sample of five nights resulted in the following number of rooms rented: 4, 7, 4, 3, and 1. The mean of this sample of 5 nights is 3.80 rooms, which we designate as $\bar{x}_1$. The bar over the x reminds us that it is a sample mean and the subscript 1 indicates it is the mean of the first sample.

$$\bar{x}_1 = \frac{\Sigma x}{n} = \frac{4 + 7 + 4 + 3 + 1}{5} = \frac{19}{5} = 3.80$$

The sampling error for the first sample is the difference between the population mean (3.13) and the first sample mean (3.80). Hence, the sampling error is $(\bar{x}_1 - \mu) = 3.80 - 3.13 = 0.67$. The second random sample of 5 days from the population of all 30 days in June revealed the following number of rooms rented: 3, 3, 2, 3, and 6. The mean of these five values is 3.40, found by

$$\bar{x}_2 = \frac{\Sigma x}{n} = \frac{3 + 3 + 2 + 3 + 6}{5} = 3.40$$

The sampling error is $(\bar{x}_2 - \mu) = 3.4 - 3.13 = 0.27$. In the third random sample, the mean was 1.80 and the sampling error was -1.33.

Each of these differences, 0.67, 0.27, and -1.33, is the sampling error made in estimating the population mean. Sometimes these errors are positive values, indicating that the sample mean overestimated the population mean; other times they are negative values, indicating the sample mean was less than the population mean.

	A	B	C	D	E	F	G
1	Day of June	Rentals			Sample 1	Sample 2	Sample 3
2	1	0			4	3	0
3	2	2			7	3	0
4	3	3			4	2	3
5	4	2			3	3	3
6	5	3			1	6	3
7	6	4		Totals	19	17	9
8	7	2		Sample means	3.80	3.40	1.80
9	8	3					
10	9	4					
11	10	7					
12	11	3					
13	12	4					
14	13	4					
15	14	4					

In this case, where we have a population of 30 values and samples of 5 values, there is a very large number of possible samples—142,506 to be exact! To find this value, use the combination formula (5–10) on page 163. Each of the 142,506 different samples has the same chance of being selected. Each sample may have a different sample mean and therefore a different sampling error. The value of the sampling error is based on the particular one of the 142,506 different possible samples selected. Therefore, the sampling errors are random and occur by chance. If you were to determine the sum of these sampling errors over a large number of samples, the result would be very close to zero. This is true because the sample mean is an *unbiased estimator* of the population mean.

LO8-3
Demonstrate the construction of a sampling distribution of the sample mean.

SAMPLING DISTRIBUTION OF THE SAMPLE MEAN

In the previous section, we defined sampling error and presented the results when we compared a sample statistic, such as the sample mean, to the population mean. To put it another way, when we use the sample mean to estimate the population mean, how can we determine how accurate the estimate is? How does:

- A quality-assurance supervisor decide if a machine is filling 20-ounce bottles with 20 ounces of cola based only on a sample of 10 filled bottles?
- CNN/*USA Today* or ABC News/*Washington Post* make accurate statements about the average years of education for voters in a presidential race based on a sample of 1,200 registered voters out of a voting population of nearly 90 million?

To answer these questions, we first develop a *sampling distribution of the sample mean*.

The sample means in the previous example/solution varied from one sample to the next. The mean of the first sample of 5 days was 3.80 rooms, and the second sample mean was 3.40 rooms. The population mean was 3.13 rooms. If we organized the means of all possible samples of 5 days into a probability distribution, the result is called the **sampling distribution of the sample mean.**

> **SAMPLING DISTRIBUTION OF THE SAMPLE MEAN** A probability distribution of all possible sample means of a given sample size.

The following example/solution illustrates the construction of a sampling distribution of the sample mean. We have intentionally used a small population to highlight the relationship between the population mean and the various sample means.

E X A M P L E

Tartus Industries has seven production employees (considered the population). The hourly earnings of each employee are given in Table 8–2.

TABLE 8–2 Hourly Earnings of the Production Employees of Tartus Industries

Employee	Hourly Earnings	Employee	Hourly Earnings
Joe	$7	Jan	$7
Sam	7	Art	8
Sue	8	Ted	9
Bob	8		

1. What is the population mean?
2. What is the sampling distribution of the sample mean for samples of size 2?
3. What is the mean of the sampling distribution?
4. What observations can be made about the population and the sampling distribution?

S O L U T I O N

Here are the solutions to the questions.

1. The population is small so it is easy to calculate the population mean. It is $7.71, found by:

$$\mu = \frac{\Sigma x}{N} = \frac{\$7 + \$7 + \$8 + \$8 + \$7 + \$8 + \$9}{7} = \$7.71$$

SAMPLING METHODS AND THE CENTRAL LIMIT THEOREM   259

We identify the population mean with the Greek letter μ. Recall from earlier chapters, Greek letters are used to represent population parameters.

2. To arrive at the sampling distribution of the sample mean, we need to select all possible samples of 2 without replacement from the population, then compute the mean of each sample. There are 21 possible samples, found by using formula (5–10) on page 163.

$$_NC_n = \frac{N!}{n!(N-n)!} = \frac{7!}{2!(7-2)!} = 21$$

where $N = 7$ is the number of items in the population and $n = 2$ is the number of items in the sample.

TABLE 8–3 Sample Means for All Possible Samples of 2 Employees

Sample	Employees	Hourly Earnings	Sum	Mean	Sample	Employees	Hourly Earnings	Sum	Mean
1	Joe, Sam	$7, $7	$14	$7.00	12	Sue, Bob	$8, $8	$16	$8.00
2	Joe, Sue	7, 8	15	7.50	13	Sue, Jan	8, 7	15	7.50
3	Joe, Bob	7, 8	15	7.50	14	Sue, Art	8, 8	16	8.00
4	Joe, Jan	7, 7	14	7.00	15	Sue, Ted	8, 9	17	8.50
5	Joe, Art	7, 8	15	7.50	16	Bob, Jan	8, 7	15	7.50
6	Joe, Ted	7, 9	16	8.00	17	Bob, Art	8, 8	16	8.00
7	Sam, Sue	7, 8	15	7.50	18	Bob, Ted	8, 9	17	8.50
8	Sam, Bob	7, 8	15	7.50	19	Jan, Art	7, 8	15	7.50
9	Sam, Jan	7, 7	14	7.00	20	Jan, Ted	7, 9	16	8.00
10	Sam, Art	7, 8	15	7.50	21	Art, Ted	8, 9	17	8.50
11	Sam, Ted	7, 9	16	8.00					

The 21 sample means from all possible samples of 2 that can be drawn from the population of 7 employees are shown in Table 8–3. These 21 sample means are used to construct a probability distribution. This is called the sampling distribution of the sample mean, and it is summarized in Table 8–4.

TABLE 8–4 Sampling Distribution of the Sample Mean for $n = 2$

Sample Mean	Number of Means	Probability
$7.00	3	.1429
7.50	9	.4285
8.00	6	.2857
8.50	3	.1429
	21	1.0000

3. Using the data in Table 8–3, the mean of the sampling distribution of the sample mean is obtained by summing the various sample means and dividing the sum by the number of samples. The mean of all the sample means is usually written $\mu_{\bar{x}}$. The μ reminds us that it is a population value because we have considered all possible samples of two employees from the population of seven employees. The subscript $\bar{x}$ indicates that it is the sampling distribution of the sample mean.

$$\mu_{\bar{x}} = \frac{\text{Sum of all sample means}}{\text{Total number of samples}} = \frac{\$7.00 + \$7.50 + \$7.50 + \cdots + \$8.00 + \$8.50}{21}$$

$$= \frac{\$162}{21} = \$7.71$$

260   CHAPTER 8

4. Refer to Chart 8–2. It shows the population distribution based on the data in Table 8–2 and the distribution of the sample mean based on the data in Table 8–4. These observations can be made:
   a. The mean of the distribution of the sample mean ($7.71) is equal to the mean of the population: $\mu = \mu_{\bar{x}}$.
   b. The spread in the distribution of the sample mean is less than the spread in the population values. The sample means range from $7.00 to $8.50, while the population values vary from $7.00 up to $9.00. If we continue to increase the sample size, the spread of the distribution of the sample mean becomes smaller.
   c. The shape of the sampling distribution of the sample mean and the shape of the frequency distribution of the population values are different. The distribution of the sample mean tends to be more bell-shaped and to approximate the normal probability distribution.

CHART 8–2 Distributions of Population Values and Sample Mean

In summary, we took all possible random samples from a population and for each sample calculated a sample statistic (the mean amount earned). This example illustrates important relationships between the population distribution and the sampling distribution of the sample mean:

1. The mean of the sample means is exactly equal to the population mean.
2. The dispersion of the sampling distribution of the sample mean is narrower than the population distribution.
3. The sampling distribution of the sample mean tends to become bell-shaped and to approximate the normal probability distribution.

Given a bell-shaped or normal probability distribution, we will be able to apply concepts from Chapter 7 to determine the probability of selecting a sample with a specified sample mean. In the next section, we will show the importance of sample size as it relates to the sampling distribution of the sample mean.

SELF-REVIEW

8–3

The years of service of the five executives employed by Standard Chemicals are:

Name	Years
Mr. Snow	20
Ms. Tolson	22
Mr. Kraft	26
Ms. Irwin	24
Mr. Jones	28

SAMPLING METHODS AND THE CENTRAL LIMIT THEOREM   261

(a) Using the combination formula, how many samples of size 2 are possible?
(b) List all possible samples of two executives from the population and compute their means.
(c) Organize the means into a sampling distribution.
(d) Compare the population mean and the mean of the sample means.
(e) Compare the dispersion in the population with that in the distribution of the sample mean.
(f) A chart portraying the population values follows. Is the distribution of population values normally distributed (bell-shaped)?

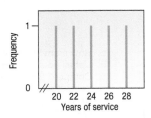

(g) Is the distribution of the sample mean computed in part (c) starting to show some tendency toward being bell-shaped?

EXERCISES

5. A population consists of the following four values: 12, 12, 14, and 16.
    a. List all samples of size 2, and compute the mean of each sample.
    b. Compute the mean of the distribution of the sample mean and the population mean. Compare the two values.
    c. Compare the dispersion in the population with that of the sample mean.
6. A population consists of the following five values: 2, 2, 4, 4, and 8.
    a. List all samples of size 2, and compute the mean of each sample.
    b. Compute the mean of the distribution of sample means and the population mean. Compare the two values.
    c. Compare the dispersion in the population with that of the sample means.
7. A population consists of the following five values: 12, 12, 14, 15, and 20.
    a. List all samples of size 3, and compute the mean of each sample.
    b. Compute the mean of the distribution of sample means and the population mean. Compare the two values.
    c. Compare the dispersion in the population with that of the sample means.
8. A population consists of the following five values: 0, 0, 1, 3, 6.
    a. List all samples of size 3, and compute the mean of each sample.
    b. Compute the mean of the distribution of sample means and the population mean. Compare the two values.
    c. Compare the dispersion in the population with that of the sample means.
9. In the law firm Tybo and Associates, there are six partners. Listed next is the number of cases each partner actually tried in court last month.

Partner	Number of Cases
Ruud	3
Wu	6
Sass	3
Flores	3
Wilhelms	0
Schueller	1

a. How many different samples of size 3 are possible?
b. List all possible samples of size 3, and compute the mean number of cases in each sample.
c. Compare the mean of the distribution of sample means to the population mean.
d. On a chart similar to Chart 8–2, compare the dispersion in the population with that of the sample means.

10. There are five sales associates at Mid-Motors Ford. The five associates and the number of cars they sold last week are:

Sales Associate	Cars Sold
Peter Hankish	8
Connie Stallter	6
Juan Lopez	4
Ted Barnes	10
Peggy Chu	6

   a. How many different samples of size 2 are possible?
   b. List all possible samples of size 2, and compute the mean of each sample.
   c. Compare the mean of the sampling distribution of the sample mean with that of the population.
   d. On a chart similar to Chart 8–2, compare the dispersion in sample means with that of the population.

LO8-4

Recite the central limit theorem and define the mean and standard error of the sampling distribution of the sample mean.

THE CENTRAL LIMIT THEOREM

In this section, we examine the **central limit theorem.** Its application to the sampling distribution of the sample mean, introduced in the previous section, allows us to use the normal probability distribution to create confidence intervals for the population mean (described in Chapter 9) and perform tests of hypothesis (described in Chapter 10). The central limit theorem states that, for large random samples, the shape of the sampling distribution of the sample mean is close to the normal probability distribution. The approximation is more accurate for large samples than for small samples. This is one of the most useful conclusions in statistics. We can reason about the distribution of the sample mean with absolutely no information about the shape of the population distribution from which the sample is taken. In other words, the central limit theorem is true for all distributions.

A formal statement of the central limit theorem follows.

> **CENTRAL LIMIT THEOREM** If all samples of a particular size are selected from any population, the sampling distribution of the sample mean is approximately a normal distribution. This approximation improves with larger samples.

If the population follows a normal probability distribution, then for any sample size the sampling distribution of the sample mean will also be normal. If the population distribution is symmetrical (but not normal), you will see the normal shape of the distribution of the sample mean emerge with samples as small as 10. On the other hand, if you start with a distribution that is skewed or has thick tails, it may require samples of 30 or more to observe the normality feature. This concept is summarized in Chart 8–3 for various population shapes. Observe the convergence to a normal distribution regardless of the shape of the population distribution.

The idea that the distribution of the sample means from a population that is not normal will converge to normality is illustrated in Charts 8–4, 8–5, and 8–6. We will discuss this example in more detail shortly, but Chart 8–4 is a graph of a discrete probability distribution that is positively skewed. There are many possible samples of 5 that might be selected from this population. Suppose we randomly select 25 samples of size 5 from the population portrayed in Chart 8–4 and compute the mean of each sample. These results are shown in Chart 8–5. Notice that the shape of the distribution of sample means has changed from the shape of the original population even though we selected only 25 of the many possible samples. To put it another way, we selected 25 random samples of 5 each from a population that is positively skewed and found the distribution of sample means has changed from the shape of the population. As we take larger samples, that is, $n = 20$ instead of $n = 5$, we will find the distribution of the

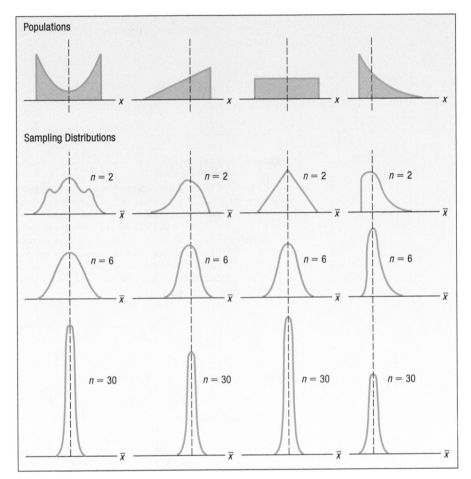

CHART 8–3 Results of the Central Limit Theorem for Several Populations

sample mean will approach the normal distribution. Chart 8–6 shows the results of 25 random samples of 20 observations each from the same population. Observe the clear trend toward the normal probability distribution. This is the point of the central limit theorem. The following example/solution will underscore this condition.

E X A M P L E

Ed Spence began his sprocket business 20 years ago. The business has grown over the years and now employs 40 people. Spence Sprockets Inc. faces some major decisions regarding health care for these employees. Before making a final decision on what health care plan to purchase, Ed decides to form a committee of five representative employees. The committee will be asked to study the health care issue carefully and make a recommendation as to what plan best fits the employees' needs. Ed feels the views of newer employees toward health care may differ from those of more experienced employees. If Ed randomly selects this committee, what can he expect in terms of the mean years with Spence Sprockets for those on the committee? How does the shape of the distribution of years of service of all employees (the population) compare with the shape of the sampling distribution of the mean? The years of service (rounded to the nearest year) of the 40 employees currently on the Spence Sprockets Inc. payroll are as follows.

11	4	18	2	1	2	0	2	2	4
3	4	1	2	2	3	3	19	8	3
7	1	0	2	7	0	4	5	1	14
16	8	9	1	1	2	5	10	2	3

SOLUTION

Chart 8–4 shows a histogram for the frequency distribution of the years of service for the population of 40 current employees. This distribution is positively skewed. Why? Because the business has grown in recent years, the distribution shows that 29 of the 40 employees have been with the company less than 6 years. Also, there are 11 employees who have worked at Spence Sprockets for more than 6 years. In particular, four employees have been with the company 12 years or more (count the frequencies above 12). So there is a long tail in the distribution of service years to the right, that is, the distribution is positively skewed.

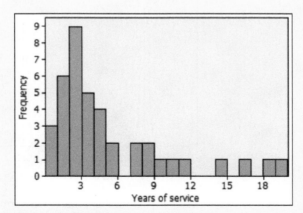

CHART 8–4 Years of Service for Spence Sprockets Inc. Employees

Let's consider the first of Ed Spence's problems. He would like to form a committee of five employees to look into the health care question and suggest what type of health care coverage would be most appropriate for the majority of workers. How should he select the committee? If he selects the committee randomly, what might he expect in terms of mean years of service for those on the committee?

To begin, Ed writes the years of service for each of the 40 employees on pieces of paper and puts them into an old baseball hat. Next, he shuffles the pieces of paper and randomly selects five slips of paper. The years of service for these five employees are 1, 9, 0, 19, and 14 years. Thus, the mean years of service for these five sampled employees is 8.60 years. How does that compare with the population mean? At this point, Ed does not know the population mean, but the number of employees in the population is only 40, so he decides to calculate the mean years of service for *all* his employees. It is 4.8 years, found by adding the years of service for *all* the employees and dividing the total by 40.

$$\mu = \frac{11 + 4 + 18 + \cdots + 2 + 3}{40} = 4.80$$

The difference between a sample mean ($\bar{x}$) and the population mean (μ) is called **sampling error**. In other words, the difference of 3.80 years between the sample mean of 8.60 and the population mean of 4.80 is the sampling error. It is due to chance. Thus, if Ed selected these five employees to constitute the committee, their mean years of service would be larger than the population mean.

What would happen if Ed put the five pieces of paper back into the baseball hat and selected another sample? Would you expect the mean of this second sample to be exactly the same as the previous one? Suppose he selects another sample of five employees and finds the years of service in this sample to be 7, 4, 4, 1, and 3. This sample mean is 3.80 years. The result of selecting 25 samples of five employees and computing the mean for each sample is shown in Table 8–5 and Chart 8–5. There are actually 658,008 possible samples of 5 from the population of 40 employees, found by the combination formula (5–9) for 40 things taken 5 at a time. Notice the difference in the shape of the population and the distribution of these sample means. The population of the years of service for employees (Chart 8–4) is positively skewed, but the

TABLE 8–5 Twenty-Five Random Samples of Five Employees

Sample	Obs 1	Obs 2	Obs 3	Obs 4	Obs 5	Sum	Mean
A	1	9	0	19	14	43	8.6
B	7	4	4	1	3	19	3.8
C	8	19	8	2	1	38	7.6
D	4	18	2	0	11	35	7.0
E	4	2	4	7	18	35	7.0
F	1	2	0	3	2	8	1.6
G	2	3	2	0	2	9	1.8
H	11	2	9	2	4	28	5.6
I	9	0	4	2	7	22	4.4
J	1	1	1	11	1	15	3.0
K	2	0	0	10	2	14	2.8
L	0	2	3	2	16	23	4.6
M	2	3	1	1	1	8	1.6
N	3	7	3	4	3	20	4.0
O	1	2	3	1	4	11	2.2
P	19	0	1	3	8	31	6.2
Q	5	1	7	14	9	36	7.2
R	5	4	2	3	4	18	3.6
S	14	5	2	2	5	28	5.6
T	2	1	1	4	7	15	3.0
U	3	7	1	2	1	14	2.8
V	0	1	5	1	2	9	1.8
W	0	3	19	4	2	28	5.6
X	4	2	3	4	0	13	2.6
Y	1	1	2	3	2	9	1.8

266   CHAPTER 8

CHART 8–5 Histogram of Mean Years of Service for 25 Samples of Five Employees

distribution of these 25 sample means does not reflect the same positive skew. There is also a difference in the range of the sample means versus the range of the population. The population ranged from 0 to 19 years, whereas the sample means range from 1.6 to 8.6 years.

Now let's change the example by increasing the size of each sample from 5 employees to 20. Table 8–6 reports the result of selecting 25 samples of 20 employees each and computing their sample means. These sample means are

TABLE 8–6 Twenty-Five Random Samples of 20 Employees

Sample	Sample Data							
	Obs 1	Obs 2	Obs 3	–	Obs 19	Obs 20	Sum	Mean
A	3	8	3	–	4	16	79	3.95
B	2	3	8	–	3	1	65	3.25
C	14	5	0	–	19	8	119	5.95
D	9	2	1	–	1	3	87	4.35
E	18	1	2	–	3	14	107	5.35
F	10	4	4	–	2	1	80	4.00
G	5	7	11	–	2	4	131	6.55
H	3	0	2	–	16	5	85	4.25
I	0	0	18	–	2	3	80	4.00
J	2	7	2	–	3	2	81	4.05
K	7	4	5	–	1	2	84	4.20
L	0	3	10	–	0	4	81	4.05
M	4	1	2	–	1	2	88	4.40
N	3	16	1	–	11	1	95	4.75
O	2	19	2	–	2	2	102	5.10
P	2	18	16	–	4	3	100	5.00
Q	3	2	3	–	3	1	102	5.10
R	2	3	1	–	0	2	73	3.65
S	2	14	19	–	0	7	142	7.10
T	0	1	3	–	2	0	61	3.05
U	1	0	1	–	9	3	65	3.25
V	1	9	4	–	2	11	137	6.85
W	8	1	9	–	8	7	107	5.35
X	4	2	0	–	2	5	86	4.30
Y	1	2	1	–	1	18	101	5.05

SAMPLING METHODS AND THE CENTRAL LIMIT THEOREM   267

shown graphically in Chart 8–6. Compare the shape of this distribution to the population (Chart 8–4) and to the distribution of sample means where the sample is $n = 5$ (Chart 8–5). You should observe two important features:

1. The shape of the distribution of the sample mean is different from that of the population. In Chart 8–4, the distribution of all employees is positively skewed. However, as we select random samples from this population, the shape of the distribution of the sample mean changes. As we increase the size of the sample, the distribution of the sample mean approaches the normal probability distribution. This illustrates the central limit theorem.
2. There is less dispersion in the sampling distribution of the sample mean than in the population distribution. In the population, the years of service ranged from 0 to 19 years. When we selected samples of 5, the sample means ranged from 1.6 to 8.6 years, and when we selected samples of 20, the means ranged from 3.05 to 7.10 years.

CHART 8–6 Histogram of Mean Years of Service for 25 Samples of 20 Employees

We can also compare the mean of the sample means to the population mean. The mean of the 25 samples of 20 employees reported in Table 8–6 is 4.676 years.

$$\mu_{\bar{X}} = \frac{3.95 + 3.25 + \cdots + 4.30 + 5.05}{25} = 4.676$$

We use the symbol $\mu_{\bar{X}}$ to identify the mean of the distribution of the sample mean. The subscript reminds us that the distribution is of the sample mean. It is read "mu sub x bar." We observe that the mean of the sample means, 4.676 years, is very close to the population mean of 4.80.

What should we conclude from this example? The central limit theorem indicates that, regardless of the shape of the population distribution, the sampling distribution of the sample mean will move toward the normal probability distribution. The larger the number of observations in each sample, the stronger the convergence. The Spence Sprockets Inc. example shows how the central limit theorem works. We began with a positively skewed population (Chart 8–4). Next, we selected 25 random samples of 5 observations, computed the mean of each sample, and finally organized these 25 sample means into a histogram (Chart 8–5). We observe a change in the shape of the sampling distribution of the sample mean from that of the population. The movement is from a positively skewed distribution to a distribution that has the shape of the normal probability distribution.

To further illustrate the effects of the central limit theorem, we increased the number of observations in each sample from 5 to 20. We selected 25 samples of 20 observations each and calculated the mean of each sample. Finally, we organized these

268   CHAPTER 8

sample means into a histogram (Chart 8–6). The shape of the histogram in Chart 8–6 is clearly moving toward the normal probability distribution.

   If you go back to Chapter 6 where several binomial distributions with a "success" proportion of .10 are shown in Chart 6–3 on page 188, you can see yet another demonstration of the central limit theorem. Observe as *n* increases from 7 through 12 and 20 up to 40 that the profile of the probability distributions moves closer and closer to a normal probability distribution. Chart 8–6 on page 267 also shows the convergence to normality as *n* increases. This again reinforces the fact that, as more observations are sampled from any population distribution, the shape of the sampling distribution of the sample mean will get closer and closer to a normal distribution.

   The central limit theorem itself (reread the definition on page 262) does not say anything about the dispersion of the sampling distribution of the sample mean or about the comparison of the mean of the sampling distribution of the sample mean to the mean of the population. However, in our Spence Sprockets example, we did observe that there was less dispersion in the distribution of the sample mean than in the population distribution by noting the difference in the range in the population and the range of the sample means. We observe that the mean of the sample means is close to the mean of the population. It can be demonstrated that the mean of the sampling distribution is the population mean (i.e., $\mu_{\bar{x}} = \mu$), and if the standard deviation in the population is σ, the standard deviation of the sample means is $\sigma/\sqrt{n}$, where *n* is the number of observations in each sample. We refer to $\sigma/\sqrt{n}$ as the **standard error of the mean.** Its longer name is actually the *standard deviation of the sampling distribution of the sample mean.*

STANDARD ERROR OF THE MEAN	$\sigma_{\bar{x}} = \dfrac{\sigma}{\sqrt{n}}$	[8–1]

   In this section, we also came to other important conclusions.

1. The mean of the distribution of sample means will be *exactly* equal to the population mean if we are able to select all possible samples of the same size from a given population. That is:

$$\mu = \mu_{\bar{x}}$$

   Even if we do not select all samples, we can expect the mean of the distribution of sample means to be close to the population mean.

2. There will be less dispersion in the sampling distribution of the sample mean than in the population. If the standard deviation of the population is σ, the standard deviation of the distribution of sample means is $\sigma/\sqrt{n}$. Note that when we increase the size of the sample, the standard error of the mean decreases.

SELF-REVIEW

8–4

Refer to the Spence Sprockets Inc. data on page 264. Select 10 random samples of five employees each. Use the methods described earlier in the chapter and the Table of Random Numbers (Appendix B.4) to find the employees to include in the sample. Compute the mean of each sample and plot the sample means on a chart similar to Chart 8–4. What is the mean of your 10 sample means?

EXERCISES

11. Appendix B.4 is a table of random numbers that are uniformly distributed. Hence, each digit from 0 to 9 has the same likelihood of occurrence.
   a. Draw a graph showing the population distribution of random numbers. What is the population mean?
   b. Following are the first 10 rows of five digits from the table of random numbers in Appendix B.4. Assume that these are 10 random samples of five values each. Determine

the mean of each sample and plot the means on a chart similar to Chart 8–4. Compare the mean of the sampling distribution of the sample mean with the population mean.

0	2	7	1	1
9	4	8	7	3
5	4	9	2	1
7	7	6	4	0
6	1	5	4	5
1	7	1	4	7
1	3	7	4	8
8	7	4	5	5
0	8	9	9	9
7	8	8	0	4

For **DATA FILE**, please visit www.mhhe.com/lind16e

12. Scrapper Elevator Company has 20 sales representatives who sell its product throughout the United States and Canada. The number of units sold last month by each representative is listed below. Assume these sales figures to be the population values.

2	3	2	3	3	4	2	4	3	2	2	7	3	4	5	3	3	3	3	5

  a. Draw a graph showing the population distribution.
  b. Compute the mean of the population.
  c. Select five random samples of 5 each. Compute the mean of each sample. Use the methods described in this chapter and Appendix B.4 to determine the items to be included in the sample.
  d. Compare the mean of the sampling distribution of the sample mean to the population mean. Would you expect the two values to be about the same?
  e. Draw a histogram of the sample means. Do you notice a difference in the shape of the distribution of sample means compared to the shape of the population distribution?
13. Consider all of the coins (pennies, nickels, quarters, etc.) in your pocket or purse as a population. Make a frequency table beginning with the current year and counting backward to record the ages (in years) of the coins. For example, if the current year is 2013, then a coin with 2011 stamped on it is 2 years old.
  a. Draw a histogram or other graph showing the population distribution.
  b. Randomly select five coins and record the mean age of the sampled coins. Repeat this sampling process 20 times. Now draw a histogram or other graph showing the distribution of the sample means.
  c. Compare the shapes of the two histograms.
14. Consider the digits in the phone numbers on a randomly selected page of your local phone book a population. Make a frequency table of the final digit of 30 randomly selected phone numbers. For example, if a phone number is 555-9704, record a 4.
  a. Draw a histogram or other graph of this population distribution. Using the uniform distribution, compute the population mean and the population standard deviation.
  b. Also record the sample mean of the final four digits (9704 would lead to a mean of 5). Now draw a histogram or other graph showing the distribution of the sample means.
  c. Compare the shapes of the two histograms.

LO8-5

Apply the central limit theorem to calculate probabilities.

USING THE SAMPLING DISTRIBUTION OF THE SAMPLE MEAN

The previous discussion is important because most business decisions are made on the basis of sample information. Here are some examples.

1. Arm & Hammer Company wants to ensure that its laundry detergent actually contains 100 fluid ounces, as indicated on the label. Historical summaries from

CHAPTER 8

the filling process indicate the mean amount per container is 100 fluid ounces and the standard deviation is 2 fluid ounces. The quality technician in her 10 a.m. check of 40 containers finds the mean amount per container is 99.8 fluid ounces. Should the technician shut down the filling operation?

2. A. C. Nielsen Company provides information to organizations advertising on television. Prior research indicates that adult Americans watch an average of 6.0 hours per day of television. The standard deviation is 1.5 hours. For a sample of 50 adults in the greater Boston area, would it be reasonable that we could randomly select a sample and find that they watch an average of 6.5 hours or more of television per day?

3. Haughton Elevator Company wishes to develop specifications for the number of people who can ride in a new oversized elevator. Suppose the mean weight for an adult is 160 pounds and the standard deviation is 15 pounds. However, the distribution of weights does not follow the normal probability distribution. It is positively skewed. What is the likelihood that for a sample of 30 adults their mean weight is 170 pounds or more?

We can answer the questions in each of these situations using the ideas discussed in the previous section. In each case, we have a population with information about its mean and standard deviation. Using this information and sample size, we can determine the distribution of sample means and compute the probability that a sample mean will fall within a certain range. The sampling distribution will be normally distributed under two conditions:

1. When the samples are taken from populations known to follow the normal distribution. In this case, the size of the sample is not a factor.

2. When the shape of the population distribution is not known or the shape is known to be nonnormal, sample size is important. In general, the sampling distribution will be normally distributed as the sample size approaches infinity. In practice, a sampling distribution will be close to a normal distribution with samples of at least 30 observations.

We use formula (7–5) from the previous chapter to convert any normal distribution to the standard normal distribution. Using formula (7–5) to compute z values, we can use the standard normal table, Appendix B.3, to find the probability that an observation is within a specific range. The formula for finding a z value is:

$$z = \frac{x - \mu}{\sigma}$$

In this formula, x is the value of the random variable, μ is the population mean, and σ is the population standard deviation.

However, most business decisions refer to a sample—not just one observation. So we are interested in the distribution of $\overline{X}$, the sample mean, instead of X, the value of one observation. That is the first change we make in formula (7–5). The second is that we use the standard error of the mean of n observations instead of the population standard deviation. That is, we use $\sigma/\sqrt{n}$ in the denominator rather than σ. Therefore, to find the likelihood of a sample mean within a specified range, we first use the following formula to find the corresponding z value. Then we use Appendix B.3 or statistical software to determine the probability.

| FINDING THE z VALUE OF $\bar{x}$ WHEN THE POPULATION STANDARD DEVIATION IS KNOWN | $z = \dfrac{\bar{x} - \mu}{\sigma/\sqrt{n}}$ | [8–2] |

The following example/solution will show the application.

EXAMPLE

The Quality Assurance Department for Cola, Inc. maintains records regarding the amount of cola in its jumbo bottle. The actual amount of cola in each bottle is critical but varies a small amount from one bottle to the next. Cola, Inc. does not wish to underfill the bottles because it will have a problem with truth in labeling. On the other hand, it cannot overfill each bottle because it would be giving cola away, hence reducing its profits. Records maintained by the Quality Assurance Department indicate that the amount of cola follows the normal probability distribution. The mean amount per bottle is 31.2 ounces and the population standard deviation is 0.4 ounce. At 8 a.m. today the quality technician randomly selected 16 bottles from the filling line. The mean amount of cola contained in the bottles is 31.38 ounces. Is this an unlikely result? Is it likely the process is putting too much soda in the bottles? To put it another way, is the sampling error of 0.18 ounce unusual?

SOLUTION

We use the results of the previous section to find the likelihood that we could select a sample of 16 (n) bottles from a normal population with a mean of 31.2 (μ) ounces and a population standard deviation of 0.4 (σ) ounce and find the sample mean to be 31.38 ($\bar{x}$) or more. We use formula (8–2) to find the value of z.

$$z = \frac{\bar{x} - \mu}{\sigma/\sqrt{n}} = \frac{31.38 - 31.20}{0.4/\sqrt{16}} = 1.80$$

The numerator of this equation, $\bar{x} - \mu = 31.38 - 31.20 = .18$, is the sampling error. The denominator, $\sigma/\sqrt{n} = 0.4/\sqrt{16} = 0.1$, is the standard error of the sampling distribution of the sample mean. So the z values express the sampling error in standard units—in other words, the standard error.

Next, we compute the likelihood of a z value greater than 1.80. In Appendix B.3, locate the probability corresponding to a z value of 1.80. It is .4641. The likelihood of a z value greater than 1.80 is .0359, found by .5000 − .4641.

What do we conclude? It is unlikely, less than a 4% chance, we could select a sample of 16 observations from a normal population with a mean of 31.2 ounces and a population standard deviation of 0.4 ounce and find the sample mean equal to or greater than 31.38 ounces. We conclude the process is putting too much cola in the bottles. The quality technician should see the production supervisor about reducing the amount of soda in each bottle. This information is summarized in Chart 8–7.

CHART 8–7 Sampling Distribution of the Mean Amount of Cola in a Jumbo Bottle

272   CHAPTER 8

SELF-REVIEW

8-5

Refer to the Cola, Inc. information. Suppose the quality technician selected a sample of 16 jumbo bottles that averaged 31.08 ounces. What can you conclude about the filling process?

EXERCISES

15. A normal population has a mean of 60 and a standard deviation of 12. You select a random sample of 9. Compute the probability the sample mean is:
   a. Greater than 63.
   b. Less than 56.
   c. Between 56 and 63.
16. A normal population has a mean of 75 and a standard deviation of 5. You select a sample of 40. Compute the probability the sample mean is:
   a. Less than 74.
   b. Between 74 and 76.
   c. Between 76 and 77.
   d. Greater than 77.
17. In a certain section of Southern California, the distribution of monthly rent for a one-bedroom apartment has a mean of $2,200 and a standard deviation of $250. The distribution of the monthly rent does not follow the normal distribution. In fact, it is positively skewed. What is the probability of selecting a sample of 50 one-bedroom apartments and finding the mean to be at least $1,950 per month?
18. According to an IRS study, it takes a mean of 330 minutes for taxpayers to prepare, copy, and electronically file a 1040 tax form. This distribution of times follows the normal distribution and the standard deviation is 80 minutes. A consumer watchdog agency selects a random sample of 40 taxpayers.
   a. What is the standard error of the mean in this example?
   b. What is the likelihood the sample mean is greater than 320 minutes?
   c. What is the likelihood the sample mean is between 320 and 350 minutes?
   d. What is the likelihood the sample mean is greater than 350 minutes?

CHAPTER SUMMARY

I. There are many reasons for sampling a population.
   A. The results of a sample may adequately estimate the value of the population parameter, thus saving time and money.
   B. It may be too time-consuming to contact all members of the population.
   C. It may be impossible to check or locate all the members of the population.
   D. The cost of studying all the items in the population may be prohibitive.
   E. Often testing destroys the sampled item and it cannot be returned to the population.
II. In an unbiased or probability sample, all members of the population have a chance of being selected for the sample. There are several probability sampling methods.
   A. In a simple random sample, all members of the population have the same chance of being selected for the sample.
   B. In a systematic sample, a random starting point is selected, and then every kth item thereafter is selected for the sample.
   C. In a stratified sample, the population is divided into several groups, called strata, and then a random sample is selected from each stratum.
   D. In cluster sampling, the population is divided into primary units, then samples are drawn from the primary units.
III. The sampling error is the difference between a population parameter and a sample statistic.

SAMPLING METHODS AND THE CENTRAL LIMIT THEOREM   273

IV. The sampling distribution of the sample mean is a probability distribution of all possible sample means of the same sample size.
   A. For a given sample size, the mean of all possible sample means selected from a population is equal to the population mean.
   B. There is less variation in the distribution of the sample mean than in the population distribution.
   C. The standard error of the mean measures the variation in the sampling distribution of the sample mean. The standard error is found by:

$$\sigma_{\bar{x}} = \frac{\sigma}{\sqrt{n}}$$ [8–1]

   D. If the population follows a normal distribution, the sampling distribution of the sample mean will also follow the normal distribution for samples of any size. If the population is not normally distributed, the sampling distribution of the sample mean will approach a normal distribution when the sample size is at least 30. Assume the population standard deviation is known. To determine the probability that a sample mean falls in a particular region, use the following formula.

$$z = \frac{\bar{x} - \mu}{\sigma/\sqrt{n}}$$ [8–2]

P R O N U N C I A T I O N   K E Y

SYMBOL	MEANING	PRONUNCIATION
$\mu_{\bar{x}}$	Mean of the sampling distribution of the sample mean	mu sub x bar
$\sigma_{\bar{x}}$	Population standard error of the sample mean	sigma sub x bar

C H A P T E R   E X E R C I S E S

19. The 25 retail stores located in the North Towne Square Mall numbered 00 through 24 are:

00	Elder-Beerman	09	Lion Store	18	County Seat
01	Sears	10	Bootleggers	19	Kid Mart
02	Deb Shop	11	Formal Man	20	Lerner
03	Frederick's of Hollywood	12	Leather Ltd.	21	Coach House Gifts
04	Petries	13	B Dalton Bookseller	22	Spencer Gifts
05	Easy Dreams	14	Pat's Hallmark	23	CPI Photo Finish
06	Summit Stationers	15	Things Remembered	24	Regis Hairstylists
07	E. B. Brown Opticians	16	Pearle Vision Express		
08	Kay-Bee Toy & Hobby	17	Dollar Tree		

   a. If the following random numbers are selected, which retail stores should be contacted for a survey? 11, 65, 86, 62, 06, 10, 12, 77, and 04
   b. Select a random sample of four retail stores. Use Appendix B.4.
   c. A systematic sampling procedure is to be used. The first store is to be contacted and then every third store. Which stores will be contacted?
20. The Medical Assurance Company is investigating the cost of a routine office visit to family-practice physicians in the Rochester, New York, area. The following is a list of 39 family-practice physicians in the region. Physicians are to be randomly selected and contacted regarding their charges. The 39 physicians have been coded from 00 to 38. Also noted is whether they are in practice by themselves (S), have a partner (P), or are in a group practice (G).

Number	Physician	Type of Practice	Number	Physician	Type of Practice
00	R. E. Scherbarth, M.D.	S	20	Gregory Yost, M.D.	P
01	Crystal R. Goveia, M.D.	P	21	J. Christian Zona, M.D.	P
02	Mark D. Hillard, M.D.	P	22	Larry Johnson, M.D.	P
03	Jeanine S. Huttner, M.D.	P	23	Sanford Kimmel, M.D.	P
04	Francis Aona, M.D.	P	24	Harry Mayhew, M.D.	S
05	Janet Arrowsmith, M.D.	P	25	Leroy Rodgers, M.D.	S
06	David DeFrance, M.D.	S	26	Thomas Tafelski, M.D.	S
07	Judith Furlong, M.D.	S	27	Mark Zilkoski, M.D.	G
08	Leslie Jackson, M.D.	G	28	Ken Bertka, M.D.	G
09	Paul Langenkamp, M.D.	S	29	Mark DeMichiei, M.D.	G
10	Philip Lepkowski, M.D.	S	30	John Eggert, M.D.	P
11	Wendy Martin, M.D.	S	31	Jeanne Fiorito, M.D.	P
12	Denny Mauricio, M.D.	P	32	Michael Fitzpatrick, M.D.	P
13	Hasmukh Parmar, M.D.	P	33	Charles Holt, D.O.	P
14	Ricardo Pena, M.D.	P	34	Richard Koby, M.D.	P
15	David Reames, M.D.	P	35	John Meier, M.D.	P
16	Ronald Reynolds, M.D.	G	36	Douglas Smucker, M.D.	S
17	Mark Steinmetz, M.D.	G	37	David Weldy, M.D.	P
18	Geza Torok, M.D.	S	38	Cheryl Zaborowski, M.D.	P
19	Mark Young, M.D.	P			

    a. The random numbers obtained from Appendix B.4 are 31, 94, 43, 36, 03, 24, 17, and 09. Which physicians should be contacted?

    b. Select a random sample of four physicians using the random numbers of Appendix B.4.

    c. A sample is to consist of every fifth physician. The number 04 is selected as the starting point. Which physicians will be contacted?

    d. A sample is to consist of two physicians in solo practice (S), two in partnership (P), and one in group practice (G). Select a sample accordingly. Explain your procedure.

21. A population consists of the following three values: 1, 2, and 3.

    a. Sampling with replacement, list all possible samples of size 2 and compute the mean of every sample.

    b. Find the means of the distribution of the sample mean and the population mean. Compare the two values.

    c. Compare the dispersion of the population with that of the sample mean.

    d. Describe the shapes of the two distributions.

22. In the Department of Education at UR University, student records suggest that the population of students spends an average of 5.5 hours per week playing organized sports. The population's standard deviation is 2.2 hours per week. Based on a sample of 121 students, Healthy Lifestyles Incorporated (HLI) would like to apply the central limit theorem to make various estimates.

    a. Compute the standard error of the sample mean.

    b. What is the chance HLI will find a sample mean between 5 and 6 hours?

    c. Calculate the probability that the sample mean will be between 5.3 and 5.7 hours.

    d. How strange would it be to obtain a sample mean greater than 6.5 hours?

23. The manufacturer of eComputers, an economy-priced computer, recently completed the design for a new laptop model. eComputer's top management would like some assistance in pricing the new laptop. Two market research firms were contacted and asked to prepare a pricing strategy. Marketing-Gets-Results tested the new eComputers laptop with 50 randomly selected consumers who indicated they plan to purchase a laptop within the next year. The second marketing research firm, called Marketing-Reaps-Profits, test-marketed the new eComputers laptop with 200 current laptop owners. Which of the marketing research companies' test results will be more useful? Discuss why.

24. Answer the following questions in one or two well-constructed sentences.

    a. What happens to the standard error of the mean if the sample size is increased?

    b. What happens to the distribution of the sample means if the sample size is increased?

SAMPLING METHODS AND THE CENTRAL LIMIT THEOREM   275

   c. When using the distribution of sample means to estimate the population mean, what is the benefit of using larger sample sizes?

25. There are 25 motels in Goshen, Indiana. The number of rooms in each motel follows:

90 72 75 60 75 72 84 72 88 74 105 115 68 74 80 64 104 82 48 58 60 80 48 58 100

   a. Using a table of random numbers (Appendix B.4), select a random sample of five motels from this population.
   b. Obtain a systematic sample by selecting a random starting point among the first five motels and then select every fifth motel.
   c. Suppose the last five motels are "cut-rate" motels. Describe how you would select a random sample of three regular motels and two cut-rate motels.

26. As a part of their customer-service program, United Airlines randomly selected 10 passengers from today's 9 a.m. Chicago–Tampa flight. Each sampled passenger is to be interviewed in depth regarding airport facilities, service, and so on. To identify the sample, each passenger was given a number on boarding the aircraft. The numbers started with 001 and ended with 250.
   a. Select 10 usable numbers at random using Appendix B.4.
   b. The sample of 10 could have been chosen using a systematic sample. Choose the first number using Appendix B.4, and then list the numbers to be interviewed.
   c. Evaluate the two methods by giving the advantages and possible disadvantages.
   d. In what other way could a random sample be selected from the 250 passengers?

27. Suppose your statistics instructor gave six examinations during the semester. You received the following grades (percent correct): 79, 64, 84, 82, 92, and 77. Instead of averaging the six scores, the instructor indicated he would randomly select two grades and compute the final percent correct based on the two percents.
   a. How many different samples of two test grades are possible?
   b. List all possible samples of size 2 and compute the mean of each.
   c. Compute the mean of the sample means and compare it to the population mean.
   d. If you were a student, would you like this arrangement? Would the result be different from dropping the lowest score? Write a brief report.

28. At the downtown office of First National Bank, there are five tellers. Last week, the tellers made the following number of errors each: 2, 3, 5, 3, and 5.
   a. How many different samples of two tellers are possible?
   b. List all possible samples of size 2 and compute the mean of each.
   c. Compute the mean of the sample means and compare it to the population mean.

29. The Quality Control Department employs five technicians during the day shift. Listed below is the number of times each technician instructed the production foreman to shut down the manufacturing process last week.

Technician	Shutdowns	Technician	Shutdowns
Taylor	4	Rousche	3
Hurley	3	Huang	2
Gupta	5		

   a. How many different samples of two technicians are possible from this population?
   b. List all possible samples of two observations each and compute the mean of each sample.
   c. Compare the mean of the sample means with the population mean.
   d. Compare the shape of the population distribution with the shape of the distribution of the sample means.

30. The Appliance Center has six sales representatives at its North Jacksonville outlet. Listed below is the number of refrigerators sold by each last month.

Sales Representative	Number Sold	Sales Representative	Number Sold
Zina Craft	54	Jan Niles	48
Woon Junge	50	Molly Camp	50
Ernie DeBrul	52	Rachel Myak	52

a. How many samples of size 2 are possible?
b. Select all possible samples of size 2 and compute the mean number sold.
c. Organize the sample means into a frequency distribution.
d. What is the mean of the population? What is the mean of the sample means?
e. What is the shape of the population distribution?
f. What is the shape of the distribution of the sample mean?

31. Power +, Inc. produces AA batteries used in remote-controlled toy cars. The mean life of these batteries follows the normal probability distribution with a mean of 35.0 hours and a standard deviation of 5.5 hours. As a part of its quality assurance program, Power +, Inc. tests samples of 25 batteries.
a. What can you say about the shape of the distribution of the sample mean?
b. What is the standard error of the distribution of the sample mean?
c. What proportion of the samples will have a mean useful life of more than 36 hours?
d. What proportion of the sample will have a mean useful life greater than 34.5 hours?
e. What proportion of the sample will have a mean useful life between 34.5 and 36.0 hours?

32. CRA CDs Inc. wants the mean lengths of the "cuts" on a CD to be 135 seconds (2 minutes and 15 seconds). This will allow the disk jockeys to have plenty of time for commercials within each 10-minute segment. Assume the distribution of the length of the cuts follows the normal distribution with a population standard deviation of 8 seconds. Suppose we select a sample of 16 cuts from various CDs sold by CRA CDs Inc.
a. What can we say about the shape of the distribution of the sample mean?
b. What is the standard error of the mean?
c. What percent of the sample means will be greater than 140 seconds?
d. What percent of the sample means will be greater than 128 seconds?
e. What percent of the sample means will be greater than 128 but less than 140 seconds?

33. Recent studies indicate that the typical 50-year-old woman spends $350 per year for personal-care products. The distribution of the amounts spent follows a normal distribution with a standard deviation of $45 per year. We select a random sample of 40 women. The mean amount spent for those sampled is $335. What is the likelihood of finding a sample mean this large or larger from the specified population?

34. Information from the American Institute of Insurance indicates the mean amount of life insurance per household in the United States is $110,000. This distribution follows the normal distribution with a standard deviation of $40,000.
a. If we select a random sample of 50 households, what is the standard error of the mean?
b. What is the expected shape of the distribution of the sample mean?
c. What is the likelihood of selecting a sample with a mean of at least $112,000?
d. What is the likelihood of selecting a sample with a mean of more than $100,000?
e. Find the likelihood of selecting a sample with a mean of more than $100,000 but less than $112,000.

35. The mean age at which men in the United States marry for the first time follows the normal distribution with a mean of 24.8 years. The standard deviation of the distribution is 2.5 years. For a random sample of 60 men, what is the likelihood that the age at which they were married for the first time is less than 25.1 years?

36. A recent study by the Greater Los Angeles Taxi Drivers Association showed that the mean fare charged for service from Hermosa Beach to Los Angeles International Airport is $21 and the standard deviation is $3.50. We select a sample of 15 fares.
a. What is the likelihood that the sample mean is between $20 and $23?
b. What must you assume to make the above calculation?

37. Crossett Trucking Company claims that the mean weight of its delivery trucks when they are fully loaded is 6,000 pounds and the standard deviation is 150 pounds. Assume that the population follows the normal distribution. Forty trucks are randomly selected and weighed. Within what limits will 95% of the sample means occur?

38. The mean amount purchased by a typical customer at Churchill's Grocery Store is $23.50, with a standard deviation of $5.00. Assume the distribution of amounts purchased follows the normal distribution. For a sample of 50 customers, answer the following questions.
a. What is the likelihood the sample mean is at least $25.00?
b. What is the likelihood the sample mean is greater than $22.50 but less than $25.00?
c. Within what limits will 90% of the sample means occur?

39. The mean performance score on a physical fitness test for Division I student-athletes is 947 with a standard deviation of 205. If you select a random sample of 60 of these students, what is the probability the mean is below 900?

SAMPLING METHODS AND THE CENTRAL LIMIT THEOREM   277

40. Suppose we roll a fair die two times.
   a. How many different samples are there?
   b. List each of the possible samples and compute the mean.
   c. On a chart similar to Chart 8–2, compare the distribution of sample means with the distribution of the population.
   d. Compute the mean and the standard deviation of each distribution and compare them.

41. Following is a list of the 50 states with the numbers 0 through 49 assigned to them.

For **DATA FILE**, please visit www.mhhe.com/lind16e

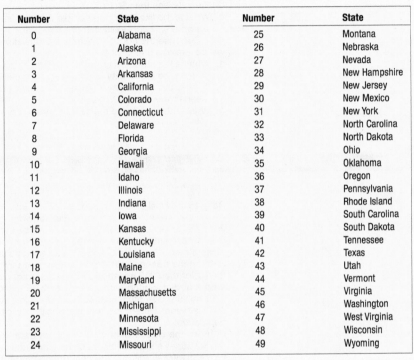

Number	State	Number	State
0	Alabama	25	Montana
1	Alaska	26	Nebraska
2	Arizona	27	Nevada
3	Arkansas	28	New Hampshire
4	California	29	New Jersey
5	Colorado	30	New Mexico
6	Connecticut	31	New York
7	Delaware	32	North Carolina
8	Florida	33	North Dakota
9	Georgia	34	Ohio
10	Hawaii	35	Oklahoma
11	Idaho	36	Oregon
12	Illinois	37	Pennsylvania
13	Indiana	38	Rhode Island
14	Iowa	39	South Carolina
15	Kansas	40	South Dakota
16	Kentucky	41	Tennessee
17	Louisiana	42	Texas
18	Maine	43	Utah
19	Maryland	44	Vermont
20	Massachusetts	45	Virginia
21	Michigan	46	Washington
22	Minnesota	47	West Virginia
23	Mississippi	48	Wisconsin
24	Missouri	49	Wyoming

   a. You wish to select a sample of eight from this list. The selected random numbers are 45, 15, 81, 09, 39, 43, 90, 26, 06, 45, 01, and 42. Which states are included in the sample?
   b. You wish to use a systematic sample of every sixth item and the digit 02 is chosen as the starting point. Which states are included?

42. Human Resource Consulting (HRC) surveyed a random sample of 60 Twin Cities construction companies to find information on the costs of their health care plans. One of the items being tracked is the annual deductible that employees must pay. The Minnesota Department of Labor reports that historically the mean deductible amount per employee is $502 with a standard deviation of $100.
   a. Compute the standard error of the sample mean for HRC.
   b. What is the chance HRC finds a sample mean between $477 and $527?
   c. Calculate the likelihood that the sample mean is between $492 and $512.
   d. What is the probability the sample mean is greater than $550?

43. Over the past decade, the mean number of hacking attacks experienced by members of the Information Systems Security Association is 510 per year with a standard deviation of 14.28 attacks. The number of attacks per year is normally distributed. Suppose nothing in this environment changes.
   a. What is the likelihood this group will suffer an average of more than 600 attacks in the next 10 years?
   b. Compute the probability the mean number of attacks over the next 10 years is between 500 and 600.
   c. What is the possibility they will experience an average of less than 500 attacks over the next 10 years?

44. An economist uses the price of a gallon of milk as a measure of inflation. She finds that the average price is $3.50 per gallon and the population standard deviation is $0.33. You decide to sample 40 convenience stores, collect their prices for a gallon of milk, and compute the mean price for the sample.
   a. What is the standard error of the mean in this experiment?
   b. What is the probability that the sample mean is between $3.46 and $3.54?
   c. What is the probability that the difference between the sample mean and the population mean is less than $0.01?
   d. What is the likelihood the sample mean is greater than $3.60?

45. Nike's annual report says that the average American buys 6.5 pairs of sports shoes per year. Suppose the population standard deviation is 2.1 and that a sample of 81 customers will be examined next year.
   a. What is the standard error of the mean in this experiment?
   b. What is the probability that the sample mean is between 6 and 7 pairs of sports shoes?
   c. What is the probability that the difference between the sample mean and the population mean is less than 0.25 pair?
   d. What is the likelihood the sample mean is greater than 7 pairs?

DATA   SET   EXERCISES

(The data for these exercises are available at the text website: www.mhhe.com/lind16e.)

46. Refer to the Real Estate data, which report information on the homes sold in the Goodyear, Arizona, area last year. Use statistical software to compute the mean and the standard deviation of the selling prices. Assume this to be the population. Select a sample of 10 homes. Compute the mean and the standard deviation of the sample. Determine the likelihood of a sample mean this large or larger from the population.

47. Refer to the Baseball 2012 data, which report information on the 30 Major League Baseball teams for the 2012 season. Over the last decade, the mean attendance per team followed a normal distribution with a mean of 2.25 million per team and a standard deviation of 0.70 million. Use statistical software to compute the mean attendance per team for the 2012 season. Determine the likelihood of a sample mean this large or larger from the population.

48. Refer to the Buena School District bus data. Information provided by manufacturers of school buses suggests the mean maintenance cost per month is $455 per bus. Use statistical software to find the mean and the standard deviation for the Buena buses. Does the Buena data seem to be in line with that reported by the manufacturer? Specifically, what is the probability of the sample mean being less than Buena's, given the manufacturer's data?

Estimation and Confidence Intervals

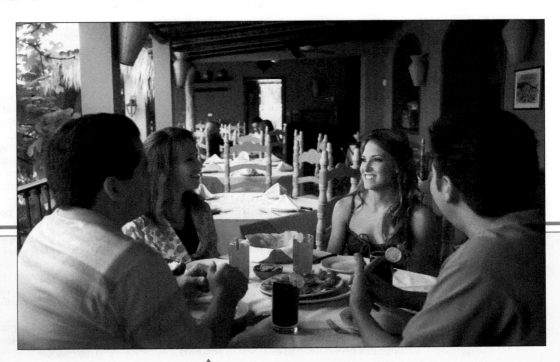

THE AMERICAN RESTAURANT ASSOCIATION collected information on the number of meals eaten outside the home per week by young married couples. A survey of 60 couples showed the sample mean number of meals eaten outside the home was 2.76 meals per week, with a standard deviation of 0.75 meal per week. Construct a 99% confidence interval for the population mean. (See Exercise 36 and **LO9-2**.)

LEARNING OBJECTIVES

When you have completed this chapter, you will be able to:

LO9-1 Compute and interpret a point estimate of a population mean.

LO9-2 Compute and interpret a confidence interval for a population mean.

LO9-3 Compute and interpret a confidence interval for a population proportion.

LO9-4 Calculate the required sample size to estimate a population proportion or population mean.

LO9-5 Adjust a confidence interval for finite populations.

280   CHAPTER 9

INTRODUCTION

The previous chapter began our discussion of statistical inference. We introduced both the reasons for, and the methods of, sampling. The reasons for sampling were:

- Contacting the entire population is too time-consuming.
- Studying all the items in the population is often too expensive.
- The sample results are usually adequate.
- Certain tests are destructive.
- Checking all the items is physically impossible.

There are several methods of sampling. Simple random sampling is the most widely used method. With this type of sampling, each member of the population has the same chance of being selected to be a part of the sample. Other methods of sampling include systematic sampling, stratified sampling, and cluster sampling.

Chapter 8 assumes information about the population, such as the mean, the standard deviation, or the shape of the population, is known. In most business situations, such information is not available. In fact, the purpose of sampling may be to estimate some of these values. For example, you select a sample from a population and use the mean of the sample to estimate the mean of the population.

This chapter considers several important aspects of sampling. We begin by studying **point estimates.** A point estimate is a single value (point) derived from a sample and used to estimate a population value. For example, suppose we select a sample of 50 junior executives and ask how many hours they worked last week. Compute the mean of this sample of 50 and use the value of the sample mean as a point estimate of the unknown population mean. However, a point estimate is a single value. A more informative approach is to present a range of values where we expect the population parameter to occur. Such a range of values is called a **confidence interval.**

Frequently in business we need to determine the size of a sample. How many voters should a polling organization contact to forecast the election outcome? How many products do we need to examine to ensure our quality level? This chapter also develops a strategy for determining the appropriate number of observations in the sample.

POINT ESTIMATE FOR A POPULATION MEAN

A point estimate is a single statistic used to estimate a population parameter. Suppose Best Buy Inc. wants to estimate the mean age of people who purchase LCD HDTV televisions. They select a random sample of 50 recent purchases, determine the age of each buyer, and compute the mean age of the buyers in the sample. The mean of this sample is a point estimate of the population mean.

LO9-1
Compute and interpret a point estimate of a population mean.

> **POINT ESTIMATE** The statistic, computed from sample information, that estimates a population parameter.

The following examples illustrate point estimates of population means.

1. Tourism is a major source of income for many Caribbean countries, such as Barbados. Suppose the Bureau of Tourism for Barbados wants an estimate of the mean amount spent by tourists visiting the country. It would not be feasible to contact each tourist. Therefore, 500 tourists are randomly selected as they depart the country and asked in detail about their spending while visiting Barbados. The mean amount spent by the sample of 500 tourists is an estimate of the unknown population parameter. That is, we let the sample mean serve as a point estimate of the population mean.

2. Litchfield Home Builders Inc. builds homes in the southeastern region of the United States. One of the major concerns of new buyers is the date when the home will be completed. Recently, Litchfield has been telling customers, "Your home will be completed 45 working days from the date we begin installing drywall." The customer relations department at Litchfield wishes to compare this pledge with recent experience. A sample of 50 homes completed this year revealed that the point estimate of the population mean is 46.7 working days from the start of drywall to the completion of the home. Is it reasonable to conclude that the population mean is still 45 days and that the difference between the sample mean (46.7 days) and the proposed population mean (45 days) is sampling error? In other words, is the sample mean significantly different from the population mean?

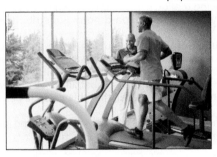

3. Recent medical studies indicate that exercise is an important part of a person's overall health. The director of human resources at OCF, a large glass manufacturer, wants an estimate of the number of hours per week employees spend exercising. A sample of 70 employees reveals the mean number of hours of exercise last week is 3.3. This value is a point estimate of the unknown population mean.

The sample mean, $\bar{x}$, is not the only point estimate of a population parameter. For example, p, a sample proportion, is a point estimate of π, the population proportion; and s, the sample standard deviation, is a point estimate of σ, the population standard deviation.

LO9-2
Compute and interpret a confidence interval for a population mean.

CONFIDENCE INTERVALS FOR A POPULATION MEAN

A point estimate, however, tells only part of the story. While we expect the point estimate to be close to the population parameter, we would like to measure how close it really is. A confidence interval serves this purpose. For example, we estimate the mean yearly income for construction workers in the New York–New Jersey area is $85,000. The range of this estimate might be from $81,000 to $89,000. We can describe how confident we are that the population parameter is in the interval. We might say, for instance, that we are 90% confident that the mean yearly income of construction workers in the New York–New Jersey area is between $81,000 and $89,000.

> **CONFIDENCE INTERVAL** A range of values constructed from sample data so that the population parameter is likely to occur within that range at a specified probability. The specified probability is called the *level of confidence*.

To compute a confidence interval for a population mean, we will consider two situations:

- We use sample data to estimate μ with $\bar{x}$, and the population standard deviation (σ) is known.
- We use sample data to estimate μ with $\bar{x}$, and the population standard deviation is unknown. In this case, we substitute the sample standard deviation (s) for the population standard deviation (σ).

There are important distinctions in the assumptions between these two situations. We first consider the case where σ is known.

282   CHAPTER 9

Population Standard Deviation, Known σ

A confidence interval is computed using two statistics: the sample mean, $\bar{x}$, and the standard deviation. From previous chapters, you know that the standard deviation is an important statistic because it measures the dispersion, or variation, of a population or sample distribution. In computing a confidence interval, the standard deviation is used to compute the limits of the confidence interval.

To demonstrate the idea of a confidence interval, we start with one simplifying assumption. That assumption is that we know the value of the population standard deviation, σ. Typically, we know the population standard deviation in situations where we have a long history of collected data. Examples are data from monitoring processes that fill soda bottles or cereal boxes, and the results of the SAT Reasoning Test (for college admission). Knowing σ allows us to simplify the development of a confidence interval because we can use the standard normal distribution from Chapter 8.

Recall that the sampling distribution of the sample mean is the distribution of all sample means, $\bar{x}$, of sample size n from a population. The population standard deviation, σ, is known. From this information, and the central limit theorem, we know that the sampling distribution follows the normal probability distribution with a mean of μ and a standard deviation $\sigma/\sqrt{n}$. Also recall that this value is called the standard error.

The results of the central limit theorem allow us to make the following general confidence interval statements using z-statistics:

1. Ninety-five percent of all confidence intervals computed from random samples selected from a population will contain the population mean. These intervals are computed using a z-statistic equal to 1.96.
2. Ninety percent of all confidence intervals computed from random samples selected from a population will contain the population mean. These confidence intervals are computed using a z-statistic equal to 1.65.

These confidence interval statements provide examples of *levels of confidence* and are called a **95% confidence interval** and a **90% confidence interval.** The *95%* and *90%* are the levels of confidence and refer to the percentage of similarly constructed intervals that would include the parameter being estimated—in this case, μ, the population mean.

How are the values of 1.96 and 1.65 obtained? First, let's look for the z value for a 95% confidence interval. The following diagram and Table 9–1 will help explain. Table 9–1 is a reproduction of Appendix B.3, the standard normal table. However, many rows and columns have been eliminated to allow us to better focus on particular rows and columns.

1. First, we divide the confidence level in half, so .9500/2 = .4750.
2. Next, we find the value .4750 in the body of Table 9–1. Note that .4750 is located in the table at the intersection of a row and a column.
3. Locate the corresponding row value in the left margin, which is 1.9, and the column value in the top margin, which is .06. Adding the row and column values gives us a z value of 1.96.
4. Thus, the probability of finding a z value between 0 and 1.96 is .4750.
5. Likewise, because the normal distribution is symmetric, the probability of finding a z value between −1.96 and 0 is also .4750.
6. When we add these two probabilities, the probability that a z value is between −1.96 and 1.96 is .9500.

For the 90% level of confidence, we follow the same steps. First, one-half of the desired confidence interval is .4500. A search of Table 9–1 does not reveal this exact value. However, it is between two values, .4495 and .4505. As in step three, we locate each value in the table. The first, .4495, corresponds to a z value of 1.64 and the second, .4505, corresponds to a z value of 1.65. To be conservative, we will select the larger of the two z values, 1.65, and the exact level of confidence is 90.1%, or 2(0.4505). Next, the probability of finding a z value between −1.65 and 0 is .4505, and the probability that a z value is between −1.65 and 1.65 is .9010.

TABLE 9–1 The Standard Normal Table for Selected Values

z	0.00	0.01	0.02	0.03	0.04	0.05	0.06	0.07
⋮	⋮	⋮	⋮	⋮	⋮	⋮	⋮	⋮
1.5	0.4332	0.4345	0.4357	0.4370	0.4382	0.4394	0.4406	0.4418
1.6	0.4452	0.4463	0.4474	0.4484	0.4495	0.4505	0.4515	0.4525
1.7	0.4554	0.4564	0.4573	0.4582	0.4591	0.4599	0.4608	0.4616
1.8	0.4641	0.4649	0.4656	0.4664	0.4671	0.4678	0.4686	0.4693
1.9	0.4713	0.4719	0.4726	0.4732	0.4738	0.4744	0.4750	0.4756
2.0	0.4772	0.4778	0.4783	0.4788	0.4793	0.4798	0.4803	0.4808
2.1	0.4821	0.4826	0.4830	0.4834	0.4838	0.4842	0.4846	0.4850
2.2	0.4861	0.4864	0.4868	0.4871	0.4875	0.4878	0.4881	0.4884

How do we determine a 95% confidence interval? The width of the interval is determined by two factors: (1) the level of confidence, as described in the previous section, and (2) the size of the standard error of the mean. To find the standard error of the mean, recall from the previous chapter [see formula (8–1) on page 268] that the standard error of the mean reports the variation in the distribution of sample means. It is really the standard deviation of the distribution of sample means. The formula is repeated below:

$$\sigma_{\bar{x}} = \frac{\sigma}{\sqrt{n}}$$

where:

$\sigma_{\bar{x}}$ is the symbol for the standard error of the mean. We use a Greek letter because it is a population value, and the subscript $\bar{x}$ reminds us that it refers to a sampling distribution of the sample means.

σ is the population standard deviation.

n is the number of observations in the sample.

284   CHAPTER 9

The size of the standard error is affected by two values. The first is the standard deviation of the population. The larger the population standard deviation, σ, the larger $\sigma/\sqrt{n}$. If the population is homogeneous, resulting in a small population standard deviation, the standard error will also be small. However, the standard error is also affected by the number of observations in the sample. A large number of observations in the sample will result in a small standard error of estimate, indicating that there is less variability in the sample means.

We can summarize the calculation for a 95% confidence interval using the following formula:

$$\bar{x} \pm 1.96 \frac{\sigma}{\sqrt{n}}$$

Similarly, a 90.1% confidence interval is computed as follows:

$$\bar{x} \pm 1.65 \frac{\sigma}{\sqrt{n}}$$

The values 1.96 and 1.65 are z values corresponding to the 95% and the 90.1% confidence intervals, respectively. However, we are not restricted to these values. We can select any confidence level between 0 and 100% and find the corresponding value for z. In general, a confidence interval for the population mean when the population follows the normal distribution and the population standard deviation is known is computed by:

CONFIDENCE INTERVAL FOR A POPULATION MEAN WITH σ KNOWN	$\bar{x} \pm z \dfrac{\sigma}{\sqrt{n}}$	[9–1]

To explain these ideas, consider the following example. Del Monte Foods distributes diced peaches in 4.5-ounce plastic cups. To ensure that each cup contains at least the required amount, Del Monte sets the filling operation to dispense 4.51 ounces of peaches and gel in each cup. Of course, not every cup will contain exactly 4.51 ounces of peaches and gel. Some cups will have more and others less. From historical data, Del Monte knows that 0.04 ounce is the standard deviation of the filling process and that the amount, in ounces, follows the normal probability distribution. The quality control technician selects a sample of 64 cups at the start of each shift, measures the amount in each cup, computes the mean fill amount, and then develops a 95% confidence interval for the population mean. Using the confidence interval, is the process filling the cups to the desired amount? This morning's sample of 64 cups had a sample mean of 4.507 ounces. Based on this information, the 95% confidence interval is:

$$\bar{x} \pm 1.96 \frac{\sigma}{\sqrt{n}} = 4.507 \pm 1.96 \frac{0.04}{\sqrt{64}} = 4.507 \pm 0.0098$$

The 95% confidence interval estimates that the population mean is between 4.4972 ounces and 4.5168 ounces of peaches and gel. Recall that the process is set to fill each cup with 4.51 ounces. Because the desired fill amount of 4.51 ounces is in this interval, we conclude that the filling process is achieving the desired results. In other words, it is reasonable to conclude that the sample mean of 4.507 could have come from a population distribution with a mean of 4.51 ounces.

In this example, we observe that the population mean of 4.51 ounces is in the confidence interval. But this is not always the case. If we selected 100 samples of

ESTIMATION AND CONFIDENCE INTERVALS   285

64 cups from the population, calculated the sample mean, and developed a confidence interval based on each sample, we would expect to find the population mean in about 95 of the 100 intervals. Or, in contrast, about five of the intervals would not contain the population mean. From Chapter 8, this is called sampling error. The following example details repeated sampling from a population.

EXAMPLE

The American Management Association is studying the income of store managers in the retail industry. A random sample of 49 managers reveals a sample mean of $45,420. The standard deviation of this population is $2,050. The association would like answers to the following questions:

1. What is the population mean?
2. What is a reasonable range of values for the population mean?
3. How do we interpret these results?

SOLUTION

Generally, distributions of salary and income are positively skewed because a few individuals earn considerably more than others, thus skewing the distribution in the positive direction. Fortunately, the central limit theorem states that the sampling distribution of the mean becomes a normal distribution as sample size increases. In this instance, a sample of 49 store managers is large enough that we can assume that the sampling distribution will follow the normal distribution. Now to answer the questions posed in the example.

1. **What is the population mean?** In this case, we do not know. We do know the sample mean is $45,420. Hence, our best estimate of the unknown population value is the corresponding sample statistic. Thus, the sample mean of $45,420 is a *point estimate* of the unknown population mean.

2. **What is a reasonable range of values for the population mean?** The association decides to use the 95% level of confidence. To determine the corresponding confidence interval, we use formula (9–1):

$$\bar{x} \pm z \frac{\sigma}{\sqrt{n}} = \$45,420 \pm 1.96 \frac{\$2,050}{\sqrt{49}} = \$45,420 \pm \$574$$

The confidence interval limits are $44,846 and $45,994. The degree or level of confidence is 95% and the confidence interval is from $44,846 to $45,994. The ±$574 is called the margin of error.

3. **How do we interpret these results?** Suppose we select many samples of 49 store managers, perhaps several hundred. For each sample, we compute the mean and then construct a 95% confidence interval, such as we did in the previous section. We could expect about 95% of these confidence intervals to contain the *population* mean. About 5% of the intervals would not contain the population mean annual income, which is μ. However, a particular confidence interval either contains the population parameter or it does not. The following diagram shows the results of selecting samples from the population of store managers in the retail industry, computing the mean of each, and then, using formula (9–1), determining a 95% confidence interval for the population mean. Note that not all intervals include the population mean. Both the endpoints of the fifth sample are less than the population mean. We attribute this to sampling error, and it is the risk we assume when we select the level of confidence.

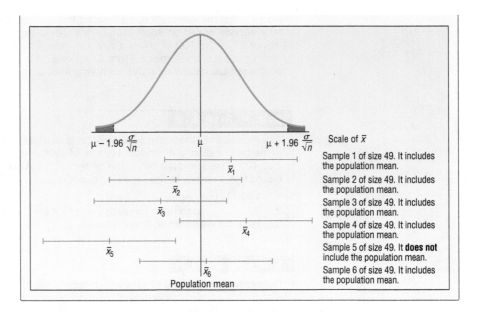

A Computer Simulation

With the aid of a computer, we can easily create random samples of a desired sample size, n, from a population. For each sample of n observations with corresponding numerical values, we can calculate the sample mean. With the sample mean, population standard deviation, and confidence level, we can determine the confidence interval for each sample. Then, using all samples and the confidence intervals, we can find the frequency that the population mean is included in the confidence intervals. The following example does just that.

EXAMPLE

From many years in the automobile leasing business, Town Bank knows that the mean distance driven on an automobile with a four-year lease is 50,000 miles and the standard deviation is 5,000 miles. These are population values. Suppose Town Bank would like to experiment with the idea of sampling to estimate the population mean of 50,000 miles. Town Bank decides to choose a sample size of 30 observations and a 95% confidence interval to estimate the population mean. Based on the experiment, we want to find the proportion of 95% confidence intervals that include the population mean of 50,000. We expect about 95%, or 57 of the 60 intervals, will include the population mean. To make the calculations easier to understand, we'll conduct the study in thousands of miles, instead of miles.

SOLUTION

Using statistical software, 60 random samples with a sample size of 30 are generated and the sample means for each sample computed. Then, using the n of 30 and a standard error of 0.913 ($\sigma/\sqrt{n} = 5/\sqrt{30}$), a 95% confidence interval is computed for each sample. The results of the experiment are shown next.

ESTIMATION AND CONFIDENCE INTERVALS   287

	Sample Observations												Sample	95% Confidence Limits	
Sample	1	2	3	4	5	–	–	–	26	27	28	29	30	Mean	Lower Limit	Upper Limit
1	56	47	47	48	58	–	–	–	55	62	48	61	57	51.6	49.811	53.389
2	55	51	52	40	53	–	–	–	47	54	55	55	45	50.77	48.981	52.559
3	42	46	48	46	41	–	–	–	50	52	50	47	45	48.63	46.841	50.419
4	52	49	55	47	49	–	–	–	46	56	49	43	50	49.9	48.111	51.689
5	48	50	53	48	45	–	–	–	46	51	61	49	47	49.03	47.241	50.819
6	49	44	47	46	48	–	–	–	51	44	51	52	43	47.73	45.941	49.519
7	50	53	39	50	46	–	–	–	55	47	43	50	57	50.2	48.411	51.989
8	47	51	49	58	44	–	–	–	49	57	54	48	48	51.17	49.381	52.959
9	51	44	47	56	45	–	–	–	45	51	49	49	52	50.33	48.541	52.119
10	45	44	52	52	56	–	–	–	52	51	52	50	48	50	48.211	51.789
11	43	52	54	46	54	–	–	–	43	46	49	52	52	51.2	49.411	52.989
12	57	53	48	42	55	–	–	–	49	44	46	46	48	49.8	48.011	51.589
13	53	39	47	51	53	–	–	–	42	44	44	55	58	49.6	47.811	51.389
14	56	55	45	43	57	–	–	–	48	51	52	55	47	49.03	47.241	50.819
15	49	50	39	45	44	–	–	–	49	43	44	51	51	49.37	47.581	51.159
16	46	44	55	53	55	–	–	–	44	53	53	43	44	50.13	48.341	51.919
17	64	52	55	55	43	–	–	–	58	46	52	58	55	52.47	50.681	54.259
18	57	51	60	40	53	–	–	–	50	51	53	46	52	50.1	48.311	51.889
19	50	49	51	57	45	–	–	–	53	52	40	45	52	49.6	47.811	51.389
20	45	46	53	57	49	–	–	–	49	43	43	53	48	49.47	47.681	51.259
21	52	45	51	52	45	–	–	–	43	49	49	58	53	50.43	48.641	52.219
22	48	48	52	49	40	–	–	–	50	47	54	51	45	47.53	45.741	49.319
23	48	50	50	53	44	–	–	–	48	57	52	44	39	49.1	47.311	50.889
24	51	51	40	54	52	–	–	–	54	45	50	57	48	50.13	48.341	51.919
25	48	63	41	52	41	–	–	–	48	50	48	44	53	49.33	47.541	51.119
26	47	45	48	59	49	–	–	–	44	47	49	55	42	49.63	47.841	51.419
27	52	45	60	51	52	–	–	–	52	50	54	46	52	49.4	47.611	51.189
28	46	48	46	57	51	–	–	–	51	50	51	41	52	49.33	47.541	51.119
29	46	48	45	42	48	–	–	–	49	43	59	46	50	48.27	46.481	50.059
30	55	48	47	48	48	–	–	–	47	59	54	51	42	50.53	48.741	52.319
31	58	49	56	46	46	–	–	–	44	51	47	51	46	50.77	48.981	52.559
32	53	54	52	58	55	–	–	–	53	52	45	44	51	50	48.211	51.789
33	50	57	56	51	51	–	–	–	58	47	50	56	46	49.7	47.911	51.489
34	61	48	49	53	54	–	–	–	46	46	56	45	54	50.03	48.241	51.819
35	43	42	43	46	49	–	–	–	49	49	56	51	45	49.43	47.641	51.219
36	39	48	48	51	44	–	–	–	54	52	47	50	52	50.07	48.281	51.859
37	48	43	57	42	54	–	–	–	52	50	59	50	52	50.17	48.381	51.959
38	55	43	49	57	45	–	–	–	41	51	51	52	52	49.5	47.711	51.289
39	47	49	58	54	54	–	–	–	50	56	51	56	58	50.37	48.581	52.159
40	47	56	41	50	54	–	–	–	46	56	61	61	45	51.6	49.811	53.389
41	48	47	42	47	62	–	–	–	44	47	49	55	43	49.43	47.641	51.219
42	46	49	43	36	52	–	–	–	45	51	46	51	43	47.67	45.881	49.459
43	44	48	49	48	51	–	–	–	47	52	51	48	49	49.63	47.841	51.419
44	45	52	54	54	49	–	–	–	49	45	53	50	52	49.07	47.281	50.859
45	54	46	54	45	48	–	–	–	55	38	56	50	62	49.53	47.741	51.319
46	48	50	49	52	51	–	–	–	53	57	58	46	50	49.9	48.111	51.689
47	54	55	46	55	50	–	–	–	56	54	50	55	51	50.5	48.711	52.289
48	45	47	47	63	44	–	–	–	45	53	42	53	50	50.1	48.311	51.889
49	47	47	48	54	56	–	–	–	50	48	54	49	51	49.93	48.141	51.719
50	45	61	51	45	54	–	–	–	55	52	47	45	53	51.03	49.241	52.819
51	49	62	43	49	48	–	–	–	49	58	42	58	52	51.07	49.281	52.859
52	54	52	62	43	54	–	–	–	51	57	49	58	55	50.17	48.381	51.959

(continued)

53	46 50 59 56 46	–	–	–	50 51 52 54 53	50.47	48.681	52.259
54	52 50 48 48 58	–	–	–	58 52 43 61 54	51.77	49.981	53.559
55	45 44 46 56 46	–	–	–	43 45 63 48 56	49.37	47.581	51.159
56	60 50 56 51 43	–	–	–	45 43 49 59 54	50.37	48.581	52.159
57	59 56 43 47 52	–	–	–	49 54 50 50 57	49.53	47.741	51.319
58	52 55 48 51 40	–	–	–	53 51 51 52 47	49.77	47.981	51.559
59	53 50 44 53 52	–	–	–	47 50 55 46 51	50.07	48.281	51.859
60	55 54 50 52 43	–	–	–	57 50 48 47 53	52.07	50.281	53.859

To explain, in the first row, the computer software computed 30 random observations based on a distribution with a mean of 50 and a standard deviation of 5. To conserve space, only observations 1 through 5 and 26 through 30 are listed. The first sample's mean is computed and listed as 51.6. In the next columns, the upper and lower limits of the 95% confidence interval for the first sample are shown. The confidence interval calculation for the first sample follows:

$$\bar{x} \pm 1.96\frac{\sigma}{\sqrt{n}} = 51.6 \pm 1.96\frac{5}{\sqrt{30}} = 51.6 \pm 1.789$$

This calculation is repeated for all the other samples. The results of the experiment show that 56, or 93.33%, of the sixty 95% confidence intervals include the population mean of 50. Four, or 6.67%, do not include the population mean. The 6.67% is close to the estimate that 5% of the intervals will not include the population mean. The particular intervals are samples 6, 17, 22, and 42. They are highlighted in yellow. This is another example of sampling error, or the possibility that a particular random sample may not be a good representation of the population and that the confidence interval based on the sample does not include the value of the population parameter.

SELF-REVIEW

9–1

The Bun-and-Run is a franchise fast-food restaurant located in the Northeast specializing in half-pound hamburgers, fish sandwiches, and chicken sandwiches. Soft drinks and French fries are also available. The Planning Department of Bun-and-Run Inc. reports that the distribution of daily sales for restaurants follows the normal distribution and that the population standard deviation is $3,000. A sample of 40 showed the mean daily sales to be $20,000.
(a)   What is the population mean?
(b)   What is the best estimate of the population mean? What is this value called?
(c)   Develop a 95% confidence interval for the population mean.
(d)   Interpret the confidence interval.

EXERCISES

1. A sample of 49 observations is taken from a normal population with a standard deviation of 10. The sample mean is 55. Determine the 99% confidence interval for the population mean.
2. A sample of 81 observations is taken from a normal population with a standard deviation of 5. The sample mean is 40. Determine the 95% confidence interval for the population mean.
3. A sample of 250 observations is selected from a normal population for which the population standard deviation is known to be 25. The sample mean is 20.
    a. Determine the standard error of the mean.
    b. Explain why we can use formula (9–1) to determine the 95% confidence interval.
    c. Determine the 95% confidence interval for the population mean.
4. Suppose you know σ and you want an 85% confidence level. What value would you use as z in formula (9–1)?

5. A research firm conducted a survey to determine the mean amount steady smokers spend on cigarettes during a week. They found the distribution of amounts spent per week followed the normal distribution with a population standard deviation of $5. A sample of 49 steady smokers revealed that $\bar{x} = \$20$.
   a. What is the point estimate of the population mean? Explain what it indicates.
   b. Using the 95% level of confidence, determine the confidence interval for μ. Explain what it indicates.

6. Refer to the previous exercise. Suppose that 64 smokers (instead of 49) were sampled. Assume the sample mean remained the same.
   a. What is the 95% confidence interval estimate of μ?
   b. Explain why this confidence interval is narrower than the one determined in the previous exercise.

7. Bob Nale is the owner of Nale's Quick Fill. Bob would like to estimate the mean number of gallons of gasoline sold to his customers. Assume the number of gallons sold follows the normal distribution with a population standard deviation of 2.30 gallons. From his records, he selects a random sample of 60 sales and finds the mean number of gallons sold is 8.60.
   a. What is the point estimate of the population mean?
   b. Develop a 99% confidence interval for the population mean.
   c. Interpret the meaning of part (b).

8. Dr. Patton is a professor of English. Recently she counted the number of misspelled words in a group of student essays. She noted the distribution of misspelled words per essay followed the normal distribution with a population standard deviation of 2.44 words per essay. For her 10 a.m. section of 40 students, the mean number of misspelled words was 6.05. Construct a 95% confidence interval for the mean number of misspelled words in the population of student essays.

Population Standard Deviation, σ Unknown

In the previous section, we assumed the population standard deviation was known. In the case involving Del Monte 4.5-ounce cups of peaches, there would likely be a long history of measurements in the filling process. Therefore, it is reasonable to assume the standard deviation of the population is available. However, in most sampling situations the population standard deviation (σ) is not known. Here are some examples where we wish to estimate the population means and it is unlikely we would know the population standard deviations. Suppose each of these studies involves students at West Virginia University.

- The Dean of the Business College wants to estimate the mean number of hours full-time students work at paying jobs each week. He selects a sample of 30 students, contacts each student, and asks them how many hours they worked last week. From the sample information, he can calculate the sample mean, but it is not likely he would know or be able to find the *population* standard deviation (σ) required in formula (9–1). He could calculate the standard deviation of the sample and use that as an estimate, but he would not likely know the population standard deviation.

- The Dean of Students wants to estimate the distance the typical commuter student travels to class. She selects a sample of 40 commuter students, contacts each, and determines the one-way distance from each student's home to the center of campus. From the sample data, she calculates the mean travel distance, that is, $\bar{x}$. It is unlikely the standard deviation of the population would be known or available, again making formula (9–1) unusable.

- The Director of Student Loans wants to estimate the mean amount owed on student loans at the time of his/her graduation. The director selects a sample of 20 graduating students and contacts each to find the information. From the sample information, the director can estimate the mean amount. However, to develop a confidence interval using formula (9–1), the population standard deviation is necessary. It is not likely this information is available.

290   CHAPTER 9

Fortunately we can use the sample standard deviation to estimate the population standard deviation. That is, we use *s*, the sample standard deviation, to estimate σ, the population standard deviation. But in doing so, we cannot use formula (9–1). Because we do not know σ, we cannot use the *z* distribution. However, there is a remedy. We use the sample standard deviation and replace the *z* distribution with the *t* distribution.

The *t* distribution is a continuous probability distribution, with many similar characteristics to the *z* distribution. William Gosset, an English brewmaster, was the first to study the *t* distribution.

He was particularly concerned with the exact behavior of the distribution of the following statistic:

$$t = \frac{\bar{x} - \mu}{s/\sqrt{n}}$$

where *s* is an estimate of σ. He was especially worried about the discrepancy between *s* and σ when *s* was calculated from a very small sample. The *t* distribution and the standard normal distribution are shown graphically in Chart 9–1. Note particularly that the *t* distribution is flatter, more spread out, than the standard normal distribution. This is because the standard deviation of the *t* distribution is larger than that of the standard normal distribution.

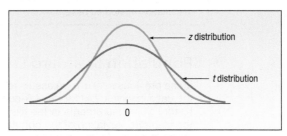

CHART 9–1 The Standard Normal Distribution and Student's *t* Distribution

The following characteristics of the *t* distribution are based on the assumption that the population of interest is normal, or nearly normal.

- It is, like the *z* distribution, a continuous distribution.
- It is, like the *z* distribution, bell-shaped and symmetrical.
- There is not one *t* distribution, but rather a family of *t* distributions. All *t* distributions have a mean of 0, but their standard deviations differ according to the sample size, *n*. There is a *t* distribution for a sample size of 20, another for a sample size of 22, and so on. The standard deviation for a *t* distribution with 5 observations is larger than for a *t* distribution with 20 observations.
- The *t* distribution is more spread out and flatter at the center than the standard normal distribution (see Chart 9–1). As the sample size increases, however, the *t* distribution approaches the standard normal distribution because the errors in using *s* to estimate σ decrease with larger samples.

Because Student's *t* distribution has a greater spread than the *z* distribution, the value of *t* for a given level of confidence is larger in magnitude than the corresponding *z* value. Chart 9–2 shows the values of *z* for a 95% level of confidence and of *t* for the same level of confidence when the sample size is *n* = 5. How we obtained the actual value of *t* will be explained shortly. For now, observe that for the same level of confidence the *t* distribution is flatter or more spread out than the standard normal distribution.

ESTIMATION AND CONFIDENCE INTERVALS   291

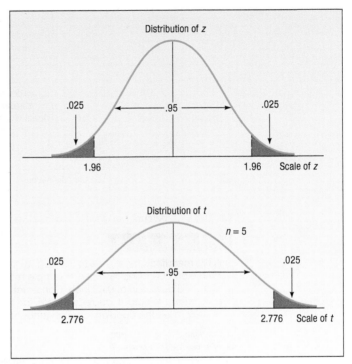

CHART 9–2 Values of z and t for the 95% Level of Confidence

To develop a confidence interval for the population mean using the t distribution, we adjust formula (9–1) as follows.

CONFIDENCE INTERVAL FOR THE POPULATION MEAN, σ UNKNOWN	$\bar{x} \pm t\dfrac{s}{\sqrt{n}}$	[9–2]

To determine a confidence interval for the population mean with an unknown standard deviation, we:

1. Assume the sampled population is either normal or approximately normal. This assumption may be questionable for small sample sizes, and becomes more valid with larger sample sizes.
2. Estimate the population standard deviation (σ) with the sample standard deviation (s).
3. Use the t distribution rather than the z distribution.

We should be clear at this point. We base the decision on whether to use the t or the z on whether or not we know σ, the population standard deviation. If we know the population standard deviation, then we use z. If we do not know the population standard deviation, then we must use t. Chart 9–3 summarizes the decision-making process.

The following example will illustrate a confidence interval for a population mean when the population standard deviation is unknown and how to find the appropriate value of t in a table.

292   CHAPTER 9

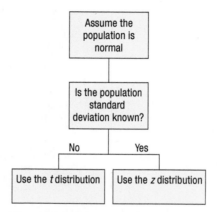

CHART 9–3 Determining When to Use the *z* Distribution or the *t* Distribution

> ### EXAMPLE
>
> A tire manufacturer wishes to investigate the tread life of its tires. A sample of 10 tires driven 50,000 miles revealed a sample mean of 0.32 inch of tread remaining with a standard deviation of 0.09 inch. Construct a 95% confidence interval for the population mean. Would it be reasonable for the manufacturer to conclude that after 50,000 miles the population mean amount of tread remaining is 0.30 inch?
>
> ### SOLUTION
>
> To begin, we assume the population distribution is normal. In this case, we don't have a lot of evidence, but the assumption is probably reasonable. We know the sample standard deviation is .09 inch. We use formula (9–2):
>
> $$\bar{x} \pm t \frac{s}{\sqrt{n}}$$
>
> From the information given, $\bar{x} = 0.32$, $s = 0.09$, and $n = 10$. To find the value of t, we use Appendix B.5, a portion of which is reproduced in Table 9–2. Appendix B.5

TABLE 9–2 A Portion of the *t* Distribution

	Confidence Intervals				
	80%	90%	95%	98%	99%
	Level of Significance for One-Tailed Test				
df	0.10	0.05	0.025	0.010	0.005
	Level of Significance for Two-Tailed Test				
	0.20	0.10	0.05	0.02	0.01
1	3.078	6.314	12.706	31.821	63.657
2	1.886	2.920	4.303	6.965	9.925
3	1.638	2.353	3.182	4.541	5.841
4	1.533	2.132	2.776	3.747	4.604
5	1.476	2.015	2.571	3.365	4.032
6	1.440	1.943	2.447	3.143	3.707
7	1.415	1.895	2.365	2.998	3.499
8	1.397	1.860	2.306	2.896	3.355
9	1.383	1.833	2.262	2.821	3.250
10	1.372	1.812	2.228	2.764	3.169

ESTIMATION AND CONFIDENCE INTERVALS   293

is also reproduced on the inside back cover of the text. The first step for locating *t* is to move across the columns identified for "Confidence Intervals" to the level of confidence requested. In this case, we want the 95% level of confidence, so we move to the column headed "95%." The column on the left margin is identified as "*df.*" This refers to the number of degrees of freedom. The number of degrees of freedom is the number of observations in the sample minus the number of samples, written $n - 1$. In this case, it is $10 - 1 = 9$. Why did we decide there were 9 degrees of freedom? When sample statistics are being used, it is necessary to determine the number of values that are *free to vary*.

To illustrate the meaning of degrees of freedom: Assume that the mean of four numbers is known to be 5. The four numbers are 7, 4, 1, and 8. The deviations of these numbers from the mean must total 0. The deviations of $+2, -1, -4$, and $+3$ do total 0. If the deviations of $+2, -1$, and -4 are known, then the value of $+3$ is fixed (restricted) in order to satisfy the condition that the sum of the deviations must equal 0. Thus, 1 degree of freedom is lost in a sampling problem involving the standard deviation of the sample because one number (the arithmetic mean) is known. For a 95% level of confidence and 9 degrees of freedom, we select the row with 9 degrees of freedom. The value of *t* is 2.262.

To determine the confidence interval, we substitute the values in formula (9–2).

$$\bar{x} \pm t \frac{s}{\sqrt{n}} = 0.32 \pm 2.262 \frac{0.09}{\sqrt{10}} = 0.32 \pm .064$$

The endpoints of the confidence interval are 0.256 and 0.384. How do we interpret this result? If we repeated this study 200 times, calculating the 95% confidence interval with each sample's mean and the standard deviation, we expect 190 of the intervals would include the population mean. Ten of the intervals would not include the population mean. This is the effect of sampling error. A further interpretation is to conclude that the population mean is in this interval. The manufacturer can be reasonably sure (95% confident) that the mean remaining tread depth is between 0.256 and 0.384 inch. Because the value of 0.30 is in this interval, it is possible that the mean of the population is 0.30.

Here is another example to clarify the use of confidence intervals. Suppose an article in your local newspaper reported that the mean time to sell a residential property in the area is 60 days. You select a random sample of 20 homes sold in the last year and find the mean selling time is 65 days. Based on the sample data, you develop a 95% confidence interval for the population mean. You find that the endpoints of the confidence interval are 62 days and 68 days. How do you interpret this result? You can be reasonably confident the population mean is within this range. The value proposed for the population mean, that is, 60 days, is not included in the interval. It is not likely that the population mean is 60 days. The evidence indicates the statement by the local newspaper may not be correct. To put it another way, it seems unreasonable to obtain the sample you did from a population that had a mean selling time of 60 days.

The following example will show additional details for determining and interpreting a confidence interval. We used Minitab to perform the calculations.

EXAMPLE

The manager of the Inlet Square Mall, near Ft. Myers, Florida, wants to estimate the mean amount spent per shopping visit by customers. A sample of 20 customers reveals the following amounts spent.

$48.16	$42.22	$46.82	$51.45	$23.78	$41.86	$54.86
37.92	52.64	48.59	50.82	46.94	61.83	61.69
49.17	61.46	51.35	52.68	58.84	43.88	

What is the best estimate of the population mean? Determine a 95% confidence interval. Interpret the result. Would it be reasonable to conclude that the population mean is $50? What about $60?

SOLUTION

The mall manager assumes that the population of the amounts spent follows the normal distribution. This is a reasonable assumption in this case. Additionally, the

confidence interval technique is quite powerful and tends to commit any errors on the conservative side if the population is not normal. We should not make the normality assumption when the population is severely skewed or when the distribution has "thick tails." In Chapter 16, we present methods for handling this issue if we cannot make the normality assumption. In this case, the normality assumption is reasonable.

The population standard deviation is not known. Hence, it is appropriate to use the t distribution and formula (9–2) to find the confidence interval. We use the Minitab system to find the mean and standard deviation of this sample. The results are shown below.

♦	C1	C2	C3	C4	C5	C6	C7	C8	C9	C10	C11
	amount										
1	48.16
2	42.22
3	46.82
4	51.45
5	23.78
6	41.86
7	54.86
8	37.92
9	52.64
10	48.59
11	50.82
12	46.94

Session

Descriptive Statistics: amount

Variable	N	N*	Mean	SE Mean	StDev	Minimum	Q1	Median	Q3	Maximum
amount	20	0	49.35	2.02	9.01	23.78	44.62	50.00	54.31	61.83

One-Sample T: amount

Variable	N	Mean	StDev	SE Mean	95% CI
amount	20	49.35	9.01	2.02	(45.13, 53.57)

The mall manager does not know the population mean. The sample mean is the best estimate of that value. From the pictured Minitab output, the mean is $49.35, which is the best estimate, the *point estimate*, of the unknown population mean.

We use formula (9–2) to find the confidence interval. The value of t is available from Appendix B.5. There are $n - 1 = 20 - 1 = 19$ degrees of freedom. We move across the row with 19 degrees of freedom to the column for the 95% confidence level. The value at this intersection is 2.093. We substitute these values into formula (9–2) to find the confidence interval.

$$\bar{x} \pm t \frac{s}{\sqrt{n}} = \$49.35 \pm 2.093 \frac{\$9.01}{\sqrt{20}} = \$49.35 \pm \$4.22$$

The endpoints of the confidence interval are $45.13 and $53.57. It is reasonable to conclude that the population mean is in that interval.

The manager of Inlet Square wondered whether the population mean could have been $50 or $60. The value of $50 is within the confidence interval. It is reasonable that the population mean could be $50. The value of $60 is not in the confidence interval. Hence, we conclude that the population mean is unlikely to be $60.

ESTIMATION AND CONFIDENCE INTERVALS   295

The calculations to construct a confidence interval are also available in Excel. The output follows. Note that the sample mean ($49.35) and the sample standard deviation ($9.01) are the same as those in the Minitab calculations. In the Excel output, the last line also includes the margin of error, which is the amount that is added and subtracted from the sample mean to form the endpoints of the confidence interval. This value is found from

$$t \frac{s}{\sqrt{n}} = 2.093 \frac{\$9.01}{\sqrt{20}} = \$4.22$$

	A	B	C	D	E
	Amount		Amount		
1	**Amount**		**Amount**		
2	48.16				
3	42.22		Mean	49.35	
4	46.82		Standard Error	2.02	
5	51.45		Median	50.00	
6	23.78		Mode	#N/A	
7	41.86		Standard Deviation	9.01	
8	54.86		Sample Variance	81.22	
9	37.92		Kurtosis	2.26	
10	52.64		Skewness	-1.00	
11	48.59		Range	38.05	
12	50.82		Minimum	23.78	
13	46.94		Maximum	61.83	
14	61.83		Sum	986.96	
15	61.69		Count	20.00	
16	49.17		Confidence Level(95.0%)	4.22	
17	61.46				
18	51.35				
19	52.68				
20	58.84				
21	43.88				

Before doing the confidence interval exercises, we would like to point out a useful characteristic of the t distribution that will allow us to use the t table to quickly find both z and t values. Earlier in this section, on page 290, we detailed the characteristics of the t distribution. The last point indicated that as we increase the sample size the t distribution approaches the z distribution. In fact, when we reach an infinitely large sample, the t distribution is exactly equal to the z distribution.

To explain, Table 9–3 is a portion of Appendix B.5, with the degrees of freedom between 4 and 99 omitted. To find the appropriate z value for a 95% confidence interval, we begin by going to the confidence interval section and selecting the column headed "95%." Move down that column to the last row, which is labeled "∞," or infinite degrees of freedom. The value reported is 1.960, the same value that we found using the standard normal distribution in Appendix B.3. This confirms the convergence of the t distribution to the z distribution.

What does this mean for us? Instead of searching in the body of the z table, we can go to the last row of the t table and find the appropriate value to build a confidence interval. An additional benefit is that the values have three decimal places. So, using this table for a 90% confidence interval, go down the column headed "90%" and see the value 1.645, which is a more precise z value that can be used for the 90%

296   CHAPTER 9

confidence level. Other z values for 98% and 99% confidence intervals are also available with three decimals. Note that we will use the *t* table, which is summarized in Table 9–3, to find the *z* values with three decimals for all following exercises and problems.

TABLE 9–3 Student's t Distribution

df (degrees of freedom)	Confidence Interval					
	80%	90%	95%	98%	99%	99.9%
	Level of Significance for One-Tailed Test, α					
	0.1	0.05	0.02	0.01	0.001	0.0005
	Level of Significance for Two-Tailed Test, α					
	0.2	0.1	0.05	0.02	0.01	0.001
1	3.078	6.314	12.706	31.821	63.657	636.619
2	1.886	2.920	4.303	6.965	9.925	31.599
3	1.638	2.353	3.182	4.541	5.841	12.924
⋮	⋮	⋮	⋮	⋮	⋮	⋮
100	1.290	1.660	1.984	2.364	2.626	3.390
120	1.289	1.658	1.980	2.358	2.617	3.373
140	1.288	1.656	1.977	2.353	2.611	3.361
160	1.287	1.654	1.975	2.350	2.607	3.352
180	1.286	1.653	1.973	2.347	2.603	3.345
200	1.286	1.653	1.972	2.345	2.601	3.340
∞	1.282	1.645	1.960	2.326	2.576	3.291

SELF-REVIEW

9–2

Dottie Kleman is the "Cookie Lady." She bakes and sells cookies at locations in the Philadelphia area. Ms. Kleman is concerned about absenteeism among her workers. The information below reports the number of days absent for a sample of 10 workers during the last two-week pay period.

| 4 | 1 | 2 | 2 | 1 | 2 | 2 | 1 | 0 | 3 |

(a) Determine the mean and the standard deviation of the sample.
(b) What is the population mean? What is the best estimate of that value?
(c) Develop a 95% confidence interval for the population mean. Assume that the population distribution is normal.
(d) Explain why the *t* distribution is used as a part of the confidence interval.
(e) Is it reasonable to conclude that the typical worker does not miss any days during a pay period?

EXERCISES

9. Use Appendix B.5 to locate the value of *t* under the following conditions.
   a. The sample size is 12 and the level of confidence is 95%.
   b. The sample size is 20 and the level of confidence is 90%.
   c. The sample size is 8 and the level of confidence is 99%.
10. Use Appendix B.5 to locate the value of *t* under the following conditions.
   a. The sample size is 15 and the level of confidence is 95%.
   b. The sample size is 24 and the level of confidence is 98%.
   c. The sample size is 12 and the level of confidence is 90%.
11. The owner of Britten's Egg Farm wants to estimate the mean number of eggs produced per chicken. A sample of 20 chickens shows they produced an average of 20 eggs per month with a standard deviation of 2 eggs per month.
   a. What is the value of the population mean? What is the best estimate of this value?
   b. Explain why we need to use the *t* distribution. What assumption do you need to make?

  c. For a 95% confidence interval, what is the value of *t*?
  d. Develop the 95% confidence interval for the population mean.
  e. Would it be reasonable to conclude that the population mean is 21 eggs? What about 25 eggs?
12. The U.S. Dairy Industry wants to estimate the mean yearly milk consumption. A sample of 16 people reveals the mean yearly consumption to be 60 gallons with a standard deviation of 20 gallons. Assume the population distribution is normal.
  a. What is the value of the population mean? What is the best estimate of this value?
  b. Explain why we need to use the *t* distribution. What assumption do you need to make?
  c. For a 90% confidence interval, what is the value of *t*?
  d. Develop the 90% confidence interval for the population mean.
  e. Would it be reasonable to conclude that the population mean is 63 gallons?
13. Merrill Lynch Securities and Health Care Retirement Inc. are two large employers in downtown Toledo, Ohio. They are considering jointly offering child care for their employees. As a part of the feasibility study, they wish to estimate the mean weekly child-care cost of their employees. A sample of 10 employees who use child care reveals the following amounts spent last week.

For **DATA FILE**, please visit www.mhhe.com/lind16e

$107	$92	$97	$95	$105	$101	$91	$99	$95	$104

Develop a 90% confidence interval for the population mean. Interpret the result.
14. The Greater Pittsburgh Area Chamber of Commerce wants to estimate the mean time workers who are employed in the downtown area spend getting to work. A sample of 15 workers reveals the following number of minutes spent traveling.

For **DATA FILE**, please visit www.mhhe.com/lind16e

29	38	38	33	38	21	45	34
40	37	37	42	30	29	35	

Develop a 98% confidence interval for the population mean. Interpret the result.

LO9-3
Compute and interpret a confidence interval for a population proportion.

A CONFIDENCE INTERVAL FOR A POPULATION PROPORTION

The material presented so far in this chapter uses the ratio scale of measurement. That is, we use such variables as incomes, weights, distances, and ages. We now want to consider situations such as the following:

- The career services director at Southern Technical Institute reports that 80% of its graduates enter the job market in a position related to their field of study.
- A company representative claims that 45% of Burger King sales are made at the drive-through window.
- A survey of homes in the Chicago area indicated that 85% of the new construction had central air conditioning.
- A recent survey of married men between the ages of 35 and 50 found that 63% felt that both partners should earn a living.

These examples illustrate the nominal scale of measurement when the outcome is limited to

STATISTICS IN ACTION

Many survey results reported in newspapers, in news magazines, and on TV use confidence intervals. For example, a recent survey of 800 TV viewers in Toledo, Ohio, found 44% watched the evening news on the local CBS affiliate. The article went on to indicate the margin of error was 3.4%. The margin of error is actually the amount that is added and subtracted from the point estimate to find the endpoints of a confidence interval. From formula (9–4) and the 95% level of confidence:

$$z\sqrt{\frac{p(1-p)}{n}}$$

$$= 1.96\sqrt{\frac{.44(1-.44)}{800}}$$

$$= 0.034$$

two values. In these cases, an observation is classified into one of two mutually exclusive groups. For example, a graduate of Southern Tech either entered the job market in a position related to his or her field of study or not. A particular Burger King customer either made a purchase at the drive-through window or did not make a purchase at the drive-through window. We can talk about the groups in terms of proportions.

> **PROPORTION** The fraction, ratio, or percent indicating the part of the sample or the population having a particular trait of interest.

As an example of a proportion, a recent survey indicated that 92 out of 100 people surveyed favored the continued use of daylight savings time in the summer. The sample proportion is 92/100, or .92, or 92%. If we let p represent the sample proportion, x the number of "successes," and n the number of items sampled, we can determine a sample proportion as follows.

> **SAMPLE PROPORTION** $p = \dfrac{x}{n}$ **[9–3]**

The population proportion is identified by π. Therefore, π refers to the percent of successes in the population. Recall from Chapter 6 that π is the proportion of "successes" in a binomial distribution. This continues our practice of using Greek letters to identify population parameters and Roman letters to identify sample statistics.

To develop a confidence interval for a proportion, we need to meet the following assumptions.

1. The binomial conditions, discussed in Chapter 6, have been met. Briefly, these conditions are:
   a. The sample data are the number of successes in n trials.
   b. There are only two possible outcomes. (We usually label one of the outcomes a "success" and the other a "failure.")
   c. The probability of a success remains the same from one trial to the next.
   d. The trials are independent. This means the outcome on one trial does not affect the outcome on another.
2. The values $n\pi$ and $n(1-\pi)$ should both be greater than or equal to 5. This condition allows us to invoke the central limit theorem and employ the standard normal distribution, that is, z, to complete a confidence interval.

Developing a point estimate for a population proportion and a confidence interval for a population proportion is similar to doing so for a mean. To illustrate, John Gail is running for Congress from the third district of Nebraska. From a random sample of 100 voters in the district, 60 indicate they plan to vote for him in the upcoming election. The sample proportion is .60, but the population proportion is unknown. That is, we do not know what proportion of voters in the *population* will vote for Mr. Gail. The sample value, .60, is the best estimate we have of the unknown population parameter. So we let p, which is .60, be an estimate of π, which is not known.

To develop a confidence interval for a population proportion, we use:

> **CONFIDENCE INTERVAL FOR A POPULATION PROPORTION** $p \pm z\sqrt{\dfrac{p(1-p)}{n}}$ **[9–4]**

An example will help to explain the details of determining a confidence interval and interpreting the result.

ESTIMATION AND CONFIDENCE INTERVALS $\hspace{8cm}$ 299

E X A M P L E

The union representing the Bottle Blowers of America (BBA) is considering a proposal to merge with the Teamsters Union. According to BBA union bylaws, at least three-fourths of the union membership must approve any merger. A random sample of 2,000 current BBA members reveals 1,600 plan to vote for the merger proposal. What is the estimate of the population proportion? Develop a 95% confidence interval for the population proportion. Basing your decision on this sample information, can you conclude that the necessary proportion of BBA members favor the merger? Why?

S O L U T I O N

First, calculate the sample proportion from formula (9–3). It is .80, found by

$$p = \frac{x}{n} = \frac{1,600}{2,000} = .80$$

Thus, we estimate that 80% of the population favor the merger proposal. We determine the 95% confidence interval using formula (9–4). The z value corresponding to the 95% level of confidence is 1.96.

$$p \pm z\sqrt{\frac{p(1-p)}{n}} = .80 \pm 1.96\sqrt{\frac{.80(1-.80)}{2,000}} = .80 \pm .018$$

The endpoints of the confidence interval are .782 and .818. The lower endpoint is greater than .75. Hence, we conclude that the merger proposal will likely pass because the interval estimate includes values greater than 75% of the union membership.

To review the interpretation of the confidence interval: If the poll was conducted 100 times with 100 different samples, we expect the confidence intervals constructed from 95 of the samples would contain the true population proportion. In addition, the interpretation of a confidence interval can be very useful in decision making and play a very important role especially on election night. For example, Cliff Obermeyer is running for Congress from the 6th District of New Jersey. Suppose 500 voters are contacted upon leaving the polls and 275 indicate they voted for Mr. Obermeyer. We will assume that the exit poll of 500 voters is a random sample of those voting in the 6th District. That means that 55% of those in the sample voted for Mr. Obermeyer. Based on formula (9–3):

$$p = \frac{x}{n} = \frac{275}{500} = .55$$

Now, to be assured of election, he must earn *more than* 50% of the votes in the population of those voting. At this point, we know a point estimate, which is .55, of the population of voters that will vote for him. But we do not know the percent in the population that will ultimately vote for the candidate. So the question is: Could we take a sample of 500 voters from a population where 50% or less of the voters support Mr. Obermeyer and find that 55% of the sample support him? To put it another way, could the sampling error, which is $p - \pi = .55 - .50 = .05$ be due to chance, or is the population of voters who support Mr. Obermeyer greater than .50? If we develop a confidence interval for the sample proportion and find that the lower endpoint is greater than .50, then we conclude that the proportion of voters supporting Mr. Obermeyer is greater than .50. What does that mean? Well, it means he should be elected! What if .50 is in the interval? Then we conclude that he is not assured of

300   CHAPTER 9

a majority and we cannot conclude he will be elected. In this case, using the 95% significance level and formula (9–4):

$$p \pm z \sqrt{\frac{p(1 - p)}{n}} = .55 \pm 1.96 \sqrt{\frac{.55(1 - .55)}{500}} = .55 \pm .044$$

So the endpoints of the confidence interval are .55 − .044 = .506 and .55 + .044 = .594. The value of .50 is not in this interval. So we conclude that probably *more than 50%* of the voters support Mr. Obermeyer and that is enough to get him elected.

Is this procedure ever used? Yes! It is exactly the procedure used by television networks, news magazines, and polling organizations on election night.

SELF-REVIEW

9–3

A market survey was conducted to estimate the proportion of homemakers who would recognize the brand name of a cleanser based on the shape and the color of the container. Of the 1,400 homemakers sampled, 420 were able to identify the brand by name.
(a) Estimate the value of the population proportion.
(b) Develop a 99% confidence interval for the population proportion.
(c) Interpret your findings.

EXERCISES

15. The owner of the West End Kwick Fill Gas Station wishes to determine the proportion of customers who use a credit card or debit card to pay at the pump. He surveys 100 customers and finds that 80 paid at the pump.
   a. Estimate the value of the population proportion.
   b. Develop a 95% confidence interval for the population proportion.
   c. Interpret your findings.
16. Ms. Maria Wilson is considering running for mayor of the town of Bear Gulch, Montana. Before completing the petitions, she decides to conduct a survey of voters in Bear Gulch. A sample of 400 voters reveals that 300 would support her in the November election.
   a. Estimate the value of the population proportion.
   b. Develop a 99% confidence interval for the population proportion.
   c. Interpret your findings.
17. The Fox TV network is considering replacing one of its prime-time crime investigation shows with a new family-oriented comedy show. Before a final decision is made, network executives commission a sample of 400 viewers. After viewing the comedy, 250 indicated they would watch the new show and suggested it replace the crime investigation show.
   a. Estimate the value of the population proportion.
   b. Develop a 99% confidence interval for the population proportion.
   c. Interpret your findings.
18. Schadek Silkscreen Printing Inc. purchases plastic cups on which to print logos for sporting events, proms, birthdays, and other special occasions. Zack Schadek, the owner, received a large shipment this morning. To ensure the quality of the shipment, he selected a random sample of 300 cups. He found 15 to be defective.
   a. What is the estimated proportion defective in the population?
   b. Develop a 95% confidence interval for the proportion defective.
   c. Zack has an agreement with his supplier that he is to return lots that are 10% or more defective. Should he return this lot? Explain your decision.

LO9-4

Calculate the required sample size to estimate a population proportion or population mean.

CHOOSING AN APPROPRIATE SAMPLE SIZE

When working with confidence intervals, one important variable is sample size. However, in practice, sample size is not a variable. It is a decision we make so that our estimate of a population parameter is a good one. Our decision is based on three variables:

1. The margin of error the researcher will tolerate.
2. The level of confidence desired, for example, 95%.
3. The variation or dispersion of the population being studied.

ESTIMATION AND CONFIDENCE INTERVALS   301

The first variable is the *margin of error.* It is designated as *E* and is the amount that is added and subtracted to the sample mean (or sample proportion) to determine the endpoints of the confidence interval. For example, in a study of wages, we may decide that we want to estimate the mean wage of the population with a margin of error of plus or minus $1,000. Or, in an opinion poll, we may decide that we want to estimate the population proportion with a margin of error of plus or minus 3.5%. The margin of error is the amount of error we are willing to tolerate in estimating a population parameter. You may wonder why we do not choose small margins of error. There is a trade-off between the margin of error and sample size. A small margin of error will require a larger sample and more money and time to collect the sample. A larger margin of error will permit a smaller sample and result in a wider confidence interval.

The second choice is the *level of confidence.* In working with confidence intervals, we logically choose relatively high levels of confidence such as 95% and 99%. To compute the sample size, we need the *z*-statistic that corresponds to the chosen level of confidence. The 95% level of confidence corresponds to a *z* value of 1.96, and a 90% level of confidence corresponds to a *z* value of 1.645 (using the *t* table). Notice that larger sample sizes (and more time and money to collect the sample) correspond with higher levels of confidence. Also, notice that we use a *z*-statistic.

The third choice to determine the sample size is the *population standard deviation.* If the population is widely dispersed, a large sample is required. On the other hand, if the population is concentrated (homogeneous), the required sample size will be smaller. Often, we do not know the population standard deviation. Here are three suggestions for finding a value for the population standard deviation.

1. **Conduct a pilot study.** This is the most common method. Suppose we want an estimate of the number of hours per week worked by students enrolled in the College of Business at the University of Texas. To test the validity of our questionnaire, we use it on a small sample of students. From this small sample, we compute the standard deviation of the number of hours worked and use this value as the population standard deviation.
2. **Use a comparable study.** Use this approach when there is an estimate of the standard deviation from another study. Suppose we want to estimate the number of hours worked per week by refuse workers. Information from certain state or federal agencies that regularly study the workforce may provide a reliable value to use for the population standard deviation.
3. **Use a range-based approach.** To use this approach, we need to know or have an estimate of the largest and smallest values in the population. Recall from Chapter 3, the Empirical Rule states that virtually all the observations could be expected to be within plus or minus 3 standard deviations of the mean, assuming that the distribution follows the normal distribution. Thus, the distance between the largest and the smallest values is 6 standard deviations. We can estimate the standard deviation as one-sixth of the range. For example, the director of operations at University Bank wants to estimate the number of checks written per month by college students. She believes that the distribution of the number of checks written follows the normal distribution. The minimum and maximum numbers written per month are 2 and 50, so the range is 48, found by (50 − 2). Then eight checks per month, 48/6, would be the value we would use for the population standard deviation.

Sample Size to Estimate a Population Mean

To estimate a population mean, we can express the interaction among these three factors and the sample size in the following formula. Notice that this formula is the margin of error used to calculate the endpoints of confidence intervals to estimate a population mean!

$$E = z \frac{\sigma}{\sqrt{n}}$$

302   CHAPTER 9

Solving this equation for *n* yields the following result.

SAMPLE SIZE FOR ESTIMATING THE POPULATION MEAN	$n = \left(\dfrac{z\sigma}{E}\right)^2$	**[9–5]**

where:
     n is the size of the sample.
     z is the standard normal value corresponding to the desired level of confidence.
     σ is the population standard deviation.
     E is the maximum allowable error.

     The result of this calculation is not always a whole number. When the outcome is not a whole number, the usual practice is to round up *any* fractional result to the next whole number. For example, 201.21 would be rounded up to 202.

EXAMPLE

A student in public administration wants to estimate the mean monthly earnings of city council members in large cities. The error in estimating the mean is to be less than $100 with a 95% level of confidence. The student found a report by the Department of Labor that reported a standard deviation of $1,000. What is the required sample size?

SOLUTION

The maximum allowable error, *E*, is $100. The value of *z* for a 95% level of confidence is 1.96, and the value of the standard deviation is $1,000. Substituting these values into formula (9–5) gives the required sample size as:

$$n = \left(\frac{z\sigma}{E}\right)^2 = \left(\frac{(1.96)(\$1,000)}{\$100}\right)^2 = (19.6)^2 = 384.16$$

The computed value of 384.16 is rounded up to 385. A sample of 385 is required to meet the specifications. If the student wants to increase the level of confidence, for example to 99%, this will require a larger sample. Using the *t* table, the *z* value for a 99% level of confidence is 2.576.

$$n = \left(\frac{z\sigma}{E}\right)^2 = \left(\frac{(2.576)(\$1,000)}{\$100}\right)^2 = (25.76)^2 = 663.58$$

We recommend a sample of 664. Observe how much the change in the confidence level changed the size of the sample. An increase from the 95% to the 99% level of confidence resulted in an increase of 279 observations, or 72% [(664/385) × 100]. This would greatly increase the cost of the study, in terms of both time and money. Hence, the level of confidence should be considered carefully.

Sample Size to Estimate a Population Proportion

To determine the sample size for a proportion, the same three variables need to be specified:

1. The margin of error.
2. The desired level of confidence.
3. The variation or dispersion of the population being studied.

ESTIMATION AND CONFIDENCE INTERVALS   303

For the binomial distribution, the margin of error is:

$$E = z \sqrt{\frac{\pi(1 - \pi)}{n}}$$

Solving this equation for n yields the following equation

SAMPLE SIZE FOR THE POPULATION PROPORTION	$n = \pi(1 - \pi)\left(\dfrac{z}{E}\right)^2$	[9–6]

where:
    n is the size of the sample.
    z is the standard normal value corresponding to the desired level of confidence.
    π is the population proportion.
    E is the maximum allowable error.

The choices for the z-statistic and the margin of error, E, are the same as the choices for estimating the population mean. However, the population variance of the binomial distribution is represented by $\pi(1 - \pi)$. To find a value of the population proportion, we would find a comparable study or conduct a pilot study. If a reliable value cannot be found, then a value of .50 should be used for π. Note that $\pi(1 - \pi)$ has the largest value using 0.50 and, therefore, without a good estimate of the population proportion, overstates the sample size. This difference will not hurt the estimate of the population proportion.

EXAMPLE

The study in the previous example also estimates the proportion of cities that have private refuse collectors. The student wants the margin of error to be within .10 of the population proportion, the desired level of confidence is 90%, and no estimate is available for the population proportion. What is the required sample size?

SOLUTION

The estimate of the population proportion is to be within .10, so $E = .10$. The desired level of confidence is .90, which corresponds to a z value of 1.645, using the t table. Because no estimate of the population proportion is available, we use .50. The suggested number of observations is

$$n = (.5)(1 - .5)\left(\frac{1.645}{.10}\right)^2 = 67.65$$

The student needs a random sample of 68 cities.

SELF-REVIEW

9–4

The registrar wants to estimate the arithmetic mean grade point average (GPA) of all graduating seniors during the past 10 years. GPAs range between 2.0 and 4.0. The mean GPA is to be estimated within plus or minus .05 of the population mean. Based on prior experience, the population standard deviation is 0.279. Use the 99% level of confidence. Will you assist the college registrar in determining how many transcripts to study?

CHAPTER 9

EXERCISES

19. A population is estimated to have a standard deviation of 10. We want to estimate the population mean within 2, with a 95% level of confidence. How large a sample is required?

20. We want to estimate the population mean within 5, with a 99% level of confidence. The population standard deviation is estimated to be 15. How large a sample is required?

21. The estimate of the population proportion is to be within plus or minus .05, with a 95% level of confidence. The best estimate of the population proportion is .15. How large a sample is required?

22. The estimate of the population proportion is to be within plus or minus .10, with a 99% level of confidence. The best estimate of the population proportion is .45. How large a sample is required?

23. A survey is being planned to determine the mean amount of time corporation executives watch television. A pilot survey indicated that the mean time per week is 12 hours, with a standard deviation of 3 hours. It is desired to estimate the mean viewing time within one-quarter hour. The 95% level of confidence is to be used. How many executives should be surveyed?

24. A processor of carrots cuts the green top off each carrot, washes the carrots, and inserts six to a package. Twenty packages are inserted in a box for shipment. To test the weight of the boxes, a few were checked. The mean weight was 20.4 pounds; the standard deviation, 0.5 pound. How many boxes must the processor sample to be 95% confident that the sample mean does not differ from the population mean by more than 0.2 pound?

25. Suppose the U.S. president wants an estimate of the proportion of the population who support his current policy toward revisions in the health care system. The president wants the estimate to be within .04 of the true proportion. Assume a 95% level of confidence. The president's political advisors estimated the proportion supporting the current policy to be .60.
   a. How large of a sample is required?
   b. How large of a sample would be necessary if no estimate were available for the proportion supporting current policy?

26. Past surveys reveal that 30% of tourists going to Las Vegas to gamble spend more than $1,000. The Visitor's Bureau of Las Vegas wants to update this percentage.
   a. The new study is to use the 90% confidence level. The estimate is to be within 1% of the population proportion. What is the necessary sample size?
   b. The Bureau feels the sample size determined above is too large. What can be done to reduce the sample? Based on your suggestion, recalculate the sample size.

LO9-5
Adjust a confidence interval for finite populations.

FINITE-POPULATION CORRECTION FACTOR

The populations we have sampled so far have been very large or infinite. What if the sampled population is not very large? We need to make some adjustments in the way we compute the standard error of the sample means and the standard error of the sample proportions.

A population that has a fixed upper bound is *finite*. For example, there are 12,179 students enrolled at Eastern Illinois University, there are 40 employees at Spence Sprockets, Chrysler assembled 917 Jeep Wranglers at the Alexis Avenue plant yesterday, or there were 65 surgical patients at St. Rose Memorial Hospital in Sarasota yesterday. A finite population can be rather small; it could be all the students registered for this class. It can also be very large, such as all senior citizens living in Florida.

For a finite population, where the total number of objects or individuals is N and the number of objects or individuals in the sample is n, we need to adjust the standard errors in the confidence interval formulas. To put it another way, to find the confidence interval for the mean, we adjust the standard error of the mean in formulas (9–1) and (9–2). If we are determining the confidence interval for a proportion, then we need to adjust the standard error of the proportion in formula (9–4).

This adjustment is called the **finite-population correction factor**. It is often shortened to *FPC* and is:

$$FPC = \sqrt{\frac{N - n}{N - 1}}$$

ESTIMATION AND CONFIDENCE INTERVALS   305

Why is it necessary to apply a factor, and what is its effect? Logically, if the sample is a substantial percentage of the population, the estimate is more precise. Note the effect of the term $(N - n)/(N - 1)$. Suppose the population is 1,000 and the sample is 100. Then this ratio is $(1,000 - 100)/(1,000 - 1)$, or 900/999. Taking the square root gives the correction factor, .9492. Multiplying this correction factor by the standard error *reduces* the standard error by about 5% $(1 - .9492 = .0508)$. This reduction in the size of the standard error yields a smaller range of values in estimating the population mean or the population proportion. If the sample is 200, the correction factor is .8949, meaning that the standard error has been reduced by more than 10%. Table 9–4 shows the effects of various sample sizes.

TABLE 9–4 Finite-Population Correction Factor for Selected Samples When the Population Is 1,000

Sample Size	Fraction of Population	Correction Factor
10	.010	.9955
25	.025	.9879
50	.050	.9752
100	.100	.9492
200	.200	.8949
500	.500	.7075

So if we wished to develop a confidence interval for the mean from a finite population and the population standard deviation was unknown, we would adjust formula (9–2) as follows:

$$\bar{x} \pm t \frac{s}{\sqrt{n}} \left(\sqrt{\frac{N - n}{N - 1}} \right)$$

We would make a similar adjustment to formula (9–4) in the case of a proportion.

The following example summarizes the steps to find a confidence interval for the mean.

EXAMPLE

There are 250 families residing in Scandia, Pennsylvania. A random sample of 40 of these families revealed the mean annual church contribution was $450 and the standard deviation of this was $75.

1. What is the population mean? What is the best estimate of the population mean?
2. Develop a 90% confidence interval for the population mean. What are the endpoints of the confidence interval?
3. Using the confidence interval, explain why the population mean could be $445. Could the population mean be $425? Why?

SOLUTION

First, note the population is finite. That is, there is a limit to the number of people residing in Scandia, in this case 250.

1. We do not know the population mean. This is the value we wish to estimate. The best estimate we have of the population mean is the sample mean, which is $450.

2. The formula to find the confidence interval for a population mean follows.

$$\bar{x} \pm t\frac{s}{\sqrt{n}}\left(\sqrt{\frac{N-n}{N-1}}\right)$$

In this case, we know $\bar{x} = 450$, $s = 75$, $N = 250$, and $n = 40$. We do not know the population standard deviation, so we use the t distribution. To find the appropriate value of t, we use Appendix B.5, and move across the top row to the column headed 90%. The degrees of freedom are $df = n - 1 = 40 - 1 = 39$, so we move to the cell where the df row of 39 intersects with the column headed 90%. The value is 1.685. Inserting these values in the formula:

$$\bar{x} \pm t\frac{s}{\sqrt{n}}\left(\sqrt{\frac{N-n}{N-1}}\right)$$

$$= \$450 \pm 1.685\frac{\$75}{\sqrt{40}}\left(\sqrt{\frac{250-40}{250-1}}\right) = \$450 \pm \$19.98\sqrt{.8434} = \$450 \pm \$18.35$$

The endpoints of the confidence interval are \$431.65 and \$468.35.

3. It is likely that the population mean is more than \$431.65 but less than \$468.35. To put it another way, could the population mean be \$445? Yes, but it is not likely that it is \$425. Why is this so? Because the value \$445 is within the confidence interval and \$425 is not within the confidence interval.

SELF-REVIEW

9–5

The same study of church contributions in Scandia revealed that 15 of the 40 families sampled attend church regularly. Construct the 95% confidence interval for the proportion of families attending church regularly.

EXERCISES

27. Thirty-six items are randomly selected from a population of 300 items. The sample mean is 35 and the sample standard deviation 5. Develop a 95% confidence interval for the population mean.

28. Forty-nine items are randomly selected from a population of 500 items. The sample mean is 40 and the sample standard deviation 9. Develop a 99% confidence interval for the population mean.

29. The attendance at the Savannah Colts minor league baseball game last night was 400. A random sample of 50 of those in attendance revealed that the mean number of soft drinks consumed per person was 1.86, with a standard deviation of 0.50. Develop a 99% confidence interval for the mean number of soft drinks consumed per person.

30. There are 300 welders employed at Maine Shipyards Corporation. A sample of 30 welders revealed that 18 graduated from a registered welding course. Construct the 95% confidence interval for the proportion of all welders who graduated from a registered welding course.

ESTIMATION AND CONFIDENCE INTERVALS   307

C H A P T E R   S U M M A R Y

I. A point estimate is a single value (statistic) used to estimate a population value (parameter).

II. A confidence interval is a range of values within which the population parameter is expected to occur.

  A. The factors that determine the width of a confidence interval for a mean are:

   1. The number of observations in the sample, n.

   2. The variability in the population, usually estimated by the sample standard deviation, s.

   3. The level of confidence.

    a. To determine the confidence limits when the population standard deviation is known, we use the z distribution. The formula is

$$\bar{x} \pm z \frac{\sigma}{\sqrt{n}} \qquad\qquad \textbf{[9–1]}$$

    b. To determine the confidence limits when the population standard deviation is unknown, we use the t distribution. The formula is

$$\bar{x} \pm t \frac{s}{\sqrt{n}} \qquad\qquad \textbf{[9–2]}$$

III. The major characteristics of the t distribution are:

  A. It is a continuous distribution.

  B. It is mound-shaped and symmetrical.

  C. It is flatter, or more spread out, than the standard normal distribution.

  D. There is a family of t distributions, depending on the number of degrees of freedom.

IV. A proportion is a ratio, fraction, or percent that indicates the part of the sample or population that has a particular characteristic.

  A. A sample proportion is found by x, the number of successes, divided by n, the number of observations.

  B. We construct a confidence interval for a sample proportion from the following formula.

$$p \pm z \sqrt{\frac{p(1 - p)}{n}} \qquad\qquad \textbf{[9–4]}$$

V. We can determine an appropriate sample size for estimating both means and proportions.

  A. There are three factors that determine the sample size when we wish to estimate the mean.

   1. The margin of error, E.

   2. The desired level of confidence.

   3. The variation in the population.

   4. The formula to determine the sample size for the mean is

$$n = \left(\frac{z\sigma}{E} \right)^2 \qquad\qquad \textbf{[9–5]}$$

  B. There are three factors that determine the sample size when we wish to estimate a proportion.

   1. The margin of error, E.

   2. The desired level of confidence.

   3. A value for π to calculate the variation in the population.

   4. The formula to determine the sample size for a proportion is

$$n = \pi(1 - \pi)\left(\frac{z}{E} \right)^2 \qquad\qquad \textbf{[9–6]}$$

VI. For a finite population, the standard error is adjusted by the factor $\sqrt{\dfrac{N - n}{N - 1}}$.

CHAPTER EXERCISES

31. A random sample of 85 group leaders, supervisors, and similar personnel at General Motors revealed that, on average, they spent 6.5 years in a particular job before being promoted. The standard deviation of the sample was 1.7 years. Construct a 95% confidence interval.

32. A state meat inspector in Iowa has been given the assignment of estimating the mean net weight of packages of ground chuck labeled "3 pounds." Of course, he realizes that the weights cannot be precisely 3 pounds. A sample of 36 packages reveals the mean weight to be 3.01 pounds, with a standard deviation of 0.03 pound.
   a. What is the estimated population mean?
   b. Determine a 95% confidence interval for the population mean.

33. As part of their business promotional package, the Milwaukee Chamber of Commerce would like an estimate of the mean cost per month to lease a one-bedroom apartment. A random sample of 40 apartments currently available for lease showed the mean cost per month was $323. The standard deviation of the sample was $25.
   a. Develop a 98% confidence interval for the population mean.
   b. Would it be reasonable to conclude that the population mean is $350 per month?

34. A recent survey of 50 executives who were laid off during a recent recession revealed it took a mean of 26 weeks for them to find another position. The standard deviation of the sample was 6.2 weeks. Construct a 95% confidence interval for the population mean. Is it reasonable that the population mean is 28 weeks? Justify your answer.

35. Marty Rowatti recently assumed the position of director of the YMCA of South Jersey. He would like some current data on how long current members of the YMCA have been members. To investigate, suppose he selects a random sample of 40 current members. The mean length of membership of those included in the sample is 8.32 years and the standard deviation is 3.07 years.
   a. What is the mean of the population?
   b. Develop a 90% confidence interval for the population mean.
   c. The previous director, in the summary report she prepared as she retired, indicated the mean length of membership was now "almost 10 years." Does the sample information substantiate this claim? Cite evidence.

36. The American Restaurant Association collected information on the number of meals eaten outside the home per week by young married couples. A survey of 60 couples showed the sample mean number of meals eaten outside the home was 2.76 meals per week, with a standard deviation of 0.75 meal per week. Construct a 99% confidence interval for the population mean.

37. The National Collegiate Athletic Association (NCAA) reported that the mean number of hours spent per week on coaching and recruiting by college football assistant coaches during the season was 70. A random sample of 50 assistant coaches showed the sample mean to be 68.6 hours, with a standard deviation of 8.2 hours.
   a. Using the sample data, construct a 99% confidence interval for the population mean.
   b. Does the 99% confidence interval include the value suggested by the NCAA? Interpret this result.
   c. Suppose you decided to switch from a 99% to a 95% confidence interval. Without performing any calculations, will the interval increase, decrease, or stay the same? Which of the values in the formula will change?

38. The Human Relations Department of Electronics Inc. would like to include a dental plan as part of the benefits package. The question is: How much does a typical employee and his or her family spend per year on dental expenses? A sample of 45 employees reveals the mean amount spent last year was $1,820, with a standard deviation of $660.
   a. Construct a 95% confidence interval for the population mean.
   b. The information from part (a) was given to the president of Electronics Inc. He indicated he could afford $1,700 of dental expenses per employee. Is it possible that the population mean could be $1,700? Justify your answer.

39. A student conducted a study and reported that the 95% confidence interval for the mean ranged from 46 to 54. He was sure that the mean of the sample was 50, that the standard deviation of the sample was 16, and that the sample size was at least 30, but could not remember the exact number. Can you help him out?

40. A recent study by the American Automobile Dealers Association revealed the mean amount of profit per car sold for a sample of 20 dealers was $290, with a standard deviation of $125. Develop a 95% confidence interval for the population mean.

ESTIMATION AND CONFIDENCE INTERVALS   309

41. A study of 25 graduates of four-year colleges by the American Banker's Association revealed the mean amount owed by a student in student loans was $14,381. The standard deviation of the sample was $1,892. Construct a 90% confidence interval for the population mean. Is it reasonable to conclude that the mean of the population is actually $15,000? Tell why or why not.

42. An important factor in selling a residential property is the number of people who look through the home. A sample of 15 homes recently sold in the Buffalo, New York, area revealed the mean number looking through each home was 24 and the standard deviation of the sample was 5 people. Develop a 98% confidence interval for the population mean.

For **DATA FILE**, please visit
www.mhhe.com/lind16e

43. Warren County Telephone Company claims in its annual report that "the typical customer spends $60 per month on local and long-distance service." A sample of 12 subscribers revealed the following amounts spent last month.

| $64 | $66 | $64 | $66 | $59 | $62 | $67 | $61 | $64 | $58 | $54 | $66 |

   a. What is the point estimate of the population mean?
   b. Develop a 90% confidence interval for the population mean.
   c. Is the company's claim that the "typical customer" spends $60 per month reasonable? Justify your answer.

For **DATA FILE**, please visit
www.mhhe.com/lind16e

44. The manufacturer of a new line of ink-jet printers would like to include as part of its advertising the number of pages a user can expect from a print cartridge. A sample of 10 cartridges revealed the following number of pages printed.

| 2,698 | 2,028 | 2,474 | 2,395 | 2,372 | 2,475 | 1,927 | 3,006 | 2,334 | 2,379 |

   a. What is the point estimate of the population mean?
   b. Develop a 95% confidence interval for the population mean.

For **DATA FILE**, please visit
www.mhhe.com/lind16e

45. Dr. Susan Benner is an industrial psychologist. She is currently studying stress among executives of Internet companies. She has developed a questionnaire that she believes measures stress. A score above 80 indicates stress at a dangerous level. A random sample of 15 executives revealed the following stress level scores.

| 94 | 78 | 83 | 90 | 78 | 99 | 97 | 90 | 97 | 90 | 93 | 94 | 100 | 75 | 84 |

   a. Find the mean stress level for this sample. What is the point estimate of the population mean?
   b. Construct a 95% confidence level for the population mean.
   c. According to Dr. Benner's test, is it reasonable to conclude that the mean stress level of Internet executives is 80? Explain.

46. As a condition of employment, Fashion Industries applicants must pass a drug test. Of the last 220 applicants, 14 failed the test. Develop a 99% confidence interval for the proportion of applicants who fail the test. Would it be reasonable to conclude that 10% of the applicants fail the test? Explain.

47. Fashion Industries randomly tests its employees throughout the year. Last year in the 400 random tests conducted, 14 employees failed the test. Develop a 99% confidence interval for the proportion of applicants that fail the test. Would it be reasonable to conclude that 5% of the employees cannot pass the random drug test? Explain.

48. During a national debate on changes to health care, a cable news service performs an opinion poll of 500 small-business owners. It shows that 65% of small-business owners do not approve of the changes. Develop a 95% confidence interval for the proportion opposing health care changes. Comment on the result.

49. There are 20,000 eligible voters in York County, South Carolina. A random sample of 500 York County voters revealed 350 plan to vote to return Louella Miller to the state senate. Construct a 99% confidence interval for the proportion of voters in the county who plan to vote for Ms. Miller. From this sample information, is it reasonable to conclude that Ms. Miller will receive a majority of the votes?

50. In a poll to estimate presidential popularity, each person in a random sample of 1,000 voters was asked to agree with one of the following statements:
   1. The president is doing a good job.
   2. The president is doing a poor job.
   3. I have no opinion.

A total of 560 respondents selected the first statement, indicating they thought the president was doing a good job.

  a. Construct a 95% confidence interval for the proportion of respondents who feel the president is doing a good job.

  b. Based on your interval in part (a), is it reasonable to conclude that a majority of the population believes the president is doing a good job?

51. Police Chief Edward Wilkin of River City reports 500 traffic citations were issued last month. A sample of 35 of these citations showed the mean amount of the fine was $54, with a standard deviation of $4.50. Construct a 95% confidence interval for the mean amount of a citation in River City.

52. The First National Bank of Wilson has 650 checking account customers. A recent sample of 50 of these customers showed 26 have a Visa card with the bank. Construct the 99% confidence interval for the proportion of checking account customers who have a Visa card with the bank.

53. It is estimated that 60% of U.S. households subscribe to cable TV. You would like to verify this statement for your class in mass communications. If you want your estimate to be within 5 percentage points, with a 95% level of confidence, how large of a sample is required?

54. You need to estimate the mean number of travel days per year for outside salespeople. The mean of a small pilot study was 150 days, with a standard deviation of 14 days. If you must estimate the population mean within 2 days, how many outside salespeople should you sample? Use the 90% confidence level.

55. You are to conduct a sample survey to determine the mean family income in a rural area of central Florida. The question is, how many families should be sampled? In a pilot sample of 10 families, the standard deviation of the sample was $500. The sponsor of the survey wants you to use the 95% confidence level. The estimate is to be within $100. How many families should be interviewed?

56. *Families USA,* a monthly magazine that discusses issues related to health and health costs, surveyed 20 of its subscribers. It found that the annual health insurance premiums for a family with coverage through an employer averaged $10,979. The standard deviation of the sample was $1,000.

  a. Based on this sample information, develop a 90% confidence interval for the population mean yearly premium.

  b. How large a sample is needed to find the population mean within $250 at 99% confidence?

57. Passenger comfort is influenced by the amount of pressurization in an airline cabin. Higher pressurization permits a closer-to-normal environment and a more relaxed flight. A study by an airline user group recorded the corresponding air pressure on 30 randomly chosen flights. The study revealed a mean equivalent pressure of 8,000 feet with a standard deviation of 300 feet.

  a. Develop a 99% confidence interval for the population mean equivalent pressure.

  b. How large a sample is needed to find the population mean within 25 feet at 95% confidence?

58. A random sample of 25 people employed by the Florida state authority established they earned an average wage (including benefits) of $65.00 per hour. The sample standard deviation was $6.25 per hour.

  a. What is the population mean? What is the best estimate of the population mean?

  b. Develop a 99% confidence interval for the population mean wage (including benefits) for these employees.

  c. How large a sample is needed to assess the population mean with an allowable error of $1.00 at 95% confidence?

59. A film alliance used a random sample of 50 U.S. citizens to estimate that the typical American spent 78 hours watching videos and DVDs last year. The standard deviation of this sample was 9 hours.

  a. Develop a 95% confidence interval for the population mean number of hours spent watching videos and DVDs last year.

  b. How large a sample should be used to be 90% confident the sample mean is within 1.0 hour of the population mean?

60. Dylan Jones kept careful records of the fuel efficiency of his new car. After the first nine times he filled up the tank, he found the mean was 23.4 miles per gallon (mpg) with a sample standard deviation of 0.9 mpg.

  a. Compute the 95% confidence interval for his mpg.

  b. How many times should he fill his gas tank to obtain a margin of error below 0.1 mpg?

ESTIMATION AND CONFIDENCE INTERVALS   311

61. A survey of 36 randomly selected "iPhone" owners showed that the purchase price has a mean of $416 with a sample standard deviation of $180.
    a. Compute the standard error of the sample mean.
    b. Compute the 95% confidence interval for the mean.
    c. How large a sample is needed to estimate the population mean within $10?

62. You plan to conduct a survey to find what proportion of the workforce has two or more jobs. You decide on the 95% confidence level and state that the estimated proportion must be within 2% of the population proportion. A pilot survey reveals that 5 of the 50 sampled hold two or more jobs. How many in the workforce should be interviewed to meet your requirements?

63. The proportion of public accountants who have changed companies within the last 3 years is to be estimated within 3%. The 95% level of confidence is to be used. A study conducted several years ago revealed that the percent of public accountants changing companies within 3 years was 21.
    a. To update this study, the files of how many public accountants should be studied?
    b. How many public accountants should be contacted if no previous estimates of the population proportion are available?

64. As part of an annual review of its accounts, a discount brokerage selects a random sample of 36 customers. Their accounts are reviewed for total account valuation, which showed a mean of $32,000, with a sample standard deviation of $8,200. What is a 90% confidence interval for the mean account valuation of the population of customers?

65. The National Weight Control Registry tries to mine secrets of success from people who have lost at least 30 pounds and kept it off for at least a year. It reports that out of 2,700 registrants, 459 were on low-carbohydrate diets (less than 90 grams a day).
    a. Develop a 95% confidence interval for this fraction.
    b. Is it possible that the population percentage is 18%?
    c. How large a sample is needed to estimate the proportion within 0.5%?

66. Near the time of an election, a cable news service performs an opinion poll of 1,000 probable voters. It shows that the Republican contender has an advantage of 52% to 48%.
    a. Develop a 95% confidence interval for the proportion favoring the Republican candidate.
    b. Estimate the probability that the Democratic candidate is actually leading.
    c. Repeat the above analysis based on a sample of 3,000 probable voters.

67. A sample of 352 subscribers to *Wired* magazine shows the mean time spent using the Internet is 13.4 hours per week, with a sample standard deviation of 6.8 hours. Find the 95% confidence interval for the mean time *Wired* subscribers spend on the Internet.

68. The Tennessee Tourism Institute (TTI) plans to sample information center visitors entering the state to learn the fraction of visitors who plan to camp in the state. Current estimates are that 35% of visitors are campers. How large a sample would you take to estimate at a 95% confidence level the population proportion with an allowable error of 2%?

D A T A   S E T   E X E R C I S E S

(The data for these exercises are available at the text website: www.mhhe.com/lind16e.)

69. Refer to the Real Estate data, which report information on homes sold in the Goodyear, Arizona, area during the last year.
    a. Develop a 95% confidence interval for the mean selling price of the homes.
    b. Develop a 95% confidence interval for the mean distance the home is from the center of the city.
    c. Develop a 95% confidence interval for the proportion of homes with an attached garage.
    d. To report your findings, write a business style memo to Gary Loftus, the president of the Goodyear Chamber of Commerce.

70. Refer to the Baseball 2012 data, which report information on the 30 Major League Baseball teams for the 2012 season. Assume the 2012 data represents a sample.
    a. Develop a 95% confidence interval for the mean number of home runs per team.
    b. Develop a 95% confidence interval for the mean number of errors committed by each team.
    c. Develop a 95% confidence interval for the mean number of stolen bases for each team.

71. Refer to the Buena School District bus data.
    a. Develop a 95% confidence interval for the mean bus maintenance.
    b. Develop a 95% confidence interval for the mean bus miles.
    c. Write a business memo to the state transportation official to report your results.

A REVIEW OF CHAPTERS 8–9

We began Chapter 8 by describing the reasons sampling is necessary. We sample because it is often impossible to study every item, or individual, in some populations. It would be too expensive and time-consuming, for example, to contact and record the annual incomes of all U.S. bank officers. Also, sampling often destroys the product. A drug manufacturer cannot test the properties of each vitamin tablet manufactured because there would be none left to sell. To estimate a population parameter, therefore, we select a sample from the population. A sample is a part of the population. Care must be taken to ensure that every member of our population has a chance of being selected; otherwise, the conclusions might be biased. A number of probability-type sampling methods can be used, including *simple random, systematic, stratified,* and *cluster sampling.*

Regardless of the sampling method selected, a sample statistic is seldom equal to the corresponding population parameter. For example, the mean of a sample is seldom exactly the same as the mean of the population. The difference between this sample statistic and the population parameter is the *sampling error.*

In Chapter 8, we demonstrated that, if we select all possible samples of a specified size from a population and calculate the mean of these samples, the result will be exactly equal to the population mean. We also showed that the dispersion in the distribution of the sample means is equal to the population standard deviation divided by the square root of the sample size. This result is called the standard error of the mean. There is less dispersion in the distribution of the sample means than in the population. In addition, as we increase the number of observations in each sample, we decrease the variation in the sampling distribution.

The central limit theorem is the foundation of statistical inference. It states that, if the population from which we select the samples follows the normal probability distribution, the distribution of the sample means will also follow the normal distribution. If the population is not normal, it will approach the normal probability distribution as we increase the size of the sample.

Our focus in Chapter 9 was point estimates and interval estimates. A point estimate is a single value used to estimate a population parameter. An interval estimate is a range of values within which we expect the population parameter to occur. For example, based on a sample, we estimate that the mean annual income of all professional house painters in Atlanta, Georgia (the population), is $45,300. That estimate is called a *point estimate.* If we state that the population mean is probably in the interval between $45,200 and $45,400, that estimate is called an *interval estimate.* The two endpoints ($45,200 and $45,400) are the *confidence limits* for the population mean. We also described procedures for establishing a confidence interval for a population mean when the population standard deviation is not known and for a population proportion. In this chapter, we also provided a method to determine the necessary sample size based on the dispersion in the population, the level of confidence desired, and the desired precision of the estimate or margin of error.

PROBLEMS

1. A recent study indicated that women took an average of 8.6 weeks of unpaid leave from their jobs after the birth of a child. Assume that this distribution follows the normal probability distribution with a standard deviation of 2.0 weeks. We select a sample of 35 women who recently returned to work after the birth of a child. What is the likelihood that the mean of this sample is at least 8.8 weeks?

2. The manager of Tee Shirt Emporium reports that the mean number of shirts sold per week is 1,210, with a standard deviation of 325. The distribution of sales follows the normal distribution. What is the likelihood of selecting a sample of 25 weeks and finding the sample mean to be 1,100 or less?

3. The owner of the Gulf Stream Café wished to estimate the mean number of lunch customers per day. A sample of 40 days revealed a mean of 160 per day, with a standard deviation of 20 per day. Develop a 98% confidence interval for the mean number of customers per day.

4. The manager of the local Hamburger Express wishes to estimate the mean time customers spend at the drive-through window. A sample of 20 customers experienced a mean waiting time of 2.65 minutes, with a standard deviation of 0.45 minute. Develop a 90% confidence interval for the mean waiting time.

5. Defiance Tool and Die has 293 sales offices throughout the world. The VP of Sales is studying the usage of its copy machines. A random sample of six of the sales offices revealed the following number of copies made in each selected office last week.

826	931	1,126	918	1,011	1,101

Develop a 95% confidence interval for the mean number of copies per week.

6. John Kleman is the host of KXYZ Radio 55 AM drive-time news in Denver. During his morning program, John asks listeners to call in and discuss current local and national news. This morning, John was concerned with the number of hours children under 12 years of age watch TV per day. The last five callers reported that their children watched the following number of hours of TV last night.

3.0	3.5	4.0	4.5	3.0

Would it be reasonable to develop a confidence interval from these data to show the mean number of hours of TV watched? If yes, construct an appropriate confidence interval and interpret the result. If no, why would a confidence interval not be appropriate?

7. Historically, Widgets Manufacturing Inc. produces 250 widgets per day. Recently the new owner bought a new machine to produce more widgets per day. A sample of 16 days' production revealed a mean of 240 units with a standard deviation of 35. Construct a confidence interval for the mean number of widgets produced per day. Does it seem reasonable to conclude that the mean daily widget production has changed? Justify your conclusion.

8. A manufacturer of cell phone batteries wants to estimate the useful life of its battery (in thousands of hours). The estimate is to be within 0.10 (100 hours). Assume a 95% level of confidence and that the standard deviation of the useful life of the battery is 0.90 (900 hours). Determine the required sample size.

9. The manager of a home improvement store wishes to estimate the mean amount of money spent in the store. The estimate is to be within $4.00 with a 95% level of confidence. The manager does not know the standard deviation of the amounts spent. However, he does estimate that the range is from $5.00 up to $155.00. How large of a sample is needed?

10. In a sample of 200 residents of Georgetown County, 120 reported they believed the county real estate taxes were too high. Develop a 95% confidence interval for the proportion of residents who believe the tax rate is too high. Does it seem reasonable to conclude that 50% of the voters believe that taxes are too high?

11. In recent times, the percent of buyers purchasing a new vehicle via the Internet has been large enough that local automobile dealers are concerned about its impact on their business. The information needed is an estimate of the proportion of purchases via the Internet. How large of a sample of purchasers is necessary for the estimate to be within 2 percentage points with a 98% level of confidence? Current thinking is that about 8% of the vehicles are purchased via the Internet.

12. Historically, the proportion of adults over the age of 24 who smoke has been .30. In recent years, much information has been published and aired on radio and TV that smoking is not good for one's health. A sample of 500 adults revealed only 25% of those sampled smoked. Develop a 98% confidence interval for the proportion of adults who currently smoke. Does it seem reasonable to conclude that the proportion of adults who smoke has changed?

13. The auditor of the state of Ohio needs an estimate of the proportion of residents who regularly play the state lottery. Historically, about 40% regularly play, but the auditor would like some current information. How large a sample is necessary for the estimate to be within 3 percentage points, with a 98% level of confidence?

CASE

Century National Bank
Refer to the description of Century National Bank at the end of the Review of Chapters 1–4 on page 125. When Mr. Selig took over as president of Century several years ago, the use of debit cards was just beginning. He would like an update on the use of these cards. Develop a 95% confidence interval for the proportion of customers using these cards. On the basis of the confidence interval, is it reasonable to conclude that more than half of the customers use a debit card? Write a brief report interpreting the results.

PRACTICE TEST

Part 1—Objective
1. If each item in the population has the same chance of being selected, this is called a _____.   1. _____
2. The difference between the population mean and the sample mean is called the _____.   2. _____

314   A REVIEW OF CHAPTERS 8–9

3. The _____ is the standard deviation of the distribution of sample means.   3. _____

4. If the sample size is increased, the variance of the sample means will _____.
(become smaller, become larger, not change)   4. _____

5. A single value used to estimate a population parameter is called a _____.   5. _____

6. A range of values within which the population parameter is expected to occur is called a _____.
                                                                                                      6. _____

7. Which of the following does *not* affect the width of a confidence interval? (sample size, variation
in the population, level of confidence, size of population)   7. _____

8. The fraction of a population that has a particular characteristic is called a _____.   8. _____

9. Which of the following is not a characteristic of the *t* distribution? (positively skewed, continuous,
mean of zero, based on degrees of freedom)   9. _____

10. To determine the required sample size of a proportion when no estimate of the population
proportion is available, what value is used?   10. _____

Part 2—Problems

1. Americans spend an average (mean) of 12.2 minutes (per day) in the shower. The distribution of times follows the normal distribution with a population standard deviation of 2.3 minutes. What is the likelihood that the mean time per day for a sample of 12 Americans was 11 minutes or less?

2. A recent study of 26 Conway, South Carolina, residents revealed they had lived at their current address an average of 9.3 years. The standard deviation of the sample was 2 years.
   a. What is the population mean?
   b. What is the best estimate of the population mean?
   c. What is the standard error of estimate?
   d. Develop a 90% confidence interval for the population mean.

3. A recent federal report indicated that 27% of children ages 2 to 5 ate a vegetable at least five times a week. How large a sample is needed to estimate the true population proportion within 2% with a 98% level of confidence? Be sure to use the information contained in the federal report.

4. The Philadelphia Area Transit Authority wishes to estimate the proportion of central city workers that use public transportation to get to work. A sample of 100 workers revealed that 64 used public transportation. Develop a 95% confidence interval for the population proportion.

One-Sample Tests of Hypothesis

10

DOLE PINEAPPLE INC. is concerned that the 16-ounce can of sliced pineapple is being overfilled. Assume the standard deviation of the process is .03 ounce. The quality control department took a random sample of 50 cans and found that the arithmetic mean weight was 16.05 ounces. At the 5% level of significance, can we conclude that the mean weight is greater than 16 ounces? Determine the *p*-value. (See Exercise 26 and LO10-5.)

LEARNING OBJECTIVES

When you have completed this chapter, you will be able to:

LO10-1 Define a hypothesis.

LO10-2 Explain the process of testing a hypothesis.

LO10-3 Apply the six-step procedure for testing a hypothesis.

LO10-4 Distinguish between a one-tailed and a two-tailed test of hypothesis.

LO10-5 Conduct a test of a hypothesis about a population mean.

LO10-6 Compute and interpret a *p*-value.

LO10-7 Use a *t* statistic to test a hypothesis.

LO10-8 Compute the probability of a Type II error.

STATISTICS IN ACTION

LASIK is a 15-minute surgical procedure that uses a laser to reshape an eye's cornea with the goal of improving eyesight. Research shows that about 5% of all surgeries involve complications such as glare, corneal haze, overcorrection or undercorrection of vision, and loss of vision. In a statistical sense, the research tests a null hypothesis that the surgery will not improve eyesight with the alternative hypothesis that the surgery will improve eyesight. The sample data of LASIK surgery shows that 5% of all cases result in complications. The 5% represents a Type I error rate. When a person decides to have the surgery, he or she expects to reject the null hypothesis. In 5% of future cases, this expectation will not be met. (Source: *American Academy of Ophthalmology Journal*, Vol. 16, no. 43.)

INTRODUCTION

Chapter 8 began our study of statistical inference. We described how we could select a random sample to estimate the value of a population parameter. For example, we selected a sample of five employees at Spence Sprockets, found the number of years of service for each sampled employee, computed the mean years of service, and used the sample mean to estimate the mean years of service for all employees. In other words, we estimated a population parameter from a sample statistic.

Chapter 9 continued the study of statistical inference by developing a confidence interval. A confidence interval is a range of values within which we expect the population parameter to occur. In this chapter, rather than develop a range of values within which we expect the population parameter to occur, we develop a procedure to test the validity of a statement about a population parameter. Some examples of statements we might want to test are:

- The mean speed of automobiles passing milepost 150 on the West Virginia Turnpike is 68 miles per hour.
- The mean number of miles driven by those leasing a Chevy Trail-Blazer for 3 years is 32,000 miles.
- The mean time an American family lives in a particular single-family dwelling is 11.8 years.
- The mean starting salary for a 2013 graduate from a four-year business program is $51,541. This is an increase of 2.2% from 2011.
- According to the Kelley Blue Book (www.kbb.com), a 2013 Ford Edge averages 19 miles per gallon in the city.
- The mean cost to remodel a home office is $10,500.

This chapter and several of the following chapters cover statistical hypothesis testing. We begin by defining what we mean by a statistical hypothesis and statistical hypothesis testing. Next, we outline the steps in statistical hypothesis testing. Then we conduct tests of hypothesis for means. In the last section of the chapter, we describe possible errors due to sampling in hypothesis testing.

WHAT IS A HYPOTHESIS?

LO10-1
Define a hypothesis.

A hypothesis is a statement about a population. Data are then collected to check the reasonableness of the statement. To begin, we need to define the word *hypothesis*. In the U.S. legal system, a person is presumed innocent until proven guilty. A jury hypothesizes that a person charged with a crime is innocent and then reviews the evidence to assess if there is enough evidence to claim that the person is not innocent or guilty as charged. In a similar sense, a patient goes to a physician and reports various symptoms. On the basis of the symptoms, the physician will order certain diagnostic tests, then, according to the symptoms and the test results, determine the treatment to be followed.

In statistical analysis, we make a claim—that is, state a hypothesis—collect data, and then use the data to test the claim. We define a statistical hypothesis as follows.

HYPOTHESIS A statement about a population parameter subject to verification.

ONE-SAMPLE TESTS OF HYPOTHESIS   317

In most cases, the population is so large that it is not feasible to study all the items, objects, or persons in the population. For example, it would not be possible to contact every systems analyst in the United States to find his or her monthly income. Likewise, the quality assurance department at Cooper Tire cannot check each tire produced to determine whether it will last more than 60,000 miles.

As noted in Chapter 8, an alternative to measuring or interviewing the entire population is to take a sample from the population. We can, therefore, test a statement to determine whether the sample does or does not support the statement concerning the population.

WHAT IS HYPOTHESIS TESTING?

LO10-2

Explain the process of testing a hypothesis.

The terms *hypothesis testing* and *testing a hypothesis* are used interchangeably. Hypothesis testing starts with a statement, or assumption, about a population parameter—such as the population mean. This statement is referred to as a hypothesis. A hypothesis might be that the mean monthly commission of sales associates in retail electronics stores, such as h. h. gregg, is $2,000. We cannot contact all h. h. gregg sales associates to determine that the mean is $2,000. The cost of locating and interviewing every h. h. gregg electronics sales associate in the United States would be exorbitant. To test the validity of the hypothesis ($\mu = \$2,000$), we must select a sample from the population of all h. h. gregg electronics sales associates, calculate sample statistics, and based on certain decision rules reject or fail to reject the hypothesis. A sample mean of $1,000 per month is much less than $2,000 per month and we would most likely reject the hypothesis. However, suppose the sample mean is $1,995. Can we attribute the $5 difference between $1,995 and $2,000 to sampling error? Or is this difference of $5 statistically significant?

> **HYPOTHESIS TESTING** A procedure based on sample evidence and probability theory to determine whether the hypothesis is a reasonable statement.

SIX-STEP PROCEDURE FOR TESTING A HYPOTHESIS

LO10-3

Apply the six-step procedure for testing a hypothesis.

There is a six-step procedure that systematizes hypothesis testing; when we get to step 5, we are ready to reject or not reject the hypothesis. However, hypothesis testing as used by statisticians does not provide proof that something is true, in the manner in which a mathematician "proves" a statement. It does provide a kind of "proof beyond a reasonable doubt," in the manner of the court system. Hence, there are specific rules of evidence, or procedures, that are followed. The steps are shown in the following diagram. We will discuss in detail each of the steps.

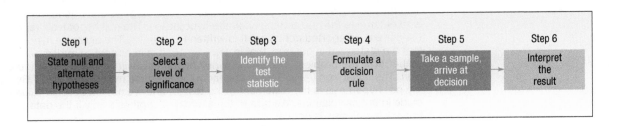

318   CHAPTER 10

Step 1: State the Null Hypothesis (H_0) and the Alternate Hypothesis (H_1)

The first step is to state the hypothesis being tested. It is called the **null hypothesis,** designated H_0, and read "*H sub zero.*" The capital letter H stands for hypothesis, and the subscript zero implies "no difference." There is usually a "not" or a "no" term in the null hypothesis, meaning that there is "no change." For example, the null hypothesis is that the mean number of miles driven on the steel-belted tire is not different from 60,000. The null hypothesis would be written H_0: μ = 60,000. Generally speaking, the null hypothesis is developed for the purpose of testing. We either reject or fail to reject the null hypothesis. The null hypothesis is a statement that is not rejected unless our sample data provide convincing evidence that it is false.

We should emphasize that, if the null hypothesis is not rejected on the basis of the sample data, we cannot say that the null hypothesis is true. To put it another way, failing to reject the null hypothesis does not prove that H_0 is true; it means we have *failed to disprove* H_0. To prove without any doubt the null hypothesis is true, the population parameter would have to be known. To actually determine it, we would have to test, survey, or count every item in the population. This is usually not feasible. The alternative is to take a sample from the population.

It should also be noted that we often begin the null hypothesis by stating, "There is no *significant* difference between . . ." or "The mean impact strength of the glass is not *significantly* different from. . . ." When we select a sample from a population, the sample statistic is usually numerically different from the hypothesized population parameter. As an illustration, suppose the hypothesized impact strength of a glass plate is 70 psi, and the mean impact strength of a sample of 12 glass plates is 69.5 psi. We must make a decision about the difference of 0.5 psi. Is it a true difference, that is, a significant difference, or is the difference between the sample statistic (69.5) and the hypothesized population parameter (70.0) due to chance (sampling)? To answer this question, we conduct a test of significance, commonly referred to as a test of hypothesis. To define what is meant by a null hypothesis:

> **NULL HYPOTHESIS** A statement about the value of a population parameter developed for the purpose of testing numerical evidence.

The **alternate hypothesis** describes what you will conclude if you reject the null hypothesis. It is written H_1 and is read "*H sub one.*" It is also referred to as the research hypothesis. The alternate hypothesis is accepted if the sample data provide us with enough statistical evidence that the null hypothesis is false.

> **ALTERNATE HYPOTHESIS** A statement that is accepted if the sample data provide sufficient evidence that the null hypothesis is false.

The following example will help clarify what is meant by the null hypothesis and the alternate hypothesis. A recent article indicated the mean age of U.S. commercial aircraft is 15 years. To conduct a statistical test regarding this statement, the first step is to determine the null and the alternate hypotheses. The null hypothesis represents the current or reported condition. It is written H_0: μ = 15. The alternate hypothesis is that the statement is not true, that is, H_1: $\mu \neq 15$. It is important to remember that no matter how the problem is stated, *the null hypothesis will always contain the equal sign.* The equal sign (=) will never appear in the alternate hypothesis. Why? Because the null hypothesis is the statement being tested, and we need a specific value to include in our calculations. We turn to the alternate hypothesis only if the data suggest the null hypothesis is untrue.

ONE-SAMPLE TESTS OF HYPOTHESIS   319

Step 2: Select a Level of Significance

After setting up the null hypothesis and alternate hypothesis, the next step is to state the level of significance.

> **LEVEL OF SIGNIFICANCE** The probability of rejecting the null hypothesis when it is true.

The level of significance is designated α, the Greek letter alpha. It is also sometimes called the level of risk. This may be a more appropriate term because it is the risk you take of rejecting the null hypothesis when it is really true.

There is no one level of significance that is applied to all tests. A decision is made to use the .05 level (often stated as the 5% level), the .01 level, the .10 level, or any other level between 0 and 1. Traditionally, the .05 level is selected for consumer research projects, .01 for quality assurance, and .10 for political polling. You, the researcher, must decide on the level of significance *before* formulating a decision rule and collecting sample data.

To illustrate how it is possible to reject a true hypothesis, suppose a firm manufacturing personal computers uses a large number of printed circuit boards. Suppliers

bid on the boards, and the one with the lowest bid is awarded a sizable contract. Suppose the contract specifies that the computer manufacturer's quality-assurance department will sample all incoming shipments of circuit boards. If more than 6% of the boards sampled are substandard, the shipment will be rejected. The null hypothesis is that the incoming shipment of boards contains 6% or less substandard boards. The alternate hypothesis is that more than 6% of the boards are defective.

A shipment of 4,000 circuit boards was received from Allied Electronics, and the quality assurance department selected a random sample of 50 circuit boards for testing. Of the 50 circuit boards sampled, 4 boards, or 8%, were substandard. The shipment was rejected because it exceeded the maximum of 6% substandard printed circuit boards. If the shipment was actually substandard, then the decision to return the boards to the supplier was correct. However, suppose the 4 substandard printed circuit boards selected in the sample of 50 were the only substandard boards in the shipment of 4,000 boards. Then only $1/10$ of 1% were defective ($4/4{,}000 = .001$). In that case, less than 6% of the entire shipment was substandard and rejecting the shipment was an error. In terms of hypothesis testing, we rejected the null hypothesis when we should have failed to reject the null hypothesis. By rejecting a true null hypothesis, we committed a Type I error. The probability of committing a Type I error is α.

> **TYPE I ERROR** Rejecting the null hypothesis, H_0, when it is true.

The probability of committing another type of error, called a Type II error, is designated by the Greek letter beta (β).

> **TYPE II ERROR** Not rejecting the null hypothesis when it is false.

The firm manufacturing personal computers would commit a Type II error if, unknown to the manufacturer, an incoming shipment of printed circuit boards from Allied Electronics contained 15% substandard boards, yet the shipment was accepted. How could this happen? Suppose 2 of the 50 boards in the sample (4%) tested were substandard, and 48 of the 50 were good boards. According to the stated procedure, because the sample contained less than 6% substandard boards, the shipment was accepted. It could be that *by chance* the 48 good boards selected in the sample were the only acceptable ones in the entire shipment consisting of thousands of boards!

In retrospect, the researcher cannot study every item or individual in the population. Thus, there is a possibility of two types of error—a Type I error, wherein the null hypothesis is rejected when it should not be rejected, and a Type II error, wherein the null hypothesis is not rejected when it should have been rejected.

We often refer to the probability of these two possible errors as *alpha,* α, and *beta,* β. Alpha (α) is the probability of making a Type I error, and beta (β) is the probability of making a Type II error. The following table summarizes the decisions the researcher could make and the possible consequences.

Null Hypothesis	Researcher	
	Does Not Reject H_0	Rejects H_0
H_0 is true	Correct decision	Type I error
H_0 is false	Type II error	Correct decision

Step 3: Select the Test Statistic

There are many test statistics. In this chapter, we use both *z* and *t* as the test statistics. In later chapters, we will use such test statistics as *F* and χ^2, called chi-square.

> **TEST STATISTIC** A value, determined from sample information, used to determine whether to reject the null hypothesis.

In hypothesis testing for the mean (μ) when σ is known, the test statistic *z* is computed by:

TESTING A MEAN, σ KNOWN	$z = \dfrac{\bar{x} - \mu}{\sigma/\sqrt{n}}$	[10–1]

The *z* value is based on the sampling distribution of $\bar{x}$, which follows the normal distribution with a mean ($\mu_{\bar{x}}$) equal to μ and a standard deviation $\sigma_{\bar{x}}$, which is equal to $\sigma/\sqrt{n}$. We can thus determine whether the difference between $\bar{x}$ and μ is statistically significant by finding the number of standard deviations $\bar{x}$ is from μ, using formula (10–1).

Step 4: Formulate the Decision Rule

A decision rule is a statement of the specific conditions under which the null hypothesis is rejected and the conditions under which it is not rejected. The region or area of rejection defines the location of all those values that are so large or so small that the probability of their occurrence under a true null hypothesis is rather remote.

Chart 10–1 portrays the rejection region for a test of significance that will be conducted later in the chapter.

STATISTICS IN ACTION

During World War II, allied military planners needed estimates of the number of German tanks. The information provided by traditional spying methods was not reliable, but statistical methods proved to be valuable. For example, espionage and reconnaissance led analysts to estimate that 1,550 tanks were produced during June 1941. However, using the serial numbers of captured tanks and statistical analysis, military planners estimated that only 244 tanks were produced. The actual number produced, as determined from German production records, was 271. The estimate using statistical analysis turned out to be much more accurate. A similar type of analysis was used to estimate the number of Iraqi tanks destroyed during Desert Storm.

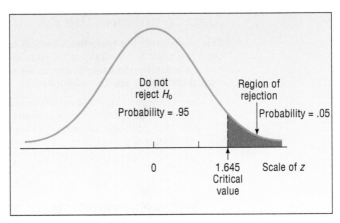

CHART 10–1 Sampling Distribution of the Statistic z, a Right-Tailed Test, .05 Level of Significance

Note in the chart that:

- The area where the null hypothesis is not rejected is to the left of 1.645. We will explain how to get the 1.645 value shortly.
- The area of rejection is to the right of 1.645.
- A one-tailed test is being applied. (This will also be explained later.)
- The .05 level of significance was chosen.
- The sampling distribution of the statistic z follows the normal probability distribution.
- The value 1.645 separates the regions where the null hypothesis is rejected and where it is not rejected.
- The value 1.645 is the **critical value.**

> **CRITICAL VALUE** The dividing point between the region where the null hypothesis is rejected and the region where it is not rejected.

Step 5: Make a Decision

The fifth step in hypothesis testing is to compute the value of the test statistic, compare its value to the critical value, and make a decision to reject or not to reject the null hypothesis. Referring to Chart 10–1, if, based on sample information, z is computed to be 2.34, the null hypothesis is rejected at the .05 level of significance. The decision to reject H_0 was made because 2.34 lies in the region of rejection, that is, beyond 1.645. We reject the null hypothesis, reasoning that it is highly improbable that a computed z value this large is due to sampling error (chance).

Had the computed value been 1.645 or less, say 0.71, the null hypothesis is not rejected. It is reasoned that such a small computed value could be attributed to chance, that is, sampling error. As we have emphasized, only one of two decisions is possible in hypothesis testing—either reject or do not reject the null hypothesis.

However, because the decision is based on a sample, it is always possible to make either of two decision errors. It is possible to make a Type I error when the null hypothesis is rejected when it should not be rejected. Or it is also possible to make a Type II error when the null hypothesis is not rejected and it should have been rejected. Fortunately, we can decide on the probability of making a Type I error, α (alpha), and we can compute the probabilities associated with a Type II error, β (beta).

322   CHAPTER 10

Step 6: Interpret the Result

The final step in the hypothesis testing procedure is to interpret the results. The process does not end with the value of a sample statistic or the decision to reject or not reject the null hypothesis. What can we say or report based on the results of the statistical test? Here are two examples:

- An investigative reporter for a Colorado newspaper reports that the mean monthly income of convenience stores in the state is $130,000. You decide to conduct a test of hypothesis to verify the report. The null hypothesis and the alternate hypothesis are:

$$H_0: \mu = \$130,000$$
$$H_1: \mu \neq \$130,000$$

A sample of convenience stores provides a sample mean and standard deviation, and you compute a z statistic. The results of the hypothesis test result in a decision to not reject the null hypothesis. How do you interpret the result? Be cautious with your interpretation because by not rejecting the null hypothesis, you did not prove the null hypothesis to be true. Based on the sample data, the difference between the sample mean and hypothesized population mean was not large enough to reject the null hypothesis.

- In a recent speech to students, the dean of the College of Business reported that the mean credit card debt for college students is $3,000. You decide to conduct a test of hypothesis to investigate the statement's truth. The null hypothesis and the alternate hypothesis are:

$$H_0: \mu = \$3,000$$
$$H_1: \mu \neq \$3,000$$

A sample of college students provides a sample mean and standard deviation, and you compute a z statistic. The results of the hypothesis test result in a decision to reject the null hypothesis. How do you interpret the result? The evidence does not support the dean's statement. You have disproved the null hypothesis with a stated probability of a Type I error, α. Based on the sample data, the mean amount of student credit card debt is different from $3,000.

SUMMARY OF THE STEPS IN HYPOTHESIS TESTING
1. Establish the null hypothesis (H_0) and the alternate hypothesis (H_1).
2. Select the level of significance, that is, α.
3. Select an appropriate test statistic.
4. Formulate a decision rule based on steps 1, 2, and 3 above.
5. Make a decision regarding the null hypothesis based on the sample information.
6. Interpret the results of the test.

Before actually conducting a test of hypothesis, we describe the difference between a one-tailed test of significance and a two-tailed test.

LO10-4

Distinguish between a one-tailed and a two-tailed test of hypothesis.

ONE-TAILED AND TWO-TAILED TESTS OF SIGNIFICANCE

Refer to Chart 10–1. It shows a one-tailed test. It is called a one-tailed test because the rejection region is only in one tail of the curve. In this case, it is in the right, or upper, tail of the curve. To illustrate, suppose that the packaging department at General Foods

ONE-SAMPLE TESTS OF HYPOTHESIS   323

Corporation is concerned that some boxes of Grape Nuts are significantly overweight. The cereal is packaged in 453-gram boxes, so the null hypothesis is H_0: $\mu \leq 453$. This is read, "the population mean (μ) is equal to or less than 453." The alternate hypothesis is, therefore, H_1: $\mu > 453$. This is read, "μ is greater than 453." Note that the inequality sign in the alternate hypothesis ($>$) points to the region of rejection in the upper tail. (See Chart 10–1.) Also observe that the null hypothesis includes the equal sign. That is, H_0: $\mu \leq 453$. The equality condition always appears in H_0, never in H_1.

Chart 10–2 portrays a situation where the rejection region is in the left (lower) tail of the standard normal distribution. As an illustration, consider the problem of automobile manufacturers, large automobile leasing companies, and other organizations that purchase large quantities of tires. They want the tires to average, say, 60,000 miles of wear under normal usage. They will, therefore, reject a shipment of tires if tests reveal that the mean life of the tires is significantly below 60,000 miles. They gladly accept a shipment if the mean life is greater than 60,000 miles! They are not concerned with this possibility, however. They are concerned only if they have sample evidence to conclude that the tires will average less than 60,000 miles of useful life. Thus, the test is set up to satisfy the concern of the automobile manufacturers that *the mean life of the tires is not less than 60,000 miles*. This statement appears in the null hypothesis. The null and alternate hypotheses in this case are written H_0: $\mu \geq 60{,}000$ and H_1: $\mu < 60{,}000$.

CHART 10–2 Sampling Distribution for the Statistic z, Left-Tailed Test, .05 Level of Significance

One way to determine the location of the rejection region is to look at the direction in which the inequality sign in the alternate hypothesis is pointing (either $<$ or $>$). In the tire wear problem, it is pointing to the left, and the rejection region is therefore in the left tail.

In summary, a test is *one-tailed* when the alternate hypothesis, H_1, states a direction, such as:

H_0: The mean income of female stockbrokers is *less than or equal to* $65,000 per year.
H_1: The mean income of female stockbrokers is *greater than* $65,000 per year.

If no direction is specified in the alternate hypothesis, we use a *two-tailed* test. Changing the previous problem to illustrate, we can say:

H_0: The mean income of female stockbrokers is $65,000 per year.
H_1: The mean income of female stockbrokers is *not equal to* $65,000 per year.

If the null hypothesis is rejected and H_1 accepted in the two-tailed case, the mean income could be significantly greater than $65,000 per year or it could be significantly less than $65,000 per year. To accommodate these two possibilities, the 5% area of

324   CHAPTER 10

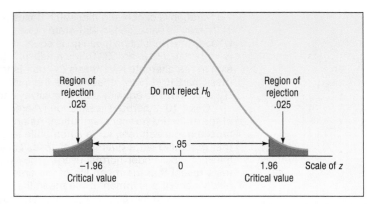

CHART 10–3 Regions of Nonrejection and Rejection for a Two-Tailed Test, .05 Level of Significance

rejection is divided equally into the two tails of the sampling distribution (2.5% each). Chart 10–3 shows the two areas and the critical values. Note that the total area in the normal distribution is 1.0000, found by .9500 + .0250 + .0250.

LO10-5

Conduct a test of a hypothesis about a population mean.

TESTING FOR A POPULATION MEAN: KNOWN POPULATION STANDARD DEVIATION

A Two-Tailed Test

An example will show the details of the six-step hypothesis testing procedure and the subsequent decision-making process. We also wish to use a two-tailed test. That is, we are *not* concerned whether the sample results are larger or smaller than the proposed population mean. Rather, we are interested in whether it is *different from* the proposed value for the population mean. We begin, as we did in the previous chapter, with a situation in which we have historical information about the population and in fact know its standard deviation.

EXAMPLE

Jamestown Steel Company manufactures and assembles desks and other office equipment at several plants in western New York State. The weekly production of the Model A325 desk at the Fredonia Plant follows a normal probability distribution with a mean of 200 and a standard deviation of 16. Recently, because of market expansion, new production methods have been introduced and new employees hired.

The vice president of manufacturing would like to investigate whether there has been a *change* in the weekly production of the Model A325 desk. Is the mean number of desks produced at the Fredonia Plant *different from* 200 at the .01 significance level?

SOLUTION

In this example, we know two important pieces of information: (1) the population of weekly production follows the normal distribution and (2) the standard deviation of this normal distribution is 16 desks per week. So it is appropriate to use the z statistic. We use the statistical hypothesis testing procedure to investigate whether the production rate has changed from 200 per week.

Step 1: **State the null hypothesis and the alternate hypothesis.** The null hypothesis is "The population mean is 200." The alternate hypothesis is "The mean is different from 200" or "The mean is not 200." These two hypotheses are written:

$$H_0: \mu = 200$$

$$H_1: \mu \neq 200$$

This is a *two-tailed test* because the alternate hypothesis does not state a direction. In other words, it does not state whether the mean production is greater than 200 or less than 200. The vice president wants only to find out whether the production rate is different from 200.

Before moving to Step 2, we wish to emphasize two points.

- The null hypothesis has the equal sign. Why? Because the value we are testing is always in the null hypothesis. Logically, the alternate hypothesis never contains the equal sign.
- Both the null hypothesis and the alternate hypothesis contain Greek letters—in this case μ, which is the symbol for the population mean. Tests of hypothesis **always** refer to population parameters, never to sample statistics. To put it another way, you will never see the symbol $\bar{x}$ as part of the null hypothesis or the alternate hypothesis.

Step 2: **Select the level of significance.** In the example description, the significance level selected is .01. This is α, the probability of committing a Type I error, and it is the probability of rejecting a true null hypothesis.

Step 3: **Select the test statistic.** The test statistic is z when the population standard deviation is known. Transforming the production data to standard units (z values) permits their use not only in this problem but also in other hypothesis-testing problems. Formula (10–1) for z is repeated next with the various letters identified.

Step 4: **Formulate the decision rule.** We formulate the decision rule by first determining the critical values of z. Because this is a two-tailed test, half of .01, or .005, is placed in each tail. The area where H_0 is not rejected, located between the two tails, is therefore .99. Using the Student's t Distribution table in Appendix B.5, move to the top margin called "Level of Significance for Two-Tailed Tests, α," select the column with $\alpha = .01$, and move to the last row, which is labeled ∞,

or infinite degrees of freedom. The z value in this cell is 2.576. For your convenience, Appendix B.5, Student's t Distribution, is repeated in the inside back cover. All the facets of this problem are shown in the diagram in Chart 10–4.

CHART 10–4 Decision Rule for the .01 Significance Level

The decision rule is: if the computed value of z is not between −2.576 and 2.576, reject the null hypothesis. If z falls between −2.576 and 2.576, do not reject the null hypothesis.

Step 5: **Make a decision.** Take a sample from the population (weekly production), compute z, apply the decision rule, and arrive at a decision to reject H_0 or not to reject H_0. The mean number of desks produced last year (50 weeks because the plant was shut down 2 weeks for vacation) is 203.5. The standard deviation of the population is 16 desks per week. Computing the z value from formula (10–1):

$$z = \frac{\bar{x} - \mu}{\sigma/\sqrt{n}} = \frac{203.5 - 200}{16/\sqrt{50}} = 1.547$$

Because 1.547 does not fall in the rejection region, we decide not to reject H_0.

Step 6: **Interpret the result.** We did not reject the null hypothesis, so we have failed to show that the population mean has changed from 200 per week. To put it another way, the difference between the population mean of 200 per week and the sample mean of 203.5 could simply be due to chance. What should we tell the vice president? The sample information fails to indicate that the new production methods resulted in a change in the 200-desks-per-week production rate.

ONE-SAMPLE TESTS OF HYPOTHESIS   327

Did we prove that the assembly rate is still 200 per week? Not really. What we did, technically, was *fail to disprove the null hypothesis.* Failing to disprove the hypothesis that the population mean is 200 is not the same thing as proving it to be true. As we suggested in the chapter introduction, the conclusion is analogous to the American judicial system. To explain, suppose a person is accused of a crime but is acquitted by a jury. If a person is acquitted of a crime, the conclusion is that there was not enough evidence to prove the person guilty. The trial did not prove that the individual was innocent, only that there was not enough evidence to prove the defendant guilty. That is what we do in statistical hypothesis testing when we do not reject the null hypothesis. The correct interpretation is that we have failed to disprove the null hypothesis.

We selected the significance level, .01 in this case, before setting up the decision rule and sampling the population. This is the appropriate strategy. The significance level should be set by the investigator, but it should be determined *before* gathering the sample evidence and not changed based on the sample evidence.

How does the hypothesis testing procedure just described compare with that of confidence intervals discussed in the previous chapter? When we conducted the test of hypothesis regarding the production of desks, we changed the units from desks per week to a z value. Then we compared the computed value of the test statistic (1.547) to that of the critical values (-2.576 and 2.576). Because the computed value was in the region where the null hypothesis was not rejected, we concluded that the population mean could be 200. To use the confidence interval approach, on the other hand, we would develop a confidence interval, based on formula (9–1). See page 284. The interval would be from 197.671 to 209.329, found by $203.5 \pm 2.576(16/\sqrt{50})$. Note that the proposed population value, 200, is within this interval. Hence, we would conclude that the population mean could reasonably be 200.

In general, H_0 is rejected if the confidence interval does not include the hypothesized value. If the confidence interval includes the hypothesized value, then H_0 is not rejected. So the "do not reject region" for a test of hypothesis is equivalent to the proposed population value occurring in the confidence interval.

SELF-REVIEW

10–1

Heinz, a manufacturer of ketchup, uses a particular machine to dispense 16 ounces of its ketchup into containers. From many years of experience with the particular dispensing machine, Heinz knows the amount of product in each container follows a normal distribution with a mean of 16 ounces and a standard deviation of 0.15 ounce. A sample of 50 containers filled last hour revealed the mean amount per container was 16.017 ounces. Does this evidence suggest that the mean amount dispensed is different from 16 ounces? Use the .05 significance level.

(a)   State the null hypothesis and the alternate hypothesis.
(b)   What is the probability of a Type I error?
(c)   Give the formula for the test statistic.
(d)   State the decision rule.
(e)   Determine the value of the test statistic.
(f)   What is your decision regarding the null hypothesis?
(g)   Interpret, in a single sentence, the result of the statistical test.

A One-Tailed Test

In the previous example/solution, we emphasized that we were concerned only with reporting to the vice president whether there had been a change in the mean number

328   CHAPTER 10

of desks assembled at the Fredonia Plant. We were not concerned with whether the change was an increase or a decrease in the production.

To illustrate a one-tailed test, let's change the problem. Suppose the vice president wants to know whether there has been an *increase* in the number of units assembled. Can we conclude, because of the improved production methods, that the mean number of desks assembled in the last 50 weeks was more than 200? Look at the difference in the way the problem is formulated. In the first case, we wanted to know whether there was a *difference* in the mean number assembled, but now we want to know whether there has been an *increase.* Because we are investigating different questions, we will set our hypotheses differently. The biggest difference occurs in the alternate hypothesis. Before, we stated the alternate hypothesis as "different from"; now we want to state it as "greater than." In symbols:

A two-tailed test:	A one-tailed test:
H_0: $\mu = 200$	H_0: $\mu \leq 200$
H_1: $\mu \neq 200$	H_1: $\mu > 200$

The critical values for a one-tailed test are different from a two-tailed test at the same significance level. In the previous example/solution, we split the significance level in half and put half in the lower tail and half in the upper tail. In a one-tailed test, we put all the rejection region in one tail. See Chart 10–5.

CHART 10–5 Rejection Regions for Two-Tailed and One-Tailed Tests, $\alpha = .01$

For the one-tailed test, the critical value of z is 2.326. Using the Student's t Distribution table in Appendix B.5 or inside the back cover, move to the top heading called "Level of Significance for One-Tailed Tests, α," select the column with $\alpha = .01$, and move to the last row, which is labeled ∞, or infinite degrees of freedom. The z value in this cell is 2.326.

LO10-6
Compute and interpret a p-value.

p-VALUE IN HYPOTHESIS TESTING

In testing a hypothesis, we compare the test statistic to a critical value. A decision is made to either reject the null hypothesis or not to reject it. So, for example, if the critical value is 1.96 and the computed value of the test statistic is 2.19, the decision is to reject the null hypothesis.

In recent years, spurred by the availability of computer software, additional information is often reported on the strength of the rejection. That is, how confident are we in rejecting the null hypothesis? This approach reports the probability (assuming that the null hypothesis is true) of getting a value of the test statistic at least as extreme as

ONE-SAMPLE TESTS OF HYPOTHESIS   329

the value actually obtained. This process compares the probability, called the **p-value,** with the significance level. If the *p*-value is smaller than the significance level, H_0 is rejected. If it is larger than the significance level, H_0 is not rejected.

> **p-VALUE** The probability of observing a sample value as extreme as, or more extreme than, the value observed, given that the null hypothesis is true.

Determining the *p*-value not only results in a decision regarding H_0, but it gives us additional insight into the strength of the decision. A very small *p*-value, such as .0001, indicates that there is little likelihood the H_0 is true. On the other hand, a *p*-value of .2033 means that H_0 is not rejected, and there is little likelihood that it is false.

How do we find the *p*-value? To calculate *p*-values, we will need to use the *z* table (Appendix B.3 or inside the back cover), and, to use this table, we will round *z* test statistics to two decimals. To illustrate how to compute a *p*-value, we will use the example in which we tested the null hypothesis that the mean number of desks produced per week at Fredonia was 200. We did not reject the null hypothesis because the *z* value of 1.547 fell in the region between −2.576 and 2.576. We agreed not to reject the null hypothesis if the computed value of *z* fell in this region. Rounding 1.547 to 1.55 and using the *z* table, the probability of finding a *z* value of 1.55 or more is .0606, found by .5000 − .4394. To put it another way, the probability of obtaining an $\overline{X}$ greater than 203.5 if $\mu = 200$ is .0606. To compute the *p*-value, we need to be concerned with the region less than −1.55 as well as the values greater than 1.55 (because the rejection region is in both tails). The two-tailed *p*-value is .1212, found by 2(.0606). The *p*-value of .1212 is greater than the significance level of .01 decided upon initially, so H_0 is not rejected. The details are shown in the following graph. Notice for the two-tailed hypothesis test, the *p*-value is represented by areas in both tails of the distribution. Then the *p*-value can easily be compared with the significance level. The same decision rule is used as in the one-sided test.

A *p*-value is a way to express the likelihood that H_0 is false. But how do we interpret a *p*-value? We have already said that if the *p*-value is less than the significance level, then we reject H_0; if it is greater than the significance level, then we do not reject H_0. Also, if the *p*-value is very large, then it is likely that H_0 is true. If the *p*-value is small, then it is likely that H_0 is not true. The following box will help to interpret *p*-values.

> **INTERPRETING THE WEIGHT OF EVIDENCE AGAINST H_0** If the *p*-value is less than
> (a) .10, we have *some* evidence that H_0 is not true.
> (b) .05, we have *strong* evidence that H_0 is not true.
> (c) .01, we have *very strong* evidence that H_0 is not true.
> (d) .001, we have *extremely strong* evidence that H_0 is not true.

330   CHAPTER 10

SELF-REVIEW

10-2

Refer to Self-Review 10–1.
(a) Suppose the next to the last sentence is changed to read: Does this evidence suggest that the mean amount dispensed is *more than* 16 ounces? State the null hypothesis and the alternate hypothesis under these conditions.
(b) What is the decision rule under the new conditions stated in part (a)?
(c) A second sample of 50 filled containers revealed the mean to be 16.040 ounces. What is the value of the test statistic for this sample?
(d) What is your decision regarding the null hypothesis?
(e) Interpret, in a single sentence, the result of the statistical test.
(f) What is the *p*-value? What is your decision regarding the null hypothesis based on the *p*-value? Is this the same conclusion reached in part (d)?

EXERCISES

For Exercises 1–4, answer the questions: (a) Is this a one- or two-tailed test? (b) What is the decision rule? (c) What is the value of the test statistic? (d) What is your decision regarding H_0? (e) What is the *p*-value? Interpret it.

1. A sample of 36 observations is selected from a normal population. The sample mean is 49, and the population standard deviation is 5. Conduct the following test of hypothesis using the .05 significance level.

$$H_0: \mu = 50$$
$$H_1: \mu \neq 50$$

2. A sample of 36 observations is selected from a normal population. The sample mean is 12, and the population standard deviation is 3. Conduct the following test of hypothesis using the .01 significance level.

$$H_0: \mu \leq 10$$
$$H_1: \mu > 10$$

3. A sample of 36 observations is selected from a normal population. The sample mean is 21, and the population standard deviation is 5. Conduct the following test of hypothesis using the .05 significance level.

$$H_0: \mu \leq 20$$
$$H_1: \mu > 20$$

4. A sample of 64 observations is selected from a normal population. The sample mean is 215, and the population standard deviation is 15. Conduct the following test of hypothesis using the .025 significance level.

$$H_0: \mu \geq 220$$
$$H_1: \mu < 220$$

For Exercises 5–8: (a) State the null hypothesis and the alternate hypothesis. (b) State the decision rule. (c) Compute the value of the test statistic. (d) What is your decision regarding H_0? (e) What is the *p*-value? Interpret it.

5. The manufacturer of the X-15 steel-belted radial truck tire claims that the mean mileage the tire can be driven before the tread wears out is 60,000 miles. Assume the mileage wear follows the normal distribution and the standard deviation of the distribution is 5,000 miles. Crosset Truck Company bought 48 tires and found that the mean mileage for its trucks is 59,500 miles. Is Crosset's experience different from that claimed by the manufacturer at the .05 significance level?

6. The waiting time for customers at MacBurger Restaurants follows a normal distribution with a population standard deviation of 1 minute. At the Warren Road MacBurger, the quality-assurance department sampled 50 customers and found that the mean waiting time was 2.75 minutes. At the .05 significance level, can we conclude that the mean waiting time is less than 3 minutes?

7. A recent national survey found that high school students watched an average (mean) of 6.8 DVDs per month with a population standard deviation of 1.8. The distribution of DVDs watched per month follows the normal distribution. A random sample of 36 college students revealed that the mean number of DVDs watched last month was 6.2. At the .05 significance level, can we conclude that college students watch fewer DVDs a month than high school students?

8. At the time she was hired as a server at the Grumney Family Restaurant, Beth Brigden was told, "You can average $80 a day in tips." Assume the population of daily tips is normally distributed with a standard deviation of $9.95. Over the first 35 days she was employed at the restaurant, the mean daily amount of her tips was $84.85. At the .01 significance level, can Ms. Brigden conclude that her daily tips average more than $80?

LO10-7

Use a t statistic to test a hypothesis.

TESTING FOR A POPULATION MEAN: POPULATION STANDARD DEVIATION UNKNOWN

In the preceding example, we knew σ, the population standard deviation, and that the population followed the normal distribution. In most cases, however, the population standard deviation is unknown. Thus, σ must be based on prior studies or estimated by the sample standard deviation, s. The population standard deviation in the following example is not known, so the sample standard deviation is used to estimate σ.

To find the value of the test statistic, we use the t distribution and revise formula (10–1) as follows:

TESTING A MEAN, σ UNKNOWN	$t = \dfrac{\bar{x} - \mu}{s/\sqrt{n}}$	[10–2]

with $n - 1$ degrees of freedom, where:
  $\bar{x}$ is the sample mean.
  μ is the hypothesized population mean.
  s is the sample standard deviation.
  n is the number of observations in the sample.

We encountered this same situation when constructing confidence intervals in the previous chapter. See pages 289–296 in Chapter 9. We summarized this problem in Chart 9–3 on page 292. Under these conditions, the correct statistical procedure is to replace the standard normal distribution with the t distribution. To review, the major characteristics of the t distribution are:

- It is a continuous distribution.
- It is bell-shaped and symmetrical.
- There is a family of t distributions. Each time the degrees of freedom change, a new distribution is created.
- As the number of degrees of freedom increases, the shape of the t distribution approaches that of the standard normal distribution.
- The t distribution is flatter, or more spread out, than the standard normal distribution.

The following example/solution shows the details.

EXAMPLE

The McFarland Insurance Company Claims Department reports the mean cost to process a claim is $60. An industry comparison showed this amount to be larger than most other insurance companies, so the company instituted cost-cutting measures. To evaluate the effect of the cost-cutting measures, the supervisor of the Claims Department selected a random sample of 26 claims processed last

332   CHAPTER 10

month and recorded the cost to process each claim. The sample information is reported below.

$45	$49	$62	$40	$43	$61
48	53	67	63	78	64
48	54	51	56	63	69
58	51	58	59	56	57
38	76				

At the .01 significance level, is it reasonable to conclude that the mean cost to process a claim is now less than $60?

SOLUTION

We will use the six-step hypothesis testing procedure.

Step 1: **State the null hypothesis and the alternate hypothesis.** The null hypothesis is that the population mean is at least $60. The alternate hypothesis is that the population mean is less than $60. We can express the null and alternate hypotheses as follows:

$$H_0: \mu \geq \$60$$

$$H_1: \mu < \$60$$

The test is *one*-tailed because we want to determine whether there has been a *reduction* in the cost. The inequality in the alternate hypothesis points to the region of rejection in the left tail of the distribution.

Step 2: **Select the level of significance.** We decided on the .01 significance level.

Step 3: **Select the test statistic.** The test statistic in this situation is the *t* distribution. Why? First, it is reasonable to conclude that the distribution of the cost per claim follows the normal distribution. We can confirm this from the histogram in the center of the following Minitab output. Observe the normal distribution superimposed on the frequency distribution.

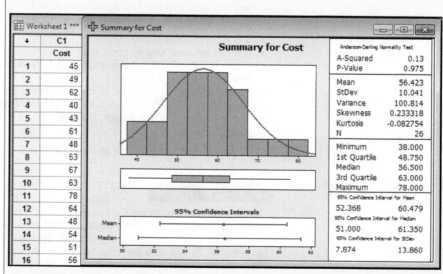

We do not know the standard deviation of the population. So we substitute the sample standard deviation. The value of the test statistic is computed by formula (10–2):

$$t = \frac{\bar{x} - \mu}{s/\sqrt{n}}$$

Step 4: **Formulate the decision rule.** The critical values of t are given in Appendix B.5, a portion of which is shown in Table 10–1. Appendix B.5 is also repeated in the back inside cover of the text. The far left column of the table is labeled "df" for degrees of freedom. The number of degrees of freedom is the total number of observations in the sample minus the number of populations sampled, written $n - 1$. In this case, the number of observations in the sample is 26, and we sampled 1 population, so there are $26 - 1 = 25$ degrees of freedom. To find the critical value, first locate the row with the appropriate degrees of freedom. This row is shaded in Table 10–1. Next, determine whether the test is one-tailed or two-tailed. In this case, we have a one-tailed test, so find the portion of the table that is labeled "one-tailed." Locate the column with the selected significance level. In this example, the significance level is .01. Move down the column labeled "0.01" until it intersects the row with 25 degrees of freedom. The value is 2.485. Because this is a one-sided test and the rejection region is in the left tail, the critical value is negative. The decision rule is to reject H_0 if the value of t is less than -2.485.

TABLE 10–1 A Portion of the t Distribution Table

	\multicolumn{6}{c	}{**Confidence Intervals**}
	80%	**90%**	**95%**	**98%**	**99%**	**99.9%**
	\multicolumn{6}{c	}{**Level of Significance for One-Tailed Test, α**}
df	**0.10**	**0.05**	**0.025**	**0.01**	**0.005**	**0.0005**
	\multicolumn{6}{c	}{**Level of Significance for Two-Tailed Test, α**}
	0.20	**0.10**	**0.05**	**0.02**	**0.01**	**0.001**
⋮	⋮	⋮	⋮	⋮	⋮	⋮
21	1.323	1.721	2.080	2.518	2.831	3.819
22	1.321	1.717	2.074	2.508	2.819	3.792
23	1.319	1.714	2.069	2.500	2.807	3.768
24	1.318	1.711	2.064	2.492	2.797	3.745
25	1.316	1.708	2.060	2.485	2.787	3.725
26	1.315	1.706	2.056	2.479	2.779	3.707
27	1.314	1.703	2.052	2.473	2.771	3.690
28	1.313	1.701	2.048	2.467	2.763	3.674
29	1.311	1.699	2.045	2.462	2.756	3.659
30	1.310	1.697	2.042	2.457	2.750	3.646

Step 5: **Make a decision.** From the Minitab output, to the right of the histogram, the mean cost per claim for the sample of 26 observations is $56.42. The standard deviation of this sample is $10.04. We insert these values in formula (10–2) and compute the value of t:

$$t = \frac{\bar{x} - \mu}{s/\sqrt{n}} = \frac{\$56.42 - \$60}{\$10.04/\sqrt{26}} = -1.818$$

Because −1.818 lies in the region to the right of the critical value of −2.485 (see Chart 10–6), the null hypothesis is not rejected at the .01 significance level.

Step 6:   Interpret the result. We have not disproved the null hypothesis. The sample of claims could have been selected from a population with a mean cost of $60 per claim. To put it another way, the difference of $3.58 ($56.42 − $60.00) between the sample mean and the population mean could be due to sampling error. The test results do not allow the claims department manager to conclude that the cost-cutting measures have been effective.

CHART 10–6 Rejection Region, *t* Distribution, .01 Significance Level

In the previous example, the mean and the standard deviation were computed using Minitab. The following example/solution shows the details when the sample mean and sample standard deviation are calculated from sample data.

EXAMPLE

The Myrtle Beach International Airport's short-term parking lot is close to the terminal, so someone meeting an incoming passenger has only a short walk to the baggage claim area, a good place to meet. To decide if the short-term lot has enough parking places, the manager of airport parking needs to know if the mean time in the lot is more than 40 minutes. A sample of 12 recent customers showed they were in the lot the following lengths of time, in minutes.

| 55 | 49 | 53 | 47 | 39 | 27 | 64 | 48 | 48 | 53 | 37 | 56 |

At the .05 significance level, is it reasonable to conclude that the mean time in the lot is more than 40 minutes?

SOLUTION

We begin by stating the null hypothesis and the alternate hypothesis. In this case, the question is whether the population mean could be more than 40 minutes. So this is a one-tailed test. We state the two hypotheses as follows:

$$H_0: \mu \le 40$$

$$H_1: \mu > 40$$

ONE-SAMPLE TESTS OF HYPOTHESIS 335

There are 11 degrees of freedom, found by $n - 1 = 12 - 1 = 11$. The critical t value is 1.796, found by referring to Appendix B.5 for a one-tailed test, using $\alpha = .05$ with 11 degrees of freedom. The decision rule is: Reject the null hypothesis if the computed t is greater than 1.796. This information is summarized in Chart 10–7.

CHART 10–7 Rejection Region, One-Tailed Test, Student's t Distribution, $\alpha = .05$

We calculate the sample mean using formula (3–2) and the sample standard deviation using formula (3–8). The sample mean is 48 hours, and the sample standard deviation is 9.835 hours. The details of the calculations are shown in Table 10–2.

TABLE 10–2 Calculations of Sample Mean and Standard Deviation Parking Times

Customer	x, Minutes	$(x - \bar{x})^2$
1	55	49
2	49	1
3	53	25
4	47	1
5	39	81
6	27	441
7	64	256
8	48	0
9	48	0
10	53	25
11	37	121
12	56	64
Total	576	1064

$$\bar{x} = \frac{\Sigma x}{n} = \frac{576}{12} = 48$$

$$s = \sqrt{\frac{\Sigma(x - \bar{x})^2}{n - 1}} = \sqrt{\frac{1064}{12 - 1}} = 9.835$$

Now we are ready to compute the value of t, using formula (10–2).

$$t = \frac{\bar{x} - \mu}{s/\sqrt{n}} = \frac{48 - 40}{9.835/\sqrt{12}} = 2.818$$

The null hypothesis that the population mean is less than or equal to 40 minutes is rejected because the computed t value of 2.818 lies in the area to the right of 1.796. We conclude that the time customers spend in the lot is more than 40 minutes. This result indicates that the airport may need to add more parking places.

336 CHAPTER 10

SELF-REVIEW

10-3

The mean life of a battery used in a digital clock is 305 days. The lives of the batteries follow the normal distribution. The battery was recently modified to last longer. A sample of 20 of the modified batteries had a mean life of 311 days with a standard deviation of 12 days. Did the modification increase the mean life of the battery?
(a) State the null hypothesis and the alternate hypothesis.
(b) Show the decision rule graphically. Use the .05 significance level.
(c) Compute the value of t. What is your decision regarding the null hypothesis? Briefly summarize your results.

EXERCISES

9. Given the following hypotheses:

$$H_0: \mu \leq 10$$
$$H_1: \mu > 10$$

A random sample of 10 observations is selected from a normal population. The sample mean was 12 and the sample standard deviation 3. Using the .05 significance level:
a. State the decision rule.
b. Compute the value of the test statistic.
c. What is your decision regarding the null hypothesis?

10. Given the following hypotheses:

$$H_0: \mu = 400$$
$$H_1: \mu \neq 400$$

A random sample of 12 observations is selected from a normal population. The sample mean was 407 and the sample standard deviation 6. Using the .01 significance level:
a. State the decision rule.
b. Compute the value of the test statistic.
c. What is your decision regarding the null hypothesis?

11. The Rocky Mountain district sales manager of Rath Publishing Inc., a college textbook publishing company, claims that the sales representatives make an average of 40 sales calls per week on professors. Several reps say that this estimate is too low. To investigate, a random sample of 28 sales representatives reveals that the mean number of calls made last week was 42. The standard deviation of the sample is 2.1 calls. Using the .05 significance level, can we conclude that the mean number of calls per salesperson per week is more than 40?

12. The management of White Industries is considering a new method of assembling its golf cart. The present method requires 42.3 minutes, on the average, to assemble a cart. The mean assembly time for a random sample of 24 carts, using the new method, was 40.6 minutes, and the standard deviation of the sample was 2.7 minutes. Using the .10 level of significance, can we conclude that the assembly time using the new method is faster?

13. The mean income per person in the United States is $40,000, and the distribution of incomes follows a normal distribution. A random sample of 10 residents of Wilmington, Delaware, had a mean of $50,000 with a standard deviation of $10,000. At the .05 level of significance, is that enough evidence to conclude that residents of Wilmington, Delaware, have more income than the national average?

For **DATA FILE**, please visit www.mhhe.com/lind16e

14. Most air travelers now use e-tickets. Electronic ticketing allows passengers to not worry about a paper ticket, and it costs the airline companies less to handle than paper ticketing. However, in recent times the airlines have received complaints from passengers regarding their e-tickets, particularly when connecting flights and a change of airlines were involved. To investigate the problem, an independent watchdog agency contacted a random sample of 20 airports and collected information on the number of complaints the airport had with e-tickets for the month of March. The information is reported below.

14	14	16	12	12	14	13	16	15	14
12	15	15	14	13	13	12	13	10	13

At the .05 significance level, can the watchdog agency conclude the mean number of complaints per airport is less than 15 per month?
a. What assumption is necessary before conducting a test of hypothesis?
b. Plot the number of complaints per airport in a frequency distribution or a dot plot. Is it reasonable to conclude that the population follows a normal distribution?
c. Conduct a test of hypothesis and interpret the results.

A Software Solution

The Minitab statistical software system, used in earlier chapters and the previous section, provides an efficient method for conducting a one-sample test of hypothesis for a population mean. The steps to generate the following output are shown in Appendix C.

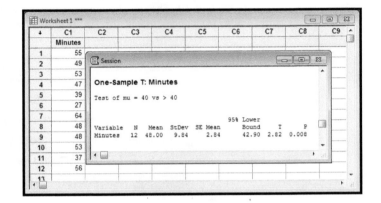

An additional feature of most statistical software packages is to report the *p*-value, which gives additional information on the null hypothesis. The *p*-value is the probability of a *t* value as extreme or more extreme than the computed *t* value, given that the null hypothesis is true. Using the Minitab analysis from the previous Parking Lot example, the *p*-value of .008 is the likelihood of a *t* value of 2.82 or larger, given a population mean of 40. Thus, comparing the *p*-value to the significance level tells us whether the null hypothesis was close to being rejected, barely rejected, and so on.

To explain further, refer to the diagram below. The *p*-value of .008 is the brown shaded area and the significance level is the total amber and brown shaded area. Because the *p*-value of .008 is less than the significance level of .05, the null hypothesis is rejected. Had the *p*-value been larger than the significance level—say, .06, .19, or .57—the null hypothesis would not be rejected.

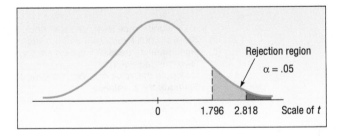

In the preceding example, the alternate hypothesis was one-sided, and the upper (right) tail of the *t* distribution contained the rejection region. The *p*-value is the area to the right of 2.818 for a *t* distribution with 11 degrees of freedom.

What if we were conducting a two-sided test, so that the rejection region is in both the upper and the lower tails? That is, in the Parking Lot example, if H_1 were stated as $\mu \neq 40$, we would have reported the *p*-value as the area to the right of 2.818 plus the value to the left of −2.818. Both of these values are .008, so the *p*-value is .008 + .008 = .016.

How can we estimate a *p*-value without a computer? To illustrate, recall that, in the example/solution regarding the length of time at the Parking Lot, we rejected the null hypothesis that $\mu \leq 40$ and accepted the alternate hypothesis that $\mu > 40$. The significance level was .05, so logically the p-value is less than .05. To estimate the p-value more accurately, go to Appendix B.5 and find the row with 11 degrees of freedom. The computed t value of 2.818 is between 2.718 and 3.106. (A portion of Appendix B.5 is reproduced as Table 10–3.) The one-tailed significance level corresponding to 2.718 is .01, and for 3.106 it is .005. Therefore, the p-value is between .005 and .01. The usual practice is to report that the p-value is less than the larger of the two significance levels. So we would report "the p-value is less than .01."

TABLE 10–3 A Portion of Student's t Distribution

	Confidence Intervals					
	80%	90%	95%	98%	99%	99.9%
	Level of Significance for One-Tailed Test, α					
df	0.10	0.05	.0025	0.01	0.005	0.0005
	Level of Significance for Two-Tailed Test, α					
	0.20	0.10	0.05	0.02	0.01	0.001
⋮	⋮	⋮	⋮	⋮	⋮	⋮
9	1.383	1.833	2.262	2.821	3.250	4.781
10	1.372	1.812	2.228	2.764	3.169	4.587
11	1.363	1.796	2.201	2.718	3.106	4.437
12	1.356	1.782	2.179	2.681	3.055	4.318
13	1.350	1.771	2.160	2.650	3.012	4.221
14	1.345	1.761	2.145	2.624	2.977	4.140
15	1.341	1.753	2.131	2.602	2.947	4.073

SELF-REVIEW

10–4

A machine is set to fill a small bottle with 9.0 grams of medicine. A sample of eight bottles revealed the following amounts (grams) in each bottle.

9.2	8.7	8.9	8.6	8.8	8.5	8.7	9.0

At the .01 significance level, can we conclude that the mean weight is less than 9.0 grams?
(a)   State the null hypothesis and the alternate hypothesis.
(b)   How many degrees of freedom are there?
(c)   Give the decision rule.
(d)   Compute the value of t. What is your decision regarding the null hypothesis?
(e)   Estimate the p-value.

EXERCISES

15. Given the following hypotheses:

$$H_0: \mu \geq 20$$

$$H_1: \mu < 20$$

A random sample of five resulted in the following values: 18, 15, 12, 19, and 21. Assume a normal population. Using the .01 significance level, can we conclude the population mean is less than 20?
a. State the decision rule.
b. Compute the value of the test statistic.
c. What is your decision regarding the null hypothesis?
d. Estimate the p-value.

16. Given the following hypotheses:

$$H_0: \mu = 100$$

$$H_1: \mu \neq 100$$

A random sample of six resulted in the following values: 118, 105, 112, 119, 105, and 111. Assume a normal population. Using the .05 significance level, can we conclude the mean is different from 100?
  a. State the decision rule.
  b. Compute the value of the test statistic.
  c. What is your decision regarding the null hypothesis?
  d. Estimate the p-value.

For **DATA FILE**, please visit www.mhhe.com/lind16e

17. The amount of water consumed each day by a healthy adult follows a normal distribution with a mean of 1.4 liters. A health campaign promotes the consumption of at least 2.0 liters per day. A sample of 10 adults after the campaign shows the following consumption in liters:

1.5	1.6	1.5	1.4	1.9	1.4	1.3	1.9	1.8	1.7

At the .01 significance level, can we conclude that water consumption has increased? Calculate and interpret the p-value.

For **DATA FILE**, please visit www.mhhe.com/lind16e

18. The liquid chlorine added to swimming pools to combat algae has a relatively short shelf life before it loses its effectiveness. Records indicate that the mean shelf life of a 5-gallon jug of chlorine is 2,160 hours (90 days). As an experiment, Holdlonger was added to the chlorine to find whether it would increase the shelf life. A sample of nine jugs of chlorine had these shelf lives (in hours):

2,159	2,170	2,180	2,179	2,160	2,167	2,171	2,181	2,185

At the .025 level, has Holdlonger increased the shelf life of the chlorine? Estimate the p-value.

For **DATA FILE**, please visit www.mhhe.com/lind16e

19. A Washington, D.C., "think tank" announces the typical teenager sent 50 text messages per day in 2013. To update that estimate, you phone a sample of 12 teenagers and ask them how many text messages they sent the previous day. Their responses were:

51	175	47	49	44	54	145	203	21	59	42	100

At the .05 level, can you conclude that the mean number is greater than 50? Estimate the p-value and describe what it tells you.

For **DATA FILE**, please visit www.mhhe.com/lind16e

20. Hugger Polls contends that an agent conducts a mean of 53 in-depth home surveys every week. A streamlined survey form has been introduced, and Hugger wants to evaluate its effectiveness. The number of in-depth surveys conducted during a week by a random sample of 15 agents are:

53	57	50	55	58	54	60	52	59	62	60	60	51	59	56

At the .05 level of significance, can we conclude that the mean number of interviews conducted by the agents is more than 53 per week? Estimate the p-value.

LO10-8
Compute the probability of a Type II error.

TYPE II ERROR

Recall that the level of significance, identified by the symbol α, is the probability that the null hypothesis is rejected when it is true. This is called a Type I error. The most common levels of significance are .05 and .01 and are set by the researcher at the outset of the test.

In a hypothesis-testing situation there is also the possibility that a null hypothesis is not rejected when it is actually false. That is, we accept a false null hypothesis. This is called a Type II error. The probability of a Type II error is identified by the Greek letter beta (β). The following example illustrates the details of determining the value of β.

EXAMPLE

Western Wire Products purchases steel bars to make cotter pins. Past experience indicates that the mean tensile strength of all incoming shipments is 10,000 psi and that the standard deviation, σ, is 400 psi.

To make a decision about incoming shipments of steel bars, Western Wire Products set up a rule for the quality-control inspector to follow: "Take a sample of 100 steel bars. At the .05 significance level, if the sample mean ($\bar{x}$) strength falls between 9,922 psi and 10,078 psi, accept the lot. Otherwise, the lot is to be rejected." Refer to Chart 10–8, Region A. It shows the region where each lot is rejected and where it is not rejected. The mean of this distribution is designated μ_0. The tails of the curve represent the probability of making a Type I error, that is, rejecting the incoming lot of steel bars when in fact it is a good lot, with a mean of 10,000 psi.

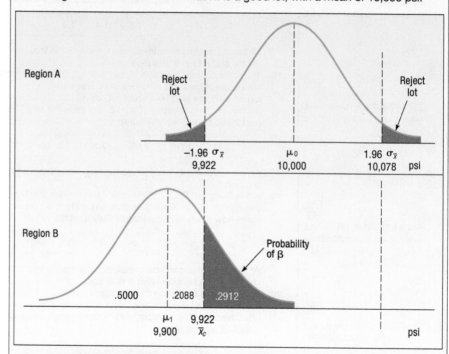

CHART 10–8 Charts Showing Type I and Type II Errors

Suppose the unknown population mean of an incoming lot, designated μ_1, is really 9,900 psi. What is the probability that the quality-control inspector will fail to reject the shipment (a Type II error)?

SOLUTION

The probability of committing a Type II error, as represented by the shaded area in Chart 10–8, Region B, is computed by determining the area under the normal curve that lies above 9,922 pounds. The calculation of the areas under the normal curve was discussed in Chapter 7. Reviewing briefly, it is necessary first to determine the probability of the sample mean falling between 9,900 and 9,922. Then this probability is subtracted from .5000 (which represents all the area beyond the mean of 9,900) to arrive at the probability of making a Type II error.

The number of standard units (z value) between the mean of the incoming lot (9,900), designated by μ_1, and $\bar{x}_c$, representing the critical value for 9,922, is computed by:

TYPE II ERROR	$$z = \dfrac{\bar{x}_c - \mu_1}{\sigma/\sqrt{n}}$$	[10–3]

With $n = 100$ and $\sigma = 400$, the value of z is 0.55:

$$z = \frac{\bar{x}_c - \mu_1}{\sigma/\sqrt{n}} = \frac{9{,}922 - 9{,}900}{400/\sqrt{100}} = \frac{22}{40} = 0.55$$

The area under the curve between 9,900 and 9,922 (a z value of 0.55) is .2088. The area under the curve beyond 9,922 pounds is .5000 − .2088, or .2912; this is the probability of making a Type II error—that is, accepting an incoming lot of steel bars when the population mean is 9,900 psi.

Another illustration, in Chart 10–9, Region C, depicts the probability of accepting a lot when the population mean is 10,120. To find the probability:

$$z = \frac{\bar{x}_c - \mu_1}{\sigma/\sqrt{n}} = \frac{10{,}078 - 10{,}120}{400/\sqrt{100}} = -1.05$$

The probability that z is less than −1.05 is .1469, found by .5000 − .3531. Therefore, β, or the probability of a Type II error, is .1469. Caution: If the difference between μ_0 and μ_1 is relatively small, the probability of a Type II error may occur in both tails. This eventuality is not considered here.

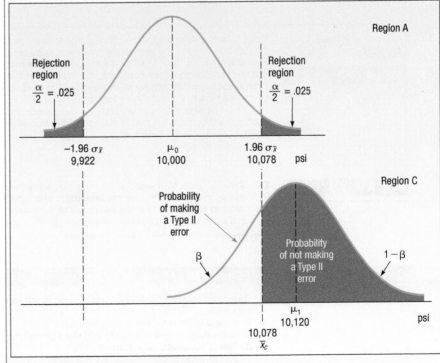

CHART 10–9 Type I and Type II Errors (Another Example)

342   CHAPTER 10

Using the methods illustrated by Charts 10–8 Region B and 10-9 Region C, the probability of accepting a hypothesis as true when it is actually false can be determined for any value of μ_1.

Type II error probabilities are shown in the center column of Table 10–4 for selected values of μ_1, given in the left column. The right column gives the probability of not making a Type II error, which is also known as the power of a test.

TABLE 10–4 Probabilities of a Type II Error for $\mu_0 = 10,000$ Pounds and Selected Alternative Means, .05 Level of Significance

Selected Alternative Mean (μ_1)	Probability of Type II Error (β)	Probability of Not Making a Type II Error $(1 - \beta)$
9,820	.0054	.9946
9,880	.1469	.8531
9,900	.2912	.7088
9,940	.6736	.3264
10,000	—*	—
10,060	.6736	.3264
10,100	.2912	.7088
10,120	.1469	.8531
10,180	.0054	.9946

*It is not possible to make a Type II error when $\mu_1 = \mu_0$.

SELF-REVIEW

10–5

Refer to the previous example. Suppose the true mean of an incoming lot of steel bars is 10,180 psi. What is the probability that the quality control inspector will accept the bars as having a mean of 10,000 psi? (It sounds implausible that steel bars will be rejected if the tensile strength is higher than specified. However, it may be that the cotter pin has a dual function in an outboard motor. It may be designed not to shear off if the motor hits a small object, but to shear off if it hits a rock. Therefore, the steel should not be *too* strong.)

The light area in Chart 10–9, Region C, represents the probability of falsely accepting the hypothesis that the mean tensile strength of the incoming steel is 10,000 psi. What is the probability of committing a Type II error?

EXERCISES

21. Refer to Table 10–4 and the example just completed. With $n = 100$, $\sigma = 400$, $\bar{x}_c = 9,922$, and $\mu_1 = 9,880$, verify that the probability of a Type II error is .1469.
22. Refer to Table 10–4 and the example just completed. With $n = 100$, $\sigma = 400$, $\bar{x}_c = 10,078$, and $\mu_1 = 10,100$, verify that the probability of a Type II error is .2912.

CHAPTER SUMMARY

I. The objective of hypothesis testing is to verify the validity of a statement about a population parameter.

II. The steps to conduct a test of hypothesis are:

A. State the null hypothesis (H_0) and the alternate hypothesis (H_1).

B. Select the level of significance.

1. The level of significance is the likelihood of rejecting a true null hypothesis.

2. The most frequently used significance levels are .01, .05, and .10, but any value between 0 and 1.00 is possible.

ONE-SAMPLE TESTS OF HYPOTHESIS   343

   C. Select the test statistic.
     1. A test statistic is a value calculated from sample information used to determine whether to reject the null hypothesis.
     2. Two test statistics were considered in this chapter.
       a. The standard normal distribution (the z distribution) is used when the population follows the normal distribution and the population standard deviation is known.
       b. The t distribution is used when the population follows the normal distribution and the population standard deviation is unknown.
   D. State the decision rule.
     1. The decision rule indicates the condition or conditions when the null hypothesis is rejected.
     2. In a two-tailed test, the rejection region is evenly split between the upper and lower tails.
     3. In a one-tailed test, all of the rejection region is in either the upper or the lower tail.
   E. Select a sample, compute the value of the test statistic, and make a decision regarding the null hypothesis.
   F. Interpret the results of your decision.
III. A p-value is the probability that the value of the test statistic is as extreme as the value computed, when the null hypothesis is true.
IV. When testing a hypothesis about a population mean:
   A. If the population standard deviation, σ, is known, the test statistic is the standard normal distribution and is determined from:

$$z = \frac{\bar{x} - \mu}{\sigma/\sqrt{n}} \qquad \text{[10–1]}$$

   B. If the population standard deviation is not known, s is substituted for σ. The test statistic is the t distribution, and its value is determined from:

$$t = \frac{\bar{x} - \mu}{s/\sqrt{n}} \qquad \text{[10–2]}$$

The major characteristics of the t distribution are:
   1. It is a continuous distribution.
   2. It is mound-shaped and symmetrical.
   3. It is flatter, or more spread out, than the standard normal distribution.
   4. There is a family of t distributions, depending on the number of degrees of freedom.
V. There are two types of errors that can occur in a test of hypothesis.
   A. A Type I error occurs when a true null hypothesis is rejected.
     1. The probability of making a Type I error is equal to the level of significance.
     2. This probability is designated by the Greek letter α.
   B. A Type II error occurs when a false null hypothesis is not rejected.
     1. The probability of making a Type II error is designated by the Greek letter β.
     2. The likelihood of a Type II error is found by

$$z = \frac{\bar{x}_c - \mu_1}{\sigma/\sqrt{n}} \qquad \text{[10–3]}$$

P R O N U N C I A T I O N   K E Y

SYMBOL	MEANING	PRONUNCIATION
H_0	Null hypothesis	*H sub zero*
H_1	Alternate hypothesis	*H sub one*
$\alpha/2$	Two-tailed significance level	*Alpha over 2*
$\bar{x}_c$	Limit of the sample mean	*x bar sub c*
μ_0	Assumed population mean	*mu sub zero*

344   CHAPTER 10

CHAPTER EXERCISES

23. According to the local union president, the mean gross income of plumbers in the Salt Lake City area follows the normal probability distribution with a mean of $45,000 and a standard deviation of $3,000. A recent investigative reporter for KYAK TV found, for a sample of 120 plumbers, the mean gross income was $45,500. At the .10 significance level, is it reasonable to conclude that the mean income is not equal to $45,000? Determine the p-value.

24. Rutter Nursery Company packages its pine bark mulch in 50-pound bags. From a long history, the production department reports that the distribution of the bag weights follows the normal distribution and the standard deviation of this process is 3 pounds per bag. At the end of each day, Jeff Rutter, the production manager, weighs 10 bags and computes the mean weight of the sample. Below are the weights of 10 bags from today's production.

For **DATA FILE**, please visit www.mhhe.com/lind16e

45.6	47.7	47.6	46.3	46.2	47.4	49.2	55.8	47.5	48.5

    a. Can Mr. Rutter conclude that the mean weight of the bags is less than 50 pounds? Use the .01 significance level.

    b. In a brief report, tell why Mr. Rutter can use the z distribution as the test statistic.

    c. Compute the p-value.

25. A new weight-watching company, Weight Reducers International, advertises that those who join will lose, on the average, 10 pounds the first two weeks with a standard deviation of 2.8 pounds. A random sample of 50 people who joined the new weight reduction program revealed the mean loss to be 9 pounds. At the .05 level of significance, can we conclude that those joining Weight Reducers on average will lose less than 10 pounds? Determine the p-value.

26. Dole Pineapple Inc. is concerned that the 16-ounce can of sliced pineapple is being overfilled. Assume the standard deviation of the process is .03 ounce. The quality-control department took a random sample of 50 cans and found that the arithmetic mean weight was 16.05 ounces. At the 5% level of significance, can we conclude that the mean weight is greater than 16 ounces? Determine the p-value.

27. According to a recent survey, Americans get a mean of 7 hours of sleep per night. A random sample of 50 students at West Virginia University revealed the mean length of time slept last night was 6 hours and 48 minutes (6.8 hours). The standard deviation of the sample was 0.9 hour. At the 5% level of significance, is it reasonable to conclude that students at West Virginia sleep less than the typical American? Compute the p-value.

28. A statewide real estate sales agency, Farm Associates, specializes in selling farm property in the state of Nebraska. Its records indicate that the mean selling time of farm property is 90 days. Because of recent drought conditions, the agency believes that the mean selling time is now greater than 90 days. A statewide survey of 100 farms sold recently revealed that the mean selling time was 94 days, with a standard deviation of 22 days. At the .10 significance level, has there been an increase in selling time?

29. According to the Census Bureau, 3.13 people reside in the typical American household. A sample of 25 households in Arizona retirement communities showed the mean number of residents per household was 2.86 residents. The standard deviation of this sample was 1.20 residents. At the .05 significance level, is it reasonable to conclude the mean number of residents in the retirement community household is less than 3.13 persons?

30. A recent article in *Vitality* magazine reported that the mean amount of leisure time per week for American men is 40.0 hours. You believe this figure is too large and decide to conduct your own test. In a random sample of 60 men, you find that the mean is 37.8 hours of leisure per week and that the standard deviation of the sample is 12.2 hours. Can you conclude that the information in the article is untrue? Use the .05 significance level. Determine the p-value and explain its meaning.

31. According to a study by the Federal Reserve Board, the rate charged on credit card debt is more than 14%. Listed below is the interest rate charged on a sample of 10 credit cards.

For **DATA FILE**, please visit www.mhhe.com/lind16e

14.6	16.7	17.4	17.0	17.8	15.4	13.1	15.8	14.3	14.5

Is it reasonable to conclude the mean rate charged is greater than 14%? Use the .01 significance level.

32. A recent article in *The Wall Street Journal* reported that the home equity loan rate is now less than 6%. A sample of eight small banks in the Midwest revealed the following home equity loan rates (in percent):

4.8	5.3	6.5	4.8	6.1	5.8	6.2	5.6

At the .01 significance level, can we conclude that the home equity loan rate for small banks is less than 6%? Estimate the *p*-value.

For **DATA FILE**, please visit www.mhhe.com/lind16e

33. A recent study revealed the typical American coffee drinker consumes an average of 3.1 cups per day. A sample of 12 senior citizens revealed they consumed the following amounts of coffee, reported in cups, yesterday.

3.1	3.3	3.5	2.6	2.6	4.3	4.4	3.8	3.1	4.1	3.1	3.2

At the .05 significance level, do these sample data suggest there is a difference between the national average and the sample mean from senior citizens?

34. The postanesthesia care area (recovery room) at St. Luke's Hospital in Maumee, Ohio, was recently enlarged. The hope was that with the enlargement the mean number of patients per day would be more than 25. A random sample of 15 days revealed the following numbers of patients.

25	27	25	26	25	28	28	27	24	26	25	29	25	27	24

At the .01 significance level, can we conclude that the mean number of patients per day is more than 25? Estimate the *p*-value and interpret it.

35. www.golfsmith.com receives an average of 6.5 returns per day from online shoppers. For a sample of 12 days, it received the following numbers of returns.

0	4	3	4	9	4	5	9	1	6	7	10

At the .01 significance level, can we conclude the mean number of returns is less than 6.5?

36. During recent seasons, Major League Baseball has been criticized for the length of the games. A report indicated that the average game lasts 3 hours and 30 minutes. A sample of 17 games revealed the following times to completion. (Note that the minutes have been changed to fractions of hours, so that a game that lasted 2 hours and 24 minutes is reported at 2.40 hours.)

2.98	2.40	2.70	2.25	3.23	3.17	2.93	3.18	2.80
2.38	3.75	3.20	3.27	2.52	2.58	4.45	2.45	

Can we conclude that the mean time for a game is less than 3.50 hours? Use the .05 significance level.

37. Watch Corporation of Switzerland claims that its watches on average will neither gain nor lose time during a week. A sample of 18 watches provided the following gains (+) or losses (−) in seconds per week.

−0.38	−0.20	−0.38	−0.32	+0.32	−0.23	+0.30	+0.25	−0.10
−0.37	−0.61	−0.48	−0.47	−0.64	−0.04	−0.20	−0.68	+0.05

Is it reasonable to conclude that the mean gain or loss in time for the watches is 0? Use the .05 significance level. Estimate the *p*-value.

38. Listed below is the rate of return for one year (reported in percent) for a sample of 12 mutual funds that are classified as taxable money market funds.

4.63	4.15	4.76	4.70	4.65	4.52	4.70	5.06	4.42	4.51	4.24	4.52

Using the .05 significance level, is it reasonable to conclude that the mean rate of return is more than 4.50%?

346   CHAPTER 10

For **DATA FILE**, please visit
www.mhhe.com/lind16e

39. Many grocery stores and large retailers such as Walmart and Kmart have installed self-checkout systems so shoppers can scan their own items and cash out themselves. How do customers like this service and how often do they use it? Listed below is the number of customers using the service for a sample of 15 days at a Walmart location.

120	108	120	114	118	91	118	92	104	104
112	97	118	108	117					

Is it reasonable to conclude that the mean number of customers using the self-checkout system is more than 100 per day? Use the .05 significance level.

For **DATA FILE**, please visit
www.mhhe.com/lind16e

40. For a recent year, the mean fare to fly from Charlotte, North Carolina, to Chicago, Illinois, on a discount ticket was $267. A random sample of 13 round-trip discount fares on this route last month gives:

$321	$286	$290	$330	$310	$250	$270	$280	$299	$265	$291	$275	$281

At the .01 significance level, can we conclude that the mean fare has increased? What is the p-value?

41. The publisher of *Celebrity Living* claims that the mean sales for personality magazines that feature people such as Angelina Jolie or Paris Hilton are 1.5 million copies per week. A sample of 10 comparable titles shows a mean weekly sales last week of 1.3 million copies with a standard deviation of 0.9 million copies. Do these data contradict the publisher's claim? Use the 0.01 significance level.

42. A United Nations report shows the mean family income for Mexican migrants to the United States is $27,000 per year. A FLOC (Farm Labor Organizing Committee) evaluation of 25 Mexican family units reveals a mean to be $30,000 with a sample standard deviation of $10,000. Does this information disagree with the United Nations report? Apply the 0.01 significance level.

43. The cost of weddings in the United States has skyrocketed in recent years. As a result, many couples are opting to have their weddings in the Caribbean. A Caribbean vacation resort recently advertised in *Bride Magazine* that the cost of a Caribbean wedding was less than $10,000. Listed below is a total cost in $000 for a sample of 8 Caribbean weddings.

9.7	9.4	11.7	9.0	9.1	10.5	9.1	9.8

At the .05 significance level, is it reasonable to conclude the mean wedding cost is less than $10,000 as advertised?

44. The American Water Works Association reports that the per capita water use in a single-family home is 69 gallons per day. Legacy Ranch is a relatively new housing development. The builders installed more efficient water fixtures, such as low-flush toilets, and subsequently conducted a survey of the residences. Thirty-six owners responded, and the sample mean water use per day was 64 gallons with a standard deviation of 8.8 gallons per day. At the .10 level of significance, is that enough evidence to conclude that residents of Legacy Ranch use less water on average?

45. A cola-dispensing machine is set to dispense 9.00 ounces of cola per cup, with a standard deviation of 1.00 ounce. The manufacturer of the machine would like to set the control limit in such a way that, for samples of 36, 5% of the sample means will be greater than the upper control limit, and 5% of the sample means will be less than the lower control limit.
   a. At what value should the control limit be set?
   b. If the population mean shifts to 8.6, what is the probability of detecting the change?
   c. If the population mean shifts to 9.6, what is the probability of detecting the change?

46. The owners of the Westfield Mall wished to study customer shopping habits. From earlier studies, the owners were under the impression that a typical shopper spends 0.75 hour at the mall, with a standard deviation of 0.10 hour. Recently the mall owners added some specialty restaurants designed to keep shoppers in the mall longer. The consulting firm, Brunner and Swanson Marketing Enterprises, was hired to evaluate the effects of the

restaurants. A sample of 45 shoppers by Brunner and Swanson revealed that the mean time spent in the mall had increased to 0.80 hour.
   a. Develop a test of hypothesis to determine if the mean time spent in the mall changed. Use the .10 significance level.
   b. Suppose the mean shopping time actually increased from 0.75 hour to 0.79 hours. What is the probability of making a Type II error?
   c. When Brunner and Swanson reported the information in part (b) to the mall owners, the owners believed that the probability of making a Type II error was too high. How could this probability be reduced?
47. The following null and alternate hypotheses are given.

$$H_0: \mu \le 50$$

$$H_1: \mu > 50$$

Suppose the population standard deviation is 10. The probability of a Type I error is set at .01 and the probability of a Type II error at .30. Assume that the population mean shifts from 50 to 55. How large a sample is necessary to meet these requirements?
48. An insurance company, based on past experience, estimates the mean damage for a natural disaster in its area is $5,000. After introducing several plans to prevent loss, it randomly samples 200 policyholders and finds the mean amount per claim was $4,800 with a standard deviation of $1,300. Does it appear the prevention plans were effective in reducing the mean amount of a claim? Use the .05 significance level.
49. A national grocer's magazine reports the typical shopper spends 8 minutes in line waiting to check out. A sample of 24 shoppers at the local Farmer Jack's showed a mean of 7.5 minutes with a standard deviation of 3.2 minutes. Is the waiting time at the local Farmer Jack's less than that reported in the national magazine? Use the .05 significance level.

DATA SET EXERCISES

(The data for these exercises are available at the text website: www.mhhe.com/lind16e.)

50. Refer to the Real Estate data, which report information on the homes sold in Goodyear, Arizona, last year.
   a. A recent article in the *Arizona Republic* indicated that the mean selling price of the homes in the area is more than $220,000. Can we conclude that the mean selling price in the Goodyear, AZ, area is more than $220,000? Use the .01 significance level. What is the *p*-value?
   b. The same article reported the mean size was more than 2,100 square feet. Can we conclude that the mean size of homes sold in the Goodyear, AZ, area is more than 2,100 square feet? Use the .01 significance level. What is the *p*-value?
51. Refer to the Baseball 2012 data, which report information on the 30 Major League Baseball teams for the 2012 season.
   a. Conduct a test of hypothesis to determine whether the mean salary of the teams was different from $80.0 million. Use the .05 significance level.
   b. Using a 5% significance level, conduct a test of hypothesis to determine whether the mean attendance was more than 2,000,000 per team.
52. Refer to the Buena School District bus data.
   a. Select the variable for the number of miles traveled last month. Conduct a test of hypothesis to determine whether the mean number of miles traveled is equal to 840. Use the .01 significance level. Find the *p*-value and explain what it means.
   b. Using the maintenance cost variable, conduct a test of hypothesis to determine whether the mean maintenance cost is less than $500 at the .05 significance level. Determine the *p*-value and interpret the result.

11

Two-Sample Tests of Hypothesis

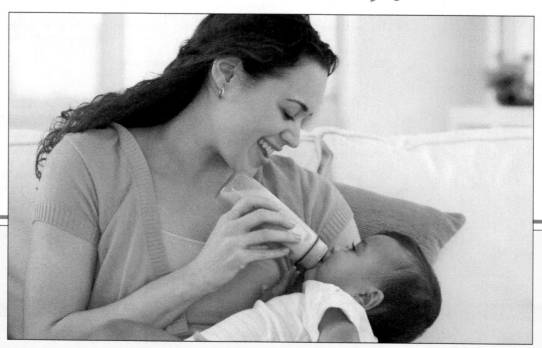

GIBBS BABY FOOD COMPANY wishes to compare the weight gain of infants using its brand versus its competitor's. A sample of 40 babies using the Gibbs products revealed a mean weight gain of 7.6 pounds in the first three months after birth. For the Gibbs brand, the population standard deviation of the sample is 2.3 pounds. A sample of 55 babies using the competitor's brand revealed a mean increase in weight of 8.1 pounds. The population standard deviation is 2.9 pounds. At the .05 significance level, can we conclude that babies using the Gibbs brand gained less weight? (See Exercise 3 and LO11-1.)

LEARNING OBJECTIVES

When you have completed this chapter, you will be able to:

LO11-1 Test a hypothesis that two independent population means are equal, assuming that the population standard deviations are known and equal.

LO11-2 Test a hypothesis that two independent population means are equal, with unknown population standard deviations.

LO11-3 Test a hypothesis about the mean population difference between paired or dependent observations.

LO11-4 Explain the difference between dependent and independent samples.

(continued on p. 350)

INTRODUCTION

Chapter 10 began our study of hypothesis testing. We described the nature of hypothesis testing and conducted tests of a hypothesis in which we compared the results of a single sample to a population value. That is, we selected a single random sample from a population and conducted a test of whether the proposed population value was reasonable. Recall in Chapter 10 that we selected a sample of the number of desks assembled per week at Jamestown Steel Company to determine whether there was a change in the production rate. Similarly, we sampled the cost to process

insurance claims to determine if cost-cutting measures resulted in a mean less than the current $60 per claim. In both cases, we compared the results of a *single* sample statistic to a population parameter.

In this chapter, we expand the idea of hypothesis testing to two populations. That is, we select random samples from two different populations to determine whether the population means are equal. Some questions we might want to test are:

1. Is there a difference in the mean value of residential real estate sold by male agents and female agents in south Florida?
2. At Grabit Software, Inc., do customer service employees receive more calls for assistance during the morning or afternoon?
3. In the fast-food industry, is there a difference in the mean number of days absent between young workers (under 21 years of age) and older workers (more than 60 years of age)?
4. Is there an increase in the production rate if music is piped into the production area?

We begin this chapter with the case in which we select random samples from two independent populations and wish to investigate whether these populations have the same mean.

TWO-SAMPLE TESTS OF HYPOTHESIS: INDEPENDENT SAMPLES

LO11-1

Test a hypothesis that two independent population means are equal, assuming that the population standard deviations are known and equal.

A city planner in Florida wishes to know whether there is a difference in the mean hourly wage rate of plumbers and electricians in central Florida. A financial accountant wishes to know whether the mean rate of return for high-yield mutual funds is different from the mean rate of return on global mutual funds. In each of these cases, there are two independent populations. In the first case, the plumbers represent one population and the electricians, the other. In the second case, high-yield mutual funds are one population and global mutual funds, the other.

In each of these cases, to investigate the question, we would select a random sample from each population and compute the mean of the two samples. If the two population means are the same, that is, the mean hourly rate is the same for the plumbers and the electricians, we would expect the *difference* between the two sample means to be zero. But what if our sample results yield a difference other than zero? Is that difference due to chance or is it because there is a real difference in the hourly earnings? A two-sample test of means will help to answer this question.

We do need to return to the results of Chapter 8. Recall that we showed that a distribution of sample means would tend to approximate the normal distribution. We need to again assume that a distribution of sample means will follow the normal

350   CHAPTER 11

distribution. It can be shown mathematically that the distribution of the differences between sample means for two normal distributions is also normal.

We can illustrate this theory in terms of the city planner in Tampa, Florida. To begin, let's assume some information that is not usually available. Suppose that the population of plumbers has a mean of $30.00 per hour and a standard deviation of $5.00 per hour. The population of electricians has a mean of $29.00 and a standard deviation of $4.50. Now, from this information it is clear that the two population means are not the same. The plumbers actually earn $1.00 per hour more than the electricians. But we cannot expect to uncover this difference each time we sample the two populations.

Suppose we select a random sample of 40 plumbers and a random sample of 35 electricians and compute the mean of each sample. Then, we determine the difference between the sample means. It is this difference between the sample means that holds our interest. If the populations have the same mean, then we would expect the difference between the two sample means to be zero. If there is a difference between the population means, then we expect to find a difference between the sample means.

To understand the theory, we need to take several pairs of samples, compute the mean of each, determine the difference between the sample means, and study the distribution of the differences in the sample means. Because of our study of the distribution of sample means in Chapter 8, we know that the distribution of the sample means follows the normal distribution. If the two distributions of sample means follow the normal distribution, then we can reason that the distribution of their differences will also follow the normal distribution. This is the first hurdle.

The second hurdle refers to the mean of this distribution of differences. If we find the mean of this distribution is zero, that implies that there is no difference in the two populations. On the other hand, if the mean of the distribution of differences is equal to some value other than zero, either positive or negative, then we conclude that the two populations do not have the same mean.

To report some concrete results, let's return to the city planner in Tampa, Florida. Table 11–1 shows the result of selecting 20 different samples of 40 plumbers and

TABLE 11–1 The Mean Hourly Earnings of 20 Random Samples of Plumbers and Electricians and the Differences between the Means

Sample	Plumbers	Electricians	Difference
1	$29.80	$28.76	$1.04
2	30.32	29.40	0.92
3	30.57	29.94	0.63
4	30.04	28.93	1.11
5	30.09	29.78	0.31
6	30.02	28.66	1.36
7	29.60	29.13	0.47
8	29.63	29.42	0.21
9	30.17	29.29	0.88
10	30.81	29.75	1.06
11	30.09	28.05	2.04
12	29.35	29.07	0.28
13	29.42	28.79	0.63
14	29.78	29.54	0.24
15	29.60	29.60	0.00
16	30.60	30.19	0.41
17	30.79	28.65	2.14
18	29.14	29.95	−0.81
19	29.91	28.75	1.16
20	28.74	29.21	−0.47

35 electricians, computing the mean of each sample, and finding the difference between the two sample means. In the first case, the sample of 40 plumbers has a mean of $29.80, and for the 35 electricians the mean is $28.76. The difference between the sample means is $1.04. This process was repeated 19 more times. Observe that in 17 of the 20 cases, the differences are positive because the mean of the plumbers is larger than the mean of the electricians. In two cases, the differences are negative because the mean of the electricians is larger than the mean of the plumbers. In one case, the means are equal.

Our final hurdle is that we need to know something about the *variability* of the distribution of differences. To put it another way, what is the standard deviation of this distribution of differences? Statistical theory shows that when we have independent populations, as in this case, the distribution of the differences has a variance (standard deviation squared) equal to the sum of the two individual variances. This means that we can add the variances of the two sampling distributions. To put it another way, the variance of the difference in sample means $(\bar{x}_1 - \bar{x}_2)$ is equal to the sum of the variance for the plumbers and the variance for the electricians.

VARIANCE OF THE DISTRIBUTION OF DIFFERENCES IN MEANS	$\sigma^2_{\bar{x}_1 - \bar{x}_2} = \dfrac{\sigma^2_1}{n_1} + \dfrac{\sigma^2_2}{n_2}$	[11–1]

The term $\sigma^2_{\bar{x}_1 - \bar{x}_2}$ looks complex but need not be difficult to interpret. The σ^2 portion reminds us that it is a variance, and the subscript $\bar{x}_1 - \bar{x}_2$ that it is a distribution of differences in the sample means.

We can put this equation in a more usable form by taking the square root, so that we have the standard deviation of the distribution or "standard error" of the differences. Finally, we standardize the distribution of the differences. The result is the following equation.

TWO-SAMPLE TEST OF MEANS—KNOWN σ	$z = \dfrac{\bar{x}_1 - \bar{x}_2}{\sqrt{\dfrac{\sigma^2_1}{n_1} + \dfrac{\sigma^2_2}{n_2}}}$	[11–2]

Before we present an example, let's review the assumptions necessary for using formula (11–2).

- The two populations follow normal distributions.
- The two samples are unrelated, that is, independent.
- The standard deviations for both populations are known.

The following example shows the details of the test of hypothesis for two population means.

E X A M P L E

Customers at the FoodTown Supermarket have a choice when paying for their groceries. They may check out and pay using the standard cashier-assisted checkout, or they may use the new Fast Lane procedure. In the standard

352   CHAPTER 11

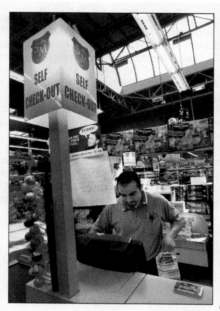

procedure, a FoodTown employee scans each item and puts it on a short conveyor, where another employee puts it in a bag and then into the grocery cart. In the Fast Lane procedure, the customer scans each item, bags it, and places the bags in the cart him- or herself. The Fast Lane procedure is designed to reduce the time a customer spends in the checkout line.

The Fast Lane facility was recently installed at the Byrne Road FoodTown location. The store manager would like to know if the mean checkout time using the standard checkout method is longer than using the Fast Lane. She gathered the following sample information. The time is measured from when the customer enters the line until all his or her bags are in the cart. Hence the time includes both waiting in line and checking out. What is the p-value?

Customer Type	Sample Mean	Population Standard Deviation	Sample Size
Standard	5.50 minutes	0.40 minute	50
Fast Lane	5.30 minutes	0.30 minute	100

SOLUTION

We use the six-step hypothesis-testing procedure to investigate the question.

Step 1: **State the null hypothesis and the alternate hypothesis.** The null hypothesis is that the mean standard checkout time is less than or equal to the mean Fast Lane checkout time. In other words, the difference of 0.20 minute between the mean checkout time for the standard method and the mean checkout time for Fast Lane is due to chance. The alternate hypothesis is that the mean checkout time is larger for those using the standard method. We will let μ_S refer to the mean checkout time for the population of standard customers and μ_F the mean checkout time for the Fast Lane customers. The null and alternative hypotheses are:

$$H_0: \mu_S \leq \mu_F$$
$$H_1: \mu_S > \mu_F$$

Step 2: **Select the level of significance.** The significance level is the probability that we reject the null hypothesis when it is actually true. This likelihood is determined prior to selecting the sample or performing any calculations. The .05 and .01 significance levels are the most common, but other values, such as .02 and .10, are also used. In theory, we may select any value between 0 and 1 for the significance level. In this case, we selected the .01 significance level.

Step 3: **Determine the test statistic.** In Chapter 10, we used the standard normal distribution (that is, z) and t as test statistics. In this case, we use the z distribution as the test statistic because we assume the

TWO-SAMPLE TESTS OF HYPOTHESIS   353

two population distributions are both normal and the standard deviations of both populations are known.

Step 4: **Formulate a decision rule.** The decision rule is based on the null and the alternate hypotheses (i.e., one-tailed or two-tailed test), the level of significance, and the test statistic used. We selected the .01 significance level and the z distribution as the test statistic, and we wish to determine whether the mean checkout time is longer using the standard method. We set the alternate hypothesis to indicate that the mean checkout time is longer for those using the standard method than the Fast Lane method. Hence, the rejection region is in the upper tail of the standard normal distribution (a one-tailed test). To find the critical value, go to Student's t distribution (Appendix B.5). In the table headings, find the row labeled **"Level of Significance for One-Tailed Test"** and select the column for an alpha of .01. Go to the bottom row with infinite degrees of freedom. The z critical value is 2.326. So the decision rule is to reject the null hypothesis if the value of the test statistic exceeds 2.326. Chart 11–1 depicts the decision rule.

CHART 11–1 Decision Rule for One-Tailed Test at .01 Significance Level

Step 5: **Make the decision regarding H_0.** We use formula (11–2) to compute the value of the test statistic.

$$z = \frac{\bar{x}_S - \bar{x}_F}{\sqrt{\dfrac{\sigma_S^2}{n_S} + \dfrac{\sigma_F^2}{n_F}}} = \frac{5.5 - 5.3}{\sqrt{\dfrac{0.40^2}{50} + \dfrac{0.30^2}{100}}} = \frac{0.2}{0.064031} = 3.123$$

The computed value of 3.123 is larger than the critical value of 2.326. Our decision is to reject the null hypothesis and accept the alternate hypothesis.

Step 6: **Interpret the result.** The difference of .20 minute between the mean checkout times is too large to have occurred by chance. We conclude the Fast Lane method is faster.

What is the p-value for the test statistic? Recall that the p-value is the probability of finding a value of the test statistic this extreme when the null hypothesis is true. To calculate the p-value, we need the probability of a z value larger than 3.123. From Appendix B.3, we cannot find the probability associated with 3.123. The largest value available is 3.09. The area corresponding to 3.09 is .4990. In this case, we can report that the p-value is less than .0010, found by .5000 − .4990. We conclude that there is very little likelihood that the null hypothesis is true!

354   CHAPTER 11

In summary, the criteria for using formula (11–2) are:

1. *The samples are from independent populations.* This means the checkout time for the Fast Lane customers is unrelated to the checkout time for the other customers. For example, Mr. Smith's checkout time does not affect any other customer's checkout time.
2. *Both populations follow the normal distribution.* In the FoodTown example, the population of times in both the standard checkout line and the Fast Lane follow normal distributions.
3. *Both population standard deviations are known.* In the FoodTown example, the population standard deviation of the Fast Lane times was 0.30 minute. The population standard deviation of the standard checkout times was 0.40 minute.

SELF-REVIEW

11-1

Tom Sevits is the owner of the Appliance Patch. Recently Tom observed a difference in the dollar value of sales between the men and women he employs as sales associates. A sample of 40 days revealed the men sold a mean of $1,400 worth of appliances per day. For a sample of 50 days, the women sold a mean of $1,500 worth of appliances per day. Assume the population standard deviation for men is $200 and for women $250. At the .05 significance level, can Mr. Sevits conclude that the mean amount sold per day is larger for the women?
(a) State the null hypothesis and the alternate hypothesis.
(b) What is the decision rule?
(c) What is the value of the test statistic?
(d) What is your decision regarding the null hypothesis?
(e) What is the *p*-value?
(f) Interpret the result.

EXERCISES

1. A sample of 40 observations is selected from one population with a population standard deviation of 5. The sample mean is 102. A sample of 50 observations is selected from a second population with a population standard deviation of 6. The sample mean is 99. Conduct the following test of hypothesis using the .04 significance level.

$$H_0: \mu_1 = \mu_2$$
$$H_1: \mu_1 \neq \mu_2$$

   a. Is this a one-tailed or a two-tailed test?
   b. State the decision rule.
   c. Compute the value of the test statistic.
   d. What is your decision regarding H_0?
   e. What is the *p*-value?

2. A sample of 65 observations is selected from one population with a population standard deviation of 0.75. The sample mean is 2.67. A sample of 50 observations is selected from a second population with a population standard deviation of 0.66. The sample mean is 2.59. Conduct the following test of hypothesis using the .08 significance level.

$$H_0: \mu_1 \leq \mu_2$$
$$H_1: \mu_1 > \mu_2$$

   a. Is this a one-tailed or a two-tailed test?
   b. State the decision rule.
   c. Compute the value of the test statistic.
   d. What is your decision regarding H_0?
   e. What is the *p*-value?

Note: Use the six-step hypothesis-testing procedure to solve the following exercises.

3. Gibbs Baby Food Company wishes to compare the weight gain of infants using its brand versus its competitor's. A sample of 40 babies using the Gibbs products revealed a mean weight gain of 7.6 pounds in the first three months after birth. For the Gibbs brand, the population standard deviation of the sample is 2.3 pounds. A sample of 55 babies using the competitor's brand revealed a mean increase in weight of 8.1 pounds. The population standard deviation is 2.9 pounds. At the .05 significance level, can we conclude that babies using the Gibbs brand gained less weight? Compute the *p*-value and interpret it.

4. As part of a study of corporate employees, the director of human resources for PNC Inc. wants to compare the distance traveled to work by employees at its office in downtown Cincinnati with the distance for those in downtown Pittsburgh. A sample of 35 Cincinnati employees showed they travel a mean of 370 miles per month. A sample of 40 Pittsburgh employees showed they travel a mean of 380 miles per month. The population standard deviations for the Cincinnati and Pittsburgh employees are 30 and 26 miles, respectively. At the .05 significance level, is there a difference in the mean number of miles traveled per month between Cincinnati and Pittsburgh employees?

5. Women's height is a suspected factor for difficult deliveries, that is, shorter women are more likely to have Caesarean sections. A medical researcher found in a sample of 45 women who had a normal delivery that their mean height was 61.4 inches. A second sample of 39 women who had a Caesarean section had a mean height of 60.6 inches. Assume that the population of heights of normal deliveries has a population standard deviation of 1.2 inches. Also assume that the heights of the population of women who had Caesarean section births has a standard deviation of 1.1 inches. Are those who had a Caesarean section shorter? Use the .05 significance level. Find the p-value and explain what it means.

6. Mary Jo Fitzpatrick is the vice president for Nursing Services at St. Luke's Memorial Hospital. Recently she noticed in the job postings for nurses that those that are unionized seem to offer higher wages. She decided to investigate and gathered the following information.

Group	Mean Wage	Population Standard Deviation	Sample Size
Union	$20.75	$2.25	40
Nonunion	$19.80	$1.90	45

Would it be reasonable for her to conclude that union nurses earn more? Use the .02 significance level. What is the p-value?

LO11-2

Test a hypothesis that two independent population means are equal, with unknown population standard deviations.

COMPARING POPULATION MEANS WITH UNKNOWN POPULATION STANDARD DEVIATIONS

In the previous section, we used the standard normal distribution and z as the test statistic to test a hypothesis that two population means from independent populations were equal. The hypothesis tests presumed that the populations were normally distributed and that we knew the population standard deviations. However, in most cases, we do not know the population standard deviations. We can overcome this problem, as we did in the one-sample case in the previous chapter, by substituting the sample standard deviation (s) for the population standard deviation (σ). See formula (10–2) on page 331.

Two-Sample Pooled Test

In this section, we describe another method for comparing the sample means of two independent populations to determine if the sampled populations could reasonably have the same mean. The method described does *not* require that we know the standard deviations of the populations. This gives us a great deal more flexibility when investigating the difference in sample means. There are two major differences in this test and the previous test described in this chapter.

1. We assume the sampled populations have equal but unknown standard deviations. Because of this assumption, we combine or "pool" the sample standard deviations.
2. We use the t distribution as the test statistic.

356   CHAPTER 11

The formula for computing the value of the test statistic t is similar to formula (11–2), but an additional calculation is necessary. The two sample standard deviations are pooled to form a single estimate of the unknown population standard deviation. In essence, we compute a weighted mean of the two sample standard deviations and use this value as an estimate of the unknown population standard deviation. The weights are the degrees of freedom that each sample provides. Why do we need to pool the sample standard deviations? Because we assume that the two populations have equal standard deviations, the best estimate we can make of that value is to combine or pool all the sample information we have about the value of the population standard deviation.

The following formula is used to pool the sample standard deviations. Notice that two factors are involved: the number of observations in each sample and the sample standard deviations themselves.

POOLED VARIANCE	$$s_p^2 = \frac{(n_1 - 1)s_1^2 + (n_2 - 1)s_2^2}{n_1 + n_2 - 2}$$	**[11–3]**

where:
s_1^2 is the variance (standard deviation squared) of the first sample.
s_2^2 is the variance of the second sample.

The value of t is computed from the following equation.

TWO-SAMPLE TEST OF MEANS—UNKNOWN σ'S	$$t = \frac{\bar{x}_1 - \bar{x}_2}{\sqrt{s_p^2\left(\frac{1}{n_1} + \frac{1}{n_2}\right)}}$$	**[11–4]**

where:
$\bar{x}_1$ is the mean of the first sample.
$\bar{x}_2$ is the mean of the second sample.
n_1 is the number of observations in the first sample.
n_2 is the number of observations in the second sample.
s_p^2 is the pooled estimate of the population variance.

The number of degrees of freedom in the test is the total number of items sampled minus the total number of samples. Because there are two samples, there are $n_1 + n_2 - 2$ degrees of freedom.

To summarize, there are three requirements or assumptions for the test.

1. The sampled populations are approximately normally distributed.
2. The sampled populations are independent.
3. The standard deviations of the two populations are equal.

The following example/solution explains the details of the test.

E X A M P L E

Owens Lawn Care Inc. manufactures and assembles lawnmowers that are shipped to dealers throughout the United States and Canada. Two different procedures have been proposed for mounting the engine on the frame of the lawnmower. The question is: Is there a difference in the mean time to mount the engines on the frames of the lawnmowers? The first procedure was developed by longtime Owens employee Herb Welles (designated as procedure W), and the other procedure was

TWO-SAMPLE TESTS OF HYPOTHESIS   357

developed by Owens Vice President of Engineering William Atkins (designated as procedure A). To evaluate the two methods, we conduct a time and motion study. A sample of five employees is timed using the Welles method and six using the Atkins method. The results, in minutes, are shown below. Is there a difference in the mean mounting times? Use the .10 significance level.

Welles (minutes)	Atkins (minutes)
2	3
4	7
9	5
3	8
2	4
	3

SOLUTION

Following the six steps to test a hypothesis, the null hypothesis states that there is no difference in mean mounting times between the two procedures. The alternate hypothesis indicates that there is a difference.

$$H_0: \mu_W = \mu_A$$
$$H_1: \mu_W \neq \mu_A$$

The required assumptions are:

- The observations in the Welles sample are *independent* of the observations in the Atkins sample.
- The two populations follow the normal distribution.
- The two populations have equal standard deviations.

Is there a difference between the mean assembly times using the Welles and the Atkins methods? The degrees of freedom are equal to the total number of items sampled minus the number of samples. In this case, that is $n_W + n_A - 2$. Five assemblers used the Welles method and six the Atkins method. Thus, there are 9 degrees of freedom, found by $5 + 6 - 2$. The critical values of t, from Appendix B.5 for $df = 9$, a two-tailed test, and the .10 significance level, are -1.833 and 1.833. The decision rule is portrayed graphically in Chart 11–2. We do not reject the null hypothesis if the computed value of t falls between -1.833 and 1.833.

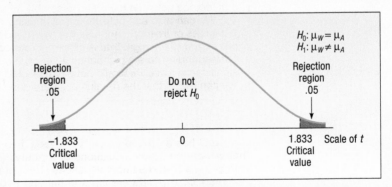

CHART 11–2 Regions of Rejection, Two-Tailed Test, $df = 9$, and .10 Significance Level

We use three steps to compute the value of t.

> **Step 1: Calculate the sample standard deviations.** To compute the sample standard deviations, we use formula (3–11) from page 81. See the details below.

Welles Method		Atkins Method	
x_W	$(x_W - \bar{x}_W)^2$	x_A	$(x_A - \bar{x}_A)^2$
2	$(2-4)^2 = 4$	3	$(3-5)^2 = 4$
4	$(4-4)^2 = 0$	7	$(7-5)^2 = 4$
9	$(9-4)^2 = 25$	5	$(5-5)^2 = 0$
3	$(3-4)^2 = 1$	8	$(8-5)^2 = 9$
2	$(2-4)^2 = 4$	4	$(4-5)^2 = 1$
$\overline{20}$	$\overline{34}$	3	$(3-5)^2 = 4$
		$\overline{30}$	$\overline{22}$

$$\bar{x}_W = \frac{\Sigma x_W}{n_W} = \frac{20}{5} = 4 \qquad \bar{x}_A = \frac{\Sigma x_A}{n_A} = \frac{30}{6} = 5$$

$$s_W = \sqrt{\frac{\Sigma(x_W - \bar{x}_W)^2}{n_W - 1}} = \sqrt{\frac{34}{5-1}} = 2.9155 \qquad s_A = \sqrt{\frac{\Sigma(x_A - \bar{x}_A)^2}{n_A - 1}} = \sqrt{\frac{22}{6-1}} = 2.0976$$

> **Step 2: Pool the sample variances.** We use formula (11–3) to pool the sample variances (standard deviations squared).

$$s_p^2 = \frac{(n_W - 1)s_W^2 + (n_A - 1)s_A^2}{n_W + n_A - 2} = \frac{(5-1)(2.9155)^2 + (6-1)(2.0976)^2}{5 + 6 - 2} = 6.2222$$

> **Step 3: Determine the value of t.** The mean mounting time for the Welles method is 4.00 minutes, found by $\bar{x}_W = 20/5$. The mean mounting time for the Atkins method is 5.00 minutes, found by $\bar{x}_A = 30/6$. We use formula (11–4) to calculate the value of t.

$$t = \frac{\bar{x}_W - \bar{x}_A}{\sqrt{s_p^2\left(\frac{1}{n_W} + \frac{1}{n_A}\right)}} = \frac{4.00 - 5.00}{\sqrt{6.2222\left(\frac{1}{5} + \frac{1}{6}\right)}} = -0.662$$

The decision is not to reject the null hypothesis because -0.662 falls in the region between -1.833 and 1.833. Our conclusion is that the sample data failed to show a difference between the mean assembly times of the two methods.

We can also estimate the p-value using Appendix B.5. Locate the row with 9 degrees of freedom, and use the two-tailed test column. Find the t value, without regard to the sign, that is closest to our computed value of 0.662. It is 1.383, corresponding to a significance level of .20. Thus, even had we used the 20% significance level, we would not have rejected the null hypothesis of equal means. We can report that the p-value is greater than .20.

Excel has a procedure called "t-Test: Two Sample Assuming Equal Variances" that will perform the calculations of formulas (11–3) and (11–4) as well as find the sample means and sample variances. The details of the procedure are provided in Appendix C. The data are input in the first two columns of the Excel spreadsheet. They are labeled "Welles" and "Atkins." The output follows. The value of t, called the "t Stat," is -0.662, and the two-tailed p-value is .525. As we would expect, the

TWO-SAMPLE TESTS OF HYPOTHESIS   359

p-value is larger than the significance level of .10. The conclusion is not to reject the null hypothesis.

	A	B	C	D	E	F
	Welles	Atkins		t-Test: Two-Sample Assuming Equal Variances		
1	Welles	Atkins				
2	2	3				
3	4	7			Welles	Atkins
4	9	5		Mean	4.000	5.000
5	3	8		Variance	8.500	4.400
6	2	4		Observations	5.000	6.000
7		3		Pooled Variance	6.222	
8				Hypothesized Mean Difference	0.000	
9				df	9.000	
10				t Stat	-0.662	
11				P(T<=t) one-tail	0.262	
12				t Critical one-tail	1.833	
13				P(T<=t) two-tail	0.525	
14				t Critical two-tail	2.262	

welles and atkins.xlsx

SELF-REVIEW

11-2

The production manager at Bellevue Steel, a manufacturer of wheelchairs, wants to compare the number of defective wheelchairs produced on the day shift with the number on the afternoon shift. A sample of the production from 6 day shifts and 8 afternoon shifts revealed the following number of defects.

Day	5	8	7	6	9	7		
Afternoon	8	10	7	11	9	12	14	9

At the .05 significance level, is there a difference in the mean number of defects per shift?
(a)   State the null hypothesis and the alternate hypothesis.
(b)   What is the decision rule?
(c)   What is the value of the test statistic?
(d)   What is your decision regarding the null hypothesis?
(e)   What is the p-value?
(f)   Interpret the result.
(g)   What are the assumptions necessary for this test?

EXERCISES

For Exercises 7 and 8: (a) state the decision rule, (b) compute the pooled estimate of the population variance, (c) compute the test statistic, (d) state your decision about the null hypothesis, and (e) estimate the p-value.

7.   The null and alternate hypotheses are:

$$H_0: \mu_1 = \mu_2$$
$$H_1: \mu_1 \neq \mu_2$$

A random sample of 10 observations from one population revealed a sample mean of 23 and a sample standard deviation of 4. A random sample of 8 observations from another population revealed a sample mean of 26 and a sample standard deviation of 5. At the .05 significance level, is there a difference between the population means?

8.   The null and alternate hypotheses are:

$$H_0: \mu_1 = \mu_2$$
$$H_1: \mu_1 \neq \mu_2$$

A random sample of 15 observations from the first population revealed a sample mean of 350 and a sample standard deviation of 12. A random sample of 17 observations from the second population revealed a sample mean of 342 and a sample standard deviation of 15. At the .10 significance level, is there a difference in the population means?

360   CHAPTER 11

Note: Use the six-step hypothesis testing procedure for the following exercises.

9. Listed below are the 25 players on the opening-day roster of the 2013 New York Yankees Major League Baseball team, their salaries, and fielding positions.

Player	Salary (US$)	Position
CC Sabathia	24,285,714	Pitcher
Hiroki Kuroda	15,000,000	Pitcher
Andy Pettitte	12,000,000	Pitcher
Mariano Rivera	10,000,000	Pitcher
Phil Hughes	7,150,000	Pitcher
Boone Logan	3,150,000	Pitcher
David Robertson	3,100,000	Pitcher
Joba Chamberlain	1,875,000	Pitcher
Shawn Kelley	935,000	Pitcher
Ivan Nova	575,600	Pitcher
David Phelps	512,425	Pitcher
Adam Warren	490,525	Pitcher
Lyle Overbay	850,000	First Base
Robinson Cano	15,000,000	Second Base
Kevin Youkilis	12,000,000	Third Base
Francisco Cervelli	515,350	Catcher
Chris Stewart	515,100	Catcher
Brett Gardner	2,850,000	Center Field
Travis Hafner	2,000,000	Designated Hitter
Vernon Wells	24,642,857	Left Field
Ben Francisco	1,200,000	Left Field
Ichiro Suzuki	6,500,000	Right Field
Brennan Boesch	1,500,000	Right Field
Jayson Nix	900,000	Shortstop
Eduardo Nunez	533,300	Shortstop

Sort the players into two groups, pitchers (P) and nonpitchers (position players). Assume equal population standard deviations for the position players and the pitchers. Test the hypothesis that mean salaries of pitchers and nonpitchers are equal using the .01 significance level.

10. A recent study compared the time spent together by single- and dual-earner couples. According to the records kept by the wives during the study, the mean amount of time spent together watching television among the single-earner couples was 61 minutes per day, with a standard deviation of 15.5 minutes. For the dual-earner couples, the mean number of minutes spent watching television was 48.4 minutes, with a standard deviation of 18.1 minutes. At the .01 significance level, can we conclude that the single-earner couples on average spend more time watching television together? There were 15 single-earner and 12 dual-earner couples studied.

11. Ms. Lisa Monnin is the budget director for Nexus Media Inc. She would like to compare the daily travel expenses for the sales staff and the audit staff. She collected the following sample information.

For **DATA FILE**, please visit www.mhhe.com/lind16e

| Sales ($) | 131 | 135 | 146 | 165 | 136 | 142 | |
| Audit ($) | 130 | 102 | 129 | 143 | 149 | 120 | 139 |

At the .10 significance level, can she conclude that the mean daily expenses are greater for the sales staff than the audit staff? What is the *p*-value?

For **DATA FILE**, please visit www.mhhe.com/lind16e

12. The Tampa Bay (Florida) Area Chamber of Commerce wanted to know whether the mean weekly salary of nurses was larger than that of school teachers. To investigate, they

collected the following information on the amounts earned last week by a sample of school teachers and nurses.

School Teachers ($)	845	826	827	875	784	809	802	820	829	830	842	832
Nurses ($)	841	890	821	771	850	859	825	829				

Is it reasonable to conclude that the mean weekly salary of nurses is higher? Use the .01 significance level. What is the *p*-value?

Unequal Population Standard Deviations

In the previous sections, it was necessary to assume that the populations had equal standard deviations. To put it another way, we did not know the population standard deviations, but we assumed they were equal. In many cases, this is a reasonable assumption, but what if it is not? In the next chapter, we present a formal method for testing this equal variance assumption. In Chapter 16 we describe a test of hypothesis that does not require either the equal variance or the normality assumption.

If it is not reasonable to assume the population standard deviations are equal, then we use a statistic very much like formula (11–2). The sample standard deviations, s_1 and s_2, are used in place of the respective population standard deviations. In addition, the degrees of freedom are adjusted downward by a rather complex approximation formula. The effect is to reduce the number of degrees of freedom in the test, which will require a larger value of the test statistic to reject the null hypothesis.

The formula for the *t* statistic is:

TEST STATISTIC FOR NO DIFFERENCE IN MEANS, UNEQUAL VARIANCES	$t = \dfrac{\bar{x}_1 - \bar{x}_2}{\sqrt{\dfrac{s_1^2}{n_1} + \dfrac{s_2^2}{n_2}}}$	**[11–5]**

The degrees of freedom statistic is found by:

DEGREES OF FREEDOM FOR UNEQUAL VARIANCE TEST	$df = \dfrac{[(s_1^2/n_1) + (s_2^2/n_2)]^2}{\dfrac{(s_1^2/n_1)^2}{n_1 - 1} + \dfrac{(s_2^2/n_2)^2}{n_2 - 1}}$	**[11–6]**

where n_1 and n_2 are the respective sample sizes and s_1 and s_2 are the respective sample standard deviations. If necessary, this fraction is rounded down to an integer value. An example will explain the details.

E X A M P L E

Personnel in a consumer testing laboratory are evaluating the absorbency of paper towels. They wish to compare a set of store brand towels to a similar group of name brand ones. For each brand they dip a ply of the paper into a tub of fluid, allow the paper to drain back into the vat for 2 minutes, and then evaluate the amount of liquid the paper has taken up from the vat. A random sample of nine store brand paper towels absorbed the following amounts of liquid in milliliters.

8	8	3	1	9	7	5	5	12

362   CHAPTER 11

An independent random sample of 12 name brand towels absorbed the following amounts of liquid in milliliters:

12	11	10	6	8	9	9	10	11	9	8	10

Use the .10 significance level and test if there is a difference in the mean amount of liquid absorbed by the two types of paper towels.

SOLUTION

To begin, let's assume that the amounts of liquid absorbed follow the normal probability distribution for both the store brand and the name brand towels. We do not know either of the population standard deviations, so we are going to use the t distribution as the test statistic. The assumption of equal population standard deviations does not appear reasonable. The amount of absorption in the store brand ranges from 1 ml to 12 ml. For the name brand, the amount of absorption ranges from 6 ml to 12 ml. That is, there is considerably more variation in the amount of absorption in the store brand than in the name brand. We observe the difference in the variation in the following dot plot provided by Minitab. The software commands to create a Minitab dot plot are given on page 746.

So we decide to use the t distribution and assume that the population standard deviations are not the same.

In the six-step hypothesis testing procedure, the first step is to state the null hypothesis and the alternate hypothesis. The null hypothesis is that there is no difference in the mean amount of liquid absorbed between the two types of paper towels. The alternate hypothesis is that there is a difference.

$$H_0: \mu_1 = \mu_2$$
$$H_0: \mu_1 \neq \mu_2$$

The significance level is .10 and the test statistic follows the t distribution. Because we do not wish to assume equal population standard deviations, we adjust the degrees of freedom using formula (11–6). To do so, we need to find the sample standard deviations. We can use the Minitab system to quickly find these results. The respective sample sizes are $n_1 = 9$ and $n_2 = 12$ and the respective standard deviations are 3.321 ml and 1.621 ml.

Variable	n	Mean	Standard Deviation
Store	9	6.444	3.321
Name	12	9.417	1.621

Inserting this information into formula (11–6):

$$df = \frac{[(s_1^2/n_1) + (s_2^2/n_2)]^2}{\dfrac{(s_1^2/n_1)^2}{n_1 - 1} + \dfrac{(s_2^2/n_2)^2}{n_2 - 1}} = \frac{[(3.321^2/9) + (1.621^2/12)]^2}{\dfrac{(3.321^2/9)^2}{9 - 1} + \dfrac{(1.621^2/12)^2}{12 - 1}} = \frac{1.4444^2}{.1877 + .0044} = 10.86$$

TWO-SAMPLE TESTS OF HYPOTHESIS   363

The usual practice is to round down to the integer, so we use 10 degrees of freedom. From Appendix B.5 with 10 degrees of freedom, a two-tailed test, and the .10 significance level, the critical t values are -1.812 and 1.812. Our decision rule is to reject the null hypothesis if the computed value of t is less than -1.812 or greater than 1.812.

To find the value of the test statistic, we use formula (11–5). Recall that the mean amount of absorption for the store paper towels is 6.444 ml and 9.417 ml for the brand.

$$t = \frac{\bar{x}_1 - \bar{x}_2}{\sqrt{\dfrac{s_1^2}{n_1} + \dfrac{s_2^2}{n_2}}} = \frac{6.444 - 9.417}{\sqrt{\dfrac{3.321^2}{9} + \dfrac{1.621^2}{12}}} = -2.474$$

The computed value of t is less than the lower critical value, so our decision is to reject the null hypothesis. We conclude that the mean absorption rate for the two towels is not the same. The Minitab output for this example follows.

	C1	C2	C3	C4	C5	C6	C7	C8	C9	C10	C11
	Store	Name									
1	8	12									
2	8	11									
3	3	10									
4	1	6									
5	9	8									
6	7	9									
7	5	9									
8	5	10									
9	12	11									
10		9									
11		8									
12		10									
13											

```
Two-Sample T-Test and CI: Store, Name

Two-sample T for Store vs Name

         N   Mean  StDev  SE Mean
Store    9   6.44   3.32     1.1
Name    12   9.42   1.62    0.47

Difference = mu (Store) - mu (Name)
Estimate for difference:  -2.97
95% CI for difference:  (-5.65, -0.29)
T-Test of difference = 0 (vs not =): T-Value = -2.47   P-Value = 0.033   DF = 10
```

SELF-REVIEW

11–3

It is often useful for companies to know who their customers are and how they became customers. A credit card company is interested in whether the owner of the card applied for the card on his or her own or was contacted by a telemarketer. The company obtained the following sample information regarding end-of-the-month balances for the two groups.

Source	Mean	Standard Deviation	Sample Size
Applied	$1,568	$356	10
Contacted	1,967	857	8

Is it reasonable to conclude the mean balance is larger for the credit card holders that were contacted by telemarketers than for those who applied on their own for the card? Assume the population standard deviations are not the same. Use the .05 significance level.
(a) State the null hypothesis and the alternate hypothesis.
(b) How many degrees of freedom are there?
(c) What is the decision rule?
(d) What is the value of the test statistic?
(e) What is your decision regarding the null hypothesis?
(f) Interpret the result.

EXERCISES

For exercises 13 and 14, assume the sample populations do not have equal standard deviations and use the .05 significance level: (a) determine the number of degrees of freedom, (b) state the decision rule, (c) compute the value of the test statistic, and (d) state your decision about the null hypothesis.

13. The null and alternate hypotheses are:

$$H_0: \mu_1 = \mu_2$$
$$H_1: \mu_1 \neq \mu_2$$

A random sample of 15 items from the first population showed a mean of 50 and a standard deviation of 5. A sample of 12 items for the second population showed a mean of 46 and a standard deviation of 15.

14. The null and alternate hypotheses are:

$$H_0: \mu_1 \leq \mu_2$$
$$H_1: \mu_1 > \mu_2$$

A random sample of 20 items from the first population showed a mean of 100 and a standard deviation of 15. A sample of 16 items for the second population showed a mean of 94 and a standard deviation of 8. Use the .05 significant level.

15. A recent survey compared the costs of adoption through public and private agencies. For a sample of 16 adoptions through a public agency, the mean cost was $21,045, with a standard deviation of $835. For a sample of 18 adoptions through a private agency, the mean cost was $22,840, with a standard deviation of $1,545. Can we conclude the mean cost is larger for adopting children through a private agency? Use the .05 significance level.

16. Suppose you are an expert on the fashion industry and wish to gather information to compare the amount earned per month by models featuring Liz Claiborne attire with those of Calvin Klein. The following is the amount ($000) earned per month by a sample of 15 Claiborne models:

$5.0	$4.5	$3.4	$3.4	$6.0	$3.3	$4.5	$4.6	$3.5	$5.2
4.8	4.4	4.6	3.6	5.0					

The following is the amount ($000) earned by a sample of 12 Klein models.

$3.1	$3.7	$3.6	$4.0	$3.8	$3.8	$5.9	$4.9	$3.6	$3.6
2.3	4.0								

Is it reasonable to conclude that Claiborne models earn more? Use the .05 significance level and assume the population standard deviations are not the same.

For **DATA FILE**, please visit www.mhhe.com/lind16e

LO11-3
Test a hypothesis about the mean population difference between paired or dependent observations.

TWO-SAMPLE TESTS OF HYPOTHESIS: DEPENDENT SAMPLES

In the example/solution beginning on page 356, we tested the difference between the means from two independent populations. We compared the mean time required to mount an engine using the Welles method to the time to mount the engine using the Atkins method. The samples were *independent*, meaning that the sample of assembly times using the Welles method was in no way related to the sample of assembly times using the Atkins method.

There are situations, however, in which the samples are not independent. To put it another way, the samples are *dependent* or *related*. As an example, Nickel Savings and Loan employs two firms, Schadek Appraisals and Bowyer Real Estate, to appraise the value of the real estate properties on which it makes loans. It is important that these two firms be similar in their appraisal values. To review the consistency of the two appraisal firms, Nickel Savings randomly selects 10 homes and has both Schadek Appraisals and Bowyer Real Estate appraise the values of the selected homes. For each home, there will

TWO-SAMPLE TESTS OF HYPOTHESIS 365

be a pair of appraisal values. That is, for each home there will be an appraised value from both Schadek Appraisals and Bowyer Real Estate. The appraised values depend on, or are related to, the home selected. This is also referred to as a **paired sample.**

For hypothesis testing, we are interested in the distribution of the *differences* in the appraised value of each home. Hence, there is only one sample. To put it more formally, we are investigating whether the mean of the distribution of differences in the appraised values is 0. The sample is made up of the *differences* between the appraised values determined by Schadek Appraisals and the values from Bowyer Real Estate. If the two appraisal firms are reporting similar estimates, then sometimes Schadek Appraisals will be the higher value and sometimes Bowyer Real Estate will have the higher value. However, the mean of the distribution of differences will be 0. On the other hand, if one of the firms consistently reports the larger appraisal values, then the mean of the distribution of the differences will not be 0.

We will use the symbol μ_d to indicate the population mean of the distribution of differences. We assume the distribution of the population of differences is approximately normally distributed. The test statistic follows the t distribution and we calculate its value from the following formula:

PAIRED t TEST	$t = \dfrac{\bar{d}}{s_d/\sqrt{n}}$	[11–7]

There are $n - 1$ degrees of freedom and

$\bar{d}$ is the mean of the difference between the paired or related observations.
s_d is the standard deviation of the differences between the paired or related observations.
n is the number of paired observations.

The standard deviation of the differences is computed by the familiar formula for the standard deviation [see formula (3–11)], except d is substituted for x. The formula is:

$$s_d = \sqrt{\frac{\Sigma(d - \bar{d})^2}{n - 1}}$$

The following example illustrates this test.

EXAMPLE

Recall that Nickel Savings and Loan wishes to compare the two companies it uses to appraise the value of residential homes. Nickel Savings selected a sample of 10 residential properties and scheduled both firms for an appraisal. The results, reported in $000, are:

Home	Schadek	Bowyer
1	235	228
2	210	205
3	231	219
4	242	240
5	205	198
6	230	223
7	231	227
8	210	215
9	225	222
10	249	245

366

CHAPTER 11

At the .05 significance level, can we conclude there is a difference between the firms' mean appraised home values?

SOLUTION

The first step is to state the null and the alternate hypotheses. In this case, a two-tailed alternative is appropriate because we are interested in determining whether there is a *difference* in the firms' appraised values. We are not interested in showing whether one particular firm appraises property at a higher value than the other. The question is whether the sample differences in the appraised values could have come from a population with a mean of 0. If the population mean of the differences is 0, then we conclude that there is no difference between the two firms' appraised values. The null and alternate hypotheses are:

$$H_0: \mu_d = 0$$

$$H_1: \mu_d \neq 0$$

There are 10 homes appraised by both firms, so $n = 10$, and $df = n - 1 = 10 - 1 = 9$. We have a two-tailed test, and the significance level is .05. To determine the critical value, go to Appendix B.5 and move across the row with 9 degrees of freedom to the column for a two-tailed test and the .05 significance level. The value at the intersection is 2.262. This value appears in the box in Table 11–2 on the next page. The decision rule is to reject the null hypothesis if the computed value of t is less than −2.262 or greater than 2.262. Here are the computational details.

Home	Schadek	Bowyer	Difference, d	$(d - \bar{d})$	$(d - \bar{d})^2$
1	235	228	7	2.4	5.76
2	210	205	5	0.4	0.16
3	231	219	12	7.4	54.76
4	242	240	2	−2.6	6.76
5	205	198	7	2.4	5.76
6	230	223	7	2.4	5.76
7	231	227	4	−0.6	0.36
8	210	215	−5	−9.6	92.16
9	225	222	3	−1.6	2.56
10	249	245	4	−0.6	0.36
			46	0	174.40

$$\bar{d} = \frac{\Sigma d}{n} = \frac{46}{10} = 4.60$$

$$s_d = \sqrt{\frac{\Sigma(d - \bar{d})^2}{n - 1}} = \sqrt{\frac{174.4}{10 - 1}} = 4.402$$

Using formula (11–7), the value of the test statistic is 3.305, found by

$$t = \frac{\bar{d}}{s_d/\sqrt{n}} = \frac{4.6}{4.402/\sqrt{10}} = \frac{4.6}{1.3920} = 3.305$$

Because the computed t falls in the rejection region, the null hypothesis is rejected. The population distribution of differences does not have a mean of 0. We conclude that there is a difference between the firms' mean appraised home values. The largest difference of $12,000 is for Home 3. Perhaps that would be an appropriate place to begin a more detailed review.

TWO-SAMPLE TESTS OF HYPOTHESIS   367

To find the *p*-value, we use Appendix B.5 and the section for a two-tailed test. Move along the row with 9 degrees of freedom and find the values of *t* that are closest to our calculated value. For a .01 significance level, the value of *t* is 3.250. The computed value is larger than this value, but smaller than the value of 4.781 corresponding to the .001 significance level. Hence, the *p*-value is less than .01. This information is highlighted in Table 11–2.

TABLE 11–2 A Portion of the *t* Distribution from Appendix B.5

	\multicolumn{5}{c}{Confidence Intervals}	*p*-value between 0.01 and 0.001
	80%	**90%**	**95%**	**98%**	**99%**	
	\multicolumn{5}{c}{Level of Significance for One-Tailed Test}	
df	**0.10**	**0.05**	**0.025**	**0.01**	**0.005**	
	\multicolumn{5}{c}{Level of Significance for Two-Tailed Test}	
	0.20	**0.10**	**0.05**	**0.02**	**0.01**	**0.001**
1	3.078	6.314	12.706	31.821	63.657	636.619
2	1.886	2.920	4.303	6.965	9.925	31.599
3	1.638	2.353	3.182	4.541	5.841	12.924
	Critical *t*-statistic for 0.05	2.132	2.776	3.747	4.604	8.610
		2.015	2.571	3.365	4.032	6.869
6	1.440	1.943	2.447	3.143	3.707	5.959
7	1.415	895	2.365	2.998	3.499	5.408
8	1.397	1.860	2.306	2.896	3.355	5.041
9	1.383	1.833	2.262	2.821	3.250	4.781
10	1.372	1.812	2.228	2.764	3.169	4.587

Excel has a procedure called "t-Test: Paired Two-Sample for Means" that will perform the calculations of formula (11–7). The output from this procedure is given below.

The computed value of *t* is 3.305, and the two-tailed *p*-value is .009. Because the *p*-value is less than .05, we reject the hypothesis that the mean of the distribution of the differences between the appraised values is zero. In fact, this *p*-value is between .01 and .001. There is a small likelihood that the null hypothesis is true.

◢	A	B	C	D	E	F	G
	\multicolumn{7}{l}{📊 paired t test}					
1	Home	Schadek	Bowyer		t-Test: Paired Two-Sample for Means		
2	1	235	228				
3	2	210	205			*Schadek*	*Bowyer*
4	3	231	219		Mean	226.800	222.200
5	4	242	240		Variance	208.844	204.178
6	5	205	198		Observations	10.000	10.000
7	6	230	223		Pearson Correlation	0.953	
8	7	231	227		Hypothesized Mean Difference	0.000	
9	8	210	215		df	9.000	
10	9	225	222		t Stat	3.305	
11	10	249	245		P(T<=t) one-tail	0.005	
12					t Critical one-tail	1.833	
13					P(T<=t) two-tail	0.009	
14					t Critical two-tail	2.262	
15							

COMPARING DEPENDENT AND INDEPENDENT SAMPLES

Beginning students are often confused by the difference between tests for independent samples [formula (11–4)] and tests for dependent samples [formula (11–7)]. How do we tell the difference between dependent and independent samples? There are two types of dependent samples: (1) those characterized by a measurement, an intervention of some type, and then another measurement; and (2) a matching or pairing of the observations. To explain further:

1. The first type of dependent sample is characterized by a measurement followed by an intervention of some kind and then another measurement. This could be called a "before" and "after" study. Two examples will help to clarify. Suppose we want to show that, by placing speakers in the production area and playing soothing music, we are able to increase production. We begin by selecting a sample of workers and measuring their output under the current conditions. The speakers are then installed in the production area, and we again measure the output of the same workers. There are two measurements, before placing the speakers in the production area and after. The intervention is placing speakers in the production area.

   A second example involves an educational firm that offers courses designed to increase test scores and reading ability. Suppose the firm wants to offer a course that will help high school juniors increase their SAT scores. To begin, each student takes the SAT in the junior year in high school. During the summer between the junior and senior year, they participate in the course that gives them tips on taking tests. Finally, during the fall of their senior year in high school, they retake the SAT. Again, the procedure is characterized by a measurement (taking the SAT as a junior), an intervention (the summer workshops), and another measurement (taking the SAT during their senior year).

2. The second type of dependent sample is characterized by matching or pairing observations. The previous example/solution regarding Nickel Savings illustrates dependent samples. A property is selected and both firms appraise the same property. As a second example, suppose an industrial psychologist wishes to study the intellectual similarities of newly married couples. She selects a sample of newlyweds. Next, she administers a standard intelligence test to both the man and woman to determine the difference in the scores. Notice the matching that occurred: comparing the scores that are paired or matched by marriage.

Why do we prefer dependent samples to independent samples? By using dependent samples, we are able to reduce the variation in the sampling distribution. To illustrate, we will use the Nickel Savings and Loan example/solution just completed. Suppose we assume that we have two independent samples of real estate property for appraisal and conduct the following test of hypothesis, using formula (11–4). The null and alternate hypotheses are:

$$H_0: \mu_1 = \mu_2$$
$$H_1: \mu_1 \neq \mu_2$$

There are now two independent samples of 10 each. So the number of degrees of freedom is $10 + 10 - 2 = 18$. From Appendix B.5, for the .05 significance level, H_0 is rejected if t is less than -2.101 or greater than 2.101.

We use Excel to find the means and standard deviations of the two independent samples as shown on page 745 in the Chapter 3 section of Appendix C. The Excel instructions to find the pooled variance and the value of the "t Stat" are on page 750 in Appendix C. These values are highlighted in yellow.

	A	B	C	D	E	F	G
					Independent t test.xlsx		
1	Home	Schadek	Bowyer		t-Test: Two-Sample Assuming Equal Variances		
2	1	235	228				
3	2	210	205			*Schadek*	*Bowyer*
4	3	231	219		Mean	226.800	222.200
5	4	242	240		Variance	208.844	204.178
6	5	205	198		Observations	10.000	10.000
7	6	230	223		Pooled Variance	206.511	
8	7	231	227		Hypothesized Mean Difference	0.000	
9	8	210	215		df	18.000	
10	9	225	222		t Stat	0.716	
11	10	249	245		P(T<=t) one-tail	0.242	
12					t Critical one-tail	1.734	
13	Mean =	226.80	222.20		P(T<=t) two-tail	0.483	
14	S =	14.45	14.29		t Critical two-tail	2.101	

The mean of the appraised value of the 10 properties by Schadek is $226,800, and the standard deviation is $14,500. For Bowyer Real Estate, the mean appraised value is $222,200, and the standard deviation is $14,290. To make the calculations easier, we use $000 instead of $. The value of the pooled estimate of the variance from formula (11–3) is

$$s_p^2 = \frac{(n_1 - 1)s_1^2 + (n_2 - 1)s_2^2}{n_1 + n_2 - 2} = \frac{(10 - 1)(14.45^2) + (10 - 1)(14.29)^2}{10 + 10 - 2} = 206.50$$

From formula (11–4), t is 0.716.

$$t = \frac{\bar{x}_1 - \bar{x}_2}{\sqrt{s_p^2\left(\frac{1}{n_1} + \frac{1}{n_2}\right)}} = \frac{226.8 - 222.2}{\sqrt{206.50\left(\frac{1}{10} + \frac{1}{10}\right)}} = \frac{4.6}{6.4265} = 0.716$$

The computed t (0.716) is less than 2.101, so the null hypothesis is not rejected. We cannot show that there is a difference in the mean appraisal value. That is not the same conclusion that we got before! Why does this happen? The numerator is the same in the paired observations test (4.6). However, the denominator is smaller. In the paired test, the denominator is 1.3920 (see the calculations on page 366). In the case of the independent samples, the denominator is 6.4265. There is more variation or uncertainty. This accounts for the difference in the t values and the difference in the statistical decisions. The denominator measures the standard error of the statistic. When the samples are *not* paired, two kinds of variation are present: differences between the two appraisal firms and the difference in the value of the real estate. Properties numbered 4 and 10 have relatively high values, whereas number 5 is relatively low. These data show how different the values of the property are, but we are really interested in the difference between the two appraisal firms.

In sum, when we can pair or match observations that measure differences for a common variable, a hypothesis test based on dependent samples is more sensitive to detecting a significant difference than a hypothesis test based on independent samples. In the case of comparing the property valuations by Schadek Appraisals and Bowyer Real Estate, the hypothesis test based on dependent samples eliminates the variation between the values of the properties and focuses only on the comparisons in the two appraisals for each property. There is a bit of bad news here. In the dependent samples test, the degrees of freedom are half of what they are if the samples are not paired. For the real estate example, the degrees of freedom drop from 18 to 9 when the observations are paired. However, in most cases, this is a small price to pay for a better test.

SELF-REVIEW

11–4

Advertisements by Sylph Fitness Center claim that completing its course will result in losing weight. A random sample of eight recent participants showed the following weights before and after completing the course. At the .01 significance level, can we conclude the students lost weight?

Name	Before	After
Hunter	155	154
Cashman	228	207
Mervine	141	147
Massa	162	157
Creola	211	196
Peterson	164	150
Redding	184	170
Poust	172	165

(a) State the null hypothesis and the alternate hypothesis.
(b) What is the critical value of t?
(c) What is the computed value of t?
(d) Interpret the result. What is the p-value?
(e) What assumption needs to be made about the distribution of the differences?

EXERCISES

17. The null and alternate hypotheses are:

$$H_0: \mu_d \leq 0$$
$$H_1: \mu_d > 0$$

The following sample information shows the number of defective units produced on the day shift and the afternoon shift for a sample of four days last month.

	Day			
	1	**2**	**3**	**4**
Day shift	10	12	15	19
Afternoon shift	8	9	12	15

At the .05 significance level, can we conclude there are more defects produced on the day shift?

18. The null and alternate hypotheses are:

$$H_0: \mu_d = 0$$
$$H_1: \mu_d \neq 0$$

The following paired observations show the number of traffic citations given for speeding by Officer Dhondt and Officer Meredith of the South Carolina Highway Patrol for the last five months.

	Number of Citations Issued				
	May	**June**	**July**	**August**	**September**
Officer Dhondt	30	22	25	19	26
Officer Meredith	26	19	20	15	19

At the .05 significance level, is there a difference in the mean number of citations given by the two officers?

Note: Use the six-step hypothesis testing procedure to solve the following exercises.

For **DATA FILE**, please visit www.mhhe.com/lind16e

19. The management of Discount Furniture, a chain of discount furniture stores in the Northeast, designed an incentive plan for salespeople. To evaluate this innovative plan, 12 salespeople

TWO-SAMPLE TESTS OF HYPOTHESIS   371

were selected at random, and their weekly incomes before and after the plan were recorded.

Salesperson	Before	After
Sid Mahone	$320	$340
Carol Quick	290	285
Tom Jackson	421	475
Andy Jones	510	510
Jean Sloan	210	210
Jack Walker	402	500
Peg Mancuso	625	631
Anita Loma	560	560
John Cuso	360	365
Carl Utz	431	431
A. S. Kushner	506	525
Fern Lawton	505	619

Was there a significant increase in the typical salesperson's weekly income due to the innovative incentive plan? Use the .05 significance level. Estimate the p-value, and interpret it.

20. The federal government recently granted funds for a special program designed to reduce crime in high-crime areas. A study of the results of the program in eight high-crime areas of Miami, Florida, yielded the following results.

	\multicolumn{8}{c}{Number of Crimes by Area}
	A	B	C	D	E	F	G	H
Before	14	7	4	5	17	12	8	9
After	2	7	3	6	8	13	3	5

Has there been a decrease in the number of crimes since the inauguration of the program? Use the .01 significance level. Estimate the p-value.

CHAPTER SUMMARY

I. In comparing two population means, we wish to know whether they could be equal.
   A. We are investigating whether the distribution of the difference between the means could have a mean of 0.
   B. The test statistic follows the standard normal distribution if the population standard deviations are known.
      1. The two populations follow normal distributions.
      2. The samples are from independent populations.
      3. The formula to compute the value of z is

$$z = \frac{\bar{x}_1 - \bar{x}_2}{\sqrt{\dfrac{\sigma_1^2}{n_1} + \dfrac{\sigma_2^2}{n_2}}}$$ [11–2]

II. The test statistic to compare two means is the t distribution if the population standard deviations are not known.
   A. Both populations are approximately normally distributed.
   B. The populations must have equal standard deviations.
   C. The samples are independent.
   D. Finding the value of t requires two steps.
      1. The first step is to pool the standard deviations according to the following formula:

$$s_p^2 = \frac{(n_1 - 1)s_1^2 + (n_2 - 1)s_2^2}{n_1 + n_2 - 2}$$ [11–3]

372   CHAPTER 11

2. The value of t is computed from the following formula:

$$t = \frac{\bar{x}_1 - \bar{x}_2}{\sqrt{s_p^2\left(\dfrac{1}{n_1} + \dfrac{1}{n_2}\right)}}$$ [11-4]

3. The degrees of freedom for the test are $n_1 + n_2 - 2$.

III. If we cannot assume the population standard deviations are equal, we adjust the degrees of freedom and the formula for finding t.

    A. We determine the degrees of freedom based on the following formula.

$$df = \frac{[(s_1^2/n_1) + (s_2^2/n_2)]^2}{\dfrac{(s_1^2/n_1)^2}{n_1 - 1} + \dfrac{(s_2^2/n_2)^2}{n_2 - 1}}$$ [11-6]

    B. The value of the test statistic is computed from the following formula.

$$t = \frac{\bar{x}_1 - \bar{x}_2}{\sqrt{\dfrac{s_1^2}{n_1} + \dfrac{s_2^2}{n_2}}}$$ [11-5]

IV. For dependent samples, we assume the distribution of the paired differences between the populations has a mean of 0.

    A. We first compute the mean and the standard deviation of the sample differences.

    B. The value of the test statistic is computed from the following formula:

$$t = \frac{\bar{d}}{s_d/\sqrt{n}}$$ [11-7]

P R O N U N C I A T I O N K E Y

SYMBOL	MEANING	PRONUNCIATION
s_p^2	Pooled sample variance	s sub p squared
$\bar{x}_1$	Mean of the first sample	x bar sub 1
$\bar{x}_2$	Mean of the second sample	x bar sub 2
$\bar{d}$	Mean of the difference between dependent observations	d bar
s_d	Standard deviation of the difference between dependent observations	s sub d

C H A P T E R E X E R C I S E S

21. A recent study focused on the number of times men and women who live alone buy take-out dinner in a month. Assume that the distributions follow the normal probability distribution and the population standard deviations are equal. The information is summarized below.

Statistic	Men	Women
Sample mean	24.51	22.69
Sample standard deviation	4.48	3.86
Sample size	35	40

At the .01 significance level, is there a difference in the mean number of times men and women order take-out dinners in a month? What is the p-value?

22. Clark Heter is an industrial engineer at Lyons Products. He would like to determine whether there are more units produced on the night shift than on the day shift. Assume the population standard deviation for the number of units produced on the day shift is 21 and is 28 on the night shift. A sample of 54 day-shift workers showed that the mean number of units produced was 345. A sample of 60 night-shift workers showed that the mean number of units produced was 351. At the .05 significance level, is the number of units produced on the night shift larger?

TWO-SAMPLE TESTS OF HYPOTHESIS 373

23. Fry Brothers Heating and Air Conditioning Inc. employs Larry Clark and George Murnen to make service calls to repair furnaces and air-conditioning units in homes. Tom Fry, the owner, would like to know whether there is a difference in the mean number of service calls they make per day. Assume the population standard deviation for Larry Clark is 1.05 calls per day and 1.23 calls per day for George Murnen. A random sample of 40 days last year showed that Larry Clark made an average of 4.77 calls per day. For a sample of 50 days George Murnen made an average of 5.02 calls per day. At the .05 significance level, is there a difference in the mean number of calls per day between the two employees? What is the *p*-value?

24. A coffee manufacturer is interested in whether the mean daily consumption of regular-coffee drinkers is less than that of decaffeinated-coffee drinkers. Assume the population standard deviation for those drinking regular coffee is 1.20 cups per day and 1.36 cups per day for those drinking decaffeinated coffee. A random sample of 50 regular-coffee drinkers showed a mean of 4.35 cups per day. A sample of 40 decaffeinated-coffee drinkers showed a mean of 5.84 cups per day. Use the .01 significance level. Compute the *p*-value.

25. A cell phone company offers two plans to its subscribers. At the time new subscribers sign up, they are asked to provide some demographic information. The mean yearly income for a sample of 40 subscribers to Plan A is $57,000 with a standard deviation of $9,200. For a sample of 30 subscribers to Plan B, the mean income is $61,000 with a standard deviation of $7,100. At the .05 significance level, is it reasonable to conclude the mean income of those selecting Plan B is larger? What is the *p*-value?

26. A computer manufacturer offers a help line that purchasers can call for help 24 hours a day, 7 days a week. Clearing these calls for help in a timely fashion is important to the company's image. After telling the caller that resolution of the problem is important, the caller is asked whether the issue is software or hardware related. The mean time it takes a technician to resolve a software issue is 18 minutes with a standard deviation of 4.2 minutes. This information was obtained from a sample of 35 monitored calls. For a study of 45 hardware issues, the mean time for the technician to resolve the problem was 15.5 minutes with a standard deviation of 3.9 minutes. This information was also obtained from monitored calls. At the .05 significance level, does it take longer to resolve software issues? What is the *p*-value?

27. One of the music industry's most pressing questions is: Can paid download stores contend nose-to-nose with free peer-to-peer download services? Data gathered over the last 12 months show Apple's iTunes was used by an average of 1.65 million households with a sample standard deviation of 0.56 million family units. Over the same 12 months WinMX (a no-cost P2P download service) was used by an average of 2.2 million families with a sample standard deviation of 0.30 million. Assume the population standard deviations are not the same. Using a significance level of .05, test the hypothesis of no difference in the mean number of households picking either variety of service to download songs.

28. Businesses, particularly those in the food preparation industry such as General Mills, Kellogg, and Betty Crocker, regularly use coupons as a brand allegiance builder to stimulate their retailing. There is uneasiness that the users of paper coupons are different from the users of e-coupons (coupons disseminated by means of the Internet). One survey recorded the age of each person who redeemed a coupon along with the type (either electronic or paper). The sample of 35 e-coupon users had a mean age of 33.6 years with a standard deviation of 10.9, while a similar sample of 25 traditional paper-coupon clippers had a mean age of 39.5 with a standard deviation of 4.8. Assume the population standard deviations are not the same. Using a significance level of .01, test the hypothesis of no difference in the mean ages of the two groups of coupon clients.

29. The owner of Bun 'N' Run Hamburgers wishes to compare the sales per day at two locations. The mean number sold for 10 randomly selected days at the Northside site was 83.55, and the standard deviation was 10.50. For a random sample of 12 days at the Southside location, the mean number sold was 78.80 and the standard deviation was 14.25. At the .05 significance level, is there a difference in the mean number of hamburgers sold at the two locations? What is the *p*-value?

30. The Engineering Department at Sims Software Inc. recently developed two chemical solutions designed to increase the usable life of computer disks. A sample of disks treated with the first solution lasted 86, 78, 66, 83, 84, 81, 84, 109, 65, and 102 hours. Those treated with the second solution lasted 91, 71, 75, 76, 87, 79, 73, 76, 79, 78, 87, 90, 76, and 72 hours. Assume the population standard deviations are not the same. At the .10 significance level, can we conclude that there is a difference in the length of time the two types of treatment lasted?

For **DATA FILE**, please visit www.mhhe.com/lind16e

For **DATA FILE**, please visit
www.mhhe.com/lind16e

31. The Willow Run Outlet Mall has two Haggar Outlet Stores, one located on Peach Street and the other on Plum Street. The two stores are laid out differently, but both store managers claim their layout maximizes the amounts customers will purchase on impulse. A sample of 10 customers at the Peach Street store revealed they spent the following amounts more than planned: $17.58, $19.73, $12.61, $17.79, $16.22, $15.82, $15.40, $15.86, $11.82, and $15.85. A sample of 14 customers at the Plum Street store revealed they spent the following amounts more than they planned: $18.19, $20.22, $17.38, $17.96, $23.92, $15.87, $16.47, $15.96, $16.79, $16.74, $21.40, $20.57, $19.79, and $14.83. At the .01 significance level, is there a difference in the mean amounts purchased on impulse at the two stores?

For **DATA FILE**, please visit
www.mhhe.com/lind16e

32. Grand Strand Family Medical Center treats minor medical emergencies for visitors to the Myrtle Beach area. There are two facilities, one in the Little River Area and the other in Murrells Inlet. The Quality Assurance Department wishes to compare the mean waiting time for patients at the two locations. Samples of the waiting times for each location, reported in minutes, follow:

Location	Waiting Time										
Little River	31.73	28.77	29.53	22.08	29.47	18.60	32.94	25.18	29.82	26.49	
Murrells Inlet	22.93	23.92	26.92	27.20	26.44	25.62	30.61	29.44	23.09	23.10	26.69	22.31

Assume the population standard deviations are not the same. At the .05 significance level, is there a difference in the mean waiting time?

For **DATA FILE**, please visit
www.mhhe.com/lind16e

33. Commercial Bank and Trust Company is studying the use of its automatic teller machines (ATMs). Of particular interest is whether young adults (under 25 years) use the machines more than senior citizens. To investigate further, samples of customers under 25 years of age and customers over 60 years of age were selected. The number of ATM transactions last month was determined for each selected individual, and the results are shown below. At the .01 significance level, can bank management conclude that younger customers use the ATMs more?

Under 25	10	10	11	15	7	11	10	9		
Over 60	4	8	7	7	4	5	1	7	4	10	5

For **DATA FILE**, please visit
www.mhhe.com/lind16e

34. Two boats, the *Prada* (Italy) and the *Oracle* (U.S.A.), are competing for a spot in the upcoming *America's Cup* race. They race over a part of the course several times. Below are a sample of times in minutes for each boat. Assume the population standard deviations are not the same. At the .05 significance level, can we conclude that there is a difference in their mean times?

Boat	Time (minutes)										
Prada (Italy)	12.9	12.5	11.0	13.3	11.2	11.4	11.6	12.3	14.2	11.3	
Oracle (U.S.A.)	14.1	14.1	14.2	17.4	15.8	16.7	16.1	13.3	13.4	13.6	10.8	19.0

For **DATA FILE**, please visit
www.mhhe.com/lind16e

35. The manufacturer of an MP3 player wanted to know whether a 10% reduction in price is enough to increase the sales of its product. To investigate, the owner randomly selected eight outlets and sold the MP3 player at the reduced price. At seven randomly selected outlets, the MP3 player was sold at the regular price. Reported below is the number of units sold last month at the regular and reduced prices at the randomly selected outlets. At the .01 significance level, can the manufacturer conclude that the price reduction resulted in an increase in sales?

Regular price	138	121	88	115	141	125	96	
Reduced price	128	134	152	135	114	106	112	120

For **DATA FILE**, please visit
www.mhhe.com/lind16e

36. A number of minor automobile accidents occur at various high-risk intersections in Teton County despite traffic lights. The Traffic Department claims that a modification in the type of light will reduce these accidents. The county commissioners have agreed to a proposed experiment. Eight intersections were chosen at random, and the lights at those intersections were modified. The numbers of minor accidents during a six-month period before and after the modifications were:

	Number of Accidents							
	A	B	C	D	E	F	G	H
Before modification	5	7	6	4	8	9	8	10
After modification	3	7	7	0	4	6	8	2

TWO-SAMPLE TESTS OF HYPOTHESIS   375

At the .01 significance level, is it reasonable to conclude that the modification reduced the number of traffic accidents?

For **DATA FILE**, please visit www.mhhe.com/lind16e

37. Lester Hollar is vice president for human resources for a large manufacturing company. In recent years, he has noticed an increase in absenteeism that he thinks is related to the general health of the employees. Four years ago, in an attempt to improve the situation, he began a fitness program in which employees exercise during their lunch hour. To evaluate the program, he selected a random sample of eight participants and found the number of days each was absent in the six months before the exercise program began and in the six months following the exercise program. Below are the results. At the .05 significance level, can he conclude that the number of absences has declined? Estimate the *p*-value.

Employee	Before	After
1	6	5
2	6	2
3	7	1
4	7	3
5	4	3
6	3	6
7	5	3
8	6	7

For **DATA FILE**, please visit www.mhhe.com/lind16e

38. The president of the American Insurance Institute wants to compare the yearly costs of auto insurance offered by two leading companies. He selects a sample of 15 families, some with only a single insured driver, others with several teenage drivers, and pays each family a stipend to contact the two companies and ask for a price quote. To make the data comparable, certain features, such as the deductible amount and limits of liability, are standardized. The data for the sample of families and their two insurance quotes are reported below. At the .10 significance level, can we conclude that there is a difference in the amounts quoted?

Family	Midstates Car Insurance	Gecko Mutual Insurance
Becker	$2,090	$1,610
Berry	1,683	1,247
Cobb	1,402	2,327
Debuck	1,830	1,367
DuBrul	930	1,461
Eckroate	697	1,789
German	1,741	1,621
Glasson	1,129	1,914
King	1,018	1,956
Kucic	1,881	1,772
Meredith	1,571	1,375
Obeid	874	1,527
Price	1,579	1,767
Phillips	1,577	1,636
Tresize	860	1,188

39. Fairfield Homes is developing two parcels near Pigeon Fork, Tennessee. In order to test different advertising approaches, it uses different media to reach potential buyers. The mean annual family income for 15 people making inquiries at the first development is $150,000, with a standard deviation of $40,000. A corresponding sample of 25 people at the second development had a mean of $180,000, with a standard deviation of $30,000. Assume the population standard deviations are the same. At the .05 significance level, can Fairfield conclude that the population means are different?

40. A candy company taste-tested two chocolate bars, one with almonds and one without almonds. A panel of testers rated the bars on a scale of 0 to 5, with 5 indicating the highest taste rating. If the bar had almonds, the rating was assigned a code of 1; if the bar did not have almonds, the rating was assigned a code of 0. Assume the population standard deviations are equal. At the .05 significance level, do the ratings show a difference between chocolate bars with or without almonds?

Rating	With/Without	Rating	With/Without
3	1	1	1
1	1	4	0
0	0	4	0
2	1	2	1
3	1	3	0
1	1	4	0

For **DATA FILE**, please visit
www.mhhe.com/lind16e

41. An investigation of the effectiveness of an antibacterial soap in reducing operating room contamination resulted in the accompanying table. The new soap was tested in a sample of eight operating rooms in the greater Seattle area during the last year. The following table reports the contamination levels before and after the use of the soap for each operating room.

	Operating Room							
	A	B	C	D	E	F	G	H
Before	6.6	6.5	9.0	10.3	11.2	8.1	6.3	11.6
After	6.8	2.4	7.4	8.5	8.1	6.1	3.4	2.0

At the .05 significance level, can we conclude the contamination measurements are lower after use of the new soap?

For **DATA FILE**, please visit
www.mhhe.com/lind16e

42. The following data on annual rates of return were collected from five randomly selected stocks listed on the New York Stock Exchange ("the big board") and five randomly selected stocks listed on NASDAQ. Assume the population standard deviations are the same. At the .10 significance level, can we conclude that the annual rates of return are higher on the big board?

NYSE	NASDAQ
17.16	15.80
17.08	16.28
15.51	16.21
8.43	17.97
25.15	7.77

For **DATA FILE**, please visit
www.mhhe.com/lind16e

43. The city of Laguna Beach operates two public parking lots. The Ocean Drive parking lot can accommodate up to 125 cars and the Rio Rancho parking lot can accommodate up to 130 cars. City planners are considering increasing the size of the lots and changing the fee structure. To begin, the Planning Office would like some information on the number of cars in the lots at various times of the day. A junior planner officer is assigned the task of visiting the two lots at random times of the day and evening and counting the number of cars in the lots. The study lasted over a period of one month. Below is the number of cars in the lots for 25 visits of the Ocean Drive lot and 28 visits of the Rio Rancho lot. Assume the population standard deviations are equal.

Ocean Drive												
89	115	93	79	113	77	51	75	118	105	106	91	54
63	121	53	81	115	67	53	69	95	121	88	64	
Rio Rancho												
128	110	81	126	82	114	93	40	94	45	84	71	74
92	66	69	100	114	113	107	62	77	80	107	90	129
105	124											

Is it reasonable to conclude that there is a difference in the mean number of cars in the two lots? Use the .05 significance level.

For **DATA FILE**, please visit
www.mhhe.com/lind16e

44. The amount of income spent on housing is an important component of the cost of living. The total costs of housing for homeowners might include mortgage payments, property taxes, and utility costs (water, heat, electricity). An economist selected a sample of

20 homeowners in New England and then calculated these total housing costs as a percent of monthly income, 5 years ago and now. The information is reported below. Is it reasonable to conclude the percent is less now than 5 years ago?

Homeowner	Five Years Ago	Now	Homeowner	Five Years Ago	Now
1	17%	10%	11	35%	32%
2	20	39	12	16	32
3	29	37	13	23	21
4	43	27	14	33	12
5	36	12	15	44	40
6	43	41	16	44	42
7	45	24	17	28	22
8	19	26	18	29	19
9	49	28	19	39	35
10	49	26	20	22	12

For **DATA FILE**, please visit
www.mhhe.com/lind16e

45. The CVS Pharmacy located on US 17 in Murrells Inlet has been one of the busiest pharmaceutical retail stores in South Carolina for many years. To try and capture more business in the area, CVS top management opened another store about 6 miles west on SC 707. After a few months, CVS management decided to compare the business volume at the two stores. One way to measure business volume is to count the number of cars in the store parking lots on random days and times. The results of the survey from the last 3 months of the year are reported below. To explain, the first observation was on October 2 at 20:52 military time (8:52 p.m.). At that time there were four cars in the US 17 lot and nine cars in the SC 707 lot. At the .05 significance level, is it reasonable to conclude that, based on vehicle counts, the US 17 store has more business volume than the SC 707 store?

		Vehicle Count	
Date	Time	US 17	SC 707
Oct 2	20:52	4	9
Oct 11	19:30	5	7
Oct 15	22:08	9	12
Oct 19	11:42	4	5
Oct 25	15:32	10	8
Oct 26	11:02	9	15
Nov 3	11:22	13	7
Nov 5	19:09	20	3
Nov 8	15:10	15	14
Nov 9	13:18	15	11
Nov 15	22:38	13	11
Nov 17	18:46	16	12
Nov 21	15:44	17	8
Nov 22	15:34	15	3
Nov 27	21:42	20	6
Nov 29	9:57	17	13
Nov 30	17:58	5	9
Dec 3	19:54	7	13
Dec 15	18:20	11	6
Dec 16	18:25	14	15
Dec 17	11:08	8	8
Dec 22	21:20	10	3
Dec 24	15:21	4	6
Dec 25	20:21	7	9
Dec 30	14:25	19	4

378   CHAPTER 11

46. A goal of financial literacy for children is to learn how to manage money wisely. One question is: How much money do children have to manage? A recent study by Schnur Educational Research Associates randomly sampled 15 children between 8 and 10 years old and 18 children between 11 and 14 years old and recorded their monthly allowance. Is it reasonable to conclude that the mean allowance received by children between 11 and 14 years is more than the allowance received by children between 8 and 10 years? Use the .01 significance level. What is the p-value?

8–10 Years	11–14 Years	8–10 Years	11–14 Years
6	19	6	11
13	14	5	8
10	12	7	14
6	8	9	9
14	9	14	20
6	11	12	19
7	9		11
7	8		12
10	8		20

D A T A   S E T   E X E R C I S E S

(The data for these exercises are available at the text website: www.mhhe.com/lind16e.)

47. Refer to the Real Estate data, which report information on the homes sold in Goodyear, Arizona, last year.
   a. At the .05 significance level, can we conclude that there is a difference in the mean selling price of homes with a pool and homes without a pool?
   b. At the .05 significance level, can we conclude that there is a difference in the mean selling price of homes with an attached garage and homes without an attached garage?
   c. At the .05 significance level, can we conclude that there is a difference in the mean selling price of homes in Township 1 and Township 2?

48. Refer to the Baseball 2012 data, which report information on the 30 Major League Baseball teams for the 2012 season.
   a. At the .05 significance level, can we conclude that there is a difference in the mean salary of teams in the American League versus teams in the National League?
   b. At the .05 significance level, can we conclude that there is a difference in the mean home attendance of teams in the American League versus teams in the National League?
   c. Compute the mean and the standard deviation of the number of wins for the 10 teams with the highest salaries. Do the same for the 10 teams with the lowest salaries. At the .05 significance level, is there a difference in the mean number of wins for the two groups?

49. Refer to the Buena School District bus data. Is there a difference in the mean maintenance cost for the diesel versus the gasoline buses? Use the .05 significance level.

Analysis of Variance

12

A SOFTWARE DESIGN COMPANY is creating a new, faster search engine. The search engine is clearly faster, but initial tests indicate there is more variation in the time to perform a search. A sample of 16 different searches showed that the standard deviation of the search time was 22 hundredths of a second for the new search engine and 12 hundredths of a second for the current search engine. At the .05 significance level, can we conclude that there is more variation in the search time of the new search engine? (See Exercise 24 and LO12-1.)

LEARNING OBJECTIVES

When you have completed this chapter, you will be able to:

LO12-1 Apply the F distribution to test a hypothesis that two population variances are equal.

LO12-2 Use ANOVA to test a hypothesis that three or more population means are equal.

LO12-3 Use confidence intervals to test and interpret differences between pairs of population means.

LO12-4 Use a blocking variable in a two-way ANOVA to test a hypothesis that three or more population means are equal.

LO12-5 Perform a two-way ANOVA with interaction and describe the results.

380   CHAPTER 12

INTRODUCTION

In this chapter, we continue our discussion of hypothesis testing. Recall that in Chapters 10 and 11 we examined the general theory of hypothesis testing. We described the case where a sample was selected from the population. We used the z distribution (the standard normal distribution) or the t distribution to determine whether it was reasonable to conclude that the population mean was equal to a specified value. We tested whether two population means are the same. In this chapter, we expand our idea of hypothesis tests. We describe a test for variances and then a test that simultaneously compares several means to determine if they came from equal populations.

COMPARING TWO POPULATION VARIANCES

In Chapter 11, we tested hypotheses about equal population means. The tests differed based on our assumptions regarding whether the population standard deviations or variances were equal or unequal. In this chapter, the assumption about equal population variances is also important. In this section, we present a way to statistically test this assumption. The test is based on the F distribution.

The F Distribution

The probability distribution used in this chapter is the F distribution. It was named to honor Sir Ronald Fisher, one of the founders of modern-day statistics. The test statistic for several situations follows this probability distribution. It is used to test whether two samples are from populations having equal variances, and it is also applied when we want to compare several population means simultaneously. The simultaneous comparison of several population means is called **analysis of variance (ANOVA)**. In both of these situations, the populations must follow a normal distribution, and the data must be at least interval-scale.

What are the characteristics of the F distribution?

1. **There is a family of F distributions.** A particular member of the family is determined by two parameters: the degrees of freedom in the numerator and the degrees of freedom in the denominator. The shape of the distribution is illustrated by the following graph. There is one F distribution for the combination of 29 degrees of freedom in the numerator (df) and 28 degrees of freedom in the denominator. There is another F distribution for 19 degrees of freedom in the numerator and 6 degrees of freedom in the denominator. The final distribution shown has 6 degrees of freedom in the numerator and 6 degrees of freedom in the denominator. We will describe the concept of degrees of freedom later in the chapter. Note that the shapes of the distributions change as the degrees of freedom change.

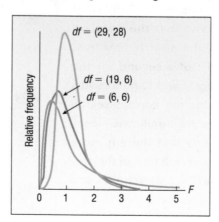

ANALYSIS OF VARIANCE   381

2. **The F distribution is continuous.** This means that it can assume an infinite number of values between zero and positive infinity.
3. **The F distribution cannot be negative.** The smallest value F can assume is 0.
4. **It is positively skewed.** The long tail of the distribution is to the right-hand side. As the number of degrees of freedom increases in both the numerator and denominator, the distribution approaches a normal distribution.
5. **It is asymptotic.** As the values of F increase, the distribution approaches the horizontal axis but never touches it. This is similar to the behavior of the normal probability distribution, described in Chapter 7.

Testing a Hypothesis of Equal Population Variances

The first application of the F distribution that we describe occurs when we test the hypothesis that the variance of one normal population equals the variance of another normal population. The following examples will show the use of the test:

- A health services corporation manages two hospitals in Knoxville, Tennessee: St. Mary's North and St. Mary's South. In each hospital, the mean waiting time in the Emergency Department is 42 minutes. The hospital administrator believes that the St. Mary's North Emergency Department has more variation in waiting time than St. Mary's South.

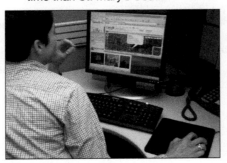

- The mean rate of return on two types of common stock may be the same, but there may be more variation in the rate of return in one than the other. A sample of 10 technology and 10 utility stocks shows the same mean rate of return, but there is likely more variation in the technology stocks.
- A study by the marketing department for a large newspaper found that men and women spent about the same amount of time per day surfing the Net. However, the same report indicated there was nearly twice as much variation in time spent per day among the men than the women.

The F distribution is also used to test assumptions for some statistical tests. Recall that in the previous chapter we used the t test to investigate whether the means of two independent populations differed. To employ that test, we sometimes assume that the variances of two normal populations are the same. See this list of assumptions on page 356. The F distribution is used to test the assumption that the variances of two normal populations are equal.

Regardless of whether we want to determine whether one population has more variation than another population or validate an assumption for a statistical test, we first state the null hypothesis. The null hypothesis is that the variance of one normal population, σ_1^2, equals the variance of another normal population, σ_2^2. The alternate hypothesis could be that the variances differ. In this instance, the null hypothesis and the alternate hypothesis are:

$$H_0: \sigma_1^2 = \sigma_2^2$$
$$H_1: \sigma_1^2 \neq \sigma_2^2$$

To conduct the test, we select a random sample of n_1 observations from one population and a random sample of n_2 observations from the second population. The test statistic is defined as follows.

382

CHAPTER 12

| TEST STATISTIC FOR COMPARING TWO VARIANCES | $F = \dfrac{s_1^2}{s_2^2}$ | [12–1] |

The terms s_1^2 and s_2^2 are the respective sample variances. If the null hypothesis is true, the test statistic follows the F distribution with $n_1 - 1$ and $n_2 - 1$ degrees of freedom. To reduce the size of the table of critical values, the *larger* sample variance is placed in the numerator; hence, the tabled F ratio is always larger than 1.00. Thus, the right-tail critical value is the only one required. The critical value of F for a two-tailed test is found by dividing the significance level in half $(\alpha/2)$ and then referring to the appropriate degrees of freedom in Appendix B.6. An example will illustrate.

EXAMPLE

Lammers Limos offers limousine service from Government Center in downtown Toledo, Ohio, to Metro Airport in Detroit. Sean Lammers, president of the company, is considering two routes. One is via U.S. 25 and the other via I-75. He wants to study the time it takes to drive to the airport using each route and then compare the results. He collected the following sample data, which is reported in minutes. Using the .10 significance level, is there a difference in the variation in the driving times for the two routes?

U.S. Route 25	Interstate 75
52	59
67	60
56	61
45	51
70	56
54	63
64	57
	65

SOLUTION

The mean driving times along the two routes are nearly the same. The mean time is 58.29 minutes for the U.S. 25 route and 59.0 minutes along the I-75 route. However, in evaluating travel times, Mr. Lammers is also concerned about the variation in the travel times. The first step is to compute the two sample variances. We'll use formula (3–11) to compute the sample standard deviations. To obtain the sample variances, we square the standard deviations.

U.S. Route 25

$$\bar{x} = \frac{\Sigma x}{n} = \frac{408}{7} = 58.29 \qquad s = \sqrt{\frac{\Sigma(x - \bar{x})^2}{n - 1}} = \sqrt{\frac{485.43}{7 - 1}} = 8.9947$$

Interstate 75

$$\bar{x} = \frac{\Sigma x}{n} = \frac{472}{8} = 59.00 \qquad s = \sqrt{\frac{\Sigma(x - \bar{x})^2}{n - 1}} = \sqrt{\frac{134}{8 - 1}} = 4.3753$$

ANALYSIS OF VARIANCE   383

There is more variation, as measured by the standard deviation, in the U.S. 25 route than in the I-75 route. This is consistent with his knowledge of the two routes; the U.S. 25 route contains more stoplights, whereas I-75 is a limited-access interstate highway. However, the I-75 route is several miles longer. It is important that the service offered be both timely and consistent, so he decides to conduct a statistical test to determine whether there really is a difference in the variation of the two routes.

We use the six-step hypothesis test procedure.

Step 1: We begin by stating the null hypothesis and the alternate hypothesis. The test is two-tailed because we are looking for a difference in the variation of the two routes. We are *not* trying to show that one route has more variation than the other. For this example/solution, the subscript 1 indicates information for U.S. 25; the subscript 2 indicates information for I-75.

$$H_0: \sigma_1^2 = \sigma_2^2$$
$$H_1: \sigma_1^2 \neq \sigma_2^2$$

Step 2: We selected the .10 significance level.

Step 3: The appropriate test statistic follows the F distribution.

Step 4: The critical value is obtained from Appendix B.6, a portion of which is reproduced as Table 12–1. Because we are conducting a two-tailed test, the tabled significance level is .05, found by $\alpha/2 = .10/2 = .05$. There are $n_1 - 1 = 7 - 1 = 6$ degrees of freedom in the numerator and $n_2 - 1 = 8 - 1 = 7$ degrees of freedom in the denominator. To find the critical value, move horizontally across the top portion of the F table (Table 12–1 or Appendix B.6) for the .05 significance level to 6 degrees of freedom in the numerator. Then move down that column to the critical value opposite 7 degrees of freedom in the denominator. The critical value is 3.87. Thus, the decision rule is: Reject the null hypothesis if the ratio of the sample variances exceeds 3.87.

TABLE 12–1 Critical Values of the F Distribution, $\alpha = .05$

Degrees of Freedom for Denominator	Degrees of Freedom for Numerator			
	5	6	7	8
1	230	234	237	239
2	19.3	19.3	19.4	19.4
3	9.01	8.94	8.89	8.85
4	6.26	6.16	6.09	6.04
5	5.05	4.95	4.88	4.82
6	4.39	4.28	4.21	4.15
7	3.97	3.87	3.79	3.73
8	3.69	3.58	3.50	3.44
9	3.48	3.37	3.29	3.23
10	3.33	3.22	3.14	3.07

Step 5: Next we compute the ratio of the two sample variances, determine the value of the test statistic, and make a decision regarding the null hypothesis. Note that formula (12–1) refers to the sample *variances,*

but we calculated the sample *standard deviations*. We need to square the standard deviations to determine the variances.

$$F = \frac{s_1^2}{s_2^2} = \frac{(8.9947)^2}{(4.3753)^2} = 4.23$$

The decision is to reject the null hypothesis because the computed *F* value (4.23) is larger than the critical value (3.87).

Step 6: We conclude there is a difference in the variation in the time to travel the two routes. Mr. Lammers will want to consider this in his scheduling.

The usual practice is to determine the *F* ratio by putting the larger of the two sample variances in the numerator. This will force the *F* ratio to be at least 1.00. This allows us to always use the right tail of the *F* distribution, thus avoiding the need for more extensive *F* tables.

A logical question arises: Is it possible to conduct one-tailed tests? For example, suppose in the previous example we suspected that the variance of the times using the U.S. 25 route, σ_1^2, is larger than the variance of the times along the I-75 route, σ_2^2. We would state the null and the alternate hypothesis as

$$H_0: \sigma_1^2 \le \sigma_2^2$$
$$H_1: \sigma_1^2 > \sigma_2^2$$

The test statistic is computed as s_1^2/s_2^2. Notice that we labeled the population with the suspected large variance as population 1. So s_1^2 appears in the numerator. The *F* ratio will be larger than 1.00, so we can use the upper tail of the *F* distribution. Under these conditions, it is not necessary to divide the significance level in half. Because Appendix B.6 gives us only the .05 and .01 significance levels, we are restricted to these levels for one-tailed tests and .10 and .02 for two-tailed tests unless we consult a more complete table or use statistical software to compute the *F* statistic.

The Excel software has a procedure to perform a test of variances. Below is the output. The computed value of *F* is the same as that determined by using formula (12–1).

	A	B	C	D	E	F	G
1	U.S. 25	Interstate 75		F-Test Two-Sample for Variances			
2	52	59			U.S. 25	Interstate 75	
3	67	60		Mean	58.29	59.00	
4	56	61		Variance	80.90	19.14	
5	45	51		Observations	7.00	8.00	
6	70	56		df	6.00	7.00	
7	54	63		F	4.23		
8	64	57		P(F<=f) one-tail	0.04		
9		65		F Critical one-tail	3.87		
10							

Variance Test

SELF-REVIEW
12–1

Steele Electric Products Inc. assembles electrical components for cell phones. For the last 10 days, Mark Nagy has averaged 9 rejects, with a standard deviation of 2 rejects per day. Debbie Richmond averaged 8.5 rejects, with a standard deviation of 1.5 rejects, over the same period. At the .05 significance level, can we conclude that there is more variation in the number of rejects per day attributed to Mark?

ANALYSIS OF VARIANCE   385

E X E R C I S E S

▼

1. What is the critical F value for a sample of six observations in the numerator and four in the denominator? Use a two-tailed test and the .10 significance level.
2. What is the critical F value for a sample of four observations in the numerator and seven in the denominator? Use a one-tailed test and the .01 significance level.
3. The following hypotheses are given.

$$H_0: \sigma_1^2 = \sigma_2^2$$
$$H_1: \sigma_1^2 \neq \sigma_2^2$$

A random sample of eight observations from the first population resulted in a standard deviation of 10. A random sample of six observations from the second population resulted in a standard deviation of 7. At the .02 significance level, is there a difference in the variation of the two populations?
4. The following hypotheses are given.

$$H_0: \sigma_1^2 \leq \sigma_2^2$$
$$H_1: \sigma_1^2 > \sigma_2^2$$

A random sample of five observations from the first population resulted in a standard deviation of 12. A random sample of seven observations from the second population showed a standard deviation of 7. At the .01 significance level, is there more variation in the first population?
5. Arbitron Media Research Inc. conducted a study of the iPod listening habits of men and women. One facet of the study involved the mean listening time. It was discovered that the mean listening time for men was 35 minutes per day. The standard deviation of the sample of the 10 men studied was 10 minutes per day. The mean listening time for the 12 women studied was also 35 minutes, but the standard deviation of the sample was 12 minutes. At the .10 significance level, can we conclude that there is a difference in the variation in the listening times for men and women?
6. A stockbroker at Critical Securities reported that the mean rate of return on a sample of 10 oil stocks was 12.6% with a standard deviation of 3.9%. The mean rate of return on a sample of 8 utility stocks was 10.9% with a standard deviation of 3.5%. At the .05 significance level, can we conclude that there is more variation in the oil stocks?

LO12-2

Use ANOVA to test a hypothesis that three or more population means are equal.

ANOVA: ANALYSIS OF VARIANCE

The F distribution is used to perform a wide variety of hypothesis tests. For example, when the equality of more than two population means is tested, the Analysis of Variance (ANOVA) technique is used and the F statistic is used as the test statistic.

ANOVA Assumptions

The ANOVA to test the equality of more than two population means requires that three assumptions are true:

1. The populations follow the normal distribution.
2. The populations have equal standard deviations (σ).
3. The populations are independent.

When these conditions are met, F is used as the distribution of the test statistic.

Why do we need to study ANOVA? Why can't we just use the test of differences in population means discussed in the previous chapter? We could compare the population means two at a time. The major reason is the unsatisfactory buildup of Type I error. To explain further, suppose we have four different methods (A, B, C, and D) of training new recruits to be firefighters. We randomly assign each of the 40 recruits in this year's class to one of the four methods. At the end of the training program, we administer to the four groups a common test to measure understanding of firefighting techniques. The question is: Is there a difference in the mean test scores among the four groups? An answer to this question will allow us to compare the four training methods.

Using the t distribution to compare the four population means, we would have to conduct six different t tests. That is, we would need to compare the mean scores for the

386

CHAPTER 12

four methods as follows: A versus B, A versus C, A versus D, B versus C, B versus D, and C versus D. For each t test, suppose we choose an $\alpha = .05$. Therefore, the probability of a Type I error, rejecting the null when it is true, is .05. The complement is the probability of .95 that we do not reject the null when it is true. Because we conduct six separate (independent) tests, the probability that all six tests result in correct decisions is:

$$P(\textit{All correct}) = (.95)(.95)(.95)(.95)(.95)(.95) = .735$$

To find the probability of at least one error due to sampling, we subtract this result from 1. Thus, the probability of at least one incorrect decision due to sampling is $1 - .735 = .265$. To summarize, if we conduct six independent tests using the t distribution, the likelihood of rejecting a true null hypothesis because of sampling error is an unsatisfactory .265. The ANOVA technique allows us to compare population means simultaneously at a selected significance level. It avoids the buildup of Type I error associated with testing many hypotheses.

ANOVA was first developed for applications in agriculture, and many of the terms related to that context remain. In particular, the term *treatment* is used to identify the different populations being examined. For example, treatment refers to how a plot of ground was treated with a particular type of fertilizer. The following illustration will clarify the term *treatment* and demonstrate an application of ANOVA.

EXAMPLE

Joyce Kuhlman manages a regional financial center. She wishes to compare the productivity, as measured by the number of customers served, among three employees. Four days are randomly selected and the number of customers served by each employee is recorded. The results are:

Wolfe	White	Korosa
55	66	47
54	76	51
59	67	46
56	71	48

SOLUTION

Is there a difference in the mean number of customers served? Chart 12–1 illustrates how the populations would appear if there were a difference in the treatment means. Note that the populations follow the normal distribution and the variation in each population is the same. However, the means are *not* the same.

CHART 12–1 Case Where Treatment Means Are Different

Suppose the populations are the same. That is, there is no difference in the (treatment) means. This is shown in Chart 12–2. This would indicate that the population means are the same. Note again that the populations follow the normal distribution and the variation in each of the populations is the same.

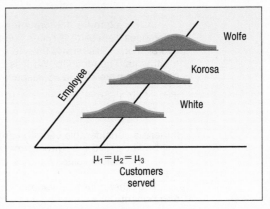

CHART 12–2 Case Where Treatment Means Are the Same

The ANOVA Test

How does the ANOVA test work? Recall that we want to determine whether the various sample means came from a single population or populations with different means. We actually compare these sample means through their variances. To explain, on page 385 we listed the assumptions required for ANOVA. One of those assumptions was that the standard deviations of the various normal populations had to be the same. We take advantage of this requirement in the ANOVA test. The underlying strategy is to estimate the population variance (standard deviation squared) two ways and then find the ratio of these two estimates. If this ratio is about 1, then logically the two estimates are the same, and we conclude that the population means are the same. If the ratio is quite different from 1, then we conclude that the population means are not the same. The F distribution serves as a referee by indicating when the ratio of the sample variances is too much greater than 1 to have occurred by chance.

Refer to the example/solution in the previous section. The manager wants to determine whether there is a difference in the mean number of customers served. To begin, find the overall mean of the 12 observations. It is 58, found by $(55 + 54 + \cdots + 48)/12$. Next, for each of the 12 observations find the difference between the particular value and the overall mean. Each of these differences is squared and these squares summed. This term is called the **total variation.**

> **TOTAL VARIATION** The sum of the squared differences between each observation and the overall mean.

In our example, the total variation is 1,082, found by $(55 - 58)^2 + (54 - 58)^2 + \cdots + (48 - 58)^2$.

Next, break this total variation into two components: that which is due to the **treatments** and that which is **random.** To find these two components, determine the mean of each of the treatments. The first source of variation is due to the treatments.

> **TREATMENT VARIATION** The sum of the squared differences between each treatment mean and the grand or overall mean.

In the example, the variation due to the treatments is the sum of the squared differences between the mean number of customers served by each employee and the overall mean. This term is 992. To calculate it, we first find the mean of each of the three treatments. The mean for Wolfe is 56 customers, found by $(55 + 54 + 59 + 56)/4$. The other means are 70 and 48, respectively. The sum of the squares due to the treatments is:

$$(56 - 58)^2 + (56 - 58)^2 + \cdots + (48 - 58)^2 = 4(56 - 58)^2 + 4(70 - 58)^2 + 4(48 - 58)^2$$
$$= 992$$

If there is considerable variation among the treatment means, it is logical that this term will be large. If the treatment means are similar, this term will be a small value. The smallest possible value would be zero. This would occur when all the treatment means are the same.

The other source of variation is referred to as the **random** component, or the error component.

> **RANDOM VARIATION** The sum of the squared differences between each observation and its treatment mean.

In the example, this term is the sum of the squared differences between each value and the mean for that particular employee. The error variation is 90.

$$(55 - 56)^2 + (54 - 56)^2 + \cdots + (48 - 48)^2 = 90$$

We determine the test statistic, which is the ratio of the two estimates of the population variance, from the following equation.

$$F = \frac{\text{Estimate of the population variance}}{\text{based on the differences among the sample means}}{\text{Estimate of the population variance}}{\text{based on the variation within the sample}}$$

Our first estimate of the population variance is based on the treatments, that is, the difference *between* the means. It is 992/2. Why did we divide by 2? Recall from Chapter 3, to find a sample variance [see formula (3–11)], we divide by the number of observations minus one. In this case, there are three treatments, so we divide by 2. Our first estimate of the population variance is 992/2.

The variance estimate *within* the treatments is the random variation divided by the total number of observations less the number of treatments—that is, $90/(12 - 3)$. Hence, our second estimate of the population variance is 90/9. This is actually a generalization of formula (11–5), where we pooled the sample variances from two populations.

The last step is to take the ratio of these two estimates.

$$F = \frac{992/2}{90/9} = 49.6$$

Because this ratio is quite different from 1, we can conclude that the treatment means are not the same. There is a difference in the mean number of customers served by the three employees.

Here's another example, which deals with samples of different sizes.

ANALYSIS OF VARIANCE   389

EXAMPLE

Recently airlines cut services, such as meals and snacks during flights, and started charging for checked luggage. A group of four carriers hired Brunner Marketing Research Inc. to survey passengers regarding their level of satisfaction with a recent flight. The survey included questions on ticketing, boarding, in-flight service, baggage handling, pilot communication, and so forth. Twenty-five questions offered a range of possible answers: excellent, good, fair, or poor. A response of excellent was given a score of 4, good a 3, fair a 2, and poor a 1. These responses were then totaled, so the total score was an indication of the satisfaction with the flight. The greater the score, the higher the level of satisfaction with the service. The highest possible score was 100.

Brunner randomly selected and surveyed passengers from the four airlines. Below is the sample information. Is there a difference in the mean satisfaction level among the four airlines? Use the .01 significance level.

Northern	WTA	Pocono	Branson
94	75	70	68
90	68	73	70
85	77	76	72
80	83	78	65
	88	80	74
		68	65
		65	

SOLUTION

We will use the six-step hypothesis-testing procedure.

Step 1: **State the null hypothesis and the alternate hypothesis.** The null hypothesis is that the mean scores are the same for the four airlines.

$$H_0: \mu_N = \mu_W = \mu_P = \mu_B$$

The alternate hypothesis is that the mean scores are not all the same for the four airlines.

H_1: The mean scores are not all equal.

We can also think of the alternate hypothesis as "at least two mean scores are not equal."

If the null hypothesis is not rejected, we conclude that there is no difference in the mean scores for the four airlines. If H_0 is rejected, we conclude that there is a difference in at least one pair of mean scores, but at this point we do not know which pair or how many pairs differ.

Step 2: **Select the level of significance.** We selected the .01 significance level.

Step 3: **Determine the test statistic.** The test statistic follows the F distribution.

Step 4: **Formulate the decision rule.** To determine the decision rule, we need the critical value. The critical value for the F statistic is found in Appendix B.6. The critical values for the .05 significance level are found on the first page and the .01 significance level on the second page. To use this table, we need to know the degrees of freedom in the numerator and the denominator. The degrees of freedom in the numerator equal the number of treatments, designated as *k,* minus 1. The degrees of freedom in the denominator are the total number of observations, *n,* minus the number of treatments. For this problem, there are four treatments and a total of 22 observations.

Degrees of freedom in the numerator $= k - 1 = 4 - 1 = 3$

Degrees of freedom in the denominator $= n - k = 22 - 4 = 18$

Refer to Appendix B.6 and the .01 significance level. Move horizontally across the top of the page to 3 degrees of freedom in the numerator. Then move down that column to the row with 18 degrees of freedom. The value at this intersection is 5.09. So the decision rule is to reject H_0 if the computed value of *F* exceeds 5.09.

Step 5: **Select the sample, perform the calculations, and make a decision.** It is convenient to summarize the calculations of the *F* statistic in an **ANOVA table.** The format for an ANOVA table is as follows. Statistical software packages also use this format.

ANOVA Table				
Source of Variation	**Sum of Squares**	**Degrees of Freedom**	**Mean Square**	**F**
Treatments	SST	$k - 1$	$SST/(k - 1) = MST$	MST/MSE
Error	SSE	$n - k$	$SSE/(n - k) = MSE$	
Total	SS total	$n - 1$		

There are three values, or sum of squares, used to compute the test statistic *F*. You can determine these values by obtaining SS total and SSE, then finding SST by subtraction. The SS total term is the total variation, SST is the variation due to the treatments, and SSE is the variation within the treatments or the random error.

We usually start the process by finding SS total. This is the sum of the squared differences between each observation and the overall mean. The formula for finding SS total is:

$$SS\ total = \Sigma(x - \bar{x}_G)^2 \qquad \textbf{[12–2]}$$

where:

x is each sample observation.
$\bar{x}_G$ is the overall or grand mean.

Next determine SSE or the sum of the squared errors. This is the sum of the squared differences between each observation and its respective treatment mean. The formula for finding SSE is:

$$SSE = \Sigma(x - \bar{x}_c)^2 \qquad \textbf{[12–3]}$$

where:
$\bar{x}_c$ is the sample mean for treatment *c*.

The SSE is calculated:

$$SSE = \Sigma(x - \bar{x}_N)^2 + \Sigma(x - \bar{x}_W)^2 + \Sigma(x - \bar{x}_P)^2 + \Sigma(x - \bar{x}_B)^2$$

The detailed calculations of SS total and SSE for this example follow. To determine the values of SS total and SSE we start by calculating the overall or grand mean. There are 22 observations and the total is 1,664, so the grand mean is 75.64.

$$\bar{x}_G = \frac{1,664}{22} = 75.64$$

	Northern	WTA	Pocono	Branson	Total
	94	75	70	68	
	90	68	73	70	
	85	77	76	72	
	80	83	78	65	
		88	80	74	
			68	65	
			65		
Column total	349	391	510	414	1,664
n	4	5	7	6	22
Mean	87.25	78.20	72.86	69.00	75.64

(Grand Mean → 1,664 / 75.64)

Next we find the deviation of each observation from the grand mean, square those deviations, and sum this result for all 22 observations. For example, the first sampled passenger had a score of 94 and the overall or grand mean is 75.64. So $(x - \bar{x}_G) = 94 - 75.64 = 18.36$. For the last passenger, $(x - \bar{x}_G) = 65 - 75.64 = -10.64$. The calculations for all other passengers follow.

Northern	WTA	Pocono	Branson
18.36	−0.64	−5.64	−7.64
14.36	−7.64	−2.64	−5.64
9.36	1.36	0.36	−3.64
4.36	7.36	2.36	−10.64
	12.36	4.36	−1.64
		−7.64	−10.64
		−10.64	

Then square each of these differences and sum all the values. Thus, for the first passenger:

$$(x - \bar{x}_G)^2 = (94 - 75.64)^2 = (18.36)^2 = 337.09$$

Finally, sum all the squared differences as formula (12–2) directs. Our SS total value is 1,485.10.

	Northern	WTA	Pocono	Branson	Total
	337.09	0.41	31.81	58.37	
	206.21	58.37	6.97	31.81	
	87.61	1.85	0.13	13.25	
	19.01	54.17	5.57	113.21	
		152.77	19.01	2.69	
			58.37	113.21	
			113.21		
Total	649.92	267.57	235.07	332.54	1,485.10

(SS Total → 1,485.10)

To compute the term SSE, find the deviation between each observation and its treatment mean. In the example, the mean of the first treatment (that is, the passengers on Northern Airlines) is 87.25, found by $\bar{x}_N = 349/4$. The subscript N refers to Northern Airlines.

392   CHAPTER 12

The first passenger rated Northern a 94, so $(x - \bar{x}_N) = (94 - 87.25) = 6.75$. The first passenger in the WTA group responded with a total score of 75, so $(x - \bar{x}_W) = (75 - 78.20) = -3.2$. The detail for all the passengers follows.

Northern	WTA	Pocono	Branson
6.75	−3.2	−2.86	−1
2.75	−10.2	0.14	1
−2.25	−1.2	3.14	3
−7.25	4.8	5.14	−4
	9.8	7.14	5
		−4.86	−4
		−7.86	

Each of these values is squared and then summed for all 22 observations. The four column totals can also be summed to find SSE.
The values are shown in the following table.

	Northern	WTA	Pocono	Branson	Total
	45.5625	10.24	8.18	1	
	7.5625	104.04	0.02	1	
	5.0625	1.44	9.86	9	
	52.5625	23.04	26.42	16	
		96.04	50.98	25	SSE
			23.62	16	
			61.78		
Total	110.7500	234.80	180.86	68	594.41

So the SSE value is 594.41. That is, $\Sigma(x - \bar{x}_c)^2 = 594.41$.
    Finally, we determine SST, the sum of the squares due to the
treatments, by subtraction.

$$SST = SS\ total - SSE \qquad\qquad \text{[12–4]}$$

For this example:

$$SST = SS\ total - SSE = 1,485.10 - 594.41 = 890.69.$$

To find the computed value of F, work your way across the ANOVA
table. The degrees of freedom for the numerator and the denominator are the same as in step 4 on page 389 when we were finding the
critical value of F. The term **mean square** is another expression for
an estimate of the variance. The mean square for treatments is SST
divided by its degrees of freedom. The result is the **mean square
for treatments** and is written MST. Compute the **mean square
error** in a similar fashion. To be precise, divide SSE by its degrees of
freedom. To complete the process and find F, divide MST by MSE.
    Insert the particular values of F into an ANOVA table and com-
pute the value of F as follows.

Source of Variation	Sum of Squares	Degrees of Freedom	Mean Square	F
Treatments	890.69	3	296.90	8.99
Error	594.41	18	33.02	
Total	1,485.10	21		

ANALYSIS OF VARIANCE 393

> The computed value of F is 8.99, which is greater than the critical value of 5.09, so the null hypothesis is rejected.
>
> **Step 6: Interpret the result.** We conclude the population means are not all equal. At this point, the results of the ANOVA only show that at least one pair of mean satisfaction scores are not the same among the four airlines. We cannot statistically show which airlines differ in satisfaction or which airlines have the highest or lowest satisfaction scores. The techniques for determining how the airlines differ are presented in the next section.

The calculations in the previous example/solution are tedious if the number of observations in each treatment is large. Many software packages will perform the calculations and output the results. In the following illustration, Excel is used to calculate the descriptive statistics and ANOVA for the previous example/solution involving airlines and passenger ratings. There are some slight differences between the software output and the previous calculations. These differences are due to rounding.

Airline Anova												
	A	B	C	D	E	F	G	H	I	J	K	L	M
1	Northern	WTA	Pocono	Branson		Anova: Single Factor							
2	94	75	70	68									
3	90	68	73	70		SUMMARY							
4	85	77	76	72		Groups	Count	Sum	Average	Variance			
5	80	83	78	65		Northern	4	349	87.250	36.917			
6		88	80	74		WTA	5	391	78.200	58.700			
7			68	65		Pocono	7	510	72.857	30.143			
8			65			Branson	6	414	69.000	13.600			
9													
10						ANOVA							
11						Source of Variation	SS	df	MS	F	P-value	F crit	
12						Between Groups	890.684	3	296.895	8.99	0.0007	3.160	
13						Within Groups	594.407	18	33.023				
14													
15						Total	1485.091	21					
16													

Notice Excel uses the term "Between Groups" for treatments and "Within Groups" for error. However, they have the same meanings. The p-value is .0007. This is the probability of finding a value of the test statistic this large or larger when the null hypothesis is true. To put it another way, it is the likelihood of calculating an F value larger than 8.99 with 3 degrees of freedom in the numerator and 18 degrees of freedom in the denominator. So when we reject the null hypothesis in this instance, there is a very small likelihood of committing a Type I error!

**SELF-REVIEW
12–2**

Citrus Clean is a new all-purpose cleaner being test-marketed by placing displays in three different locations within various supermarkets. The number of 12-ounce bottles sold from each location within the supermarket is reported below.

Near bread	18	14	19	17
Near beer	12	18	10	16
Other cleaners	26	28	30	32

At the .05 significance level, is there a difference in the mean number of bottles sold at the three locations?
(a) State the null hypothesis and the alternate hypothesis.
(b) What is the decision rule?
(c) Compute the values of SS total, SST, and SSE.
(d) Develop an ANOVA table.
(e) What is your decision regarding the null hypothesis?

7. The following are four observations collected from each of three treatments. Test the hypothesis that the treatment means are equal. Use the .05 significance level.

Treatment 1	Treatment 2	Treatment 3
8	3	3
6	2	4
10	4	5
9	3	4

   a. State the null and the alternate hypotheses.
   b. What is the decision rule?
   c. Compute SST, SSE, and SS total.
   d. Complete an ANOVA table.
   e. State your decision regarding the null hypothesis.

8. The following are six observations collected from treatment 1, four observations collected from treatment 2, and five observations collected from treatment 3. Test the hypothesis at the .05 significance level that the treatment means are equal.

Treatment 1	Treatment 2	Treatment 3
9	13	10
7	20	9
11	14	15
9	13	14
12		15
10		

   a. State the null and the alternate hypotheses.
   b. What is the decision rule?
   c. Compute SST, SSE, and SS total.
   d. Complete an ANOVA table.
   e. State your decision regarding the null hypothesis.

9. A real estate developer is considering investing in a shopping mall on the outskirts of Atlanta, Georgia. Three parcels of land are being evaluated. Of particular importance is the income in the area surrounding the proposed mall. A random sample of four families is selected near each proposed mall. Following are the sample results. At the .05 significance level, can the developer conclude there is a difference in the mean income? Use the usual six-step hypothesis testing procedure.

For **DATA FILE**, please visit
www.mhhe.com/lind16e

Southwyck Area ($000)	Franklin Park ($000)	Old Orchard ($000)
64	74	75
68	71	80
70	69	76
60	70	78

10. The manager of a computer software company wishes to study the number of hours senior executives by type of industry spend at their desktop computers. The manager selected a sample of five executives from each of three industries. At the .05 significance level, can she conclude there is a difference in the mean number of hours spent per week by industry?

For **DATA FILE**, please visit
www.mhhe.com/lind16e

Banking	Retail	Insurance
12	8	10
10	8	8
10	6	6
12	8	8
10	10	10

LO12-3

Use confidence intervals to test and interpret differences between pairs of population means.

INFERENCES ABOUT PAIRS OF TREATMENT MEANS

Suppose we carry out the ANOVA procedure and make the decision to reject the null hypothesis. This allows us to conclude that all the treatment means are not the same. Sometimes we may be satisfied with this conclusion, but in other instances we may want to know which treatment means differ. This section provides the details for such a test.

Recall in the previous example/solution regarding airline passenger ratings, we concluded that there was a difference in the treatment means. That is, the null hypothesis was rejected and the alternate hypothesis accepted. If the passenger ratings do differ, the question is: Between which groups do the treatment means differ?

Several procedures are available to answer this question. The simplest is through the use of confidence intervals, that is, formula (9–2). From the computer output of the previous example (see page 393), the sample mean score for those passengers rating Northern's service is 87.25, and for those rating Branson's service, the sample mean score is 69.00. Is there enough disparity to justify the conclusion that there is a significant difference in the mean satisfaction scores of the two airlines?

The t distribution, described in Chapters 10 and 11, is used as the basis for this test. Recall that one of the assumptions of ANOVA is that the population variances are the same for all treatments. This common population value is the **mean square error,** or MSE, and is determined by $SSE/(n - k)$. A confidence interval for the difference between two populations is found by:

CONFIDENCE INTERVAL FOR THE DIFFERENCE IN TREATMENT MEANS	$(\bar{x}_1 - \bar{x}_2) \pm t\sqrt{MSE\left(\dfrac{1}{n_1} + \dfrac{1}{n_2}\right)}$	**[12–5]**

where:

$\bar{x}_1$ is the mean of the first sample.
$\bar{x}_2$ is the mean of the second sample.
t is obtained from Appendix B.5. The degrees of freedom are equal to $n - k$.
MSE is the mean square error term obtained from the ANOVA table [$SSE/(n - k)$].
n_1 is the number of observations in the first sample.
n_2 is the number of observations in the second sample.

How do we decide whether there is a difference in the treatment means? If the confidence interval includes zero, there is *not* a difference between the treatment means. For example, if the left endpoint of the confidence interval has a negative sign and the right endpoint has a positive sign, the interval includes zero and the two means do not differ. So if we develop a confidence interval from formula (12–5) and find the difference in the sample means was 5.00—that is, if $\bar{x}_1 - \bar{x}_2 = 5$ and $t\sqrt{MSE\left(\dfrac{1}{n_1} + \dfrac{1}{n_2}\right)} = 12$—the confidence interval would range from −7.00 up to 17.00. To put it in symbols:

$$(\bar{x}_1 - \bar{x}_2) \pm t\sqrt{MSE\left(\frac{1}{n_1} + \frac{1}{n_2}\right)} = 5.00 \pm 12.00 = -7.00 \text{ up to } 17.00$$

Note that zero is in this interval. Therefore, we conclude that there is no significant difference in the selected treatment means.

On the other hand, if the endpoints of the confidence interval have the same sign, this indicates that the treatment means differ. For example, if $\bar{x}_1 - \bar{x}_2 = -0.35$ and $t\sqrt{MSE\left(\dfrac{1}{n_1} + \dfrac{1}{n_2}\right)} = 0.25$, the confidence interval would range from −0.60 up to −0.10. Because −0.60 and −0.10 have the same sign, both negative, zero is not in the interval and we conclude that these treatment means differ.

396   CHAPTER 12

Using the previous airline example, let us compute the confidence interval for the difference between the mean scores of passengers on Northern and Branson. With a 95% level of confidence, the endpoints of the confidence interval are 10.457 and 26.043.

$$(\bar{x}_N - \bar{x}_B) \pm t\sqrt{MSE\left(\frac{1}{n_N} + \frac{1}{n_B}\right)} = (87.25 - 69.00) \pm 2.101\sqrt{33.023\left(\frac{1}{4} + \frac{1}{6}\right)}$$

$$= 18.25 \pm 7.793$$

where:

$\bar{x}_N$ is 87.25.

$\bar{x}_B$ is 69.00.

t is 2.101: from Appendix B.5 with $(n - k) = 22 - 4 = 18$ degrees of freedom.

MSE is 33.023: from the ANOVA table with $SSE/(n - k) = 594.4/18$.

N_N is 4.

N_B is 6.

The 95% confidence interval ranges from 10.457 up to 26.043. Both endpoints are positive; hence, we can conclude these treatment means differ significantly. That is, passengers on Northern Airlines rated service significantly different from those on Branson Airlines.

The differences between each pair of means can be obtained directly from Minitab using the one-way ANOVA analysis and Fisher's method to compare means. The Minitab output follows.

```
Branson subtracted from:

            Lower   Center   Upper    -----+---------+---------+---------+-----
Pocono     -2.860    3.857   10.574              (----*---)
WTA         1.889    9.200   16.511                 (----*----)
Northern   10.457   18.250   26.043                        (----*----)
                                       -----+---------+---------+---------+-----
                                          -15        0        15        30


Pocono subtracted from:

            Lower   Center   Upper    -----+---------+---------+---------+-----
WTA        -1.726    5.343   12.412              (----*---)
Northern    6.826   14.393   21.960                     (----*----)
                                       -----+---------+---------+---------+-----
                                          -15        0        15        30


WTA subtracted from:

            Lower   Center   Upper    -----+---------+---------+---------+-----
Northern    0.951    9.050   17.149                 (----*----)
                                       -----+---------+---------+---------+-----
                                          -15        0        15        30
```

The output shows the confidence intervals for the difference between each pair of treatment means. Starting at the top of the table, the confidence intervals for the difference between the Branson treatment mean and each of the other treatment means are shown. On the left, each row shows the center or difference between the treatment means and the lower and upper endpoints of the confidence interval. Again, if zero is not in the interval, then the two treatment means are significantly different. Note that the confidence interval for the difference between Branson and Northern is the same as the results above. These two treatment means are significantly different.

On the right side of the output is a graphic showing the confidence interval for the difference between each pair of treatment means. The asterisk (*) indicates the center location of the difference between the treatment means. The open and closed parentheses show the endpoints of the interval. Using the graphic, we can easily see which intervals do not include zero and indicate the significantly different treatment means. The Branson treatment mean is different from the WTA and Northern means; the Pocono treatment mean is different from the Northern mean; and the WTA treatment mean is different from the Northern mean.

ANALYSIS OF VARIANCE   397

We should emphasize that this investigation is a step-by-step process. The initial step is to conduct the ANOVA test. Only if the null hypothesis that the treatment means are equal is rejected should any analysis of the individual treatment means be attempted.

SELF-REVIEW

12–3

The following data are the semester tuition charges ($000) for a sample of five private colleges in the Northeast region of the United States, four in the Southeast region, and five in the West region. At the .05 significance level, can we conclude there is a difference in the mean tuition rates for the various regions?

Northeast ($000)	Southeast ($000)	West ($000)
10	8	7
11	9	8
12	10	6
10	8	7
12		6

(a) State the null and the alternate hypotheses.
(b) What is the decision rule?
(c) Develop an ANOVA table. What is the value of the test statistic?
(d) What is your decision regarding the null hypothesis?
(e) Could there be a significant difference between the mean tuition in the Northeast and that of the West? If so, develop a 95% confidence interval for that difference.

EXERCISES

11. The following are three observations collected from treatment 1, five observations collected from treatment 2, and four observations collected from treatment 3. Test the hypothesis that the treatment means are equal at the .05 significance level.

Treatment 1	Treatment 2	Treatment 3
8	3	3
11	2	4
10	1	5
	3	4
	2	

a. State the null hypothesis and the alternate hypothesis.
b. What is the decision rule?
c. Compute SST, SSE, and SS total.
d. Complete an ANOVA table.
e. State your decision regarding the null hypothesis.
f. If H_0 is rejected, can we conclude that treatment 1 and treatment 2 differ? Use the 95% level of confidence.

For **DATA FILE**, please visit
www.mhhe.com/lind16e

12. The following are six observations collected from treatment 1, ten observations collected from treatment 2, and eight observations collected from treatment 3. Test the hypothesis that the treatment means are equal at the .05 significance level.

Treatment 1	Treatment 2	Treatment 3
3	9	6
2	6	3
5	5	5
1	6	5
3	8	5
1	5	4
	4	1
	7	5
	6	
	4	

a. State the null hypothesis and the alternate hypothesis.
b. What is the decision rule?
c. Compute SST, SSE, and SS total.
d. Complete an ANOVA table.
e. State your decision regarding the null hypothesis.
f. If H_0 is rejected, can we conclude that treatment 2 and treatment 3 differ? Use the 95% level of confidence.

13. A senior accounting major at Midsouth State University has job offers from four CPA firms. To explore the offers further, she asked a sample of recent trainees how many months each worked for the firm before receiving a raise in salary. The sample information is submitted to Minitab with the following results:

```
Analysis of Variance
Source    DF      SS      MS      F       P
Factor     3    32.33   10.78   2.36    0.133
Error     10    45.67    4.57
Total     13    78.00
```

At the .05 level of significance, is there a difference in the mean number of months before a raise was granted among the four CPA firms?

14. A stock analyst wants to determine whether there is a difference in the mean rate of return for three types of stock: utility, retail, and banking stocks. The following output is obtained:

```
Source   DF      SS      MS      F       P
Factor    2    81.11   40.56   15.61   0.000
Error    14    36.37    2.60
Total    16   117.48

S = 1.612   R-Sq = 69.04%   R-Sq(adj) = 64.62%

Level              N    Mean    StDev
Utility Stocks     5   16.520   1.611
Retail Stocks      6   11.492   0.378
Banking Stocks     6   15.547   2.249


Utility Stocks subtracted from:

                  Lower    Center    Upper
Retail Stocks    -7.121   -5.028   -2.935
Banking Stocks   -3.066   -0.972    1.121


                   +---------+---------+---------+---------
Retail Stocks      (-----*-----)
Banking Stocks                  (-----*-----)
                   +---------+---------+---------+---------
                 -7.0       -3.5       0.0       3.5


Retail Stocks subtracted from:

                  Lower    Center    Upper
Banking Stocks    2.060    4.056    6.051


                   +---------+---------+---------+---------
Banking Stocks                                 (-----*----)
                   +---------+---------+---------+---------
                 -7.0       -3.5       0.0       3.5
```

a. Using the .05 level of significance, is there a difference in the mean rate of return among the three types of stock?
b. Can the analyst conclude there is a difference between the mean rates of return for utility and retail stocks? For utility and banking stocks? For banking and retail stocks? Explain.

TWO-WAY ANALYSIS OF VARIANCE

LO12-4
Use a blocking variable in a two-way ANOVA to test a hypothesis that three or more population means are equal.

In the example/solution in the previous section, we divided the total variation in passenger ratings of the airlines into two categories: the variation between the treatments and the variation within the treatments. We also called the variation within the treatments the error or the random variation. To put it another way, we considered only two sources of variation: that due to the treatments and the random differences. In the airline passenger ratings example, there may be other causes of variation. These factors might include, for example, the season of the year, the particular airport, or the number of passengers on the flight.

The benefit of considering other factors is that we can reduce the error variance. That is, if we can reduce the denominator of the F statistic (reducing the error variance or, more directly, the SSE term), the value of F will be larger, causing us to reject the hypothesis of equal treatment means. In other words, if we can explain more of the variation, then there is less "error." An example will clarify the reduction in the error variance.

EXAMPLE

WARTA, the Warren Area Regional Transit Authority, is expanding bus service from the suburb of Starbrick into the central business district of Warren. There are four routes being considered from Starbrick to downtown Warren: (1) via U.S. 6, (2) via the West End, (3) via the Hickory Street Bridge, and (4) via Route 59. WARTA conducted several tests to determine whether there was a difference in the mean travel times along the four routes. Because there will be many different drivers, the test was set up so each driver drove along each of the four routes. Below is the travel time, in minutes, for each driver–route combination.

	Travel Time from Starbrick to Warren (minutes)			
Driver	U.S. 6	West End	Hickory St.	Rte. 59
Deans	18	17	21	22
Snaverly	16	23	23	22
Ormson	21	21	26	22
Zollaco	23	22	29	25
Filbeck	25	24	28	28

At the .05 significance level, is there a difference in the mean travel time along the four routes? If we remove the effect of the drivers, is there a difference in the mean travel time?

SOLUTION

To begin, we conduct a test of hypothesis using a one-way ANOVA. That is, we consider only the four routes. Under this condition, differences in travel times are due to either treatment or random variation. In this example/solution, the subscripts correspond to the treatments or routes: 1 for U.S. 6, 2 for West End, 3 for Hickory Street, and 4 for Route 59. The null hypothesis and the alternate hypothesis for comparing the mean travel time along the four routes are:

H_0: $\mu_1 = \mu_2 = \mu_3 = \mu_4$
H_1: Not all treatment means are the same.

There are four routes, so for the numerator the degrees of freedom is $k - 1 = 4 - 1 = 3$. There are 20 observations, so the degrees of freedom in the denominator is $n - k = 20 - 4 = 16$. From Appendix B.6, at the .05 significance level, the critical value of F is 3.24. The decision rule is to reject the null hypothesis if the computed value of F is greater than 3.24.

We use Excel to perform the calculations and output the results. The computed value of F is 2.483, so our decision is to not reject the null hypothesis. We conclude there is no difference in the mean travel time along the four routes. There is no reason to select one of the routes as faster than the other.

Drivers and Routes.xlsx

Anova: Single Factor

Driver	U.S 6	West End	Hickory St.	Route 59
Deans	18	17	21	22
Snaverly	16	23	23	22
Ormson	21	21	26	22
Zollaco	23	22	29	25
Filbeck	25	24	28	28

(Routes is the heading spanning U.S 6, West End, Hickory St., Route 59)

SUMMARY

Groups	Count	Sum	Average	Variance
U.S 6	5	103	20.6	13.3
West End	5	107	21.4	7.3
Hickory St.	5	127	25.4	11.3
Route 59	5	119	23.8	7.2

Treatment (Block)

Error

ANOVA

Source of Variation	SS	df	MS	F	P-value	F crit
Between Groups	72.8	3	24.267	2.483	0.098	3.239
Within Groups	156.4	16	9.775			
Total	229.2	19				

From the above Excel output, the mean travel times along the routes were 20.6 minutes along U.S. 6, 21.4 minutes along the West End route, 25.4 minutes using Hickory Street, and 23.8 minutes using Route 59. We conclude these differences could reasonably be attributed to chance. From the ANOVA table, we note SST is 72.8, SSE is 156.4, and SS total is 229.2.

In this example, we considered the variation due to the treatments (routes) and took all the remaining variation to be random. If we could consider the effect of the several drivers, this would allow us to reduce the SSE term, which would lead to a larger value of F. The second treatment variable, the drivers in this case, is referred to as a **blocking variable.**

> **BLOCKING VARIABLE** A second treatment variable that when included in the ANOVA analysis will have the effect of reducing the SSE term.

In this case, we let the drivers be the blocking variable, and removing the effect of the drivers from the SSE term will change the F ratio for the treatment variable. First, we need to determine the sum of squares due to the blocks.

In a two-way ANOVA, the sum of squares due to blocks is found by the following formula.

$$SSB = k\Sigma(\bar{x}_b - \bar{x}_G)^2 \qquad \text{[12–6]}$$

where:

k is the number of treatments.
b is the number of blocks.
$\bar{x}_b$ is the sample mean of block b.
$\bar{x}_G$ is the overall or grand mean.

From the calculations on the next page, the means for the respective drivers are 19.5 minutes, 21 minutes, 22.5 minutes, 24.75 minutes, and 26.25 minutes. The overall mean is 22.8 minutes, found by adding the travel time for all 20 drives (456 minutes) and dividing by 20.

ANALYSIS OF VARIANCE 401

Travel Time from Starbrick to Warren (minutes)						
Driver	**U.S. 6**	**West End**	**Hickory St.**	**Rte. 59**	**Driver Sums**	**Driver Means**
Deans	18	17	21	22	78	19.50
Snaverly	16	23	23	22	84	21.00
Ormson	21	21	26	22	90	22.50
Zollaco	23	22	29	25	99	24.75
Filbeck	25	24	28	28	105	26.25

Substituting this information into formula (12–6) we determine SSB, the sum of squares due to the drivers (the blocking variable), is 119.7.

$$SSB = k\Sigma(\bar{x}_b - \bar{x}_G)^2$$
$$= 4(19.5 - 22.8)^2 + 4(21.0 - 22.8)^2 + 4(22.5 - 22.8)^2$$
$$+ 4(24.75 - 22.8)^2 + 4(26.25 - 22.8)^2$$
$$= 119.7$$

The same format is used in the two-way ANOVA table as in the one-way case, except there is an additional row for the blocking variable. SS total and SST are calculated as before, and SSB is found from formula (12–6). The SSE term is found by subtraction.

SUM OF SQUARES ERROR, TWO-WAY   SSE = SS total − SST − SSB   **[12–7]**

The values for the various components of the ANOVA table are computed as follows.

Source of Variation	Sum of Squares	Degrees of Freedom	Mean Square	*F*
Treatments	SST	$k - 1$	$SST/(k-1) = MST$	MST/MSE
Blocks	SSB	$b - 1$	$SSB/(b-1) = MSB$	MSB/MSE
Error	SSE	$(k-1)(b-1)$	$SSE/(k-1)(b-1) = MSE$	
Total	SS total	$n - 1$		

SSE is found by formula (12–7).

$$SSE = SS\ total - SST - SSB = 229.2 - 72.8 - 119.7 = 36.7$$

Source of Variation	(1) Sum of Squares	(2) Degrees of Freedom	(3) Mean Square (1)/(2)
Treatments	72.8	3	24.27
Blocks	119.7	4	29.93
Error	36.7	12	3.06
Total	229.2	19	

There is disagreement at this point. If the purpose of the blocking variable (the drivers in this example) was only to reduce the error variation, we should not conduct a test of hypothesis for the difference in block means. That is, if our goal was to reduce the MSE term, then we should not test a hypothesis regarding the blocking variable. On the other hand, we may wish to give the blocks the same status as the treatments and conduct a test of hypothesis. In the latter case, when the blocks are important enough to be considered as a second factor, we refer to this as a **two-factor experiment.** In many cases the decision is not clear. In our example we are

CHAPTER 12

concerned about the difference in the travel time for the different drivers, so we will conduct the test of hypothesis. For the hypothesis of equal block means, the subscripts are the first letter of each driver's name. The two sets of hypotheses are:

1. H_0: The treatment means are the same ($\mu_1 = \mu_2 = \mu_3 = \mu_4$).
   H_1: The treatment means are not the same.
2. H_0: The block means are the same ($\mu_D = \mu_S = \mu_O = \mu_Z = \mu_F$).
   H_1: The block means are not the same.

First, we will test the hypothesis concerning the treatment means. There are $k - 1 = 4 - 1 = 3$ degrees of freedom in the numerator and $(b - 1)(k - 1) = (5 - 1)(4 - 1) = 12$ degrees of freedom in the denominator. Using the .05 significance level, the critical value of F is 3.49. The null hypothesis that the mean times for the four routes are the same is rejected if the F ratio exceeds 3.49.

$$F = \frac{\text{MST}}{\text{MSE}} = \frac{24.27}{3.06} = 7.93$$

The null hypothesis is rejected and the alternate accepted. We conclude that the mean travel time is not the same for all routes. WARTA will want to conduct some tests to determine which treatment means differ.

Next, we test to find whether the travel time is the same for the various drivers. The degrees of freedom in the numerator for blocks are $b - 1 = 5 - 1 = 4$. The degrees of freedom for the denominator are the same as before: $(b - 1)(k - 1) = (5 - 1)(4 - 1) = 12$. The null hypothesis that the block means are the same is rejected if the F ratio exceeds 3.26.

$$F = \frac{\text{MSB}}{\text{MSE}} = \frac{29.93}{3.06} = 9.78$$

The null hypothesis is rejected, and the alternate is accepted. The mean time is not the same for the various drivers. Thus, WARTA management can conclude, based on the sample results, that there is a difference in the routes and in the drivers.

The Excel spreadsheet has a two-factor ANOVA procedure. The output for the WARTA example just completed follows. This output also includes the p-values. The p-value for the null hypothesis regarding the drivers is .001 and .004 for the routes. These p-values confirm that the null hypotheses for treatments and blocks should both be rejected because the p-value is less than the significance level.

Drivers and Routes.xlsx

	A	B	C	D	E	F	G	H	I	J	K	L	M
1													
2													
3			Routes				Anova: Two-Factor Without Replication						
4	Driver	U.S 6	West End	Hickory St.	Route 59								
5	Deans	18	17	21	22		SUMMARY	Count	Sum	Average	Variance		
6	Snaverly	16	23	23	22		Deans	4	78	19.50	5.67		
7	Ormson	21	21	26	22		Snaverly	4	84	21.00	11.33		
8	Zollaco	23	22	29	25		Ormson	4	90	22.50	5.67		
9	Filbeck	25	24	28	28		Zollaco	4	99	24.75	9.58		
10							Filbeck	4	105	26.25	4.25		
11													
12							U.S 6	5	103	20.60	13.30		
13							West End	5	107	21.40	7.30		
14							Hickory St.	5	127	25.40	11.30		
15							Route 59	5	119	23.80	7.20		
16													
17													
18							ANOVA						
19				Block (Driver)			Source of Variation	SS	df	MS	F	P-value	F crit
20							Rows	119.7	4	29.925	9.785	0.001	3.259
21							Columns	72.8	3	24.267	7.935	0.004	3.490
22				Treatment (Route)			Error	36.7	12	3.058			
23													
24							Total	229.2	19				

ANALYSIS OF VARIANCE

SELF-REVIEW

12–4

Rudduck Shampoo sells three shampoos, one each for dry, normal, and oily hair. Sales, in millions of dollars, for the past 5 months are given in the following table. Using the .05 significance level, test whether the mean sales differ for the three types of shampoo or by month.

Month	Sales ($ million)		
	Dry	Normal	Oily
June	7	9	12
July	11	12	14
August	13	11	8
September	8	9	7
October	9	10	13

EXERCISES

For exercises 15 and 16, conduct a test of hypothesis to determine whether the block or the treatment means differ. Using the .05 significance level: (a) state the null and alternate hypotheses for treatments; (b) state the decision rule for treatments; and (c) state the null and alternate hypotheses for blocks. Also, state the decision rule for blocks, then: (d) compute SST, SSB, SS total, and SSE; (e) complete an ANOVA table; and (f) give your decision regarding the two sets of hypotheses and interpret the results.

15. The following data are given for a two-factor ANOVA with two treatments and three blocks.

Block	Treatment	
	1	2
A	46	31
B	37	26
C	44	35

16. The following data are given for a two-factor ANOVA with three treatments and three blocks.

Block	Treatment		
	1	2	3
A	12	14	8
B	9	11	9
C	7	8	8

17. Chapin Manufacturing Company operates 24 hours a day, 5 days a week. The workers rotate shifts each week. Management is interested in whether there is a difference in the number of units produced when the employees work on various shifts. A sample of five workers is selected and their output recorded on each shift. At the .05 significance level, can we conclude there is a difference in the mean production rate by shift or by employee?

For **DATA FILE**, please visit www.mhhe.com/lind16e

Employee	Units Produced		
	Day	Afternoon	Night
Skaff	31	25	35
Lum	33	26	33
Clark	28	24	30
Treece	30	29	28
Morgan	28	26	27

404   CHAPTER 12

For **DATA FILE**, please visit
www.mhhe.com/lind16e

18. There are three hospitals in the Tulsa, Oklahoma, area. The following data show the number of outpatient surgeries performed on Monday, Tuesday, Wednesday, Thursday, and Friday at each hospital last week. At the .05 significance level, can we conclude there is a difference in the mean number of surgeries performed by hospital or by day of the week?

	Number of Surgeries Performed		
Day	St. Luke's	St. Vincent	Mercy
Monday	14	18	24
Tuesday	20	24	14
Wednesday	16	22	14
Thursday	18	20	22
Friday	20	28	24

LO12-5

Perform a two-way ANOVA with interaction and describe the results.

TWO-WAY ANOVA WITH INTERACTION

In the previous section, we studied the separate or independent effects of two variables, or factors, on a response variable, travel time. In the example/solution, the two factors were the bus routes and the drivers and the response was travel time. The analysis shows two significant results. First, the mean travel times between routes, averaged over all drivers, are different. Second, the mean travel times between the five drivers, averaged over all the routes, are different. What could explain these differences? The differences between routes may simply be related to differences in the distance of the routes. We really didn't study the distance of the various routes. Perhaps the differences are explained by how fast, on average, the drivers drive regardless of the route.

There is another effect that may influence travel time that we have not considered. This is called the **interaction effect** between route and driver on travel time. That is, differences in travel time may depend on both the driver and the route. For example, it is possible that one of the drivers is especially good driving one of the routes. Perhaps one driver knows how to effectively time the traffic lights or how to avoid heavily congested intersections for one or more of the routes. In this case, differences in mean travel time may depend on the combined effect of driver and route. The results of the interaction of driver and route can provide interesting information.

> **INTERACTION** The effect of one factor on a response variable differs depending on the value of another factor.

Interaction Plots

An everyday illustration of interaction is the effect of diet and exercise on body weight. It is generally agreed that body weight (the response variable) can be affected by two factors, diet and exercise. However, research shows there is also a combined or *interaction* effect of diet and exercise on weight loss. That is, the amount of weight loss will be different and depend on diet AND whether people exercise.

The following graph, or interaction plot, illustrates the interaction of diet and exercise. First, for people who do not exercise, the mean weight losses for Diet 1 and Diet 2 are plotted. These are connected with the blue line. Clearly, there is a difference in weight loss for the two diets. Second, for people who did exercise, the mean weight losses for Diet 1 and Diet 2 are plotted. These are connected with the green line. Again, there is a clear difference in weight loss between Diet 1 and Diet 2 for people who exercise. The plot also shows an interaction effect between diet and exercise on weight loss. Notice the two lines are not parallel to each other. For Diet 1, the mean weight loss is more when people also exercise. For Diet 2, the mean weight loss is also more when people also exercise, but the weight loss is much greater than for Diet 1. So, what is the effect of diet and exercise on weight loss? It depends on the combined, or interaction, effects of diet and exercise.

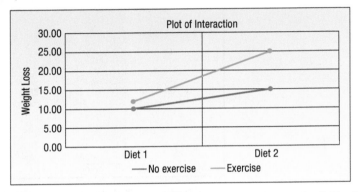

How would the interaction plot look if there were no interaction? The following graph shows an analysis of diet and exercise with no interaction.

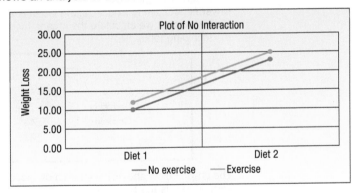

In this case the lines are parallel. Comparing the means, the effect of exercise on weight loss for Diet 1 and Diet 2 is the same. The estimated weight loss is about two pounds. In addition, the effect of diet is the same whether people exercise or not. It is about 13 pounds.

Testing for Interaction

To test for an interaction effect, we use a two-way ANOVA with interaction. To illustrate, we return to the previous WARTA example/solution. Restating the issue facing WARTA management: They want to expand bus service from downtown Warren to Starbrick. So far they have concluded, based on statistical analysis, that there is a difference in the mean travel time along the four proposed routes and a difference in the mean travel times of the five drivers. But it is possible that the combination, or the interaction between routes and drivers, has a significant effect on mean travel time.

In this analysis, we call the two variables, route and driver, **factors.** We refer to the variable, travel time, as the **response** variable. To test for interaction, the sample data must be replicated for each route. In this case, each driver drives each route three times so there are three observed times for each route/driver combination. This information is summarized in the following Excel spreadsheet.

406   CHAPTER 12

	Routes				Means for Drivers
	US 6	West End	Hickory St	Route 59	
Deans	18	17	21	22	
	15	14	20	19	
	21	20	22	25	19.50
Snaverly	16	23	23	22	
	19	19	24	20	
	13	25	22	24	20.83
Ormson	21	21	26	22	
	19	23	24	24	
	14	25	28	20	22.25
Zollaco	23	22	29	25	
	21	24	30	20	
	25	20	28	26	24.42
Filbeck	25	24	28	28	
	24	25	29	30	Grand Mean
	26	23	27	26	26.25
Means for Routes	20.00	21.67	25.40	23.53	22.65

To evaluate interaction effects, a useful first step is to plot the means for each driver/route combination. For the driver/route combination Driver Deans using Route 6, the mean is 18 minutes, found by (18 + 15 + 21)/3. For the driver/route combination Driver Filbeck using Route 59, the mean is 28 minutes, found by (28 + 30 + 26)/3. In a similar manner we calculate the means for the other cells and summarize the results in the following table.

Drivers	Routes			
	US 6	West End	Hickory St	Route 59
Deans	18	17	21	22
Snaverly	16	22.33	23	22
Ormson	18	23	26	22
Zollaco	23	22	29	23.67
Filbeck	25	24	28	28

The graph below shows the interaction plot using the information in the above table. The vertical axis is the travel time in minutes. The four routes are labeled on the horizontal axis and each line plots the mean travel times for each driver for all four routes. For example, the green line reports average travel times for Deans for each of the four routes.

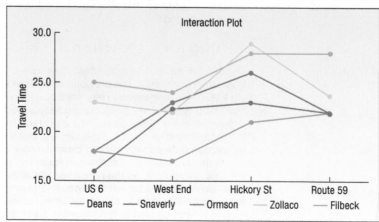

From the graph, what observations can be made about the interaction of driver and route on travel time? Most importantly, the lines are not parallel. Because the five lines are clearly not parallel, there is an interaction effect of driver and route on travel time; that is, travel time depends on the combined effect of driver and route.

Note the differences in travel times. For the U.S. 6 route, Snaverly has the lowest or fastest mean travel time. Deans has the lowest mean travel time for the West End and Hickory Street routes. Zollaco has the slowest average time for the Hickory Street route. There are many other observations that lead to the general observation that travel time is related to the combined effects of driver AND route. The critical question is whether the observed interactions are significant or the differences are due to chance.

Hypothesis Tests for Interaction

The next step is to conduct statistical tests to further investigate the possible interaction effects. In summary, our study of travel times has several questions:

- Is there an interaction between routes and drivers on mean travel times?
- Are the mean travel times for drivers the same?
- Are the mean travel times for the routes the same?

Of the three questions, we are most interested in the test for interactions.
We formalize these ideas into three sets of hypotheses:

1. H_0: There is no interaction between drivers and routes.
    H_1: There is interaction between drivers and routes.
2. H_0: The driver means are the same.
    H_1: The driver means are *not* the same.
3. H_0: The route means are the same.
    H_1: The route means are *not* the same.

We test each of these hypotheses as we did in the previous section using the F distribution. The tests are summarized with the following ANOVA table. It is similar to the two-way ANOVA in the previous section with the addition of the Interaction source of variation. In addition, we refer to the driver effect as **Factor A** and the route effect as **Factor B.** Each of these hypotheses is tested using the familiar F statistic.

Source of Variation	Sum of Squares	df	Mean Square	F
Factor A (driver)	SSA	$k - 1$	$MSA = SSA/(k - 1)$	MSA/MSE
Factor B (route)	SSB	$b - 1$	$MSB = SSA/(b - 1)$	MSB/MSE
Interaction	SSI	$(k - 1)(b - 1)$	$MSI = SSI/[(k - 1)(b - 1)]$	MSI/MSE
Error	SSE	$n - kb$	$MSE = SSE/(n - kb)$	
Total		$n - 1$		

To test the hypotheses for a two-way ANOVA with interaction, we use the ANOVA: Two-Factor with Replication in the Data Analysis add-in for Excel. The details of using Excel are summarized in Appendix C. The following ANOVA table shows the results of the analysis. We use the p-values to test each hypothesis. Using the .05 significance level, the null hypotheses are rejected if the computed p-value is less than .05.

ANOVA						
Source of Variation	SS	df	MS	F	P-value	F crit
Drivers	353.5667	4	88.39167	17.21916	0.0000	2.605975
Routes	244.9833	3	81.66111	15.90801	0.0000	2.838745
Interaction	125.7667	12	10.48056	2.041667	0.0456	2.003459
Error	205.3333	40	5.133333			
Total	929.65	59				

Reviewing the results of the ANOVA, the p-value for the interaction effect of .0456 is less than our significance level of. 05, so our decision is to reject the null hypothesis of no interaction and conclude that the combination of route and driver has a significant effect on the response variable, travel time.

A significant interaction effect provides important information about the combined effects of the variables. If interaction is present, then a test of differences in the factor means using a one-way ANOVA for each level of the other factor is the next step. This analysis requires some time and work to complete, but the results are usually enlightening.

We will continue the analysis by conducting a one-way ANOVA for each route by testing the hypothesis H_0: Driver travel times are equal. The results follow.

US 6; H_0: Driver times are equal						
Source of Variation	SS	df	MS	F	P-value	F crit
Between Groups	174	4	43.5	6.04167	0.010	3.478
Within Groups	72	10	7.2			
Total	246	14				

West End; H_0: Driver times are equal						
Source of Variation	SS	df	MS	F	P-value	F crit
Between Groups	88.6667	4	22.1667	4.05488	0.033	3.478
Within Groups	54.6667	10	5.46667			
Total	143.333	14				

Hickory; H_0: Driver times are equal						
Source of Variation	SS	df	MS	F	P-value	F crit
Between Groups	135.6	4	33.9	21.1875	0.000	3.478
Within Groups	16	10	1.6			
Total	151.6	14				

Route 59; H_0: Driver times are equal						
Source of Variation	SS	df	MS	F	P-value	F crit
Between Groups	81.0667	4	20.2667	3.23404	0.060	3.478
Within Groups	62.6667	10	6.26667			
Total	143.733	14				

The results of the one-way ANOVA show there are significant differences in the mean travel times among the drivers for every route, except Route 59 with a p-value of 0.06. A review of the interaction plot may reveal some of the differences. For example, for the West End route, the graph suggests that Deans has the best mean travel time. Further statistical analysis would test pairs of mean travel times to determine the significant differences between driver travel times for each route that has a significant p-value.

ANALYSIS OF VARIANCE 409

SELF-REVIEW

12–5

See the following ANOVA table.

ANOVA					
Source of Variation	**SS**	**df**	**MS**	**F**	**p-value**
Factor A	6.41	3	2.137	3.46	0.0322
Factor B	5.01	2	2.507	4.06	0.0304
Interaction	33.15	6	5.525	8.94	0.0000
Error	14.83	24	0.618		
Total	59.41	35			

Use the .05 significance level to answer the following questions.
(a) How many levels does Factor A have? Is there a significant difference among the Factor A means? How do you know?
(b) How many levels does Factor B have? Is there a significant difference among the Factor B means? How do you know?
(c) How many observations are there in each cell? Is there a significant interaction between Factor A and Factor B on the response variable? How do you know?

EXERCISES

For **DATA FILE**, please visit
www.mhhe.com/lind16e

19. Consider the following sample data for a two-factor ANOVA analysis. There are two levels (heavy and light) of factor A (weight), and three levels (small, medium, and large) of factor B (size). For each combination of size and weight, there are three observations.

		Size		
		Small	**Medium**	**Large**
Weight	Heavy	23	20	11
		21	32	20
		25	26	20
	Light	13	20	11
		32	17	23
		17	15	8

Compute an ANOVA with statistical software, and use the .05 significance level to answer the following questions.
a. Is there a difference in the Size means?
b. Is there a difference in the Weight means?
c. Is there a significant interaction between Weight and Size?

20. Consider the following partially completed two-way ANOVA table. Suppose there are four levels of Factor A and three levels of Factor B. The number of replications per cell is 5. Complete the table and test to determine if there is a significant difference in Factor A means, Factor B means, or the interaction means. Use the .05 significance level. (Hint: estimate the values from the F table.)

ANOVA				
Source	**SS**	**df**	**MS**	**F**
Factor A	75			
Factor B	25			
Interaction	300			
Error	600			
Total	1000			

For **DATA FILE**, please visit
www.mhhe.com/lind16e

21. The distributor of the *Wapakoneta Daily News,* a regional newspaper serving western Ohio, is considering three types of dispensing machines or "racks." Management wants to know if the different machines affect sales. These racks are designated as J-1000, D-320, and UV-57. Management also wants to know if the placement of the racks either inside or outside supermarkets affects sales. Each of six similar stores was randomly assigned a machine and location combination. The data below are the number of papers sold over four days.

Position/Machine	J-1000	D-320	UV-57
Inside	33, 40, 30, 31	29, 28, 33, 33	47, 39, 39, 45
Outside	43, 36, 41, 40	48, 45, 40, 44	37, 32, 36, 35

   a. Draw the interaction graph. Based on your observations, is there an interaction effect? Based on the graph, describe the interaction effect of machine and position.
   b. Compute an ANOVA with statistical software, and use the 0.05 level to test for position, machine, and interaction effects on sales. Report the statistical results.
   c. Compare the inside and outside mean sales for each machine using statistical techniques. What do you conclude?

22. A large company is organized into three functional areas: manufacturing, marketing, and research and development. The employees claim that the company pays women less than men for similar jobs. The company randomly selected four males and four females in each area and recorded their weekly salaries in dollars.

For **DATA FILE**, please visit
www.mhhe.com/lind16e

Area/Gender	Female	Male
Manufacturing	1016, 1007, 875, 968	978, 1056, 982, 748
Marketing	1045, 895, 848, 904	1154, 1091, 878, 876
Research and Development	770, 733, 844, 771	926, 1055, 1066, 1088

   a. Draw the interaction graph. Based on your observations, is there an interaction effect? Based on the graph, describe the interaction effect of gender and area on salary.
   b. Compute an ANOVA with statistical software, and use the 0.05 level to test for gender, area, and interaction effects on salary. Report the statistical results.
   c. Compare the male and female mean sales for each area using statistical techniques. What do you recommend to the distributor?

CHAPTER SUMMARY

I. The characteristics of the *F* distribution are:
   A. It is continuous.
   B. Its values cannot be negative.
   C. It is positively skewed.
   D. There is a family of *F* distributions. Each time the degrees of freedom in either the numerator or the denominator change, a new distribution is created.
II. The *F* distribution is used to test whether two population variances are the same.
   A. The sampled populations must follow the normal distribution.
   B. The larger of the two sample variances is placed in the numerator, forcing the ratio to be at least 1.00.
   C. The value of *F* is computed using the following equation:

$$F = \frac{s_1^2}{s_2^2}$$

[12–1]

III. A one-way ANOVA is used to compare several treatment means.
   A. A treatment is a source of variation.
   B. The assumptions underlying ANOVA are:
      1. The samples are from populations that follow the normal distribution.
      2. The populations have equal standard deviations.
      3. The populations are independent.

ANALYSIS OF VARIANCE   411

C. The information for finding the value of F is summarized in an ANOVA table.
1. The formula for SS total, the sum of squares total, is:

$$\text{SS total} = \Sigma(x - \bar{x}_G)^2 \qquad \qquad \textbf{[12–2]}$$

2. The formula for SSE, the sum of squares error, is:

$$\text{SSE} = \Sigma(x - \bar{x}_c)^2 \qquad \qquad \textbf{[12–3]}$$

3. The formula for the SST, the sum of squares treatment, is found by subtraction.

$$\text{SST} = \text{SS total} - \text{SSE} \qquad \qquad \textbf{[12–4]}$$

4. This information is summarized in the following ANOVA table and the value of F is determined.

Source of Variation	Sum of Squares	Degrees of Freedom	Mean Square	F
Treatments	SST	$k - 1$	$\text{SST}/(k - 1) = \text{MST}$	MST/MSE
Error	SSE	$n - k$	$\text{SSE}/(n - k) = \text{MSE}$	
Total	SS total	$n - 1$		

IV. If a null hypothesis of equal treatment means is rejected, we can identify the pairs of means that differ from the following confidence interval.

$$(\bar{x}_1 - \bar{x}_2) \pm t\sqrt{\text{MSE}\left(\frac{1}{n_1} + \frac{1}{n_2}\right)} \qquad \qquad \textbf{[12–5]}$$

V. In a two-way ANOVA, we consider a second treatment variable.
   A. The second treatment variable is called the blocking variable.
   B. It is determined using the following equation:

$$\text{SSB} = k\Sigma(\bar{x}_b - \bar{x}_G)^2 \qquad \qquad \textbf{[12–6]}$$

   C. The SSE term, or sum of squares error, is found from the following equation.

$$\text{SSE} = \text{SS total} - \text{SST} - \text{SSB} \qquad \qquad \textbf{[12–7]}$$

   D. The F statistics for the treatment variable and the blocking variable are determined in the following table.

Source of Variation	Sum of Squares	Degrees of Freedom	Mean Square	F
Treatments	SST	$k - 1$	$\text{SST}/(k - 1) = \text{MST}$	MST/MSE
Blocks	SSB	$b - 1$	$\text{SSB}/(b - 1) = \text{MSB}$	MSB/MSE
Error	SSE	$(k - 1)(b - 1)$	$\text{SSE}/[(k - 1)(b - 1)] = \text{MSE}$	
Total	SS total	$n - 1$		

VI. In a two-way ANOVA with repeated observations, we consider two treatment variables and the possible interaction between the variables. The complete ANOVA table including interactions is:

Source	Sum of Squares	df	Mean Square	F
Factor A	SSA	$k - 1$	$\text{SSA}/(k - 1) = \text{MSA}$	MSA/MSE
Factor B	SSB	$b - 1$	$\text{SSB}/(b - 1) = \text{MSB}$	MSB/MSE
Interaction	SSI	$(k - 1)(b - 1)$	$\text{SSI}/[(k - 1)(b - 1)] = \text{MSI}$	MSI/MSE
Error	SSE	$n - kb$	$\text{SSE}/(n - kb) = \text{MSE}$	
Total	SS total	$n - 1$		

412   CHAPTER 12

SYMBOL	MEANING	PRONUNCIATION
SS total	Sum of squares total	S S total
SST	Sum of squares treatment	S S T
SSE	Sum of squares error	S S E
MSE	Mean square error	M S E
SSB	Block sum of squares	S S B
SSI	Sum of squares interaction	S S I

C H A P T E R   E X E R C I S E S

23. A real estate agent in the coastal area of Georgia wants to compare the variation in the selling price of homes on the oceanfront with those one to three blocks from the ocean. A sample of 21 oceanfront homes sold within the last year revealed the standard deviation of the selling prices was $45,600. A sample of 18 homes, also sold within the last year, that were one to three blocks from the ocean revealed that the standard deviation was $21,330. At the .01 significance level, can we conclude that there is more variation in the selling prices of the oceanfront homes?

24. A software design company is creating a new, faster search engine. The search engine is clearly faster, but initial tests indicate there is more variation in the time to perform a search. A sample of 16 different searches showed that the standard deviation of the search time was 22 hundredths of a second for the new search engine and 12 hundredths of a second for the current search engine. At the .05 significance level, can we conclude that there is more variation in the search time of the new search engine?

For **DATA FILE**, please visit www.mhhe.com/lind16e

25. There are two Chevrolet dealers in Jamestown, New York. The mean monthly sales at Sharkey Chevy and Dave White Chevrolet are about the same. However, Tom Sharkey, the owner of Sharkey Chevy, believes his sales are more consistent. Below are the numbers of new cars sold at Sharkey in the last 7 months and for the last 8 months at Dave White. Do you agree with Mr. Sharkey? Use the .01 significance level.

Sharkey	98	78	54	57	68	64	70	
Dave White	75	81	81	30	82	46	58	101

26. Random samples of five were selected from each of three populations. The sum of squares total was 100. The sum of squares due to the treatments was 40.
  a. Set up the null hypothesis and the alternate hypothesis.
  b. What is the decision rule? Use the .05 significance level.
  c. Complete the ANOVA table. What is the value of F?
  d. What is your decision regarding the null hypothesis?

27. In an ANOVA table, MSE was equal to 10. Random samples of six were selected from each of four populations, where the sum of squares total was 250.
  a. Set up the null hypothesis and the alternate hypothesis.
  b. What is the decision rule? Use the .05 significance level.
  c. Complete the ANOVA table. What is the value of F?
  d. What is your decision regarding the null hypothesis?

28. The following is a partial ANOVA table.

Source	Sum of Squares	df	Mean Square	F
Treatment		2		
Error			20	
Total	500	11		

ANALYSIS OF VARIANCE

413

Complete the table and answer the following questions. Use the .05 significance level.
a. How many treatments are there?
b. What is the total sample size?
c. What is the critical value of F?
d. Write out the null and alternate hypotheses.
e. What is your conclusion regarding the null hypothesis?

29. A consumer organization wants to know whether there is a difference in the price of a particular toy at three different types of stores. The price of the toy was checked in a sample of five discount stores, five variety stores, and five department stores. The results are shown below. Use the .05 significance level.

For **DATA FILE**, please visit
www.mhhe.com/lind16e

Discount	Variety	Department
$12	$15	$19
13	17	17
14	14	16
12	18	20
15	17	19

30. Jacob Lee is a frequent traveler between Los Angeles and San Francisco. For the past month, he wrote down the flight times on three different airlines. The results are:

For **DATA FILE**, please visit
www.mhhe.com/lind16e

Goust	Jet Red	Cloudtran
51	50	52
51	53	55
52	52	60
42	62	64
51	53	61
57	49	49
47	50	49
47	49	
50	58	
60	54	
54	51	
49	49	
48	49	
48	50	

a. Use the .05 significance level and the six-step hypothesis-testing process to check if there is a difference in the mean flight times among the three airlines.
b. Develop a 95% confidence interval for the difference in the means between Goust and Cloudtran.

31. The City of Maumee comprises four districts. Chief of Police Andy North wants to determine whether there is a difference in the mean number of crimes committed among the four districts. He examined the records from six randomly selected days and recorded the number of crimes. At the .05 significance level, can Chief North conclude that there is a difference in the mean number of crimes among the four districts?

For **DATA FILE**, please visit
www.mhhe.com/lind16e

Number of Crimes			
Rec Center	Key Street	Monclova	Whitehouse
13	21	12	16
15	13	14	17
14	18	15	18
15	19	13	15
14	18	12	20
15	19	15	18

CHAPTER 12

For **DATA FILE**, please visit
www.mhhe.com/lind16e

32. A study of the effect of television commercials on 12-year-old children measured their attention span, in seconds. The commercials were for clothes, food, and toys. At the .05 significance level, is there a difference in the mean attention span of the children for the various commercials? Are there significant differences between pairs of means? Would you recommend dropping one of the three commercial types?

Clothes	Food	Toys
26	45	60
21	48	51
43	43	43
35	53	54
28	47	63
31	42	53
17	34	48
31	43	58
20	57	47
	47	51
	44	51
	54	

For **DATA FILE**, please visit
www.mhhe.com/lind16e

33. When only two treatments are involved, ANOVA and the Student's t test (Chapter 11) result in the same conclusions. Also, $t^2 = F$. As an example, 14 randomly selected Introduction to History students were divided into two groups, one consisting of 6 students and the other of 8. One group took the course in the normal lecture format. The other group of 8 students took the course via the Internet. At the end of the course, each group was given a 50-item test. The following is a list of the number correct for each of the two groups.

Traditional Lecture	Internet
19	32
17	28
23	31
22	26
17	23
16	24
	27
	25

   a. Using analysis of variance techniques, test H_0 that the two mean test scores are equal; $\alpha = .05$.
   b. Using the t test from Chapter 11, compute t.
   c. Interpret the results.

34. There are four auto body shops in Bangor, Maine, and all claim to promptly serve customers. To check if there is any difference in service, customers are randomly selected from each repair shop and their waiting times in days are recorded. The output from a statistical software package is:

Summary				
Groups	Count	Sum	Average	Variance
Body Shop A	3	15.4	5.133333	0.323333
Body Shop B	4	32	8	1.433333
Body Shop C	5	25.2	5.04	0.748
Body Shop D	4	25.9	6.475	0.595833

ANALYSIS OF VARIANCE   415

ANOVA

Source of Variation	SS	df	MS	F	p-value
Between Groups	23.37321	3	7.791069	9.612506	0.001632
Within Groups	9.726167	12	0.810514		
Total	33.09938	15			

Is there evidence to suggest a difference in the mean waiting times at the four body shops? Use the .05 significance level.

35. The fuel efficiencies for a sample of 27 compact, midsize, and large cars are entered into a statistical software package. Analysis of variance is used to investigate if there is a difference in the mean mileage of the three cars. What do you conclude? Use the .01 significance level.

Summary

Groups	Count	Sum	Average	Variance
Compact	12	268.3	22.35833	9.388106
Midsize	9	172.4	19.15556	7.315278
Large	6	100.5	16.75	7.303

Additional results are shown below.

ANOVA

Source of Variation	SS	df	MS	F	p-value
Between Groups	136.4803	2	68.24014	8.258752	0.001866
Within Groups	198.3064	24	8.262766		
Total	334.7867	26			

36. Three assembly lines are used to produce a certain component for an airliner. To examine the production rate, a random sample of six hourly periods is chosen for each assembly line and the number of components produced during these periods for each line is recorded. The output from a statistical software package is:

Summary

Groups	Count	Sum	Average	Variance
Line A	6	250	41.66667	0.266667
Line B	6	260	43.33333	0.666667
Line C	6	249	41.5	0.7

ANOVA

Source of Variation	SS	df	MS	F	p-value
Between Groups	12.33333	2	6.166667	11.32653	0.001005
Within Groups	8.166667	15	0.544444		
Total	20.5	17			

a. Use a .01 level of significance to test if there is a difference in the mean production of the three assembly lines.
b. Develop a 99% confidence interval for the difference in the means between Line B and Line C.

37. The postal service sorts mail as Priority Mail Express, Priority Mail, First-Class Mail, or Standard Mail. Over a period of 3 weeks, 18 of each type were mailed from the Network Distribution Center in Altanta, Georgia, to Des Moines, Iowa. The total delivery time in days was recorded. Minitab was used to perform the ANOVA. The results follow:

```
Source  DF      SS      MS       F       P
Factor   3   30.298  10.099  11.90   0.000
Error   68   57.705   0.849
Total   71   88.003

S = 0.9212    R-Sq = 34.43%    R-Sq(adj) = 31.54%

Level                  N    Mean    StDev
Priority Mail Express  18  1.0694   0.7652
Priority Mail          18  1.7210   1.0829
First-Class Mail       18  2.5211   0.9097
Standard Mail          18  2.6840   0.8991


Priority Mail Express subtracted from:

                  Lower   Center   Upper
Priority Mail    0.0389   0.6516  1.2644
First-Class Mail 0.8390   1.4517  2.0645
Standard Mail    1.0018   1.6146  2.2273


                 ------+---------+---------+---------+---
Priority Mail                      (------*-----)
First-Class Mail                        (------*-----)
Standard Mail                            (-----*-----)
                 ------+---------+---------+---------+---
                    -1.0       0.0       1.0       2.0

Priority Mail subtracted from:

                  Lower   Center   Upper
First-Class Mail 0.1874   0.8001  1.4128
Standard Mail    0.3502   0.9629  1.5757


                 ------+---------+---------+---------+---
First-Class Mail                   (-----*-----)
Standard Mail                     (-----*-----)
                 ------+---------+---------+---------+---
                    -1.0       0.0       1.0       2.0

First-Class Mail subtracted from:

                   Lower   Center   Upper
Standard Mail    -0.4499   0.1628  0.7756


                 ------+---------+---------+---------+---
Standard Mail                     (-----*-----)
                 ------+---------+---------+---------+---
                    -1.0       0.0       1.0       2.0
```

Using the ANOVA results, compare the average delivery times of the four different types of mail.

38. For your e-mail, you use a filter to block spam from your inbox. The number of items blocked by day of week is recorded and Minitab is used to perform the analysis that follows. Here are the results:

```
Source   DF      SS     MS     F      P
Factor    6  1242.5  207.1  6.66  0.000
Error    48  1493.1   31.1
Total    54  2735.7

S = 5.577   R-Sq = 45.42%   R-Sq(adj) = 38.60%


Level       N    Mean   StDev
Monday     10  71.926   5.435
Tuesday     9  64.329   6.890
Wednesday   7  73.322   2.936
Thursday    8  60.539   4.268
Friday      8  73.709   5.369
Saturday    5  64.436   6.729
Sunday      8  68.810   6.384


Monday subtracted from:
            Lower   Center   Upper  ---------+---------+---------+---------+
Tuesday   -12.749   -7.597  -2.444       (----*-----)
Wednesday  -4.130    1.396   6.922                (----*-----)
Thursday  -16.706  -11.387  -6.068   (-----*----)
Friday     -3.536    1.783   7.103                (-----*----)
Saturday  -13.632   -7.490  -1.348       (------*-----)
Sunday     -8.436   -3.117   2.203            (----*----)
                                     ---------+---------+---------+---------+
                                           -10        0        10       20

Tuesday subtracted from:
            Lower   Center   Upper  ---------+---------+---------+---------+
Wednesday   3.341    8.993  14.644                      (-----*-----)
Thursday   -9.239   -3.790   1.659          (----*-----)
Friday      3.931    9.380  14.829                      (----*-----)
Saturday   -6.148    0.107   6.362              (-----*-----)
Sunday     -0.969    4.480   9.929                (----*-----)
                                     ---------+---------+---------+---------+
                                           -10        0        10       20

Wednesday subtracted from:
            Lower   Center   Upper  ---------+---------+---------+---------+
Thursday  -18.587  -12.783  -6.979  (-----*-----)
Friday     -5.416    0.388   6.191                (----*-----)
Saturday  -15.452   -8.886  -2.319     (-----*------)
Sunday    -10.316   -4.512   1.291          (----*-----)
                                     ---------+---------+---------+---------+
                                           -10        0        10       20

Thursday subtracted from:
            Lower   Center   Upper  ---------+---------+---------+---------+
Friday      7.563   13.170  18.777                        (----*-----)
Saturday   -2.496    3.897  10.290               (------*-----)
Sunday      2.663    8.270  13.877                    (----*-----)
                                     ---------+---------+---------+---------+
                                           -10        0        10       20

Friday subtracted from:
            Lower   Center   Upper  ---------+---------+---------+---------+
Saturday  -15.666   -9.273  -2.880    (------*-----)
Sunday    -10.507   -4.900   0.707         (-----*-----)
                                     ---------+---------+---------+---------+
                                           -10        0        10       20

Saturday subtracted from:
            Lower   Center   Upper  ---------+---------+---------+---------+
Sunday     -2.020    4.373  10.766               (-----*------)
                                     ---------+---------+---------+---------+
                                           -10        0        10
```

Using the ANOVA results, compare the average number of items blocked for each day of the week.

418   CHAPTER 12

39. Shank's Inc., a nationwide advertising firm, wants to know whether the size of an advertisement and the color of the advertisement make a difference in the response of magazine readers. A random sample of readers is shown ads of four different colors and three different sizes. Each reader is asked to give the particular combination of size and color a rating between 1 and 10. Assume that the ratings follow the normal distribution. The rating for each combination is shown in the following table (for example, the rating for a small red ad is 2).

For **DATA FILE**, please visit www.mhhe.com/lind16e

| | | Color of Ad | | |
Size of Ad	Red	Blue	Orange	Green
Small	2	3	3	8
Medium	3	5	6	7
Large	6	7	8	8

Is there a difference in the effectiveness of an advertisement by color and by size? Use the .05 level of significance.

40. There are four McBurger restaurants in the Columbus, Georgia, area. The numbers of burgers sold at the respective restaurants for each of the last 6 weeks are shown below. At the .05 significance level, is there a difference in the mean number sold among the four restaurants when the factor of week is considered?

For **DATA FILE**, please visit www.mhhe.com/lind16e

| | | Restaurant | | |
Week	Metro	Interstate	University	River
1	124	160	320	190
2	234	220	340	230
3	430	290	290	240
4	105	245	310	170
5	240	205	280	180
6	310	260	270	205

a. Is there a difference in the treatment means?
b. Is there a difference in the block means?

41. The city of Tucson, Arizona, employs people to assess the value of homes for the purpose of establishing real estate tax. The city manager sends each assessor to the same five homes and then compares the results. The information is given below, in thousands of dollars. Can we conclude that there is a difference in the assessors? Use the .05 significance level.

For **DATA FILE**, please visit www.mhhe.com/lind16e

| | | Assessor | | |
Home	Zawodny	Norman	Cingle	Holiday
A	$53.0	$55.0	$49.0	$45.0
B	50.0	51.0	52.0	53.0
C	48.0	52.0	47.0	53.0
D	70.0	68.0	65.0	64.0
E	84.0	89.0	92.0	86.0

a. Is there a difference in the treatment means?
b. Is there a difference in the block means?

42. Martin Motors has in stock three cars of the same make and model. The Sales Manager would like to compare the gas consumption of the three cars (labeled car A, car B, and car C) using four different types of gasoline. For each trial, a gallon of gasoline was added to an empty tank, and the car was driven until it ran out of gas. The following table shows the number of miles driven in each trial.

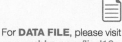

For **DATA FILE**, please visit www.mhhe.com/lind16e

| | Distance (miles) | | |
Types of Gasoline	Car A	Car B	Car C
Regular	22.4	20.8	21.5
Super regular	17.0	19.4	20.7
Unleaded	19.2	20.2	21.2
Premium unleaded	20.3	18.6	20.4

ANALYSIS OF VARIANCE 419

Using the .05 level of significance:
a. Is there a difference among types of gasoline?
b. Is there a difference in the cars?

For **DATA FILE**, please visit www.mhhe.com/lind16e

43. A research firm wants to compare the miles per gallon of unleaded regular, mid-grade, and super premium gasolines. Because of differences in the performance of different automobiles, seven different automobiles were selected and treated as blocks. Therefore, each brand of gasoline was tested with each type of automobile. The results of the trials, in miles per gallon, are shown in the following table. At the .05 significance level, is there a difference in the gasolines or automobiles?

Automobile	Regular	Mid-grade	Super Premium
1	21	23	26
2	23	22	25
3	24	25	27
4	24	24	26
5	26	26	30
6	26	24	27
7	28	27	32

For **DATA FILE**, please visit www.mhhe.com/lind16e

44. Three supermarket chains in the Denver area each claims to have the lowest overall prices. As part of an investigative study on supermarket advertising, the *Denver Daily News* conducted a study. First, a random sample of nine grocery items was selected. Next, the price of each selected item was checked at each of the three chains on the same day. At the .05 significance level, is there a difference in the mean prices at the supermarkets or for the items?

Item	Super$	Ralph's	Lowblaws
1	$1.12	$1.02	$1.07
2	1.14	1.10	1.21
3	1.72	1.97	2.08
4	2.22	2.09	2.32
5	2.40	2.10	2.30
6	4.04	4.32	4.15
7	5.05	4.95	5.05
8	4.68	4.13	4.67
9	5.52	5.46	5.86

For **DATA FILE**, please visit www.mhhe.com/lind16e

45. Listed below are the weights (in grams) of a sample of M&M's Plain candies, classified according to color. Use a statistical software system to determine whether there is a difference in the mean weights of candies of different colors. Use the .05 significance level.

Red	Orange	Yellow	Brown	Tan	Green
0.946	0.902	0.929	0.896	0.845	0.935
1.107	0.943	0.960	0.888	0.909	0.903
0.913	0.916	0.938	0.906	0.873	0.865
0.904	0.910	0.933	0.941	0.902	0.822
0.926	0.903	0.932	0.838	0.956	0.871
0.926	0.901	0.899	0.892	0.959	0.905
1.006	0.919	0.907	0.905	0.916	0.905
0.914	0.901	0.906	0.824	0.822	0.852
0.922	0.930	0.930	0.908		0.965
1.052	0.883	0.952	0.833		0.898
0.903		0.939			
0.895		0.940			
		0.882			
		0.906			

46. There are four radio stations in Midland. The stations have different formats (hard rock, classical, country/western, and easy listening), but each is concerned with the number of minutes of music played per hour. From a sample of 10 randomly selected hours from each station, the sum of squared differences between each observation and the mean for its respective radio station, $\Sigma(x - \bar{x}_C)^2$, are:

Hard rock station:	126.29	Country/western station:	166.79
Classical station:	233.34	Easy listening station:	77.57

The total sum of squares for the data is: SS total = 1,099.61.
a. Determine SSE.
b. Determine SST.
c. Complete an ANOVA table.
d. At the .05 significance level, is there a difference in the treatment means?
e. If the mean for the hard rock station is 51.32 and the mean for the country/western station is 50.85, determine if there is a difference using the .05 significance level.

For **DATA FILE**, please visit www.mhhe.com/lind16e

47. The American Accounting Association recently conducted a study to compare the weekly wages of men and women employed in either the public or private sector of accounting. Random samples of five men and five women were selected in each group.

	Sector	
Gender	**Public**	**Private**
Men	$ 978	$1,335
	1,035	1,167
	964	1,236
	996	1,317
	1,117	1,192
Women	$ 863	$1,079
	975	1,160
	999	1,063
	1,019	1,110
	1,037	1,093

a. Draw an interaction plot of men and women means by sector.
b. Compute an ANOVA with statistical software and, using the .05 significance level, test the interaction effect of gender and sector on wages.
c. Based on your results in part (b), conduct the appropriate tests of hypotheses for differences in factor means.
d. Interpret the results in a brief report.

For **DATA FILE**, please visit www.mhhe.com/lind16e

48. Robert Altoff is vice president for engineering for a manufacturer of household washing machines. As part of new product development, he wishes to determine the optimal length of time for the washing cycle. A part of the development is to study the relationship between the detergent used (four brands) and the length of the washing cycle (18, 20, 22, or 24 minutes). In order to run the experiment, 32 standard household laundry loads (having equal amounts of dirt and the same total weights) are randomly assigned to the 16 detergent–washing cycle combinations. The results (in pounds of dirt removed) are shown below.

	Cycle Time (min)			
Detergent Brand	**18**	**20**	**22**	**24**
A	0.13	0.12	0.19	0.15
	0.11	0.11	0.17	0.18
B	0.14	0.15	0.18	0.20
	0.10	0.14	0.17	0.18
C	0.16	0.15	0.18	0.19
	0.17	0.14	0.19	0.21
D	0.09	0.12	0.16	0.15
	0.13	0.13	0.16	0.17

a. Draw an interaction plot of the detergent means by cycle time.
b. Compute the ANOVA with statistical software and, using the .05 significance level, test the interaction effect of brand and cycle time on "dirt removed."
c. Based on your results in part (b), conduct the appropriate tests of hypotheses for differences in factor means.
d. Interpret the results in a brief report.

D A T A   S E T   E X E R C I S E S

(The data for these exercises are available at the text website: www.mhhe.com/lind16e.)

49. Refer to the Real Estate data, which report information on the homes sold in the Goodyear, Arizona, area last year.
    a. At the .02 significance level, is there a difference in the variability of the selling prices of the homes that have a pool versus those that do not have a pool?
    b. At the .02 significance level, is there a difference in the variability of the selling prices of the homes with an attached garage versus those that do not have an attached garage?
    c. At the .05 significance level, is there a difference in the mean selling price of the homes among the five townships?
50. Refer to the Baseball 2012 data, which report information on the 30 Major League Baseball teams for the 2012 season.
    a. At the .10 significance level, is there a difference in the variation in team salary among the American and National League teams?
    b. Create a variable that classifies a team's total attendance into three groups: less than 2.0 (million), 2.0 up to 3.0, and 3.0 or more. At the .05 significance level, is there a difference in the mean number of games won among the three groups?
    c. Using the same attendance variable developed in part (b), is there a difference in the mean number of home runs hit per team? Use the .05 significance level.
    d. Using the same attendance variable developed in part (b), is there a difference in the mean salary of the three groups? Use the .05 significance level.
51. Refer to the Buena School District bus data.
    a. Conduct a test of hypothesis to reveal whether the mean maintenance cost is equal for each of the bus manufacturers. Use the .01 significance level.
    b. Conduct a test of hypothesis to determine whether the mean miles traveled is equal for each bus manufacturer. Use the .05 significance level.
    c. Develop a 95% confidence interval for the disparity in the average maintenance cost between buses made by Bluebird and Thompson.

A REVIEW OF CHAPTERS 10–12

This section is a review of the major concepts and terms introduced in Chapters 10, 11, and 12. Chapter 10 began our study of hypothesis testing. A hypothesis is a statement about the value of a population parameter. In statistical hypothesis testing, we begin by making a statement about the value of the population parameter in the null hypothesis. We establish the null hypothesis for the purpose of testing. When we complete the testing, our decision is either to reject or to fail to reject the null hypothesis. If we reject the null hypothesis, we conclude that the alternate hypothesis is true. The alternate hypothesis is "accepted" only if we show that the null hypothesis is false. We also refer to the alternate hypothesis as the research hypothesis. Most of the time we want to prove the alternate hypothesis.

In Chapter 10, we selected random samples from a single population and tested whether it was reasonable that the population parameter under study equaled a particular value. For example, we wish to investigate whether the mean tenure of those holding the position of CEO in large firms is 12 years. We select a sample of CEOs, compute the sample mean, and compare the mean of the sample to the population. The single population under consideration is the length of tenure of CEOs of large firms. We described methods for conducting the test when the population standard deviation was available and when it was not available.

In Chapter 11, we extended the idea of hypothesis testing to whether two independent random samples came from populations having the same or equal population means. For example, St. Mathews Hospital operates an urgent care facility on both the north and south sides of Knoxville, Tennessee. The research question is: Is the mean waiting time for patients visiting the two facilities the same? To investigate, we select a random sample from each of the facilities and compute the sample means. We test the null hypothesis that the mean waiting time is the same at the two facilities. The alternate hypothesis is that the mean waiting time is not the same for the two facilities. If the population standard deviations are known, we use the z distribution as the test statistic. If the population standard deviations are not known, the test statistic follows the t distribution.

Our discussion in Chapter 11 also concerned dependent samples. The test statistic is the t distribution and we assume that the distribution of differences follows the normal distribution. One typical paired sample problem calls for recording an individual's blood pressure before administering medication and then again afterward in order to evaluate the effectiveness of the medication. We also considered the case of testing two population proportions. For example, the production manager wished to compare the proportion of defects on the day shift with that of the second shift.

Chapter 11 dealt with the difference between two population means. Chapter 12 presented tests for variances and a procedure called the *analysis of variance, or ANOVA*. ANOVA is used to simultaneously determine whether several independent normal populations have the same mean. This is accomplished by comparing the variances of the random samples selected from these populations. We apply the usual hypothesis-testing procedure, but we use the F distribution as the test statistic. Often the calculations are tedious, so a software package is recommended.

As an example of analysis of variance, a test could be conducted to resolve whether there is any difference in effectiveness among five fertilizers on the weight of popcorn ears. This type of analysis is referred to as *one-factor ANOVA* because we are able to draw conclusions about only one factor, called a *treatment*. If we want to draw conclusions about the simultaneous effects of more than one factor or variable, we use the *two-factor ANOVA* technique. Both the one-factor and two-factor tests use the F *distribution* as the distribution of the test statistic. The F distribution is also the distribution of the test statistic used to find whether one normal population has more variation than another.

An additional feature of the two-factor ANOVA is the possibility that interactions may exist between the factors. There is an *interaction* if the response to one of the factors depends on the level of the other factor. Fortunately, the ANOVA is easily extended to include a test for interactions.

P R O B L E M S

For problems 1–6, state: (a) the null and the alternate hypotheses, (b) the decision rule, and (c) the decision regarding the null hypothesis, (d) then interpret the result.

1. A machine is set to produce tennis balls so the mean bounce is 36 inches when the ball is dropped from a platform of a certain height. The production supervisor suspects that the mean bounce has changed and is less than 36 inches. As an experiment, a sample of 12 balls was dropped from the platform and the mean height of the bounce was 35.5 inches, with a standard deviation of 0.9 inch. At the .05 significance level, can the supervisor conclude that the mean bounce height is less than 36 inches?

For **DATA FILE**, please visit
www.mhhe.com/lind16e

2. It was hypothesized that road construction workers do not engage in productive work 20 minutes on the average out of every hour. Some claimed the nonproductive time is greater than 20 minutes. An actual study was conducted at a construction site, using a stopwatch and other ways of checking the work habits. A random check of workers revealed the following unproductive times, in minutes, during a one-hour period (exclusive of regularly scheduled breaks):

10	25	17	20	28	30	18	23	18

Using the .05 significance level, is it reasonable to conclude the mean unproductive time is greater than 20 minutes?

3. A test is to be conducted involving the mean holding power of two glues designed for plastic. First, a small plastic hook was coated at one end with Epox glue and fastened to a sheet of plastic. After it dried, weight was added to the hook until it separated from the sheet of plastic. The weight was then recorded. This was repeated until 12 hooks were tested. The same procedure was followed for Holdtite glue, but only 10 hooks were used. The sample results, in pounds, were:

	Epox	Holdtite
Sample mean	250	252
Sample standard deviation	5	8
Sample size	12	10

At the .01 significance level, is there a difference between the mean holding power of Epox and that of Holdtite?

For **DATA FILE**, please visit
www.mhhe.com/lind16e

4. Pittsburgh Paints wishes to test an additive formulated to increase the life of paints used in the hot and arid conditions of the Southwest. The top half of a piece of wood was painted using the regular paint. The bottom half was painted with the paint including the additive. The same procedure was followed for a total of 10 pieces. Then each piece was subjected to brilliant light. The data, the number of hours each piece lasted before it faded beyond a certain point, follow:

	Number of Hours by Sample									
	A	**B**	**C**	**D**	**E**	**F**	**G**	**H**	**I**	**J**
Without additive	325	313	320	340	318	312	319	330	333	319
With additive	323	313	326	343	310	320	313	340	330	315

Using the .05 significance level, determine whether the additive is effective in prolonging the life of the paint.

5. A Buffalo, New York, cola distributor is featuring a super-special sale on 12-packs. She wonders where in the grocery store to place the cola for maximum attention. Should it be near the front door of the grocery stores, in the cola section, at the checkout registers, or near the milk and other dairy products? Four stores with similar total sales cooperated in an experiment. In one store, the 12-packs were stacked near the front door, in another they were placed near the checkout registers, and so on. Sales were checked at specified times in each store for exactly four minutes. The results were:

Cola at the Door	In Soft Drink Section	Near Registers	Dairy Section
$6	$5	$7	$10
8	10	10	9
3	12	9	6
7	4	4	11
	9	5	
		7	

The Buffalo distributor wants to find out whether there is a difference in the mean sales for cola stacked at the four locations in the store. Use the .05 significance level.

For **DATA FILE**, please visit www.mhhe.com/lind16e

6. Williams Corporation is investigating the effects of educational background on employee performance. A potential relevant variable in this case is the self-rated social status of the employee. The company has recorded the annual sales volumes (in $000) achieved by sales employees in each of the categories below. Perform a complete two-way analysis of variance (including the possibility of interactions) on the data and describe what your results suggest.

Self-Rated Social Status	School Type		
	Ivy League	State-supported	Small Private
Low	62, 61	68, 64	70, 70
Medium	68, 64	74, 68	62, 65
High	70, 71	57, 60	57, 56

7. A school supervisor is reviewing initial wages of former students (in $000). Samples were taken over 3 years for four different majors (accounting, administration, finance, and marketing). For each combination of major and year, three former students were sampled.

Major/Year	2010	2011	2012
Accounting	75.4, 69.8, 62.3	73.9, 78.8, 62.0	64.2, 80.8, 68.2
Administration	61.5, 59.9, 62.1	63.9, 57.6, 66.5	74.2, 67.5, 58.1
Finance	63.6, 70.2, 72.2	69.2, 72.5, 67.2	74.7, 66.4, 77.9
Marketing	71.3, 69.2, 66.4	74.0, 67.6, 61.7	60.0, 61.3, 62.5

a. Here is an interaction plot of the information. What does it reveal?

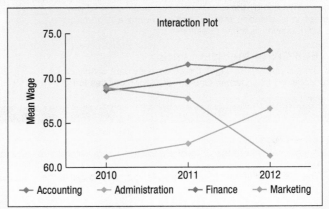

b. Write out all of the pairs of null and alternative hypotheses you would apply for a two-way ANOVA.

c. Here is the statistical software output. Use the 0.05 level to check for interactions.

Source	DF	SS	MS	F	P
Major	3	329.20	109.732	3.39	0.034
Year	2	7.32	3.659	0.11	0.894
Interaction	6	183.57	30.595	0.94	0.482
Error	24	777.29	32.387		
Total	35	1297.37			

d. If proper, test the other hypotheses at the .05 significance level. If it is not appropriate, describe why you should not do the tests.

CASES

A. Century National Bank

Refer to the description of Century National Bank at the end of the Review of Chapters 1–4 on page 128.

With many other options available, customers no longer let their money sit in a checking account. For many years the mean checking balance has been $1,600. Do the sample data indicate that the mean account balance has declined from this value?

Recent years have also seen an increase in the use of ATM machines. When Mr. Selig took over the bank, the mean number of transactions per month per customer was 8; now he believes it has increased to more than 10. In fact, the advertising agency that prepares TV commercials for Century would like to use this on the new commercial being designed. Is there sufficient evidence to conclude that the mean number of transactions per customer is more than 10 per month? Could the advertising agency say the mean is more than 9 per month?

The bank has branch offices in four different cities: Cincinnati, Ohio; Atlanta, Georgia; Louisville, Kentucky; and Erie, Pennsylvania. Mr. Selig would like to know whether there is a difference in the mean checking account balances among the four branches. If there are differences, between which branches do these differences occur?

Mr. Selig is also interested in the bank's ATMs. Is there a difference in ATM use among the branches? Also, do customers who have debit cards tend to use ATMs differently from those who do not have debit cards? Is there a difference in ATM use by those with checking accounts that pay interest versus those that do not? Prepare a report for Mr. Selig answering these questions.

B. Bell Grove Medical Center

Ms. Gene Dempsey manages the emergency care center at Bell Grove Medical Center. One of her responsibilities is to have enough nurses so that incoming patients needing service can be handled promptly. It is stressful for patients to wait a long time for emergency care even when their care needs are not life threatening. Ms. Dempsey gathered the following information regarding the number of patients over the last several weeks. The center is not open on weekends. Does it appear that there are any differences in the number of patients served by the day of the week? If there are differences, which days seem to be the busiest? Write a brief report summarizing your findings.

Date	Day	Patients
9-29-06	Monday	38
9-30-06	Tuesday	28
10-1-06	Wednesday	28
10-2-06	Thursday	30
10-3-06	Friday	35
10-6-06	Monday	35
10-7-06	Tuesday	25
10-8-06	Wednesday	22
10-9-06	Thursday	21
10-10-06	Friday	32
10-13-06	Monday	37
10-14-06	Tuesday	29
10-15-06	Wednesday	27
10-16-06	Thursday	28
10-17-06	Friday	35
10-20-06	Monday	37
10-21-06	Tuesday	26
10-22-06	Wednesday	28
10-23-06	Thursday	23
10-24-06	Friday	33

PRACTICE TEST

Part 1—Objective

1. A statement about the value of a population parameter that always includes the equal sign is called the _____.

2. The likelihood of rejecting a true null hypothesis is called the _____.

1. _____

2. _____

3. Assuming the null hypothesis is true, the likelihood of finding a value of the test statistic at least as extreme as the one found in the sample is called the _____.

4. When conducting a test of hypothesis about a single population mean, the z distribution is used as the test statistic only when the _____ is known.

5. In a two-sample test of hypothesis for means, if the population standard deviations are not known, *what must we assume about the shape of the populations?*

6. A value calculated from sample information used to determine whether to reject the null hypothesis is called the _____.

7. In a two-tailed test, the rejection region is _____. (all in the upper tail, all in the lower tail, split evenly between the two tails, none of these—pick one)

8. Which of the following is not a characteristic of the F distribution? (continuous, positively skewed, range from $-\infty$ to ∞, family of distributions)

9. To perform a one-way ANOVA, the treatments must be _____. (independent, mutually exclusive, continuous)

10. In a one-way ANOVA, there are four treatments and six observations in each treatment. What are the degrees of freedom for the F distribution?

3. _____
4. _____
5. _____
6. _____
7. _____
8. _____
9. _____
10. _____

Part 2—Problems

For problems 1 and 2, state the null and alternate hypotheses and the decision rule, make a decision regarding the null hypothesis, and interpret the result.

1. The Park Manager at Fort Fisher State Park in North Carolina believes the typical summer visitor spends more than 90 minutes in the park. A sample of 18 visitors during the months of June, July, and August revealed the mean time in the park for visitors was 96 minutes, with a standard deviation of 12 minutes. At the .01 significance level, is it reasonable to conclude the mean time in the park is greater than 90 minutes?

2. Is there a difference in the mean miles traveled per week by each of two taxicab companies operating in the Grand Strand area? The *Sun News,* the local paper, is investigating and obtained the following sample information. At the .05 significance level, is it reasonable to conclude there is a difference in the mean miles traveled? Assume equal population variances.

Variable	Yellow Cab	Horse and Buggy Cab Company
Mean miles	837	797
Standard deviation	30	40
Sample size	14	12

3. The results of a one-way ANOVA are reported below. Use the .05 significance level.

ANOVA				
Source of Variation	SS	df	MS	F
Between groups	6.892202	2	3.446101	4.960047
Within groups	12.50589	18	0.694772	
Total	19.3981	20		

Answer the following questions.
a. How many treatments are in the study?
b. What is the total sample size?
c. What is the critical value of F?
d. Write out the null hypothesis and the alternate hypothesis.
e. What is your decision regarding the null hypothesis?
f. Can we conclude the treatment means differ?

13

Correlation and Linear Regression

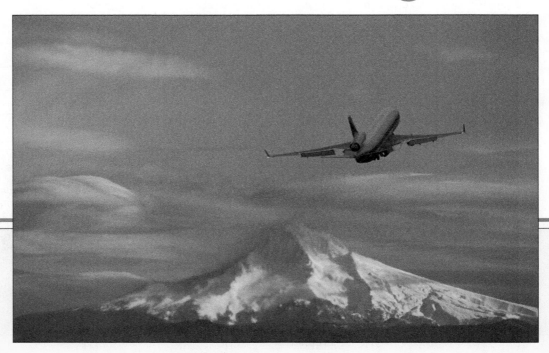

AN AIR TRAVEL SERVICE samples domestic airline flights to explore the relationship between airfare and distance. The service would like to know if there is a correlation between airfare and flight distance. If there is a correlation, what percentage of the variation in airfare is accounted for by distance? How much does each additional mile add to the fare? (See Exercise 61 and LO13-2, LO13-3, and LO13-5.)

LEARNING OBJECTIVES

When you have completed this chapter, you will be able to:

LO13-1 Explain the purpose of correlation analysis.

LO13-2 Calculate a correlation coefficient to test and interpret the relationship between two variables.

LO13-3 Apply regression analysis to estimate the linear relationship between two variables.

LO13-4 Evaluate the significance of the slope of the regression equation.

LO13-5 Evaluate a regression equation's ability to predict using the standard estimate of the error and the coefficient of determination.

LO13-6 Calculate and interpret confidence and prediction intervals.

LO13-7 Use a log function to transform a nonlinear relationship.

CORRELATION AND LINEAR REGRESSION 427

INTRODUCTION

Chapters 2 through 4 presented *descriptive statistics.* We organized raw data into a frequency distribution and computed several measures of location and measures of dispersion to describe the major characteristics of the distribution. In Chapters 5 through 7, we described probability, and from probability statements, we created probability distributions. In Chapter 8, we began the study of *statistical inference,* where we collected a sample to estimate a population parameter such as the population mean or population proportion. In addition, we used the sample data to test a hypothesis about a population mean or a population proportion, the difference between two population means, or the equality of several population means. Each of these tests involved just *one* interval- or ratio-level variable, such as the profit made on a car sale, the income of bank presidents, or the number of patients admitted each month to a particular hospital.

In this chapter, we shift the emphasis to the study of relationships between two interval- or ratio-level variables. In all business fields, identifying and studying relationships between variables can provide information on ways to increase profits, methods to decrease costs, or variables to predict demand. In marketing products, many firms use price reductions through coupons and discount pricing to increase sales. In this example, we are interested in the relationship between two variables: price reductions and sales. To collect the data, a company can test-market a variety of price reduction methods and observe sales. We hope to confirm a relationship that decreasing price leads to increased sales. In economics, you will find many relationships between two variables that are the basis of economics, such as price and demand.

As another familiar example, recall in Chapter 4 we used the Applewood Auto Group data to show the relationship between two variables with a scatter diagram. We plotted the profit for each vehicle sold on the vertical axis and the age of the buyer on the horizontal axis. See the statistical software output on page 95. In that graph, we observed that as the age of the buyer increased, the profit for each vehicle also increased.

Other examples of relationships between two variables are:

- Does the amount Healthtex spends per month on training its sales force affect its monthly sales?
- Is the number of square feet in a home related to the cost to heat the home in January?
- In a study of fuel efficiency, is there a relationship between miles per gallon and the weight of a car?
- Does the number of hours that students study for an exam influence the exam score?

In this chapter, we carry this idea further. That is, we develop numerical measures to express the relationship between two variables. Is the relationship strong or weak? Is it direct or inverse? In addition, we develop an equation to express the relationship between variables. This will allow us to estimate one variable on the basis of another.

To begin our study of relationships between two variables, we examine the meaning and purpose of **correlation analysis.** We continue by developing an equation that will allow us to estimate the value of one variable based on the value of another. This is called **regression analysis.** We will also evaluate the ability of the equation to accurately make estimations.

WHAT IS CORRELATION ANALYSIS?

When we study the relationship between two interval- or ratio-scale variables, we often start with a scatter diagram. This procedure provides a visual representation of the relationship between the variables. The next step is usually to calculate the correlation

TABLE 13–1 Number of Sales Calls and Copiers Sold for 15 Salespeople

Sales Representative	Sales Calls	Copiers Sold
Brian Virost	96	41
Carlos Ramirez	40	41
Carol Saia	104	51
Greg Fish	128	60
Jeff Hall	164	61
Mark Reynolds	76	29
Meryl Rumsey	72	39
Mike Kiel	80	50
Ray Snarsky	36	28
Rich Niles	84	43
Ron Broderick	180	70
Sal Spina	132	56
Soni Jones	120	45
Susan Welch	44	31
Tom Keller	84	30

coefficient. It provides a quantitative measure of the strength of the relationship between two variables. As an example, the sales manager of North American Copier Sales, which has a large sales force throughout the United States and Canada, wants to determine whether there is a relationship between the number of sales calls made in a month and the number of copiers sold that month. The manager selects a random sample of 15 representatives and determines, for each representative, the number of sales calls made and the number of copiers sold. This information is reported in Table 13–1.

By reviewing the data, we observe that there does seem to be some relationship between the number of sales calls and the number of units sold. That is, the salespeople who made the most sales calls sold the most units. However, the relationship is not "perfect" or exact. For example, Soni Jones made fewer sales calls than Jeff Hall, but she sold more units.

In addition to the graphical techniques in Chapter 4, we will develop numerical measures to precisely describe the relationship between the two variables, sales calls and copiers sold. This group of statistical techniques is called **correlation analysis.**

> **CORRELATION ANALYSIS** A group of techniques to measure the relationship between two variables.

The basic idea of correlation analysis is to report the relationship between two variables. The usual first step is to plot the data in a **scatter diagram.** An example will show how a scatter diagram is used.

E X A M P L E

North American Copier Sales sells copiers to businesses of all sizes throughout the United States and Canada. Ms. Marcy Bancer was recently promoted to the position of national sales manager. At the upcoming sales meeting, the sales representatives from all over the country will be in attendance. She would like to impress upon them the importance of making that extra sales call each day. She decides to gather some information on the relationship between the number of sales calls and the number of copiers sold. She selects a random sample of 15 sales representatives and determines the number of sales calls they made last month and the number of copiers they sold. The sample information is reported in

Table 13–1. What observations can you make about the relationship between the number of sales calls and the number of copiers sold? Develop a scatter diagram to display the information.

SOLUTION

Based on the information in Table 13–1, Ms. Bancer suspects there is a relationship between the number of sales calls made in a month and the number of copiers sold. Ron Broderick sold the most copiers last month and made 180 sales calls. On the other hand, Ray Snarsky, Carlos Ramirez, and Susan Welch made the fewest calls: 36, 40, and 44. They also had the lowest number of copiers sold among the sampled representatives.

The implication is that the number of copiers sold is related to the number of sales calls made. As the number of sales calls increases, it appears the number of copiers sold also increases. We refer to number of sales calls as the **independent variable** and number of copiers sold as the **dependent variable.**

The independent variable provides the basis for estimating or predicting the dependent variable. For example, we would like to predict the expected number of copiers sold if a salesperson makes 100 sales calls. In the randomly selected sample data, the independent variable—sales calls—is a random number.

The dependent variable is the variable that is being predicted or estimated. It can also be described as the result or outcome for a particular value of the independent variable. The dependent variable is random. That is, for a given value of the independent variable, there are many possible outcomes for the dependent variable.

It is common practice to scale the dependent variable (copiers sold) on the vertical or Y-axis and the independent variable (number of sales calls) on the horizontal or X-axis. To develop the scatter diagram of the North American Copier Sales information, we begin with the first sales representative, Brian Virost. Brian made 96 sales calls last month and sold 41 copiers, so $x = 96$ and $y = 41$. To plot this point, move along the horizontal axis to $x = 96$, then go vertically to $y = 41$ and place a dot at the intersection. This process is continued until all the paired data are plotted, as shown in Chart 13–1.

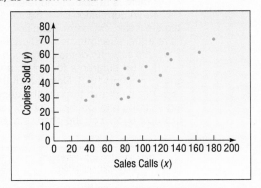

CHART 13–1 Scatter Diagram Showing Sales Calls and Copiers Sold

The scatter diagram shows graphically that the sales representatives who make more calls tend to sell more copiers. It is reasonable for Ms. Bancer, the national sales manager, to tell her salespeople that the more sales calls they make, the more copiers they can expect to sell. Note that, while there appears to be a positive relationship between the two variables, all the points do not fall on a line. In the following section, you will measure the strength and direction of this relationship between two variables by determining the correlation coefficient.

THE CORRELATION COEFFICIENT

Originated by Karl Pearson about 1900, the **correlation coefficient** describes the strength of the relationship between two sets of interval-scaled or ratio-scaled variables. Designated r, it is often referred to as *Pearson's r* and as the *Pearson product-moment correlation coefficient*. It can assume any value from -1.00 to $+1.00$ inclusive. A correlation coefficient of -1.00 or $+1.00$ indicates *perfect correlation*. For example, a correlation coefficient for the preceding example computed to be $+1.00$ would indicate that the number of sales calls and the number of copiers sold are perfectly related in a positive linear sense. A computed value of -1.00 would reveal that sales calls and the number of copiers sold are perfectly related in an inverse linear sense. How the scatter diagram would appear if the relationship between the two variables were linear and perfect is shown in Chart 13–2.

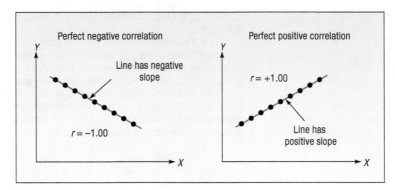

CHART 13–2 Scatter Diagrams Showing Perfect Negative Correlation and Perfect Positive Correlation

If there is absolutely no relationship between the two sets of variables, Pearson's r is zero. A correlation coefficient r close to 0 (say, .08) shows that the linear relationship is quite weak. The same conclusion is drawn if $r = -.08$. Coefficients of $-.91$ and $+.91$ have equal strength; both indicate very strong correlation between the two variables. Thus, *the strength of the correlation does not depend on the direction (either $-$ or $+$).*

Scatter diagrams for $r = 0$, a weak r (say, $-.23$), and a strong r (say, $+.87$) are shown in Chart 13–3. Note that, if the correlation is weak, there is considerable scatter about a line drawn through the center of the data. For the scatter diagram representing a strong relationship, there is very little scatter about the line. This indicates, in the example shown on the chart, that hours studied is a good predictor of exam score.

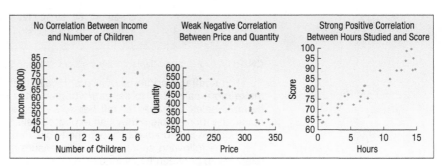

CHART 13–3 Scatter Diagrams Depicting Zero, Weak, and Strong Correlation

CORRELATION AND LINEAR REGRESSION   431

The following drawing summarizes the strength and direction of the correlation coefficient.

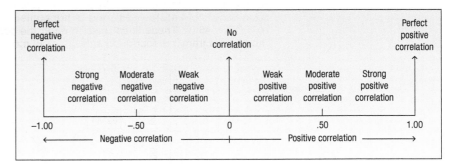

> **CORRELATION COEFFICIENT** A measure of the strength of the linear relationship between two variables.

The characteristics of the correlation coefficient are summarized below.

> **CHARACTERISTICS OF THE CORRELATION COEFFICIENT**
> 1. The sample correlation coefficient is identified by the lowercase letter r.
> 2. It shows the direction and strength of the linear relationship between two interval- or ratio-scale variables.
> 3. It ranges from -1 up to and including $+1$.
> 4. A value near 0 indicates there is little linear relationship between the variables.
> 5. A value near 1 indicates a direct or positive linear relationship between the variables.
> 6. A value near -1 indicates an inverse or negative linear relationship between the variables.

How is the value of the correlation coefficient determined? We will use the North American Copier Sales in Table 13–1 as an example. It is replicated in Table 13–2 for

TABLE 13–2 Number of Sales Calls and Copiers Sold for 15 Salespeople

Sales Representative	Sales Calls	Copiers Sold
Brian Virost	96	41
Carlos Ramirez	40	41
Carol Saia	104	51
Greg Fish	128	60
Jeff Hall	164	61
Mark Reynolds	76	29
Meryl Rumsey	72	39
Mike Kiel	80	50
Ray Snarsky	36	28
Rich Niles	84	43
Ron Broderick	180	70
Sal Spina	132	56
Soni Jones	120	45
Susan Welch	44	31
Tom Keller	84	30
Total	1440	675

your convenience. We begin with a scatter diagram, similar to Chart 13–2. Draw a vertical line through the data values at the mean of the x-values and a horizontal line at the mean of the y-values. In Chart 13–4, we've added a vertical line at 96 calls ($\bar{x} = \Sigma x/n = 1440/15 = 96$) and a horizontal line at 45.0 copiers ($\bar{y} = \Sigma y/n = 675/15 = 45.0$). These lines pass through the "center" of the data and divide the scatter diagram into four quadrants. Think of moving the origin from (0, 0) to (96, 45).

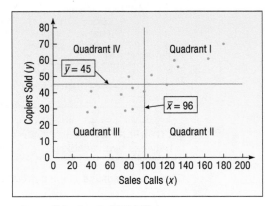

CHART 13–4 Computation of the Correlation Coefficient

Two variables are positively related when the number of copiers sold is above the mean and the number of sales calls is also above the mean. These points appear in the upper-right quadrant (labeled Quadrant I) of Chart 13–4. Similarly, when the number of copiers sold is less than the mean, so is the number of sales calls. These points fall in the lower-left quadrant of Chart 13–4 (labeled Quadrant III). For example, the third person on the list in Table 13–2, Carol Saia, made 104 sales calls and sold 51 copiers. These values are above their respective means, so this point is located in Quadrant I, which is in the upper-right quadrant. She made 8 more calls than the mean number of sales calls and sold 6 more than the mean number sold. Tom Keller, the last name on the list in Table 13–2, made 84 sales calls and sold 30 copiers. Both of these values are less than their respective means, hence this point is in the lower-left quadrant. Tom made 12 fewer sales calls and sold 15 fewer copiers than the respective means. The deviations from the mean number of sales calls and the mean number of copiers sold are summarized in Table 13–3 for the 15 sales representatives. The sum of the products of the deviations from the respective means is 6672. That is, the term $\Sigma(x - \bar{x})(y - \bar{y}) = 6672$.

In both the upper-right and the lower-left quadrants, the product of $(x - \bar{x})(y - \bar{y})$ is positive because both of the factors have the same sign. In our example, this happens for all sales representatives except Mike Kiel. Mike made 80 sales calls (which is less than the mean) but sold 50 machines (which is more than the mean). We can therefore expect the correlation coefficient to have a positive value.

If the two variables are inversely related, one variable will be above the mean and the other below the mean. Most of the points in this case occur in the upper-left and lower-right quadrants, that is, Quadrants II and IV. Now $(x - \bar{x})$ and $(y - \bar{y})$ will have opposite signs, so their product is negative. The resulting correlation coefficient is negative.

What happens if there is no linear relationship between the two variables? The points in the scatter diagram will appear in all four quadrants. The negative products of $(x - \bar{x})(y - \bar{y})$ offset the positive products, so the sum is near zero. This leads to a correlation coefficient near zero. So, the term $\Sigma(x - \bar{x})(y - \bar{y})$ drives the strength as well as the sign of the relationship between the two variables.

CORRELATION AND LINEAR REGRESSION   433

TABLE 13–3 Deviations from the Mean and Their Products

Sales Representative	Sales Calls (x)	Copiers Sold (y)	$x - \bar{x}$	$y - \bar{y}$	$(x - \bar{x})(y - \bar{y})$
Brian Virost	96	41	0	−4	0
Carlos Ramirez	40	41	−56	−4	224
Carol Saia	104	51	8	6	48
Greg Fish	128	60	32	15	480
Jeff Hall	164	61	68	16	1,088
Mark Reynolds	76	29	−20	−16	320
Meryl Rumsey	72	39	−24	−6	144
Mike Kiel	80	50	−16	5	−80
Ray Snarsky	36	28	−60	−17	1,020
Rich Niles	84	43	−12	−2	24
Ron Broderick	180	70	84	25	2,100
Sal Spina	132	56	36	11	396
Soni Jones	120	45	24	0	0
Susan Welch	44	31	−52	−14	728
Tom Keller	84	30	−12	−15	180
Totals	1440	675	0	0	6,672

The correlation coefficient is also unaffected by the units of the two variables. For example, if we had used hundreds of copiers sold instead of the number sold, the correlation coefficient would be the same. The correlation coefficient is independent of the scale used if we divide the term $\Sigma(x - \bar{x})(y - \bar{y})$ by the sample standard deviations. It is also made independent of the sample size and bounded by the values +1.00 and −1.00 if we divide by $(n - 1)$.

This reasoning leads to the following formula:

CORRELATION COEFFICIENT	$$r = \frac{\Sigma(x - \bar{x})(y - \bar{y})}{(n - 1)s_x s_y}$$	[13–1]

To compute the correlation coefficient, we use the standard deviations of the sample of 15 sales calls and 15 copiers sold. We could use formula (3–12) to calculate the sample standard deviations or we could use a software package. For the specific Excel and Minitab commands, see the **Software Commands** in Appendix C. The following is the Excel output. The standard deviation of the number of sales calls is 42.76 and of the number of copiers sold 12.89.

	A	B	C	D	E	F	G	H
1		Sales Representative	Sales Calls (x)	Copiers Sold (y)			Sales Calls (x)	Copiers Sold (y)
2		Brian Virost	96	41		Mean	96.00	45.00
3		Carlos Ramirez	40	41		Standard Error	11.04	3.33
4		Carol Saia	104	51		Median	84.00	43.00
5		Greg Fish	128	60		Mode	84.00	41.00
6		Jeff Hall	164	61		Standard Deviation	42.76	12.89
7		Mark Reynolds	76	29		Sample Variance	1828.57	166.14
8		Meryl Rumsey	72	39		Kurtosis	-0.32	-0.73
9		Mike Kiel	80	50		Skewness	0.46	0.36
10		Ray Snarsky	36	28		Range	144.00	42.00
11		Rich Niles	84	43		Minimum	36.00	28.00
12		Ron Broderick	180	70		Maximum	180.00	70.00
13		Sal Spina	132	56		Sum	1440.00	675.00
14		Soni Jones	120	45		Count	15.00	15.00
15		Susan Welch	44	31				
16		Tom Keller	84	30				
17		Total	1440	675				

We now insert these values into formula (13–1) to determine the correlation coefficient:

$$r = \frac{\Sigma(x - \bar{x})(y - \bar{y})}{(n-1)s_x s_y} = \frac{6672}{(15-1)(42.76)(12.89)} = 0.865$$

How do we interpret a correlation of 0.865? First, it is positive, so we conclude there is a direct relationship between the number of sales calls and the number of copiers sold. This confirms our reasoning based on the scatter diagram, Chart 13–4. The value of 0.865 is fairly close to 1.00, so we conclude that the association is strong.

We must be careful with the interpretation. The correlation of 0.865 indicates a strong positive linear association between the variables. Ms. Bancer would be correct to encourage the sales personnel to make that extra sales call because the number of sales calls made is related to the number of copiers sold. However, does this mean that more sales calls *cause* more sales? No, we have not demonstrated cause and effect here, only that the two variables—sales calls and copiers sold—are related.

If there is a strong relationship (say, .97) between two variables, we are tempted to assume that an increase or decrease in one variable *causes* a change in the other variable. For example, historically, the consumption of Georgia peanuts and the consumption of aspirin have a strong correlation. However, this does not indicate that an increase in the consumption of peanuts *caused* the consumption of aspirin to increase. Likewise, the incomes of professors and the number of inmates in mental institutions have increased proportionately. Further, as the population of donkeys has decreased, there has been an increase in the number of doctoral degrees granted. Relationships such as these are called **spurious correlations.** What we can conclude when we find two variables with a strong correlation is that there is a relationship or association between the two variables, not that a change in one causes a change in the other.

EXAMPLE

The Applewood Auto Group's marketing department believes younger buyers purchase vehicles on which lower profits are earned and the older buyers purchase vehicles on which higher profits are earned. They would like to use this information as part of an upcoming advertising campaign to try to attract older buyers, for whom the profits tend to be higher. Develop a scatter diagram depicting the relationship between vehicle profits and age of the buyer. Use statistical software to determine the correlation coefficient. Would this be a useful advertising feature?

SOLUTION

Using the Applewood Auto Group example, the first step is to graph the data using a scatter plot. It is shown in Chart 13–5.

CHART 13–5 Scatter Diagram of Profit versus Age for the Applewood Auto Group Data

CORRELATION AND LINEAR REGRESSION   435

The scatter diagram suggests that a positive relationship does exist between age and profit; however, that relationship does not appear strong.

The next step is to calculate the correlation coefficient to evaluate the relative strength of the relationship. Statistical software provides an easy way to calculate the value of the correlation coefficient. The Excel output follows.

	Age	*Profit*
Age	1	
Profit	0.262	1

For these data, $r = 0.262$. To evaluate the relationship between a buyer's age and the profit on a car sale:

1. The relationship is positive or direct. Why? Because the sign of the correlation coefficient is positive. This confirms that as the age of the buyer increases, the profit on a car sale also increases.
2. The relationship between the two variables is weak. For a positive relationship, values of the correlation coefficient close to one indicate stronger relationships. In this case, $r = 0.262$. It is closer to zero, and we would observe that the relationship is not very strong.

It is not recommended that Applewood use this information as part of an advertising campaign to attract older, more profitable buyers.

SELF-REVIEW

13–1

Haverty's Furniture is a family business that has been selling to retail customers in the Chicago area for many years. The company advertises extensively on radio, TV, and the Internet, emphasizing low prices and easy credit terms. The owner would like to review the relationship between sales and the amount spent on advertising. Below is information on sales and advertising expense for the last four months.

Month	Advertising Expense ($ million)	Sales Revenue ($ million)
July	2	7
August	1	3
September	3	8
October	4	10

(a) The owner wants to forecast sales on the basis of advertising expense. Which variable is the dependent variable? Which variable is the independent variable?
(b) Draw a scatter diagram.
(c) Determine the correlation coefficient.
(d) Interpret the strength of the correlation coefficient.

EXERCISES

1. The following sample observations were randomly selected.

x	4	5	3	6	10
y	4	6	5	7	7

Determine the correlation coefficient and interpret the relationship between x and y.

436   CHAPTER 13

2. The following sample observations were randomly selected.

x	5	3	6	3	4	4	6	8
y	13	15	7	12	13	11	9	5

Determine the correlation coefficient and interpret the relationship between x and y.

3. Bi-lo Appliance Super-Store has outlets in several large metropolitan areas in New England. The general sales manager aired a commercial for a digital camera on selected local TV stations prior to a sale starting on Saturday and ending Sunday. She obtained the information for Saturday–Sunday digital camera sales at the various outlets and paired it with the number of times the advertisement was shown on the local TV stations. The purpose is to find whether there is any relationship between the number of times the advertisement was aired and digital camera sales. The pairings are:

Location of TV Station	Number of Airings	Saturday–Sunday Sales ($ thousands)
Providence	4	15
Springfield	2	8
New Haven	5	21
Boston	6	24
Hartford	3	17

a. What is the dependent variable?
b. Draw a scatter diagram.
c. Determine the correlation coefficient.
d. Interpret these statistical measures.

4. The production department of Celltronics International wants to explore the relationship between the number of employees who assemble a subassembly and the number produced. As an experiment, two employees were assigned to assemble the subassemblies. They produced 15 during a one-hour period. Then four employees assembled them. They produced 25 during a one-hour period. The complete set of paired observations follows.

Number of Assemblers	One-Hour Production (units)
2	15
4	25
1	10
5	40
3	30

The dependent variable is production; that is, it is assumed that different levels of production result from a different number of employees.

a. Draw a scatter diagram.
b. Based on the scatter diagram, does there appear to be any relationship between the number of assemblers and production? Explain.
c. Compute the correlation coefficient.

5. The city council of Pine Bluffs is considering increasing the number of police in an effort to reduce crime. Before making a final decision, the council asked the chief of police to survey other cities of similar size to determine the relationship between the number of police and the number of crimes reported. The chief gathered the following sample information.

City	Police	Number of Crimes	City	Police	Number of Crimes
Oxford	15	17	Holgate	17	7
Starksville	17	13	Carey	12	21
Danville	25	5	Whistler	11	19
Athens	27	7	Woodville	22	6

CORRELATION AND LINEAR REGRESSION   437

a. Which variable is the dependent variable and which is the independent variable? Hint: Which of the following makes better sense: Cities with more police have fewer crimes, or cities with fewer crimes have more police? Explain your choice.
b. Draw a scatter diagram.
c. Determine the correlation coefficient.
d. Interpret the correlation coefficient. Does it surprise you that the correlation coefficient is negative?

6. The owner of Maumee Ford-Mercury-Volvo wants to study the relationship between the age of a car and its selling price. Listed below is a random sample of 12 used cars sold at the dealership during the last year.

For **DATA FILE**, please visit
www.mhhe.com/lind16e

Car	Age (years)	Selling Price ($000)	Car	Age (years)	Selling Price ($000)
1	9	8.1	7	8	7.6
2	7	6.0	8	11	8.0
3	11	3.6	9	10	8.0
4	12	4.0	10	12	6.0
5	8	5.0	11	6	8.6
6	7	10.0	12	6	8.0

a. Draw a scatter diagram.
b. Determine the correlation coefficient.
c. Interpret the correlation coefficient. Does it surprise you that the correlation coefficient is negative?

Testing the Significance of the Correlation Coefficient

Recall that the sales manager of North American Copier Sales found the correlation between the number of sales calls and the number of copiers sold was 0.865. This indicated a strong positive association between the two variables. However, only 15 salespeople were sampled. Could it be that the correlation in the population is actually 0? This would mean the correlation of 0.865 was due to chance. The population in this example is all the salespeople employed by the firm.

Resolving this dilemma requires a test to answer the obvious question: Could there be zero correlation in the population from which the sample was selected? To put it another way, did the computed r come from a population of paired observations with zero correlation? To continue our convention of allowing Greek letters to represent a population parameter, we will let ρ represent the correlation in the population. It is pronounced "rho."

We will continue with the illustration involving sales calls and copiers sold. We employ the same hypothesis testing steps described in Chapter 10. The null hypothesis and the alternate hypothesis are:

H_0: $\rho = 0$ (The correlation in the population is zero.)
H_1: $\rho \neq 0$ (The correlation in the population is different from zero.)

From the way H_1 is stated, we know that the test is two-tailed.
The formula for t is:

t TEST FOR THE CORRELATION COEFFICIENT	$t = \dfrac{r\sqrt{n-2}}{\sqrt{1-r^2}}$ with $n-2$ degrees of freedom	**[13–2]**

Using the .05 level of significance, the decision rule states that if the computed t falls in the area between plus 2.160 and minus 2.160, the null hypothesis is not rejected. To locate the critical value of 2.160, refer to Appendix B.5 for $df = n - 2 = 15 - 2 = 13$. See Chart 13–6.

438   CHAPTER 13

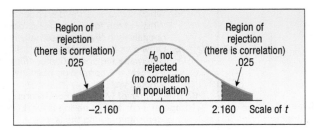

CHART 13-6 Decision Rule for Test of Hypothesis at .05 Significance Level and 13 *df*

Applying formula (13–2) to the example regarding the number of sales calls and units sold:

$$t = \frac{r\sqrt{n-2}}{\sqrt{1-r^2}} = \frac{.865\sqrt{15-2}}{\sqrt{1-.865^2}} = 6.216$$

The computed *t* is in the rejection region. Thus, H_0 is rejected at the .05 significance level. Hence we conclude the correlation in the population is not zero. This indicates to the sales manager that there is correlation with respect to the number of sales calls made and the number of copiers sold in the population of salespeople.

We can also interpret the test of hypothesis in terms of *p*-values. A *p*-value is the likelihood of finding a value of the test statistic more extreme than the one computed, when H_0 is true. To determine the *p*-value, go to the *t* distribution in Appendix B.5 and find the row for 13 degrees of freedom. The value of the test statistic is 6.216, so in the row for 13 degrees of freedom and a two-tailed test, find the value closest to 6.216. For a two-tailed test at the 0.001 significance level, the critical value is 4.221. Because 6.216 is greater than 4.221, we conclude that the *p*-value is less than 0.001.

Both Minitab and Excel will report the correlation between two variables. In addition to the correlation, Minitab reports the *p*-value for the test of hypothesis that the correlation in the population between the two variables is 0. The Minitab output follows.

	C1-T	C2	C3	C4	C5	C6	C7	C8	C9	C10	C11
	Name	Sales Calls	Copiers Sold								
1	Brian Virost	96	41								
2	Carlos Ramirez	40	41								
3	Carol Saia	104	51								
4	Greg Fish	128	60								
5	Jeff Hall	164	61								
6	Mark Reynolds	76	29								
7	Meryl Rumsey	72	39								
8	Mike Kiel	80	50								
9	Ray Snarsky	36	28								
10	Rich Niles	84	43								
11	Ron Broderick	180	70								
12	Sal Spina	132	56								
13	Soni Jones	120	45								
14	Susan Welch	44	31								
15	Tom Keller	84	30								

Session

Correlations: Sales Calls, Copiers Sold

Pearson correlation of Sales Calls and Copiers Sold = 0.865
P-Value = 0.000

E X A M P L E

In the example on page 435, we found that the correlation coefficient between the profit on the sale of a vehicle by the Applewood Auto Group and the age of the person that purchased the vehicle was 0.262. Because the sign of the correlation coefficient was positive, we concluded there was a direct relationship between the two variables. However, because the amount of correlation was low—that is, near

CORRELATION AND LINEAR REGRESSION   439

zero—we concluded that an advertising campaign directed toward the older buyers, where there is a large profit, was not warranted. We can test our conclusion by conducting a hypothesis test that the correlation coefficient is greater than zero using the .05 significance level.

SOLUTION

To test the hypothesis, we need to clarify the sample and population issues. Let's assume that the data collected on the 180 vehicles sold by the Applewood Group is a sample from the population of *all* vehicles sold over many years by the Applewood Auto Group. The Greek letter ρ is the correlation coefficient in the population and r the correlation coefficient in the sample.

Our next step is to set up the null hypothesis and the alternate hypothesis. We test the null hypothesis that the correlation coefficient is equal to or less than zero. The alternate hypothesis is that there is positive correlation between the two variables.

H_0: $\rho \leq 0$ (The correlation in the population is negative or equal to zero.)
H_1: $\rho > 0$ (The correlation in the population is positive.)

This is a one-tailed test because we are interested in confirming a positive association between the variables. The test statistic follows the t distribution with $n - 2$ degrees of freedom, so the degrees of freedom are $180 - 2 = 178$. However, the value for 178 degrees of freedom is not in Appendix B.5. The closest value is 180, so we will use that value. Our decision rule is to reject the null hypothesis if the computed value of the test statistic is greater than 1.653.

We use formula (13–2) to find the value of the test statistic.

$$t = \frac{r\sqrt{n-2}}{\sqrt{1-r^2}} = \frac{0.262\sqrt{180-2}}{\sqrt{1-0.262^2}} = 3.622$$

Comparing the value of our test statistic of 3.622 to the critical value of 1.653, we reject the null hypothesis. We conclude that the sample correlation coefficient of 0.262 is too large to have come from a population with no correlation. To put our results another way, there is a positive correlation between profits and age in the population.

This result is confusing and seems contradictory. On one hand, we observed that the correlation coefficient did not indicate a very strong relationship and that the Applewood Auto Group marketing department should not use this information for its promotion and advertising decisions. On the other hand, the hypothesis test indicated that the correlation coefficient is not equal to zero and that a positive relationship between age and profit exists. How can this be? We must be very careful about the application of the hypothesis test results. The hypothesis test shows a statistically significant result. However, this result does not necessarily support a practical decision to start a new marketing and promotion campaign to older purchasers. In fact, the relatively low correlation coefficient is an indication that the outcome of a new marketing and promotion campaign to older potential purchasers is, at best, uncertain.

SELF-REVIEW

13–2

A sample of 25 mayoral campaigns in medium-sized cities with populations between 50,000 and 250,000 showed that the correlation between the percent of the vote received and the amount spent on the campaign by the candidate was .43. At the .05 significance level, is there a positive association between the variables?

EXERCISES

▼

For **DATA FILE**, please visit
www.mhhe.com/lind16e

7. The following hypotheses are given.

$$H_0: \rho \le 0$$
$$H_1: \rho > 0$$

A random sample of 12 paired observations indicated a correlation of .32. Can we conclude that the correlation in the population is greater than zero? Use the .05 significance level.

8. The following hypotheses are given.

$$H_0: \rho \ge 0$$
$$H_1: \rho < 0$$

A random sample of 15 paired observations has a correlation of −.46. Can we conclude that the correlation in the population is less than zero? Use the .05 significance level.

9. Pennsylvania Refining Company is studying the relationship between the pump price of gasoline and the number of gallons sold. For a sample of 20 stations last Tuesday, the correlation was .78. At the .01 significance level, is the correlation in the population greater than zero?

10. A study of 20 worldwide financial institutions showed the correlation between their assets and pretax profit to be .86. At the .05 significance level, can we conclude that there is positive correlation in the population?

11. The Airline Passenger Association studied the relationship between the number of passengers on a particular flight and the cost of the flight. It seems logical that more passengers on the flight will result in more weight and more luggage, which in turn will result in higher fuel costs. For a sample of 15 flights, the correlation between the number of passengers and total fuel cost was .667. Is it reasonable to conclude that there is positive association in the population between the two variables? Use the .01 significance level.

12. The Student Government Association at Middle Carolina University wanted to demonstrate the relationship between the number of beers a student drinks and his or her blood alcohol content (BAC). A random sample of 18 students participated in a study in which each participating student was randomly assigned a number of 12-ounce cans of beer to drink. Thirty minutes after they consumed their assigned number of beers, a member of the local sheriff's office measured their blood alcohol content. The sample information is reported below.

Student	Beers	BAC	Student	Beers	BAC
1	6	0.10	10	3	0.07
2	7	0.09	11	3	0.05
3	7	0.09	12	7	0.08
4	4	0.10	13	1	0.04
5	5	0.10	14	4	0.07
6	3	0.07	15	2	0.06
7	3	0.10	16	7	0.12
8	6	0.12	17	2	0.05
9	6	0.09	18	1	0.02

Use a statistical software package to answer the following questions.

a. Develop a scatter diagram for the number of beers consumed and BAC. Comment on the relationship. Does it appear to be strong or weak? Does it appear to be positive or inverse?

b. Determine the correlation coefficient.

c. At the .01 significance level, is it reasonable to conclude that there is a positive relationship in the population between the number of beers consumed and the BAC? What is the p-value?

LO13-3

Apply regression analysis to estimate the linear relationship between two variables.

REGRESSION ANALYSIS

In the previous sections of this chapter, we evaluated the direction and the significance of the linear relationship between two variables by finding the correlation coefficient. Regression analysis is another method to examine a linear relationship between two variables. This analysis uses the basic concepts of correlation but provides much more information by expressing the linear relationship between two variables in the form of an equation. Using this equation, we will be able to estimate the value of the dependent variable Y based on a selected value of the independent variable X. The technique used to develop the equation and provide the estimates is called **regression analysis.**

In Table 13–1, we reported the number of sales calls and the number of units sold for a sample of 15 sales representatives employed by North American Copier Sales. Chart 13–1 portrayed this information in a scatter diagram. Recall that we tested the significance of the correlation coefficient ($r = 0.865$) and concluded that a significant relationship exists between the two variables. Now we want to develop a linear equation that expresses the relationship between the number of sales calls, the independent variable, and the number of units sold, the dependent variable. The equation for the line used to estimate Y on the basis of X is referred to as the **regression equation.**

> **REGRESSION EQUATION** An equation that expresses the linear relationship between two variables.

Least Squares Principle

In regression analysis, our objective is to use the data to position a line that best represents the relationship between the two variables. Our first approach is to use a scatter diagram to visually position the line.

The scatter diagram in Chart 13–1 is reproduced in Chart 13–7, with a line drawn with a ruler through the dots to illustrate that a line would probably fit the data. However, the line drawn using a straight edge has one disadvantage: Its position is based in part on the judgment of the person drawing the line. The hand-drawn lines in Chart 13–8 represent the judgments of four people. All the lines except line A seem to be reasonable. That is, each line is centered among the graphed data. However, each would result in a different estimate of units sold for a particular number of sales calls.

CHART 13–7 Sales Calls and Copiers Sold for 15 Sales Representatives

CHART 13–8 Four Lines Superimposed on the Scatter Diagram

We would prefer a method that results in a single, best regression line. This method is called the least squares principle. It gives what is commonly referred to as the "best-fitting" line.

> **LEAST SQUARES PRINCIPLE** A mathematical procedure that uses the data to position a line with the objective of minimizing the sum of the squares of the vertical distances between the actual y values and the predicted values of y.

To illustrate this concept, the same data are plotted in the three charts that follow. The dots are the actual values of y, and the asterisks are the predicted values of y for a given value of x. The regression line in Chart 13–9 was determined using the least squares method. It is the best-fitting line because the sum of the squares of the vertical deviations about it is at a minimum. The first plot ($x = 3$, $y = 8$) deviates by 2 from the line, found by $10 - 8$. The deviation squared is 4. The squared deviation for the plot $x = 4$, $y = 18$ is 16. The squared deviation for the plot $x = 5$, $y = 16$ is 4. The sum of the squared deviations is 24, found by $4 + 16 + 4$.

Assume that the lines in Charts 13–10 and 13–11 were drawn with a straight edge. The sum of the squared vertical deviations in Chart 13–10 is 44. For Chart 13–11, it is 132. Both sums are greater than the sum for the line in Chart 13–9, found by using the least squares method.

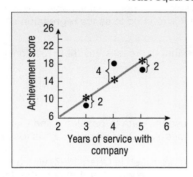

CHART 13–9   The Least Squares Line

CHART 13–10   Line Drawn with a Straight Edge

CHART 13–11   Different Line Drawn with a Straight Edge

The equation of a line has the form

GENERAL FORM OF LINEAR REGRESSION EQUATION	$\hat{y} = a + bx$	[13–3]

where:

     $\hat{y}$, read y hat, is the estimated value of the y variable for a selected x value.

     a is the y-intercept. It is the estimated value of Y when $x = 0$. Another way to put it is: a is the estimated value of y where the regression line crosses the Y-axis when x is zero.

     b is the slope of the line, or the average change in $\hat{y}$ for each change of one unit (either increase or decrease) in the independent variable x.

     x is any value of the independent variable that is selected.

The general form of the linear regression equation is exactly the same form as the equation of any line. a is the Y intercept and b is the slope. The purpose of regression analysis is to calculate the values of a and b to develop a linear equation that best fits the data.

The formulas for a and b are:

SLOPE OF THE REGRESSION LINE	$b = r\left(\dfrac{s_y}{s_x}\right)$	[13–4]

where:

     r is the correlation coefficient.

     s_y is the standard deviation of y (the dependent variable).

     s_x is the standard deviation of x (the independent variable).

Y-INTERCEPT	$a = \bar{y} - b\bar{x}$	[13–5]

where:

$\bar{y}$ is the mean of *y* (the dependent variable).
$\bar{x}$ is the mean of *x* (the independent variable).

E X A M P L E

Recall the example involving North American Copier Sales. The sales manager gathered information on the number of sales calls made and the number of copiers sold for a random sample of 15 sales representatives. As a part of her presentation at the upcoming sales meeting, Ms. Bancer, the sales manager, would like to offer specific information about the relationship between the number of sales calls and the number of copiers sold. Use the least squares method to determine a linear equation to express the relationship between the two variables. What is the expected number of copiers sold by a representative who made 100 calls?

S O L U T I O N

The first step in determining the regression equation is to find the slope of the least squares regression line. That is, we need the value of *b*. On page 434, we determined the correlation coefficient *r* (0.865). In the Excel output on page 433, we determined the standard deviation of the independent variable *x* (42.76) and the standard deviation of the dependent variable *y* (12.89). The values are inserted in formula (13–4).

$$b = r\left(\frac{s_y}{s_x}\right) = .865\left(\frac{12.89}{42.76}\right) = 0.2608$$

Next, we need to find the value of *a*. To do this, we use the value for *b* that we just calculated as well as the means for the number of sales calls and the number of copiers sold. These means are also available in the Excel worksheet on page 433. From formula (13–5):

$$a = \bar{y} - b\bar{x} = 45 - .2608(96) = 19.9632$$

Thus, the regression equation is $\hat{y} = 19.9632 + 0.2608x$. So if a salesperson makes 100 calls, he or she can expect to sell 46.0432 copiers, found by $\hat{y} = 19.9632 + 0.2608x = 19.9632 + 0.2608(100)$. The *b* value of .2608 indicates that for each additional sales call, the sales representative can expect to increase the number of copiers sold by about 0.2608. To put it another way, 20 additional sales calls in a month will result in about five more copiers being sold, found by $0.2608(20) = 5.216$.

The *a* value of 19.9632 is the point where the equation crosses the *Y*-axis. A literal translation is that if no sales calls are made, that is *x* = 0, 19.9632 copiers will be sold. Note that *x* = 0 is outside the range of values included in the sample and, therefore, should not be used to estimate the number of copiers sold. The sales calls ranged from 36 to 180, so estimates should be limited to that range.

Drawing the Regression Line

The least squares equation $\hat{y} = 19.9632 + 0.2608x$ can be drawn on the scatter diagram. The fifth sales representative in the sample is Jeff Hall. He made 164 calls. His estimated number of copiers sold is $\hat{y} = 19.9632 + 0.2608(164) = 62.7344$. The plot *x* = 164 and $\hat{y} = 62.7344$ is located by moving to 164 on the *X*-axis and then going

CHART 13–12 The Line of Regression Drawn on the Scatter Diagram

vertically to 62.7344. The other points on the regression equation can be determined by substituting a particular value of x into the regression equation and calculating $\hat{y}$. All the points are connected to give the line. See Chart 13–12.

Sales Representative	Sales Calls (x)	Copiers Sold (y)	Estimated Sales ($\hat{y}$)
Brian Virost	96	41	45.0000
Carlos Ramirez	40	41	30.3952
Carol Saia	104	51	47.0864
Greg Fish	128	60	53.3456
Jeff Hall	164	61	62.7344
Mark Reynolds	76	29	39.7840
Meryl Rumsey	72	39	38.7408
Mike Kiel	80	50	40.8272
Ray Snarsky	36	28	29.3520
Rich Niles	84	43	41.8704
Ron Broderick	180	70	66.9072
Sal Spina	132	56	54.3888
Soni Jones	120	45	51.2592
Susan Welch	44	31	31.4384
Tom Keller	84	30	41.8704

The least squares regression line has some interesting and unique features. First, it will always pass through the point $(\bar{x}, \bar{y})$. To show this is true, we can use the mean number of sales calls to predict the number of copiers sold. In this example, the mean number of sales calls is 96, found by $\bar{x} = 1440/15$. The mean number of copiers sold is 45.0, found by $\bar{y} = 675/15$. If we let $x = 96$ and then use the regression equation to find the estimated value for $\hat{y}$, the result is:

$$\hat{y} = 19.9632 + 0.2608(96) = 45$$

The estimated number of copiers sold is exactly equal to the mean number of copiers sold. This simple example shows the regression line will pass through the point represented by the two means. In this case, the regression equation will pass through the point $x = 96$ and $y = 45$.

Second, as we discussed earlier in this section, there is no other line through the data where the sum of the squared deviations is smaller. To put it another way, the term $\Sigma(y - \hat{y})^2$ is smaller for the least squares regression equation than for any other equation. We use the Excel system to demonstrate this result in the following printout.

CORRELATION AND LINEAR REGRESSION   445

	A	B	C	D	E	F	G	H	I	J
1	Sales Rep	Sales Calls (x)	Copiers Sold (y)	Estimated Sales $\hat{y}$	$(y-\bar{y})$	$(y-\bar{y})^2$	y^*	$(y \cdot y^*)^2$	y^{**}	$(y \cdot y^{**})^2$
2	Brian Virost	96	41	45.0000	-4.0000	16.0000	44.4000	11.5600	41.6000	0.3600
3	Carlos Ramirez	40	41	30.3952	10.6048	112.4618	29.0000	144.0000	29.0000	144.0000
4	Carol Saia	104	51	47.0864	3.9136	15.3163	46.6000	19.3600	43.4000	57.7600
5	Greg Fish	128	60	53.3456	6.6544	44.2810	53.2000	46.2400	48.8000	125.4400
6	Jeff Hall	164	61	62.7344	-1.7344	3.0081	63.1000	4.4100	56.9000	16.8100
7	Mark Reynolds	76	29	39.7840	-10.7840	116.2947	38.9000	98.0100	37.1000	65.6100
8	Meryl Rumsey	72	39	38.7408	0.2592	0.0672	37.8000	1.4400	36.2000	7.8400
9	Mike Kiel	80	50	40.8272	9.1728	84.1403	40.0000	100.0000	38.0000	144.0000
10	Ray Snarsky	36	28	29.3520	-1.3520	1.8279	27.9000	0.0100	28.1000	0.0100
11	Rich Niles	84	43	41.8704	1.1296	1.2760	41.1000	3.6100	38.9000	16.8100
12	Ron Broderick	180	70	66.9072	3.0928	9.5654	67.5000	6.2500	60.5000	90.2500
13	Sal Spina	132	56	54.3888	1.6112	2.5960	54.3000	2.8900	49.7000	39.6900
14	Soni Jones	120	45	51.2592	-6.2592	39.1776	51.0000	36.0000	47.0000	4.0000
15	Susan Welch	44	31	31.4384	-0.4384	0.1922	30.1000	0.8100	29.9000	1.2100
16	Tom Keller	84	30	41.8704	-11.8704	140.9064	41.1000	123.2100	38.9000	79.2100
17	**Total**				**0.0000**	**587.1108**		**597.8000**		**793.0000**

In Columns A, B, and C in the Excel spreadsheet above, we duplicated the sample information on sales and copiers sold from Table 13–1. In column D, we provide the estimated sales values, the $\hat{y}$ values, as calculated above.

In column E, we calculate the **residuals,** or the error values. This is the difference between the actual values and the predicted values. That is, column E is $(y - \hat{y})$. For Soni Jones,

$$\hat{y} = 19.9632 + 0.2608(120) = 51.2592$$

Her actual value is 45. So the residual, or error of estimate, is

$$(y - \hat{y}) = (45 - 51.2592) = -6.2592$$

This value reflects the amount the predicted value of sales is "off" from the actual sales value.

Next, in Column F, we square the residuals for each of the sales representatives and total the result. The total is 587.111.

$$\Sigma(y - \hat{y})^2 = 16.0000 + 112.4618 + \cdots + 140.9064 = 587.1108$$

This is the sum of the squared differences or the least squares value. There is no other line through these 15 data points where the sum of the squared differences is smaller.

We can demonstrate the least squares criterion by choosing two arbitrary equations that are close to the least squares equation and determining the sum of the squared differences for these equations. In column G, we use the equation $y^* = 18 + 0.275x$ to find the predicted value. Notice this equation is very similar to the least squares equation. In Column H, we determine the residuals and square these residuals. For the first sales representative, Brian Virost,

$$y^* = 18 + 0.275(96) = 44.4$$

$$(y - y^*)^2 = (41 - 44.4)^2 = 11.56$$

This procedure is continued for the other 14 sales representatives and the squared residuals totaled. The result is 597.8. This is a larger value (597.8 is more than 587.1108) than the residuals for the least squares line.

In columns I and J on the output, we repeat the above process for yet another equation $y^{**} = 20 + 0.225x$. Again, this equation is similar to the least squares equation. The details for Brian Virost are:

$$y^{**} = 20 + 0.225x = 20 + 0.225(96) = 41.6$$

$$(y - y^{**})^2 = (41 - 41.6)^2 = 0.36$$

This procedure is continued for the other 14 sales representatives and the residuals totaled. The result is 793, which is also larger than the least squares values.

What have we shown with the example? The sum of the squared residuals $[\Sigma(y - \hat{y})^2]$ for the least squares equation is smaller than for other selected lines. The bottom line is you will not be able to find a line passing through these data points where the sum of the squared residuals is smaller.

SELF-REVIEW

13–3

Refer to Self-Review 13–1, where the owner of Haverty's Furniture Company was studying the relationship between sales and the amount spent on advertising. The advertising expense and sales revenue, both in millions of dollars, for the last 4 months are repeated below.

Month	Advertising Expense ($ million)	Sales Revenue ($ million)
July	2	7
August	1	3
September	3	8
October	4	10

(a) Determine the regression equation.
(b) Interpret the values of a and b.
(c) Estimate sales when $3 million is spent on advertising.

EXERCISES

For **DATA FILE**, please visit www.mhhe.com/lind16e

For **DATA FILE**, please visit www.mhhe.com/lind16e

For **DATA FILE**, please visit www.mhhe.com/lind16e

For **DATA FILE**, please visit www.mhhe.com/lind16e

13. The following sample observations were randomly selected.

x:	4	5	3	6	10
y:	4	6	5	7	7

a. Determine the regression equation.
b. Determine the value of $\hat{y}$ when x is 7.

14. The following sample observations were randomly selected.

x:	5	3	6	3	4	4	6	8
y:	13	15	7	12	13	11	9	5

a. Determine the regression equation.
b. Determine the value of $\hat{y}$ when x is 7.

15. Bradford Electric Illuminating Company is studying the relationship between kilowatt-hours (thousands) used and the number of rooms in a private single-family residence. A random sample of 10 homes yielded the following.

Number of Rooms	Kilowatt-Hours (thousands)	Number of Rooms	Kilowatt-Hours (thousands)
12	9	8	6
9	7	10	8
14	10	10	10
6	5	5	4
10	8	7	7

a. Determine the regression equation.
b. Determine the number of kilowatt-hours, in thousands, for a six-room house.

16. Mr. James McWhinney, president of Daniel-James Financial Services, believes there is a relationship between the number of client contacts and the dollar amount of sales. To document this assertion, Mr. McWhinney gathered the following sample information. The x column indicates the number of client contacts last month and the y column shows the value of sales ($ thousands) last month for each client sampled.

Number of Contacts, x	Sales ($ thousands), y	Number of Contacts, x	Sales ($ thousands), y
14	24	23	30
12	14	48	90
20	28	50	85
16	30	55	120
46	80	50	110

a. Determine the regression equation.
b. Determine the estimated sales if 40 contacts are made.

17. A recent article in *Bloomberg Businessweek* listed the "Best Small Companies." We are interested in the current results of the companies' sales and earnings. A random sample of 12 companies was selected and the sales and earnings, in millions of dollars, are reported below.

For **DATA FILE**, please visit www.mhhe.com/lind16e

Company	Sales ($ millions)	Earnings ($ millions)	Company	Sales ($ millions)	Earnings ($ millions)
Papa John's International	$89.2	$4.9	Checkmate Electronics	$17.5	$ 2.6
Applied Innovation	18.6	4.4	Royal Grip	11.9	1.7
Integracare	18.2	1.3	M-Wave	19.6	3.5
Wall Data	71.7	8.0	Serving-N-Slide	51.2	8.2
Davidson & Associates	58.6	6.6	Daig	28.6	6.0
Chico's FAS	46.8	4.1	Cobra Golf	69.2	12.8

Let sales be the independent variable and earnings be the dependent variable.
a. Draw a scatter diagram.
b. Compute the correlation coefficient.
c. Determine the regression equation.
d. For a small company with $50.0 million in sales, estimate the earnings.

18. We are studying mutual bond funds for the purpose of investing in several funds. For this particular study, we want to focus on the assets of a fund and its five-year performance. The question is: Can the five-year rate of return be estimated based on the assets of the fund? Nine mutual funds were selected at random, and their assets and rates of return are shown below.

For **DATA FILE**, please visit www.mhhe.com/lind16e

Fund	Assets ($ millions)	Return (%)	Fund	Assets ($ millions)	Return (%)
AARP High Quality Bond	$622.2	10.8	MFS Bond A	$494.5	11.6
Babson Bond L	160.4	11.3	Nichols Income	158.3	9.5
Compass Capital Fixed Income	275.7	11.4	T. Rowe Price Short-term	681.0	8.2
Galaxy Bond Retail	433.2	9.1	Thompson Income B	241.3	6.8
Keystone Custodian B-1	437.9	9.2			

a. Draw a scatter diagram.
b. Compute the correlation coefficient.
c. Write a brief report of your findings for parts (a) and (b).
d. Determine the regression equation. Use assets as the independent variable.
e. For a fund with $400.0 million in sales, determine the five-year rate of return (in percent).

19. Refer to Exercise 5. Assume the dependent variable is number of crimes.
a. Determine the regression equation.
b. Estimate the number of crimes for a city with 20 police officers.
c. Interpret the regression equation.

20. Refer to Exercise 6.
a. Determine the regression equation.
b. Estimate the selling price of a 10-year-old car.
c. Interpret the regression equation.

LO13-4

Evaluate the significance of the slope of the regression equation.

TESTING THE SIGNIFICANCE OF THE SLOPE

In the prior section, we showed how to find the equation of the regression line that best fits the data. The method for finding the equation is based on the *least squares principle*. The purpose of the regression equation is to quantify a linear relationship between two variables.

The next step is to analyze the regression equation by conducting a test of hypothesis to see if the slope of the regression line is different from zero. Why is this important? If we can show that the slope of the line in the population is different from zero, then we can conclude that using the regression equation adds to our ability to predict or forecast the dependent variable based on the independent variable. If we cannot demonstrate that this slope is different from zero, then we conclude there is no merit to using the independent variable as a predictor. To put it another way, if we cannot show the slope of the line is different from zero, we might as well use the mean of the dependent variable as a predictor, rather than use the regression equation.

Following from the hypothesis-testing procedure in Chapter 10, the null and alternative hypotheses are:

$$H_0: \beta = 0$$
$$H_1: \beta \neq 0$$

We use β (the Greek letter beta) to represent the population slope for the regression equation. This is consistent with our policy to identify population parameters by Greek letters. We assumed the information regarding North American Copier Sales, Table 13–2, is a sample. Be careful here. Remember, this is a single sample, but when we selected a particular salesperson we identified two pieces of information: how many customers they called on and how many copiers they sold. It is still a single sample, however.

We identified the slope value as b. So our computed slope b is based on a sample and is an estimate of the population's slope, identified as β. The null hypothesis is that the slope of the regression equation in the population is zero. If this is the case, the regression line is horizontal and there is no relationship between the independent variable, X, and the dependent variable, Y. In other words, the value of the dependent variable is the same for any value of the independent variable and does not offer us any help in estimating the value of the dependent variable.

What if the null hypothesis is rejected? If the null hypothesis is rejected and the alternate hypothesis accepted, this indicates that the slope of the regression line for the population is not equal to zero. That is, knowing the value of the independent variable allows us to make a better estimate of the dependent variable. To put it another way, a significant relationship exists between the two variables.

Before we test the hypothesis, we use statistical software to determine the needed regression statistics. We continue to use the North American Copier Sales data from Table 13–2 and use Excel to perform the necessary calculations. The following spreadsheet shows three tables to the right of the sample data.

	A	B	C	D	E	F	G	H	I	J
1	Sales Representative	Sales calls (x)	Copiers Sold (y)		SUMMARY OUTPUT					
2	Brian Virost	96	41							
3	Carlos Ramirez	40	41		*Regression Statistics*					
4	Carol Saia	104	51		Multiple R	0.865				
5	Greg Fish	128	60		R Square	0.748				
6	Jeff Hall	164	61		Adjusted R Square	0.728				
7	Mark Reynolds	76	29		Standard Error	6.720				
8	Meryl Rumsey	72	39		Observations	15				
9	Mike Kiel	80	50							
10	Ray Snarsky	36	28		ANOVA					
11	Rich Niles	84	43			*df*	*SS*	*MS*	*F*	*Significance F*
12	Ron Broderick	180	70		Regression	1	1738.89	1738.89	38.5031	3.19277E-05
13	Sal Spina	132	56		Residual	13	587.11	45.1623		
14	Sani Jones	120	45		Total	14	2326			
15	Susan Welch	44	31							
16	Tom Keller	84	30			*Coefficients*	*Standard Error*	*t Stat*	*P-value*	
17					Intercept	19.9800	4.389675533	4.55159	0.00054	
18					Sales calls (x)	0.2606	0.042001817	6.20509	3.2E-05	

1. Starting on the top are the *Regression Statistics.* We will use this information later in the chapter, but notice that the "Multiple R" value is familiar. It is .865, which is the correlation coefficient we calculated using formula (13–1).
2. Next is an ANOVA table. This is a useful table for summarizing regression information. We will refer to it later in this chapter and use it extensively in the next chapter when we study multiple regression.
3. At the bottom, highlighted in blue, is the information needed to conduct our test of hypothesis regarding the slope of the line. It includes the value of the slope, which is 0.2606, and the intercept, which is 19.98. (Note that these values for the slope and the intercept are slightly different from those computed on page 443. These small differences are due to rounding.) In the column to the right of the regression coefficient is a column labeled "Standard Error." This is a value similar to the standard error of the mean. Recall that the standard error of the mean reports the variation in the sample means. In a similar fashion, these standard errors report the possible variation in slope and intercept values. The standard error of the slope coefficient is 0.0420.

To test the null hypothesis, we use the *t*-distribution with $(n - 2)$ and the following formula.

TEST FOR THE SLOPE	$t = \dfrac{b - 0}{s_b}$ with $n - 2$ degrees of freedom	**[13–6]**

where:
  b is the estimate of the regression line's slope calculated from the sample information.
  s_b is the standard error of the slope estimate, also determined from sample information.

Our first step is to set the null and the alternative hypotheses. They are:

$$H_0: \beta \leq 0$$
$$H_1: \beta > 0$$

Notice that we have a one-tailed test. If we do not reject the null hypothesis, we conclude that the slope of the regression line in the population could be zero. This means the independent variable is of no value in improving our estimate of the dependent variable. In our case, this means that knowing the number of sales calls made by a representative does not help us predict the sales.

If we reject the null hypothesis and accept the alternative, we conclude the slope of the line is greater than zero. Hence, the independent variable is an aid in predicting the dependent variable. Thus, if we know the number of sales calls made by a representative, this will help us forecast that representative's sales. We also know, because we have demonstrated that the slope of the line is greater than zero—that is, positive—that more sales calls will result in the sale of more copiers.

The *t*-distribution is the test statistic; there are 13 degrees of freedom, found by $n - 2 = 15 - 2$. We use the .05 significance level. From Appendix B.5, the critical value is 1.771. Our decision rule is to reject the null hypothesis if the value computed from formula (13–6) is greater than 1.771. We apply formula (13–6) to find *t*.

$$t = \frac{b - 0}{s_b} = \frac{0.2606 - 0}{0.042} = 6.205$$

The computed value of 6.205 exceeds our critical value of 1.771, so we reject the null hypothesis and accept the alternative hypothesis. We conclude that the slope of the line is greater than zero. The independent variable, number of sales calls, is useful in estimating copier sales.

The table also provides us information on the p-value of this test. This cell is highlighted in purple. So we could select a significance level, say .05, and compare that value with the p-value. In this case, the calculated p-value in the table is reported in exponential notation and is equal to 0.0000319, so our decision is to reject the null hypothesis. An important caution is that the p-values reported in the statistical software are usually for a two-*tailed test.*

Before moving on, here is an interesting note. Observe that on page 439, when we conducted a test of hypothesis regarding the correlation coefficient for these same data using formula (13–2), we obtained the same value of the t-statistic, $t = 6.205$. Actually, when comparing the results of simple linear regression and correlation analysis, the two tests are equivalent and will always yield exactly the same values of t and the same p-values.

SELF-REVIEW

13–4

Refer to Self-Review 13–1, where the owner of Haverty's Furniture Company studied the relationship between the amount spent on advertising in a month and sales revenue for that month. The amount of sales is the dependent variable and advertising expense, the independent variable. The regression equation in that study was $\hat{y} = 1.5 + 2.2x$ for a sample of 5 months. Conduct a test of hypothesis to show there is a positive relationship between advertising and sales. From statistical software, the standard error of the regression coefficient is 0.42. Use the .05 significance level.

EXERCISES

▼

21. Refer to Exercise 5. The regression equation is $\hat{y} = 29.29 - 0.96x$, the sample size is 8, and the standard error of the slope is 0.22. Use the .05 significance level. Can we conclude that the slope of the regression line is less than zero?
22. Refer to Exercise 6. The regression equation is $\hat{y} = 11.18 - 0.49x$, the sample size is 12, and the standard error of the slope is 0.23. Use the .05 significance level. Can we conclude that the slope of the regression line is less than zero?
23. Refer to Exercise 17. The regression equation is $\hat{y} = 1.85 + .08x$, the sample size is 12, and the standard error of the slope is 0.03. Use the .05 significance level. Can we conclude that the slope of the regression line is *different from zero*?
24. Refer to Exercise 18. The regression equation is $\hat{y} = 9.9198 - 0.00039x$, the sample size is 9, and the standard error of the slope is 0.0032. Use the .05 significance level. Can we conclude that the slope of the regression line is less than zero?

LO13-5

Evaluate a regression equation's ability to predict using the standard estimate of the error and the coefficient of determination.

EVALUATING A REGRESSION EQUATION'S ABILITY TO PREDICT

The Standard Error of Estimate

The results of the regression analysis for North American Copier Sales show a significant relationship between number of sales calls and the number of sales made. By substituting the names of the variables into the equation, it can be written as:

Number of copiers sold = 19.9632 + 0.2608 (Number of sales calls)

The equation can be used to estimate the number of copiers sold for any given "number of sales calls" within the range of the data. For example, if the number of sales calls is 84, then we can predict the number of copiers sold. It is 41.8704, found by 19.9632 + 0.2608(84). However, the data show two sales representatives with 84 sales calls and 30 and 43 copiers sold. So, is the regression equation a good predictor of "Number of copiers sold"?

Perfect prediction, which is finding the exact outcome, is practically impossible in almost all disciplines including economics and business. For example:

- A large electronics firm, with production facilities throughout the United States, has a stock option plan for employees. Suppose there is a relationship between the number of years employed and the number of shares owned. This relationship is likely because, as number of years of service increases, the number of shares an employee earns also increases. If we observe all employees with 20 years of service, they would most likely own different numbers of shares.
- A real estate developer in the southwest United States studied the relationship between the income of buyers and the size, in square feet, of the home they purchased. The developer's analysis shows that as the income of a purchaser increases, the size of the home purchased will also increase. However, all buyers with an income of $70,000 will not purchase a home of exactly the same size.

What is needed, then, is a measure that describes how precise the prediction of Y is based on X or, conversely, how inaccurate the estimate might be. This measure is called the **standard error of estimate.** The standard error of estimate is symbolized by $s_{y \cdot x}$. The subscript, $y \cdot x$, is interpreted as the standard error of y for a given value of x. It is the same concept as the standard deviation discussed in Chapter 3. The standard deviation measures the dispersion around the mean. The standard error of estimate measures the dispersion about the regression line for a given value of x.

> **STANDARD ERROR OF ESTIMATE** A measure of the dispersion, or scatter, of the observed values around the line of regression for a given value of x.

The standard error of estimate is found using formula (13–7).

> **STANDARD ERROR OF ESTIMATE** $$s_{y \cdot x} = \sqrt{\frac{\Sigma(y - \hat{y})^2}{n - 2}}$$ **[13–7]**

The calculation of the standard error of estimate requires the sum of the squared differences between each observed value of y and the predicted value of y, which is identified as $\hat{y}$ in the numerator. This calculation is illustrated in the spreadsheet on page 445. See cell G13 in the spreadsheet. It is a very important value. It is the numerator in the calculation of the standard error of estimate.

$$s_{y \cdot x} = \sqrt{\frac{\Sigma(y - \hat{y})^2}{n - 2}} = \sqrt{\frac{587.11}{15 - 2}} = 6.720$$

The standard error of estimate can be calculated using statistical software such as Excel. It is included in Excel's regression analysis and highlighted in yellow on page 448. Its value is 6.720.

If the standard error of estimate is small, this indicates that the data are relatively close to the regression line and the regression equation can be used to predict y with little error. If the standard error of estimate is large, this indicates that the data are widely scattered around the regression line and the regression equation will not provide a precise estimate of y.

The Coefficient of Determination

Using the standard error of estimate provides a relative measure of a regression equation's ability to predict. We will use it to provide more specific information about a

452   CHAPTER 13

prediction in the next section. In this section, another statistic is explained that will provide a more interpretable measure of a regression equation's ability to predict. It is called the coefficient of determination, or R-square.

> **COEFFICIENT OF DETERMINATION** The proportion of the total variation in the dependent variable Y that is explained, or accounted for, by the variation in the independent variable X.

The coefficient of determination is easy to compute. It is the correlation coefficient squared. Therefore, the term R-square is also used. With the North American Copier Sales data, the correlation coefficient for the relationship between the number of copiers sold and the number of sales calls is 0.865. If we compute $(0.865)^2$, the coefficient of determination is 0.748. See the blue (Multiple R) and green (R-square) highlighted cells in the spreadsheet on page 448. To better interpret the coefficient of determination, convert it to a percentage. Hence, we say that 74.8% of the variation in the number of copiers sold is explained, or accounted for, by the variation in the number of sales calls.

How well can the regression equation predict number of copiers sold with number of sales calls made? If it were possible to make perfect predictions, the coefficient of determination would be 100%. That would mean that the independent variable, number of sales calls, explains or accounts for all the variation in the number of copiers sold. A coefficient of determination of 100% is associated with a correlation coefficient of $+1.0$ or -1.0. Refer to Chart 13–2, which shows that a perfect prediction is associated with a perfect linear relationship where all the data points form a perfect line in a scatter diagram. Our analysis shows that only 74.8% of the variation in copiers sold is explained by the number of sales calls. Clearly, these data do not form a perfect line. Instead, the data are scattered around the best-fitting, least squares regression line, and there will be error in the predictions. In the next section, the standard error of estimate is used to provide more specific information regarding the error associated with using the regression equation to make predictions.

SELF-REVIEW

13–5

Refer to Self-Review 13–1, where the owner of Haverty's Furniture Company studied the relationship between the amount spent on advertising in a month and sales revenue for that month. The amount of sales is the dependent variable and advertising expense is the independent variable.
(a) Determine the standard error of estimate.
(b) Determine the coefficient of determination.
(c) Interpret the coefficient of determination.

EXERCISES

(You may wish to use a software package such as Excel, Minitab, or Megastat to assist in your calculations.)

25. Refer to Exercise 5. Determine the standard error of estimate and the coefficient of determination. Interpret the coefficient of determination.
26. Refer to Exercise 6. Determine the standard error of estimate and the coefficient of determination. Interpret the coefficient of determination.
27. Refer to Exercise 15. Determine the standard error of estimate and the coefficient of determination. Interpret the coefficient of determination.
28. Refer to Exercise 16. Determine the standard error of estimate and the coefficient of determination. Interpret the coefficient of determination.

Relationships among the Correlation Coefficient, the Coefficient of Determination, and the Standard Error of Estimate

On page 451, we described the standard error of estimate. Recall that it measures how close the actual values are to the regression line. When the standard error is small, it indicates that the two variables are closely related. In the calculation of the standard error, the key term is

$$\Sigma(y - \hat{y})^2$$

If the value of this term is small, then the standard error will also be small.

The correlation coefficient measures the strength of the linear association between two variables. When the points on the scatter diagram appear close to the line, we note that the correlation coefficient tends to be large. Therefore, the correlation coefficient and the standard error of the estimate are inversely related. As the strength of a linear relationship between two variables increases, the correlation coefficient increases and the standard error of the estimate decreases.

We also noted that the square of the correlation coefficient is the coefficient of determination. The coefficient of determination measures the percentage of the variation in Y that is explained by the variation in X.

A convenient vehicle for showing the relationship among these three measures is an ANOVA table. See the highlighted portion of the spreadsheet below. This table is similar to the analysis of variance table developed in Chapter 12. In that chapter, the total variation was divided into two components: variation due to the *treatments* and that due to *random error*. The concept is similar in regression analysis. The total variation is divided into two components: (1) variation explained by the *regression* (explained by the independent variable) and (2) the *error,* or *residual.* This is the unexplained variation. These three sources of variance (total, regression, and residual) are identified in the first column of the spreadsheet ANOVA table. The column headed "*df*" refers to the degrees of freedom associated with each category. The total number of degrees of freedom is $n - 1$. The number of degrees of freedom in the regression is 1 because there is only one independent variable. The number of degrees of freedom associated with the error term is $n - 2$. The term SS located in the middle of the ANOVA table refers to the sum of squares. You should note that the total degrees of freedom are equal to the sum of the regression and residual (error) degrees of freedom, and the total sum of squares is equal to the sum of the regression and residual (error) sum of squares. This is true for any ANOVA table.

	A	B	C	D	E	F	G	H	I	J
1	Sales Representive	Sales Calls (x)	Copiers Sold (y)		SUMMARY OUTPUT					
2	Brian Virost	96	41							
3	Carlos Ramirez	40	41		*Regression Statistics*					
4	Carol Saia	104	51		Multiple R	0.865				
5	Greg Fish	128	60		R Square	0.748				
6	Jeff Hall	164	61		Adjusted R Square	0.728				
7	Mark Reynolds	76	29		Standard Error	6.720				
8	Meryl Rumsey	72	39		Observations	15				
9	Mike Kiel	80	50							
10	Ray Snarsky	36	28		ANOVA					
11	Rich Niles	84	43			df	SS	MS	F	Significance F
12	Ron Broderick	180	70		Regression	1	1738.89	1738.89	38.50312548	3.19277E-05
13	Sal Spina	132	56		Residual	13	587.11	45.162308		
14	Sani Jones	120	45		Total	14	2326			
15	Susan Welch	44	31							
16	Tom Keller	84	30			Coefficients	Standard Error	t Stat	P-value	
17					Intercept	19.9800	4.389675533	4.5515893	0.000543565	
18					Sales Calls (X)	0.2606	0.042001817	6.2050887	3.19277E-05	

The ANOVA sum of squares are:

$$\text{Regression Sum of Squares} = \text{SSR} = \Sigma(\hat{y} - \bar{y})^2 = 1738.89$$

$$\text{Residual or Error Sum of Squares} = \text{SSE} = \Sigma(y - \hat{y})^2 = 587.11$$

$$\text{Total Sum of Squares} = \text{SS Total} = \Sigma(y - \bar{y})^2 = 2326.0$$

Recall that the coefficient of determination is defined as the percentage of the total variation (SS Total) explained by the regression equation (SSR). Using the ANOVA table, the reported value of R-square can be validated.

COEFFICIENT OF DETERMINATION	$r^2 = \dfrac{SSR}{SS\ Total} = 1 - \dfrac{SSE}{SS\ Total}$ **[13–8]**

Using the values from the ANOVA table, the coefficient of determination is $1738.89/2326.0 = 0.748$. Therefore, the more variation of the dependent variable (SS Total) explained by the independent variable (SSR), the higher the coefficient of determination.

We can also express the coefficient of determination in terms of the error or residual variation:

$$r^2 = 1 - \frac{SSE}{SS\ Total} = 1 - \frac{587.11}{2326.0} = 1 - 0.252 = 0.748$$

As illustrated in formula 13–8, the coefficient of determination and the residual or error sum of squares are inversely related. The higher the unexplained or error variation as a percentage of the total variation, the lower is the coefficient of determination. In this case, 25.2% of the total variation in the dependent variable is error or residual variation.

The final observation that relates the correlation coefficient, the coefficient of determination, and the standard error of estimate is to show the relationship between the standard error of estimate and SSE. By substituting [SSE Residual or Error Sum of Squares = SSE = $\Sigma(y - \hat{y})^2$] into the formula for the standard error of estimate, we find:

STANDARD ERROR OF ESTIMATE	$s_{y \cdot x} = \sqrt{\dfrac{SSE}{n - 2}}$ **[13–9]**

In sum, regression analysis provides two statistics to evaluate the predictive ability of a regression equation: the standard error of the estimate and the coefficient of determination. When reporting the results of a regression analysis, the findings must be clearly explained, especially when using the results to make predictions of the dependent variable. The report must always include a statement regarding the coefficient of determination so that the relative precision of the prediction is known to the reader of the report. Objective reporting of statistical analysis is required so that the readers can make their own decisions.

EXERCISES

29. Given the following ANOVA table:

Source	DF	SS	MS	F
Regression	1	1000.0	1000.0	26.00
Error	13	500.0	38.46	
Total	14	1500.0		

a. Determine the coefficient of determination.
b. Assuming a direct relationship between the variables, what is the correlation coefficient?
c. Determine the standard error of estimate.

30. On the first statistics exam, the coefficient of determination between the hours studied and the grade earned was 80%. The standard error of estimate was 10. There were 20 students in the class. Develop an ANOVA table for the regression analysis of hours studied as a predictor of the grade earned on the first statistics exam.

LO13-6

Calculate and interpret confidence and prediction intervals.

STATISTICS IN ACTION

Studies indicate that for both men and women, those who are considered good looking earn higher wages than those who are not. In addition, for men there is a correlation between height and salary. For each additional inch of height, a man can expect to earn an additional $250 per year. So a man 6'6" tall receives a $3,000 "stature" bonus over his 5'6" counterpart. Being overweight or underweight is also related to earnings, particularly among women. A study of young women showed the heaviest 10% earned about 6% less than their lighter counterparts.

INTERVAL ESTIMATES OF PREDICTION

The standard error of estimate and the coefficient of determination are two statistics that provide an overall evaluation of the ability of a regression equation to predict a dependent variable. Another way to report the ability of a regression equation to predict is specific to a stated value of the independent variable. For example, we can predict the number of copiers sold (y) for a selected value of number of sales calls made (x). In fact, we can calculate a confidence interval for the predicted value of the dependent variable for a selected value of the independent variable.

Assumptions Underlying Linear Regression

Before we present the confidence intervals, the assumptions for properly applying linear regression should be reviewed. Chart 13–13 illustrates these assumptions.

1. For each value of x, there are corresponding y values. These y values follow the normal distribution.
2. The means of these normal distributions lie on the regression line.
3. The standard deviations of these normal distributions are all the same. The best estimate we have of this common standard deviation is the standard error of estimate ($s_{y \cdot x}$).
4. The y values are statistically independent. This means that in selecting a sample, a particular x does not depend on any other value of x. This assumption is particularly important when data are collected over a period of time. In such situations, the errors for a particular time period are often correlated with those of other time periods.

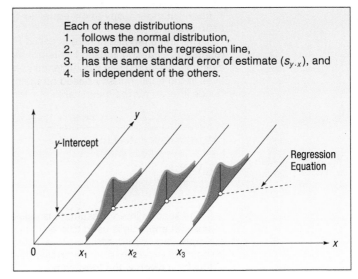

CHART 13–13 Regression Assumptions Shown Graphically

Recall from Chapter 7 that if the values follow a normal distribution, then the mean plus or minus one standard deviation will encompass 68% of the observations, the mean plus or minus two standard deviations will encompass 95% of the observations, and the mean plus or minus three standard deviations will encompass virtually all of the observations. The same relationship exists between the predicted values $\hat{y}$ and the standard error of estimate ($s_{y \cdot x}$).

1. $\hat{y} \pm s_{y \cdot x}$ will include the middle 68% of the observations.
2. $\hat{y} \pm 2s_{y \cdot x}$ will include the middle 95% of the observations.
3. $\hat{y} \pm 3s_{y \cdot x}$ will include virtually all the observations.

We can now relate these assumptions to North American Copier Sales, where we studied the relationship between the number of sales calls and the number of copiers sold. If we drew a parallel line 6.72 units above the regression line and another 6.72 units below the regression line, about 68% of the points would fall between the two lines. Similarly, a line $13.44 [2s_{y \cdot x} = 2(6.72)]$ units above the regression line and another 13.44 units below the regression line should include about 95% of the data values.

As a rough check, refer to column E in the Excel spreadsheet on page 445. Four of the 15 deviations exceed one standard error of estimate. That is, the deviations of Carlos Ramirez, Mark Reynolds, Mike Keil, and Tom Keller all exceed 6.72 (one standard error). All values are less than 13.44 units away from the regression line. In short, 11 of the 15 deviations are within one standard error and all are within two standard errors. That is a fairly good result for a relatively small sample.

Constructing Confidence and Prediction Intervals

When using a regression equation, two different predictions can be made for a selected value of the independent variable. The differences are subtle but very important and are related to the assumptions stated in the last section. Recall that for any selected value of the independent variable (X), the dependent variable (Y) is a random variable that is normally distributed with a mean $\hat{Y}$. Each distribution of Y has a standard deviation equal to the regression analysis's standard error of estimate.

The first interval estimate is called a **confidence interval.** This is used when the regression equation is used to predict the mean value of Y for a given value of x. For example, we would use a confidence interval to estimate the mean salary of all executives in the retail industry based on their years of experience. To determine the confidence interval for the mean value of y for a given x, the formula is:

CONFIDENCE INTERVAL FOR THE MEAN OF Y, GIVEN X	$\hat{y} \pm ts_{y \cdot x} \sqrt{\dfrac{1}{n} + \dfrac{(x - \bar{x})^2}{\Sigma(x - \bar{x})^2}}$	**[13–10]**

The second interval estimate is called a prediction interval. This is used when the regression equation is used to predict an individual y ($n = 1$) for a given value of x. For example, we would estimate the salary of a particular retail executive who has 20 years of experience. To determine the prediction interval for an estimate of an individual for a given x, the formula is:

PREDICTION INTERVAL FOR Y, GIVEN X	$\hat{y} \pm ts_{y \cdot x} \sqrt{1 + \dfrac{1}{n} + \dfrac{(x - \bar{x})^2}{\Sigma(x - \bar{x})^2}}$	**[13–11]**

EXAMPLE

We return to the North American Copier Sales illustration. Determine a 95% confidence interval for all sales representatives who make 50 calls, and determine a prediction interval for Sheila Baker, a West Coast sales representative who made 50 calls.

SOLUTION

We use formula (13–10) to determine a confidence level. Table 13–4 includes the necessary totals and a repeat of the information of Table 13–2 on page 431.

TABLE 13–4 Determining Confidence and Prediction Intervals

Sales Representative	Sales Calls (x)	Copiers Sold (y)	$(x - \bar{x})$	$(x - \bar{x})^2$
Brian Virost	96	41	0	0
Carlos Ramirez	40	41	−56	3,136
Carol Saia	104	51	8	64
Greg Fish	128	60	32	1,024
Jeff Hall	164	61	68	4,624
Mark Reynolds	76	29	−20	400
Meryl Rumsey	72	39	−24	576
Mike Kiel	80	50	−16	256
Ray Snarsky	36	28	−60	3,600
Rich Niles	84	43	−12	144
Ron Broderick	180	70	84	7,056
Sal Spina	132	56	36	1,296
Sani Jones	120	45	24	576
Susan Welch	44	31	−52	2,704
Tom Keller	84	30	−12	144
Total	1440	675	0	25,600

The first step is to determine the number of copiers we expect a sales representative to sell if he or she makes 50 calls. It is 33.0032, found by

$$\hat{y} = 19.9632 + 0.2608x = 19.9632 + 0.2608(50) = 33.0032$$

To find the t value, we need to first know the number of degrees of freedom. In this case, the degrees of freedom are $n - 2 = 15 - 2 = 13$. We set the confidence level at 95%. To find the value of t, move down the left-hand column of Appendix B.5 to 13 degrees of freedom, then move across to the column with the 95% level of confidence. The value of t is 2.160.

In the previous section, we calculated the standard error of estimate to be 6.720. We let $x = 50$, and from Table 13–4, the mean number of sales calls is 96.0 (1440/15) and $\Sigma(x - \bar{x})^2 = 25,600$. Inserting these values in formula (13–10), we can determine the confidence interval.

$$\text{Confidence Interval} = \hat{y} \pm ts_{y \cdot x}\sqrt{\frac{1}{n} + \frac{(x - \bar{x})^2}{\Sigma(x - \bar{x})^2}}$$

$$= 33.0032 \pm 2.160(6.720)\sqrt{\frac{1}{15} + \frac{(50 - 96)^2}{25,600}}$$

$$= 33.0032 \pm 5.6090$$

Thus, the 95% confidence interval for all sales representatives who make 50 calls is from 27.3942 up to 38.6122. To interpret, let's round the values. If a sales representative makes 50 calls, he or she can expect to sell 33 copiers. It is likely the sales will range from 27.4 to 38.6 copiers.

Suppose we want to estimate the number of copiers sold by Sheila Baker, who made 50 sales calls. The 95% prediction interval is determined as follows:

$$\text{Prediction Interval} = \hat{y} \pm t s_{y \cdot x} \sqrt{1 + \frac{1}{n} + \frac{(x - \bar{x})^2}{\Sigma (x - \bar{x})^2}}$$

$$= 33.0032 \pm 2.160(6.720) \sqrt{1 + \frac{1}{15} + \frac{(50 - 96)^2}{25,600}}$$

$$= 33.0032 \pm 15.5612$$

Thus, the interval is from 17.442 up to 48.5644 copiers. We conclude that the number of office machines sold will be between about 17.4 and 48.6 for a particular sales representative, such as Sheila Baker, who makes 50 calls. This interval is quite large. It is much larger than the confidence interval for all sales representatives who made 50 calls. It is logical, however, that there should be more variation in the sales estimate for an individual than for a group.

The following Minitab graph shows the relationship between the least squares regression line (in the center), the confidence interval (shown in crimson), and the prediction interval (shown in green). The bands for the prediction interval are always further from the regression line than those for the confidence interval. Also, as the values of x move away from the mean number of calls (96) in either direction, the confidence interval and prediction interval bands widen. This is caused by the numerator of the right-hand term under the radical in formulas (13–10) and (13–11). That is, as the term increases, the widths of the confidence interval and the prediction interval also increase. To put it another way, there is less precision in our estimates as we move away, in either direction, from the mean of the independent variable.

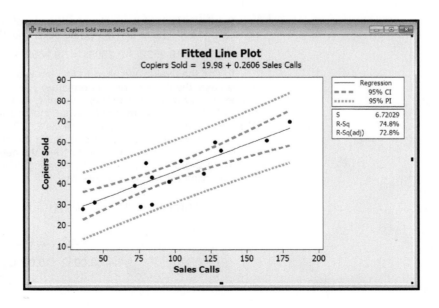

We wish to emphasize again the distinction between a confidence interval and a prediction interval. A confidence interval refers to the mean of all cases for a given value of x and is computed by formula (13–10). A prediction interval refers to a particular, single case for a given value of x and is computed using formula (13–11). The prediction interval will always be wider because of the extra 1 under the radical in the second equation.

SELF-REVIEW

13–6

Refer to the sample data in Self-Review 13–1, where the owner of Haverty's Furniture was studying the relationship between sales and the amount spent on advertising. The advertising expense and sales revenue, both in millions of dollars, for the last 4 months are repeated below.

Month	Advertising Expense ($ million)	Sales Revenue ($ million)
July	2	7
August	1	3
September	3	8
October	4	10

The regression equation was computed to be $\hat{y} = 1.5 + 2.2x$, and the standard error 0.9487. Both variables are reported in millions of dollars. Determine the 90% confidence interval for the typical month in which $3 million was spent on advertising.

EXERCISES

31. Refer to Exercise 13.
    a. Determine the .95 confidence interval for the mean predicted when $x = 7$.
    b. Determine the .95 prediction interval for an individual predicted when $x = 7$.
32. Refer to Exercise 14.
    a. Determine the .95 confidence interval for the mean predicted when $x = 7$.
    b. Determine the .95 prediction interval for an individual predicted when $x = 7$.
33. Refer to Exercise 15.
    a. Determine the .95 confidence interval, in thousands of kilowatt-hours, for the mean of all six-room homes.
    b. Determine the .95 prediction interval, in thousands of kilowatt-hours, for a particular six-room home.
34. Refer to Exercise 16.
    a. Determine the .95 confidence interval, in thousands of dollars, for the mean of all sales personnel who make 40 contacts.
    b. Determine the .95 prediction interval, in thousands of dollars, for a particular salesperson who makes 40 contacts.

LO13-7

Use a log function to transform a nonlinear relationship.

TRANSFORMING DATA

Regression analysis describes the relationship between two variables. A requirement is that this relationship be linear. The same is true of the correlation coefficient. It measures the strength of a linear relationship between two variables. But what if the relationship is not linear? The remedy is to rescale one or both of the variables so the new relationship is linear. For example, instead of using the actual values of the dependent variable, y, we would create a new dependent variable by computing the log to the base 10 of y, Log(y). This calculation is called a transformation. Other common transformations include taking the square root, taking the reciprocal, or squaring one or both of the variables.

Thus, two variables could be closely related, but their relationship is not linear. Be cautious when you are interpreting the correlation coefficient or a regression equation. These statistics may indicate there is no linear relationship, but there could be a relationship of some other nonlinear or curvilinear form. The following example explains the details.

EXAMPLE

GroceryLand Supermarkets is a regional grocery chain with over 300 stores located in the midwestern United States. The corporate director of marketing for GroceryLand wishes to study the effect of price on the weekly sales of two-liter bottles of their private-brand diet cola. The objectives of the study are:

1. To determine whether there is a relationship between selling price and weekly sales. Is this relationship direct or indirect? Is it strong or weak?
2. To determine the effect of price increases or decreases on sales. Can we effectively forecast sales based on the price?

SOLUTION

To begin the project, the marketing director meets with the vice president of sales and other company staff members. They decide that it would be reasonable to price the two-liter bottle of their private-brand diet cola from $0.50 up to $2.00. To collect the data needed to analyze the relationship between price and sales, the marketing director selects a random sample of 20 stores and then randomly assigns a selling price for the two-liter bottle of diet cola between $0.50 and $2.00 to each selected store. The director contacts each of the 20 store managers included in the study to tell them the selling price and ask them to report the sales for the product at the end of the week. The results are reported below. For example, store number 17 sold 181 two-liter bottles of diet cola at $0.50 each.

GroceryLand Sales and Price Data			GroceryLand Sales and Price Data		
Store Number	Price	Sales	Store Number	Price	Sales
17	0.50	181	30	0.76	91
121	1.35	33	127	1.79	13
227	0.79	91	266	1.57	22
135	1.71	13	117	1.27	34
6	1.38	34	132	0.96	74
282	1.22	47	120	0.52	164
172	1.03	73	272	0.64	129
296	1.84	11	120	1.05	55
143	1.73	15	194	0.72	107
66	1.62	20	105	0.75	119

To examine the relationship between Price and Sales, we use regression analysis setting *Price* as the independent variable and *Sales* as the dependent

CORRELATION AND LINEAR REGRESSION   461

variable. The analysis will provide important information about the relationship between the variables. The analysis is summarized in the following Minitab output.

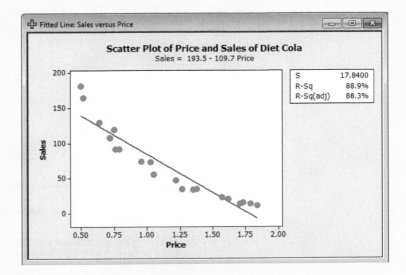

From the output, we can make these conclusions:

1. The relationship between the two variables is inverse or indirect. As the *Price* of the cola increases, the *Sales* of the product decreases. Given basic economic theory of price and demand, this is expected.
2. There is a strong relationship between the two variables. The coefficient of determination is 88.9%. So 88.9% of the variation in *Sales* is accounted for by the variation in *Price*. From the coefficient of determination, we can compute the correlation coefficient as the square root of the coefficient of determination. The correlation coefficient is the square root of 0.889, or 0.943. The sign of the correlation coefficient is negative because sales are inversely related to price. Therefore, the correlation coefficient is −0.943.
3. Before continuing our summary of conclusions, we should look carefully at the scatter diagram and the plot of the regression line. The assumption of a linear relationship is tenuous. If the relationship is linear, the data points should be distributed both above and below the line over the entire range of the independent variable. However, for the highest and lowest prices, the data points are above the regression line. For the selling prices in the middle, most of the data points are below the regression line. So the linear regression equation does not effectively describe the relationship between *Price* and *Sales*. A transformation of the data is needed to create a linear relationship.

By transforming one of the variables, we may be able to change the nonlinear relationship between the variables to a linear relationship. Of the possible choices, the director of marketing decides to transform the dependent variable, *Sales*, by taking the logarithm to the base 10 of each *Sales* value. Note the new variable, *Log-Sales*, in the following analysis. Now, the regression analysis uses *Log-Sales* as the dependent variable and *Price* as the independent variable. This analysis is reported below.

What can we conclude from the regression analysis using the transformation of the dependent variable *Sales?*

1. By transforming the dependent variable, *Sales,* we increase the coefficient of determination from 0.889 to 0.989. So *Price* now explains nearly all of the variation in *Log-Sales.*
2. Compare this result with the scatter diagram before we transformed the dependent variable. The transformed data seem to fit the linear relationship requirement much better. Observe that the data points are both above and below the regression line over the range of *Price.*
3. The regression equation is $\hat{y} = 2.685 - 0.8738x$. The sign of the slope value is negative, confirming the inverse association between the variables. We can use the new equation to estimate sales and study the effect of changes in price. For example, if we decided to sell the two-liter bottle of diet cola for $1.25, the predicted *Log-Sales* is:

$$\hat{y} = 2.685 - 0.8738x = 2.685 - 0.8738(1.25) = 1.593$$

Remember that the regression equation now predicts the log, base10, of *Sales.* Therefore, we must undo the transformation by taking the antilog of 1.593, which is $10^{1.593}$, or 39.174. So, if we price the two-liter diet cola product at $1.25, the predicted weekly sales are 39 bottles. If we increase the price to $2.00, the regression equation would predict a value of .9374. Taking the antilog, $10^{.9374}$, the predicted sales decrease to 8.658, or, rounding, 9 two-liter bottles per week. Clearly, as price increases, sales decrease. This relationship will be very helpful to GroceryLand when making pricing decisions for this product.

EXERCISES

35. Given the following sample of five observations, develop a scatter diagram, using x as the independent variable and y as the dependent variable, and compute the correlation coefficient. Does the relationship between the variables appear to be linear? Try squaring the x variable and then develop a scatter diagram and determine the correlation coefficient. Summarize your analysis.

x	−8	−16	12	2	18
y	58	247	153	3	341

CORRELATION AND LINEAR REGRESSION   463

For **DATA FILE**, please visit
www.mhhe.com/lind16e

36. Every April, The Masters—one of the most prestigious golf tournaments on the PGA golf tour—is played in Augusta, Georgia. In 2013, 60 players received prize money. The 2013 winner, Adam Scott of Australia, earned a prize of $1,440,000. Miguel Cabrera finished in second place, earning $864,000. Jason Day finished in third place, earning $544,000. The data are briefly summarized below. Each player has three corresponding variables: finishing position or rank, score, and prize (in dollars). The complete file is in the data sets available on the text website, www.mhhe.com/lind16e, labeled as Ex13-36. We want to study the relationship between score and prize.

Position	Player	Score	Prize
1	Scott	279	$1,440,000
2	Cabrera	279	$864,000
3	Day	281	$544,000
Tied 4	Woods	283	$352,000
Tied 4	Leishman	283	$352,000
.	.	.	.
.	.	.	.
Tied 54	Bradley	297	$18,320
Tied 54	Lyle	297	$18,320
Tied 54	Mickelson	297	$18,320
Tied 54	Piercy	297	$18,320
58	Na	301	$17,920
59	Peterson	302	$17,760
60	Pettersson	304	$17,600

a. Using *Score* as the independent variable and *Prize* as the dependent variable, develop a scatter diagram. Does the relationship appear to be linear? Does it seem reasonable that as *Score* increases the *Prize* decreases?
b. What percentage of the variation in the dependent variable, *Prize,* is accounted for by the independent variable, *Score*?
c. Calculate a new variable, *Log-Prize,* computing the log to the base 10 of *Prize*. Draw a scatter diagram with *Log-Prize* as the dependent variable and *Score* as the independent variable.
d. Develop a regression equation and compute the coefficient of determination using *Log-Prize* as the dependent variable.
e. Compare the coefficient of determination in parts (b) and (d). What do you conclude?
f. Write out the regression equation developed in part (d). If a player shot a total of 280 for the four rounds, how much would you expect that player to earn?

CHAPTER SUMMARY

I. A scatter diagram is a graphic tool to portray the relationship between two variables.
  A. The dependent variable is scaled on the Y-axis and is the variable being estimated.
  B. The independent variable is scaled on the X-axis and is the variable used as the predictor.
II. The correlation coefficient measures the strength of the linear association between two variables.
  A. Both variables must be at least the interval scale of measurement.
  B. The correlation coefficient can range from −1.00 to 1.00.
  C. If the correlation between the two variables is 0, there is no association between them.
  D. A value of 1.00 indicates perfect positive correlation, and a value of −1.00 indicates perfect negative correlation.

E. A positive sign means there is a direct relationship between the variables, and a negative sign means there is an inverse relationship.

F. It is designated by the letter r and found by the following equation:

$$r = \frac{\Sigma(x - \bar{x})(y - \bar{y})}{(n - 1)s_x s_y}$$ [13–1]

G. To test a hypothesis that a population correlation is different from 0, we use the following statistic:

$$t = \frac{r\sqrt{n - 2}}{\sqrt{1 - r^2}}$$ with $n - 2$ degrees of freedom   [13–2]

III. In regression analysis, we estimate one variable based on another variable.
  A. The variable being estimated is the dependent variable.
  B. The variable used to make the estimate or predict the value is the independent variable.
   1. The relationship between the variables is linear.
   2. Both the independent and the dependent variables must be interval or ratio scale.
   3. The least squares criterion is used to determine the regression equation.
IV. The least squares regression line is of the form $\hat{y} = a + bx$.
  A. $\hat{y}$ is the estimated value of y for a selected value of x.
  B. a is the constant or intercept.
   1. It is the value of $\hat{y}$ when $x = 0$.
   2. a is computed using the following equation.

$$a = \bar{y} - b\bar{x}$$ [13–5]

  C. b is the slope of the fitted line.
   1. It shows the amount of change in $\hat{y}$ for a change of one unit in x.
   2. A positive value for b indicates a direct relationship between the two variables. A negative value indicates an inverse relationship.
   3. The sign of b and the sign of r, the correlation coefficient, are always the same.
   4. b is computed using the following equation.

$$b = r\left(\frac{s_y}{s_x}\right)$$ [13–4]

  D. x is the value of the independent variable.
V. For a regression equation, the slope is tested for significance.
  A. We test the hypothesis that the slope of the line in the population is 0.
   1. If we do not reject the null hypothesis, we conclude there is no relationship between the two variables.
   2. The test is equivalent to the test for the correlation coefficient.
  B. When testing the null hypothesis about the slope, the test statistic is with $n - 2$ degrees of freedom:

$$t = \frac{b - 0}{s_b}$$ [13–6]

VI. The standard error of estimate measures the variation around the regression line.
  A. It is in the same units as the dependent variable.
  B. It is based on squared deviations from the regression line.
  C. Small values indicate that the points cluster closely about the regression line.
  D. It is computed using the following formula.

$$s_{y \cdot x} = \sqrt{\frac{\Sigma(y - \hat{y})^2}{n - 2}}$$ [13–7]

VII. The coefficient of determination is the proportion of the variation of a dependent variable explained by the independent variable.
  A. It ranges from 0 to 1.0.
  B. It is the square of the correlation coefficient.
  C. It is found from the following formula.

$$r^2 = \frac{SSR}{SS\ Total} = 1 - \frac{SSE}{SS\ Total}$$ [13–8]

CORRELATION AND LINEAR REGRESSION   465

VIII. Inference about linear regression is based on the following assumptions.
    A. For a given value of x, the values of Y are normally distributed about the line of regression.
    B. The standard deviation of each of the normal distributions is the same for all values of x and is estimated by the standard error of estimate.
    C. The deviations from the regression line are independent, with no pattern to the size or direction.
IX. There are two types of interval estimates.
    A. In a confidence interval, the mean value of y is estimated for a given value of x.
        1. It is computed from the following formula.

$$\hat{y} \pm ts_{y \cdot x} \sqrt{\frac{1}{n} + \frac{(x - \bar{x})^2}{\Sigma(x - \bar{x})^2}}$$ **[13–10]**

        2. The width of the interval is affected by the level of confidence, the size of the standard error of estimate, and the size of the sample, as well as the value of the independent variable.
    B. In a prediction interval, the individual value of y is estimated for a given value of x.
        1. It is computed from the following formula.

$$\hat{y} \pm ts_{y \cdot x} \sqrt{1 + \frac{1}{n} + \frac{(x - \bar{x})^2}{\Sigma(x - \bar{x})^2}}$$ **[13–11]**

        2. The difference between formulas (13–10) and (13–11) is the 1 under the radical.
        a. The prediction interval will be wider than the confidence interval.
        b. The prediction interval is also based on the level of confidence, the size of the standard error of estimate, the size of the sample, and the value of the independent variable.

PRONUNCIATION KEY

SYMBOL	MEANING	PRONUNCIATION
Σxy	Sum of the products of x and y	*Sum x y*
ρ	Correlation coefficient in the population	*Rho*
$\hat{y}$	Estimated value of Y	*y hat*
$s_{y \cdot x}$	Standard error of estimate	*s sub y dot x*
r^2	Coefficient of determination	*r square*

CHAPTER EXERCISES

37. A regional commuter airline selected a random sample of 25 flights and found that the correlation between the number of passengers and the total weight, in pounds, of luggage stored in the luggage compartment is 0.94. Using the .05 significance level, can we conclude that there is a positive association between the two variables?

38. A sociologist claims that the success of students in college (measured by their GPA) is related to their family's income. For a sample of 20 students, the correlation coefficient is 0.40. Using the 0.01 significance level, can we conclude that there is a positive correlation between the variables?

39. An Environmental Protection Agency study of 12 automobiles revealed a correlation of 0.47 between engine size and emissions. At the .01 significance level, can we conclude that there is a positive association between these variables? What is the *p*-value? Interpret.

466   CHAPTER 13

For **DATA FILE**, please visit
www.mhhe.com/lind16e

40. A suburban hotel derives its revenue from its hotel and restaurant operations. The owners are interested in the relationship between the number of rooms occupied on a nightly basis and the revenue per day in the restaurant. Below is a sample of 25 days (Monday through Thursday) from last year showing the restaurant income and number of rooms occupied.

Day	Revenue	Occupied	Day	Revenue	Occupied
1	$1,452	23	14	$1,425	27
2	1,361	47	15	1,445	34
3	1,426	21	16	1,439	15
4	1,470	39	17	1,348	19
5	1,456	37	18	1,450	38
6	1,430	29	19	1,431	44
7	1,354	23	20	1,446	47
8	1,442	44	21	1,485	43
9	1,394	45	22	1,405	38
10	1,459	16	23	1,461	51
11	1,399	30	24	1,490	61
12	1,458	42	25	1,426	39
13	1,537	54			

Use a statistical software package to answer the following questions.
a. Does the revenue seem to increase as the number of occupied rooms increases? Draw a scatter diagram to support your conclusion.
b. Determine the correlation coefficient between the two variables. Interpret the value.
c. Is it reasonable to conclude that there is a positive relationship between revenue and occupied rooms? Use the .10 significance level.
d. What percent of the variation in revenue in the restaurant is accounted for by the number of rooms occupied?

For **DATA FILE**, please visit
www.mhhe.com/lind16e

41. The table below shows the number of cars (in millions) sold in the United States for various years and the percent of those cars manufactured by GM.

Year	Cars Sold (millions)	Percent GM	Year	Cars Sold (millions)	Percent GM
1950	6.0	50.2	1985	15.4	40.1
1955	7.8	50.4	1990	13.5	36.0
1960	7.3	44.0	1995	15.5	31.7
1965	10.3	49.9	2000	17.4	28.6
1970	10.1	39.5	2005	16.9	26.9
1975	10.8	43.1	2010	11.6	19.1
1980	11.5	44.0			

Use a statistical software package to answer the following questions.
a. Is the number of cars sold directly or indirectly related to GM's percentage of the market? Draw a scatter diagram to show your conclusion.
b. Determine the correlation coefficient between the two variables. Interpret the value.
c. Is it reasonable to conclude that there is a negative association between the two variables? Use the .01 significance level.
d. How much of the variation in GM's market share is accounted for by the variation in cars sold?

42. For a sample of 32 large U.S. cities, the correlation between the mean number of square feet per office worker and the mean monthly rental rate in the central business district is −.363. At the .05 significance level, can we conclude that there is a negative association between the two variables?

43. For each of the 32 National Football League teams, the numbers of points scored and allowed during the 2012 season are shown below.

Team	Conference	Points Scored	Points Allowed	Team	Conference	Points Scored	Points Allowed
Chicago Bears	NFC	375	277	Cincinnati Bengals	AFC	391	320
Green Bay Packers	NFC	433	336	Baltimore Ravens	AFC	398	344
Minnesota Vikings	NFC	379	348	Pittsburgh Steelers	AFC	336	314
Detroit Lions	NFC	372	437	Cleveland Browns	AFC	302	368
Seattle Seahawks	NFC	412	245	New England Patriots	AFC	557	331
San Francisco 49ers	NFC	397	273	Miami Dolphins	AFC	288	317
St. Louis Rams	NFC	299	348	Buffalo Bills	AFC	344	435
Arizona Cardinals	NFC	250	357	New York Jets	AFC	281	375
Atlanta Falcons	NFC	419	299	Denver Broncos	AFC	481	289
New Orleans Saints	NFC	461	454	San Diego Chargers	AFC	350	350
Tampa Bay Buccaneers	NFC	389	394	Oakland Raiders	AFC	290	443
Carolina Panthers	NFC	357	363	Kansas City Chiefs	AFC	211	425
New York Giants	NFC	429	344	Houston Texans	AFC	416	331
Washington Redskins	NFC	436	388	Indianapolis Colts	AFC	357	387
Dallas Cowboys	NFC	376	400	Tennessee Titans	AFC	330	471
Philadelphia Eagles	NFC	280	444	Jacksonville Jaguars	AFC	255	444

Assuming these are sample data, answer the following questions. You may use statistical software to assist you.

a. What is the correlation coefficient between these variables? Are you surprised the association is negative? Interpret your results.

b. Find the coefficient of determination. What does it say about the relationship?

c. At the .05 significance level, can you conclude there is a negative association between "points scored" and "points allowed"?

d. At the .05 significance level, can you conclude there is a negative association between "points scored" and "points allowed" for each conference?

For **DATA FILE**, please visit www.mhhe.com/lind16e

44. The Cotton Mill is an upscale chain of women's clothing stores, located primarily in the southwest United States. Due to recent success, The Cotton Mill's top management is planning to expand by locating new stores in other regions of the country. The director of planning has been asked to study the relationship between yearly sales and the store size. As part of the study, the director selects a sample of 25 stores and determines the size of the store in square feet and the sales for last year. The sample data follow. The use of statistical software is suggested.

Store Size (thousands of square feet)	Sales (millions $)	Store Size (thousands of square feet)	Sales (millions $)
3.7	9.18	0.4	0.55
2.0	4.58	4.2	7.56
5.0	8.22	3.1	2.23
0.7	1.45	2.6	4.49
2.6	6.51	5.2	9.90
2.9	2.82	3.3	8.93
5.2	10.45	3.2	7.60
5.9	9.94	4.9	3.71
3.0	4.43	5.5	5.47
2.4	4.75	2.9	8.22
2.4	7.30	2.2	7.17
0.5	3.33	2.3	4.35
5.0	6.76		

a. Draw a scatter diagram. Use store size as the independent variable. Does there appear to be a relationship between the two variables. Is it positive or negative?
b. Determine the correlation coefficient and the coefficient of determination. Is the relationship strong or weak? Why?
c. At the .05 significance level, can we conclude there is a significant positive correlation?

For **DATA FILE**, please visit www.mhhe.com/lind16e

45. The manufacturer of Cardio Glide exercise equipment wants to study the relationship between the number of months since the glide was purchased and the time, in hours, the equipment was used last week.

Person	Months Owned	Hours Exercised	Person	Months Owned	Hours Exercised
Rupple	12	4	Massa	2	8
Hall	2	10	Sass	8	3
Bennett	6	8	Karl	4	8
Longnecker	9	5	Malrooney	10	2
Phillips	7	5	Veights	5	5

a. Plot the information on a scatter diagram. Let hours of exercise be the dependent variable. Comment on the graph.
b. Determine the correlation coefficient. Interpret.
c. At the .01 significance level, can we conclude that there is a negative association between the variables?

46. The following regression equation was computed from a sample of 20 observations:

$$\hat{y} = 15 - 5x$$

SSE was found to be 100 and SS total, 400.
a. Determine the standard error of estimate.
b. Determine the coefficient of determination.
c. Determine the correlation coefficient. (Caution: Watch the sign!)

For **DATA FILE**, please visit www.mhhe.com/lind16e

47. City planners believe that larger cities are populated by older residents. To investigate the relationship, data on population and median age in 10 large cities were collected.

City	Population (in millions)	Median Age
Chicago, IL	2.833	31.5
Dallas, TX	1.233	30.5
Houston, TX	2.144	30.9
Los Angeles, CA	3.849	31.6
New York, NY	8.214	34.2
Philadelphia, PA	1.448	34.2
Phoenix, AZ	1.513	30.7
San Antonio, TX	1.297	31.7
San Diego, CA	1.257	32.5
San Jose, CA	0.930	32.6

a. Plot these data on a scatter diagram with median age as the dependent variable.
b. Find the correlation coefficient.
c. A regression analysis was performed and the resulting regression equation is Median Age = 31.4 + 0.272 Population. Interpret the meaning of the slope.
d. Estimate the median age for a city of 2.5 million people.
e. Here is a portion of the regression software output. What does it tell you?

```
Predictor      Coef     SE Coef       T        P
Constant     31.3672    0.6158     50.94    0.000
Population    0.2722    0.1901      1.43    0.190
```

f. Using the .10 significance level, test the significance of the slope. Interpret the result. Is there a significant relationship between the two variables?

CORRELATION AND LINEAR REGRESSION 469

For **DATA FILE**, please visit
www.mhhe.com/lind16e

48. Emily Smith decides to buy a fuel-efficient used car. Here are several vehicles she is considering, with the estimated cost to purchase and the age of the vehicle.

Vehicle	Estimated Cost	Age
Honda Insight	$5,555	8
Toyota Prius	$17,888	3
Toyota Prius	$9,963	6
Toyota Echo	$6,793	5
Honda Civic Hybrid	$10,774	5
Honda Civic Hybrid	$16,310	2
Chevrolet Prizm	$2,475	8
Mazda Protege	$2,808	10
Toyota Corolla	$7,073	9
Acura Integra	$8,978	8
Scion xB	$11,213	2
Scion xA	$9,463	3
Mazda3	$15,055	2
Mini Cooper	$20,705	2

a. Plot these data on a scatter diagram with estimated cost as the dependent variable.
b. Find the correlation coefficient.
c. A regression analysis was performed and the resulting regression equation is Estimated Cost = 18358 − 1534 Age. Interpret the meaning of the slope.
d. Estimate the cost of a five-year-old car.
e. Here is a portion of the regression software output. What does it tell you?

```
Predictor        Coef      SE Coef        T          P
Constant        18358         1817     10.10      0.000
Age           -1533.6        306.3     -5.01      0.000
```

f. Using the .10 significance level, test the significance of the slope. Interpret the result. Is there a significant relationship between the two variables?

For **DATA FILE**, please visit
www.mhhe.com/lind16e

49. The National Highway Association is studying the relationship between the number of bidders on a highway project and the winning (lowest) bid for the project. Of particular interest is whether the number of bidders increases or decreases the amount of the winning bid.

Project	Number of Bidders, x	Winning Bid ($ millions), y	Project	Number of Bidders, x	Winning Bid ($ millions), y
1	9	5.1	9	6	10.3
2	9	8.0	10	6	8.0
3	3	9.7	11	4	8.8
4	10	7.8	12	7	9.4
5	5	7.7	13	7	8.6
6	10	5.5	14	7	8.1
7	7	8.3	15	6	7.8
8	11	5.5			

a. Determine the regression equation. Interpret the equation. Do more bidders tend to increase or decrease the amount of the winning bid?
b. Estimate the amount of the winning bid if there were seven bidders.
c. A new entrance is to be constructed on the Ohio Turnpike. There are seven bidders on the project. Develop a 95% prediction interval for the winning bid.
d. Determine the coefficient of determination. Interpret its value.

For **DATA FILE**, please visit www.mhhe.com/lind16e

50. Mr. William Profit is studying companies going public for the first time. He is particularly interested in the relationship between the size of the offering and the price per share. A sample of 15 companies that recently went public revealed the following information.

Company	Size ($ millions), x	Price per Share, y	Company	Size ($ millions), x	Price per Share, y
1	9.0	10.8	9	160.7	11.3
2	94.4	11.3	10	96.5	10.6
3	27.3	11.2	11	83.0	10.5
4	179.2	11.1	12	23.5	10.3
5	71.9	11.1	13	58.7	10.7
6	97.9	11.2	14	93.8	11.0
7	93.5	11.0	15	34.4	10.8
8	70.0	10.7			

a. Determine the regression equation.
b. Conduct a test to determine whether the slope of the regression line is positive.
c. Determine the coefficient of determination. Do you think Mr. Profit should be satisfied with using the size of the offering as the independent variable?

51. Bardi Trucking Co., located in Cleveland, Ohio, makes deliveries in the Great Lakes region, the Southeast, and the Northeast. Jim Bardi, the president, is studying the relationship between the distance a shipment must travel and the length of time, in days, it takes the shipment to arrive at its destination. To investigate, Mr. Bardi selected a random sample of 20 shipments made last month. Shipping distance is the independent variable and shipping time is the dependent variable. The results are as follows:

For **DATA FILE**, please visit www.mhhe.com/lind16e

Shipment	Distance (miles)	Shipping Time (days)	Shipment	Distance (miles)	Shipping Time (days)
1	656	5	11	862	7
2	853	14	12	679	5
3	646	6	13	835	13
4	783	11	14	607	3
5	610	8	15	665	8
6	841	10	16	647	7
7	785	9	17	685	10
8	639	9	18	720	8
9	762	10	19	652	6
10	762	9	20	828	10

a. Draw a scatter diagram. Based on these data, does it appear that there is a relationship between how many miles a shipment has to go and the time it takes to arrive at its destination?
b. Determine the correlation coefficient. Can we conclude that there is a positive correlation between distance and time? Use the .05 significance level.
c. Determine and interpret the coefficient of determination.
d. Determine the standard error of estimate.
e. Would you recommend using the regression equation to predict shipping time? Why or why not.

52. Super Markets Inc. is considering expanding into the Scottsdale, Arizona, area. You, as director of planning, must present an analysis of the proposed expansion to the operating committee of the board of directors. As a part of your proposal, you need to include information on the amount people in the region spend per month for grocery items. You would also like to include information on the relationship between the amount spent for grocery items and income. Your assistant gathered the following sample information.

For **DATA FILE**, please visit www.mhhe.com/lind16e

Household	Amount Spent	Monthly Income
1	$ 555	$4,388
2	489	4,558
⋮	⋮	⋮
39	1,206	9,862
40	1,145	9,883

a. Let the amount spent be the dependent variable and monthly income the independent variable. Create a scatter diagram, using a software package.
b. Determine the regression equation. Interpret the slope value.
c. Determine the correlation coefficient. Can you conclude that it is greater than 0?

53. Below is information on the price per share and the dividend for a sample of 30 companies.

Company	Price per Share	Dividend
1	$20.00	$ 3.14
2	22.01	3.36
⋮	⋮	⋮
29	77.91	17.65
30	80.00	17.36

For **DATA FILE**, please visit www.mhhe.com/lind16e

a. Calculate the regression equation using selling price based on the annual dividend.
b. Test the significance of the slope.
c. Determine the coefficient of determination. Interpret its value.
d. Determine the correlation coefficient. Can you conclude that it is greater than 0 using the .05 significance level?

54. A highway employee performed a regression analysis of the relationship between the number of construction work-zone fatalities and the number of unemployed people in a state. The regression equation is Fatalities = 12.7 + 0.000114 (Unemp). Some additional output is:

```
Predictor          Coef          SE Coef        T        P
Constant           12.726          8.115       1.57     0.134
Unemp           0.00011386      0.00002896     3.93     0.001

Analysis of Variance
Source          DF        SS        MS       F        P
Regression       1      10354     10354    15.46    0.001
Residual Error   18     12054       670
Total            19     22408
```

a. How many states were in the sample?
b. Determine the standard error of estimate.
c. Determine the coefficient of determination.
d. Determine the correlation coefficient.
e. At the .05 significance level, does the evidence suggest there is a positive association between fatalities and the number unemployed?

55. A regression analysis relating the current market value in dollars to the size in square feet of homes in Greene County, Tennessee, follows. The regression equation is: Value = −37,186 + 65.0 Size.

```
Predictor      Coef      SE Coef      T        P
Constant      -37186      4629      -8.03    0.000
Size          64.993      3.047     21.33    0.000

Analysis of Variance
Source          DF          SS              MS           F        P
Regression       1      13548662082     13548662082    454.98    0.000
Residual Error   33       982687392       29778406
Total            34      14531349474
```

472   CHAPTER 13

a. How many homes were in the sample?
b. Compute the standard error of estimate.
c. Compute the coefficient of determination.
d. Compute the correlation coefficient.
e. At the .05 significance level, does the evidence suggest a positive association between the market value of homes and the size of the home in square feet?

56. The following table shows the mean annual percent return on capital (profitability) and the mean annual percentage sales growth for eight aerospace and defense companies.

For **DATA FILE**, please visit www.mhhe.com/lind16e

Company	Profitability	Growth
Alliant Techsystems	23.1	8.0
Boeing	13.2	15.6
General Dynamics	24.2	31.2
Honeywell	11.1	2.5
L-3 Communications	10.1	35.4
Northrop Grumman	10.8	6.0
Rockwell Collins	27.3	8.7
United Technologies	20.1	3.2

a. Compute the correlation coefficient. Conduct a test of hypothesis to determine if it is reasonable to conclude that the population correlation is greater than zero. Use the .05 significance level.
b. Develop the regression equation for profitability based on growth. Can we conclude that the slope of the regression line is negative?
c. Use a software package to determine the residual for each observation. Which company has the largest residual?

57. The following data show the retail price for 12 randomly selected laptop computers along with their corresponding processor speeds in gigahertz.

For **DATA FILE**, please visit www.mhhe.com/lind16e

Computers	Speed	Price	Computers	Speed	Price
1	2.0	$2,017	7	2.0	$2,197
2	1.6	922	8	1.6	1,387
3	1.6	1,064	9	2.0	2,114
4	1.8	1,942	10	1.6	2,002
5	2.0	2,137	11	1.0	937
6	1.2	1,012	12	1.4	869

a. Develop a linear equation that can be used to describe how the price depends on the processor speed.
b. Based on your regression equation, is there one machine that seems particularly over- or underpriced?
c. Compute the correlation coefficient between the two variables. At the .05 significance level, conduct a test of hypothesis to determine if the population correlation is greater than zero.

58. A consumer buying cooperative tested the effective heating area of 20 different electric space heaters with different wattages. Here are the results.

For **DATA FILE**, please visit www.mhhe.com/lind16e

Heater	Wattage	Area	Heater	Wattage	Area
1	1,500	205	11	1,250	116
2	750	70	12	500	72
3	1,500	199	13	500	82
4	1,250	151	14	1,500	206
5	1,250	181	15	2,000	245
6	1,250	217	16	1,500	219
7	1,000	94	17	750	63
8	2,000	298	18	1,500	200
9	1,000	135	19	1,250	151
10	1,500	211	20	500	44

CORRELATION AND LINEAR REGRESSION   473

a. Compute the correlation between the wattage and heating area. Is there a direct or an indirect relationship?
b. Conduct a test of hypothesis to determine if it is reasonable that the coefficient is greater than zero. Use the .05 significance level.
c. Develop the regression equation for effective heating based on wattage.
d. Which heater looks like the "best buy" based on the size of the residual?

59. A dog trainer is exploring the relationship between the size of the dog (weight in pounds) and its daily food consumption (measured in standard cups). Below is the result of a sample of 18 observations.

For **DATA FILE**, please visit www.mhhe.com/lind16e

Dog	Weight	Consumption	Dog	Weight	Consumption
1	41	3	10	91	5
2	148	8	11	109	6
3	79	5	12	207	10
4	41	4	13	49	3
5	85	5	14	113	6
6	111	6	15	84	5
7	37	3	16	95	5
8	111	6	17	57	4
9	41	3	18	168	9

a. Compute the correlation coefficient. Is it reasonable to conclude that the correlation in the population is greater than zero? Use the .05 significance level.
b. Develop the regression equation for cups based on the dog's weight. How much does each additional cup change the estimated weight of the dog?
c. Is one of the dogs a big undereater or overeater?

60. Waterbury Insurance Company wants to study the relationship between the amount of fire damage and the distance between the burning house and the nearest fire station. This information will be used in setting rates for insurance coverage. For a sample of 30 claims for the last year, the director of the actuarial department determined the distance from the fire station (x) and the amount of fire damage, in thousands of dollars (y). The MegaStat output is reported below.

```
ANOVA table
Source                SS       df             MS          F
Regression      1,864.5782      1      1,864.5782      38.83
Residual        1,344.4934     28         48.0176
Total           3,209.0716     29

Regression output
Variables        Coefficients        Std. Error     t(df = 28)
Intercept            12.3601             3.2915          3.755
Distance—X            4.7956             0.7696          6.231
```

Answer the following questions.
a. Write out the regression equation. Is there a direct or indirect relationship between the distance from the fire station and the amount of fire damage?
b. How much damage would you estimate for a fire 5 miles from the nearest fire station?
c. Determine and interpret the coefficient of determination.
d. Determine the correlation coefficient. Interpret its value. How did you determine the sign of the correlation coefficient?
e. Conduct a test of hypothesis to determine if there is a significant relationship between the distance from the fire station and the amount of damage. Use the .01 significance level and a two-tailed test.

For **DATA FILE**, please visit
www.mhhe.com/lind16e

61. An air travel service samples domestic airline flights to explore the relationship between airfare and distance. The service would like to know if there is a correlation between airfare and flight distance. If there is a correlation, what percentage of the variation in airfare is accounted for by distance? How much does each additional mile add to the fare? The data follow.

Origin	Destination	Distance	Fare
Detroit, MI	Myrtle Beach, SC	636	$109
Baltimore, MD	Sacramento, CA	2,395	252
Las Vegas, NV	Philadelphia, PA	2,176	221
Sacramento, CA	Seattle, WA	605	151
Atlanta, GA	Orlando, FL	403	138
Boston, MA	Miami, FL	1,258	209
Chicago, IL	Covington, KY	264	254
Columbus, OH	Minneapolis, MN	627	259
Fort Lauderdale, FL	Los Angeles, CA	2,342	215
Chicago, IL	Indianapolis, IN	177	128
Philadelphia, PA	San Francisco, CA	2,521	348
Houston, TX	Raleigh/Durham, NC	1,050	224
Houston, TX	Midland/Odessa, TX	441	175
Cleveland, OH	Dallas/Ft.Worth, TX	1,021	256
Baltimore, MD	Columbus, OH	336	121
Boston, MA	Covington, KY	752	252
Kansas City, MO	San Diego, CA	1,333	206
Milwaukee, WI	Phoenix, AZ	1,460	167
Portland, OR	Washington, DC	2,350	308
Phoenix, AZ	San Jose, CA	621	152
Baltimore, MD	St. Louis, MO	737	175
Houston, TX	Orlando, FL	853	191
Houston, TX	Seattle, WA	1,894	231
Burbank, CA	New York, NY	2,465	251
Atlanta, GA	San Diego, CA	1,891	291
Minneapolis, MN	New York, NY	1,028	260
Atlanta, GA	West Palm Beach, FL	545	123
Kansas City, MO	Seattle, WA	1,489	211
Baltimore, MD	Portland, ME	452	139
New Orleans, LA	Washington, DC	969	243

a. Draw a scatter diagram with *Distance* as the independent variable and *Fare* as the dependent variable. Is the relationship direct or indirect?
b. Compute the correlation coefficient. At the .05 significance level, is it reasonable to conclude that the correlation coefficient is greater than zero?
c. What percentage of the variation in *Fare* is accounted for by *Distance* of a flight?
d. Determine the regression equation. How much does each additional mile add to the fare? Estimate the fare for a 1,500-mile flight.
e. A traveler is planning to fly from Atlanta to London Heathrow. The distance is 4,218 miles. She wants to use the regression equation to estimate the fare. Explain why it would not be a good idea to estimate the fare for this international flight with the regression equation.

DATA   SET   EXERCISES

(The data for these exercises are available at the text website: www.mhhe.com/lind16e.)

62. Refer to the Real Estate data, which reports information on homes sold in Goodyear, Arizona, last year.
  a. Let selling price be the dependent variable and size of the home the independent variable. Determine the regression equation. Estimate the selling price for a home with an

CORRELATION AND LINEAR REGRESSION   475

   area of 2,200 square feet. Determine the 95% confidence interval and the 95% prediction interval for the selling price of a home with 2,200 square feet.
   b. Let selling price be the dependent variable and distance from the center of the city the independent variable. Determine the regression equation. Estimate the selling price of a home 20 miles from the center of the city. Determine the 95% confidence interval and the 95% prediction interval for homes 20 miles from the center of the city.
   c. Can you conclude that the independent variables "distance from the center of the city" and "selling price" are negatively correlated and that the area of the home and the selling price are positively correlated? Use the .05 significance level. Report the *p*-value of the test. Summarize your results in a brief report.
63. Refer to the Baseball 2012 data, which reports information on the 2012 Major League Baseball season. Let attendance be the dependent variable and total team salary, in millions of dollars, be the independent variable. Determine the regression equation and answer the following questions.
   a. Draw a scatter diagram. From the diagram, does there seem to be a direct relationship between the two variables?
   b. What is the expected attendance for a team with a salary of $80.0 million?
   c. If the owners pay an additional $30 million, how many more people could they expect to attend?
   d. At the .05 significance level, can we conclude that the slope of the regression line is positive? Conduct the appropriate test of hypothesis.
   e. What percentage of the variation in attendance is accounted for by salary?
   f. Determine the correlation between attendance and team batting average and between attendance and team ERA. Which is stronger? Conduct an appropriate test of hypothesis for each set of variables.
64. Refer to the Buena School bus data. Develop a regression equation that expresses the relationship between age of the bus and maintenance. The age of the bus is the independent variable.
   a. Draw a scatter diagram. What does this diagram suggest as to the relationship between the two variables? Is it direct or indirect? Does it appear to be strong or weak?
   b. Develop a regression equation. How much does an additional year add to the maintenance cost. What is the estimated maintenance cost for a 10-year-old bus?
   c. Conduct a test of hypothesis to determine whether the slope of the regression line is greater than zero. Use the .05 significance level. Interpret your findings from parts (a), (b), and (c) in a brief report.

14

Multiple Regression Analysis

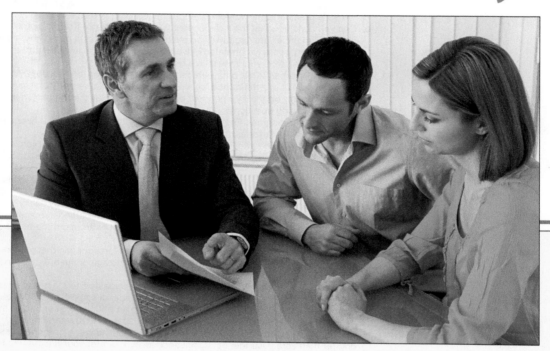

THE MORTGAGE DEPARTMENT of the Bank of New England is studying data from recent loans. Of particular interest is how such factors as the value of the home being purchased, education level of the head of the household, age of the head of the household, current monthly mortgage payment, and gender of the head of the household relate to the family income. Are the proposed variables effective predictors of the dependent variable family income? (See the example/solution on page 508, LO14-1.)

LEARNING OBJECTIVES

When you have completed this chapter, you will be able to:

LO14-1 Use multiple regression analysis to describe and interpret a relationship between several independent variables and a dependent variable.

LO14-2 Evaluate how well a multiple regression equation fits the data.

LO14-3 Test hypotheses about the relationships inferred by a multiple regression model.

LO14-4 Evaluate the assumptions of multiple regression.

LO14-5 Use and interpret a qualitative, dummy variable in multiple regression.

LO14-6 Include and interpret an interaction effect in multiple regression analysis.

LO14-7 Apply stepwise regression to develop a multiple regression model.

LO14-8 Apply multiple regression techniques to develop a linear model.

INTRODUCTION

In Chapter 13, we described the relationship between a pair of interval- or ratio-scaled variables. We began the chapter by studying the correlation coefficient, which measures the strength of the relationship. A coefficient near plus or minus 1.00 ($-.88$ or $.78$, for example) indicates a very strong linear relationship, whereas a value near 0 ($-.12$ or $.18$, for example) indicates that the relationship is weak. Next we developed a procedure to determine a linear equation to express the relationship between the two variables. We referred to this as a *regression line*. This line describes the relationship between the variables. It also describes the overall pattern of a dependent variable (y) to a single independent or explanatory variable (x).

In multiple linear correlation and regression, we use additional independent variables (denoted $x_1, x_2, \ldots$, and so on) that help us better explain or predict the dependent variable (y). Almost all of the ideas we saw in simple linear correlation and regression extend to this more general situation. However, the additional independent variables do lead to some new considerations. Multiple regression analysis can be used either as a descriptive or as an inferential technique.

MULTIPLE REGRESSION ANALYSIS

LO14-1

Use multiple regression analysis to describe and interpret a relationship between several independent variables and a dependent variable.

The general descriptive form of a multiple linear equation is shown in formula (14–1). We use k to represent the number of independent variables. So k can be any positive integer.

GENERAL MULTIPLE REGRESSION EQUATION	$\hat{y} = a + b_1x_1 + b_2x_2 + b_3x_3 + \cdots + b_kx_k$	**[14–1]**

where:
- a is the intercept, the value of $\hat{y}$ when all the X's are zero.
- b_j is the amount by which $\hat{y}$ changes when that particular x_j increases by one unit, with the values of all other independent variables held constant. The subscript j is simply a label that helps to identify each independent variable; it is not used in any calculations. Usually the subscript is an integer value between 1 and k, which is the number of independent variables. However, the subscript can also be a short or abbreviated label. For example, age could be used as a subscript.

In Chapter 13, the regression analysis described and tested the relationship between a dependent variable, $\hat{y}$, and a single independent variable, x. The relationship between $\hat{y}$ and x was graphically portrayed by a line. When there are two independent variables, the regression equation is

$$\hat{y} = a + b_1x_1 + b_2x_2$$

Because there are two independent variables, this relationship is graphically portrayed as a plane and is shown in Chart 14–1. The chart shows the residuals as the difference between the actual y and the fitted $\hat{y}$ on the plane. If a multiple regression analysis includes more than two independent variables, we cannot use a graph to illustrate the analysis since graphs are limited to three dimensions.

To illustrate the interpretation of the intercept and the two regression coefficients, suppose the selling price of a home is directly related to the number of rooms and *inversely* related to its age. We let x_1 refer to the number of rooms, x_2 to the age of the home in years, and y to the selling price of the home in thousands of dollars ($000).

CHART 14–1 Regression Plane with 10 Sample Points

Suppose the regression equation, calculated using statistical software, is:

$$\hat{y} = 21.2 + 18.7x_1 - 0.25x_2$$

The intercept value of 21.2 indicates the regression equation (plane) intersects the y-axis at 21.2. This happens when both the number of rooms and the age of the home are zero. We could say that $21,200 is the average value of a property without a house.

The first regression coefficient, 18.7, indicates that for each increase of one room in the size of a home, the selling price will increase by $18.7 thousand ($18,700), regardless of the age of the home. The second regression coefficient, −0.25, indicates that for each increase of one year in age, the selling price will *decrease* by $.25 thousand ($250), regardless of the number of rooms. As an example, a seven-room home that is 30 years old is expected to sell for $144,600.

$$\hat{y} = 21.2 + 18.7x_1 - 0.25x_2 = 21.2 + 18.7(7) - 0.25(30) = 144.6$$

The values for the coefficients in the multiple linear equation are found by using the method of least squares. Recall from the previous chapter that the least squares method makes the sum of the squared differences between the fitted and actual values of y as small as possible, that is, the term $\Sigma(y - \hat{y})^2$ is minimized. The calculations are very tedious, so they are usually performed by a statistical software package.

In the following example, we show a multiple regression analysis using three independent variables employing Excel that produces a standard set of statistics and reports. Statistical software such as Minitab, Megastat, and others provide advanced regression analysis techniques.

EXAMPLE

Salsberry Realty sells homes along the East Coast of the United States. One of the questions most frequently asked by prospective buyers is: If we purchase this home, how much can we expect to pay to heat it during the winter? The research department at Salsberry has been asked to develop some guidelines regarding heating costs for single-family homes. Three variables are thought to relate to the heating costs: (1) the mean daily outside temperature, (2) the number of inches of insulation in the attic, and (3) the age in years of the furnace. To investigate, Salsberry's research department selected a random sample of 20 recently sold homes. It determined the cost to heat each home last January, as well as the January outside temperature in the region, the number of inches of insulation in the attic, and the age of the furnace. The sample information is reported in Table 14–1.

TABLE 14–1 Factors in January Heating Cost for a Sample of 20 Homes

Home	Heating Cost ($)	Mean Outside Temperature (°F)	Attic Insulation (inches)	Age of Furnace (years)
1	$250	35	3	6
2	360	29	4	10
3	165	36	7	3
4	43	60	6	9
5	92	65	5	6
6	200	30	5	5
7	355	10	6	7
8	290	7	10	10
9	230	21	9	11
10	120	55	2	5
11	73	54	12	4
12	205	48	5	1
13	400	20	5	15
14	320	39	4	7
15	72	60	8	6
16	272	20	5	8
17	94	58	7	3
18	190	40	8	11
19	235	27	9	8
20	139	30	7	5

The data in Table 14–1 are available in Excel worksheet format at the textbook website, **www.mhhe.com/lind16e**. The basic instructions for using Excel for these data are in the Software Commands in Appendix C.

Determine the multiple regression equation. Which variables are the independent variables? Which variable is the dependent variable? Discuss the regression coefficients. What does it indicate if some coefficients are positive and some coefficients are negative? What is the intercept value? What is the estimated heating cost for a home if the mean outside temperature is 30 degrees, there are 5 inches of insulation in the attic, and the furnace is 10 years old?

SOLUTION

We begin the analysis by defining the dependent and independent variables. The dependent variable is the January heating cost. It is represented by y. There are three independent variables:

- The mean outside temperature in January, represented by x_1.
- The number of inches of insulation in the attic, represented by x_2.
- The age in years of the furnace, represented by x_3.

Given these definitions, the general form of the multiple regression equation follows. The value $\hat{y}$ is used to estimate the value of y.

$$\hat{y} = a + b_1 x_1 + b_2 x_2 + b_3 x_3$$

Now that we have defined the regression equation, we are ready to use Excel to compute all the statistics needed for the analysis. The output from Excel is shown on the following page.

To use the regression equation to predict the January heating cost, we need to know the values of the regression coefficients, b_j. These are highlighted in the software reports. The software uses the variable names or labels associated with each independent variable. The regression equation intercept, *a,* is labeled "intercept" in the Excel output.

	A	B	C	D	E	F	G	H	I	J	K
1	Cost	Temp	Insul	Age		SUMMARY OUTPUT					
2	250	35	3	6							
3	360	29	4	10		*Regression Statistics*					
4	165	36	7	3		Multiple R	0.897				
5	43	60	6	9		R Square	0.804				
6	92	65	5	6		Adjusted R Square	0.767				
7	200	30	5	5		Standard Error	51.049				
8	355	10	6	7		Observations	20				
9	290	7	10	10							
10	230	21	9	11		ANOVA					
11	120	55	2	5			*df*	*SS*	*MS*	*F*	*Significance F*
12	73	54	12	4		Regression	3	171220.473	57073.491	21.901	0.000
13	205	48	5	1		Residual	16	41695.277	2605.955		
14	400	20	5	15		Total	19	212915.750			
15	320	39	4	7							
16	72	60	8	6			*Coefficients*	*Standard Error*	*t Stat*	*P-value*	
17	272	20	5	8		Intercept	427.194	59.601	7.168	0.000	
18	94	58	7	3		Temp	-4.583	0.772	-5.934	0.000	
19	190	40	8	11		Insul	-14.831	4.754	-3.119	0.007	
20	235	27	9	8		Age	6.101	4.012	1.521	0.148	
21	139	30	7	5							

In this case, the estimated regression equation is:

$$\hat{y} = 427.194 - 4.583x_1 - 14.831x_2 + 6.101x_3$$

We can now estimate or predict the January heating cost for a home if we know the mean outside temperature, the inches of insulation, and the age of the furnace. For an example home, the mean outside temperature for the month is 30 degrees (x_1), there are 5 inches of insulation in the attic (x_2), and the furnace is 10 years old (x_3). By substituting the values for the independent variables:

$$\hat{y} = 427.194 - 4.583(30) - 14.831(5) + 6.101(10) = 276.56$$

The estimated January heating cost is $276.56.

The regression coefficients, and their algebraic signs, also provide information about their individual relationships with the January heating cost. The regression coefficient for mean outside temperature is −4.583. The coefficient is negative and shows an inverse relationship between heating cost and temperature. This is not surprising. As the outside temperature increases, the cost to heat the home decreases. The numeric value of the regression coefficient provides more information. If we increase temperature by 1 degree and hold the other two independent variables constant, we can estimate a decrease of $4.583 in monthly heating cost. So if the mean temperature in Boston is 25 degrees and it is 35 degrees in Philadelphia, all other things being the same (insulation and age of furnace), we expect the heating cost would be $45.83 less in Philadelphia.

The attic insulation variable also shows an inverse relationship: the more insulation in the attic, the less the cost to heat the home. So the negative sign for this coefficient is logical. For each additional inch of insulation, we expect the cost to heat the home to decline $14.83 per month, holding the outside temperature and the age of the furnace constant.

The age of the furnace variable shows a direct relationship. With an older furnace, the cost to heat the home increases. Specifically, for each additional year older the furnace is, we expect the cost to increase $6.10 per month.

MULTIPLE REGRESSION ANALYSIS   481

SELF-REVIEW

14-1

There are many restaurants in northeastern South Carolina. They serve beach vacationers in the summer, golfers in the fall and spring, and snowbirds in the winter. Bill and Joyce Tuneall manage several restaurants in the North Jersey area and are considering moving to Myrtle Beach, SC, to open a new restaurant. Before making a final decision, they wish to investigate existing restaurants and what variables seem to be related to profitability. They gather sample information where profit (reported in $000) is the dependent variable and the independent variables are:

x_1 the number of parking spaces near the restaurant.
x_2 the number of hours the restaurant is open per week.
x_3 the distance from the SkyWheel, a landmark in Myrtle Beach.
x_4 the number of servers employed.
x_5 the number of years the current owner operated the restaurant.

The following is part of the output obtained using statistical software.

Predictor	Coefficient	SE Coefficient	t
Constant	2.50	1.50	1.667
x_1	3.00	1.50	2.000
x_2	4.00	3.00	1.333
x_3	-3.00	0.20	-15.000
x_4	0.20	0.05	4.000
x_5	1.00	1.50	0.667

(a) What is the amount of profit for a restaurant with 40 parking spaces that is open 72 hours per week, is 10 miles from the SkyWheel, has 20 servers, and has been operated by the current owner for 5 years?
(b) Interpret the values of b_2 and b_3 in the multiple regression equation.

EXERCISES

1. The director of marketing at Reeves Wholesale Products is studying monthly sales. Three independent variables were selected as estimators of sales: regional population, per capita income, and regional unemployment rate. The regression equation was computed to be (in dollars):

$$\hat{y} = 64{,}100 + 0.394x_1 + 9.6x_2 - 11{,}600x_3$$

    a. What is the full name of the equation?
    b. Interpret the number 64,100.
    c. What are the estimated monthly sales for a particular region with a population of 796,000, per capita income of $6,940, and an unemployment rate of 6.0%?
2. Thompson Photo Works purchased several new, highly sophisticated processing machines. The production department needed some guidance with respect to qualifications needed by an operator. Is age a factor? Is the length of service as an operator (in years) important? In order to explore further the factors needed to estimate performance on the new processing machines, four variables were listed:

x_1 = Length of time an employee was in the industry
x_2 = Mechanical aptitude test score
x_3 = Prior on-the-job rating
x_4 = Age

Performance on the new machine is designated y.
    Thirty employees were selected at random. Data were collected for each, and their performances on the new machines were recorded. A few results are:

Name	Performance on New Machine, y	Length of Time in Industry, x_1	Mechanical Aptitude Score, x_2	Prior on-the-Job Performance, x_3	Age, x_4
Mike Miraglia	112	12	312	121	52
Sue Trythall	113	2	380	123	27

The equation is:

$$\hat{y} = 11.6 + 0.4x_1 + 0.286x_2 + 0.112x_3 + 0.002x_4$$

   a. What is this equation called?
   b. How many dependent variables are there? Independent variables?
   c. What is the number 0.286 called?
   d. As age increases by one year, how much does estimated performance on the new machine increase?
   e. Carl Knox applied for a job at Photo Works. He has been in the business for 6 years and scored 280 on the mechanical aptitude test. Carl's prior on-the-job performance rating is 97, and he is 35 years old. Estimate Carl's performance on the new machine.

3. A consulting group was hired by the Human Resources Department at General Mills, Inc. to survey company employees regarding their degree of satisfaction with their quality of life. A special index, called the index of satisfaction, was used to measure satisfaction. Six factors were studied, namely, age at the time of first marriage (x_1), annual income (x_2), number of children living (x_3), value of all assets (x_4), status of health in the form of an index (x_5), and the average number of social activities per week—such as bowling and dancing (x_6). Suppose the multiple regression equation is:

$$\hat{y} = 16.24 + 0.017x_1 + 0.0028x_2 + 42x_3 + 0.0012x_4 + 0.19x_5 + 26.8x_6$$

   a. What is the estimated index of satisfaction for a person who first married at 18, has an annual income of $26,500, has three children living, has assets of $156,000, has an index of health status of 141, and has 2.5 social activities a week on the average?
   b. Which would add more to satisfaction, an additional income of $10,000 a year or two more social activities a week?

4. Cellulon, a manufacturer of home insulation, wants to develop guidelines for builders and consumers on how the thickness of the insulation in the attic of a home and the outdoor temperature affect natural gas consumption. In the laboratory, it varied the insulation thickness and temperature. A few of the findings are:

Monthly Natural Gas Consumption (cubic feet), y	Thickness of Insulation (inches), x_1	Outdoor Temperature (°F), x_2
30.3	6	40
26.9	12	40
22.1	8	49

On the basis of the sample results, the regression equation is:

$$\hat{y} = 62.65 - 1.86x_1 - 0.52x_2$$

   a. How much natural gas can homeowners expect to use per month if they install 6 inches of insulation and the outdoor temperature is 40 degrees F?
   b. What effect would installing 7 inches of insulation instead of 6 have on the monthly natural gas consumption (assuming the outdoor temperature remains at 40 degrees F)?
   c. Why are the regression coefficients b_1 and b_2 negative? Is this logical?

EVALUATING A MULTIPLE REGRESSION EQUATION

Many statistics and statistical methods are used to evaluate the relationship between a dependent variable and more than one independent variable. Our first step was to write the relationship in terms of a multiple regression equation. The next step follows on the concepts presented in Chapter 13 by using the information in an ANOVA table to evaluate how well the equation fits the data.

The ANOVA Table

As in Chapter 13, the statistical analysis of a multiple regression equation is summarized in an ANOVA table. To review, the total variation of the dependent variable, y, is divided into two components: (1) *regression,* or the variation of y explained by all the independent variables, and (2) *the error or residual,* or unexplained variation of y. These two categories are identified in the first column of an ANOVA table below. The column headed "*df*" refers to the degrees of freedom associated with each category. The total number of degrees of freedom is $n - 1$. The number of degrees of freedom in the regression is equal to the number of independent variables in the multiple regression equation. We call the regression degrees of freedom k. The number of degrees of freedom associated with the error term is equal to the total degrees of freedom minus the regression degrees of freedom. In multiple regression, the degrees of freedom are $n - (k + 1)$.

Source	df	SS	MS	F
Regression	k	SSR	MSR = SSR/k	MSR/MSE
Residual or error	$n - (k + 1)$	SSE	MSE = SSE/$[n - (k + 1)]$	
Total	$n - 1$	SS total		

The term "SS" located in the middle of the ANOVA table refers to the sum of squares. Notice that there is a sum of squares for each source of variation. The sum of squares column shows the amount of variation attributable to each source. The total variation of the dependent variable, y, is summarized in SS total. You should note that this is simply the numerator of the usual formula to calculate any variation—in other words, the sum of the squared deviations from the mean. It is computed as:

$$\text{Total Sum of Squares} = \text{SS total} = \Sigma(y - \bar{y})^2$$

As we have seen, the total sum of squares is the sum of the regression and residual sum of squares. The regression sum of squares is the sum of the squared differences between the estimated or predicted values, $\hat{y}$, and the overall mean of y. The regression sum of squares is found by:

$$\text{Regression Sum of Squares} = \text{SSR} = \Sigma(\hat{y} - \bar{y})^2$$

The residual sum of squares is the sum of the squared differences between the observed values of the dependent variable, y, and their corresponding estimated or predicted values, $\hat{y}$. Notice that this difference is the error of estimating or predicting the dependent variable with the multiple regression equation. It is calculated as:

$$\text{Residual or Error Sum of Squares} = \text{SSE} = \Sigma(y - \hat{y})^2$$

We will use the ANOVA table information from the previous example to evaluate the regression equation to estimate January heating costs.

	A	B	C	D	G	H	I	J	K	L	M
1	Cost	Temp	Insul	Age		SUMMARY OUTPUT					
2	250	35	3	6							
3	360	29	4	10		*Regression Statistics*					
4	165	36	7	3		Multiple R	0.897				
5	43	60	6	9		R Square	0.804				
6	92	65	5	6		Adjusted R Square	0.767				
7	200	30	5	5		Standard Error	51.049				
8	355	10	6	7		Observations	20				
9	290	7	10	10							
10	230	21	9	11		ANOVA					
11	120	55	2	5			*df*	*SS*	*MS*	*F*	*Significance F*
12	73	54	12	4		Regression	3	171220.473	57073.491	21.901	0.000
13	205	48	5	1		Residual	16	41695.277	2605.955		
14	400	20	5	15		Total	19	212915.750			
15	320	39	4	7							
16	72	60	8	6			*Coefficients*	*Standard Error*	*t Stat*	*P-value*	
17	272	20	5	8		Intercept	427.194	59.601	7.168	0.000	
18	94	58	7	3		Temp	-4.583	0.772	-5.934	0.000	
19	190	40	8	11		Insul	-14.831	4.754	-3.119	0.007	
20	235	27	9	8		Age	6.101	4.012	1.521	0.148	

Multiple Standard Error of Estimate

We begin with the **multiple standard error of estimate.** Recall that the standard error of estimate is comparable to the standard deviation. To explain the details of the standard error of estimate, refer to the first sampled home in row 2 in the Excel spreadsheet on the previous page. The actual heating cost for the first observation, y, is $250; the outside temperature, x_1, is 35 degrees; the depth of insulation, x_2, is 3 inches; and the age of the furnace, x_3, is 6 years. Using the regression equation developed in the previous section, the estimated heating cost for this home is:

$$\hat{y} = 427.194 - 4.583x_1 - 14.831x_2 + 6.101x_3$$

$$= 427.194 - 4.583(35) - 14.831(3) + 6.101(6)$$

$$= 258.90$$

So we would estimate that a home with a mean January outside temperature of 35 degrees, 3 inches of insulation, and a 6-year-old furnace would cost $258.90 to heat. The actual heating cost was $250, so the residual—which is the difference between the actual value and the estimated value—is $y - \hat{y} = 250 - 258.90 = -8.90$. This difference of $8.90 is the random or unexplained error for the first home sampled. Our next step is to square this difference—that is, find $(y - \hat{y})^2 = (250 - 258.90)^2 = (-8.90)^2 = 79.21$.

If we repeat this calculation for the other 19 observations and sum all 20 squared differences, the total will be the residual or error sum of squares from the ANOVA table. Using this information, we can calculate the multiple standard error of the estimate as:

MULTIPLE STANDARD ERROR OF ESTIMATE	$$S_{Y.123\ldots k} = \sqrt{\frac{\Sigma(y - \hat{y})^2}{n - (k + 1)}} = \sqrt{\frac{SSE}{n - (k + 1)}}$$	**[14–2]**

where:
   y is the actual observation.
   $\hat{y}$ is the estimated value computed from the regression equation.
   n is the number of observations in the sample.
   k is the number of independent variables.
   SSE is the Residual Sum of Squares from an ANOVA table.

There is more information in the ANOVA table that can be used to compute the multiple standard error of estimate. The column headed "MS" reports the mean squares for the regression and residual variation. These values are calculated as the sum of squares divided by the corresponding degrees of freedom. The multiple standard error of estimate is equal to the square root of the residual MS, which is also called the mean square error or the MSE.

$$s_{Y.123\ldots K} = \sqrt{MSE} = \sqrt{2605.995} = \$51.05$$

How do we interpret the standard error of estimate of 51.05? It is the typical "error" when we use this equation to predict the cost. First, the units are the same as the dependent variable, so the standard error is in dollars, $51.05. Second, we expect the residuals to be approximately normally distributed, so about 68% of the residuals will be within ±$51.05 and about 95% within ±2(51.05), or ±$102.10. As before with similar measures of dispersion, such as the standard error of estimate in Chapter 13, a smaller multiple standard error indicates a better or more effective predictive equation.

Coefficient of Multiple Determination

Next, let's look at the coefficient of multiple determination. Recall from the previous chapter the coefficient of determination is defined as the percent of variation in the dependent variable explained, or accounted for, by the independent variable. In the multiple regression case, we extend this definition as follows.

> **COEFFICIENT OF MULTIPLE DETERMINATION** The percent of variation in the dependent variable, y, explained by the set of independent variables, x_1, x_2, x_3, . . . x_k.

The characteristics of the coefficient of multiple determination are:

1. **It is symbolized by a capital R squared.** In other words, it is written as R^2 because it behaves like the square of a correlation coefficient.
2. **It can range from 0 to 1.** A value near 0 indicates little association between the set of independent variables and the dependent variable. A value near 1 means a strong association.
3. **It cannot assume negative values.** Any number that is squared or raised to the second power cannot be negative.
4. **It is easy to interpret.** Because R^2 is a value between 0 and 1, it is easy to interpret, compare, and understand.

We can calculate the coefficient of determination from the information found in the ANOVA table. We look in the sum of squares column, which is labeled SS in the Excel output, and use the regression sum of squares, SSR, then divide by the total sum of squares, SS total.

COEFFICIENT OF MULTIPLE DETERMINATION	$R^2 = \dfrac{\text{SSR}}{\text{SS total}}$	**[14–3]**

We can use the regression and the total sum of squares from the ANOVA table highlighted in the Excel output on page 483 and compute the coefficient of determination.

$$R^2 = \frac{\text{SSR}}{\text{SS total}} = \frac{171{,}220.473}{212{,}915.750} = .804$$

How do we interpret this value? We conclude that the independent variables (outside temperature, amount of insulation, and age of furnace) explain, or account for, 80.4% of the variation in heating cost. To put it another way, 19.6% of the variation is due to other sources, such as random error or variables not included in the analysis. Using the ANOVA table, 19.6% is the error sum of squares divided by the total sum of squares. Knowing that the SSR + SSE = SS total, the following relationship is true.

$$1 - R^2 = 1 - \frac{\text{SSR}}{\text{SS total}} = \frac{\text{SSE}}{\text{SS total}} = \frac{41{,}695.277}{212{,}915.750} = .196$$

Adjusted Coefficient of Determination

The coefficient of determination tends to increase as more independent variables are added to the multiple regression model. Each new independent variable causes the predictions to be more accurate. That, in turn, makes SSE smaller and SSR larger. Hence, R^2 increases only because the total number of independent variables increases and not because the added independent variable is a good predictor of the dependent variable. In fact, if the number of variables, k, and the sample size, n, are equal, the coefficient of determination is 1.0. In practice, this situation is rare and would also be ethically questionable. To balance the effect that the number of independent variables has on the coefficient of multiple determination, statistical software packages use an *adjusted* coefficient of multiple determination.

ADJUSTED COEFFICIENT OF DETERMINATION	$R^2_{adj} = 1 - \dfrac{\dfrac{SSE}{n - (k + 1)}}{\dfrac{SS\,total}{n - 1}}$	[14–4]

The error and total sum of squares are divided by their degrees of freedom. Notice especially the degrees of freedom for the error sum of squares include k, the number of independent variables. For the cost of heating example, the adjusted coefficient of determination is:

$$R^2_{adj} = 1 - \dfrac{\dfrac{41{,}695.277}{20 - (3 + 1)}}{\dfrac{212{,}915.750}{20 - 1}} = 1 - \dfrac{2{,}605.955}{11{,}206.092} = 1 - .233 = .767$$

If we compare the R^2 (0.80) to the adjusted R^2 (0.767), the difference in this case is small.

SELF-REVIEW

14–2

Refer to Self-Review 14–1 on the subject of restaurants in Myrtle Beach. The ANOVA portion of the regression output is presented below.

```
Analysis of Variance
Source          DF    SS    MS
Regression       5   100    20
Residual Error  20    40     2
Total           25   140
```

(a) How large was the sample?
(b) How many independent variables are there?
(c) How many dependent variables are there?
(d) Compute the standard error of estimate. About 95% of the residuals will be between what two values?
(e) Determine the coefficient of multiple determination. Interpret this value.
(f) Find the coefficient of multiple determination, adjusted for the degrees of freedom.

EXERCISES

5. Consider the ANOVA table that follows.

```
Analysis of Variance
Source          DF      SS        MS       F       P
Regression       2   77.907    38.954    4.14    0.021
Residual Error  62  583.693     9.414
Total           64  661.600
```

   a. Determine the standard error of estimate. About 95% of the residuals will be between what two values?
   b. Determine the coefficient of multiple determination. Interpret this value.
   c. Determine the coefficient of multiple determination, adjusted for the degrees of freedom.

6. Consider the ANOVA table that follows.

```
Analysis of Variance
Source          DF       SS        MS       F
Regression       5   3710.00    742.00   12.89
Residual Error  46   2647.38     57.55
Total           51   6357.38
```

   a. Determine the standard error of estimate. About 95% of the residuals will be between what two values?
   b. Determine the coefficient of multiple determination. Interpret this value.
   c. Determine the coefficient of multiple determination, adjusted for the degrees of freedom.

LO14-3
Test hypotheses about
the relationships inferred
by a multiple regression
model.

INFERENCES IN MULTIPLE LINEAR REGRESSION

Thus far, multiple regression analysis has been viewed only as a way to describe the relationship between a dependent variable and several independent variables. However, the least squares method also has the ability to draw inferences or generalizations about the relationship for an entire population. Recall that when you create confidence intervals or perform hypothesis tests as a part of inferential statistics, you view the data as a random sample taken from some population.

In the multiple regression setting, we assume there is an unknown population regression equation that relates the dependent variable to the k independent variables. This is sometimes called a **model** of the relationship. In symbols we write:

$$Y = \alpha + \beta_1 X_1 + \beta_2 X_2 + \cdots + \beta_k X_k$$

This equation is analogous to formula (14–1) except the coefficients are now reported as Greek letters. We use the Greek letters to denote *population parameters*. Then under a certain set of assumptions, which will be discussed shortly, the computed values of a and b_j are sample statistics. These sample statistics are point estimates of the corresponding population parameters α and β_j. For example, the sample regression coefficient b_2 is a point estimate of the population parameter β_2. The sampling distribution of these point estimates follows the normal probability distribution. These sampling distributions are each centered at their respective parameter values. To put it another way, the means of the sampling distributions are equal to the parameter values to be estimated. Thus, by using the properties of the sampling distributions of these statistics, inferences about the population parameters are possible.

Global Test: Testing the Multiple Regression Model

We can test the ability of the independent variables $X_1, X_2, \ldots, X_k$ to explain the behavior of the dependent variable Y. To put this in question form: Can the dependent variable be estimated without relying on the independent variables? The test used is referred to as the **global test.** Basically, it investigates whether it is possible all the independent variables have zero regression coefficients.

To relate this question to the heating cost example, we will test whether the independent variables (amount of insulation in the attic, mean daily outside temperature, and age of furnace) effectively estimate home heating costs. In testing a hypothesis, we first state the null hypothesis and the alternate hypothesis. In the heating cost example, there are three independent variables. Recall that b_1, b_2, and b_3 are sample regression coefficients. The corresponding coefficients in the population are given the symbols β_1, β_2, and β_3. We now test whether the regression coefficients in the population are all zero. The null hypothesis is:

$$H_0: \beta_1 = \beta_2 = \beta_3 = 0$$

The alternate hypothesis is:

$$H_1: \text{Not all the } \beta_i\text{'s are 0.}$$

If the null hypothesis is true, it implies the regression coefficients are all zero and, logically, are of no value in estimating the dependent variable (heating cost). Should that be the case, we would have to search for some other independent variables—or take a different approach—to predict home heating costs.

To test the null hypothesis that the multiple regression coefficients are all zero, we employ the F distribution introduced in Chapter 12. We will use the .05 level of significance. Recall these characteristics of the F distribution:

1. **There is a family of F distributions.** Each time the degrees of freedom in either the numerator or the denominator change, a new F distribution is created.

2. **The _F_ distribution cannot be negative.** The smallest possible value is 0.
3. **It is a continuous distribution.** The distribution can assume an infinite number of values between 0 and positive infinity.
4. **It is positively skewed.** The long tail of the distribution is to the right-hand side. As the number of degrees of freedom increases in both the numerator and the denominator, the distribution approaches the normal probability distribution. That is, the distribution will move toward a symmetric distribution.
5. **It is asymptotic.** As the values of X increase, the F curve will approach the horizontal axis, but will never touch it.

The F-statistic to test the global hypothesis follows. As in Chapter 12, it is the ratio of two variances. In this case, the numerator is the regression sum of squares divided by its degrees of freedom, k. The denominator is the residual sum of squares divided by its degrees of freedom, $n - (k + 1)$. The formula follows.

GLOBAL TEST	$$F = \frac{SSR/k}{SSE/[n - (k + 1)]}$$	**[14–5]**

Using the values from the ANOVA table on page 480, the F-statistic is

$$F = \frac{SSR/k}{SSE/[n - (k + 1)]} = \frac{171{,}220.473/3}{41{,}695.277/[20 - (3 + 1)]} = 21.90$$

Remember that the F-statistic tests the basic null hypothesis that two variances or, in this case, two mean squares are equal. In our global multiple regression hypothesis test, we will reject the null hypothesis, H_0, that all regression coefficients are zero when the regression mean square is larger in comparison to the residual mean square. If this is true, the F-statistic will be relatively large and in the far right tail of the F distribution, and the p-value will be small, that is, less than our choice of significance level of 0.05. Thus, we will reject the null hypothesis.

As with other hypothesis-testing methods, the decision rule can be based on either of two methods: (1) comparing the test statistic to a critical value or (2) calculating a p-value based on the test statistic and comparing the p-value to the significance level. The critical value method using the F-statistic requires three pieces of information: (1) the numerator degrees of freedom, (2) the denominator degrees of freedom, and (3) the significance level. The degrees of freedom for the numerator and the denominator are reported in the Excel ANOVA table that follows. The ANOVA output is highlighted in light green. The top number in the column marked "_df_" is 3, indicating there are 3 degrees of freedom in the numerator. This value corresponds to the number of independent variables. The middle number in the "_df_" column (16) indicates that there are 16 degrees of freedom in the denominator. The number 16 is found by $n - (k - 1) = 20 - (3 - 1) = 16$.

	A	B	C	D	G	H	I	J	K	L	M
1	Cost	Temp	Insul	Age		SUMMARY OUTPUT					
2	250	35	3	6							
3	360	29	4	10		_Regression Statistics_					
4	165	36	7	3		Multiple R	0.897				
5	43	60	6	9		R Square	0.804				
6	92	65	5	6		Adjusted R Square	0.767				
7	200	30	5	5		Standard Error	51.049				
8	355	10	6	7		Observations	20				
9	290	7	10	10							
10	230	21	9	11		ANOVA					
11	120	55	2	5			_df_	_SS_	_MS_	_F_	_Significance F_
12	73	54	12	4		Regression	3	171220.473	57073.491	21.901	0.000
13	205	48	5	1		Residual	16	41695.277	2605.955		
14	400	20	5	15		Total	19	212915.750			
15	320	39	4	7							
16	72	60	8	6			_Coefficients_	_Standard Error_	_t Stat_	_P-value_	
17	272	20	5	8		Intercept	427.194	59.601	7.168	0.000	
18	94	58	7	3		Temp	-4.583	0.772	-5.934	0.000	
19	190	40	8	11		Insul	-14.831	4.754	-3.119	0.007	
20	235	27	9	8		Age	6.101	4.012	1.521	0.148	

MULTIPLE REGRESSION ANALYSIS   489

The critical value of F is found in Appendix B.6. Using the table for the .05 significance level, move horizontally to 3 degrees of freedom in the numerator, then down to 16 degrees of freedom in the denominator, and read the critical value. It is 3.24. The region where H_0 is not rejected and the region where H_0 is rejected are shown in the following diagram.

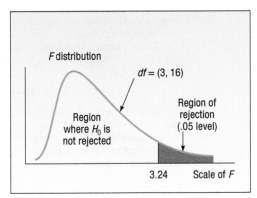

Continuing with the global test, the decision rule is: Do not reject the null hypothesis, H_0, that all the regression coefficients are 0 if the computed value of F is less than or equal to 3.24. If the computed F is greater than 3.24, reject H_0 and accept the alternate hypothesis, H_1.

The computed value of F is 21.90, which is in the rejection region. The null hypothesis that all the multiple regression coefficients are zero is therefore rejected. This means that at least one of the independent variables has the ability to explain the variation in the dependent variable (heating cost). We expected this decision. Logically, the outside temperature, the amount of insulation, or the age of the furnace has a great bearing on heating costs. The global test assures us that they do.

Testing the null hypothesis can also be based on a p-value, which is reported in the statistical software output for all hypothesis tests. In the case of the F-statistic, the p-value is defined as the probability of observing an F-value as large or larger than the F test statistic, assuming the null hypothesis is true. If the p-value is less than our selected significance level, then we decide to reject the null hypothesis. The ANOVA shows the F-statistic's p-value is equal to 0.000. It is clearly less than our significance level of 0.05. Therefore, we decide to reject the global null hypothesis and conclude that at least one of the regression coefficients is not equal to zero.

Evaluating Individual Regression Coefficients

So far we have shown that at least one, but not necessarily all, of the regression coefficients is not equal to zero and thus useful for predictions. The next step is to test the independent variables *individually* to determine which regression coefficients may be 0 and which are not.

Why is it important to know if any of the β_j's equal 0? If a β could equal 0, it implies that this particular independent variable is of no value in explaining any variation in the dependent value. If there are coefficients for which H_0 cannot be rejected, we may want to eliminate them from the regression equation.

Our strategy is to use three sets of hypotheses: one for temperature, one for insulation, and one for age of the furnace.

For temperature:	For insulation:	For furnace age:
H_0: $\beta_1 = 0$	H_0: $\beta_2 = 0$	H_0: $\beta_3 = 0$
H_1: $\beta_1 \neq 0$	H_1: $\beta_2 \neq 0$	H_1: $\beta_3 \neq 0$

CHAPTER 14

We will test the hypotheses at the .05 level. Note that these are two-tailed tests.

The test statistic follows Student's t distribution with $n - (k + 1)$ degrees of freedom. The number of sample observations is n. There are 20 homes in the study, so $n = 20$. The number of independent variables is k, which is 3. Thus, there are $n - (k + 1) = 20 - (3 + 1) = 16$ degrees of freedom.

The critical value for t is in Appendix B.5. For a two-tailed test with 16 degrees of freedom using the .05 significance level, H_0 is rejected if t is less than -2.120 or greater than 2.120.

Refer to the Excel output in the previous section. (See page 488.) The column highlighted in orange, headed Coefficients, shows the values for the multiple regression equation:

$$\hat{y} = 427.194 - 4.583x_1 - 14.831x_2 + 6.101x_3$$

Interpreting the term $-4.583x_1$ in the equation: For each degree increase in temperature, we predict that heating cost will decrease \$4.58, holding the insulation and age of the furnace variables constant.

The column in the Excel output labeled "Standard Error" shows the standard error of the sample regression coefficients. Recall that Salsberry Realty selected a sample of 20 homes along the East Coast of the United States. If Salsberry Realty selected a second random sample and computed the regression coefficients for that sample, the values would not be exactly the same. If the sampling process was repeated many times, we could construct a sampling distribution for each of these regression coefficients. The column labeled "Standard Error" estimates the variability for each of these regression coefficients. The sampling distributions of the coefficients follow the t distribution with $n - (k + 1)$ degrees of freedom. Hence, we are able to test the independent variables individually to determine whether the regression coefficients differ from zero. The formula is:

TESTING INDIVIDUAL REGRESSION COEFFICIENTS	$t = \dfrac{b_i - 0}{s_{b_i}}$	**[14–6]**

The b_i refers to any one of the regression coefficients, and s_b refers to the standard deviation of that distribution of the regression coefficient. We include 0 in the equation because the null hypothesis is $\beta_i = 0$.

To illustrate this formula, refer to the test of the regression coefficient for the independent variable temperature. From the output on page 488, the regression coefficient for temperature is -4.583. The standard deviation of the sampling distribution of the regression coefficient for the independent variable temperature is 0.772. Inserting these values in formula (14–6):

$$t = \frac{b_1 - 0}{s_{b_1}} = \frac{-4.583 - 0}{0.772} = -5.937$$

The computed value of t is -5.937 for temperature (the small difference between the computed value and that shown on the Excel output is due to rounding) and -3.119 for insulation. Both of these t-values are in the rejection region to the left of -2.120. Thus, we conclude that the regression coefficients for the temperature and insulation variables are *not* zero. The computed t for the age of the furnace is 1.521, so we conclude that the coefficient could equal 0. The independent variable age of the furnace is not a significant predictor of heating cost. The results of these hypothesis tests indicate that the analysis should focus on temperature and insulation as predictors of heating cost.

We can also use p-values to test the individual regression coefficients. Again, these are commonly reported in statistical software output. The computed value of t for temperature on the Excel output is -5.934 and has a p-value of 0.000. Because the p-value is less than 0.05, the regression coefficient for the independent variable temperature is not equal to zero and should be included in the equation to predict heating costs. For insulation, the value of t is -3.119 and has a p-value of 0.007. As with temperature, the p-value is less than 0.05, so we conclude that the insulation regression coefficient is not equal to zero and should be included in the equation to predict heating cost. In contrast to temperature and insulation, the p-value to test the "age of the furnace" regression coefficient is 0.148. It is clearly greater than 0.05, so we conclude that the "age of furnace" regression coefficient could equal 0. Further, as an independent variable it is not a significant predictor of heating cost. Thus, age of furnace should not be included in the equation to predict heating costs.

At this point, we need to develop a strategy for deleting independent variables. In the Salsberry Realty case, there were three independent variables. For the age of the furnace variable, we failed to reject the null hypothesis that the regression coefficient was zero. It is clear that we should drop that variable and rerun the regression equation. Below is the Excel output where heating cost is the dependent variable and outside temperature and amount of insulation are the independent variables.

	A	B	C	D	E	F	G	H	I	J	K
1	Cost	Temp	Insul	Age		SUMMARY OUTPUT					
2	250	35	3	6							
3	360	29	4	10		*Regression Statistics*					
4	165	36	7	3		Multiple R	0.881				
5	43	60	6	9		R Square	0.776				
6	92	65	5	6		Adjusted R Square	0.749				
7	200	30	5	5		Standard Error	52.982				
8	355	10	6	7		Observations	20				
9	290	7	10	10							
10	230	21	9	11		ANOVA					
11	120	55	2	5			*df*	*SS*	*MS*	*F*	*Significance F*
12	73	54	12	4		Regression	2	165194.521	82597.261	29.424	0.000
13	205	48	5	1		Residual	17	47721.229	2807.131		
14	400	20	5	15		Total	19	212915.750			
15	320	39	4	7							
16	72	60	8	6			*Coefficients*	*Standard Error*	*t Stat*	*P-value*	
17	272	20	5	8		Intercept	490.286	44.410	11.040	0.000	
18	94	58	7	3		Temp	-5.150	0.702	-7.337	0.000	
19	190	40	8	11		Insul	-14.718	4.934	-2.983	0.008	
20	235	27	9	8							

Summarizing the results from this new output:

1. The new regression equation is:

$$\hat{y} = 490.286 - 5.150x_1 - 14.718x_2$$

    Notice that the regression coefficients for outside temperature (x_1) and amount of insulation (x_2) are similar to but not exactly the same as when we included the independent variable age of the furnace. Compare the above equation to that in the Excel output on page 488. Both of the regression coefficients are negative as in the earlier equation.

2. The details of the global test are as follows:

$$H_0: \beta_1 = \beta_2 = 0$$
$$H_1: \text{Not all of the } \beta_i\text{'s} = 0$$

    The F distribution is the test statistic and there are $k = 2$ degrees of freedom in the numerator and $n - (k + 1) = 20 - (2 + 1) = 17$ degrees of freedom in the denominator. Using the .05 significance level and Appendix B.6, the decision rule is to reject H_0 if F is greater than 3.59. We compute the value of F as follows:

$$F = \frac{SSR/k}{SSE/[n - (k + 1)]} = \frac{165,194.521/2}{47,721.229/[20 - (2 + 1)]} = 29.424$$

    Because the computed value of F (29.424) is greater than the critical value (3.59), the null hypothesis is rejected and the alternate accepted. We conclude that at least one of the regression coefficients is different from 0.

Using the p-value, the F test statistic (29.424) has a p-value (0.000), which is clearly less than 0.05. Therefore, we reject the null hypothesis and accept the alternate. We conclude that at least one of the regression coefficients is different from 0.

3. The next step is to conduct a test of the regression coefficients individually. We want to determine if one or both of the regression coefficients are different from 0. The null and alternate hypotheses for each of the independent variables are:

Outside Temperature	Insulation
$H_0: \beta_1 = 0$	$H_0: \beta_2 = 0$
$H_1: \beta_1 \neq 0$	$H_1: \beta_2 \neq 0$

The test statistic is the t distribution with $n - (k + 1) = 20 - (2 + 1) = 17$ degrees of freedom. Using the .05 significance level and Appendix B.5, the decision rule is to reject H_0 if the computed value of t is less than -2.110 or greater than 2.110.

Outside Temperature

$$t = \frac{b_1 - 0}{s_{b_1}} = \frac{-5.150 - 0}{0.702} = -7.337$$

Insulation

$$t = \frac{b_2 - 0}{s_{b_2}} = \frac{-14.718 - 0}{4.934} = -2.983$$

In both tests, we reject H_0 and accept H_1. We conclude that each of the regression coefficients is different from 0. Both outside temperature and amount of insulation are useful variables in explaining the variation in heating costs.

Using p-values, the p-value for the temperature t-statistic is 0.000 and the p-value for the insulation t-statistic is 0.008. Both p-values are less than 0.05, so in both tests we reject the null hypothesis and conclude that each of the regression coefficients is different from 0. Both outside temperature and amount of insulation are useful variables in explaining the variation in heating costs.

In the heating cost example, it was clear which independent variable to delete. However, in some instances which variable to delete may not be as clear-cut. To explain, suppose we develop a multiple regression equation based on five independent variables. We conduct the global test and find that some of the regression coefficients are different from zero. Next, we test the regression coefficients individually and find that three are significant and two are not. The preferred procedure is to drop the single independent variable with the *smallest absolute* t *value* or *largest* p-*value* and rerun the regression equation with the four remaining variables, then, on the new regression equation with four independent variables, conduct the individual tests. If there are still regression coefficients that are not significant, again drop the variable with the smallest absolute t value or the largest, nonsignificant p-value. To describe the process in another way, we should delete only one variable at a time. Each time we delete a variable, we need to rerun the regression equation and check the remaining variables.

This process of selecting variables to include in a regression model can be automated, using Excel, Minitab, MegaStat, or other statistical software. Most of the software systems include methods to sequentially remove and/or add independent variables and at the same time provide estimates of the percentage of variation explained (the R-square term). Two of the common methods are **stepwise regression** and **best subset regression.** It may take a long time, but in the extreme we could compute every regression between the dependent variable and any possible subset of the independent variables.

Unfortunately, on occasion, the software may work "too hard" to find an equation that fits all the quirks of your particular data set. The suggested equation may not represent the relationship in the population. Judgment is needed to choose among the equations presented. Consider whether the results are logical. They should have a simple interpretation and be consistent with your knowledge of the application under study.

SELF-REVIEW

14–3

The regression output about eating places in Myrtle Beach is repeated below (see earlier self-reviews).

Predictor	Coefficient	SE Coefficient	t	p-value
Constant	2.50	1.50	1.667	0.111
x_1	3.00	1.50	2.000	0.056
x_2	4.00	3.00	1.333	0.194
x_3	-3.00	0.20	-15.000	0.000
x_4	0.20	0.05	4.000	0.000
x_5	1.00	1.50	0.667	0.511

Analysis of Variance

Source	DF	SS	MS	F	p-value
Regression	5	100	20	10	0.000
Residual Error	20	40	2		
Total	25	140			

(a) Perform a global test of hypothesis to check if any of the regression coefficients are different from 0. What do you decide? Use the .05 significance level.
(b) Do an individual test of each independent variable. Which variables would you consider eliminating? Use the .05 significance level.
(c) Outline a plan for possibly removing independent variables.

EXERCISES

7. Given the following regression output,

Predictor	Coefficient	SE Coefficient	t	p-value
Constant	84.998	1.863	45.62	0.000
x_1	2.391	1.200	1.99	0.051
x_2	-0.409	0.172	-2.38	0.021

Analysis of Variance

Source	DF	SS	MS	F	p-value
Regression	2	77.907	38.954	4.138	0.021
Residual Error	62	583.693	9.414		
Total	64	661.600			

answer the following questions:
a. Write the regression equation.
b. If x_1 is 4 and x_2 is 11, what is the expected or predicted value of the dependent variable?
c. How large is the sample? How many independent variables are there?
d. Conduct a global test of hypothesis to see if any of the set of regression coefficients could be different from 0. Use the .05 significance level. What is your conclusion?
e. Conduct a test of hypothesis for each independent variable. Use the .05 significance level. Which variable would you consider eliminating?
f. Outline a strategy for deleting independent variables in this case.

8. The following regression output was obtained from a study of architectural firms. The dependent variable is the total amount of fees in millions of dollars.

Predictor	Coefficient	SE Coefficient	t	p-value
Constant	7.987	2.967	2.690	0.010
x_1	0.122	0.031	3.920	0.000
x_2	-1.220	0.053	-2.270	0.028
x_3	-0.063	0.039	-1.610	0.114
x_4	0.523	0.142	3.690	0.001
x_5	-0.065	0.040	-1.620	0.112

Analysis of Variance

Source	DF	SS	MS	F	p-value
Regression	5	371000	742	12.89	0.000
Residual Error	46	2647.38	57.55		
Total	51	6357.38			

x_1 is the number of architects employed by the company.
x_2 is the number of engineers employed by the company.
x_3 is the number of years involved with health care projects.
x_4 is the number of states in which the firm operates.
x_5 is the percent of the firm's work that is health care–related.

a. Write out the regression equation.
b. How large is the sample? How many independent variables are there?
c. Conduct a global test of hypothesis to see if any of the set of regression coefficients could be different from 0. Use the .05 significance level. What is your conclusion?
d. Conduct a test of hypothesis for each independent variable. Use the .05 significance level. Which variable would you consider eliminating first?
e. Outline a strategy for deleting independent variables in this case.

CHAPTER 14

LO14-4

Evaluate the assumptions
of multiple regression.

EVALUATING THE ASSUMPTIONS
OF MULTIPLE REGRESSION

In the previous section, we described the methods to statistically evaluate the multiple regression equation. The results of the test let us know if at least one of the coefficients was not equal to zero and we described a procedure of evaluating each regression coefficient. We also discussed the decision-making process for including and excluding independent variables in the multiple regression equation.

It is important to know that the validity of the statistical global and individual tests rely on several assumptions. So if the assumptions are not true, the results might be biased or misleading. However, strict adherence to the following assumptions is not always possible. Fortunately, the statistical techniques discussed in this chapter work well even when one or more of the assumptions are violated. Even if the values in the multiple regression equation are "off" slightly, our estimates using a multiple regression equation will be closer than any that could be made otherwise. Usually the statistical procedures are robust enough to overcome violations of some assumptions.

In Chapter 13, we listed the necessary assumptions for regression when we considered only a single independent variable. (See page 455.) The assumptions for multiple regression are similar.

1. **There is a linear relationship.** That is, there is a straight-line relationship between the dependent variable and the set of independent variables.
2. **The variation in the residuals is the same for both large and small values of $\hat{y}$.** To put it another way, $(y - \hat{y})$ is unrelated to whether $\hat{y}$ is large or small.
3. **The residuals follow the normal probability distribution.** Recall the residual is the difference between the actual value of y and the estimated value $\hat{y}$. So the term $(y - \hat{y})$ is computed for every observation in the data set. These residuals should approximately follow a normal probability distribution. In addition, the mean of the residuals is 0.
4. **The independent variables should not be correlated.** That is, we would like to select a set of independent variables that are not themselves correlated.
5. **The residuals are independent.** This means that successive observations of the dependent variable are not correlated. This assumption is often violated when time is involved with the sampled observations.

In this section, we present a brief discussion of each of these assumptions. In addition, we provide methods to validate these assumptions and indicate the consequences if these assumptions cannot be met. For those interested in additional discussion, Kutner, Nachtscheim, Neter, and Li, *Applied Linear Statistical Models,* 5th ed. (McGraw-Hill: 2005), is an excellent reference.

Linear Relationship

Let's begin with the linearity assumption. The idea is that the relationship between the set of independent variables and the dependent variable is linear. If we are considering two independent variables, we can visualize this assumption. The two independent variables and the dependent variable would form a three-dimensional space. The regression equation would then form a plane as shown on page 478. We can evaluate this assumption with scatter diagrams and residual plots.

Using Scatter Diagrams   The evaluation of a multiple regression equation should always include a scatter diagram that plots the dependent variable against each independent variable. These graphs help us to visualize the relationships and provide some initial information about the direction (positive or negative), linearity, and strength of the relationship. For example, the scatter diagrams for the home heating example follow. The plots suggest a fairly strong negative, linear relationship between heating cost and temperature, and a negative relationship between heating cost and insulation.

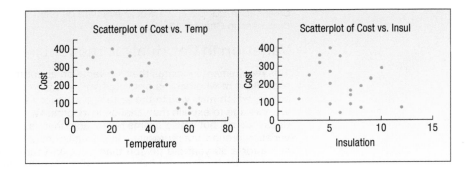

Using Residual Plots   Recall that a residual $(y - \hat{y})$ can be computed using the multiple regression equation for each observation in a data set. In Chapter 13, we discussed the idea that the best regression line passed through the center of the data in a scatter plot. In this case, you would find a good number of the observations above the regression line (these residuals would have a positive sign) and a good number of the observations below the line (these residuals would have a negative sign). Further, the observations would be scattered above and below the line over the entire range of the independent variable.

The same concept is true for multiple regression, but we cannot graphically portray the multiple regression. However, plots of the residuals can help us evaluate the linearity of the multiple regression equation. To investigate, the residuals are plotted on the vertical axis against the predictor variable, $\hat{y}$. The graph on the left below shows the residual plots for the home heating cost example. Notice the following:

- The residuals are plotted on the vertical axis and are centered around zero. There are both positive and negative residuals.
- The residual plots show a random distribution of positive and negative values across the entire range of the variable plotted on the horizontal axis.
- The points are scattered and there is no obvious pattern, so there is no reason to doubt the linearity assumption.

This plot supports the assumption of linearity.

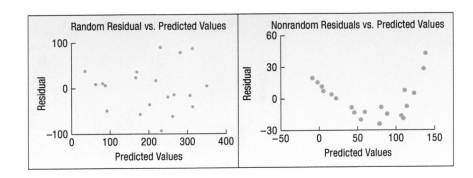

If there is a pattern to the points in the scatter plot, further investigation is necessary. For example, the graph at the bottom of the previous page shows nonrandom residuals. See that the residual plot does *not* show a random distribution of positive and negative values across the entire range of the variable plotted on the horizontal axis. In fact, the graph shows a curvature to the residual plots. This indicates the relationship may not be linear. In this case, we would evaluate different transformations of the equation as discussed in Chapter 13.

Variation in Residuals Same for Large and Small $\hat{y}$ Values

This requirement indicates that the variation about the predicted values is constant, regardless of whether the predicted values are large or small. To cite a specific example, which may violate the assumption, suppose we use the single independent variable age to explain the variation in income. We suspect that as age increases so does income, but it also seems reasonable that as age increases there may be more variation around the regression line. That is, there will likely be more variation in income for a 50-year-old person than for a 35-year-old person. The requirement for constant variation around the regression line is called **homoscedasticity.**

> **HOMOSCEDASTICITY** The variation around the regression equation is the same for all of the values of the independent variables.

To check for homoscedasticity, the residuals are plotted against the fitted values of *y*. This is the same graph that we used to evaluate the assumption of linearity. (See page 495.) Based on the scatter diagram in that software output, it is reasonable to conclude that this assumption has not been violated.

Distribution of Residuals

To be sure that the inferences we make in the global and individual hypothesis tests are valid, we evaluate the distribution of residuals. Ideally, the residuals should follow a normal probability distribution.

To evaluate this assumption, we can organize the residuals into a frequency distribution. The Histogram of Residuals graph is shown on the left for the home heating cost example. Although it is difficult to show that the residuals follow a normal distribution with only 20 observations, it does appear the normality assumption is reasonable.

Excel offers another graph that helps to evaluate the assumption of normally distributed residuals. It is a called a Normal Probability Plot and is shown to the right of the histogram. The normal probability plot supports the assumption of normally distributed residuals if the plotted points are fairly close to a straight line drawn from the lower left to the upper right of the graph. This plot supports the assumption of normally distributed residuals.

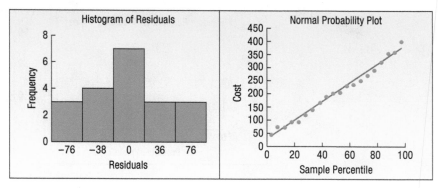

In this case, both graphs support the assumption that the residuals follow the normal probability distribution. Therefore, the inferences that we made based on the global and individual hypothesis tests are supported with the results of this evaluation.

Multicollinearity

Multicollinearity exists when independent variables are correlated. Correlated independent variables make it difficult to make inferences about the individual regression coefficients and their individual effects on the dependent variable. In practice, it is nearly impossible to select variables that are completely unrelated. To put it another way, it is nearly impossible to create a set of independent variables that are not correlated to some degree. However, a general understanding of the issue of multicollinearity is important.

First, multicollinearity does not affect a multiple regression equation's ability to predict the dependent variable. However, when we are interested in evaluating the relationship between each independent variable and the dependent variable, multicollinearity may show unexpected results.

For example, if we use two highly multicollinear variables, high school GPA and high school class rank, to predict the GPA of incoming college freshmen (dependent variable), we would expect that both independent variables would be positively related to the dependent variable. However, because the independent variables are highly correlated, one of the independent variables may have an unexpected and inexplicable negative sign. In essence, these two independent variables are redundant in that they explain the same variation in the dependent variable.

A second reason to avoid correlated independent variables is they may lead to erroneous results in the hypothesis tests for the individual independent variables. This is due to the instability of the standard error of estimate. Several clues that indicate problems with multicollinearity include the following:

1. An independent variable known to be an important predictor ends up having a regression coefficient that is not significant.
2. A regression coefficient that should have a positive sign turns out to be negative, or vice versa.
3. When an independent variable is added or removed, there is a drastic change in the values of the remaining regression coefficients.

In our evaluation of a multiple regression equation, an approach to reducing the effects of multicollinearity is to carefully select the independent variables that are included in the regression equation. A general rule is if the correlation between two independent variables is between -0.70 and 0.70, there likely is not a problem using both of the independent variables. A more precise test is to use the **variance inflation factor**. It is usually written *VIF*. The value of *VIF* is found as follows:

VARIANCE INFLATION FACTOR	$$VIF = \frac{1}{1 - R_j^2}$$	**[14–7]**

The term R_j^2 refers to the coefficient of determination, where the selected *independent variable* is used as a dependent variable and the remaining independent variables are used as independent variables. A *VIF* greater than 10 is considered unsatisfactory, indicating that the independent variable should be removed from the analysis. The following example will explain the details of finding the *VIF*.

EXAMPLE

Refer to the data in Table 14–1, which relate the heating cost to the independent variables outside temperature, amount of insulation, and age of furnace. Develop a correlation matrix for all the independent variables. Does it appear there is a problem with multicollinearity? Find and interpret the variance inflation factor for each of the independent variables.

SOLUTION

We begin by finding the correlation matrix for the dependent variable and the three independent variables. A correlation matrix shows the correlation between all pairs of the variables. A portion of that output follows:

	Cost	Temp	Insul	Age
Cost	1.000			
Temp	−0.812	1.000		
Insul	−0.257	−0.103	1.000	
Age	0.537	−0.486	0.064	1.000

The highlighted area indicates the correlation among the independent variables. Because all of the correlations are between −.70 and .70, we do not suspect problems with multicollinearity. The largest correlation among the independent variables is −0.486 between age and temperature.

To confirm this conclusion, we compute the *VIF* for each of the three independent variables. We will consider the independent variable temperature first. We use Excel to find the multiple coefficient of determination with temperature as the *dependent variable* and amount of insulation and age of the furnace as independent variables. The relevant Excel output follows.

SUMMARY OUTPUT

Regression Statistics	
Multiple R	0.491
R Square	0.241
Adjusted R Square	0.152
Standard Error	16.031
Observations	20

ANOVA

	df	SS	MS	F	Significance F
Regression	2	1390.291	695.145	2.705	0.096
Residual	17	4368.909	256.995		
Total	19	5759.200			

The coefficient of determination is .241, so inserting this value into the *VIF* formula:

$$VIF = \frac{1}{1 - R_1^2} = \frac{1}{1 - .241} = 1.32$$

The *VIF* value of 1.32 is less than the upper limit of 10. This indicates that the independent variable temperature is not strongly correlated with the other independent variables.

Again, to find the *VIF* for insulation we would develop a regression equation with insulation as the *dependent variable* and temperature and age of furnace as independent variables. For this equation, the R^2 is .011 and, using formula (14–7), the *VIF* for insulation would be 1.011. To find the *VIF* for age, we would develop a regression equation with age as the dependent variable and temperature and insulation as the independent variables. For this equation, the R^2 is .236 and, using formula (14–7), the *VIF* for age would be 1.310. All the *VIF* values are less than 10. Hence, we conclude there is not a problem with multicollinearity in this example.

Independent Observations

The fifth assumption about regression and correlation analysis is that successive residuals should be independent. This means that there is not a pattern to the residuals, the residuals are not highly correlated, and there are not long runs of positive or negative residuals. When successive residuals are correlated, we refer to this condition as **autocorrelation.**

Autocorrelation frequently occurs when the data are collected over a period of time. For example, we wish to predict yearly sales of Ages Software Inc. based on the time and the amount spent on advertising. The dependent variable is yearly sales and the independent variables are time and amount spent on advertising. It is likely that for a period of time the actual points will be above the regression plane (remember there are two independent variables) and then for a period of time the points will be below the regression plane. The graph below shows the residuals plotted on the vertical axis and the fitted values $\hat{y}$ on the horizontal axis. Note the run of residuals above the mean of the residuals, followed by a run below the mean. A scatter plot such as this would indicate possible autocorrelation.

There is a test for autocorrelation, called the Durbin-Watson. It is discussed in Chapter 18.

LO14-5

Use and interpret a qualitative, dummy variable in multiple regression.

QUALITATIVE INDEPENDENT VARIABLES

In the previous example/solution regarding heating cost, the two independent variables outside temperature and insulation were quantitative; that is, numerical in nature. Frequently we wish to use nominal-scale variables—such as gender, whether the home has a swimming pool, or whether the sports team was the home or the visiting team—in our analysis. These are called **qualitative variables** because they describe a particular quality, such as male or female. To use a qualitative variable in regression analysis, we use a scheme of **dummy variables** in which one of the two possible conditions is coded 0 and the other 1.

> **DUMMY VARIABLE** A variable in which there are only two possible outcomes. For analysis, one of the outcomes is coded a 1 and the other a 0.

For example, we are interested in estimating an executive's salary on the basis of years of job experience and whether he or she graduated from college. "Graduation from college" can take on only one of two conditions: yes or no. Thus, it is considered a qualitative variable.

Suppose in the Salsberry Realty example that the independent variable "garage" is added. For those homes without an attached garage, 0 is used; for homes with an attached garage, a 1 is used. We will refer to the "garage" variable as x_4. The data from Table 14–2 are entered into the Excel system. Recall that the variable "age of the furnace" is not included in the analysis because we determined that it was not signifi-cantly related to heating cost.

TABLE 14–2 Home Heating Costs, Temperature, Insulation, and Presence of a Garage for a Sample of 20 Homes

Cost, y	Temperature, x_1	Insulation, x_2	Garage, x_4
$250	35	3	0
360	29	4	1
165	36	7	0
43	60	6	0
92	65	5	0
200	30	5	0
355	10	6	1
290	7	10	1
230	21	9	0
120	55	2	0
73	54	12	0
205	48	5	1
400	20	5	1
320	39	4	1
72	60	8	0
272	20	5	1
94	58	7	0
190	40	8	1
235	27	9	0
139	30	7	0

The output from Excel is:

	A	B	C	D	E	F	G	H	I	J	K
1	Cost	Temp	Insul	Garage		SUMMARY OUTPUT					
2	250	35	3	0							
3	360	29	4	1		*Regression Statistics*					
4	165	36	7	0		Multiple R	0.933				
5	43	60	6	0		R Square	0.870				
6	92	65	5	0		Adjusted R Square	0.845				
7	200	30	5	0		Standard Error	41.618				
8	355	10	6	1		Observations	20				
9	290	7	10	1							
10	230	21	9	0		ANOVA					
11	120	55	2	0			*df*	*SS*	*MS*	*F*	*Significance F*
12	73	54	12	0		Regression	3	185202.269	61734.090	35.641	0.000
13	205	48	5	1		Residual	16	27713.481	1732.093		
14	400	20	5	1		Total	19	212915.750			
15	320	39	4	1							
16	72	60	8	0			*Coefficients*	*Standard Error*	*t Stat*	*P-value*	
17	272	20	5	1		Intercept	393.666	45.001	8.748	0.000	
18	94	58	7	0		Temp	-3.963	0.653	-6.072	0.000	
19	190	40	8	1		Insul	-11.334	4.002	-2.832	0.012	
20	235	27	9	0		Garage	77.432	22.783	3.399	0.004	

What is the effect of the garage variable? Should it be included in the analy-sis? To show the effect of the variable, suppose we have two houses exactly alike

MULTIPLE REGRESSION ANALYSIS   501

next to each other in Buffalo, New York; one has an attached garage and the other does not. Both homes have 3 inches of insulation, and the mean January temperature in Buffalo is 20 degrees. For the house without an attached garage, a 0 is substituted for x_4 in the regression equation. The estimated heating cost is $280.404, found by:

$$\hat{y} = 393.666 - 3.963x_1 - 11.334x_2 + 77.432x_4$$
$$= 393.666 - 3.963(20) - 11.334(3) + 77.432(0) = 280.404$$

For the house with an attached garage, a 1 is substituted for x_4 in the regression equation. The estimated heating cost is $357.836, found by:

$$\hat{y} = 393.666 - 3.963x_1 - 11.334x_2 + 77.432x_4$$
$$= 393.666 - 3.963(20) - 11.334(3) + 77.432(1) = 357.836$$

The difference between the estimated heating costs is $77.432 ($357.836 − $280.404). Hence, we can expect the cost to heat a house with an attached garage to be $77.432 more than the cost for an equivalent house without a garage.

We have shown the difference between the two types of homes to be $77.432, but is the difference significant? We conduct the following test of hypothesis.

$$H_0: \beta_4 = 0$$
$$H_1: \beta_4 \neq 0$$

The information necessary to answer this question is in the output at the bottom of the previous page. The regression coefficient for the independent variable garage is $77.432, and the standard deviation of the sampling distribution is 22.783. We identify this as the fourth independent variable, so we use a subscript of 4. (Remember we dropped age of the furnace, the third independent variable.) Finally, we insert these values in formula (14–6).

$$t = \frac{b_4 - 0}{s_{b_4}} = \frac{77.432 - 0}{22.783} = 3.399$$

There are three independent variables in the analysis, so there are $n - (k + 1) =$ $20 - (3 + 1) = 16$ degrees of freedom. The critical value from Appendix B.5 is 2.120. The decision rule, using a two-tailed test and the .05 significance level, is to reject H_0 if the computed t is to the left of −2.120 or to the right of 2.120. Because the computed value of 3.399 is to the right of 2.120, the null hypothesis is rejected. We conclude that the regression coefficient is not zero. The independent variable garage should be included in the analysis.

Using the p-value approach, the computed t value of 3.399 has a p-value of 0.004. This value is less than the .05 significance level. Therefore, we reject the null hypothesis. We conclude that the regression coefficient is not zero and the independent variable garage should be included in the analysis.

Is it possible to use a qualitative variable with more than two possible outcomes? Yes, but the coding scheme becomes more complex and will require a series of dummy variables. To explain, suppose a company is studying its sales as they relate to advertising expense by quarter for the last 5 years. Let sales be the dependent variable and advertising expense be the first independent variable, x_1. To include the qualitative information regarding the quarter, we use three additional independent variables. For the variable x_2, the five observations referring to the first quarter of each of the 5 years are coded 1 and the other quarters 0. Similarly, for x_3 the five observations referring to the second quarter are coded 1 and the other quarters 0. For x_4, the five observations referring to the third quarter are coded 1 and the other quarters 0. An observation that does not refer to any of the first three quarters must refer to the fourth quarter, so a distinct independent variable referring to this quarter is not necessary.

SELF-REVIEW

14–4

A study by the American Realtors Association investigated the relationship between the commissions earned by sales associates last year and the number of months since the associates earned their real estate licenses. Also of interest in the study is the gender of the sales associate. Below is a portion of the regression output. The dependent variable is commissions, which is reported in $000, and the independent variables are months since the license was earned and gender (female = 1 and male = 0).

```
                    Regression Analysis

                  Regression Statistics
          Multiple R              0.801
          R Square               0.642
          Adjusted R Square      0.600
          Standard Error         3.219
          Observations              20

    ANOVA
                    df        SS          MS          F       p-value
    Regression       2    315.9291    157.9645    15.2468    0.0002
    Residual        17    176.1284     10.36049
    Total           19    492.0575

                Coefficients    Standard Error    t Stat    p-value
    Intercept        15.7625         3.0782        5.121     .0001
    Months            0.4415         0.0839        5.262     .0001
    Gender            3.8598         1.4724        2.621     .0179
```

(a) Write out the regression equation. How much commission would you expect a female agent to make who earned her license 30 months ago?

(b) Do the female agents on the average make more or less than the male agents? How much more?

(c) Conduct a test of hypothesis to determine if the independent variable gender should be included in the analysis. Use the .05 significance level. What is your conclusion?

LO14-6

Include and interpret an interaction effect in a multiple regression analysis.

REGRESSION MODELS WITH INTERACTION

In Chapter 12, we discussed interaction among independent variables. To explain, suppose we are studying weight loss and assume, as the current literature suggests, that diet and exercise are related. So the dependent variable is amount of change in weight and the independent variables are diet (yes or no) and exercise (none, moderate, significant). We are interested in whether there is interaction among the independent variables. That is, if those studied maintain their diet and exercise significantly, will that increase the mean amount of weight lost? Is total weight loss more than the sum of the loss due to the diet effect and the loss due to the exercise effect?

We can expand on this idea. Instead of having two nominal-scale variables, diet and exercise, we can examine the effect (interaction) of several ratio-scale variables. For example, suppose we want to study the effect of room temperature (68, 72, 76, or 80 degrees Fahrenheit) and noise level (60, 70, or 80 decibels) on the number of units produced. To put it another way, does the combination of noise level in the room and the temperature of the room have an effect on the productivity of the workers? Would the workers in a quiet, cool room produce more units than those in a hot, noisy room?

In regression analysis, interaction is examined as a separate independent variable. An interaction prediction variable can be developed by multiplying the data values in one independent variable by the values in another independent variable, thereby creating a new independent variable. A two-variable model that includes an interaction term is:

$$Y = \alpha + \beta_1 X_1 + \beta_2 X_2 + \beta_3 X_1 X_2$$

The term X_1X_2 is the *interaction term*. We create this variable by multiplying the values of X_1 and X_2 to create the third independent variable. We then develop a regression equation using the three independent variables and test the significance of the third independent variable using the individual test for independent variables, described earlier in the chapter. An example will illustrate the details.

EXAMPLE

Refer to the heating cost example and the data in Table 14–1. Is there an interaction between the outside temperature and the amount of insulation? If both variables are increased, is the effect on heating cost greater than the sum of savings from warmer temperature and the savings from increased insulation separately?

SOLUTION

The information from Table 14–1 for the independent variables temperature and insulation is repeated below. We create the interaction variable by multiplying the temperature variable by the insulation. For the first sampled home, the value temperature is 35 degrees and insulation is 3 inches so the value of the interaction variable is 35 × 3 = 105. The values of the other interaction products are found in a similar fashion.

	A	B	C	D	E	F	G	H	I	J	K
1	Cost	Temp	Insul	Temp X Insul		SUMMARY OUTPUT					
2	250	35	3	105							
3	360	29	4	116		*Regression Statistics*					
4	165	36	7	252		Multiple R	0.893				
5	43	60	6	360		R Square	0.798				
6	92	65	5	325		Adjusted R Square	0.760				
7	200	30	5	150		Standard Error	51.846				
8	355	10	6	60		Observations	20				
9	290	7	10	70							
10	230	21	9	189		ANOVA					
11	120	55	2	110			*df*	*SS*	*MS*	*F*	*Significance F*
12	73	54	12	648		Regression	3	169908.452	56636.151	21.070	0.000
13	205	48	5	240		Residual	16	43007.298	2687.956		
14	400	20	5	100		Total	19	212915.750			
15	320	39	4	156							
16	72	60	8	480			*Coefficients*	*Standard Error*	*t Stat*	*P-value*	
17	272	20	5	100		Intercept	598.070	92.265	6.482	0.000	
18	94	58	7	406		Temp	-7.811	2.124	-3.678	0.002	
19	190	40	8	320		Insul	-30.161	12.621	-2.390	0.030	
20	235	27	9	243		Temp X Insul	0.385	0.291	1.324	0.204	
21	139	30	7	210							

We find the multiple regression using temperature, insulation, and the interaction of temperature and insulation as independent variables. The regression equation is reported below.

$$\hat{y} = 598.070 - 7.811x_1 - 30.161x_2 + 0.385x_1x_2$$

The question we wish to answer is whether the interaction variable is significant. We will use the .05 significance level. In terms of a hypothesis:

$$H_0: \beta_3 = 0$$

$$H_1: \beta_3 \neq 0$$

There are $n - (k + 1) = 20 - (3 + 1) = 16$ degrees of freedom. Using the .05 significance level and a two-tailed test, the critical values of t are -2.120 and 2.120. We reject the null hypothesis if t is less than -2.120 or t is greater than 2.120. From the output, $b_3 = 0.385$ and $s_{b_3} = 0.291$. To find the value of t, we use formula (14–6).

$$t = \frac{b_3 - 0}{s_{b_3}} = \frac{0.385 - 0}{0.291} = 1.324$$

Because the computed value of 1.324 is less than the critical value of 2.120, we do not reject the null hypothesis. In addition, the *p*-value of .204 exceeds .05. We conclude that there is not a significant interaction between temperature and insulation.

There are other situations that can occur when studying interaction among independent variables.

1. It is possible to have a three-way interaction among the independent variables. In our heating example, we might have considered the three-way interaction between temperature, insulation, and age of the furnace.
2. It is possible to have an interaction where one of the independent variables is nominal scale. In our heating cost example, we could have studied the interaction between temperature and garage.

Studying all possible interactions can become very complex. However, careful consideration to possible interactions among independent variables can often provide useful insight into the regression models.

LO14-7

Apply stepwise regression to develop a multiple regression model.

STEPWISE REGRESSION

In our heating cost example (see sample information in Table 14–1), we considered three independent variables: the mean outside temperature, the amount of insulation in the home, and the age of the furnace. To obtain the equation, we first ran a global or "all at once" test to determine if any of the regression coefficients were significant. When we found at least one to be significant, we tested the regression coefficients individually to determine which were important. We kept the independent variables that had significant regression coefficients and left the others out. By retaining the independent variables with significant coefficients, we found the regression equation that used the fewest independent variables. This made the regression equation easier to interpret. Then we considered the qualitative variable, garage, and found that it was significantly related to heating cost. The variable, garage, was added to the equation.

We are now going to describe a technique called **stepwise regression.** This technique is more efficient for building an equation that only includes independent variables with significant regression coefficients.

> **STEPWISE REGRESSION** A step-by-step method to determine a regression equation that begins with a single independent variable and adds or deletes independent variables one by one. Only independent variables with nonzero regression coefficients are included in the regression equation.

In the stepwise method, we develop a sequence of equations. The first equation contains only one independent variable. However, this independent variable is the one from the set of proposed independent variables that explains the most variation in the dependent variable. Stated differently, if we compute all the simple correlations between each independent variable and the dependent variable, the stepwise method first selects the independent variable with the strongest correlation with the dependent variable.

Next, the stepwise method looks at the remaining independent variables and then selects the one that will explain the largest percentage of the variation yet unexplained. We continue this process until all the independent variables with significant regression coefficients are included in the regression equation. The advantages to the stepwise method are:

1. Only independent variables with significant regression coefficients are entered into the equation.
2. The steps involved in building the regression equation are clear.
3. It is efficient in finding the regression equation with only significant regression coefficients.
4. The changes in the multiple standard error of estimate and the coefficient of determination are shown.

The stepwise Minitab output for the heating cost problem follows. Note that the final equation, which is reported in the column labeled 3, includes the independent variables temperature, garage, and insulation. These are the same independent variables that were included in our equation using the global test and the test for individual independent variables. (See page 500.) The independent variable age, for age of the furnace, is not included because it is not a significant predictor of cost.

	C1	C2	C3	C4
	Cost	Temp	Insul	Garage
1	250	35	3	0
2	360	29	4	1
3	165	36	7	0
4	43	60	6	0
5	92	65	5	0
6	200	30	5	0
7	355	10	6	1
8	290	7	10	1
9	230	21	9	0
10	120	55	2	0
11	73	54	12	0
12	205	48	5	1
13	400	20	5	1
14	320	39	4	1
15	72	60	8	0
16	272	20	5	1
17	94	58	7	0
18	190	40	8	1
19	235	27	9	0
20	139	30	7	0

Stepwise Regression: Cost versus Temp, Insul, Garage

Alpha-to-Enter: 0.15   Alpha-to-Remove: 0.15

Response is Cost on 3 predictors, with N = 20

Step	1	2	3
Constant	388.8	300.3	393.7
Temp	-4.93	-3.56	-3.96
T-Value	-5.89	-4.70	-6.07
P-Value	0.000	0.000	0.000
Garage		93	77
T-Value		3.56	3.40
P-Value		0.002	0.004
Insul			-11.3
T-Value			-2.83
P-Value			0.012
S	63.6	49.5	41.6
R-Sq	65.85	80.46	86.98
R-Sq(adj)	63.96	78.16	84.54
Mallows Cp	26.0	10.0	4.0

Reviewing the steps and interpreting output:

1. The stepwise procedure selects the independent variable temperature first. This variable explains more of the variation in heating cost than any of the other three proposed independent variables. Temperature explains 65.85% of the variation in heating cost. The regression equation is:

$$\hat{y} = 388.8 - 4.93x_1$$

There is an inverse relationship between heating cost and temperature. For each degree the temperature increases, heating cost is reduced by $4.93.

2. The next independent variable to enter the regression equation is garage. When this variable is added to the regression equation, the coefficient of determination is increased from 65.85% to 80.46%. That is, by adding garage as an independent variable, we increase the coefficient of determination by 14.61 percentage points. The regression equation after step 2 is:

$$\hat{y} = 300.3 - 3.56x_1 + 93.0x_2$$

Usually the regression coefficients will change from one step to the next. In this case, the coefficient for temperature retained its negative sign, but it changed from -4.93 to -3.56. This change is reflective of the added influence of the independent variable garage. Why did the stepwise method select the independent variable garage instead of either insulation or age? The increase in R^2, the coefficient of determination, is larger if garage is included rather than either of the other two variables.

3. At this point, there are two unused variables remaining, insulation and age. Notice on the third step the procedure selects insulation and then stops. This indicates

506   CHAPTER 14

the variable insulation explains more of the remaining variation in heating cost than the age variable does. After the third step, the regression equation is:

$$\hat{y} = 393.7 - 3.96x_1 + 77.0x_2 - 11.3x_3$$

At this point, 86.98% of the variation in heating cost is explained by the three independent variables temperature, garage, and insulation. This is the same R^2 value and regression equation we found on page 500 except for rounding differences.

4.   Here, the stepwise procedure stops. This means the independent variable age does not add significantly to the coefficient of determination.

The stepwise method developed the same regression equation, selected the same independent variables, and found the same coefficient of determination as the global and individual tests described earlier in the chapter. The advantage to the stepwise method is that it is more direct than using a combination of the global and individual procedures.

Other methods of variable selection are available. The stepwise method is also called the **forward selection method** because we begin with no independent variables and add one independent variable to the regression equation at each iteration. There is also the **backward elimination method,** which begins with the entire set of variables and eliminates one independent variable at each iteration.

The methods described so far look at one variable at a time and decide whether to include or eliminate that variable. Another approach is the **best-subset regression.** With this method, we look at the best model using one independent variable, the best model using two independent variables, the best model with three, and so on. The criterion is to find the model with the largest R^2 value, regardless of the number of independent variables. Also, each independent variable does not necessarily have a nonzero regression coefficient. Since each independent variable could either be included or not included, there are $2^k - 1$ possible models, where k refers to the number of independent variables. In our heating cost example, we considered four independent variables so there are 15 possible regression models, found by $2^4 - 1 = 16 - 1 = 15$. We would examine all regression models using one independent variable, all combinations using two variables, all combinations using three independent variables, and the possibility of using all four independent variables. The advantages to the best-subset method is it may examine combinations of independent variables not considered in the stepwise method. The process is available in Minitab and MegaStat.

For **DATA FILE**, please visit
www.mhhe.com/lind16e

9.   The production manager of High Point Sofa and Chair, a large furniture manufacturer located in North Carolina, is studying the job performance ratings of a sample of 15 electrical repairmen employed by the company. An aptitude test is required by the human resources department to become an electrical repairman. The production manager was able to get the score for each repairman in the sample. In addition, he determined which of the repairmen were union members (code = 1) and which were not (code = 0). The sample information is reported below.

Worker	Job Performance Score	Aptitude Test Score	Union Membership
Abbott	58	5	0
Anderson	53	4	0
Bender	33	10	0
Bush	97	10	0
Center	36	2	0
Coombs	83	7	0
Eckstine	67	6	0
Gloss	84	9	0
Herd	98	9	1

(continued)

MULTIPLE REGRESSION ANALYSIS   507

Worker	Job Performance Score	Aptitude Test Score	Union Membership
Householder	45	2	1
lori	97	8	1
Lindstrom	90	6	1
Mason	96	7	1
Pierse	66	3	1
Rohde	82	6	1

a. Use a statistical software package to develop a multiple regression equation using the job performance score as the dependent variable and aptitude test score and union membership as independent variables.

b. Comment on the regression equation. Be sure to include the coefficient of determination and the effect of union membership. Are these two variables effective in explaining the variation in job performance?

c. Conduct a test of hypothesis to determine if union membership should be included as an independent variable.

d. Repeat the analysis considering possible interaction terms.

For **DATA FILE**, please visit
www.mhhe.com/lind16e

10. Cincinnati Paint Company sells quality brands of paints through hardware stores throughout the United States. The company maintains a large sales force whose job it is to call on existing customers as well as look for new business. The national sales manager is investigating the relationship between the number of sales calls made and the miles driven by the sales representative. Also, do the sales representatives who drive the most miles and make the most calls necessarily earn the most in sales commissions? To investigate, the vice president of sales selected a sample of 25 sales representatives and determined:

- The amount earned in commissions last month (y)
- The number of miles driven last month (x_1)
- The number of sales calls made last month (x_2)

The information is reported below.

Commissions ($000)	Calls	Driven
22	139	2,371
13	132	2,226
33	144	2,731
⋮	⋮	⋮
25	127	2,671
43	154	2,988
34	147	2,829

Develop a regression equation including an interaction term. Is there a significant interaction between the number of sales calls and the miles driven?

11. An art collector is studying the relationship between the selling price of a painting and two independent variables. The two independent variables are the number of bidders at the particular auction and the age of the painting, in years. A sample of 25 paintings revealed the following sample information.

For **DATA FILE**, please visit
www.mhhe.com/lind16e

Painting	Auction Price	Bidders	Age
1	3,470	10	67
2	3,500	8	56
3	3,700	7	73
⋮	⋮	⋮	⋮
23	4,660	5	94
24	4,710	3	88
25	4,880	1	84

a. Develop a multiple regression equation using the independent variables number of bidders and age of painting to estimate the dependent variable auction price. Discuss the equation. Does it surprise you that there is an inverse relationship between the number of bidders and the price of the painting?

b. Create an interaction variable and include it in the regression equation. Explain the meaning of the interaction. Is this variable significant?

c. Use the stepwise method and the independent variables for the number of bidders, the age of the painting, and the interaction between the number of bidders and the age of the painting. Which variables would you select?

12. A real estate developer wishes to study the relationship between the size of home a client will purchase (in square feet) and other variables. Possible independent variables include the family income, family size, whether there is a senior adult parent living with the family (1 for yes, 0 for no), and the total years of education beyond high school for the husband and wife. The sample information is reported below.

For **DATA FILE**, please visit
www.mhhe.com/lind16e

Family	Square Feet	Income (000s)	Family Size	Senior Parent	Education
1	2,240	60.8	2	0	4
2	2,380	68.4	2	1	6
3	3,640	104.5	3	0	7
4	3,360	89.3	4	1	0
5	3,080	72.2	4	0	2
6	2,940	114	3	1	10
7	4,480	125.4	6	0	6
8	2,520	83.6	3	0	8
9	4,200	133	5	0	2
10	2,800	95	3	0	6

Develop an appropriate multiple regression equation. Which independent variables would you include in the final regression equation? Use the stepwise method.

Apply multiple regression techniques to develop a linear model.

REVIEW OF MULTIPLE REGRESSION

We described many topics involving multiple regression in this chapter. In this section of the chapter, we focus on a single example with a solution that reviews the procedure and guides your application of multiple regression analysis.

EXAMPLE

The Bank of New England is a large financial institution serving the New England states as well as New York and New Jersey. The mortgage department of the Bank of New England is studying data from recent loans. Of particular interest is how such factors as the value of the home being purchased ($000), education level of the head of the household (number of years, beginning with first grade), age of the head of the household, current monthly mortgage payment (in dollars), and gender of the head of the household (male = 1, female = 0) relate to the family income. The mortgage department would like to know whether these variables are effective predictors of family income.

SOLUTION

Consider a random sample of 25 loan applications submitted to the Bank of New England last month. A portion of the sample information is shown in Table 14–3. The entire data set is available at the website (www.mhhe.com/lind16e) and is identified as Bank of New England.

TABLE 14–3 Information on Sample of 25 Loans by the Bank of New England

Loan	Income ($000)	Value ($000)	Education	Age	Mortgage	Gender
1	100.7	190	14	53	230	1
2	99.0	121	15	49	370	1
3	102.0	161	14	44	397	1
⋮	⋮	⋮	⋮	⋮	⋮	⋮
23	102.3	163	14	46	142	1
24	100.2	150	15	50	343	0
25	96.3	139	14	45	373	0

We begin by calculating the correlation matrix shown below. It shows the relationship between each of the independent variables and the dependent variable. It helps to identify the independent variables that are more closely related to the dependent variable (family income). The correlation matrix also reveals the independent variables that are highly correlated and possibly redundant.

	Income	Value	Education	Age	Mortgage	Gender
Income	1					
Value	0.720	1				
Education	0.188	−0.144	1			
Age	0.243	0.220	0.621	1		
Mortgage	0.116	0.358	−0.210	−0.038	1	
Gender	0.486	0.184	0.062	0.156	−0.129	1

What can we learn from this correlation matrix?

1. The first column shows the correlations between each of the independent variables and the dependent variable family income. Observe that each of the independent variables is positively correlated with family income. The value of the home has the strongest correlation with family income. The level of education of the person applying for the loan and the current mortgage payment have a weak correlation with family income. These two variables are candidates to be dropped from the regression equation.
2. All possible correlations among the independent variables are identified with the green background. Our standard is to look for correlations that exceed an absolute value of .700. None of the independent variables are strongly correlated with each other. This indicates that multicollinearity is not likely.

Next, we compute the multiple regression equation using all the independent variables. The software output follows.

	A	B	C	D	E	F
1	SUMMARY OUTPUT					
2						
3	*Regression Statistics*					
4	Multiple R	0.866				
5	R Square	0.750				
6	Adjusted R Square	0.684				
7	Standard Error	1.478				
8	Observations	25				
9						
10	ANOVA					
11		*df*	*SS*	*MS*	*F*	*P-value*
12	Regression	5	124.322	24.864	11.385	0.000
13	Residual	19	41.494	2.184		
14	Total	24	165.815			
15						
16		*Coefficients*	*Standard Error*	*t Stat*	*P-value*	
17	Intercept	70.606	7.464	9.459	0.000	
18	Value ($000)	0.072	0.012	5.769	0.000	
19	Education	1.624	0.603	2.693	0.014	
20	Age	-0.122	0.078	-1.566	0.134	
21	Mortgage	-0.001	0.003	-0.319	0.753	
22	Gender	1.807	0.623	2.901	0.009	

The coefficients of determination, that is, both R^2 and adjusted R^2, are reported at the top of the summary output and highlighted in yellow. The R^2 value is 75.0%, so the five independent variables account for three-quarters of the variation in family income. The adjusted R^2 measures the strength of the relationship between the set of independent variables and family income and also accounts for the number of variables in the regression equation. The adjusted R^2 indicates that the five variables account for 68.4% of the variance of family income. Both of these suggest that the proposed independent variables are useful in predicting family income.

The output also includes the regression equation.

$$\hat{y} = 70.606 + 0.072(Value) + 1.624(Education) - 0.122(Age)$$
$$- 0.001(Mortgage) + 1.807(Gender)$$

Be careful in this interpretation. Both income and the value of the home are in thousands of dollars. Here is a summary:

1. An increase of $1,000 in the value of the home suggests an increase of $72 in family income. An increase of 1 year of education increases income by $1,624, another year older reduces income by $122, and an increase of $1,000 in the mortgage reduces income by $1.
2. If a male is head of the household, the value of family income will increase by $1,807. Remember that "female" was coded 0 and "male" was coded 1, so a male head of household is positively related to home value.
3. The age of the head of household and monthly mortgage payment are inversely related to family income. This is true because the sign of the regression coefficient is negative.

MULTIPLE REGRESSION ANALYSIS

Next we conduct the global hypothesis test. Here we check to see if any of the regression coefficients are different from 0. We use the .05 significance level.

$$H_0: \beta_1 = \beta_2 = \beta_3 = \beta_4 = \beta_5 = 0$$

$$H_1: \text{Not all the } \beta\text{s are } 0.$$

The p-value from the table (cell F12) is 0.000. Because the p-value is less than the significance level, we reject the null hypothesis and conclude that at least one of the regression coefficients is not equal to zero.

Next we evaluate the individual regression coefficients. The p-values to test each regression coefficient are reported in cells E18 through E22 in the software output on the previous page. The null hypothesis and the alternate hypothesis are:

$$H_0: \beta_i = 0$$

$$H_1: \beta_i \neq 0$$

The subscript i represents any particular independent variable. Again using .05 significance levels, the p-values for the regression coefficients for home value, years of education, and gender are all less than .05. We conclude that these regression coefficients are not equal to zero and are significant predictors of family income. The p-value for age and mortgage amount are greater than the significance level of .05, so we do not reject the null hypotheses for these variables. The regression coefficients are not different from zero and are not related to family income.

Based on the results of testing each of the regression coefficients, we conclude that the variables age and mortgage amount are not effective predictors of family income. Thus, they should be removed from the multiple regression equation. Remember that we must remove one independent variable at a time and redo the analysis to evaluate the overall effect of removing the variable. Our strategy is to remove the variable with the smallest t-statistic or the largest p-value. This variable is mortgage amount. The result of the regression analysis without the mortgage variable follows.

	A	B	C	D	E	F
1	SUMMARY OUTPUT					
2						
3	*Regression Statistics*					
4	Multiple R	0.865				
5	R Square	0.748				
6	Adjusted R Square	0.698				
7	Standard Error	1.444				
8	Observations	25				
9						
10	ANOVA					
11		*df*	*SS*	*MS*	*F*	*P-value*
12	Regression	4	124.099	31.025	14.874	0.000
13	Residual	20	41.716	2.086		
14	Total	24	165.815			
15						
16		*Coefficients*	*Standard Error*	*t Stat*	*P-value*	
17	Intercept	70.159	7.165	9.791	0.000	
18	Value ($000)	0.070	0.011	6.173	0.000	
19	Education	1.647	0.585	2.813	0.011	
20	Age	-0.122	0.076	-1.602	0.125	
21	Gender	1.846	0.596	3.096	0.006	

Observe that the R^2 and adjusted R^2 change very little without the mortgage variable. Also observe that the p-value associated with age is greater than the .05

significance level. So next we remove the age variable and redo the analysis. The regression output with the variables age and mortgage amount removed follows.

	A	B	C	D	E	F
1	SUMMARY OUTPUT					
2						
3	*Regression Statistics*					
4	Multiple R	0.846				
5	R Square	0.716				
6	Adjusted R Square	0.676				
7	Standard Error	1.497				
8	Observations	25				
9						
10	ANOVA					
11		*df*	*SS*	*MS*	*F*	*P-value*
12	Regression	3	118.743	39.581	17.658	0.000
13	Residual	21	47.072	2.242		
14	Total	24	165.815			
15						
16		*Coefficients*	*Standard Error*	*t Stat*	*P-value*	
17	Intercept	74.527	6.870	10.849	0.000	
18	Value ($000)	0.063	0.011	5.803	0.000	
19	Education	1.016	0.449	2.262	0.034	
20	Gender	1.770	0.616	2.872	0.009	

From this output, we conclude:

1. The R^2 and adjusted R^2 values have declined but only slightly. Using all five independent variables, the R^2 value was .750. With the two nonsignificant variables removed, the R^2 and adjusted R^2 values are .716 and .676, respectively. We prefer the equation with the fewer number of independent variables. It is easier to interpret.
2. In ANOVA, we observe that the p-value is less than .05. Hence, at least one of the regression coefficients is not equal to zero.
3. Reviewing the significance of the individual coefficients, the p-values associated with each of the remaining independent variables are less than .05. We conclude that all the regression coefficients are different from zero. Each independent variable is a useful predictor of family income.

Our final step is to examine the regression assumptions, listed on page 494, with our regression model. The first assumption is that there is a linear relationship between each independent variable and the dependent variable. It is not necessary to review the dummy variable Gender because there are only two possible outcomes. Below are the scatter plots of family income versus home value and family income versus years of education.

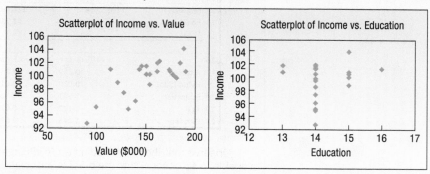

MULTIPLE REGRESSION ANALYSIS   513

The scatter plot of income versus home value shows a general increasing trend. As the home value increases, so does family income. The points appear to be linear. That is, there is no observable nonlinear pattern in the data. The scatter plot on the right, of income versus years of education, shows that the data are measured to the nearest year. The measurement is to the nearest year and is a discrete variable. Given the measurement method, it is difficult to determine if the relationship is linear or not.

A plot of the residuals is also useful to evaluate the overall assumption of linearity. Recall that a residual is $(y - \hat{y})$, the difference between the actual value of the dependent variable (y) and the predicted value of the dependent variable $(\hat{y})$. Assuming a linear relationship, the distribution of the residuals should show about an equal proportion of negative residuals (points above the line) and positive residuals (points below the line) centered on zero. There should be no observable pattern to the plots. The graph follows.

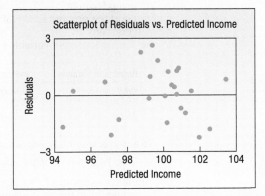

There is no discernable pattern to the plot, so we conclude that the linearity assumption is reasonable.

If the linearity assumption is valid, then the distribution of residuals should follow the normal probability distribution with a mean of zero. To evaluate this assumption, we will use a histogram and a normal probability plot.

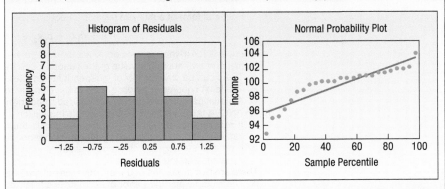

In general, the histogram on the left shows the major characteristics of a normal distribution, that is, a majority of observations in the middle and centered on the mean of zero, with lower frequencies in the tails of the distribution. The normal probability plot on the right is based on a cumulative normal probability distribution. The line shows the standardized cumulative normal distribution. The green dots show the cumulative distribution of the residuals. To confirm the normal distribution of the residuals, the green dots should be close to the line. This is true for most of the plot. However, we would note that there are departures and even perhaps a nonlinear pattern in the residuals in the lower part of the graph. As before, we are looking for serious departures from linearity and these are not indicated in these graphs.

The final assumption refers to multicollinearity. This means that the independent variables should not be highly correlated. We suggested a rule of thumb that multicollinearity would be a concern if the correlations among independent variables were close to 0.7 or -0.7. There are no violations of this guideline.

There is a statistic that is used to more precisely evaluate multicollinearity, the variance inflation factor (VIF). To calculate the VIFs, we need to do a regression analysis for each independent variable as a function of the other independent variables. From each of these regression analyses, we need the R^2 to compute the VIF using formula (14–7). The following table shows the R^2 for each regression analysis and the computed VIF. If the VIFs are less than 10, then multicollinearity is not a concern. In this case, the VIFs are all less than 10, so multicollinearity among the independent variables is not a concern.

Dependent Variable	Independent Variables	R-square	VIF
Value	Education and Gender	0.058	1.062
Education	Gender and Value	0.029	1.030
Gender	Value and Education	0.042	1.044

To summarize, the multiple regression equation is

$$\hat{y} = 74.527 + 0.063(Value) + 1.016(Education) + 1.770(Gender)$$

This equation explains 71.6% of the variation in family income. There are no major departures from the multiple regression assumptions of linearity, normally distributed residuals, and multicollinearity.

C H A P T E R   S U M M A R Y

I. The general form of a multiple regression equation is:

$$\hat{y} = a + b_1x_1 + b_2x_2 + \cdots + b_kx_k \qquad \text{[14–1]}$$

where a is the Y-intercept when all x's are zero, b_j refers to the sample regression coefficients, and x_j refers to the value of the various independent variables.
  A. There can be any number of independent variables.
  B. The least squares criterion is used to develop the regression equation.
  C. A statistical software package is needed to perform the calculations.
II. An ANOVA table summarizes the multiple regression analysis.
  A. It reports the total amount of the variation in the dependent variable and divides this variation into that explained by the set of independent variables and that not explained.
  B. It reports the degrees of freedom associated with the independent variables, the error variation, and the total variation.
III. There are two measures of the effectiveness of the regression equation.
  A. The multiple standard error of estimate is similar to the standard deviation.
    1. It is measured in the same units as the dependent variable.
    2. It is based on squared deviations from the regression equation.
    3. It ranges from 0 to plus infinity.
    4. It is calculated from the following equation.

$$s_{Y.123\dots k} = \sqrt{\frac{\Sigma(y - \hat{y})^2}{n - (k + 1)}} \qquad \text{[14–2]}$$

B. The coefficient of multiple determination reports the percent of the variation in the dependent variable explained by the variation in the set of independent variables.
  1. It may range from 0 to 1.
  2. It is also based on squared deviations from the regression equation.
  3. It is found by the following equation.

$$R^2 = \frac{SSR}{SS\ total}$$ [14–3]

  4. When the number of independent variables is large, we adjust the coefficient of determination for the degrees of freedom as follows.

$$R_{adj}^2 = 1 - \frac{\dfrac{SSE}{n - (k + 1)}}{\dfrac{SS\ total}{n - 1}}$$ [14–4]

IV. A global test is used to investigate whether any of the independent variables have a regression coefficient that differs significantly from zero.
  A. The null hypothesis is: All the regression coefficients are zero.
  B. The alternate hypothesis is: At least one regression coefficient is not zero.
  C. The test statistic is the F distribution with k (the number of independent variables) degrees of freedom in the numerator and $n - (k + 1)$ degrees of freedom in the denominator, where n is the sample size.
  D. The formula to calculate the value of the test statistic for the global test is:

$$F = \frac{SSR/k}{SSE/[n - (k + 1)]}$$ [14–5]

V. The test for individual variables determines which independent variables have regression coefficients that differ significantly from zero.
  A. The variables that have zero regression coefficients are usually dropped from the analysis.
  B. The test statistic is the t distribution with $n - (k + 1)$ degrees of freedom.
  C. The formula to calculate the value of the test statistic for the individual test is:

$$t = \frac{b_i - 0}{s_{b_i}}$$ [14–6]

VI. There are five assumptions to use multiple regression analysis.
  A. The relationship between the dependent variable and the set of independent variables must be linear.
    1. To verify this assumption, develop a scatter diagram and plot the residuals on the vertical axis and the fitted values on the horizontal axis.
    2. If the plots appear random, we conclude the relationship is linear.
  B. The variation is the same for both large and small values of $\hat{y}$.
    1. Homoscedasticity means the variation is the same for all fitted values of the dependent variable.
    2. This condition is checked by developing a scatter diagram with the residuals on the vertical axis and the fitted values on the horizontal axis.
    3. If there is no pattern to the plots—that is, they appear random—the residuals meet the homoscedasticity requirement.
  C. The residuals follow the normal probability distribution.
    1. This condition is checked by developing a histogram of the residuals or a normal probability plot.
    2. The mean of the distribution of the residuals is 0.
  D. The independent variables are not correlated.
    1. A correlation matrix will show all possible correlations among independent variables. Signs of trouble are correlations larger than 0.70 or less than −0.70.
    2. Signs of correlated independent variables include when an important predictor variable is found insignificant, when an obvious reversal occurs in signs in one or more of

516   CHAPTER 14

the independent variables, or when a variable is removed from the solution, there is a large change in the regression coefficients.
   3. The variance inflation factor is used to identify correlated independent variables.

$$VIF = \frac{1}{1 - R_j^2}$$ [14–7]

  E. Each residual is independent of other residuals.
    1. Autocorrelation occurs when successive residuals are correlated.
    2. When autocorrelation exists, the value of the standard error will be biased and will return poor results for tests of hypothesis regarding the regression coefficients.
VII. Several techniques help build a regression model.
  A. A dummy or qualitative independent variable can assume one of two possible outcomes.
    1. A value of 1 is assigned to one outcome and 0 to the other.
    2. Use formula (14–6) to determine if the dummy variable should remain in the equation.
  B. Interaction is the case in which one independent variable (such as x_2) affects the relationship with another independent variable (x_1) and the dependent variable (y).
  C. Stepwise regression is a step-by-step process to find the regression equation.
    1. Only independent variables with nonzero regression coefficients enter the equation.
    2. Independent variables are added one at a time to the regression equation.

P R O N U N C I A T I O N   K E Y

SYMBOL	MEANING	PRONUNCIATION
b_1	Regression coefficient for the first independent variable	b sub 1
b_k	Regression coefficient for any independent variable	b sub k
$s_{Y.123...k}$	Multiple standard error of estimate	s sub Y dot 1, 2, 3 . . . k

C H A P T E R   E X E R C I S E S

13. A multiple regression equation yields the following partial results.

Source	Sum of Squares	df
Regression	750	4
Error	500	35

  a. What is the total sample size?
  b. How many independent variables are being considered?
  c. Compute the coefficient of determination.
  d. Compute the standard error of estimate.
  e. Test the hypothesis that none of the regression coefficients is equal to zero. Let $\alpha = .05$.
14. In a multiple regression equation, two independent variables are considered, and the sample size is 25. The regression coefficients and the standard errors are as follows.

$$b_1 = 2.676 \qquad s_{b_1} = 0.56$$
$$b_2 = -0.880 \qquad s_{b_2} = 0.71$$

Conduct a test of hypothesis to determine whether either independent variable has a coefficient equal to zero. Would you consider deleting either variable from the regression equation? Use the .05 significance level.

MULTIPLE REGRESSION ANALYSIS 517

15. The following output was obtained.

Analysis of Variance			
Source	DF	SS	MS
Regression	5	100	20
Residual Error	20	40	2
Total	25	140	

Predictor	Coefficient	SE Coefficient	t
Constant	3.00	1.50	2.00
x_1	4.00	3.00	1.33
x_2	3.00	0.20	15.00
x_3	0.20	0.05	4.00
x_4	-2.50	1.00	-2.50
x_5	3.00	4.00	0.75

a. What is the sample size?
b. Compute the value of R^2.
c. Compute the multiple standard error of estimate.
d. Conduct a global test of hypothesis to determine whether any of the regression coefficients are significant. Use the .05 significance level.
e. Test the regression coefficients individually. Would you consider omitting any variable(s)? If so, which one(s)? Use the .05 significance level.

16. In a multiple regression equation, $k = 5$ and $n = 20$, the MSE value is 5.10, and SS total is 519.68. At the .05 significance level, can we conclude that any of the regression coefficients are not equal to 0?

17. The district manager of Jasons, a large discount electronics chain, is investigating why certain stores in her region are performing better than others. She believes that three factors are related to total sales: the number of competitors in the region, the population in the surrounding area, and the amount spent on advertising. From her district, consisting of several hundred stores, she selects a random sample of 30 stores. For each store, she gathered the following information.

y = total sales last year (in $ thousands)
x_1 = number of competitors in the region
x_2 = population of the region (in millions)
x_3 = advertising expense (in $ thousands)

The sample data were run on Minitab, with the following results.

Analysis of Variance			
Source	DF	SS	MS
Regression	3	3050	1016.67
Residual Error	26	2200	84.62
Total	29	5250	

Predictor	Coefficient	SE Coefficient	t
Constant	14.00	7.00	2.00
x_1	-1.00	0.70	-1.43
x_2	30.00	5.20	5.77
x_3	0.20	0.08	2.50

a. What are the estimated sales for the Bryne store, which has four competitors, a regional population of 0.4 (400,000), and an advertising expense of 30 ($30,000)?
b. Compute the R^2 value.
c. Compute the multiple standard error of estimate.
d. Conduct a global test of hypothesis to determine whether any of the regression coefficients are not equal to zero. Use the .05 level of significance.
e. Conduct tests of hypothesis to determine which of the independent variables have significant regression coefficients. Which variables would you consider eliminating? Use the .05 significance level.

518

CHAPTER 14

18. Suppose that the sales manager of a large automotive parts distributor wants to estimate as early as April the total annual sales of a region. On the basis of regional sales, the total sales for the company can also be estimated. If, based on past experience, it is found that the April estimates of annual sales are reasonably accurate, then in future years the April forecast could be used to revise production schedules and maintain the correct inventory at the retail outlets.

Several factors appear to be related to sales, including the number of retail outlets in the region stocking the company's parts, the number of automobiles in the region registered as of April 1, and the total personal income for the first quarter of the year. Five independent variables were finally selected as being the most important (according to the sales manager). Then the data were gathered for a recent year. The total annual sales for that year for each region were also recorded. Note in the following table that for region 1 there were 1,739 retail outlets stocking the company's automotive parts, there were 9,270,000 registered automobiles in the region as of April 1, and so on. The sales for that year were $37,702,000.

Annual Sales ($ millions), y	Number of Retail Outlets, x_1	Number of Automobiles Registered (millions), x_2	Personal Income ($ billions), x_3	Average Age of Automobiles (years), x_4	Number of Supervisors, x_5
37.702	1,739	9.27	85.4	3.5	9.0
24.196	1,221	5.86	60.7	5.0	5.0
32.055	1,846	8.81	68.1	4.4	7.0
3.611	120	3.81	20.2	4.0	5.0
17.625	1,096	10.31	33.8	3.5	7.0
45.919	2,290	11.62	95.1	4.1	13.0
29.600	1,687	8.96	69.3	4.1	15.0
8.114	241	6.28	16.3	5.9	11.0
20.116	649	7.77	34.9	5.5	16.0
12.994	1,427	10.92	15.1	4.1	10.0

a. Consider the following correlation matrix. Which single variable has the strongest correlation with the dependent variable? The correlations between the independent variables outlets and income and between cars and outlets are fairly strong. Could this be a problem? What is this condition called?

	sales	outlets	cars	income	age
outlets	0.899				
cars	0.605	0.775			
income	0.964	0.825	0.409		
age	−0.323	−0.489	−0.447	−0.349	
bosses	0.286	0.183	0.395	0.155	0.291

b. The output for all five variables is shown below. What percent of the variation is explained by the regression equation?

```
The regression equation is
Sales = −19.7 − 0.00063 outlets + 1.74 cars + 0.410 income
        + 2.04 age − 0.034 bosses

            Predictor        Coef       SE Coef        T         P
            Constant       −19.672        5.422      −3.63     0.022
            outlets      −0.000629      0.002638      −0.24     0.823
            cars            1.7399        0.5530       3.15     0.035
            income         0.40994       0.04385       9.35     0.001
            age             2.0357        0.8779       2.32     0.081
            bosses         −0.0344        0.1880      −0.18     0.864

Analysis of Variance
            SOURCE          DF        SS         MS         F         P
            Regression       5    1593.81     318.76    140.36     0.000
            Residual Error   4       9.08       2.27
            Total            9    1602.89
```

MULTIPLE REGRESSION ANALYSIS   519

c. Conduct a global test of hypothesis to determine whether any of the regression coefficients are not zero. Use the .05 significance level.

d. Conduct a test of hypothesis on each of the independent variables. Would you consider eliminating "outlets" and "bosses"? Use the .05 significance level.

e. The regression has been rerun below with "outlets" and "bosses" eliminated. Compute the coefficient of determination. How much has R^2 changed from the previous analysis?

```
The regression equation is
Sales = −18.9 + 1.61 cars + 0.400 income + 1.96 age

          Predictor        Coef      SE Coef           T         P
          Constant      −18.924        3.636       −5.20     0.002
          cars           1.6129       0.1979        8.15     0.000
          income        0.40031      0.01569       25.52     0.000
          age            1.9637       0.5846        3.36     0.015

Analysis of Variance
          SOURCE             DF           SS          MS          F         P
          Regression          3      1593.66      531.22     345.25     0.000
          Residual Error      6         9.23        1.54
          Total               9      1602.89
```

f. Following is a histogram of the residuals. Does the normality assumption appear reasonable?

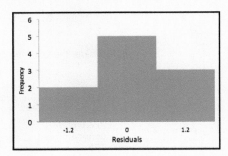

g. Following is a plot of the fitted values of y (i.e., $\hat{y}$) and the residuals. Do you see any violations of the assumptions?

19. The administrator of a new paralegal program at Seagate Technical College wants to estimate the grade point average in the new program. He thought that high school GPA, the verbal score on the Scholastic Aptitude Test (SAT), and the mathematics score on the SAT would be good predictors of paralegal GPA. The data on nine students are:

Student	High School GPA	SAT Verbal	SAT Math	Paralegal GPA
1	3.25	480	410	3.21
2	1.80	290	270	1.68
3	2.89	420	410	3.58
4	3.81	500	600	3.92
5	3.13	500	490	3.00
6	2.81	430	460	2.82
7	2.20	320	490	1.65
8	2.14	530	480	2.30
9	2.63	469	440	2.33

a. Consider the following correlation matrix. Which variable has the strongest correlation with the dependent variable? Some of the correlations among the independent variables are strong. Does this appear to be a problem?

	legal	gpa	verbal
gpa	0.911		
verbal	0.616	0.609	
math	0.487	0.636	0.599

b. Consider the following output. Compute the coefficient of multiple determination.

```
The regression equation is
Legal = −0.411 + 1.20 GPA + 0.00163 Verbal − 0.00194 Math

Predictor            Coef           SE Coef          T          P
Constant          −0.4111           0.7823        −0.53      0.622
GPA                1.2014           0.2955         4.07      0.010
Verbal            0.001629         0.002147        0.76      0.482
Math             −0.001939         0.002074       −0.94      0.393

Analysis of Variance
SOURCE              DF          SS            MS          F          P
Regression           3       4.3595        1.4532      10.33      0.014
Residual Error       5       0.7036        0.1407
Total                8       5.0631

SOURCE      DF     Seq SS
GPA          1     4.2061
Verbal       1     0.0303
Math         1     0.1231
```

c. Conduct a global test of hypothesis from the preceding output. Does it appear that any of the regression coefficients are not equal to zero?
d. Conduct a test of hypothesis on each independent variable. Would you consider eliminating the variables "verbal" and "math"? Let $\alpha = .05$.
e. The analysis has been rerun without "verbal" and "math." See the following output. Compute the coefficient of determination. How much has R^2 changed from the previous analysis?

```
The regression equation is
Legal = −0.454 + 1.16 GPA

Predictor       Coef      SE Coef        T         P
Constant      −0.4542     0.5542      −0.82      0.439
GPA            1.1589     0.1977       5.86      0.001

Analysis of Variance
SOURCE           DF      SS       MS       F        P
Regression        1    4.2061   4.2061   34.35    0.001
Residual Error    7    0.8570   0.1224
Total             8    5.0631
```

f. Following is a histogram of the residuals. Does the normality assumption for the residuals seem reasonable?

g. Following is a plot of the residuals and the $\hat{y}$ values. Do you see any violation of the assumptions?

For **DATA FILE**, please visit
www.mhhe.com/lind16e

20. Mike Wilde is president of the teachers' union for Otsego School District. In preparing for upcoming negotiations, he would like to investigate the salary structure of classroom teachers in the district. He believes there are three factors that affect a teacher's salary: years of experience, a rating of teaching effectiveness given by the principal, and whether the teacher has a master's degree. A random sample of 20 teachers resulted in the following data.

522   CHAPTER 14

Salary ($ thousands), y	Years of Experience, x_1	Principal's Rating, x_2	Master's Degree,* x_3
31.1	8	35	0
33.6	5	43	0
29.3	2	51	1
⋮	⋮	⋮	⋮
30.7	4	62	0
32.8	2	80	1
42.8	8	72	0

*1 = yes, 0 = no.

a. Develop a correlation matrix. Which independent variable has the strongest correlation with the dependent variable? Does it appear there will be any problems with multicollinearity?
b. Determine the regression equation. What salary would you estimate for a teacher with 5 years' experience, a rating by the principal of 60, and no master's degree?
c. Conduct a global test of hypothesis to determine whether any of the regression coefficients differ from zero. Use the .05 significance level.
d. Conduct a test of hypothesis for the individual regression coefficients. Would you consider deleting any of the independent variables? Use the .05 significance level.
e. If your conclusion in part (d) was to delete one or more independent variables, run the analysis again without those variables.
f. Determine the residuals for the equation of part (e). Use a stem-and-leaf chart or a histogram to verify that the distribution of the residuals is approximately normal.
g. Plot the residuals computed in part (f) in a scatter diagram with the residuals on the Y-axis and the $\hat{y}$ values on the X-axis. Does the plot reveal any violations of the assumptions of regression?

21. A consumer analyst collected the following data on the screen sizes of popular LCD televisions sold recently at a large retailer:

For **DATA FILE**, please visit www.mhhe.com/lind16e

Manufacturer	Screen	Price	Manufacturer	Screen	Price
Sharp	46	$1473.00	Sharp	37	$1314.50
Samsung	52	2300.00	Sharp	32	853.50
Samsung	46	1790.00	Sharp	52	2778.00
Sony	40	1250.00	Samsung	40	1749.50
Sharp	42	1546.50	Sharp	32	1035.00
Samsung	46	1922.50	Samsung	52	2950.00
Samsung	40	1372.00	Sony	40	1908.50
Sharp	37	1149.50	Sony	52	3103.00
Sharp	46	2000.00	Sony	46	2606.00
Sony	40	1444.50	Sony	46	2861.00
Sony	52	2615.00	Sony	52	3434.00
Samsung	32	747.50			

a. Does there appear to be a linear relationship between the screen size and the price?
b. Which variable is the "dependent" variable?
c. Using statistical software, determine the regression equation. Interpret the value of the slope in the regression equation.
d. Include the manufacturer in a multiple linear regression analysis using a "dummy" variable. Does it appear that some manufacturers can command a premium price? *Hint:* You will need to use a set of indicator variables.
e. Test each of the individual coefficients to see if they are significant.
f. Make a plot of the residuals and comment on whether they appear to follow a normal distribution.
g. Plot the residuals versus the fitted values. Do they seem to have the same amount of variation?

MULTIPLE REGRESSION ANALYSIS   523

For **DATA FILE**, please visit
www.mhhe.com/lind16e

22. A regional planner is studying the demographics in a region of a particular state. She has gathered the following data on nine counties.

County	Median Income	Median Age	Coastal
A	$48,157	57.7	1
B	48,568	60.7	1
C	46,816	47.9	1
D	34,876	38.4	0
E	35,478	42.8	0
F	34,465	35.4	0
G	35,026	39.5	0
H	38,599	65.6	0
J	33,315	27.0	0

a. Is there a linear relationship between the median income and median age?
b. Which variable is the "dependent" variable?
c. Use statistical software to determine the regression equation. Interpret the value of the slope in a simple regression equation.
d. Include the aspect that the county is "coastal" or not in a multiple linear regression analysis using a "dummy" variable. Does it appear to be a significant influence on incomes?
e. Test each of the individual coefficients to see if they are significant.
f. Make a plot of the residuals and comment on whether they appear to follow a normal distribution.
g. Plot the residuals versus the fitted values. Do they seem to have the same amount of variation?

For **DATA FILE**, please visit
www.mhhe.com/lind16e

23. Great Plains Roofing and Siding Company Inc. sells roofing and siding products to home repair retailers, such as Lowe's and Home Depot, and commercial contractors. The owner is interested in studying the effects of several variables on the value of shingles sold ($000). The marketing manager is arguing that the company should spend more money on advertising, while a market researcher suggests it should focus more on making its brand and product more distinct from its competitors.

The company has divided the United States into 26 marketing districts. In each district, it collected information on the following variables: volume of sales (in thousands of dollars), advertising dollars (in thousands), number of active accounts, number of competing brands, and a rating of district potential.

Sales (000s)	Advertising Dollars (000s)	Number of Accounts	Number of Competitors	Market Potential
79.3	5.5	31	10	8
200.1	2.5	55	8	6
163.2	8.0	67	12	9
200.1	3.0	50	7	16
146.0	3.0	38	8	15
177.7	2.9	71	12	17
⋮	⋮	⋮	⋮	⋮
93.5	4.2	26	8	3
259.0	4.5	75	8	19
331.2	5.6	71	4	9

Conduct a multiple regression analysis to find the best predictors of sales.
a. Draw a scatter diagram comparing sales volume with each of the independent variables. Comment on the results.
b. Develop a correlation matrix. Do you see any problems? Does it appear there are any redundant independent variables?
c. Develop a regression equation. Conduct the global test. Can we conclude that some of the independent variables are useful in explaining the variation in the dependent variable?

d. Conduct a test of each of the independent variables. Are there any that should be dropped?

e. Refine the regression equation so the remaining variables are all significant.

f. Develop a histogram of the residuals and a normal probability plot. Are there any problems?

g. Determine the variance inflation factor for each of the independent variables. Are there any problems?

For **DATA FILE**, please visit www.mhhe.com/lind16e

24. The *Times-Observer* is a daily newspaper in Metro City. Like many city newspapers, the *Times-Observer* is suffering through difficult financial times. The circulation manager is studying other newspapers in similar cities in the United States and Canada. She is particularly interested in what variables relate to the number of subscriptions to the newspaper. She is able to obtain the following sample information on 25 newspapers in similar cities. The following notation is used:

       Sub = Number of subscriptions (in thousands)
     Popul = The metropolitan population (in thousands)
       Adv = The advertising budget of the newspaper (in $ hundreds)
  Income = The median family income in the metropolitan area (in $ thousands)

Paper	Sub	Popul	Adv	Income
1	37.95	588.9	13.2	35.1
2	37.66	585.3	13.2	34.7
3	37.55	566.3	19.8	34.8
⋮	⋮	⋮	⋮	⋮
23	38.83	629.6	22.0	35.3
24	38.33	680.0	24.2	34.7
25	40.24	651.2	33.0	35.8

a. Determine the regression equation.

b. Conduct a global test of hypothesis to determine whether any of the regression coefficients are not equal to zero.

c. Conduct a test for the individual coefficients. Would you consider deleting any coefficients?

d. Determine the residuals and plot them against the fitted values. Do you see any problems?

e. Develop a histogram of the residuals. Do you see any problems with the normality assumption?

For **DATA FILE**, please visit www.mhhe.com/lind16e

25. Fred G. Hire is the manager of human resources at Crescent Tool and Die Inc. As part of his yearly report to the CEO, he is required to present an analysis of the salaried employees. Because there are over 1,000 employees, he does not have the staff to gather information on each salaried employee, so he selects a random sample of 30. For each employee, he records monthly salary; service at Crescent, in months; gender (1 = male, 0 = female); and whether the employee has a technical or clerical job. Those working technical jobs are coded 1, and those who are clerical 0.

Sampled Employee	Monthly Salary	Length of Service	Age	Gender	Job
1	$1,769	93	42	1	0
2	1,740	104	33	1	0
3	1,941	104	42	1	1
⋮	⋮	⋮	⋮	⋮	⋮
28	1,791	131	56	0	1
29	2,001	95	30	1	1
30	1,874	98	47	1	0

a. Determine the regression equation, using salary as the dependent variable and the other four variables as independent variables.

b. What is the value of R^2? Comment on this value.

MULTIPLE REGRESSION ANALYSIS   525

   c. Conduct a global test of hypothesis to determine whether any of the independent variables are different from 0.
   d. Conduct an individual test to determine whether any of the independent variables can be dropped.
   e. Rerun the regression equation, using only the independent variables that are significant. How much more does a man earn per month than a woman? Does it make a difference whether the employee has a technical or a clerical job?

For **DATA FILE**, please visit www.mhhe.com/lind16e

26. Many regions along the coast in North and South Carolina and Georgia have experienced rapid population growth over the last 10 years. It is expected that the growth will continue over the next 10 years. This has motivated many of the large grocery store chains to build new stores in the region. The Kelley's Super Grocery Stores Inc. chain is no exception. The director of planning for Kelley's Super Grocery Stores wants to study adding more stores in this region. He believes there are two main factors that indicate the amount families spend on groceries. The first is their income and the other is the number of people in the family. The director gathered the following sample information.

Family	Food	Income	Size
1	$5.04	$ 73.98	4
2	4.08	54.90	2
3	5.76	94.14	4
⋮	⋮	⋮	⋮
23	4.56	38.16	3
24	5.40	43.74	7
25	4.80	48.42	5

Food and income are reported in thousands of dollars per year, and the variable size refers to the number of people in the household.
   a. Develop a correlation matrix. Do you see any problems with multicollinearity?
   b. Determine the regression equation. Discuss the regression equation. How much does an additional family member add to the amount spent on food?
   c. What is the value of R^2? Can we conclude that this value is greater than 0?
   d. Would you consider deleting either of the independent variables?
   e. Plot the residuals in a histogram. Is there any problem with the normality assumption?
   f. Plot the fitted values against the residuals. Does this plot indicate any problems with homoscedasticity?

For **DATA FILE**, please visit www.mhhe.com/lind16e

27. An investment advisor is studying the relationship between a common stock's price to earnings (P/E) ratio and factors that she thinks would influence it. She has the following data on the earnings per share (EPS) and the dividend percentage (Yield) for a sample of 20 stocks.

Stock	P/E	EPS	Yield
1	20.79	$2.46	1.42
2	3.03	2.69	4.05
3	44.46	−0.28	4.16
⋮	⋮	⋮	⋮
18	30.21	1.71	3.07
19	32.88	0.35	2.21
20	15.19	5.02	3.50

   a. Develop a multiple linear regression with P/E as the dependent variable.
   b. Are either of the two independent variables an effective predictor of P/E?
   c. Interpret the regression coefficients.
   d. Do any of these stocks look particularly undervalued?
   e. Plot the residuals and check the normality assumption. Plot the fitted values against the residuals.
   f. Does there appear to be any problems with homoscedasticity?
   g. Develop a correlation matrix. Do any of the correlations indicate multicollinearity?

526   CHAPTER 14

For **DATA FILE**, please visit
www.mhhe.com/lind16e

28. The Conch Café, located in Gulf Shores, Alabama, features casual lunches with a great view of the Gulf of Mexico. To accommodate the increase in business during the summer vacation season, Fuzzy Conch, the owner, hires a large number of servers as seasonal help. When he interviews a prospective server, he would like to provide data on the amount a server can earn in tips. He believes that the amount of the bill and the number of diners are both related to the amount of the tip. He gathered the following sample information.

Customer	Amount of Tip	Amount of Bill	Number of Diners
1	$7.00	$48.97	5
2	4.50	28.23	4
3	1.00	10.65	1
⋮	⋮	⋮	⋮
28	2.50	26.25	2
29	9.25	56.81	5
30	8.25	50.65	5

a. Develop a multiple regression equation with the amount of tips as the dependent variable and the amount of the bill and the number of diners as independent variables. Write out the regression equation. How much does another diner add to the amount of the tips?

b. Conduct a global test of hypothesis to determine if at least one of the independent variables is significant. What is your conclusion?

c. Conduct an individual test on each of the variables. Should one or the other be deleted?

d. Use the equation developed in part (c) to determine the coefficient of determination. Interpret the value.

e. Plot the residuals. Is it reasonable to assume they follow the normal distribution?

f. Plot the residuals against the fitted values. Is it reasonable to conclude they are random?

For **DATA FILE**, please visit
www.mhhe.com/lind16e

29. The president of Blitz Sales Enterprises sells kitchen products through television commercials, often called infomercials. He gathered data from the last 15 weeks of sales to determine the relationship between sales and the number of infomercials.

Infomercials	Sales ($000s)	Infomercials	Sales ($000s)
20	3.2	22	2.5
15	2.6	15	2.4
25	3.4	25	3.0
10	1.8	16	2.7
18	2.2	12	2.0
18	2.4	20	2.6
15	2.4	25	2.8
12	1.5		

a. Determine the regression equation. Are the sales predictable from the number of commercials?

b. Determine the residuals and plot a histogram. Does the normality assumption seem reasonable?

For **DATA FILE**, please visit
www.mhhe.com/lind16e

30. The director of special events for Sun City believed that the amount of money spent on fireworks displays on the 4th of July was predictive of attendance at the Fall Festival held in October. She gathered the following data to test her suspicion.

4th of July ($000)	Fall Festival (000)	4th of July ($000)	Fall Festival (000)
10.6	8.8	9.0	9.5
8.5	6.4	10.0	9.8
12.5	10.8	7.5	6.6
9.0	10.2	10.0	10.1
5.5	6.0	6.0	6.1
12.0	11.1	12.0	11.3
8.0	7.5	10.5	8.8
7.5	8.4		

Determine the regression equation. Is the amount spent on fireworks related to attendance at the Fall Festival? Evaluate regression assumptions by examining the residuals.

31. You are a new hire at Laurel Woods Real Estate, which specializes in selling foreclosed homes via public auction. Your boss has asked you to use the following data (mortgage balance, monthly payments, payments made before default, and final auction price) on a random sample of recent sales in order to estimate what the actual auction price will be.

For **DATA FILE**, please visit www.mhhe.com/lind16e

Loan	Monthly Payments	Payments Made	Auction Price
$ 85,600	$ 985.87	1	$16,900
115,300	902.56	33	75,800
103,100	736.28	6	43,900
⋮	⋮	⋮	⋮
119,400	1,021.23	58	69,000
90,600	836.46	3	35,600
104,500	1,056.37	22	63,000

   a. Carry out a global test of hypothesis to verify if any of the regression coefficients are different from zero.

   b. Do an individual test of the independent variables. Would you remove any of the variables?

   c. If it seems one or more of the independent variables is not needed, remove it and work out the revised regression equation.

32. Think about the figures from the previous exercise. Add a new variable that describes the potential interaction between the loan amount and the number of payments made. Then do a test of hypothesis to check if the interaction is significant.

DATA SET EXERCISES

(The data for these exercises are available at the text website: www.mhhe.com/lind16e.)

33. Refer to the Real Estate data, which report information on homes sold in Goodyear, Arizona. Use the selling price of the home as the dependent variable and determine the regression equation with number of bedrooms, size of the house, center of the city, and number of bathrooms as independent variables.

   a. Use a statistical software package to determine the multiple regression equation. Discuss each of the variables. For example, are you surprised that the regression coefficient for distance from the center of the city is negative? How much does a garage or a swimming pool add to the selling price of a home?

   b. Determine the value of the Intercept.

   c. Develop a correlation matrix. Which independent variables have strong or weak correlations with the dependent variable? Do you see any problems with multicollinearity?

   d. Conduct the global test on the set of independent variables. Interpret.

   e. Conduct a test of hypothesis on each of the independent variables. Would you consider deleting any of the variables? If so, which ones?

    f. Rerun the analysis until only significant regression coefficients remain in the analysis. Identify these variables.

    g. Develop a histogram or a stem-and-leaf display of the residuals from the final regression equation developed in part (f). Is it reasonable to conclude that the normality assumption has been met?

    h. Plot the residuals against the fitted values from the final regression equation developed in part (f). Plot the residuals on the vertical axis and the fitted values on the horizontal axis.

34. Refer to the Baseball 2012 data, which report information on the 30 Major League Baseball teams for the 2012 season. Let the number of games won be the dependent variable and the following variables be independent variables: team batting average, number of stolen bases, number of errors committed, team ERA, number of home runs, and whether the team plays in the American or the National League.

    a. Use a statistical software package to determine the multiple regression equation. Discuss each of the variables. For example, are you surprised that the regression coefficient for ERA is negative? Is the number of wins affected by whether the team plays in the National or the American League?

    b. Find the coefficient of determination for this set of independent variables.

    c. Develop a correlation matrix. Which independent variables have strong or weak correlations with the dependent variable? Do you see any problems with multicollinearity?

    d. Conduct a global test on the set of independent variables. Interpret.

    e. Conduct a test of hypothesis on each of the independent variables. Would you consider deleting any of the variables? If so, which ones?

    f. Rerun the analysis until only significant regression coefficients remain in the analysis. Identify these variables.

    g. Develop a histogram or a stem-and-leaf display of the residuals from the final regression equation developed in part (f). Is it reasonable to conclude that the normality assumption has been met?

    h. Plot the residuals against the fitted values from the final regression equation developed in part (f). Plot the residuals on the vertical axis and the fitted values on the horizontal axis.

35. Refer to the Buena School District bus data. First, add a variable to change the type of bus (diesel or gasoline) to a qualitative variable. If the bus type is diesel, then set the qualitative variable to 0. If the bus type is gasoline, then set the qualitative variable to 1. Develop a regression equation using statistical software with maintenance as the dependent variable and age, miles, and bus type as the independent variables.

    a. Write out the multiple regression equation analysis. Discuss each of the variables.

    b. Determine the value of R^2. Interpret.

    c. Develop a correlation matrix. Which independent variables have strong or weak correlations with the dependent variable? Do you see any problems with multicollinearity?

    d. Conduct the global test on the set of independent variables. Interpret.

    e. Conduct a test of hypothesis on each of the independent variables. Would you consider deleting any of the variables? If so, which ones?

    f. Rerun the analysis until only significant regression coefficients remain in the analysis. Identify these variables.

    g. Develop a histogram or a stem-and-leaf display of the residuals from the final regression equation developed in part (f). Is it reasonable to conclude that the normality assumption has been met?

    h. Plot the residuals against the fitted values from the final regression equation developed in part (f) against the fitted values of Y. Plot the residuals on the vertical axis and the fitted values on the horizontal axis.

A REVIEW OF CHAPTERS 13–14

This section is a review of the major concepts and terms introduced in Chapters 13 and 14. Chapter 13 noted that the strength of the relationship between the independent variable and the dependent variable can be measured by the *correlation coefficient*. The correlation coefficient is designated by the letter *r*. It can assume any value between −1.00 and +1.00 inclusive. Coefficients of −1.00 and +1.00 indicate a perfect relationship, and 0 indicates no relationship. A value near 0, such as −.14 or .14, indicates a weak relationship. A value near −1 or +1, such as −.90 or +.90, indicates a strong relationship. Squaring r gives the *coefficient of determination,* also called R^2. It indicates the proportion of the total variation in the dependent variable explained by the independent variable.

Likewise, the strength of the relationship between several independent variables and a dependent variable is measured by the *coefficient of multiple determination, R^2*. It measures the proportion of the variation in y explained by two or more independent variables.

The linear relationship in the simple case involving one independent variable and one dependent variable is described by the equation $\hat{y} = a + bx$. For k independent variables, $x_1, x_2, \ldots x_k$, the same multiple regression equation is

$$\hat{y} = a + b_1x_1 + b_2x_2 + \cdots + b_kx_k$$

Solving for $b_1, b_2, \ldots, b_k$ would involve tedious calculations. Fortunately, this type of problem can be quickly solved using one of the many statistical software packages and spreadsheet packages. Various measures, such as the coefficient of determination, the multiple standard error of estimate, the results of the global test, and the test of the individual variables, are reported in the output of most statistical software programs.

PROBLEMS

1. The accounting department at Box and Go Apparel wishes to estimate the net profit for each of the chain's many stores on the basis of the number of employees in the store, overhead costs, average markup, and theft loss. A few statistics from the stores are:

Store	Net Profit ($ thousands)	Number of Employees	Overhead Cost ($ thousands)	Average Markup (percent)	Theft Loss ($ thousands)
1	$846	143	$79	69%	$52
2	513	110	64	50	45

   a. The dependent variable is _____.
   b. The general equation for this problem is _____.
   c. The multiple regression equation was computed to be $\hat{y} = 67 + 8x_1 - 10x_2 + 0.004x_3 - 3x_4$. What are the predicted sales for a store with 112 employees, an overhead cost of $65,000, a markup rate of 50%, and a loss from theft of $50,000?
   d. Suppose R^2 was computed to be .86. Explain.
   e. Suppose that the multiple standard error of estimate was 3 (in $ thousands). Explain what this means in this problem.

2. Quick-print firms in a large downtown business area spend most of their advertising dollars on displays on bus benches. A research project involves predicting monthly sales based on the annual amount spent on placing ads on bus benches. A sample of quick-print firms revealed these advertising expenses and sales:

Firm	Annual Bus Bench Advertising ($ thousands)	Monthly Sales ($ thousands)
A	2	10
B	4	40
C	5	30
D	7	50
E	3	20

   a. Draw a scatter diagram.
   b. Determine the correlation coefficient.
   c. What is the coefficient of determination?

    d. Compute the regression equation.

    e. Estimate the monthly sales of a quick-print firm that spends $4,500 on bus bench advertisements.

    f. Summarize your findings.

3. The following ANOVA output is given.

Analysis of Variance			
Source	DF	SS	MS
Regression	4	1050.8	262.70
Residual Error	20	83.8	4.19
Total	24	1134.6	
Predictor	Coefficient	SE Coefficient	t
Constant	70.06	2.13	32.89
x_1	0.42	0.17	2.47
x_2	0.27	0.21	1.29
x_3	0.75	0.30	2.50
x_4	0.42	0.07	6.00

    a. Compute the coefficient of determination.

    b. Compute the multiple standard error of estimate.

    c. Conduct a test of hypothesis to determine whether any of the regression coefficients are different from zero.

    d. Conduct a test of hypothesis on the individual regression coefficients. Can any of the variables be deleted?

CASES

A. The Century National Bank

Refer to the Century National Bank data. Using checking account balance as the dependent variable and using as independent variables the number of ATM transactions, the number of other services used, whether the individual has a debit card, and whether interest is paid on the particular account, write a report indicating which of the variables seem related to the account balance and how well they explain the variation in account balances. Should all of the independent variables proposed be used in the analysis or can some be dropped?

B. Terry and Associates: The Time to Deliver Medical Kits

Terry and Associates is a specialized medical testing center in Denver, Colorado. One of the firm's major sources of revenue is a kit used to test for elevated amounts of lead in the blood. Workers in auto body shops, those in the lawn care industry, and commercial house painters are exposed to large amounts of lead and thus must be randomly tested. It is expensive to conduct the test, so the kits are delivered on demand to a variety of locations throughout the Denver area.

Kathleen Terry, the owner, is concerned about setting appropriate costs for each delivery. To investigate, Ms. Terry gathered information on a random sample of 50 recent deliveries. Factors thought to be related to the cost of delivering a kit were:

Prep   The time in minutes between when the customized order is phoned into the company and when it is ready for delivery.

Delivery   The actual travel time in minutes from Terry's plant to the customer.

Mileage   The distance in miles from Terry's plant to the customer.

Sample Number	Cost	Prep	Delivery	Mileage	Sample Number	Cost	Prep	Delivery	Mileage
1	$32.60	10	51	20	6	$22.63	9	20	11
2	23.37	11	33	12	7	22.63	9	39	11
3	31.49	6	47	19	8	21.53	10	23	10
4	19.31	9	18	8	9	21.16	13	20	8
5	28.35	8	88	17	10	21.53	10	32	10

Sample Number	Cost	Prep	Delivery	Mileage	Sample Number	Cost	Prep	Delivery	Mileage
11	$28.17	5	35	16	31	$24.29	7	35	13
12	20.42	7	23	9	32	19.56	2	12	6
13	21.53	9	21	10	33	22.63	8	30	11
14	27.55	7	37	16	34	21.16	5	13	8
15	23.37	9	25	12	35	21.16	11	20	8
16	17.10	15	15	6	36	19.68	5	19	8
17	27.06	13	34	15	37	18.76	5	14	7
18	15.99	8	13	4	38	17.96	5	11	4
19	17.96	12	12	4	39	23.37	10	25	12
20	25.22	6	41	14	40	25.22	6	32	14
21	24.29	3	28	13	41	27.06	8	44	16
22	22.76	4	26	10	42	21.96	9	28	9
23	28.17	9	54	16	43	22.63	8	31	11
24	19.68	7	18	8	44	19.68	7	19	8
25	25.15	6	50	13	45	22.76	8	28	10
26	20.36	9	19	7	46	21.96	13	18	9
27	21.16	3	19	8	47	25.95	10	32	14
28	25.95	10	45	14	48	26.14	8	44	15
29	18.76	12	12	5	49	24.29	8	34	13
30	18.76	8	16	5	50	24.35	3	33	12

1. Develop a multiple linear regression equation that describes the relationship between the cost of delivery and the other variables. Do these three variables explain a reasonable amount of the variation in the dependent variable? Estimate the delivery cost for a kit that takes 10 minutes for preparation, takes 30 minutes to deliver, and must cover a distance of 14 miles.

2. Test to determine that at least one regression coefficient differs from zero. Also test to see whether any of the variables can be dropped from the analysis. If some of the variables can be dropped, rerun the regression equation until only significant variables are included.

3. Write a brief report interpreting the final regression equation.

P R A C T I C E   T E S T

Part 1—Objective

1. In a scatter diagram, the dependent variable is always scaled on which axis?   1. _____
2. What level of measurement is required to compute the correlation coefficient?   2. _____
3. If there is no correlation between two variables, what is the value of the correlation coefficient?   3. _____
4. Which of the following values indicates the strongest correlation between two variables? (.65, −.77, 0, −.12)   4. _____
5. Under what conditions will the coefficient of determination assume a value greater than 1?   5. _____

Given the following regression equation, $\hat{Y} = 7 - .5X$, and that the coefficient of determination is .81, answer questions 6, 7, and 8.

6. At what point does the regression equation cross the Y-axis?   6. _____
7. An increase of 1 unit in the independent variable will result in what amount of an increase or decrease in the dependent variable?   7. _____
8. What is the correlation coefficient? (Be careful of the sign.)   8. _____
9. If all the data points in a scatter diagram were on the regression line, what would be the value of the standard error of estimate?   9. _____
10. In a multiple regression equation, what is the maximum number of independent variables allowed? (2, 10, 30, unlimited)   10. _____
11. In multiple regression analysis, we assume what type of relationship between the dependent variable and the set of independent variables? (linear, multiple, curved, none of these)   11. _____
12. The difference between Y and $\hat{Y}$ is called a _____.   12. _____

13. For a particular dummy variable, such as gender, how many different outcomes are possible?   13. _____

14. What is the term given to a table that shows all possible correlation coefficients between the dependent variable and all the independent variables and among all the independent variables?   14. _____

15. If there is a linear relationship between the dependent variable and the set of independent variables, a graph of the residuals will show what type of distribution?   15. _____

Part 2—Problems

1. Given the following software output:

Regression Analysis

ANOVA Table					
Source	**SS**	**df**	**MS**	**F**	**p-value**
Regression	129.7275	1	129.7275	14.50	.0007
Residual	250.4391	28	8.9443		
Total	380.1667	29			

Regression Output			
Variables	**Coefficients**	**Standard Error**	**t (df = 28)**
Intercept	90.6190	1.5322	59.141
Slope	−0.9401	0.2468	−3.808

  a. What is the sample size?
  b. Write out the regression equation. Interpret the slope and intercept values.
  c. If the value of the independent variable is 10, what is the value of the dependent variable?
  d. Calculate the coefficient of determination. Interpret this value.
  e. Calculate the correlation coefficient. Conduct a test of hypothesis to determine if there is a significant negative association between the variables.

2. Given the following software output.

Regression Analysis

ANOVA Table					
Source	**SS**	**df**	**MS**	**F**	**p-value**
Regression	227.0928	4	56.7732	9.27	0.000
Residual	153.0739	25	6.1230		
Total	380.1667	29			

Regression Output				
Variables	**Coefficients**	**Standard Error**	**t (df = 25)**	**p-value**
Intercept	68.3366	8.9752	7.614	0.000
x_1	0.8595	0.3087	2.784	0.010
x_2	−0.3380	0.8381	−0.403	0.690
x_3	−0.8179	0.2749	−2.975	0.006
x_4	−0.5824	0.2541	−2.292	0.030

  a. How large is the sample size?
  b. How many independent variables are in the study?
  c. Determine the coefficient of determination.
  d. Conduct a global test of hypothesis. Can you conclude at least one of the independent variables does not equal zero? Use the .01 significance level.
  e. Conduct an individual test of hypothesis on each of the independent variables. Would you consider dropping any of the independent variables? If so, which variable or variables would you drop? Use the .01 significance level.

Nonparametric Methods:

NOMINAL LEVEL HYPOTHESIS TESTS

15

FOR MANY YEARS, TV executives used the guideline that 30% of the audience were watching each of the traditional big three prime-time networks and 10% were watching cable stations on a weekday night. A random sample of 500 viewers in the Tampa–St. Petersburg, Florida, area last Monday night showed that 165 homes were tuned in to the ABC affiliate, 140 to the CBS affiliate, 125 to the NBC affiliate, and the remainder were viewing a cable station. At the .05 significance level, can we conclude that the guideline is still reasonable? (See Exercise 24 and LO15-3.)

LEARNING OBJECTIVES

When you have completed this chapter, you will be able to:

LO15-1 Test a hypothesis about a population proportion.

LO15-2 Test a hypothesis about two population proportions.

LO15-3 Test a hypothesis comparing an observed set of frequencies to an expected frequency distribution.

LO15-4 Explain the limitations of using the chi-square statistic in goodness-of-fit tests.

LO15-5 Test a hypothesis that an observed frequency distribution is normally distributed.

LO15-6 Perform a chi-square test for independence on a contingency table.

534   CHAPTER 15

INTRODUCTION

In Chapters 9 through 12 we describe tests of hypothesis for data of interval or ratio scale. Examples of interval and ratio scale data include the scores on the first statistics examination in your class, the incomes of corporate executive officers in technology companies, or years of employment of production workers at the BMW plant in Greer, South Carolina.

We conducted hypothesis tests about a single population mean (Chapter 10), about two population means (Chapter 11), and about three or more population means (Chapter 12). For these tests we use interval or ratio data and assume the populations follow the normal probability distribution. However, there are hypothesis tests that do not require any assumption regarding the shape of the population. Hence, the assumption of a normal population is not necessary. These tests are referred to as nonparametric hypothesis tests.

In this chapter, we begin with tests of hypothesis for nominal scale data. Recall that nominal scale data are simply classified into mutually exclusive categories. In the first two sections of this chapter we describe tests of proportions. In these tests individuals or objects are classified into one of two mutually exclusive groups. Examples include gender (male or female), quality (acceptable or unacceptable), diabetes (yes or no), and airline flight arrivals (on time or late).

We also expand the nominal scale tests to include situations where data are classified into several mutually exclusive categories. The scale of measurement is still nominal, but there are several categories. Examples include the colors of M&M Plain Candies (red, green, blue, yellow, orange, and brown), brand of peanut butter purchased (Peter Pan, Jif, Skippy, and others), or days of the workweek (Monday, Tuesday, Wednesday, Thursday, and Friday). We introduce the chi-square distribution as a new test statistic. It is most often used when there are more than two nominal scale categories.

LO15-1

Test a hypothesis about a population proportion.

TEST A HYPOTHESIS OF A POPULATION PROPORTION

Beginning on page 297 in Chapter 9, we discussed confidence intervals for proportions. We can also conduct a test of hypothesis for a proportion. Recall that a proportion is the ratio of the number of successes to the number of observations. We let X refer to the number of successes and n the number of observations, so the proportion of successes in a fixed number of trials is X/n. Thus, the formula for computing a sample proportion, p, is $p = X/n$. Consider the following potential hypothesis-testing situations.

- Historically, General Motors reports that 70% of leased vehicles are returned with less than 36,000 miles. A recent sample of 200 vehicles returned at the end of their lease showed 158 had less than 36,000 miles. Has the proportion increased?
- The American Association of Retired Persons (AARP) reports that 60% of retired people under the age of 65 would return to work on a full-time basis if a suitable job were available. A sample of 500 retirees under 65 revealed 315 would return to work. Can we conclude that more than 60% would return to work?
- Able Moving and Storage Inc. advises its clients for long-distance residential moves that their household goods will be delivered in 3 to 5 days from the time they are picked up. Able's records show it is successful 90% of the time with this claim. A recent audit revealed it was successful 190 times out of 200. Can the company conclude its success rate has increased?

Some assumptions must be made and conditions met before testing a population proportion. To test a hypothesis about a population proportion, a random sample is chosen from the population. It is assumed that the binomial assumptions discussed in Chapter 6 are met: (1) the sample data collected are the result of counts; (2) the outcome of an experiment is classified into one of two mutually exclusive categories— a "success" or a "failure"; (3) the probability of a success is the same for each trial; and (4) the trials are independent, meaning the outcome of one trial does not affect the outcome of any other trial. This test is appropriate when both $n\pi$ and $n(1 - \pi)$ are at least 5. n is the sample size, and π is the population proportion. It takes advantage of the fact that a binomial distribution can be approximated by the normal distribution.

EXAMPLE

A Republican governor of a western state is thinking about running for reelection. Historically, to be reelected, a Republican candidate needs to earn at least 80% of the vote in the northern section of the state. The governor hires a polling organization to survey the voters in the northern section of the state and determine what percent would vote for him. The polling organization will survey 2,000 voters. Use a statistical hypothesis-testing procedure to assess the governor's chances of reelection.

SOLUTION

This situation regarding the governor's reelection meets the binomial conditions.

- There are only two possible outcomes. That is, a sampled voter will either vote or not vote for the governor.
- The probability of a success is the same for each trial. In this case, the likelihood a particular sampled voter will support reelection is .80.
- The trials are independent. This means, for example, the likelihood the 23rd voter sampled will support reelection is not affected by what the 24th or 52nd voter does.
- The sample data are the result of counts. We are going to count the number of voters who support reelection in the sample of 2,000.

We can use a normal approximation to the binomial distribution if both $n\pi$ and $n(1 - \pi)$ exceed 5. In this case, $n = 2,000$ and $\pi = 0.80$. (π is the proportion of the vote in the northern part of the state, or 80%, needed to be elected.) Thus, $n\pi = 2,000(.80) = 1,600$ and $n(1 - \pi) = 2,000(1 - .80) = 400$. Both 1,600 and 400 are clearly greater than 5.

Step 1: **State the null hypothesis and the alternate hypothesis.** The null hypothesis, H_0, is that the population proportion π is .80 or larger. The alternate hypothesis, H_1, is that the proportion is less than .80. From a practical standpoint, the incumbent governor is concerned only when the proportion is less than .80. If it is equal to or greater than .80, he will have no problem; that is, the sample data would indicate he will probably be reelected. These hypotheses are written symbolically as:

$$H_0: \pi \geq .80$$

$$H_1: \pi < .80$$

H_1 states a direction. Thus, as noted previously, the test is one-tailed with the inequality sign pointing to the tail of the distribution containing the region of rejection.

Step 2: **Select the level of significance.** The level of significance is .05. This is the likelihood that a true hypothesis will be rejected.

Step 3: **Select the test statistic.** z is the appropriate statistic, found by:

TEST OF HYPOTHESIS, ONE PROPORTION	$z = \dfrac{p - \pi}{\sqrt{\dfrac{\pi(1 - \pi)}{n}}}$	[15–1]

where:

π is the population proportion.

p is the sample proportion.

n is the sample size.

Step 4: **Formulate the decision rule.** The critical value or values of z form the dividing point or points between the regions where H_0 is rejected and where it is not rejected. Because the alternate hypothesis states a direction, this is a one-tailed test. The sign of the inequality points to the left, so only the left side of the curve is used. (See Chart 15–1.) The significance level is .05. This probability is in the left tail and determines the region of rejection. The area between zero and the critical value is .4500, found by .5000 − .0500. Referring to Appendix B.3, go to the column indicating a .05 significance level for a one-tailed test, find the row with infinite degrees of freedom, and read the z value of 1.645. The decision rule is, therefore: Reject the null hypothesis and accept the alternate hypothesis if the computed value of z falls to the left of −1.645; otherwise do not reject H_0.

CHART 15–1 Rejection Region for the .05 Level of Significance, One-Tailed Test

Step 5: **Make a decision.** Select a sample and make a decision about H_0. A sample survey of 2,000 potential voters in the northern part of the state revealed that 1,550 planned to vote for the incumbent governor. Is the sample proportion of .775 (found by 1,550/2,000) close enough to .80 to conclude that the difference is due to sampling error? In this case:

p is .775, the proportion in the sample who plan to vote for the governor.

n is 2,000, the number of voters surveyed.

π is .80, the hypothesized population proportion.

z is a normally distributed test statistic when the hypothesis is true and the other assumptions are true.

Using formula (15–1) and computing z gives

$$z = \frac{p - \pi}{\sqrt{\dfrac{\pi(1 - \pi)}{n}}} = \frac{\dfrac{1{,}550}{2{,}000} - .80}{\sqrt{\dfrac{.80(1 - .80)}{2{,}000}}} = \frac{.775 - .80}{\sqrt{.00008}} = -2.80$$

The computed value of z (−2.80) is less than the critical value, so the null hypothesis is rejected at the .05 level. The difference of 2.5 percentage points between the sample percent (77.5%) and the hypothesized population percent in the northern part of the state necessary to carry the state (80%) is statistically significant. From Appendix B.3, the probability of a z value between zero and −2.80 is .4974. So the p-value is .0026, found by .5000 − .4974. Because the p-value is less than the significance level, the null hypothesis is rejected.

Step 6: Interpret the result. The governor can conclude that he does not have the necessary support in the northern section of the state to win reelection. To put it another way, the evidence at this point does not support the claim that the incumbent governor will return to the governor's mansion for another 4 years.

SELF-REVIEW

15–1

A recent insurance industry report indicated that 40% of those persons involved in minor traffic accidents this year have been involved in at least one other traffic accident in the last 5 years. An advisory group decided to investigate this claim, believing it was too large. A sample of 200 traffic accidents this year showed 74 persons were also involved in another accident within the last 5 years. Use the .01 significance level.
(a) Can we use z as the test statistic? Tell why or why not.
(b) State the null hypothesis and the alternate hypothesis.
(c) Show the decision rule graphically.
(d) Compute the value of z and state your decision regarding the null hypothesis.
(e) Determine and interpret the p-value.

EXERCISES

1. The following hypotheses are given.

$$H_0: \pi \leq .70$$
$$H_1: \pi > .70$$

A sample of 100 observations revealed that $p = .75$. At the .05 significance level, can the null hypothesis be rejected?
   a. State the decision rule.
   b. Compute the value of the test statistic.
   c. What is your decision regarding the null hypothesis?
2. The following hypotheses are given.

$$H_0: \pi = .40$$
$$H_1: \pi \neq .40$$

A sample of 120 observations revealed that $p = .30$. At the .05 significance level, can the null hypothesis be rejected?
   a. State the decision rule.
   b. Compute the value of the test statistic.
   c. What is your decision regarding the null hypothesis?

Note: It is recommended that you use the six-step hypothesis-testing procedure in solving the following problems.

3. The National Safety Council reported that 52% of American turnpike drivers are men. A sample of 300 cars traveling southbound on the New Jersey Turnpike yesterday revealed that 170 were driven by men. At the .01 significance level, can we conclude that a larger proportion of men were driving on the New Jersey Turnpike than the national statistics indicate?
4. A recent article reported that a job awaits only one in three new college graduates. The major reasons given were an overabundance of college graduates and a weak economy. A survey of 200 recent graduates from your school revealed that 80 students had jobs. At the .01 significance level, can we conclude that a larger proportion of students at your school have jobs?
5. Chicken Delight claims that 90% of its orders are delivered within 10 minutes of the time the order is placed. A sample of 100 orders revealed that 82 were delivered within the promised time. At the .10 significance level, can we conclude that less than 90% of the orders are delivered in less than 10 minutes?
6. Research at the University of Toledo indicates that 50% of students change their major area of study after their first year in a program. A random sample of 100 students in the College of Business revealed that 48 had changed their major area of study after their first year of the program. Has there been a significant decrease in the proportion of students who change their major after the first year in this program? Test at the .05 level of significance.

TWO-SAMPLE TESTS ABOUT PROPORTIONS

LO15-2
Test a hypothesis about two population proportions.

In the previous section, we considered a test of a single population proportion. However, we are often interested also in whether two sample proportions come from populations that are equal. Here are several examples.

- The vice president of human resources wishes to know whether there is a difference in the proportion of hourly employees who miss more than 5 days of work per year at the Atlanta and the Houston plants.
- General Motors is considering a new design for the Chevy Malibu. The design is shown to a group of potential buyers under 30 years of age and another group over 60 years of age. General Motors wishes to know whether there is a difference in the proportion of the two groups who like the new design.
- A consultant to the airline industry is investigating the fear of flying among adults. Specifically, the company wishes to know whether there is a difference in the proportion of men versus women who are fearful of flying.

In the above cases, each sampled item or individual can be classified as a "success" or a "failure." That is, in the Chevy Malibu example, each potential buyer is classified as "liking the new design" or "not liking the new design." We then compare the proportion in the under-30 group with the proportion in the over-60 group who indicated they liked the new design. Can we conclude that the differences are due to chance? In this study, there is no measurement obtained, only classifying the individuals or objects.

To conduct the test, we assume each sample is large enough that the normal distribution will serve as a good approximation of the binomial distribution. The test statistic follows the standard normal distribution. We compute the value of z from the following formula:

TWO-SAMPLE TEST OF PROPORTIONS
$$z = \frac{p_1 - p_2}{\sqrt{\dfrac{p_c(1 - p_c)}{n_1} + \dfrac{p_c(1 - p_c)}{n_2}}}$$ [15–2]

where:

n_1 is the number of observations in the first sample.
n_2 is the number of observations in the second sample.
p_1 is the proportion in the first sample possessing the trait.
p_2 is the proportion in the second sample possessing the trait.
p_c is the pooled proportion possessing the trait in the combined samples. It is called the pooled estimate of the population proportion and is computed from the following formula.

POOLED PROPORTION	$p_c = \dfrac{x_1 + x_2}{n_1 + n_2}$	[15–3]

where:

x_1 is the number possessing the trait in the first sample.
x_2 is the number possessing the trait in the second sample.

The following example will illustrate the two-sample test of proportions.

EXAMPLE

Manelli Perfume Company recently developed a new fragrance that it plans to market under the name Heavenly. A number of market studies indicate that Heavenly has very good market potential. The sales department at Manelli is particularly interested in whether there is a difference in the proportions of young and older women who would purchase Heavenly if it were marketed. There are two independent populations, a population consisting of the young women and a population consisting of the older women. Each sampled woman will be asked to smell Heavenly and indicate whether she likes the fragrance well enough to purchase a bottle.

SOLUTION

We will use the usual six-step hypothesis-testing procedure.

Step 1: State H_0 and H_1. In this case, the null hypothesis is: "There is no difference in the proportion of young women and older women who prefer Heavenly." We designate π_1 as the proportion of young women who would purchase Heavenly and π_2 as the proportion of older women who would purchase it. The alternate hypothesis is that the two proportions are not equal.

$$H_0: \pi_1 = \pi_2$$
$$H_1: \pi_1 \neq \pi_2$$

Step 2: Select the level of significance. We choose the .05 significance level in this example.

Step 3: Determine the test statistic. The test statistic follows the standard normal distribution. The value of the test statistic can be computed from formula (15–2).

Step 4: Formulate the decision rule. Recall that the alternate hypothesis from **Step 1** does not state a direction, so this is a two-tailed test. To find the critical value, go to Student's t distribution (Appendix B.5). In the table headings, find the row labeled **"Level of Significance for Two-Tailed Test"** and select the column for an alpha of .05. Go to the bottom row with infinite degrees of freedom. The z critical value is 1.960, so the critical values are −1.960 and 1.960. As before, if the computed test statistic is less than −1.960 or greater than 1.960, the null hypothesis is rejected. This information is summarized in Chart 15–2.

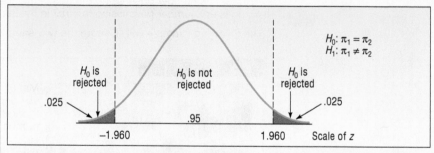

CHART 15–2 Decision Rules for Heavenly Fragrance Test, .05 Significance Level

Step 5: Select a sample and make a decision. A random sample of 100 young women revealed 19 liked the Heavenly fragrance well enough to purchase it. Similarly, a sample of 200 older women revealed 62 liked the fragrance well enough to make a purchase. We let p_1 refer to the young women and p_2 to the older women.

$$p_1 = \frac{x_1}{n_1} = \frac{19}{100} = .19 \qquad p_2 = \frac{x_2}{n_2} = \frac{62}{200} = .31$$

The research question is whether the difference of .12 in the two sample proportions is due to chance or whether there is a difference in the proportion of young and older women who like the Heavenly fragrance.

Next, we combine or pool the sample proportions. We use formula (15–3).

$$p_c = \frac{x_1 + x_2}{n_1 + n_2} = \frac{19 + 62}{100 + 200} = \frac{81}{300} = 0.27$$

Note that the pooled proportion is closer to .31 than to .19 because more older women than young women were sampled.

We use formula (15–2) to find the value of the test statistic.

$$z = \frac{p_1 - p_2}{\sqrt{\dfrac{p_c(1 - p_c)}{n_1} + \dfrac{p_c(1 - p_c)}{n_2}}} = \frac{.19 - .31}{\sqrt{\dfrac{.27(1 - .27)}{100} + \dfrac{.27(1 - .27)}{200}}} = -2.207$$

The computed value of -2.207 is in the area of rejection; that is, it is to the left of -1.960. Therefore, the null hypothesis is rejected at the .05 significance level. To put it another way, we reject the null hypothesis that the proportion of young women who would purchase Heavenly is equal to the proportion of older women who would purchase Heavenly.

To find the p-value, we need to round the z test statistic from -2.207 to -2.21 so that we can use the table Areas under the Normal Curve in Appendix B.3. In the table, find the likelihood, or probability, of a z value less than -2.21 or greater than 2.21. The probability corresponding to 2.21 is .4864, so the likelihood of finding the value of the test statistic to be less than -2.21 or greater than 2.21 is:

$$p\text{-value} = 2(.5000 - .4864) = 2(.0136) = .0272$$

The p-value of .0272 is less than the significance level of .05, so our decision is to reject the null hypothesis.

Step 6: Interpret the result. The results of the hypothesis test indicate younger and older women purchase Heavenly at different rates or proportions.

The MegaStat add-in for Excel has a procedure to determine the value of the test statistic and compute the p-value. Notice that the MegaStat output includes the two sample proportions, the value of z, and the p-value. The difference in the p-value is rounding. The results follow.

Hypothesis test for two independent proportions			
$p1$	$p2$	p_c	
0.19	0.31	0.27	p (as decimal)
19/100	62/200	81/300	p (as fraction)
19.	62.	81.	X
100	200	300	n
		-0.12	difference
		0.	hypothesized difference
		0.0544	std. error
		-2.21	z
		.0273	p-value (two-tailed)

SELF-REVIEW

15–2

Of 150 adults who tried a new peach-flavored Peppermint Pattie, 87 rated it excellent. Of 200 children sampled, 123 rated it excellent. Using the .10 level of significance, can we conclude that there is a significant difference in the proportion of adults and the proportion of children who rate the new flavor excellent?

(a) State the null hypothesis and the alternate hypothesis.
(b) What is the probability of a Type I error?
(c) Is this a one-tailed or a two-tailed test?
(d) What is the decision rule?
(e) What is the value of the test statistic?
(f) What is your decision regarding the null hypothesis?
(g) What is the p-value? Explain what it means in terms of this problem.

542   CHAPTER 15

EXERCISES

▼

7. The null and alternate hypotheses are:

$$H_0: \pi_1 \le \pi_2$$
$$H_1: \pi_1 > \pi_2$$

A sample of 100 observations from the first population indicated that X_1 is 70. A sample of 150 observations from the second population revealed X_2 to be 90. Use the .05 significance level to test the hypothesis.
   a. State the decision rule.
   b. Compute the pooled proportion.
   c. Compute the value of the test statistic.
   d. What is your decision regarding the null hypothesis?

8. The null and alternate hypotheses are:

$$H_0: \pi_1 = \pi_2$$
$$H_1: \pi_1 \ne \pi_2$$

A sample of 200 observations from the first population indicated that x_1 is 170. A sample of 150 observations from the second population revealed x_2 to be 110. Use the .05 significance level to test the hypothesis.
   a. State the decision rule.
   b. Compute the pooled proportion.
   c. Compute the value of the test statistic.
   d. What is your decision regarding the null hypothesis?

Note: Use the six-step hypothesis-testing procedure in solving the following exercises.

9. The Damon family owns a large grape vineyard in western New York along Lake Erie. The grapevines must be sprayed at the beginning of the growing season to protect against various insects and diseases. Two new insecticides have just been marketed: Pernod 5 and Action. To test their effectiveness, three long rows were selected and sprayed with Pernod 5, and three others were sprayed with Action. When the grapes ripened, 400 of the vines treated with Pernod 5 were checked for infestation. Likewise, a sample of 400 vines sprayed with Action were checked. The results are:

Insecticide	Number of Vines Checked (sample size)	Number of Infested Vines
Pernod 5	400	24
Action	400	40

At the .05 significance level, can we conclude that there is a difference in the proportion of vines infested using Pernod 5 as opposed to Action?

10. GfK Custom Research North America conducted identical surveys 5 years apart. One question asked of women was "Are most men basically kind, gentle, and thoughtful?" The earlier survey revealed that, of the 3,000 women surveyed, 2,010 said that they were. The later revealed 1,530 of the 3,000 women surveyed thought that men were kind, gentle, and thoughtful. At the .05 level, can we conclude that women think men are less kind, gentle, and thoughtful in the later survey compared with the earlier one?

11. A nationwide sample of influential Republicans and Democrats was asked as a part of a comprehensive survey whether they favored lowering environmental standards so that high-sulfur coal could be burned in coal-fired power plants. The results were:

	Republicans	Democrats
Number sampled	1,000	800
Number in favor	200	168

At the .02 level of significance, can we conclude that there is a larger proportion of Democrats in favor of lowering the standards? Determine the *p*-value.

12. The research department at the home office of New Hampshire Insurance conducts ongoing research on the causes of automobile accidents, the characteristics of the drivers, and so on. A random sample of 400 policies written on single persons revealed 120 had at

least one accident in the previous three-year period. Similarly, a sample of 600 policies written on married persons revealed that 150 had been in at least one accident. At the .05 significance level, is there a significant difference in the proportions of single and married persons having an accident during a three-year period? Determine the *p*-value.

LO15-3

Test a hypothesis comparing an observed set of frequencies to an expected frequency distribution.

GOODNESS-OF-FIT TESTS: COMPARING OBSERVED AND EXPECTED FREQUENCY DISTRIBUTIONS

Next, we compare two distributions of nominal scale data that are summarized by several categories. For example, a life insurance company classified its policies into four categories: whole life, level term, decreasing term, and others. The table below shows the historical relative frequency distribution of the policy types.

Policy Type	Percent
Whole life	40
Level term	25
Decreasing term	15
Other	20

The insurance company wishes to compare this distribution with the distribution of policy types purchased by a sample of 2,000 young married adults. In situations where the data are nominally scaled and we wish to compare two distributions, we call this a goodness-of-fit test. A goodness-of-fit test is one of the most commonly used statistical tests. It is particularly useful because it requires only the nominal level of measurement. So we can conduct a test of hypothesis on data that have been classified into categories or groups.

Hypothesis Test of Equal Expected Frequencies

Our first illustration of a goodness-of-fit test involves the case when the expected frequencies are equal. As the full name implies, the purpose of the goodness-of-fit test is to compare an observed frequency distribution to an expected frequency distribution. An example will describe the hypothesis-testing situation.

EXAMPLE

Bubba's Fish and Pasta is a chain of restaurants located along the Gulf Coast of Florida. Bubba, the owner, is considering adding steak to his menu. Before doing so, he decides to hire Magnolia Research, LLC, to conduct a survey of adults as to their favorite meal when eating out. Magnolia selected a sample 120 adults and asked each to indicate his or her favorite meal when dining out. The results are reported below.

TABLE 15–1 Favorite Entrée as Selected by a Sample of 120 Adults

Favorite Entrée	Frequency
Chicken	32
Fish	24
Meat	35
Pasta	29
Total	120

Is it reasonable to conclude there is no preference among the four entrées?

SOLUTION

If there is no difference in the popularity of the four entrées, we would expect the observed frequencies to be equal—or nearly equal. To put it another way, we would expect as many adults to indicate they preferred chicken as fish. Thus, any discrepancy in the observed and expected frequencies is attributed to sampling error or chance.

What is the level of measurement in this problem? Notice that when a person is selected, we can only classify the selected adult as to the entrée pre-

ferred. We do not get a reading or a measurement of any kind. The "measurement" or "classification" is based on the selected entrée. In addition, there is no natural order to the favorite entrée. No one entrée is assumed better than another. Therefore, the nominal scale is appropriate.

If the entrées are equally popular, we would expect 30 adults to select each meal. Why is this so? If there are 120 adults in the sample and four categories, we expect that one-fourth of those surveyed would select each entrée. So 30, found by 120/4, is the expected frequency for each category or cell, assuming there is no preference for any of the entrées. This information is summarized in Table 15–2. An examination of the data indicates meat is the entrée selected most frequently (35 out of 120) and fish is selected least frequently (24 out of 120). Is the difference in the number of times each entrée is selected due to chance, or should we conclude that the entrées are not equally preferred?

TABLE 15–2 Observed and Expected Frequencies for Survey of 120 Adults

Favorite Meal	Observed Frequency, f_o	Expected Frequency, f_e
Chicken	32	30
Fish	24	30
Meat	35	30
Pasta	29	30
Total	120	120

To investigate the issue, we use the six-step hypothesis-testing procedure.

Step 1: State the null hypothesis and the alternate hypothesis. The null hypothesis, H_0, is that there is no difference between the set of observed frequencies and the set of expected frequencies. In other words, any difference between the two sets of frequencies is attributed to sampling error. The alternate hypothesis, H_1, is that there is a difference between the observed and expected sets of frequencies. If the null hypothesis is rejected and the alternate hypothesis is accepted, we conclude the preferences are not equally distributed among the four categories (cells).

H_0: There is no difference in the proportion of adults selecting each entrée.

H_1: There is a difference in the proportion of adults selecting each entrée.

Step 2: **Select the level of significance.** We selected the .05 significance level. The probability is .05 that a true null hypothesis is rejected.

Step 3: **Select the test statistic.** The test statistic follows the chi-square distribution, designated by χ^2.

$$\text{CHI-SQUARE TEST STATISTIC} \qquad \chi^2 = \Sigma \left[\frac{(f_o - f_e)^2}{f_e} \right] \qquad \textbf{[15–4]}$$

with $k - 1$ degrees of freedom, where:

k is the number of categories.

f_o is an observed frequency in a particular category.

f_e is an expected frequency in a particular category.

We will examine the characteristics of the chi-square distribution in more detail shortly.

Step 4: **Formulate the decision rule.** Recall that the decision rule in hypothesis testing is the value that separates the region where we do not reject H_0 from the region where H_0 is rejected. This number is called the *critical value*. As we will soon see, the chi-square distribution is really a family of distributions. Each distribution has a slightly different shape, depending on the number of degrees of freedom. The number of degrees of freedom is $k - 1$, where k is the number of categories. In this particular problem, there are four categories, the four meal entrées. Because there are four categories, there are $k - 1 = 4 - 1 = 3$ degrees of freedom. As noted, a category is called a *cell*, and there are four cells. The critical value for 3 degrees of freedom and the .05 level of significance is found in Appendix B.7. A portion of that table is shown in Table 15–3. The critical value is 7.815, found by locating 3 degrees of freedom in the left margin and then moving horizontally (to the right) and reading the critical value in the .05 column.

TABLE 15–3 A Portion of the Chi-Square Table

Degrees of Freedom	Right-Tail Area			
df	.10	.05	.02	.01
1	2.706	3.841	5.412	6.635
2	4.605	5.991	7.824	9.210
3	6.251	7.815	9.837	11.345
4	7.779	9.488	11.668	13.277
5	9.236	11.070	13.388	15.086

The decision rule is to reject the null hypothesis if the computed value of chi-square is greater than 7.815. If it is less than or equal to 7.815, we fail to reject the null hypothesis. Chart 15–3 shows the decision rule.

CHART 15–3 Chi-Square Probability Distribution for 3 Degrees of Freedom, Showing the Region of Rejection, .05 Level of Significance

The decision rule indicates that if there are large differences between the observed and expected frequencies, resulting in a computed χ^2 of more than 7.815, the null hypothesis should be rejected. However, if the differences between f_o and f_e are small, the computed χ^2 value will be 7.815 or less, and the null hypothesis should not be rejected. The reasoning is that such small differences between the observed and expected frequencies are probably due to chance. Remember, the 120 observations are a sample of the population.

Step 5: **Compute the value of chi-square and make a decision.** Of the 120 adults in the sample, 32 indicated their favorite entrée was chicken. The counts were reported in Table 15–1. The calculations for chi-square follow. (Note again that the expected frequencies are the same for each cell.)

Column D: Determine the differences between each f_o and f_e. That is, $f_o - f_e$. The sum of these differences is zero.

Column E: Square the difference between each observed and expected frequency, that is, $(f_o - f_e)^2$.

Column F: Divide the result for each observation by the expected frequency, that is, $(f_o - f_e)^2/f_e$. Finally, sum these values. The result is the value of χ^2, which is 2.20.

	A	B	C	D	E	F	G
1	Favorite Entrée	f_o	f_e	$(f_o - f_e)$	$(f_o - f_e)^2$	$(f_o - f_e)^2/f_e$	
2	Chicken	32	30	2	4	0.133	
3	Fish	24	30	-6	36	1.200	
4	Meat	35	30	5	25	0.833	χ^2 Value
5	Pasta	29	30	-1	1	0.033	
6	Total	120	120			2.200	

The computed χ^2 of 2.20 is not in the rejection region. It is less than the critical value of 7.815. The decision, therefore, is to not reject the null hypothesis.

Step 6: **Interpret the results.** We conclude that the differences between the observed and the expected frequencies could be due to chance. The data do not suggest that the preferences among the four entrées are different.

We can use Megastat to compute the goodness-of-fit test as follows. The steps are shown in the **Software Commands** in Appendix C. The computed value of

NONPARAMETRIC METHODS: NOMINAL LEVEL HYPOTHESIS TESTS   547

chi-square is 2.20, the same value obtained in our earlier calculations. Also note the *p*-value is .5319, much larger than .05.

```
Goodness-of-Fit Test

  observed       expected        O - E      (O - E)²/E      % of chisq
        32         30.000         2.000          0.133            6.06
        24         30.000        -6.000          1.200           54.55
        35         30.000         5.000          0.833           37.88
        29         30.000        -1.000          0.033            1.52
       120        120.000         0.000          2.200          100.00

      2.20      chi-square
         3      df
     .5319      p-value
```

The distribution of the chi-square statistic has the following characteristics.

1. **Chi-square values are never negative.** This is because the difference between f_o and f_e is squared, that is, $(f_o - f_e)^2$.
2. **There is a family of chi-square distributions.** There is a chi-square distribution for 1 degree of freedom, another for 2 degrees of freedom, another for 3 degrees of freedom, and so on. In this type of problem, the number of degrees of freedom is determined by $k - 1$, where k is the number of categories. Therefore, the shape of the chi-square distribution does *not* depend on the size of the sample, but on the number of categories used. For example, if 200 employees of an airline were classified into one of three categories—flight personnel, ground support, and administrative personnel—there would be $k - 1 = 3 - 1 = 2$ degrees of freedom.
3. **The chi-square distribution is positively skewed.** However, as the number of degrees of freedom increases, the distribution begins to approximate the normal probability distribution. Chart 15–4 shows the distributions for selected degrees of freedom. Notice that for 10 degrees of freedom the curve is approaching a normal distribution.

CHART 15–4 Chi-Square Distributions for Selected Degrees of Freedom

548   CHAPTER 15

SELF-REVIEW

15-3

The human resources director at Georgetown Paper Inc. is concerned about absenteeism among hourly workers. She decides to sample the company records to determine whether absenteeism is distributed evenly throughout the six-day workweek. The hypotheses are:

H_0: Absenteeism is evenly distributed throughout the workweek.
H_1: Absenteeism is *not* evenly distributed throughout the workweek.

The sample results are:

	Number Absent		Number Absent
Monday	12	Thursday	10
Tuesday	9	Friday	9
Wednesday	11	Saturday	9

(a) What are the numbers 12, 9, 11, 10, 9, and 9 called?
(b) How many categories (cells) are there?
(c) What is the *expected* frequency for each day?
(d) How many degrees of freedom are there?
(e) What is the chi-square critical value at the 1% significance level?
(f) Compute the χ^2 test statistic.
(g) What is the decision regarding the null hypothesis?
(h) Specifically, what does this indicate to the human resources director?

EXERCISES

13. In a particular chi-square goodness-of-fit test, there are four categories and 200 observations. Use the .05 significance level.
  a. How many degrees of freedom are there?
  b. What is the critical value of chi-square?
14. In a particular chi-square goodness-of-fit test, there are six categories and 500 observations. Use the .01 significance level.
  a. How many degrees of freedom are there?
  b. What is the critical value of chi-square?
15. The null hypothesis and the alternate hypothesis are:

H_0: The frequencies are equal.
H_1: The frequencies are not equal.

Category	f_o
A	10
B	20
C	30

  a. State the decision rule, using the .05 significance level.
  b. Compute the value of chi-square.
  c. What is your decision regarding H_0?
16. The null hypothesis and the alternate hypothesis are:

H_0: The frequencies are equal.
H_1: The frequencies are not equal.

Category	f_o
A	10
B	20
C	30
D	20

  a. State the decision rule, using the .05 significance level.
  b. Compute the value of chi-square.
  c. What is your decision regarding H_0?

17. A six-sided die is rolled 30 times and the numbers 1 through 6 appear as shown in the following frequency distribution. At the .10 significance level, can we conclude that the die is fair?

Outcome	Frequency	Outcome	Frequency
1	3	4	3
2	6	5	9
3	2	6	7

18. Classic Golf Inc. manages five courses in the Jacksonville, Florida, area. The director of golf wishes to study the number of rounds of golf played per weekday at the five courses. He gathered the following sample information. At the .05 significance level, is there a difference in the number of rounds played by day of the week?

Day	Rounds
Monday	124
Tuesday	74
Wednesday	104
Thursday	98
Friday	120

For **DATA FILE**, please visit
www.mhhe.com/lind16e

19. A group of department store buyers viewed a new line of dresses and gave their opinions of them. The results were:

Opinion	Number of Buyers	Opinion	Number of Buyers
Outstanding	47	Good	39
Excellent	45	Fair	35
Very good	40	Undesirable	34

Because the largest number (47) indicated the new line is outstanding, the head designer thinks that this is a mandate to go into mass production of the dresses. The head sweeper (who somehow became involved in this) believes that there is not a clear mandate and claims that the opinions are evenly distributed among the six categories. He further states that the slight differences among the various counts are probably due to chance. Test the null hypothesis that there is no significant difference among the opinions of the buyers. Test at the .01 level of risk. Follow a formal approach; that is, state the null hypothesis, the alternate hypothesis, and so on.

For **DATA FILE**, please visit
www.mhhe.com/lind16e

20. The safety director of a large steel mill took samples at random from company records of minor work-related accidents and classified them according to the time the accident took place.

Time	Number of Accidents	Time	Number of Accidents
8 up to 9 a.m.	6	1 up to 2 p.m.	7
9 up to 10 a.m.	6	2 up to 3 p.m.	8
10 up to 11 a.m.	20	3 up to 4 p.m.	19
11 up to 12 p.m.	8	4 up to 5 p.m.	6

Using the goodness-of-fit test and the .01 level of significance, determine whether the accidents are evenly distributed throughout the day. Write a brief explanation of your conclusion.

Hypothesis Test of Unequal Expected Frequencies

The expected frequencies (f_e) in the previous example/solution involving preferred entrées were all equal. According to the null hypothesis, it was expected that of the

550   CHAPTER 15

120 adults in the study, an equal number would select each of the four entrées. So we expect 30 to select chicken, 30 to select fish, and so on. The chi-square test can also be used if the expected frequencies are not equal.

The following example illustrates the case of unequal frequencies and also gives a practical use of the chi-square goodness-of-fit test—namely, to find whether a local experience differs from the national experience.

EXAMPLE

The American Hospital Administrators Association (AHAA) reports the following information concerning the number of times senior citizens are admitted to a hospital during a one-year period. Forty percent are not admitted; 30% are admitted once; 20% are admitted twice, and the remaining 10% are admitted three or more times.

A survey of 150 residents of Bartow Estates, a community devoted to active seniors located in central Florida, revealed 55 residents were not admitted during the last year, 50 were admitted to a hospital once, 32 were admitted twice, and the rest of those in the survey were admitted three or more times. Can we conclude the survey at Bartow Estates is consistent with the information reported by the AHAA? Use the .05 significance level.

SOLUTION

We begin by organizing the above information into Table 15–4. Clearly, we cannot compare percentages given in the study by AHAA to the frequencies reported for the Bartow Estates. However, these percentages can be converted to expected frequencies, f_e. According to AHAA, 40% of the Bartow residents in the survey did not require hospitalization. Thus, if there is no difference between the national experience and those of Bartow Estates, then 40% of the 150 seniors surveyed (60 residents) would not have been hospitalized. Further, 30% of those surveyed were admitted once (45 residents), and so on. The observed frequencies for Bartow residents and the expected frequencies based on the percents in the national study are given in Table 15–4.

STATISTICS IN ACTION

Many state governments operate lotteries to help fund education. In many lotteries, numbered balls are mixed and selected by a machine. In a Select Three game, numbered balls are selected randomly from three groups of balls numbered zero through nine. Randomness would predict that the frequency of each number is equal. How would you test if the machine ensured a random selection process? A chi-square, goodness-of-fit test could be used to investigate this question.

TABLE 15–4 Summary of Study by AHAA and a Survey of Bartow Estates

Number of Times Admitted	AHAA Percent of Total	Number of Bartow Residents (f_o)	Expected Number of Bartow Residents (f_e)
0	40	55	60
1	30	50	45
2	20	32	30
3 or more	10	13	15
Total	100	150	

The null hypothesis and the alternate hypothesis are:

H_0: There is no difference between local and national experience for hospital admissions.

H_1: There is a difference between local and national experience for hospital admissions.

To find the decision rule, we use Appendix B.7 and the .05 significance level. There are four admitting categories, so the degrees of freedom are $df = 4 - 1 = 3$.

CHART 15–5 Decision Criteria for the Bartow Estates Research Study

The critical value is 7.815. Therefore, the decision rule is to reject the null hypothesis if $\chi^2 > 7.815$. The decision rule is portrayed in Chart 15–5.

Now to compute the chi-square test statistic:

Number of Times Admitted	f_o	f_e	$(f_o - f_e)$	$(f_o - f_e)^2$	$(f_o - f_e)^2/f_e$
0	55	60	−5	25	0.4167
1	50	45	5	25	0.5556
2	32	30	2	4	0.1333
3 or more	13	15	−2	4	0.2667
Total	150				1.3723

χ^2 value → 1.3723

The computed value of χ^2 (1.3723) lies to the left of 7.815. Thus, we cannot reject the null hypothesis. We conclude that the survey results do not provide evidence of a difference between the local and national experience for hospital admissions.

LO15-4

Explain the limitations of using the chi-square statistic in goodness-of-fit tests.

LIMITATIONS OF CHI-SQUARE

If there is an unusually small expected frequency in a cell, chi-square (if applied) might result in an erroneous conclusion. This can happen because f_e appears in the denominator, and dividing by a very small number makes the quotient quite large! Two generally accepted policies regarding small cell frequencies are:

1. If there are only two cells, the *expected* frequency in each cell should be at least 5. The computation of chi-square would be permissible in the following problem, involving a minimum f_e of 6.

Individual	f_o	f_e
Literate	641	642
Illiterate	7	6

2. For more than two cells, chi-square should *not* be used if more than 20% of the f_e cells have expected frequencies less than 5. According to this policy, it would not be appropriate to use the goodness-of-fit test on the following data. Three of the seven cells, or 43%, have expected frequencies (f_e) of less than 5.

Level of Management	f_o	f_e
Foreman	30	32
Supervisor	110	113
Manager	86	87
Middle management	23	24
Assistant vice president	5	2
Vice president	5	4
Senior vice president	4	1
Total	263	263

To show the reason for the 20% policy, we conducted the goodness-of-fit test on the above data on the levels of management. The MegaStat output follows.

Goodness of Fit Test

observed	expected	O - E	$(O - E)^2 / E$	% of chisq
30	32.000	-2.000	0.125	0.89
110	113.000	-3.000	0.080	0.57
86	87.000	-1.000	0.011	0.08
23	24.000	-1.000	0.042	0.30
5	2.000	3.000	4.500	32.12
5	4.000	1.000	0.250	1.78
4	1.000	3.000	9.000	64.25
263	263.000	0.000	14.008	100.00

14.01 chi-square
6 df
.0295 p-value

For this test at the .05 significance level, H_0 is rejected if the computed value of chi-square is greater than 12.592. The computed value is 14.008, so we reject the null hypothesis that the observed frequencies represent a random sample from the population of the expected values. Examine the MegaStat output. More than 98% of the computed chi-square value is accounted for by the three vice president categories [(4.500 + .250 + 9.000)/14.008 = 0.9815]. Logically, too much weight is being given to these categories.

The issue can be resolved by combining categories if it is logical to do so. In the above example, we combine the three vice president categories, which satisfies the 20% policy.

Level of Management	f_o	f_e
Foreman	30	32
Supervisor	110	113
Manager	86	87
Middle management	23	24
Vice president	14	7
Total	263	263

The computed value of chi-square with the revised categories is 7.258. See the following MegaStat output. This value is less than the critical value of 9.488 for the .05 significance level. The null hypothesis is, therefore, not rejected at the .05 significance level. This indicates there is not a significant difference between the observed distribution and the expected distribution.

Goodness-of-Fit Test

Observed	Expected	O - E	$(O - E)^2 / E$	% of chisq
30	32.000	-2.000	0.125	1.72
110	113.000	-3.000	0.080	1.10
86	87.000	-1.000	0.011	0.16
23	24.000	-1.000	0.042	0.57
14	7.000	7.000	7.000	96.45
263	263.000	0.000	7.258	100.00

7.26 chi-square
4 df
.1229 p-value

SELF-REVIEW 15–4

The American Accounting Association classifies accounts receivable as "current," "late," and "not collectible." Industry figures show that 60% of accounts receivable are current, 30% are late, and 10% are not collectible. Massa and Barr, a law firm in Greenville, Ohio, has 500 accounts receivable: 320 are current, 120 are late, and 60 are not collectible. Are these numbers in agreement with the industry distribution? Use the .05 significance level.

EXERCISES

21. The following hypotheses are given:

H_0: Forty percent of the observations are in category A, 40% are in B, and 20% are in C.
H_1: The distribution of the observations is not as described in H_0.

We took a sample of 60, with the results below.

Category	f_o
A	30
B	20
C	10

   a. State the decision rule using the .01 significance level.
   b. Compute the value of chi-square.
   c. What is your decision regarding H_0?

22. The chief of security for Mall of the Dakotas was directed to study the problem of missing goods. He selected a sample of 100 boxes that had been tampered with and ascertained that, for 60 of the boxes, the missing pants, shoes, and so on were attributed to shoplifting. For 30 other boxes, employees had stolen the goods, and for the remaining 10 boxes he blamed poor inventory control. In his report to the mall management, can he say that shoplifting is *twice* as likely to be the cause of the loss as compared with either employee theft or poor inventory control and that employee theft and poor inventory control are equally likely? Use the .02 significance level.

23. The bank credit card department of Carolina Bank knows from experience that 5% of its card holders have had some high school, 15% have completed high school, 25% have had some college, and 55% have completed college. Of the 500 card holders whose cards

have been called in for failure to pay their charges this month, 50 had some high school, 100 had completed high school, 190 had some college, and 160 had completed college. Can we conclude that the distribution of card holders who do not pay their charges is different from all others? Use the .01 significance level.

24. For many years, TV executives used the guideline that 30% of the audience were watching each of the traditional big three prime-time networks and 10% were watching cable stations on a weekday night. A random sample of 500 viewers in the Tampa–St. Petersburg, Florida, area last Monday night showed that 165 homes were tuned in to the ABC affiliate, 140 to the CBS affiliate, and 125 to the NBC affiliate, with the remainder viewing a cable station. At the .05 significance level, can we conclude that the guideline is still reasonable?

LO15-5

Test a hypothesis that an observed frequency distribution is normally distributed.

TESTING THE HYPOTHESIS THAT A DISTRIBUTION IS NORMAL

We use a goodness-of-fit test to compare an observed frequency distribution to an expected frequency distribution. In the example/solution regarding Bubba's Fish and Pasta (page 543), the observed frequencies are the count of each entrée selected for a sample of 120 adults. We determine the expected frequencies by assuming there is no preference for any of the four entrées, so we expect that one-fourth of the sample, or 30 adults, selects each entrée. In this section, we want to test a hypothesis that a distribution is normal by using the goodness-of-fit test to compare an observed frequency distribution to an expected frequency distribution that is normal. Why is this test important? In Chapter 11, when we tested for differences in two population means, we assumed the two populations followed the normal distribution. We made the same assumption in Chapter 12 when we tested if several population means were equal. In Chapter 13 on page 455 we assume the distribution of the residuals in a least squares regression analysis follow the normal probability distribution.

The following example/solution provides the details of a goodness-of-fit test to investigate the reasonableness of the normality assumption.

E X A M P L E

On page 28 in Chapter 2 we use a frequency distribution to organize the profits from the Applewood Auto Group's sale of 180 vehicles. The frequency distribution is repeated in Table 15–5.

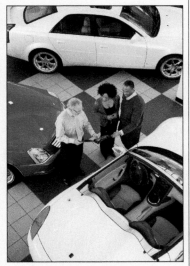

TABLE 15–5 Frequency Distribution of Profits for Vehicles Sold Last Month by Applewood Auto Group

Profit	Frequency
$ 200 up to $ 600	8
600 up to 1,000	11
1,000 up to 1,400	23
1,400 up to 1,800	38
1,800 up to 2,200	45
2,200 up to 2,600	32
2,600 up to 3,000	19
3,000 up to 3,400	4
Total	180

Using statistical software, on page 63 in Chapter 3 we determined that the mean profit on a vehicle for the Applewood Auto Group was $1,843.17 and that the standard deviation was $643.63. Is it reasonable to conclude that the profit data is a sample obtained from a normal population? To put it another way, do the profit data follow a normal population? We use the .05 significance level.

SOLUTION

To test for a normal distribution, we need to find the expected frequencies for each class in the distribution, assuming that the expected distribution follows a normal probability distribution. We start with the normal distribution by calculating probabilities for each class. Then we use these probabilities to compute the expected frequencies for each class.

To begin, we need to find the area, or probability, for each of the eight classes in Table 15–5, assuming a normal population with a mean of $1,843.17 and a standard deviation of $643.63. To find this probability, we adapt formula (7–1) from Chapter 7 replacing μ with $\bar{x}$ and σ with s. So we use the following formula to determine the various values of z.

$$z = \frac{x - \bar{x}}{s}$$

In this case, z is the value of the standard normal statistic; $\bar{x}$, $1,843.17, is the sample mean; and s, $643.63, is the sample standard deviation. To illustrate, we select class $200 up to $600 from Table 15–5. We want to determine the expected frequency in this class, assuming the distribution of profits follows a normal distribution. First, we find the z value corresponding to $200.

$$z = \frac{x - \bar{x}}{s} = \frac{\$200 - \$1,843.17}{\$643.63} = -2.55$$

This indicates that the lower limit of this class is 2.55 standard deviations below the mean. From Appendix B.3, the probability of finding a z value less than −2.55 is .5000 − .4946 = .0054.

For the upper limit of the $200 up to $600 class:

$$z = \frac{x - \bar{x}}{s} = \frac{\$600 - \$1,843.17}{\$643.63} = -1.93$$

The area to the left of $600 is the probability of a z value less than −1.93. To find this value, we again use Appendix B.3 and reason that .5000 − .4732 = .0268.

Finally, to find the area between $200 and $600:

$$P(\$200 < x < \$600) = P(-2.55 < z < -1.93) = .0268 - .0054 = .0214$$

That is, about 2.14% of the vehicles sold will result in a profit of between $200 and $600.

There is a chance that the profit earned is less than $200. To find this probability:

$$P(x < \$200) = P(z < -2.55) = .5000 - .4946 = .0054$$

We enter these two probabilities in the second and third rows of column 3 in Table 15–6.

TABLE 15–6 Profits at Applewood Auto Group, z Values, Areas under the Normal Distribution, and Expected Frequencies

Profit	z Values	Area	Found by	Expected Frequency
Under $200	Under −2.55	.0054	0.5000 − 0.4946	0.97
$ 200 up to $ 600	−2.55 up to −1.93	.0214	0.4946 − 0.4732	3.85
600 up to 1,000	−1.93 up to −1.31	.0683	0.4732 − 0.4049	12.29
1,000 up to 1,400	−1.31 up to −0.69	.1500	0.4049 − 0.2549	27.00
1,400 up to 1,800	−0.69 up to −0.07	.2270	0.2549 − 0.0279	40.86
1,800 up to 2,200	−0.07 up to 0.55	.2367	0.0279 + 0.2088	42.61
2,200 up to 2,600	0.55 up to 1.18	.1722	0.3810 − 0.2088	31.00
2,600 up to 3,000	1.18 up to 1.80	.0831	0.4641 − 0.3810	14.96
3,000 up to 3,400	1.80 up to 2.42	.0281	0.4922 − 0.4641	5.06
3,400 or more	2.42 or more	.0078	0.5000 − 0.4922	1.40
Total		1.0000		180.00

Logically, if we sold 180 vehicles, we would expect to earn a profit of between $200 and $600 on 3.852 vehicles, found by .0214(180). We would expect to sell 0.972 vehicle with a profit of less than $200, found by 180(.0054). We continue this process for the remaining classes. This information is summarized in Table 15–7. Don't be concerned that we are reporting fractional vehicles.

TABLE 15–7 Computations of the Chi-Square Statistic

Profit	f_o	f_e	$(f_o - f_e)$	$(f_o - f_e)^2$	$(f_o - f_e)^2/f_e$
Under $600	8	4.82	3.18	10.1124	2.098
$ 600 up to $1,000	11	12.29	−1.29	1.6641	.135
1,000 up to 1,400	23	27.00	−4.00	16.0000	.593
1,400 up to 1,800	38	40.86	−2.86	8.1796	.200
1,800 up to 2,200	45	42.61	2.39	5.7121	.134
2,200 up to 2,600	32	31.00	1.00	1.0000	.032
2,600 up to 3,000	19	14.96	4.04	16.3216	1.091
3,000 and over	4	6.46	−2.46	6.0516	.937
Total	180	180.00	0		5.220

Before continuing, we should emphasize one of the limitations of tests using chi-square as the test statistic. The second limitation on page 551 indicates that if more than 20% of the cells have *expected frequencies* of less than 5, some of the categories should be combined. In Table 15–6, there are three classes in which the expected frequencies are less than 5. Hence, we combine the "Under $200" class with the "$200 up to $600" class and the "$3,400 or more" class with the "$3,000 up to $3,400" class. So the expected frequency in the "Under $600" class is now 4.82, found by 0.97 plus 3.85. We do the same for the "$3,000 and over" class: 5.06 + 1.40 = 6.46. The results are shown in Table 15–7. The computed value of chi-square is 5.220.

Now let's put this information into the formal hypothesis-testing format. The null and alternate hypotheses are:

H_0: The population of profits follows the normal distribution.
H_1: The population of profits does not follow the normal distribution.

NONPARAMETRIC METHODS: NOMINAL LEVEL HYPOTHESIS TESTS   557

To determine the critical value of chi-square, we need to know the degrees of freedom. In this case, there are 8 categories, or classes, so the degrees of freedom are $k - 1 = 8 - 1 = 7$. In addition, the values $1,843.17, the mean profit, and $643.63, the standard deviation of the Applewood Auto Group profits, were computed from a sample. When we estimate population parameters from sample data, we lose a degree of freedom for each estimate. So we lose two more degrees of freedom for estimating the population mean and the population standard deviation. Thus, the number of degrees of freedom in this problem is 5, found by $k - 2 - 1 = 8 - 2 - 1 = 5$.

From Appendix B.7, using the .05 significance level, the critical value of chi-square is 11.070. Our decision rule is to reject the null hypothesis if the computed value of chi-square is more than 11.070.

Now, to compute the value of chi-square, we use formula (15–4):

$$\chi^2 = \sum \frac{(f_o - f_e)^2}{f_e} = \frac{(8 - 4.82)^2}{4.82} + \cdots + \frac{(4 - 6.46)^2}{6.46} = 5.220$$

The values for each class are shown in the right-hand column of Table 15–7, as well as the column total, which is 5.220. Because the computed value of 5.220 is less than the critical value, we do not reject the null hypothesis. We conclude the evidence does not suggest the distribution of profits is other than normal.

To expand on the calculation of the number of degrees of freedom, if we know the mean and the standard deviation of a population and wish to find whether some sample data conform to a normal, the degrees of freedom are $k - 1$. On the other hand, suppose we have sample data grouped into a frequency distribution, but we do not know the value of the population mean and the population standard deviation. In this case, the degrees of freedom are $k - 2 - 1$. In general, when we use sample statistics to estimate population parameters, we lose a degree of freedom for each parameter we estimate. This is parallel to the situation on page 488 of Chapter 14, the chapter on multiple regression, where we lost a degree of freedom in the denominator of the F statistic for each independent variable considered.

EXERCISES

For **DATA FILE**, please visit
www.mhhe.com/lind16e

25. The IRS is interested in the number of individual tax forms prepared by small accounting firms. The IRS randomly sampled 50 public accounting firms with 10 or fewer employees in the Dallas–Fort Worth area. The following frequency table reports the results of the study. Assume the sample mean is 44.8 clients and the sample standard deviation is 9.37 clients. Is it reasonable to conclude that the sample data are from a population that follows a normal probability distribution? Use the .05 significance level.

Number of Clients	Frequency
20 up to 30	1
30 up to 40	15
40 up to 50	22
50 up to 60	8
60 up to 70	4

For **DATA FILE**, please visit
www.mhhe.com/lind16e

26. Advertising expenses are a significant component of the cost of goods sold. Listed below is a frequency distribution showing the advertising expenditures for 60 manufacturing companies located in the Southwest. The mean expense is $52.0 million and the standard

558   CHAPTER 15

deviation is $11.32 million. Is it reasonable to conclude the sample data are from a population that follows a normal probability distribution? Use the .05 significance level.

Advertising Expense ($ Million)	Number of Companies
25 up to 35	5
35 up to 45	10
45 up to 55	21
55 up to 65	16
65 up to 75	8
Total	60

LO15-6

Perform a chi-square test for independence on a contingency table.

CONTINGENCY TABLE ANALYSIS

In Chapter 4, we discussed bivariate data, where we studied the relationship between two variables. We described a contingency table, which simultaneously summarizes two nominal-scale variables of interest. For example, a sample of students enrolled in the School of Business is classified by gender (male or female) and major (accounting, management, finance, marketing, or quantitative methods). This classification is based on the nominal scale because there is no natural order to the classifications.

We discussed contingency tables in Chapter 5. On page 150, we illustrated the relationship between the number of movies attended per month and the age of the attendee. We can use the chi-square distribution to test whether two nominal-scaled variables are related or not. To put it another way, is one variable *independent* of the other?

Here are some examples where we are interested in testing whether two nominal-scaled variables are related.

- Ford Motor Company operates an assembly plant in Dearborn, Michigan. The plant operates three shifts per day, 5 days a week. The quality control manager wishes to compare the quality level on the three shifts. Vehicles are classified by quality level (acceptable, unacceptable) and shift (day, afternoon, night). Is there a difference in the quality level on the three shifts? That is, is the quality of the product related to the shift when it was manufactured? Or is the quality of the product independent of the shift on which it was manufactured?
- A sample of 100 drivers who were stopped for speeding violations was classified by gender and whether or not they were wearing a seat belt. For this sample, is wearing a seatbelt related to gender?
- Does a male released from federal prison make a different adjustment to civilian life if he returns to his hometown or if he goes elsewhere to live? The two variables are adjustment to civilian life and place of residence. Note that both variables are measured on the nominal scale.

The following example/solution provides the details of the analysis and possible conclusions.

EXAMPLE

Rainbow Chemical, Inc. employs hourly and salaried employees. The vice president of human resources surveyed a random sample of 380 employees about his/her satisfaction level with the current health care benefits program. The employees were then classified according to the pay type, i.e., salary or hourly. The results are shown in Table 15–8.

TABLE 15–8 Health Care Satisfaction Level for Rainbow Chemical Employees

Pay Type	Satisfied	Neutral	Dissatisfied	Total
Salary	30	17	8	55
Hourly	140	127	58	325
Total	170	144	66	380

At the .05 significance level, is it reasonable to conclude that pay type and level of satisfaction with the health care benefits are related?

SOLUTION

The first step is to state the null hypothesis and the alternate hypothesis.

H_0: There is no relationship between level of satisfaction and pay type.
H_1: There is a relationship between level of satisfaction and pay type.

The significance level, as requested by the HR vice president, is .05. The level of measurement for pay type is the nominal scale. The satisfaction level with health benefits is actually the ordinal scale, but we use it as a nominal-scale variable. Each sampled employee is classified by two criteria: the level of satisfaction with benefits and pay type. The information is tabulated into Table 15–8, which is called a contingency table.

We use the chi-square distribution as the test statistic. To determine the critical value of chi-square, we need to know the degrees of freedom (df) calculated as:

$$df = (\text{Number of rows} - 1)(\text{Number of columns} - 1) = (r - 1)(c - 1)$$

In this example/solution there are 2 rows and 3 columns, so there are 2 degrees of freedom.

$$df = (r - 1)(c - 1) = (2 - 1)(3 - 1) = 2$$

To find the critical value for 2 degrees of freedom and the .05 level, refer to Appendix B.7. Move down the degrees of freedom column in the left margin to the row with 2 degrees of freedom. Move across this row to the column headed .05. At the intersection, the chi-square critical value is 5.991. The decision rule is to reject the null hypothesis if the computed value of χ^2 is greater than 5.991. See Chart 15–6.

CHART 15–6 Chi-Square Distribution for 2 Degree of Freedom

CHAPTER 15

Next we compute the chi-square value χ^2, using formula (15–4). The observed frequencies, f_o, are shown in Table 15–9. How are the corresponding expected frequencies, f_e, determined? To begin, notice from Table 15–8 that 55 of the 380 Rainbow Chemical employees sampled are salaried. So the fraction of salaried employees in the sample is 55/380 = .14474. *If there is no relationship* between pay type and level of satisfaction with the health care benefits program, we would expect about the same fraction of the employees who are satisfied with the health care to be salaried. There are 170 employees who are satisfied with the health care program, so the expected number of satisfied employees who are salaried is 24.61, found by (.14474)(170). Thus, the expected frequency for the upper-left cell is 24.61. Likewise, if there were no relationship between satisfaction level and pay type, we would expect .14474 of the 144 employees, or 20.84, who were neutral about the health care program to be salaried. We continue this process, filling in the remaining cells. It is not necessary to calculate each of these cell values; some may be determined by subtraction.

The expected frequency for any cell is determined by:

| EXPECTED FREQUENCY | $f_e = \dfrac{(\text{Row total})(\text{Column total})}{(\text{Grand total})}$ | [15–5] |

From this formula, the expected frequency for the upper-left cell in Table 15–8 is:

$$f_e = \frac{(\text{Row total})(\text{Column total})}{(\text{Grand total})} = \frac{(55)(170)}{380} = 24.61$$

The observed frequencies, f_o, and the expected frequencies, f_e, for all of the cells in the contingency table are listed in Table 15–9. Note there are slight differences due to rounding.

TABLE 15–9 Observed and Expected Frequencies

| | Satisfaction Level with Health Care | | | | | | |
| | Satisfied | | Neutral | | Dissatisfied | | |
Pay Type	f_o	f_e	f_o	f_e	f_o	f_e	Total
Salary	30	24.61	17	20.84	8	9.55	55
Hourly	140	145.39	127	123.16	58	56.45	325
Total	170	170.00	144	144.00	66	66.00	380

We use formula (15–4) to determine the value of chi-square. Starting with the upper-left cell:

$$\chi^2 = \sum \frac{(f_o - f_e)^2}{f_e} = \frac{(30 - 24.61)^2}{24.61} + \frac{(17 - 20.84)^2}{20.84} + \cdots + \frac{(58 - 56.45)^2}{56.45}$$

$$= 1.181 + .708 + \cdots + .043 = 2.506$$

Because the computed value of chi-square (2.506) lies in the region to the left of 5.991, the null hypothesis is not rejected at the .05 significance level. What do we conclude? The sample data do not provide evidence that pay type and satisfaction level with health care benefits are related.

NONPARAMETRIC METHODS: NOMINAL LEVEL HYPOTHESIS TESTS   561

The following output is from the Megastat Excel add-in.

Chi-square Contingency Table Test for Independence

Pay Type		Satisfied	Neutral	Dissatisfied	Total
Salary	Observed	**30**	**17**	**8**	55
	Expected	24.61	20.84	9.55	55.00
Hourly	Observed	**140**	**127**	**58**	325
	Expected	145.39	123.16	56.45	325.00
Total	Observed	170	144	66	380
	Expected	170.00	144.00	66.00	380.00

The "Satisfied", "Neutral", "Dissatisfied" columns fall under the heading **Satisfaction Level with Health Care**.

2.506 chi-square
2 df
0.286 p-value

Observe that the value of chi-square is the same as that computed earlier, 2.506. In addition, the *p*-value, .286, is reported. So the probability of finding a value of the test statistic as large or larger, assuming the null hypothesis is true, is .286. The *p*-value also results in the same decision: do not reject the null hypothesis.

SELF-REVIEW

15–5

A social scientist sampled 140 people and classified them according to income level and whether or not they played a state lottery in the last month. The sample information is reported below. Is it reasonable to conclude that playing the lottery is related to income level? Use the .05 significance level.

	Low	Middle	High	Total
Played	46	28	21	95
Did not play	14	12	19	45
Total	60	40	40	140

The "Low", "Middle", "High" columns fall under the heading **Income**.

(a) What is this table called?
(b) State the null hypothesis and the alternate hypothesis.
(c) What is the decision rule?
(d) Determine the value of chi-square.
(e) Make a decision on the null hypothesis. Interpret the result.

EXERCISES

For **DATA FILE**, please visit
www.mhhe.com/lind16e

27. The director of advertising for the *Carolina Sun Times,* the largest newspaper in the Carolinas, is studying the relationship between the type of community in which a subscriber resides and the section of the newspaper he or she reads first. For a sample of readers, she collected the sample information in the following table.

	National News	Sports	Comics
City	170	124	90
Suburb	120	112	100
Rural	130	90	88

At the .05 significance level, can we conclude there is a relationship between the type of community where the person resides and the section of the paper read first?

562   CHAPTER 15

For **DATA FILE**, please visit
www.mhhe.com/lind16e

28. Four brands of lightbulbs are being considered for use in the final assembly area of the Ford F-150 truck plant in Dearborn, Michigan. The director of purchasing asked for samples of 100 from each manufacturer. The numbers of acceptable and unacceptable bulbs from each manufacturer are shown below. At the .05 significance level, is there a difference in the quality of the bulbs?

	Manufacturer			
	A	B	C	D
Unacceptable	12	8	5	11
Acceptable	88	92	95	89
Total	100	100	100	100

For **DATA FILE**, please visit
www.mhhe.com/lind16e

29. The quality control department at Food Town Inc., a grocery chain in upstate New York, conducts a monthly check on the comparison of scanned prices to posted prices. The chart below summarizes the results of a sample of 500 items last month. Company management would like to know whether there is any relationship between error rates on regularly priced items and specially priced items. Use the .01 significance level.

	Regular Price	Advertised Special Price
Undercharge	20	10
Overcharge	15	30
Correct price	200	225

30. The use of cellular phones in automobiles has increased dramatically in the last few years. Of concern to traffic experts, as well as manufacturers of cellular phones, is the effect on accident rates. Is someone who is using a cellular phone more likely to be involved in a traffic accident? What is your conclusion from the following sample information? Use the .05 significance level.

	Had Accident in the Last Year	Did Not Have an Accident in the Last Year
Uses a cell phone	25	300
Does not use a cell phone	50	400

CHAPTER SUMMARY

I. This chapter considered tests of hypothesis for nominal level data.

II. When we sample from a single population and the variable of interest has only two possible outcomes, we call this a test of proportion.

   A. The binomial conditions must be met.

   B. Both $n\pi$ and $n(1-\pi)$ must be at least 5.

   C. The test statistic is

$$z = \frac{p - \pi}{\sqrt{\dfrac{\pi(1 - \pi)}{n}}} \qquad \text{[15–1]}$$

III. We can also test whether two samples came from populations with an equal proportion of successes.

   A. The two sample proportions are pooled using the following formula:

$$p_c = \frac{x_1 + x_2}{n_1 + n_2} \qquad \text{[15–3]}$$

B. We compute the value of the test statistic from the following formula:

$$z = \frac{p_1 - p_2}{\sqrt{\dfrac{p_c(1 - p_c)}{n_1} + \dfrac{p_c(1 - p_c)}{n_2}}}$$ [15–2]

IV. The characteristics of the chi-square distribution are:
  A. The value of chi-square is never negative.
  B. The chi-square distribution is positively skewed.
  C. There is a family of chi-square distributions.
   1. Each time the degrees of freedom change, a new distribution is formed.
   2. As the degrees of freedom increase, the distribution approaches a normal distribution.
V. A goodness-of-fit test will show whether an observed set of frequencies could have come from a hypothesized population distribution.
  A. The degrees of freedom are $k - 1$, where k is the number of categories.
  B. The formula for computing the value of chi-square is

$$\chi^2 = \sum \frac{(f_o - f_e)^2}{f_e}$$ [15–4]

VI. A goodness-of-fit test can also be used to determine whether a sample of observations is from a normal population.
  A. First, find the mean and standard deviation of the sample data.
  B. Group the data into a frequency distribution.
  C. Convert the class limits to z values and find the standard normal probability distribution for each class.
  D. For each class, find the expected normally distributed frequency by multiplying the standard normal probability distribution by the class frequency.
  E. Calculate the chi-square goodness-of-fit statistic based on the observed and expected class frequencies.
  F. Find the expected frequency in each cell by determining the product of the probability of finding a value in each cell by the total number of observations.
  G. If we use the information on the sample mean and the sample standard deviation from the sample data, the degrees of freedom are $k - 3$.
VII. A contingency table is used to test whether two traits or characteristics are related.
  A. Each observation is classified according to two traits.
  B. The expected frequency is determined as follows:

$$f_e = \frac{(\text{Row total})(\text{Column total})}{\text{Grand total}}$$ [15–5]

  C. The degrees of freedom are found by:

$$df = (\text{Rows} - 1)(\text{Columns} - 1)$$

  D. The usual hypothesis testing procedure is used.

PRONUNCIATION KEY

SYMBOL	MEANING	PRONUNCIATION
p_c	Pooled proportion	p sub c
χ^2	Probability distribution	ki square
f_o	Observed frequency	f sub oh
f_e	Expected frequency	f sub e

CHAPTER EXERCISES

31. A coin toss is used to decide which team gets the ball first in most sports. It involves little effort and is believed to give each side the same chance. In 47 Super Bowl games, the National Football Conference has won the coin flip 31 times. Meanwhile, the American

Football Conference has won only 16 times. Use the six-step hypothesis-testing procedure at the .01 significance level to test whether these data suggest a fair coin flip.

a. Why can you employ Z as the test statistic?

b. State the null and alternate hypotheses.

c. Make a diagram of the decision rule.

d. Evaluate the test statistic and make the decision.

e. What is the p-value and what does that imply?

32. According to a study by the American Pet Food Dealers Association, 63% of U.S. households own pets. A report is being prepared for an editorial in the *San Francisco Chronicle*. As a part of the editorial, a random sample of 300 households showed 210 own pets. Do these data disagree with the Pet Food Dealers Association's data? Use a .05 level of significance.

33. Tina Dennis is the comptroller for Meek Industries. She believes that the current cash-flow problem at Meek is due to the slow collection of accounts receivable. She believes that more than 60% of the accounts are in arrears more than 3 months. A random sample of 200 accounts showed that 140 were more than 3 months old. At the .01 significance level, can she conclude that more than 60% of the accounts are in arrears for more than three months?

34. The policy of the Suburban Transit Authority is to add a bus route if more than 55% of the potential commuters indicate they would use the particular route. A sample of 70 commuters revealed that 42 would use a proposed route from Bowman Park to the downtown area. Does the Bowman-to-downtown route meet the STA criterion? Use the .05 significance level.

35. Past experience at the Crowder Travel Agency indicated that 44% of those persons who wanted the agency to plan a vacation for them wanted to go to Europe. During the most recent season, a sampling of 1,000 persons was selected at random from the files. It was found that 480 persons wanted to go to Europe on vacation. Has there been a significant shift upward in the percentage of persons who want to go to Europe? Test at the .05 significance level.

36. Research in the gaming industry showed that 10% of all slot machines in the United States stop working each year. Short's Game Arcade has 60 slot machines and only 3 failed last year. At the .05 significance level, test whether these data contradict the research report.

a. Why can you employ z as the test statistic?

b. State the null and alternate hypotheses.

c. Evaluate the test statistic and make the decision.

d. What is the p-value and what does that imply?

37. An urban planner claims that, nationally, 20% of all families renting condominiums move during a given year. A random sample of 200 families renting condominiums in the Dallas Metroplex revealed that 56 moved during the past year. At the .01 significance level, does this evidence suggest that a larger proportion of condominium owners moved in the Dallas area? Determine the p-value.

38. After a losing season, there is a great uproar to fire the head football coach. In a random sample of 200 college alumni, 80 favor keeping the coach. Test at the .05 level of significance whether the proportion of alumni who support the coach is less than 50%.

39. During the 1990s, the fatality rate for lung cancer was 80 per 100,000 people. After the turn of the century and the establishment of newer treatments and adjustment in public health advertising, a random sample of 10,000 people exhibits only six deaths due to lung cancer. Test at the .05 significance level whether that data are proof of a reduced fatality rate for lung cancer.

40. Each month the National Association of Purchasing Managers surveys purchasing managers and publishes the NAPM index. One of the questions asked on the survey is: Do you think the economy is contracting? Last month, of the 300 responding managers, 160 answered yes to the question. This month, 170 of the 290 managers indicated they felt the economy was contracting. At the .05 significance level, can we conclude that a larger proportion of the purchasing managers believe the economy is contracting this month?

41. As part of a recent survey among dual-wage-earner couples, an industrial psychologist found that 990 men out of the 1,500 surveyed believed the division of household duties was fair. A sample of 1,600 women found 970 believed the division of household duties was fair. At the .01 significance level, is it reasonable to conclude that the proportion of men who believe the division of household duties is fair is larger? What is the p-value?

NONPARAMETRIC METHODS: NOMINAL LEVEL HYPOTHESIS TESTS   565

42. There are two major cell phone providers in the Colorado Springs, Colorado, area, one called HTC and the other, Mountain Communications. We want to investigate whether there is a difference in the proportion of times a customer is able to successfully access the Internet. During a one-week period, 500 calls were placed at random times throughout the day and night to HTC; 450 of the calls were successful. A similar one-week study with Mountain Communications showed that 352 of 400 calls were successful. At the .01 significance level, is there a difference in the percent of time that cell phone connections are successful?

43. The Consumer Confidence Survey is a monthly review that measures consumer confidence in the U.S. economy. It is based on a typical sample of 5,000 U.S. households. Last month 9.1% of consumers said conditions were "good." In the prior month, only 8.5% said they were "good." Use the six-step hypothesis-testing method at the .05 level of significance to see whether you can determine if there is an increase in the share asserting conditions are "good." Find the *p*-value and explain what it means.

44. A study was conducted to determine if there was a difference in the humor content in British and American trade magazine advertisements. In an independent random sample of 270 American trade magazine advertisements, 56 were humorous. An independent random sample of 203 British trade magazines contained 52 humorous ads. Do these data provide evidence at the .05 significance level that there is a difference in the proportion of humorous ads in British versus American trade magazines?

45. The AP-Petside.com poll contacted 300 married women and 200 married men. All owned pets. One hundred of the women and 36 of the men replied that their pets are better listeners than their spouses. At the .05 significance level, is there a difference between the responses of women and men?

46. The National Basketball Association had 39 African-American top executives (presidents or vice presidents) among its 388 senior managers. Meanwhile, Major League Baseball had only 11 African Americans among its 307 top administrators. Test at the .05 significance level if this reveals the NBA has significantly more African-American participation in higher levels of management.

47. Vehicles heading west on Front Street may turn right, turn left, or go straight ahead at Elm Street. The city traffic engineer believes that half of the vehicles will continue straight through the intersection. Of the remaining half, equal proportions will turn right and left. Two hundred vehicles were observed, with the following results. Can we conclude that the traffic engineer is correct? Use the .10 significance level.

	Straight	Right Turn	Left Turn
Frequency	112	48	40

48. The publisher of a sports magazine plans to offer new subscribers one of three gifts: a sweatshirt with the logo of their favorite team, a coffee cup with the logo of their favorite team, or a pair of earrings also with the logo of their favorite team. In a sample of 500 new subscribers, the number selecting each gift is reported below. At the .05 significance level, is there a preference for the gifts or should we conclude that the gifts are equally well liked?

Gift	Frequency
Sweatshirt	183
Coffee cup	175
Earrings	142

49. In a particular metro area, there are three commercial television stations, each with its own news program from 6:00 to 6:30 p.m. According to a report in this morning's local newspaper, a random sample of 150 viewers last night revealed 53 watched the news on WNAE (channel 5), 64 watched on WRRN (channel 11), and 33 on WSPD (channel 13). At the .05 significance level, is there a difference in the proportion of viewers watching the three channels?

For **DATA FILE**, please visit
www.mhhe.com/lind16e

50. There are four entrances to the Government Center Building in downtown Philadelphia. The building maintenance supervisor would like to know if the entrances are equally utilized. To

investigate, 400 people were observed entering the building. The number using each entrance is reported below. At the .01 significance level, is there a difference in the use of the four entrances?

Entrance	Frequency
Main Street	140
Broad Street	120
Cherry Street	90
Walnut Street	50
Total	400

For **DATA FILE**, please visit
www.mhhe.com/lind16e

51. The owner of a mail-order catalog would like to compare her sales with the geographic distribution of the population. According to the U.S. Bureau of the Census, 21% of the population lives in the Northeast, 24% in the Midwest, 35% in the South, and 20% in the West. Listed below is a breakdown of a sample of 400 orders randomly selected from those shipped last month. At the .01 significance level, does the distribution of the orders reflect the population?

Region	Frequency
Northeast	68
Midwest	104
South	155
West	73
Total	400

For **DATA FILE**, please visit
www.mhhe.com/lind16e

52. Banner Mattress and Furniture Company wishes to study the number of credit applications received per day for the last 300 days. The sample information is reported below.

Number of Credit Applications	Frequency (Number of Days)
0	50
1	77
2	81
3	48
4	31
5 or more	13

To interpret, there were 50 days on which no credit applications were received, 77 days on which only one application was received, and so on. Would it be reasonable to conclude that the population distribution is Poisson with a mean of 2.0? Use the .05 significance level. (*Hint:* To find the expected frequencies use the Poisson distribution with a mean of 2.0. Find the probability of exactly one success given a Poisson distribution with a mean of 2.0. Multiply this probability by 300 to find the expected frequency for the number of days in which there was exactly one application. Determine the expected frequency for the other days in a similar manner.)

53. Each of the digits in a raffle is thought to have the same chance of occurrence. The table shows the frequency of each digit for consecutive drawings in a California lottery. Perform the chi-square test to see if you reject the hypothesis at the .05 significance level that the digits are from a uniform population.

For **DATA FILE**, please visit
www.mhhe.com/lind16e

Digit	Frequency	Digit	Frequency
0	44	5	24
1	32	6	31
2	23	7	27
3	27	8	28
4	23	9	21

For **DATA FILE**, please visit
www.mhhe.com/lind16e

54. John Isaac Inc., a designer and installer of industrial signs, employs 60 people. The company recorded the type of the most recent visit to a doctor by each employee. A national assessment conducted in 2014 found that 53% of all physician visits were to primary care physicians, 19% to medical specialists, 17% to surgical specialists, and 11% to emergency departments. Test at the .01 significance level if Isaac employees differ significantly from the survey distribution. Here are their results:

Visit Type	Number of Visits
Primary care	29
Medical specialist	11
Surgical specialist	16
Emergency	4

For **DATA FILE**, please visit
www.mhhe.com/lind16e

55. The Eckel Manufacturing Company believes that their hourly wages follow a normal probability distribution. To confirm this, 270 employees were sampled, organized into the following frequency distribution. Use the methods on pages 82–83 of Chapter 3 to find the mean and standard deviation of these data grouped into a frequency distribution. At the .10 significance level, is it reasonable to conclude that the distribution of hourly wages follows a normal distribution?

Hourly Wage	Frequency
$5.50 up to $ 6.50	20
6.50 up to 7.50	24
7.50 up to 8.50	130
8.50 up to 9.50	68
9.50 up to 10.50	28
Total	270

For **DATA FILE**, please visit
www.mhhe.com/lind16e

56. The National Cable and Telecommunications Association recently reported that the mean number of HDTVs per household in the United States is 2.30 with a standard deviation of 1.474 sets. A sample of 100 homes in Boise, Idaho, revealed the following sample information.

Number of HDTVs	Number of Households
0	7
1	27
2	28
3	18
4	10
5 or more	10
Total	100

At the .05 significance level, is it reasonable to conclude that the number of HDTVs per household follows a normal distribution? (*Hint:* Use limits such as 0.5 up to 1.5, 1.5 up to 2.5, and so on.)

For **DATA FILE**, please visit
www.mhhe.com/lind16e

57. A survey investigated the public's attitude toward the federal deficit. Each sampled citizen was classified as to whether he or she felt the government should reduce the deficit or increase the deficit, or if the individual had no opinion. The sample results of the study by gender are reported below.

Gender	Reduce the Deficit	Increase the Deficit	No Opinion
Female	244	194	68
Male	305	114	25

At the .05 significance level, is it reasonable to conclude that gender is independent of a person's position on the deficit?

58. A study regarding the relationship between age and the amount of pressure sales personnel feel in relation to their jobs revealed the following sample information. At the .01 significance level, is there a relationship between job pressure and age?

	Degree of Job Pressure		
Age (years)	Low	Medium	High
Less than 25	20	18	22
25 up to 40	50	46	44
40 up to 60	58	63	59
60 and older	34	43	43

For **DATA FILE**, please visit
www.mhhe.com/lind16e

59. The claims department at Wise Insurance Company believes that younger drivers have more accidents and, therefore, should be charged higher insurance rates. Investigating a sample of 1,200 Wise policyholders revealed the following breakdown on whether a claim had been filed in the last 3 years and the age of the policyholder. Is it reasonable to conclude that there is a relationship between the age of the policyholder and whether or not the person filed a claim? Use the .05 significance level.

Age Group	No Claim	Claim
16 up to 25	170	74
25 up to 40	240	58
40 up to 55	400	44
55 or older	190	24
Total	1,000	200

For **DATA FILE**, please visit
www.mhhe.com/lind16e

60. A sample of employees at a large chemical plant was asked to indicate a preference for one of three pension plans. The results are given in the following table. Does it seem that there is a relationship between the pension plan selected and the job classification of the employees? Use the .01 significance level.

	Pension Plan		
Job Class	Plan A	Plan B	Plan C
Supervisor	10	13	29
Clerical	19	80	19
Labor	81	57	22

For **DATA FILE**, please visit
www.mhhe.com/lind16e

61. Did you ever purchase a bag of M&M's candies and wonder about the distribution of colors? You can go to the website www.baking.m-ms.com and click the United States on the map, then click **About M&M's,** then **Products** and **Peanut,** and find the percentage breakdown according to the manufacturer, as well as a brief history of the product. Did you know in the beginning they were all brown? For peanut M&M's, 12% are brown, 15% yellow, 12% red, 23% blue, 23% orange, and 15% green. A 6-oz. bag purchased at the Book Store at Coastal Carolina University had 14 brown, 13 yellow, 14 red, 12 blue, 7 orange, and 12 green. Is it reasonable to conclude that the actual distribution agrees with the expected distribution? Use the .05 significance level. Conduct your own trial. Be sure to share with your instructor.

DATA SET EXERCISES

(The data for these exercises are available at the text website: www.mhhe.com/lind16e.)

62. Refer to the Real Estate data, which report information on homes sold in Goodyear, Arizona, and the surrounding area last year.
   a. Determine the proportion of homes that have an attached garage. At the .05 significance level, can we conclude that more than 60% of the homes sold in the Goodyear, Arizona, area had an attached garage? What is the p-value?
   b. Determine the proportion of homes that have a pool. At the .05 significance level, can we conclude that more than 60% of the homes sold in the Goodyear, Arizona, area had a pool? What is the p-value?
   c. Develop a contingency table that shows whether a home has a pool and the township in which the house is located. Is there an association between the variables pool and township? Use the .05 significance level.
   d. Develop a contingency table that shows whether a home has an attached garage and the township in which the home is located. Is there an association between the variables attached garage and township? Use the .05 significance level.
63. Refer to the Baseball 2012 data, which report information on the 30 Major League Baseball teams for the 2012 season. Set up a variable that divides the teams into two groups, those that had a winning season and those that did not. There are 162 games in the season, so define a winning season as having won 81 or more games. Next, find the median team salary and divide the teams into two salary groups. Let the 15 teams with the largest salaries be in one group and the 15 teams with the smallest salaries be in the other. At the .05 significance level, is there a relationship between salaries and winning?
64. Refer to the Buena School District bus data.
   a. Suppose we consider a bus "old" if it has been in service more than 8 years. At the .01 significance level, can we conclude that less than 40% of the district's buses are old? Report the p-value.
   b. Find the median maintenance cost and the median age of the buses. Organize the data into a two-by-two contingency table, with buses above and below the median of each variable. Determine whether the age of the bus is related to the amount of the maintenance cost. Use the .05 significance level.
   c. Is there a relationship between the maintenance cost and the manufacturer of the bus? Use the breakdown in part (b) for the buses above and below the median maintenance cost and the bus manufacturers to create a contingency table. Use the .05 significance level.

Appendixes

APPENDIX A: DATA SETS

A.1   Data Set 1—Goodyear, Arizona, Real Estate Sales Data

Variables

x_1 = Selling price in $000
x_2 = Number of bedrooms
x_3 = Size of the home in square feet
x_4 = Pool (1 = yes, 0 = no)
x_5 = Distance from the center of the city in miles
x_6 = Township
x_7 = Garage attached (1 = yes, 0 = no)
x_8 = Number of bathrooms
105 homes sold

x_1	x_2	x_3	x_4	x_5	x_6	x_7	x_8
263.1	4	2,300	0	17	5	1	2.0
182.4	4	2,100	1	19	4	0	2.0
242.1	3	2,300	1	12	3	0	2.0
213.6	2	2,200	1	16	2	0	2.5
139.9	2	2,100	1	28	1	0	1.5
245.4	2	2,100	0	12	1	1	2.0
327.2	6	2,500	1	15	3	1	2.0
271.8	2	2,100	1	9	2	1	2.5
221.1	3	2,300	0	18	1	0	1.5
266.6	4	2,400	1	13	4	1	2.0
292.4	4	2,100	1	14	3	1	2.0
209.0	2	1,700	1	8	4	1	1.5
270.8	6	2,500	1	7	4	1	2.0
246.1	4	2,100	1	18	3	1	2.0
194.4	2	2,300	1	11	3	0	2.0
281.3	3	2,100	1	16	2	1	2.0
172.7	4	2,200	0	16	3	0	2.0
207.5	5	2,300	0	21	4	0	2.5
198.9	3	2,200	0	10	4	1	2.0
209.3	6	1,900	0	15	4	1	2.0
252.3	4	2,600	1	8	4	1	2.0
192.9	4	1,900	0	14	2	1	2.5
209.3	5	2,100	1	20	5	0	1.5
345.3	8	2,600	1	9	4	1	2.0
326.3	6	2,100	1	11	5	1	3.0
173.1	2	2,200	0	21	5	1	1.5
187.0	2	1,900	1	26	4	0	2.0
257.2	2	2,100	1	9	4	1	2.0
233.0	3	2,200	1	14	3	1	1.5
180.4	2	2,000	1	11	5	0	2.0
234.0	2	1,700	1	19	3	1	2.0
207.1	2	2,000	1	11	5	1	2.0
247.7	5	2,400	1	16	2	1	2.0
166.2	3	2,000	0	16	2	1	2.0
177.1	2	1,900	1	10	5	1	2.0

(continued)

A.1   Data Set 1—Goodyear, Arizona, Real Estate Sales Data (*continued*)

X_1	X_2	X_3	X_4	X_5	X_6	X_7	X_8
182.7	4	2,000	0	14	4	0	2.5
216.0	4	2,300	1	19	2	0	2.0
312.1	6	2,600	1	7	5	1	2.5
199.8	3	2,100	1	19	3	1	2.0
273.2	5	2,200	1	16	2	1	3.0
206.0	3	2,100	0	9	3	0	1.5
232.2	3	1,900	0	16	1	1	1.5
198.3	4	2,100	0	19	1	1	1.5
205.1	3	2,000	0	20	4	0	2.0
175.6	4	2,300	0	24	4	1	2.0
307.8	3	2,400	0	21	2	1	3.0
269.2	5	2,200	1	8	5	1	3.0
224.8	3	2,200	1	17	1	1	2.5
171.6	3	2,000	0	16	4	0	2.0
216.8	3	2,200	1	15	1	1	2.0
192.6	6	2,200	0	14	1	0	2.0
236.4	5	2,200	1	20	3	1	2.0
172.4	3	2,200	1	23	3	0	2.0
251.4	3	1,900	1	12	2	1	2.0
246.0	6	2,300	1	7	3	1	3.0
147.4	6	1,700	0	12	1	0	2.0
176.0	4	2,200	1	15	1	1	2.0
228.4	3	2,300	1	17	5	1	1.5
166.5	3	1,600	0	19	3	0	2.5
189.4	4	2,200	1	24	1	1	2.0
312.1	7	2,400	1	13	3	1	3.0
289.8	6	2,000	1	21	3	1	3.0
269.9	5	2,200	0	11	4	1	2.5
154.3	2	2,000	1	13	2	0	2.0
222.1	2	2,100	1	9	5	1	2.0
209.7	5	2,200	0	13	2	1	2.0
190.9	3	2,200	0	18	3	1	2.0
254.3	4	2,500	0	15	3	1	2.0
207.5	3	2,100	0	10	2	0	2.0
209.7	4	2,200	0	19	2	1	2.0
294.0	2	2,100	1	13	2	1	2.5
176.3	2	2,000	0	17	3	0	2.0
294.3	7	2,400	1	8	4	1	2.0
224.0	3	1,900	0	6	1	1	2.0
125.0	2	1,900	1	18	4	0	1.5
236.8	4	2,600	0	17	5	1	2.0
164.1	4	2,300	1	19	4	0	2.0
217.8	3	2,500	1	12	3	0	2.0
192.2	2	2,400	1	16	2	0	2.5
125.9	2	2,400	1	28	1	0	1.5

(*continued*)

A.1 Data Set 1—Goodyear, Arizona, Real Estate Sales Data (*concluded*)

x_1	x_2	x_3	x_4	x_5	x_6	x_7	x_8
220.9	2	2,300	0	12	1	1	2.0
294.5	6	2,700	1	15	3	1	2.0
244.6	2	2,300	1	9	2	1	2.5
199.0	3	2,500	0	18	1	0	1.5
240.0	4	2,600	1	13	4	1	2.0
263.2	4	2,300	1	14	3	1	2.0
188.1	2	1,900	1	8	4	1	1.5
243.7	6	2,700	1	7	4	1	2.0
221.5	4	2,300	1	18	3	1	2.0
175.0	2	2,500	1	11	3	0	2.0
253.2	3	2,300	1	16	2	1	2.0
155.4	4	2,400	0	16	3	0	2.0
186.7	5	2,500	0	21	4	0	2.5
179.0	3	2,400	0	10	4	1	2.0
188.3	6	2,100	0	15	4	1	2.0
227.1	4	2,900	1	8	4	1	2.0
173.6	4	2,100	0	14	2	1	2.5
188.3	5	2,300	1	20	5	0	1.5
310.8	8	2,900	1	9	4	1	2.0
293.7	6	2,400	1	11	5	1	3.0
179.0	3	2,400	1	8	4	1	2.0
188.3	6	2,100	0	14	2	1	2.5
227.1	4	2,900	1	20	5	0	1.5
173.6	4	2,100	1	9	4	1	2.0
188.3	5	2,300	1	11	5	1	3.0

A.2   Data Set 2—Baseball Statistics, 2012 Season

Variables
x_1 = Team
x_2 = League (American = 1, National = 0)
x_3 = Built (year stadium was built)
x_4 = Size (stadium capacity)
x_5 = Salary (total 2012 team salary, $ millions)
x_6 = Wins
x_7 = Attendance (total for team in millions)
x_8 = BA (team batting average)
x_9 = ERA (team earned run average)
x_{10} = HR (team home runs)
x_{11} = Errors (team errors)
x_{12} = SB (team stolen bases)
x_{13} = Year
x_{14} = Average player salary ($)

(continued)

A.2 Data Set 2—Baseball Statistics, 2012 Season (concluded)

Team x_1	League x_2	Opened x_3	Capacity Seating x_4	Salary 2012 x_5	Wins x_6	Attendance x_7	BA x_8	ERA x_9	HR x_{10}	Errors x_{11}	SB x_{12}
Arizona Diamondbacks	0	1998	48633	74.3	81	2.18	0.26	3.93	165	90	93
Atlanta Braves	0	1996	49586	83.3	94	2.42	0.25	3.42	149	86	101
Baltimore Orioles	1	1992	45971	81.4	93	2.1	0.25	3.9	214	106	58
Boston Red Sox	0	1912	37495	173.2	69	3.04	0.26	4.7	165	101	97
Chicago Cubs	1	1914	41009	88.2	61	2.88	0.24	4.51	137	105	94
Chicago White Sox	1	1991	40615	96.9	85	1.97	0.26	4.02	211	70	109
Cincinnati Reds	0	2003	42319	82.2	97	2.35	0.25	3.34	172	89	87
Cleveland Indians	1	1994	43429	78.4	68	1.6	0.25	4.78	136	96	110
Colorado Rockies	0	1995	50398	78.1	64	2.63	0.27	5.22	166	122	100
Detroit Tigers	1	2000	41255	132.3	88	3.03	0.27	3.75	163	99	59
Houston Astros	0	2000	40981	60.7	55	1.61	0.24	4.56	146	118	105
Kansas City Royals	1	1973	37903	60.9	72	1.74	0.27	4.3	131	113	132
Los Angeles Angels	1	1966	45957	154.5	89	3.06	0.27	4.02	187	98	134
Los Angeles Dodgers	0	1962	56000	95.1	86	3.32	0.24	3.34	116	98	104
Miami Marlins	0	2012	36742	118.1	69	2.22	0.24	4.09	137	103	149
Milwaukee Brewers	0	2001	41900	97.7	83	2.83	0.26	4.22	202	99	158
Minnesota Twins	1	2010	39504	94.1	66	2.78	0.26	4.77	131	107	135
New York Mets	0	2009	41922	93.4	95	2.24	0.25	4.09	139	101	79
New York Yankees	1	2009	50287	198	74	3.54	0.27	3.85	245	74	93
Oakland Athletics	1	1966	35067	55.4	94	1.68	0.24	3.48	195	111	122
Philadelphia Phillies	0	2004	43651	174.5	81	3.57	0.26	3.83	158	101	116
Pittsburgh Pirates	0	2001	38362	63.4	79	2.09	0.24	3.86	170	112	73
San Diego Padres	0	2004	42691	55.2	76	2.12	0.25	4.01	121	121	155
San Francisco Giants	0	2000	41915	117.6	94	3.38	0.27	3.68	103	115	118
Seattle Mariners	1	1999	47860	82	75	1.72	0.23	3.76	149	72	104
St. Louis Cardinals	0	2006	43975	110.3	88	3.26	0.27	3.71	159	107	91
Tampa Bay Rays	1	1990	34078	64.2	90	1.56	0.24	3.19	175	114	134
Texas Rangers	1	1994	48194	120.5	93	3.46	0.27	3.99	200	85	91
Toronto Blue Jays	1	1989	49260	75.5	73	2.1	0.25	4.64	198	101	123
Washington Nationals	0	2008	41487	81.3	98	2.37	0.26	3.33	194	94	105

	Average Salary
1989	$ 512,930
1990	578,930
1991	891,188
1992	1,084,408
1993	1,120,254
1994	1,188,679
1995	1,071,029
1996	1,176,967
1997	1,383,578
1998	1,441,406
1999	1,720,050
2000	1,988,034
2001	2,264,403
2002	2,383,235
2003	2,555,476
2004	2,486,609
2005	2,632,655
2006	2,866,544
2007	2,944,556
2008	3,154,845
2009	3,240,206
2010	3,297,828
2011	3,305,393
2012	3,440,000

A.3   Data Set 3—Buena School District Bus Data

Variables
x_1 = Bus number
x_2 = Maintenance cost ($)
x_3 = Age
x_4 = Miles
x_5 = Bus type (diesel or gasoline)
x_6 = Bus manufacturer (Bluebird, Keiser, Thompson)
x_7 = Passengers

Bus Number, x_1	Maintenance Cost, x_2	Age, x_3	Miles, x_4	Bus Type, x_5	Bus Manufacturer, x_6	Passengers, x_7
135	329	7	853	Diesel	Bluebird	55
120	503	10	883	Diesel	Keiser	42
200	505	10	822	Diesel	Bluebird	55
40	466	10	865	Gasoline	Bluebird	55
427	359	7	751	Gasoline	Keiser	55
759	546	8	870	Diesel	Keiser	55
10	427	5	780	Gasoline	Keiser	14
880	474	9	857	Gasoline	Keiser	55
481	382	3	818	Gasoline	Keiser	6
387	422	8	869	Gasoline	Bluebird	55
326	433	9	848	Diesel	Bluebird	55
861	474	10	845	Gasoline	Bluebird	55
122	558	10	885	Gasoline	Bluebird	55
156	561	12	838	Diesel	Thompson	55
887	357	8	760	Diesel	Bluebird	6
686	329	3	741	Diesel	Bluebird	55
490	497	10	859	Gasoline	Bluebird	55
370	459	8	826	Gasoline	Keiser	55
464	355	3	806	Gasoline	Bluebird	55
875	489	9	858	Diesel	Bluebird	55
883	436	2	785	Gasoline	Bluebird	55
57	455	7	828	Diesel	Bluebird	55
482	514	11	980	Gasoline	Bluebird	55
704	503	8	857	Diesel	Bluebird	55
989	380	9	803	Diesel	Keiser	55
731	432	6	819	Diesel	Bluebird	42
75	478	6	821	Diesel	Bluebird	55
162	406	3	798	Gasoline	Keiser	55
732	471	9	815	Diesel	Keiser	42
751	444	2	757	Diesel	Keiser	14
600	493	10	1008	Diesel	Bluebird	55
948	452	9	831	Diesel	Keiser	42
358	461	6	849	Diesel	Bluebird	55
833	496	8	839	Diesel	Thompson	55
692	469	8	812	Diesel	Bluebird	55

(continued)

A.3 Data Set 3—Buena School District Bus Data (*concluded*)

Bus Number, x_1	Maintenance Cost, x_2	Age, x_3	Miles, x_4	Bus Type, x_5	Bus Manufacturer, x_6	Passengers, x_7
61	442	9	809	Diesel	Keiser	55
9	414	4	864	Gasoline	Keiser	55
314	459	11	859	Diesel	Thompson	6
396	457	2	815	Diesel	Thompson	55
365	462	6	799	Diesel	Keiser	55
398	570	9	844	Diesel	Thompson	14
43	439	9	832	Gasoline	Bluebird	55
500	369	5	842	Gasoline	Bluebird	55
279	390	2	792	Diesel	Bluebird	55
693	469	9	775	Gasoline	Keiser	55
884	381	9	882	Diesel	Bluebird	55
977	501	7	874	Diesel	Bluebird	55
38	432	6	837	Gasoline	Keiser	14
725	392	5	774	Diesel	Bluebird	55
982	441	1	823	Diesel	Bluebird	55
724	448	8	790	Diesel	Keiser	42
603	468	4	800	Diesel	Keiser	14
168	467	7	827	Gasoline	Thompson	55
45	478	6	830	Diesel	Keiser	55
754	515	14	895	Diesel	Keiser	14
39	411	6	804	Gasoline	Bluebird	55
671	504	8	866	Gasoline	Thompson	55
418	504	9	842	Diesel	Bluebird	55
984	392	8	851	Diesel	Bluebird	55
953	423	10	835	Diesel	Bluebird	55
507	410	7	866	Diesel	Bluebird	55
540	529	4	846	Gasoline	Bluebird	55
695	477	2	802	Diesel	Bluebird	55
193	540	11	847	Diesel	Thompson	55
321	450	6	856	Diesel	Bluebird	6
918	390	5	799	Diesel	Bluebird	55
101	424	4	827	Diesel	Bluebird	55
714	433	7	817	Diesel	Bluebird	42
678	428	7	842	Diesel	Keiser	55
768	494	7	815	Diesel	Bluebird	42
29	396	6	784	Gasoline	Bluebird	55
554	458	4	817	Diesel	Bluebird	14
767	493	6	816	Diesel	Keiser	55
699	475	9	816	Gasoline	Bluebird	55
954	476	10	827	Diesel	Bluebird	42
705	403	4	806	Diesel	Keiser	42
660	337	6	819	Gasoline	Bluebird	55
520	492	10	836	Diesel	Bluebird	55
814	426	4	757	Diesel	Bluebird	55
353	449	4	817	Gasoline	Keiser	55

A.4   Data Set 4—Applewood Auto Group

x_1 = **Age**—the age of the buyer at the time of the purchase
x_2 = **Profit**—the amount earned by the dealership on the sale of each vehicle
x_3 = **Location**—the dealership where the vehicle was purchased
x_4 = **Vehicle type**—SUV, sedan, compact, hybrid, or truck
x_5 = **Previous**—the number of vehicles previously purchased at any of the four Applewood dealerships by the customer

Age x_1	Profit x_2	Location x_3	Vehicle-Type x_4	Previous x_5	Age x_1	Profit x_2	Location x_3	Vehicle-Type x_4	Previous x_5
21	$1,387	Tionesta	Sedan	0	40	$1,485	Sheffield	Compact	0
23	1,754	Sheffield	SUV	1	40	1,509	Kane	SUV	2
24	1,817	Sheffield	Hybrid	1	40	1,638	Sheffield	Sedan	0
25	1,040	Sheffield	Compact	0	40	1,961	Sheffield	Sedan	1
26	1,273	Kane	Sedan	1	40	2,127	Olean	Truck	0
27	1,529	Sheffield	Sedan	1	40	2,430	Tionesta	Sedan	1
27	3,082	Kane	Truck	0	41	1,704	Sheffield	Sedan	1
28	1,951	Kane	SUV	1	41	1,876	Kane	Sedan	2
28	2,692	Tionesta	Compact	0	41	2,010	Tionesta	Sedan	1
29	1,206	Sheffield	Sedan	0	41	2,165	Tionesta	SUV	0
29	1,342	Kane	Sedan	2	41	2,231	Tionesta	SUV	2
30	443	Kane	Sedan	3	41	2,389	Kane	Truck	1
30	754	Olean	Sedan	2	42	335	Olean	SUV	1
30	1,621	Sheffield	Truck	1	42	963	Kane	Sedan	0
31	870	Tionesta	Sedan	1	42	1,298	Tionesta	Sedan	1
31	1,174	Kane	Truck	0	42	1,410	Kane	SUV	2
31	1,412	Sheffield	Sedan	1	42	1,553	Tionesta	Compact	0
31	1,809	Tionesta	Sedan	1	42	1,648	Olean	SUV	0
31	2,415	Kane	Sedan	0	42	2,071	Kane	SUV	0
32	1,546	Sheffield	Truck	3	42	2,116	Kane	Compact	2
32	2,148	Tionesta	SUV	2	43	1,500	Tionesta	Sedan	0
32	2,207	Sheffield	Compact	0	43	1,549	Kane	SUV	2
32	2,252	Tionesta	SUV	0	43	2,348	Tionesta	Sedan	0
33	1,428	Kane	SUV	2	43	2,498	Tionesta	SUV	1
33	1,889	Olean	SUV	1	44	294	Kane	SUV	1
34	1,166	Olean	Sedan	1	44	1,115	Kane	Truck	0
34	1,320	Tionesta	Sedan	1	44	1,124	Tionesta	Compact	2
34	2,265	Olean	Sedan	0	44	1,532	Tionesta	SUV	3
35	1,323	Olean	Sedan	2	44	1,688	Kane	Sedan	4
35	1,761	Kane	Sedan	1	44	1,822	Kane	SUV	0
35	1,919	Tionesta	SUV	1	44	1,897	Sheffield	Compact	0
36	2,357	Kane	SUV	2	44	2,445	Kane	SUV	0
36	2,866	Kane	Sedan	1	44	2,886	Olean	SUV	1
37	732	Olean	SUV	1	45	820	Kane	Compact	1
37	1,464	Olean	Sedan	3	45	1,266	Olean	Sedan	0
37	1,626	Tionesta	Compact	4	45	1,741	Olean	Compact	2
37	1,761	Olean	SUV	1	45	1,772	Olean	Compact	1
37	1,915	Tionesta	SUV	2	45	1,932	Tionesta	Sedan	1
37	2,119	Kane	Hybrid	1	45	2,350	Sheffield	Compact	0
38	1,766	Sheffield	SUV	0	45	2,422	Kane	Sedan	1
38	2,201	Sheffield	Truck	2	45	2,446	Olean	Compact	1
39	996	Kane	Compact	2	46	369	Olean	Sedan	1
39	2,813	Tionesta	SUV	0	46	978	Kane	Sedan	1
40	323	Kane	Sedan	0	46	1,238	Sheffield	Compact	1
40	352	Sheffield	Compact	0	46	1,818	Kane	SUV	0
40	482	Olean	Sedan	1	46	1,824	Olean	Truck	0
40	1,144	Tionesta	Truck	0	46	1,907	Olean	Sedan	0

(*continued*)

A.4   Data Set 4—Applewood Auto Group (*concluded*)

Age x_1	Profit x_2	Location x_3	Vehicle-Type x_4	Previous x_5	Age x_1	Profit x_2	Location x_3	Vehicle-Type x_4	Previous x_5
46	$1,938	Kane	Sedan	0	53	$1,401	Tionesta	SUV	2
46	1,940	Kane	Truck	3	53	2,175	Olean	Sedan	1
46	2,197	Sheffield	Sedan	1	54	1,118	Sheffield	Compact	1
46	2,646	Tionesta	Sedan	2	54	2,584	Olean	Compact	2
47	1,461	Kane	Sedan	0	54	2,666	Tionesta	Truck	0
47	1,731	Tionesta	Compact	0	54	2,991	Tionesta	SUV	0
47	2,230	Tionesta	Sedan	1	55	934	Sheffield	Truck	1
47	2,341	Sheffield	SUV	1	55	2,063	Kane	SUV	1
47	3,292	Olean	Sedan	2	55	2,083	Sheffield	Sedan	1
48	1,108	Sheffield	Sedan	1	55	2,856	Olean	Hybrid	1
48	1,295	Sheffield	SUV	1	55	2,989	Tionesta	Compact	1
48	1,344	Sheffield	SUV	0	56	910	Sheffield	SUV	0
48	1,906	Kane	Sedan	1	56	1,536	Kane	SUV	0
48	1,952	Tionesta	Compact	1	56	1,957	Sheffield	SUV	1
48	2,070	Kane	SUV	1	56	2,240	Olean	Sedan	0
48	2,454	Kane	Sedan	1	56	2,695	Kane	Sedan	2
49	1,606	Olean	Compact	0	57	1,325	Olean	Sedan	1
49	1,680	Kane	SUV	3	57	2,250	Sheffield	Sedan	2
49	1,827	Tionesta	Truck	3	57	2,279	Sheffield	Hybrid	1
49	1,915	Tionesta	SUV	1	57	2,626	Sheffield	Sedan	2
49	2,084	Tionesta	Sedan	0	58	1,501	Sheffield	Hybrid	1
49	2,639	Sheffield	SUV	0	58	1,752	Kane	Sedan	3
50	842	Kane	SUV	0	58	2,058	Kane	SUV	1
50	1,963	Sheffield	Sedan	1	58	2,370	Tionesta	Compact	0
50	2,059	Sheffield	Sedan	1	58	2,637	Sheffield	SUV	1
50	2,338	Tionesta	SUV	0	59	1,426	Sheffield	Sedan	0
50	3,043	Kane	Sedan	0	59	2,944	Olean	SUV	2
51	1,059	Kane	SUV	1	60	2,147	Olean	Compact	2
51	1,674	Sheffield	Sedan	1	61	1,973	Kane	SUV	3
51	1,807	Tionesta	Sedan	1	61	2,502	Olean	Sedan	0
51	2,056	Sheffield	Hybrid	0	62	783	Sheffield	Hybrid	1
51	2,236	Tionesta	SUV	2	62	1,538	Olean	Truck	1
51	2,928	Kane	SUV	0	63	2,339	Olean	Compact	1
52	1,269	Tionesta	Sedan	1	64	2,700	Kane	Truck	0
52	1,717	Sheffield	SUV	3	65	2,222	Kane	Truck	1
52	1,797	Kane	Sedan	1	65	2,597	Sheffield	Truck	0
52	1,955	Olean	Hybrid	2	65	2,742	Tionesta	SUV	2
52	2,199	Tionesta	SUV	0	68	1,837	Sheffield	Sedan	1
52	2,482	Olean	Compact	0	69	2,842	Kane	SUV	0
52	2,701	Sheffield	SUV	0	70	2,434	Olean	Sedan	4
52	3,210	Olean	Truck	4	72	1,640	Olean	Sedan	1
53	377	Olean	SUV	1	72	1,821	Tionesta	SUV	1
53	1,220	Olean	Sedan	0	73	2,487	Olean	Compact	4

A.5 Banking Data Set—Century National Bank Case

x_1 = Account balance in $
x_2 = Number of ATM transactions in the month
x_3 = Number of other bank services used
x_4 = Has a debit card (1 = yes, 0 = no)
x_5 = Receives interest on the account (1 = yes, 0 = no)
x_6 = City where banking is done
60 Accounts

x_1	x_2	x_3	x_4	x_5	x_6	x_1	x_2	x_3	x_4	x_5	x_6
1,756	13	4	0	1	2	1,958	6	2	1	0	2
748	9	2	1	0	1	634	2	7	1	0	4
1,501	10	1	0	0	1	580	4	1	0	0	1
1,831	10	4	0	1	3	1,320	4	5	1	0	1
1,622	14	6	0	1	4	1,675	6	7	1	0	2
1,886	17	3	0	1	1	789	8	4	0	0	4
740	6	3	0	0	3	1,735	12	7	0	1	3
1,593	10	8	1	0	1	1,784	11	5	0	0	1
1,169	6	4	0	0	4	1,326	16	8	0	0	3
2,125	18	6	0	0	2	2,051	14	4	1	0	4
1,554	12	6	1	0	3	1,044	7	5	1	0	1
1,474	12	7	1	0	1	1,885	10	6	1	1	2
1,913	6	5	0	0	1	1,790	11	4	0	1	3
1,218	10	3	1	0	1	765	4	3	0	0	4
1,006	12	4	0	0	1	1,645	6	9	0	1	4
2,215	20	3	1	0	4	32	2	0	0	0	3
137	7	2	0	0	3	1,266	11	7	0	0	4
167	5	4	0	0	4	890	7	1	0	1	1
343	7	2	0	0	1	2,204	14	5	0	0	2
2,557	20	7	1	0	4	2,409	16	8	0	0	2
2,276	15	4	1	0	3	1,338	14	4	1	0	2
1,494	11	2	0	1	1	2,076	12	5	1	0	2
2,144	17	3	0	0	3	1,708	13	3	1	0	1
1,995	10	7	0	0	2	2,138	18	5	0	1	4
1,053	8	4	1	0	3	2,375	12	4	0	0	2
1,526	8	4	0	1	2	1,455	9	5	1	1	3
1,120	8	6	1	0	3	1,487	8	4	1	0	4
1,838	7	5	1	1	3	1,125	6	4	1	0	2
1,746	11	2	0	0	2	1,989	12	3	0	1	2
1,616	10	4	1	1	2	2,156	14	5	1	0	2

APPENDIX B: TABLES

B.1 Binomial Probability Distribution

$n = 1$
Probability

x	0.05	0.10	0.20	0.30	0.40	0.50	0.60	0.70	0.80	0.90	0.95
0	0.950	0.900	0.800	0.700	0.600	0.500	0.400	0.300	0.200	0.100	0.050
1	0.050	0.100	0.200	0.300	0.400	0.500	0.600	0.700	0.800	0.900	0.950

$n = 2$
Probability

x	0.05	0.10	0.20	0.30	0.40	0.50	0.60	0.70	0.80	0.90	0.95
0	0.903	0.810	0.640	0.490	0.360	0.250	0.160	0.090	0.040	0.010	0.003
1	0.095	0.180	0.320	0.420	0.480	0.500	0.480	0.420	0.320	0.180	0.095
2	0.003	0.010	0.040	0.090	0.160	0.250	0.360	0.490	0.640	0.810	0.903

$n = 3$
Probability

x	0.05	0.10	0.20	0.30	0.40	0.50	0.60	0.70	0.80	0.90	0.95
0	0.857	0.729	0.512	0.343	0.216	0.125	0.064	0.027	0.008	0.001	0.000
1	0.135	0.243	0.384	0.441	0.432	0.375	0.288	0.189	0.096	0.027	0.007
2	0.007	0.027	0.096	0.189	0.288	0.375	0.432	0.441	0.384	0.243	0.135
3	0.000	0.001	0.008	0.027	0.064	0.125	0.216	0.343	0.512	0.729	0.857

$n = 4$
Probability

x	0.05	0.10	0.20	0.30	0.40	0.50	0.60	0.70	0.80	0.90	0.95
0	0.815	0.656	0.410	0.240	0.130	0.063	0.026	0.008	0.002	0.000	0.000
1	0.171	0.292	0.410	0.412	0.346	0.250	0.154	0.076	0.026	0.004	0.000
2	0.014	0.049	0.154	0.265	0.346	0.375	0.346	0.265	0.154	0.049	0.014
3	0.000	0.004	0.026	0.076	0.154	0.250	0.346	0.412	0.410	0.292	0.171
4	0.000	0.000	0.002	0.008	0.026	0.063	0.130	0.240	0.410	0.656	0.815

$n = 5$
Probability

x	0.05	0.10	0.20	0.30	0.40	0.50	0.60	0.70	0.80	0.90	0.95
0	0.774	0.590	0.328	0.168	0.078	0.031	0.010	0.002	0.000	0.000	0.000
1	0.204	0.328	0.410	0.360	0.259	0.156	0.077	0.028	0.006	0.000	0.000
2	0.021	0.073	0.205	0.309	0.346	0.313	0.230	0.132	0.051	0.008	0.001
3	0.001	0.008	0.051	0.132	0.230	0.313	0.346	0.309	0.205	0.073	0.021
4	0.000	0.000	0.006	0.028	0.077	0.156	0.259	0.360	0.410	0.328	0.204
5	0.000	0.000	0.000	0.002	0.010	0.031	0.078	0.168	0.328	0.590	0.774

(continued)

B.1   Binomial Probability Distribution (*continued*)

n = 6
Probability

x	0.05	0.10	0.20	0.30	0.40	0.50	0.60	0.70	0.80	0.90	0.95
0	0.735	0.531	0.262	0.118	0.047	0.016	0.004	0.001	0.000	0.000	0.000
1	0.232	0.354	0.393	0.303	0.187	0.094	0.037	0.010	0.002	0.000	0.000
2	0.031	0.098	0.246	0.324	0.311	0.234	0.138	0.060	0.015	0.001	0.000
3	0.002	0.015	0.082	0.185	0.276	0.313	0.276	0.185	0.082	0.015	0.002
4	0.000	0.001	0.015	0.060	0.138	0.234	0.311	0.324	0.246	0.098	0.031
5	0.000	0.000	0.002	0.010	0.037	0.094	0.187	0.303	0.393	0.354	0.232
6	0.000	0.000	0.000	0.001	0.004	0.016	0.047	0.118	0.262	0.531	0.735

n = 7
Probability

x	0.05	0.10	0.20	0.30	0.40	0.50	0.60	0.70	0.80	0.90	0.95
0	0.698	0.478	0.210	0.082	0.028	0.008	0.002	0.000	0.000	0.000	0.000
1	0.257	0.372	0.367	0.247	0.131	0.055	0.017	0.004	0.000	0.000	0.000
2	0.041	0.124	0.275	0.318	0.261	0.164	0.077	0.025	0.004	0.000	0.000
3	0.004	0.023	0.115	0.227	0.290	0.273	0.194	0.097	0.029	0.003	0.000
4	0.000	0.003	0.029	0.097	0.194	0.273	0.290	0.227	0.115	0.023	0.004
5	0.000	0.000	0.004	0.025	0.077	0.164	0.261	0.318	0.275	0.124	0.041
6	0.000	0.000	0.000	0.004	0.017	0.055	0.131	0.247	0.367	0.372	0.257
7	0.000	0.000	0.000	0.000	0.002	0.008	0.028	0.082	0.210	0.478	0.698

n = 8
Probability

x	0.05	0.10	0.20	0.30	0.40	0.50	0.60	0.70	0.80	0.90	0.95
0	0.663	0.430	0.168	0.058	0.017	0.004	0.001	0.000	0.000	0.000	0.000
1	0.279	0.383	0.336	0.198	0.090	0.031	0.008	0.001	0.000	0.000	0.000
2	0.051	0.149	0.294	0.296	0.209	0.109	0.041	0.010	0.001	0.000	0.000
3	0.005	0.033	0.147	0.254	0.279	0.219	0.124	0.047	0.009	0.000	0.000
4	0.000	0.005	0.046	0.136	0.232	0.273	0.232	0.136	0.046	0.005	0.000
5	0.000	0.000	0.009	0.047	0.124	0.219	0.279	0.254	0.147	0.033	0.005
6	0.000	0.000	0.001	0.010	0.041	0.109	0.209	0.296	0.294	0.149	0.051
7	0.000	0.000	0.000	0.001	0.008	0.031	0.090	0.198	0.336	0.383	0.279
8	0.000	0.000	0.000	0.000	0.001	0.004	0.017	0.058	0.168	0.430	0.663

(*continued*)

B.1 Binomial Probability Distribution (*continued*)

n = 9
Probability

x	0.05	0.10	0.20	0.30	0.40	0.50	0.60	0.70	0.80	0.90	0.95
0	0.630	0.387	0.134	0.040	0.010	0.002	0.000	0.000	0.000	0.000	0.000
1	0.299	0.387	0.302	0.156	0.060	0.018	0.004	0.000	0.000	0.000	0.000
2	0.063	0.172	0.302	0.267	0.161	0.070	0.021	0.004	0.000	0.000	0.000
3	0.008	0.045	0.176	0.267	0.251	0.164	0.074	0.021	0.003	0.000	0.000
4	0.001	0.007	0.066	0.172	0.251	0.246	0.167	0.074	0.017	0.001	0.000
5	0.000	0.001	0.017	0.074	0.167	0.246	0.251	0.172	0.066	0.007	0.001
6	0.000	0.000	0.003	0.021	0.074	0.164	0.251	0.267	0.176	0.045	0.008
7	0.000	0.000	0.000	0.004	0.021	0.070	0.161	0.267	0.302	0.172	0.063
8	0.000	0.000	0.000	0.000	0.004	0.018	0.060	0.156	0.302	0.387	0.299
9	0.000	0.000	0.000	0.000	0.000	0.002	0.010	0.040	0.134	0.387	0.630

n = 10
Probability

x	0.05	0.10	0.20	0.30	0.40	0.50	0.60	0.70	0.80	0.90	0.95
0	0.599	0.349	0.107	0.028	0.006	0.001	0.000	0.000	0.000	0.000	0.000
1	0.315	0.387	0.268	0.121	0.040	0.010	0.002	0.000	0.000	0.000	0.000
2	0.075	0.194	0.302	0.233	0.121	0.044	0.011	0.001	0.000	0.000	0.000
3	0.010	0.057	0.201	0.267	0.215	0.117	0.042	0.009	0.001	0.000	0.000
4	0.001	0.011	0.088	0.200	0.251	0.205	0.111	0.037	0.006	0.000	0.000
5	0.000	0.001	0.026	0.103	0.201	0.246	0.201	0.103	0.026	0.001	0.000
6	0.000	0.000	0.006	0.037	0.111	0.205	0.251	0.200	0.088	0.011	0.001
7	0.000	0.000	0.001	0.009	0.042	0.117	0.215	0.267	0.201	0.057	0.010
8	0.000	0.000	0.000	0.001	0.011	0.044	0.121	0.233	0.302	0.194	0.075
9	0.000	0.000	0.000	0.000	0.002	0.010	0.040	0.121	0.268	0.387	0.315
10	0.000	0.000	0.000	0.000	0.000	0.001	0.006	0.028	0.107	0.349	0.599

n = 11
Probability

x	0.05	0.10	0.20	0.30	0.40	0.50	0.60	0.70	0.80	0.90	0.95
0	0.569	0.314	0.086	0.020	0.004	0.000	0.000	0.000	0.000	0.000	0.000
1	0.329	0.384	0.236	0.093	0.027	0.005	0.001	0.000	0.000	0.000	0.000
2	0.087	0.213	0.295	0.200	0.089	0.027	0.005	0.001	0.000	0.000	0.000
3	0.014	0.071	0.221	0.257	0.177	0.081	0.023	0.004	0.000	0.000	0.000
4	0.001	0.016	0.111	0.220	0.236	0.161	0.070	0.017	0.002	0.000	0.000
5	0.000	0.002	0.039	0.132	0.221	0.226	0.147	0.057	0.010	0.000	0.000
6	0.000	0.000	0.010	0.057	0.147	0.226	0.221	0.132	0.039	0.002	0.000
7	0.000	0.000	0.002	0.017	0.070	0.161	0.236	0.220	0.111	0.016	0.001
8	0.000	0.000	0.000	0.004	0.023	0.081	0.177	0.257	0.221	0.071	0.014
9	0.000	0.000	0.000	0.001	0.005	0.027	0.089	0.200	0.295	0.213	0.087
10	0.000	0.000	0.000	0.000	0.001	0.005	0.027	0.093	0.236	0.384	0.329
11	0.000	0.000	0.000	0.000	0.000	0.000	0.004	0.020	0.086	0.314	0.569

(continued)

B.1   Binomial Probability Distribution (*continued*)

n = 12
Probability

x	0.05	0.10	0.20	0.30	0.40	0.50	0.60	0.70	0.80	0.90	0.95
0	0.540	0.282	0.069	0.014	0.002	0.000	0.000	0.000	0.000	0.000	0.000
1	0.341	0.377	0.206	0.071	0.017	0.003	0.000	0.000	0.000	0.000	0.000
2	0.099	0.230	0.283	0.168	0.064	0.016	0.002	0.000	0.000	0.000	0.000
3	0.017	0.085	0.236	0.240	0.142	0.054	0.012	0.001	0.000	0.000	0.000
4	0.002	0.021	0.133	0.231	0.213	0.121	0.042	0.008	0.001	0.000	0.000
5	0.000	0.004	0.053	0.158	0.227	0.193	0.101	0.029	0.003	0.000	0.000
6	0.000	0.000	0.016	0.079	0.177	0.226	0.177	0.079	0.016	0.000	0.000
7	0.000	0.000	0.003	0.029	0.101	0.193	0.227	0.158	0.053	0.004	0.000
8	0.000	0.000	0.001	0.008	0.042	0.121	0.213	0.231	0.133	0.021	0.002
9	0.000	0.000	0.000	0.001	0.012	0.054	0.142	0.240	0.236	0.085	0.017
10	0.000	0.000	0.000	0.000	0.002	0.016	0.064	0.168	0.283	0.230	0.099
11	0.000	0.000	0.000	0.000	0.000	0.003	0.017	0.071	0.206	0.377	0.341
12	0.000	0.000	0.000	0.000	0.000	0.000	0.002	0.014	0.069	0.282	0.540

n = 13
Probability

x	0.05	0.10	0.20	0.30	0.40	0.50	0.60	0.70	0.80	0.90	0.95
0	0.513	0.254	0.055	0.010	0.001	0.000	0.000	0.000	0.000	0.000	0.000
1	0.351	0.367	0.179	0.054	0.011	0.002	0.000	0.000	0.000	0.000	0.000
2	0.111	0.245	0.268	0.139	0.045	0.010	0.001	0.000	0.000	0.000	0.000
3	0.021	0.100	0.246	0.218	0.111	0.035	0.006	0.001	0.000	0.000	0.000
4	0.003	0.028	0.154	0.234	0.184	0.087	0.024	0.003	0.000	0.000	0.000
5	0.000	0.006	0.069	0.180	0.221	0.157	0.066	0.014	0.001	0.000	0.000
6	0.000	0.001	0.023	0.103	0.197	0.209	0.131	0.044	0.006	0.000	0.000
7	0.000	0.000	0.006	0.044	0.131	0.209	0.197	0.103	0.023	0.001	0.000
8	0.000	0.000	0.001	0.014	0.066	0.157	0.221	0.180	0.069	0.006	0.000
9	0.000	0.000	0.000	0.003	0.024	0.087	0.184	0.234	0.154	0.028	0.003
10	0.000	0.000	0.000	0.001	0.006	0.035	0.111	0.218	0.246	0.100	0.021
11	0.000	0.000	0.000	0.000	0.001	0.010	0.045	0.139	0.268	0.245	0.111
12	0.000	0.000	0.000	0.000	0.000	0.002	0.011	0.054	0.179	0.367	0.351
13	0.000	0.000	0.000	0.000	0.000	0.000	0.001	0.010	0.055	0.254	0.513

B.1   Binomial Probability Distribution (*concluded*)

n = 14
Probability

x	0.05	0.10	0.20	0.30	0.40	0.50	0.60	0.70	0.80	0.90	0.95
0	0.488	0.229	0.044	0.007	0.001	0.000	0.000	0.000	0.000	0.000	0.000
1	0.359	0.356	0.154	0.041	0.007	0.001	0.000	0.000	0.000	0.000	0.000
2	0.123	0.257	0.250	0.113	0.032	0.006	0.001	0.000	0.000	0.000	0.000
3	0.026	0.114	0.250	0.194	0.085	0.022	0.003	0.000	0.000	0.000	0.000
4	0.004	0.035	0.172	0.229	0.155	0.061	0.014	0.001	0.000	0.000	0.000
5	0.000	0.008	0.086	0.196	0.207	0.122	0.041	0.007	0.000	0.000	0.000
6	0.000	0.001	0.032	0.126	0.207	0.183	0.092	0.023	0.002	0.000	0.000
7	0.000	0.000	0.009	0.062	0.157	0.209	0.157	0.062	0.009	0.000	0.000
8	0.000	0.000	0.002	0.023	0.092	0.183	0.207	0.126	0.032	0.001	0.000
9	0.000	0.000	0.000	0.007	0.041	0.122	0.207	0.196	0.086	0.008	0.000
10	0.000	0.000	0.000	0.001	0.014	0.061	0.155	0.229	0.172	0.035	0.004
11	0.000	0.000	0.000	0.000	0.003	0.022	0.085	0.194	0.250	0.114	0.026
12	0.000	0.000	0.000	0.000	0.001	0.006	0.032	0.113	0.250	0.257	0.123
13	0.000	0.000	0.000	0.000	0.000	0.001	0.007	0.041	0.154	0.356	0.359
14	0.000	0.000	0.000	0.000	0.000	0.000	0.001	0.007	0.044	0.229	0.488

n = 15
Probability

x	0.05	0.10	0.20	0.30	0.40	0.50	0.60	0.70	0.80	0.90	0.95
0	0.463	0.206	0.035	0.005	0.000	0.000	0.000	0.000	0.000	0.000	0.000
1	0.366	0.343	0.132	0.031	0.005	0.000	0.000	0.000	0.000	0.000	0.000
2	0.135	0.267	0.231	0.092	0.022	0.003	0.000	0.000	0.000	0.000	0.000
3	0.031	0.129	0.250	0.170	0.063	0.014	0.002	0.000	0.000	0.000	0.000
4	0.005	0.043	0.188	0.219	0.127	0.042	0.007	0.001	0.000	0.000	0.000
5	0.001	0.010	0.103	0.206	0.186	0.092	0.024	0.003	0.000	0.000	0.000
6	0.000	0.002	0.043	0.147	0.207	0.153	0.061	0.012	0.001	0.000	0.000
7	0.000	0.000	0.014	0.081	0.177	0.196	0.118	0.035	0.003	0.000	0.000
8	0.000	0.000	0.003	0.035	0.118	0.196	0.177	0.081	0.014	0.000	0.000
9	0.000	0.000	0.001	0.012	0.061	0.153	0.207	0.147	0.043	0.002	0.000
10	0.000	0.000	0.000	0.003	0.024	0.092	0.186	0.206	0.103	0.010	0.001
11	0.000	0.000	0.000	0.001	0.007	0.042	0.127	0.219	0.188	0.043	0.005
12	0.000	0.000	0.000	0.000	0.002	0.014	0.063	0.170	0.250	0.129	0.031
13	0.000	0.000	0.000	0.000	0.000	0.003	0.022	0.092	0.231	0.267	0.135
14	0.000	0.000	0.000	0.000	0.000	0.000	0.005	0.031	0.132	0.343	0.366
15	0.000	0.000	0.000	0.000	0.000	0.000	0.000	0.005	0.035	0.206	0.463

B.2   Poisson Distribution

					μ				
x	0.1	0.2	0.3	0.4	0.5	0.6	0.7	0.8	0.9
0	0.9048	0.8187	0.7408	0.6703	0.6065	0.5488	0.4966	0.4493	0.4066
1	0.0905	0.1637	0.2222	0.2681	0.3033	0.3293	0.3476	0.3595	0.3659
2	0.0045	0.0164	0.0333	0.0536	0.0758	0.0988	0.1217	0.1438	0.1647
3	0.0002	0.0011	0.0033	0.0072	0.0126	0.0198	0.0284	0.0383	0.0494
4	0.0000	0.0001	0.0003	0.0007	0.0016	0.0030	0.0050	0.0077	0.0111
5	0.0000	0.0000	0.0000	0.0001	0.0002	0.0004	0.0007	0.0012	0.0020
6	0.0000	0.0000	0.0000	0.0000	0.0000	0.0000	0.0001	0.0002	0.0003
7	0.0000	0.0000	0.0000	0.0000	0.0000	0.0000	0.0000	0.0000	0.0000

					μ				
x	1.0	2.0	3.0	4.0	5.0	6.0	7.0	8.0	9.0
0	0.3679	0.1353	0.0498	0.0183	0.0067	0.0025	0.0009	0.0003	0.0001
1	0.3679	0.2707	0.1494	0.0733	0.0337	0.0149	0.0064	0.0027	0.0011
2	0.1839	0.2707	0.2240	0.1465	0.0842	0.0446	0.0223	0.0107	0.0050
3	0.0613	0.1804	0.2240	0.1954	0.1404	0.0892	0.0521	0.0286	0.0150
4	0.0153	0.0902	0.1680	0.1954	0.1755	0.1339	0.0912	0.0573	0.0337
5	0.0031	0.0361	0.1008	0.1563	0.1755	0.1606	0.1277	0.0916	0.0607
6	0.0005	0.0120	0.0504	0.1042	0.1462	0.1606	0.1490	0.1221	0.0911
7	0.0001	0.0034	0.0216	0.0595	0.1044	0.1377	0.1490	0.1396	0.1171
8	0.0000	0.0009	0.0081	0.0298	0.0653	0.1033	0.1304	0.1396	0.1318
9	0.0000	0.0002	0.0027	0.0132	0.0363	0.0688	0.1014	0.1241	0.1318
10	0.0000	0.0000	0.0008	0.0053	0.0181	0.0413	0.0710	0.0993	0.1186
11	0.0000	0.0000	0.0002	0.0019	0.0082	0.0225	0.0452	0.0722	0.0970
12	0.0000	0.0000	0.0001	0.0006	0.0034	0.0113	0.0263	0.0481	0.0728
13	0.0000	0.0000	0.0000	0.0002	0.0013	0.0052	0.0142	0.0296	0.0504
14	0.0000	0.0000	0.0000	0.0001	0.0005	0.0022	0.0071	0.0169	0.0324
15	0.0000	0.0000	0.0000	0.0000	0.0002	0.0009	0.0033	0.0090	0.0194
16	0.0000	0.0000	0.0000	0.0000	0.0000	0.0003	0.0014	0.0045	0.0109
17	0.0000	0.0000	0.0000	0.0000	0.0000	0.0001	0.0006	0.0021	0.0058
18	0.0000	0.0000	0.0000	0.0000	0.0000	0.0000	0.0002	0.0009	0.0029
19	0.0000	0.0000	0.0000	0.0000	0.0000	0.0000	0.0001	0.0004	0.0014
20	0.0000	0.0000	0.0000	0.0000	0.0000	0.0000	0.0000	0.0002	0.0006
21	0.0000	0.0000	0.0000	0.0000	0.0000	0.0000	0.0000	0.0001	0.0003
22	0.0000	0.0000	0.0000	0.0000	0.0000	0.0000	0.0000	0.0000	0.0001

B.3 Areas under the Normal Curve

Example:
If $z = 1.96$, then
$P(0$ to $z) = 0.4750$.

0.4750

$z \longrightarrow$ 0   1.96

z	0.00	0.01	0.02	0.03	0.04	0.05	0.06	0.07	0.08	0.09
0.0	0.0000	0.0040	0.0080	0.0120	0.0160	0.0199	0.0239	0.0279	0.0319	0.0359
0.1	0.0398	0.0438	0.0478	0.0517	0.0557	0.0596	0.0636	0.0675	0.0714	0.0753
0.2	0.0793	0.0832	0.0871	0.0910	0.0948	0.0987	0.1026	0.1064	0.1103	0.1141
0.3	0.1179	0.1217	0.1255	0.1293	0.1331	0.1368	0.1406	0.1443	0.1480	0.1517
0.4	0.1554	0.1591	0.1628	0.1664	0.1700	0.1736	0.1772	0.1808	0.1844	0.1879
0.5	0.1915	0.1950	0.1985	0.2019	0.2054	0.2088	0.2123	0.2157	0.2190	0.2224
0.6	0.2257	0.2291	0.2324	0.2357	0.2389	0.2422	0.2454	0.2486	0.2517	0.2549
0.7	0.2580	0.2611	0.2642	0.2673	0.2704	0.2734	0.2764	0.2794	0.2823	0.2852
0.8	0.2881	0.2910	0.2939	0.2967	0.2995	0.3023	0.3051	0.3078	0.3106	0.3133
0.9	0.3159	0.3186	0.3212	0.3238	0.3264	0.3289	0.3315	0.3340	0.3365	0.3389
1.0	0.3413	0.3438	0.3461	0.3485	0.3508	0.3531	0.3554	0.3577	0.3599	0.3621
1.1	0.3643	0.3665	0.3686	0.3708	0.3729	0.3749	0.3770	0.3790	0.3810	0.3830
1.2	0.3849	0.3869	0.3888	0.3907	0.3925	0.3944	0.3962	0.3980	0.3997	0.4015
1.3	0.4032	0.4049	0.4066	0.4082	0.4099	0.4115	0.4131	0.4147	0.4162	0.4177
1.4	0.4192	0.4207	0.4222	0.4236	0.4251	0.4265	0.4279	0.4292	0.4306	0.4319
1.5	0.4332	0.4345	0.4357	0.4370	0.4382	0.4394	0.4406	0.4418	0.4429	0.4441
1.6	0.4452	0.4463	0.4474	0.4484	0.4495	0.4505	0.4515	0.4525	0.4535	0.4545
1.7	0.4554	0.4564	0.4573	0.4582	0.4591	0.4599	0.4608	0.4616	0.4625	0.4633
1.8	0.4641	0.4649	0.4656	0.4664	0.4671	0.4678	0.4686	0.4693	0.4699	0.4706
1.9	0.4713	0.4719	0.4726	0.4732	0.4738	0.4744	0.4750	0.4756	0.4761	0.4767
2.0	0.4772	0.4778	0.4783	0.4788	0.4793	0.4798	0.4803	0.4808	0.4812	0.4817
2.1	0.4821	0.4826	0.4830	0.4834	0.4838	0.4842	0.4846	0.4850	0.4854	0.4857
2.2	0.4861	0.4864	0.4868	0.4871	0.4875	0.4878	0.4881	0.4884	0.4887	0.4890
2.3	0.4893	0.4896	0.4898	0.4901	0.4904	0.4906	0.4909	0.4911	0.4913	0.4916
2.4	0.4918	0.4920	0.4922	0.4925	0.4927	0.4929	0.4931	0.4932	0.4934	0.4936
2.5	0.4938	0.4940	0.4941	0.4943	0.4945	0.4946	0.4948	0.4949	0.4951	0.4952
2.6	0.4953	0.4955	0.4956	0.4957	0.4959	0.4960	0.4961	0.4962	0.4963	0.4964
2.7	0.4965	0.4966	0.4967	0.4968	0.4969	0.4970	0.4971	0.4972	0.4973	0.4974
2.8	0.4974	0.4975	0.4976	0.4977	0.4977	0.4978	0.4979	0.4979	0.4980	0.4981
2.9	0.4981	0.4982	0.4982	0.4983	0.4984	0.4984	0.4985	0.4985	0.4986	0.4986
3.0	0.4987	0.4987	0.4987	0.4988	0.4988	0.4989	0.4989	0.4989	0.4990	0.4990

B.4   Table of Random Numbers

02711	08182	75997	79866	58095	83319	80295	79741	74599	84379
94873	90935	31684	63952	09865	14491	99518	93394	34691	14985
54921	78680	06635	98689	17306	25170	65928	87709	30533	89736
77640	97636	37397	93379	56454	59818	45827	74164	71666	46977
61545	00835	93251	87203	36759	49197	85967	01704	19634	21898
17147	19519	22497	16857	42426	84822	92598	49186	88247	39967
13748	04742	92460	85801	53444	65626	58710	55406	17173	69776
87455	14813	50373	28037	91182	32786	65261	11173	34376	36408
08999	57409	91185	10200	61411	23392	47797	56377	71635	08601
78804	81333	53809	32471	46034	36306	22498	19239	85428	55721
82173	26921	28472	98958	07960	66124	89731	95069	18625	92405
97594	25168	89178	68190	05043	17407	48201	83917	11413	72920
73881	67176	93504	42636	38233	16154	96451	57925	29667	30859
46071	22912	90326	42453	88108	72064	58601	32357	90610	32921
44492	19686	12495	93135	95185	77799	52441	88272	22024	80631
31864	72170	37722	55794	14636	05148	54505	50113	21119	25228
51574	90692	43339	65689	76539	27909	05467	21727	51141	72949
35350	76132	92925	92124	92634	35681	43690	89136	35599	84138
46943	36502	01172	46045	46991	33804	80006	35542	61056	75666
22665	87226	33304	57975	03985	21566	65796	72915	81466	89205
39437	97957	11838	10433	21564	51570	73558	27495	34533	57808
77082	47784	40098	97962	89845	28392	78187	06112	08169	11261
24544	25649	43370	28007	06779	72402	62632	53956	24709	06978
27503	15558	37738	24849	70722	71859	83736	06016	94397	12529
24590	24545	06435	52758	45685	90151	46516	49644	92686	84870
48155	86226	40359	28723	15364	69125	12609	57171	86857	31702
20226	53752	90648	24362	83314	00014	19207	69413	97016	86290
70178	73444	38790	53626	93780	18629	68766	24371	74639	30782
10169	41465	51935	05711	09799	79077	88159	33437	68519	03040
81084	03701	28598	70013	63794	53169	97054	60303	23259	96196
69202	20777	21727	81511	51887	16175	53746	46516	70339	62727
80561	95787	89426	93325	86412	57479	54194	52153	19197	81877
08199	26703	95128	48599	09333	12584	24374	31232	61782	44032
98883	28220	39358	53720	80161	83371	15181	11131	12219	55920
84568	69286	76054	21615	80883	36797	82845	39139	90900	18172
04269	35173	95745	53893	86022	77722	52498	84193	22448	22571
10538	13124	36099	13140	37706	44562	57179	44693	67877	01549
77843	24955	25900	63843	95029	93859	93634	20205	66294	41218
12034	94636	49455	76362	83532	31062	69903	91186	65768	55949
10524	72829	47641	93315	80875	28090	97728	52560	34937	79548
68935	76632	46984	61772	92786	22651	07086	89754	44143	97687
89450	65665	29190	43709	11172	34481	95977	47535	25658	73898
90696	20451	24211	97310	60446	73530	62865	96574	13829	72226
49006	32047	93086	00112	20470	17136	28255	86328	07293	38809
74591	87025	52368	59416	34417	70557	86746	55809	53628	12000
06315	17012	77103	00968	07235	10728	42189	33292	51487	64443
62386	09184	62092	46617	99419	64230	95034	85481	07857	42510
86848	82122	04028	36959	87827	12813	08627	80699	13345	51695
65643	69480	46598	04501	40403	91408	32343	48130	49303	90689
11084	46534	78957	77353	39578	77868	22970	84349	09184	70603

B.5 Student's *t* Distribution

Confidence interval

Left-tailed test

Right-tailed test

Two-tailed test

	Confidence Intervals, *c*								Confidence Intervals, *c*					
	80%	90%	95%	98%	99%	99.9%		80%	90%	95%	98%	99%	99.9%
	Level of Significance for One-Tailed Test, α							Level of Significance for One-Tailed Test, α					
df	0.10	0.05	0.025	0.01	0.005	0.0005	*df*	0.10	0.05	0.025	0.01	0.005	0.0005
	Level of Significance for Two-Tailed Test, α							Level of Significance for Two-Tailed Test, α					
	0.20	0.10	0.05	0.02	0.01	0.001		0.20	0.10	0.05	0.02	0.01	0.001
1	3.078	6.314	12.706	31.821	63.657	636.619	36	1.306	1.688	2.028	2.434	2.719	3.582
2	1.886	2.920	4.303	6.965	9.925	31.599	37	1.305	1.687	2.026	2.431	2.715	3.574
3	1.638	2.353	3.182	4.541	5.841	12.924	38	1.304	1.686	2.024	2.429	2.712	3.566
4	1.533	2.132	2.776	3.747	4.604	8.610	39	1.304	1.685	2.023	2.426	2.708	3.558
5	1.476	2.015	2.571	3.365	4.032	6.869	40	1.303	1.684	2.021	2.423	2.704	3.551
6	1.440	1.943	2.447	3.143	3.707	5.959	41	1.303	1.683	2.020	2.421	2.701	3.544
7	1.415	1.895	2.365	2.998	3.499	5.408	42	1.302	1.682	2.018	2.418	2.698	3.538
8	1.397	1.860	2.306	2.896	3.355	5.041	43	1.302	1.681	2.017	2.416	2.695	3.532
9	1.383	1.833	2.262	2.821	3.250	4.781	44	1.301	1.680	2.015	2.414	2.692	3.526
10	1.372	1.812	2.228	2.764	3.169	4.587	45	1.301	1.679	2.014	2.412	2.690	3.520
11	1.363	1.796	2.201	2.718	3.106	4.437	46	1.300	1.679	2.013	2.410	2.687	3.515
12	1.356	1.782	2.179	2.681	3.055	4.318	47	1.300	1.678	2.012	2.408	2.685	3.510
13	1.350	1.771	2.160	2.650	3.012	4.221	48	1.299	1.677	2.011	2.407	2.682	3.505
14	1.345	1.761	2.145	2.624	2.977	4.140	49	1.299	1.677	2.010	2.405	2.680	3.500
15	1.341	1.753	2.131	2.602	2.947	4.073	50	1.299	1.676	2.009	2.403	2.678	3.496
16	1.337	1.746	2.120	2.583	2.921	4.015	51	1.298	1.675	2.008	2.402	2.676	3.492
17	1.333	1.740	2.110	2.567	2.898	3.965	52	1.298	1.675	2.007	2.400	2.674	3.488
18	1.330	1.734	2.101	2.552	2.878	3.922	53	1.298	1.674	2.006	2.399	2.672	3.484
19	1.328	1.729	2.093	2.539	2.861	3.883	54	1.297	1.674	2.005	2.397	2.670	3.480
20	1.325	1.725	2.086	2.528	2.845	3.850	55	1.297	1.673	2.004	2.396	2.668	3.476
21	1.323	1.721	2.080	2.518	2.831	3.819	56	1.297	1.673	2.003	2.395	2.667	3.473
22	1.321	1.717	2.074	2.508	2.819	3.792	57	1.297	1.672	2.002	2.394	2.665	3.470
23	1.319	1.714	2.069	2.500	2.807	3.768	58	1.296	1.672	2.002	2.392	2.663	3.466
24	1.318	1.711	2.064	2.492	2.797	3.745	59	1.296	1.671	2.001	2.391	2.662	3.463
25	1.316	1.708	2.060	2.485	2.787	3.725	60	1.296	1.671	2.000	2.390	2.660	3.460
26	1.315	1.706	2.056	2.479	2.779	3.707	61	1.296	1.670	2.000	2.389	2.659	3.457
27	1.314	1.703	2.052	2.473	2.771	3.690	62	1.295	1.670	1.999	2.388	2.657	3.454
28	1.313	1.701	2.048	2.467	2.763	3.674	63	1.295	1.669	1.998	2.387	2.656	3.452
29	1.311	1.699	2.045	2.462	2.756	3.659	64	1.295	1.669	1.998	2.386	2.655	3.449
30	1.310	1.697	2.042	2.457	2.750	3.646	65	1.295	1.669	1.997	2.385	2.654	3.447
31	1.309	1.696	2.040	2.453	2.744	3.633	66	1.295	1.668	1.997	2.384	2.652	3.444
32	1.309	1.694	2.037	2.449	2.738	3.622	67	1.294	1.668	1.996	2.383	2.651	3.442
33	1.308	1.692	2.035	2.445	2.733	3.611	68	1.294	1.668	1.995	2.382	2.650	3.439
34	1.307	1.691	2.032	2.441	2.728	3.601	69	1.294	1.667	1.995	2.382	2.649	3.437
35	1.306	1.690	2.030	2.438	2.724	3.591	70	1.294	1.667	1.994	2.381	2.648	3.435

(continued)

B.5   Student's *t* Distribution (*concluded*)

	Confidence Intervals, *c*					
	80%	90%	95%	98%	99%	99.9%
	Level of Significance for One-Tailed Test, α					
df	0.10	0.05	0.025	0.01	0.005	0.0005
	Level of Significance for Two-Tailed Test, α					
	0.20	0.10	0.05	0.02	0.01	0.001
71	1.294	1.667	1.994	2.380	2.647	3.433
72	1.293	1.666	1.993	2.379	2.646	3.431
73	1.293	1.666	1.993	2.379	2.645	3.429
74	1.293	1.666	1.993	2.378	2.644	3.427
75	1.293	1.665	1.992	2.377	2.643	3.425
76	1.293	1.665	1.992	2.376	2.642	3.423
77	1.293	1.665	1.991	2.376	2.641	3.421
78	1.292	1.665	1.991	2.375	2.640	3.420
79	1.292	1.664	1.990	2.374	2.640	3.418
80	1.292	1.664	1.990	2.374	2.639	3.416
81	1.292	1.664	1.990	2.373	2.638	3.415
82	1.292	1.664	1.989	2.373	2.637	3.413
83	1.292	1.663	1.989	2.372	2.636	3.412
84	1.292	1.663	1.989	2.372	2.636	3.410
85	1.292	1.663	1.988	2.371	2.635	3.409
86	1.291	1.663	1.988	2.370	2.634	3.407
87	1.291	1.663	1.988	2.370	2.634	3.406
88	1.291	1.662	1.987	2.369	2.633	3.405

	Confidence Intervals, *c*					
	80%	90%	95%	98%	99%	99.9%
	Level of Significance for One-Tailed Test, α					
df	0.10	0.05	0.025	0.01	0.005	0.0005
	Level of Significance for Two-Tailed Test, α					
	0.20	0.10	0.05	0.02	0.01	0.001
89	1.291	1.662	1.987	2.369	2.632	3.403
90	1.291	1.662	1.987	2.368	2.632	3.402
91	1.291	1.662	1.986	2.368	2.631	3.401
92	1.291	1.662	1.986	2.368	2.630	3.399
93	1.291	1.661	1.986	2.367	2.630	3.398
94	1.291	1.661	1.986	2.367	2.629	3.397
95	1.291	1.661	1.985	2.366	2.629	3.396
96	1.290	1.661	1.985	2.366	2.628	3.395
97	1.290	1.661	1.985	2.365	2.627	3.394
98	1.290	1.661	1.984	2.365	2.627	3.393
99	1.290	1.660	1.984	2.365	2.626	3.392
100	1.290	1.660	1.984	2.364	2.626	3.390
120	1.289	1.658	1.980	2.358	2.617	3.373
140	1.288	1.656	1.977	2.353	2.611	3.361
160	1.287	1.654	1.975	2.350	2.607	3.352
180	1.286	1.653	1.973	2.347	2.603	3.345
200	1.286	1.653	1.972	2.345	2.601	3.340
∞	1.282	1.645	1.960	2.326	2.576	3.291

B.6A   Critical Values of the *F* Distribution ($\alpha = .05$)

		Degrees of Freedom for the Numerator														
	1	**2**	**3**	**4**	**5**	**6**	**7**	**8**	**9**	**10**	**12**	**15**	**20**	**24**	**30**	**40**
1	161	200	216.	225	230	234	237	239	241	242	244	246	248	249	250	251
2	18.5	19.0	19.2	19.2	19.3	19.3	19.4	19.4	19.4	19.4	19.4	19.4	19.4	19.5	19.5	19.5
3	10.1	9.55	9.28	9.12	9.01	8.94	8.89	8.85	8.81	8.79	8.74	8.70	8.66	8.64	8.62	8.59
4	7.71	6.94	6.59	6.39	6.26	6.16	6.09	6.04	6.00	5.96	5.91	5.86	5.80	5.77	5.75	5.72
5	6.61	5.79	5.41	5.19	5.05	4.95	4.88	4.82	4.77	4.74	4.68	4.62	4.56	4.53	4.50	4.46
6	5.99	5.14	4.76	4.53	4.39	4.28	4.21	4.15	4.10	4.06	4.00	3.94	3.87	3.84	3.81	3.77
7	5.59	4.74	4.35	4.12	3.97	3.87	3.79	3.73	3.68	3.64	3.57	3.51	3.44	3.41	3.38	3.34
8	5.32	4.46	4.07	3.84	3.69	3.58	3.50	3.44	3.39	3.35	3.28	3.22	3.15	3.12	3.08	3.04
9	5.12	4.26	3.86	3.63	3.48	3.37	3.29	3.23	3.18	3.14	3.07	3.01	2.94	2.90	2.86	2.83
10	4.96	4.10	3.71	3.48	3.33	3.22	3.14	3.07	3.02	2.98	2.91	2.85	2.77	2.74	2.70	2.66
11	4.84	3.98	3.59	3.36	3.20	3.09	3.01	2.95	2.90	2.85	2.79	2.72	2.65	2.61	2.57	2.53
12	4.75	3.89	3.49	3.26	3.11	3.00	2.91	2.85	2.80	2.75	2.69	2.62	2.54	2.51	2.47	2.43
13	4.67	3.81	3.41	3.18	3.03	2.92	2.83	2.77	2.71	2.67	2.60	2.53	2.46	2.42	2.38	2.34
14	4.60	3.74	3.34	3.11	2.96	2.85	2.76	2.70	2.65	2.60	2.53	2.46	2.39	2.35	2.31	2.27
15	4.54	3.68	3.29	3.06	2.90	2.79	2.71	2.64	2.59	2.54	2.48	2.40	2.33	2.29	2.25	2.20
16	4.49	3.63	3.24	3.01	2.85	2.74	2.66	2.59	2.54	2.49	2.42	2.35	2.28	2.24	2.19	2.15
17	4.45	3.59	3.20	2.96	2.81	2.70	2.61	2.55	2.49	2.45	2.38	2.31	2.23	2.19	2.15	2.10
18	4.41	3.55	3.16	2.93	2.77	2.66	2.58	2.51	2.46	2.41	2.34	2.27	2.19	2.15	2.11	2.06
19	4.38	3.52	3.13	2.90	2.74	2.63	2.54	2.48	2.42	2.38	2.31	2.23	2.16	2.11	2.07	2.03
20	4.35	3.49	3.10	2.87	2.71	2.60	2.51	2.45	2.39	2.35	2.28	2.20	2.12	2.08	2.04	1.99
21	4.32	3.47	3.07	2.84	2.68	2.57	2.49	2.42	2.37	2.32	2.25	2.18	2.10	2.05	2.01	1.96
22	4.30	3.44	3.05	2.82	2.66	2.55	2.46	2.40	2.34	2.30	2.23	2.15	2.07	2.03	1.98	1.94
23	4.28	3.42	3.03	2.80	2.64	2.53	2.44	2.37	2.32	2.27	2.20	2.13	2.05	2.01	1.96	1.91
24	4.26	3.40	3.01	2.78	2.62	2.51	2.42	2.36	2.30	2.25	2.18	2.11	2.03	1.98	1.94	1.89
25	4.24	3.39	2.99	2.76	2.60	2.49	2.40	2.34	2.28	2.24	2.16	2.09	2.01	1.96	1.92	1.87
30	4.17	3.32	2.92	2.69	2.53	2.42	2.33	2.27	2.21	2.16	2.09	2.01	1.93	1.89	1.84	1.79
40	4.08	3.23	2.84	2.61	2.45	2.34	2.25	2.18	2.12	2.08	2.00	1.92	1.84	1.79	1.74	1.69
60	4.00	3.15	2.76	2.53	2.37	2.25	2.17	2.10	2.04	1.99	1.92	1.84	1.75	1.70	1.65	1.59
120	3.92	3.07	2.68	2.45	2.29	2.18	2.09	2.02	1.96	1.91	1.83	1.75	1.66	1.61	1.55	1.50
∞	3.84	3.00	2.60	2.37	2.21	2.10	2.01	1.94	1.88	1.83	1.75	1.67	1.57	1.52	1.46	1.39

Degrees of Freedom for the Denominator

736

B.6B   Critical Values of the *F* Distribution ($\alpha = .01$)

		Degrees of Freedom for the Numerator															
		1	2	3	4	5	6	7	8	9	10	12	15	20	24	30	40
	1	4052	5000	5403	5625	5764	5859	5928	5981	6022	6056	6106	6157	6209	6235	6261	6287
	2	98.5	99.0	99.2	99.2	99.3	99.3	99.4	99.4	99.4	99.4	99.4	99.4	99.4	99.5	99.5	99.5
	3	34.1	30.8	29.5	28.7	28.2	27.9	27.7	27.5	27.3	27.2	27.1	26.9	26.7	26.6	26.5	26.4
	4	21.2	18.0	16.7	16.0	15.5	15.2	15.0	14.8	14.7	14.5	14.4	14.2	14.0	13.9	13.8	13.7
	5	16.3	13.3	12.1	11.4	11.0	10.7	10.5	10.3	10.2	10.1	9.89	9.72	9.55	9.47	9.38	9.29
	6	13.7	10.9	9.78	9.15	8.75	8.47	8.26	8.10	7.98	7.87	7.72	7.56	7.40	7.31	7.23	7.14
	7	12.2	9.55	8.45	7.85	7.46	7.19	6.99	6.84	6.72	6.62	6.47	6.31	6.16	6.07	5.99	5.91
	8	11.3	8.65	7.59	7.01	6.63	6.37	6.18	6.03	5.91	5.81	5.67	5.52	5.36	5.28	5.20	5.12
	9	10.6	8.02	6.99	6.42	6.06	5.80	5.61	5.47	5.35	5.26	5.11	4.96	4.81	4.73	4.65	4.57
	10	10.0	7.56	6.55	5.99	5.64	5.39	5.20	5.06	4.94	4.85	4.71	4.56	4.41	4.33	4.25	4.17
Degrees of Freedom for the Denominator	11	9.65	7.21	6.22	5.67	5.32	5.07	4.89	4.74	4.63	4.54	4.40	4.25	4.10	4.02	3.94	3.86
	12	9.33	6.93	5.95	5.41	5.06	4.82	4.64	4.50	4.39	4.30	4.16	4.01	3.86	3.78	3.70	3.62
	13	9.07	6.70	5.74	5.21	4.86	4.62	4.44	4.30	4.19	4.10	3.96	3.82	3.66	3.59	3.51	3.43
	14	8.86	6.51	5.56	5.04	4.69	4.46	4.28	4.14	4.03	3.94	3.80	3.66	3.51	3.43	3.35	3.27
	15	8.68	6.36	5.42	4.89	4.56	4.32	4.14	4.00	3.89	3.80	3.67	3.52	3.37	3.29	3.21	3.13
	16	8.53	6.23	5.29	4.77	4.44	4.20	4.03	3.89	3.78	3.69	3.55	3.41	3.26	3.18	3.10	3.02
	17	8.40	6.11	5.18	4.67	4.34	4.10	3.93	3.79	3.68	3.59	3.46	3.31	3.16	3.08	3.00	2.92
	18	8.29	6.01	5.09	4.58	4.25	4.01	3.84	3.71	3.60	3.51	3.37	3.23	3.08	3.00	2.92	2.84
	19	8.18	5.93	5.01	4.50	4.17	3.94	3.77	3.63	3.52	3.43	3.30	3.15	3.00	2.92	2.84	2.76
	20	8.10	5.85	4.94	4.43	4.10	3.87	3.70	3.56	3.46	3.37	3.23	3.09	2.94	2.86	2.78	2.69
	21	8.02	5.78	4.87	4.37	4.04	3.81	3.64	3.51	3.40	3.31	3.17	3.03	2.88	2.80	2.72	2.64
	22	7.95	5.72	4.82	4.31	3.99	3.76	3.59	3.45	3.35	3.26	3.12	2.98	2.83	2.75	2.67	2.58
	23	7.88	5.66	4.76	4.26	3.94	3.71	3.54	3.41	3.30	3.21	3.07	2.93	2.78	2.70	2.62	2.54
	24	7.82	5.61	4.72	4.22	3.90	3.67	3.50	3.36	3.26	3.17	3.03	2.89	2.74	2.66	2.58	2.49
	25	7.77	5.57	4.68	4.18	3.85	3.63	3.46	3.32	3.22	3.13	2.99	2.85	2.70	2.62	2.54	2.45
	30	7.56	5.39	4.51	4.02	3.70	3.47	3.30	3.17	3.07	2.98	2.84	2.70	2.55	2.47	2.39	2.30
	40	7.31	5.18	4.31	3.83	3.51	3.29	3.12	2.99	2.89	2.80	2.66	2.52	2.37	2.29	2.20	2.11
	60	7.08	4.98	4.13	3.65	3.34	3.12	2.95	2.82	2.72	2.63	2.50	2.35	2.20	2.12	2.03	1.94
	120	6.85	4.79	3.95	3.48	3.17	2.96	2.79	2.66	2.56	2.47	2.34	2.19	2.03	1.95	1.86	1.76
	∞	6.63	4.61	3.78	3.32	3.02	2.80	2.64	2.51	2.41	2.32	2.18	2.04	1.88	1.79	1.70	1.59

B.7   Critical Values of Chi-Square

This table contains the values of χ^2 that correspond to a specific right-tail area and specific number of degrees of freedom.

Example: With 17 *df* and a .02 area in the upper tail, $\chi^2 = 30.995$

Degrees of Freedom, df	Right-Tail Area			
	0.10	0.05	0.02	0.01
1	2.706	3.841	5.412	6.635
2	4.605	5.991	7.824	9.210
3	6.251	7.815	9.837	11.345
4	7.779	9.488	11.668	13.277
5	9.236	11.070	13.388	15.086
6	10.645	12.592	15.033	16.812
7	12.017	14.067	16.622	18.475
8	13.362	15.507	18.168	20.090
9	14.684	16.919	19.679	21.666
10	15.987	18.307	21.161	23.209
11	17.275	19.675	22.618	24.725
12	18.549	21.026	24.054	26.217
13	19.812	22.362	25.472	27.688
14	21.064	23.685	26.873	29.141
15	22.307	24.996	28.259	30.578
16	23.542	26.296	29.633	32.000
17	24.769	27.587	30.995	33.409
18	25.989	28.869	32.346	34.805
19	27.204	30.144	33.687	36.191
20	28.412	31.410	35.020	37.566
21	29.615	32.671	36.343	38.932
22	30.813	33.924	37.659	40.289
23	32.007	35.172	38.968	41.638
24	33.196	36.415	40.270	42.980
25	34.382	37.652	41.566	44.314
26	35.563	38.885	42.856	45.642
27	36.741	40.113	44.140	46.963
28	37.916	41.337	45.419	48.278
29	39.087	42.557	46.693	49.588
30	40.256	43.773	47.962	50.892

B.8   Wilcoxon *T* Values

n	2α .15 / α .075	2α .10 / α .050	2α .05 / α .025	2α .04 / α .020	2α .03 / α .015	2α .02 / α .010	2α .01 / α .005
4	0						
5	1	0					
6	2	2	0	0			
7	4	3	2	1	0	0	
8	7	5	3	3	2	1	0
9	9	8	5	5	4	3	1
10	12	10	8	7	6	5	3
11	16	13	10	9	8	7	5
12	19	17	13	12	11	9	7
13	24	21	17	16	14	12	9
14	28	25	21	19	18	15	12
15	33	30	25	23	21	19	15
16	39	35	29	28	26	23	19
17	45	41	34	33	30	27	23
18	51	47	40	38	35	32	27
19	58	53	46	43	41	37	32
20	65	60	52	50	47	43	37
21	73	67	58	56	53	49	42
22	81	75	65	63	59	55	48
23	89	83	73	70	66	62	54
24	98	91	81	78	74	69	61
25	108	100	89	86	82	76	68
26	118	110	98	94	90	84	75
27	128	119	107	103	99	92	83
28	138	130	116	112	108	101	91
29	150	140	126	122	117	110	100
30	161	151	137	132	127	120	109
31	173	163	147	143	137	130	118
32	186	175	159	154	148	140	128
33	199	187	170	165	159	151	138
34	212	200	182	177	171	162	148
35	226	213	195	189	182	173	159
40	302	286	264	257	249	238	220
50	487	466	434	425	413	397	373
60	718	690	648	636	620	600	567
70	995	960	907	891	872	846	805
80	1,318	1,276	1,211	1,192	1,168	1,136	1,086
90	1,688	1,638	1,560	1,537	1,509	1,471	1,410
100	2,105	2,045	1,955	1,928	1,894	1,850	1,779

B.9A   Critical Values for the Durbin–Watson *d* Statistic (α = .05)

n	k = 1		k = 2		k = 3		k = 4		k = 5	
	$d_{L,.05}$	$d_{U,.05}$	$d_{L,.05}$	$d_{U,.05}$	$d_{L,.05}$	$d_{U,.05}$	$d_{L,.05}$	$d_{U,.05}$	$d_{L,.05}$	$d_{U,.05}$
15	1.08	1.36	0.95	1.54	0.82	1.75	0.69	1.97	0.56	2.21
16	1.10	1.37	0.98	1.54	0.86	1.73	0.74	1.93	0.62	2.15
17	1.13	1.38	1.02	1.54	0.90	1.71	0.78	1.90	0.67	2.10
18	1.16	1.39	1.05	1.53	0.93	1.69	0.82	1.87	0.71	2.06
19	1.18	1.40	1.08	1.53	0.97	1.68	0.86	1.85	0.75	2.02
20	1.20	1.41	1.10	1.54	1.00	1.68	0.90	1.83	0.79	1.99
21	1.22	1.42	1.13	1.54	1.03	1.67	0.93	1.81	0.83	1.96
22	1.24	1.43	1.15	1.54	1.05	1.66	0.96	1.80	0.86	1.94
23	1.26	1.44	1.17	1.54	1.08	1.66	0.99	1.79	0.90	1.92
24	1.27	1.45	1.19	1.55	1.10	1.66	1.01	1.78	0.93	1.90
25	1.29	1.45	1.21	1.55	1.12	1.66	1.04	1.77	0.95	1.89
26	1.30	1.46	1.22	1.55	1.14	1.65	1.06	1.76	0.98	1.88
27	1.32	1.47	1.24	1.56	1.16	1.65	1.08	1.76	1.01	1.86
28	1.33	1.48	1.26	1.56	1.18	1.65	1.10	1.75	1.03	1.85
29	1.34	1.48	1.27	1.56	1.20	1.65	1.12	1.74	1.05	1.84
30	1.35	1.49	1.28	1.57	1.21	1.65	1.14	1.74	1.07	1.83
31	1.36	1.50	1.30	1.57	1.23	1.65	1.16	1.74	1.09	1.83
32	1.37	1.50	1.31	1.57	1.24	1.65	1.18	1.73	1.11	1.82
33	1.38	1.51	1.32	1.58	1.26	1.65	1.19	1.73	1.13	1.81
34	1.39	1.51	1.33	1.58	1.27	1.65	1.21	1.73	1.15	1.81
35	1.40	1.52	1.34	1.58	1.28	1.65	1.22	1.73	1.16	1.80
36	1.41	1.52	1.35	1.59	1.29	1.65	1.24	1.73	1.18	1.80
37	1.42	1.53	1.36	1.59	1.31	1.66	1.25	1.72	1.19	1.80
38	1.43	1.54	1.37	1.59	1.32	1.66	1.26	1.72	1.21	1.79
39	1.43	1.54	1.38	1.60	1.33	1.66	1.27	1.72	1.22	1.79
40	1.44	1.54	1.39	1.60	1.34	1.66	1.29	1.72	1.23	1.79
45	1.48	1.57	1.43	1.62	1.38	1.67	1.34	1.72	1.29	1.78
50	1.50	1.59	1.46	1.63	1.42	1.67	1.38	1.72	1.34	1.77
55	1.53	1.60	1.49	1.64	1.45	1.68	1.41	1.72	1.38	1.77
60	1.55	1.62	1.51	1.65	1.48	1.69	1.44	1.73	1.41	1.77
65	1.57	1.63	1.54	1.66	1.50	1.70	1.47	1.73	1.44	1.77
70	1.58	1.64	1.55	1.67	1.52	1.70	1.49	1.74	1.46	1.77
75	1.60	1.65	1.57	1.68	1.54	1.71	1.51	1.74	1.49	1.77
80	1.61	1.66	1.59	1.69	1.56	1.72	1.53	1.74	1.51	1.77
85	1.62	1.67	1.60	1.70	1.57	1.72	1.55	1.75	1.52	1.77
90	1.63	1.68	1.61	1.70	1.59	1.73	1.57	1.75	1.54	1.78
95	1.64	1.69	1.62	1.71	1.60	1.73	1.58	1.75	1.56	1.78
100	1.65	1.69	1.63	1.72	1.61	1.74	1.59	1.76	1.57	1.78

B.9B   Critical Values for the Durbin–Watson d Statistic ($\alpha = .025$)

	$k = 1$		$k = 2$		$k = 3$		$k = 4$		$k = 5$	
n	$d_{L,.025}$	$d_{U,.025}$	$d_{L,.025}$	$d_{U,.025}$	$d_{L,.025}$	$d_{U,.025}$	$d_{L,.025}$	$d_{U,.025}$	$d_{L,.025}$	$d_{U,.025}$
15	0.95	1.23	0.83	1.40	0.71	1.61	0.59	1.84	0.48	2.09
16	0.98	1.24	0.86	1.40	0.75	1.59	0.64	1.80	0.53	2.03
17	1.01	1.25	0.90	1.40	0.79	1.58	0.68	1.77	0.57	1.98
18	1.03	1.26	0.93	1.40	0.82	1.56	0.72	1.74	0.62	1.93
19	1.06	1.28	0.96	1.41	0.86	1.55	0.76	1.72	0.66	1.90
20	1.08	1.28	0.99	1.41	0.89	1.55	0.79	1.70	0.70	1.87
21	1.10	1.30	1.01	1.41	0.92	1.54	0.83	1.69	0.73	1.84
22	1.12	1.31	1.04	1.42	0.95	1.54	0.86	1.68	0.77	1.82
23	1.14	1.32	1.06	1.42	0.97	1.54	0.89	1.67	0.80	1.80
24	1.16	1.33	1.08	1.43	1.00	1.54	0.91	1.66	0.83	1.79
25	1.18	1.34	1.10	1.43	1.02	1.54	0.94	1.65	0.86	1.77
26	1.19	1.35	1.12	1.44	1.04	1.54	0.96	1.65	0.88	1.76
27	1.21	1.36	1.13	1.44	1.06	1.54	0.99	1.64	0.91	1.75
28	1.22	1.37	1.15	1.45	1.08	1.54	1.01	1.64	0.93	1.74
29	1.24	1.38	1.17	1.45	1.10	1.54	1.03	1.63	0.96	1.73
30	1.25	1.38	1.18	1.46	1.12	1.54	1.05	1.63	0.98	1.73
31	1.26	1.39	1.20	1.47	1.13	1.55	1.07	1.63	1.00	1.72
32	1.27	1.40	1.21	1.47	1.15	1.55	1.08	1.63	1.02	1.71
33	1.28	1.41	1.22	1.48	1.16	1.55	1.10	1.63	1.04	1.71
34	1.29	1.41	1.24	1.48	1.17	1.55	1.12	1.63	1.06	1.70
35	1.30	1.42	1.25	1.48	1.19	1.55	1.13	1.63	1.07	1.70
36	1.31	1.43	1.26	1.49	1.20	1.56	1.15	1.63	1.09	1.70
37	1.32	1.43	1.27	1.49	1.21	1.56	1.16	1.62	1.10	1.70
38	1.33	1.44	1.28	1.50	1.23	1.56	1.17	1.62	1.12	1.70
39	1.34	1.44	1.29	1.50	1.24	1.56	1.19	1.63	1.13	1.69
40	1.35	1.45	1.30	1.51	1.25	1.57	1.20	1.63	1.15	1.69
45	1.39	1.48	1.34	1.53	1.30	1.58	1.25	1.63	1.21	1.69
50	1.42	1.50	1.38	1.54	1.34	1.59	1.30	1.64	1.26	1.69
55	1.45	1.52	1.41	1.56	1.37	1.60	1.33	1.64	1.30	1.69
60	1.47	1.54	1.44	1.57	1.40	1.61	1.37	1.65	1.33	1.69
65	1.49	1.55	1.46	1.59	1.43	1.62	1.40	1.66	1.36	1.69
70	1.51	1.57	1.48	1.60	1.45	1.63	1.42	1.66	1.39	1.70
75	1.53	1.58	1.50	1.61	1.47	1.64	1.45	1.67	1.42	1.70
80	1.54	1.59	1.52	1.62	1.49	1.65	1.47	1.67	1.44	1.70
85	1.56	1.60	1.53	1.63	1.51	1.65	1.49	1.68	1.46	1.71
90	1.57	1.61	1.55	1.64	1.53	1.66	1.50	1.69	1.48	1.71
95	1.58	1.62	1.56	1.65	1.54	1.67	1.52	1.69	1.50	1.71
100	1.59	1.63	1.57	1.65	1.55	1.67	1.53	1.70	1.51	1.72

SOURCE: J. Durbin and G. S. Watson, "Testing for Serial Correlation in Least Squares Regression, II," *Biometrika* 30 (1951), pp. 159–178. Reproduced by permission of the Biometrika Trustees.

B.9C   Critical Values for the Durbin–Watson *d* Statistic ($\alpha = .01$)

n	k = 1		k = 2		k = 3		k = 4		k = 5	
	$d_{L,.01}$	$d_{U,.01}$	$d_{L,.01}$	$d_{U,.01}$	$d_{L,.01}$	$d_{U,.01}$	$d_{L,.01}$	$d_{U,.01}$	$d_{L,.01}$	$d_{U,.01}$
15	0.81	1.07	0.70	1.25	0.59	1.46	0.49	1.70	0.39	1.96
16	0.84	1.09	0.74	1.25	0.63	1.44	0.53	1.66	0.44	1.90
17	0.87	1.10	0.77	1.25	0.67	1.43	0.57	1.63	0.48	1.85
18	0.90	1.12	0.80	1.26	0.71	1.42	0.61	1.60	0.52	1.80
19	0.93	1.13	0.83	1.26	0.74	1.41	0.65	1.58	0.56	1.77
20	0.95	1.15	0.86	1.27	0.77	1.41	0.68	1.57	0.60	1.74
21	0.97	1.16	0.89	1.27	0.80	1.41	0.72	1.55	0.63	1.71
22	1.00	1.17	0.91	1.28	0.83	1.40	0.75	1.54	0.66	1.69
23	1.02	1.19	0.94	1.29	0.86	1.40	0.77	1.53	0.70	1.67
24	1.04	1.20	0.96	1.30	0.88	1.41	0.80	1.53	0.72	1.66
25	1.05	1.21	0.98	1.30	0.90	1.41	0.83	1.52	0.75	1.65
26	1.07	1.22	1.00	1.31	0.93	1.41	0.85	1.52	0.78	1.64
27	1.09	1.23	1.02	1.32	0.95	1.41	0.88	1.51	0.81	1.63
28	1.10	1.24	1.04	1.32	0.97	1.41	0.90	1.51	0.83	1.62
29	1.12	1.25	1.05	1.33	0.99	1.42	0.92	1.51	0.85	1.61
30	1.13	1.26	1.07	1.34	1.01	1.42	0.94	1.51	0.88	1.61
31	1.15	1.27	1.08	1.34	1.02	1.42	0.96	1.51	0.90	1.60
32	1.16	1.28	1.10	1.35	1.04	1.43	0.98	1.51	0.92	1.60
33	1.17	1.29	1.11	1.36	1.05	1.43	1.00	1.51	0.94	1.59
34	1.18	1.30	1.13	1.36	1.07	1.43	1.01	1.51	0.95	1.59
35	1.19	1.31	1.14	1.37	1.08	1.44	1.03	1.51	0.97	1.59
36	1.21	1.32	1.15	1.38	1.10	1.44	1.04	1.51	0.99	1.59
37	1.22	1.32	1.16	1.38	1.11	1.45	1.06	1.51	1.00	1.59
38	1.23	1.33	1.18	1.39	1.12	1.45	1.07	1.52	1.02	1.58
39	1.24	1.34	1.19	1.39	1.14	1.45	1.09	1.52	1.03	1.58
40	1.25	1.34	1.20	1.40	1.15	1.46	1.10	1.52	1.05	1.58
45	1.29	1.38	1.24	1.42	1.20	1.48	1.16	1.53	1.11	1.58
50	1.32	1.40	1.28	1.45	1.24	1.49	1.20	1.54	1.16	1.59
55	1.36	1.43	1.32	1.47	1.28	1.51	1.25	1.55	1.21	1.59
60	1.38	1.45	1.35	1.48	1.32	1.52	1.28	1.56	1.25	1.60
65	1.41	1.47	1.38	1.50	1.35	1.53	1.31	1.57	1.28	1.61
70	1.43	1.49	1.40	1.52	1.37	1.55	1.34	1.58	1.31	1.61
75	1.45	1.50	1.42	1.53	1.39	1.56	1.37	1.59	1.34	1.62
80	1.47	1.52	1.44	1.54	1.42	1.57	1.39	1.60	1.36	1.62
85	1.48	1.53	1.46	1.55	1.43	1.58	1.41	1.60	1.39	1.63
90	1.50	1.54	1.47	1.56	1.45	1.59	1.43	1.61	1.41	1.64
95	1.51	1.55	1.49	1.57	1.47	1.60	1.45	1.62	1.42	1.64
100	1.52	1.56	1.50	1.58	1.48	1.60	1.46	1.63	1.44	1.65

SOURCE: J. Durbin and G. S. Watson, "Testing for Serial Correlation in Least Squares Regression, II," *Biometrika* 30 (1951), pp. 159–178. Reproduced by permission of the Biometrika Trustees.

B.10 Factors for Control Charts

Number of Items in Sample, n	Chart for Averages	Chart for Ranges		
	Factors for Control Limits	Factors for Central Line	Factors for Control Limits	
	A_2	d_2	D_3	D_4
2	1.880	1.128	0	3.267
3	1.023	1.693	0	2.575
4	.729	2.059	0	2.282
5	.577	2.326	0	2.115
6	.483	2.534	0	2.004
7	.419	2.704	.076	1.924
8	.373	2.847	.136	1.864
9	.337	2.970	.184	1.816
10	.308	3.078	.223	1.777
11	.285	3.173	.256	1.744
12	.266	3.258	.284	1.716
13	.249	3.336	.308	1.692
14	.235	3.407	.329	1.671
15	.223	3.472	.348	1.652

SOURCE: Adapted from American Society for Testing and Materials, *Manual on Quality Control of Materials*, 1951, Table B2, p. 115. For a more detailed table and explanation, see J. Duncan Acheson, *Quality Control and Industrial Statistics*, 3d ed. (Homewood, Ill.: Richard D. Irwin, 1974), Table M, p. 927.

APPENDIX C: SOFTWARE COMMANDS

CHAPTER 2

2–1. The Excel commands to use the PivotTable Wizard to create the frequency table, bar chart, and pie chart on page 22 are:
a. Open the Applewood Auto Group data file.
b. Click on a cell somewhere in the data set, such as cell *C5*.
c. Click on the *Insert* menu on the toolbar. Then click *Pivot-Table* on the far left of the *Ribbon*.

d. The following screen will appear. Click on "*Select a table or range*" to select the data range as shown in the *Table/ Range* row. Next, click on "*Existing Worksheet*" and select a cell location, such a *N1*, and click *OK*.

e. On the right-hand side of the spreadsheet, a *PivotTable Field List* will appear with a list of the data set variables. To summarize the "Vehicle-Type" variable, click on the "Vehicle-Type" variable and it will appear in the lower left box called *Row Label*. You will note that the frequency table is started in cell *N1* with the rows labeled with the values of the variable "Vehicle-Type." Next, return to the top box, and select and drag the "Vehicle-Type" variable to the "Σ Values" box. A column of frequencies will be added to the table. Note that you can format the table to center the values and also relabel the column headings as needed.
f. To create the bar chart, select any cell in the PivotTable. Next, select the *Insert* menu from the tool bar and within the *Charts* group, select a bar chart from the *Column* drop-down menu. A bar chart appears. Click on the chart heading and label the chart as needed.
g. To create the pie chart, the frequencies should be converted to relative frequencies. Click in the body of the PivotTable and the *PivotTable Field List* will appear to the right. In the "Σ Values" box, click on the pull-down menu for "Count of Vehicle Type" and select the *Value Field Settings* option. You will see a number of different selections that can be used to summarize the variables in a PivotTable. Click on the tab "*Show Values As*" and, in the pull-down menu, select "*% of Grand Total*." The frequencies will be converted to relative frequencies.

To create the pie chart, select any cell in the PivotTable. Next, select the *Insert* menu from the tool bar, and within the *Charts* group, select a pie chart from the *Column* drop-down menu. A pie chart appears. Click on the chart heading and label the chart as needed. To add the percentages, click on the pie chart and a menu will appear. Click on "Add Data Labels."

2–2. The Excel commands to use the PivotTable Wizard to create the frequency and relative frequency distributions on page 30 and the histogram on page 33 follow.
a. Open the Applewood Auto Group data file.
b. Click on a cell somewhere in the data set, such as cell *C5*.
c. Click on the *Insert* menu on the toolbar. Then click on *PivotTable* on the far left of the *Ribbon*.
d. The following screen will appear. Click on "*Select a table or range*" to select the data range as shown in the *Table/ Range* row. Next, click on "*New Worksheet*" and the Pivot-Table will be created in a new worksheet.
e. On the right-hand side of the spreadsheet, a *PivotTable Field List* will appear with a list of the data set variables. To summarize the "Profit" variable, click on the "Profit" variable and drag it to the "Row Labels" box. Then return to the top box, click on "Profits" again and drag it to the "Σ Values" box. Staying in this box, click on the pull-down menu for "Sum of Profit." You will see a number of different selections that can be used to summarize the variables

in a PivotTable. In the "*Summarize Values As*" tab, select "Count" to create frequencies for the variable "Profit." A PivotTable will appear in the new worksheet.

f. In the PivotTable, the left column shows each value of the variable "Profit." To create classes for "Profit," select any cell in the column and right-click. A menu appears. Select "Group" from the menu to create the classes. First, un-check both boxes. Then, in the dialogue box, enter the lower limit of the first class as the "Starting at" value. Enter the upper limit of the last class as the "Ending at" value. Then enter the class interval as the "By" value. Click OK. A frequency distribution appears.

g. To create a relative frequency distribution, point and click on one of the cells in the PivotTable and the "PivotTable Field List" appears to the right. Click and drag the variable "Profits" to the "Σ Values" box. A second "Counts of Profit" appears. In the "Σ Values," click on the second "Counts of Profit" and select the "Value Fields Setting." You will see a number of different selections that can be used to summarize the variables in a PivotTable. Click on the tab "*Show Values As*" and, in the pull-down menu, select "*% of Grand Total*." The relative frequencies will be added to the table. You can format the table by relabeling the column headings such as "Frequency" and "Relative Frequency."

h. To create a histogram, select a cell in the PivotTable, choose the *Insert* menu from the tool bar, and within the *Charts* group, select a *column* chart from the *Column* drop-down menu. A histogram appears with both "Count of Profit" and "Count of Profit2." On the "Count of Profit2" bubble at the top of the chart, right-click and select "Remove Field." Then the chart and PivotTable only report the frequencies. To eliminate the space between the bars, select the entire chart area, and "PivotChart Tools" will appear at the top. Select "Design." In the "Chart Layouts" choices, select the option that shows no spaces between the bars. The option is illustrated in the figure to the right. To add data labels, select the histo-gram, right-click, and select "Add Data Labels." Relabel the chart and axes as needed.

CHAPTER 3

3–1. The Excel Commands for the descriptive statistics on page 63 are:

a. From the website, www.mhhe.com/lind16e, retrieve the Applewood data.

b. From the menu bar, select **Data** and then **Data Analysis.** Select **Descriptive Statistics** and then click **OK.**

c. For the **Input Range,** type *C1:C181,* indicate that the data are grouped by column and that the labels are in the first

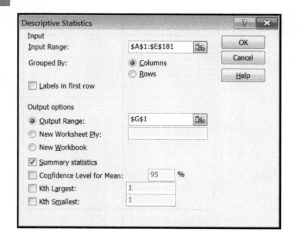

row. Click on **Output Range,** indicate that the output should go in *G1* (or any place you wish), click on **Summary statistics,** then click **OK.**

   d. After you get your results, double-check the count in the output to be sure it contains the correct number of items.

CHAPTER 4

4–1. The Minitab commands for the dot plot on page 95 are:
   a. Enter the number of vehicles serviced at Tionesta Ford Lincoln Mercury in column *C1* and Sheffield Motors in *C2.* Name the variables accordingly.
   b. Select **Graph** and **Dotplot.** In the first dialog box, select **Multiple Y's, Simple** in the lower left corner, and click **OK.** In the next dialog box, select **Tionesta** and **Sheffield** as the variables to **Graph,** click on **Labels,** and write an appropriate title. Then click **OK.**
   c. To calculate the descriptive statistics shown in the output, select **Stat, Basic statistics,** and then **Display Descriptive statistics.** In the dialog box, select **Tionesta** and **Sheffield** as the variables, click on **Statistics,** select the desired statistics to be output, and finally click **OK** twice.

4–2. The Minitab commands for the stem-and-leaf display on page 98 are:
   a. Import the data for **Table 4–1** from www.mhhe.com/ lind16e.
   b. Select **Graph,** and click on **Stem-and-Leaf.**
   c. Select the variable **Spots,** enter *10* for the **Increment,** and then click **OK.**

4–3. The Minitab commands for the descriptive summary on page 104 are:
   a. Input the data on the Smith Barney commissions from the Example on page 102.
   b. From the toolbar, select **Stat, Basic Statistics,** and **Display Descriptive Statistics.** In the dialog box, select **Commissions** as the **Variable,** and then click **OK.**

4–4. The Excel commands for the quartiles on page 104 follow.
   a. Input the data on the Smith Barney commissions from the example on page 102 in column A.
   If you are using Excel 2010 and wish to compute quartiles using formula (4–1), the steps are:
   b. In cell *C3* type **Formula (4–1),** in *C4* write **Quartile 1,** and in *C6* type **Quartile 3.**
   c. In cell *D4* type **"=QUARTILE.EXC(A2:A16,1)"** and hit **Enter.** In cell *D6* type **"=QUARTILE.EXC(A2:A16,3)"** and hit **Enter.**
   If you are using either Excel 2007 or 2010 and wish to compute quartiles using the Excel Method:
   b. In cell *C8* type **Excel Method,** in *C9* write **Quartile 1,** and in *C11* type **Quartile 3.**
   c. In cell *D8* type **"=QUARTILE(A2:A16,1)"** and hit **Enter.** In cell *D11* type **"=QUARTILE(A2:A16,3)"** and hit **Enter.**

4–5. The Minitab commands for the box plot on page 107 are:
   a. Import the Applewood Auto Group data from www.mhhe .com/lind16e.

   b. Select **Graph** and then **Boxplot.** In the dialog box, select **Simple** in the upper left corner and click **OK.** Select **Age** as the **Graph Variable,** click on **Labels** and include an appropriate heading, and then click **OK.**

4–6. The Minitab commands for the descriptive summary on page 112 are:
   a. Enter the data in the first column. In the cell below *C1,* enter the variable *Earnings.*
   b. Select **Stat, Basic Statistics,** and then click on **Graphical Summary.** Select **Earnings** as the variable, and then click **OK.**

4–7. The Excel commands for the scatter diagram on page 115 are:
   a. Retrieve the Applewood Auto data.
   b. Using the mouse, highlight the column of age and profit. Include the first row.
   c. Select the **Insert** tab. Select **Scatter** from the **Chart** options. Select the top left option. The scatter plot will appear.
   d. With **Chart Tools** displayed at the top, select the **Layout** tab. Select **Chart Title** and type in a title for the plot. Next, under the same **Layout** tab, select **AxisTitles.** Using **Primary Vertical Axis Title,** name the vertical axis *Profit.* Using the **Primary Horizontal Axis Title,** name the horizontal axis *Age.* Next, select **Legend** and select **None.**

CHAPTER 5

5–1. The Excel Commands to determine the number of permutations shown on page 164 are:
  a. Click on the **Formulas** tab in the top menu, then, on the far left, select **Insert Function *fx*.**

  b. In the **Insert Function** box, select **Statistical** as the category, then scroll down to **PERMUT** in the **Select a function list.** Click **OK.**
  c. In the **PERM** box after **Number,** enter *8* and in the **Number_chosen** box enter *3*. The correct answer of *336* appears twice in the box.

5–2. The Excel Commands to determine the number of combinations shown on page 164 are:
  a. Click on the **Formulas** tab in the top menu, then, on the far left, select **Insert Function *fx*.**

  b. In the **Insert Function** box, select **Math & Trig** as the category, then scroll down to **COMBIN** in the **Select a function list.** Click **OK.**
  c. In the **COMBIN** box after **Number,** enter *7,* and in the **Number_chosen** box enter *3*. The correct answer of *35* appears twice in the box.

CHAPTER 6

6–1. The Excel commands necessary to determine the binomial probability distribution on page 187 are:
  a. On a blank Excel worksheet, write the word *Success* in cell A1 and the word *Probability* in B1. In cells A2 through A17, write the integers *0* to *15*. Click on *B2* as the active cell.
  b. Click on the **Formulas** tab in the top menu, then, on the far left, select **Insert Function *fx*.**
  c. In the first dialog box, select **Statistical** in the function category and **BINOM.DIST** in the function name category, then click **OK.**
  d. In the second dialog box, enter the four items necessary to compute a binomial probability.
    1. Enter *0* for the **Number_s.**
    2. Enter *40* for the **Trials.**
    3. Enter *.09* for the probability of a success.
    4. Enter the word *false* or the *0* for **Cumulative** and click on **OK.**

  5. Excel will compute the probability of 0 successes in 40 trials, with a .09 probability of success. The result, .02299618, is stored in cell B2.
  e. To complete the probability distribution for successes of 1 through 15, double-click on cell **B2.** The binomial function should appear. Replace the **0** to the right of the open parentheses with the cell reference **A2.**
  f. Move the mouse to the lower right corner of cell B2 until a solid black + symbol appears, then click and hold and highlight the B column to cell B17. The probability of a success for the various values of the random variable will appear.

6–2. The Excel commands necessary to determine the hypergeometric distribution on page 193 are:
  a. On a blank Excel worksheet, write the word *Union Members* in cell A1 and the word *Probability* in B1. In cells A2 through A7, enter the numbers *0* through *5*. Click on cell **B2.**
  b. Click the **Formulas** tab in the top menu, then, on the far left, select **Insert Function *fx*.**

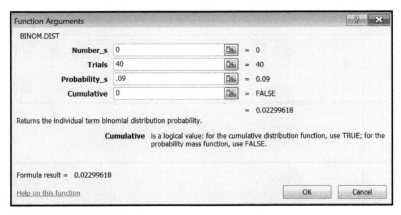

c. In the first dialog box, select **Statistical** and **HYPGEOM. DIST** and then click **OK.**

d. In the second dialog box, enter the four items necessary to compute a hypergeometric probability.
  1. Enter *0* for the **Sample_s.**
  2. Enter *5* for the **Number_sample.**
  3. Enter *40* for the **Population_s.**
  4. Enter *50* for the **Number_pop.**
  5. Enter *0* for the **Cumulative** and click **OK.**

6. Excel will compute the probability of 0 successes in 5 trials (.000118937) and store that result in cell **B2.**

e. To complete the probability distribution for successes of 1 through 5, double-click on cell **B2.** The hypergeometric function should appear. Replace the **0** to the right of the open parentheses with the cell reference **A2.**

f. Move the mouse to the lower right corner of cell **B2** till a solid black + symbol appears, then click and hold and highlight the **B** column to cell **B7.** The probability of a success for the various outcomes will appear.

6–3. The Excel commands necessary to determine the Poisson probability distribution on page 196 are:

a. On a blank Excel worksheet, write the word *Success* in cell **A1** and the word *Probability* in **B1.** In cells **A2** through **A9,** write the integers *0* to *7.* Click on **B2** as the active cell.

b. Click on the **Formulas** tab in the top menu, then, on the far left, select **Insert Function** *fx.*

c. In the first dialog box, select **Statistical** in the function category and **POISSON.DIST** in the function name category, then click **OK.**

d. In the second dialog box, enter the three items necessary to compute a Poisson probability.
  1. Enter *0* for **X.**
  2. Enter *0.3* for the **Mean.**

3. Enter the word *false* or the number *0* for **Cumulative** and click **OK.**

4. Excel will compute the probability of 0 successes for a Poisson probability distribution with a mean of 0.3. The result, .74081822, is stored in cell **B2.**

e. To complete the probability distribution for successes of 1 through 7, double-click on cell **B2.** The Poisson function should appear. Replace the **0** to the right of the open parentheses with the cell reference **A2.**

f. Move the mouse to the lower right corner of cell **B2** until a solid black + symbol appears, then click and hold and highlight the **B** column to cell **B9.** The probability of a success for the various values of the random variable will appear.

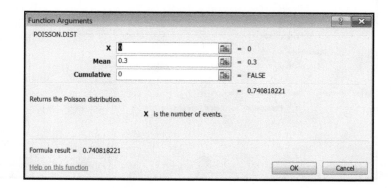

CHAPTER 7

7–1. The Excel commands necessary to produce the output on page 219 are:
    a. Click on the **Formulas** tab in the top menu, then, on the far left, select **Insert Function fx.** Then from the category box, select **Statistical** and below that **NORM.DIST** and click **OK.**
    b. In the dialog box, put *1100* in the box for **X,** *1000* for the **Mean,** *100* for the **Standard_dev,** and *True* in the **Cumulative** box, and click **OK.**
    c. The result will appear in the dialog box. If you click **OK,** the answer appears in your spreadsheet.

7–2. The Excel commands necessary to produce the output on page 225 are:
    a. Click the **Formulas** tab in the top menu, then, on the far left, select **Insert Function fx.** Then from the category box, select **Statistical** and below that **NORM.INV** and click **OK.**
    b. In the dialog box, set the **Probability** to *.04,* the **Mean** to *67900,* and the **Standard_dev** to *2050.*
    c. The results will appear in the dialog box. Note that the answer is different from page 225 because of rounding error. If you click **OK,** the answer also appears in your spreadsheet.
    d. Try entering a **Probability** of *.04,* a **Mean** of *0,* and a **Standard_dev** of *1.* The *z* value will be computed.

CHAPTER 8

8–1. The Excel commands to select a simple random sample from the rental data on page 250 are:
    a. Select the **Data** tab on the top of the menu. Then on the far right select **Data Analysis,** then **Sampling** and **OK.**
    b. For **Input Range,** insert *B1:B31.* Since the column is named, click the **Labels** box. Select **Random,** and enter the sample size for the **Number of Samples,** in this case *5.* Click on **Output Range** and indicate the place in the spreadsheet where you want the sample information. Note that your sample results will differ from those in the text. Also recall that Excel samples with replacement, so it is possible for a population value to appear more than once in the sample.

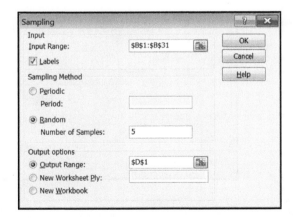

CHAPTER 9

9–1. The Minitab commands for the confidence interval for the amount spent at the Inlet Square Mall on page 294 are:
    a. Enter the 20 amounts spent in column **C1** and name the variable *Amount.*

    b. On the Toolbar, select **Stat, Basic Statistics,** and click on **1-Sample t.**
    c. Select **Samples in columns:** and select **Amount** and click **OK.**

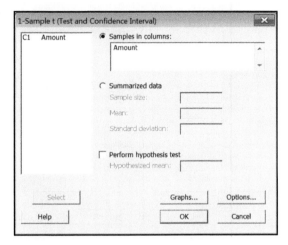

9–2. The Excel commands for the confidence interval for the amounts spent at the Inlet Square Mall on page 295 are:
    a. Select the **Data** tab on the top menu. Then, on the far right, select **Data Analysis,** and then **Descriptive Statistics,** and click **OK.**
    b. For the **Input Range,** type *A1:A21,* click on **Labels in first row,** type *C1* as the **Output Range,** click on **Summary statistics** and **Confidence Level for Mean,** and then click on **OK.**

CHAPTER 10

10–1. The Minitab commands for the histogram and the descriptive statistics on page 332 are:
    a. Enter the 26 sample observations in column **C1** and name the variable *Cost.*

b. From the menu bar, select **Stat, Basic Statistics,** and **Graphical Summary.** In the dialog box, select **Cost** as the variable and click **OK.**

10–2. The Minitab commands for the one-sample *t* test on page 337 are:
a. Enter the sample data into column **C1** and name the variable *Minutes.*
b. From the menu bar, select **Stat, Basic Statistics,** and **1-Sample** *t,* and then hit **Enter.**
c. Select **Minutes** as the variable, select **Perform hypothesized mean,** insert the value *40.* Click **Options.** Under **Alternate,** select **greater than.** Finally, click **OK** twice.

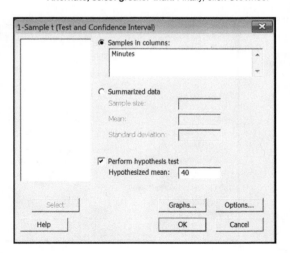

CHAPTER 11

11–1. The Excel commands for the two-sample *t*-test on page 359 are:
a. Enter the data into columns A and B (or any other columns) in the spreadsheet. Use the first row of each column to enter the variable name.

b. Select the **Data** tab on the top menu. Then, on the far right, select **Data Analysis.** Select **t-Test: Two Sample Assuming Equal Variances,** and then click **OK.**
c. In the dialog box, indicate that the range of **Variable 1** is from *A1* to *A6* and **Variable 2** from *B1* to *B7,* the **Hypothesized Mean Difference** is *0,* click **Labels, Alpha** is *0.05,* and the **Output Range** is *D1.* Click **OK.**

11–2. The Minitab commands for the two-sample *t*-test on page 363 are:
a. Put the amount absorbed by the Store brand in *C1* and the amount absorbed by the Name brand paper towel in *C2.*
b. From the toolbar, select **Stat, Basic Statistics,** and then **2-Sample,** and click **OK.**
c. In the next dialog box, select **Samples in different columns,** select *C1* Store for the **First** column and *C2* Name of the **Second,** click the box next to **Assume equal variances,** and click **OK.**

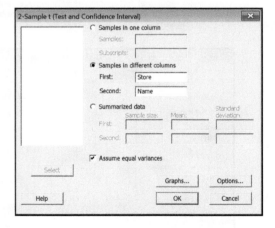

11–3. The Excel commands for the paired *t*-test on page 367 are:
a. Enter the data into columns B and C (or any other two columns) in the spreadsheet, with the variable names in the first row.
b. Select the **Data** tab on the top menu. Then, on the far right, select **Data Analysis.** Select **t-Test: Paired Two Sample for Means,** and then click **OK.**

c. In the dialog box, indicate that the range of **Variable 1** is from *B1* to *B11* and **Variable 2** from *C1* to *C11*, the **Hypothesized Mean Difference** is *0*, click **Labels**, **Alpha** is *.05*, and the **Output Range** is *E1*. Click **OK.**

CHAPTER 12

12–1. The Excel commands for the test of variances on page 384 are:
  a. Enter the data for U.S. 25 in column A and for I-75 in column B. Label the two columns.
  b. Select the **Data** tab on the top menu. Then, on the far right, select **Data Analysis.** Select **F-Test: Two-Sample for Variances,** then click **OK.**
  c. The range of the first variable is *A1:A8,* and *B1:B9* for the second. Click on **Labels,** enter *0.05* for **Alpha,** select *D1* for the **Output Range,** and click **OK.**

12–2. The Excel commands for the one-way ANOVA on page 393 are:
  a. Key in data into four columns labeled *Northern, WTA, Pocono,* and *Branson.*
  b. Select the **Data** tab on the top menu. Then, on the far right, select **Data Analysis.** Select **ANOVA: Single Factor,** then click **OK.**
  c. In the subsequent dialog box, make the input range *A1:D8,* click on **Grouped by Columns,** click on **Labels in first row,** the **Alpha** text box is *0.05*, and finally select **Output Range** as *F1* and click **OK.**

12–3. The Minitab commands for the pairwise comparisons on page 396 are:
  a. Input the data into four columns and identify the columns as *Northern, WTA, Pocono,* and *Branson.*
  b. Select **Stat, ANOVA,** and **One-way (Unstacked),** select and enter the variable names into the **Responses** box by clicking on the variable names in the following order: *Branson, Pocono, WTA,* and *Northern.* Then select **Comparisons** and then select **Fisher's, individual error rate.** Then **OK.**

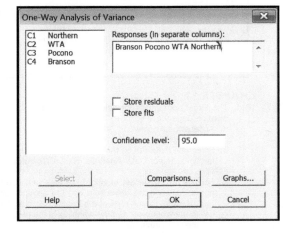

12–4. The Excel commands for the two-way ANOVA on page 400 are:
  a. In the first row of the first column, write the word *Driver,* then list the five drivers in the first column. In the first row of the next four columns, enter the names of the routes. Enter the data under each route name.
  b. Select the **Data** tab on the top menu. Then, on the far right, select **Data Analysis.** Select **ANOVA: Two-Factor Without Replication,** then click **OK.**
  c. In the dialog box, the **Input Range** is *A3:E8,* click on **Labels,** enter *0.05* for **Alpha,** select *G3* for the **Output Range,** and then click **OK.**

12–5. The Excel commands for the two-way ANOVA with interaction on page 408 are:
  a. Enter the data into Excel as shown on page 406.
  b. Select the **Data** tab on the top menu. Then, on the far right, select **Data Analysis**. Select **ANOVA: Two-Factor With Replication,** then click **OK.**
  c. In the dialog box, for the **Input Range** highlight the entire range for the data including row and column labels, enter **Rows per sample** as *3,* enter *0.05* for **Alpha, Output Range** and cell H1.

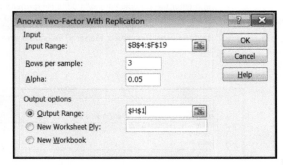

CHAPTER 13
13–1. The Excel commands for calculating the correlation coefficient on page 435 are:
  a. Access the Applewood Auto Group dataset (www.mhhe .com/lind16e).
  b. Select the **Data** tab on the top of the ribbon. Then, on the far right, select **Data Analysis**. Select **Correlation,** and click **OK.**
  c. For the **Input Range,** highlight the **Age** and **Profit** columns, including the labels in row 1. The data are grouped by **Columns.** Check the **Labels in first row** box. Select a cell in the worksheet as the beginning of the range to output the correlation. Click **OK.**

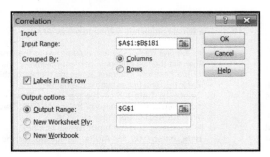

13–2. The computer commands for the Excel output on page 448 are:
  a. Enter the variable names in row 1 of columns A, B, and C. Enter the data in rows 2 through 16 in the same columns.
  b. Select the **Data** tab on the top of the menu. Then, on the far right, select **Data Analysis**. Select **Regression,** then click **OK.**
  c. For our spreadsheet, we have *Calls* in column B and *Sales* in column C. The **Input Y Range** is *C1:C16* and the **Input X Range** is *B1:B16.* Click on **Labels,** select *E1* as the **Output Range,** and click **OK.**

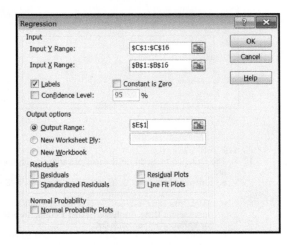

13–3. The Minitab commands to the confidence intervals and prediction intervals on page 458 are:
  a. Select **Stat, Regression,** and **Fitted line plot.**
  b. In the next dialog box, the **Response (Y)** is *Copiers Sold* and **Predictor (X)** is *Sales Calls.* Select **Linear** for the type of regression model and then click on **Options.**
  c. In the **Options** dialog box, click on **Display confidence interval and prediction interval,** use the **95.0 for confidence level,** type an appropriate heading in the **Title** box, then click **OK** and then **OK** again.

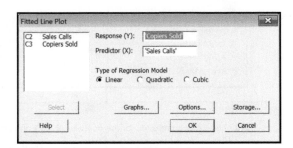

CHAPTER 14
Note: We do not show steps for all the statistical software in Chapter 14. The following shows the basic steps.
14–1. The Excel commands to produce the multiple regression output on page 480 are:
  a. Import the data from the text website: www.mhhe.com/ lind16e. The file name is **Tbl14.**

b. Select the **Data** tab on the top menu. Then on the far right, select **Data analysis.** Select **Regression** and click **OK.**

c. Make the **Input Y Range** *A1:A21*, the **Input X Range** *B1:D21*, check the **Labels** box, the **Output Range** is *F1*, then click **OK.**

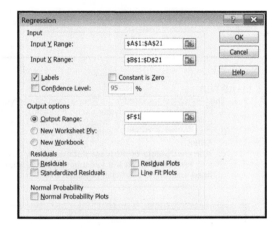

CHAPTER 15

15–1. The MegaStat commands for the two-sample test of proportions on page 541 are:

a. Select **MegaStat** from the **Add-Ins** tab. From the menu, select **Hypothesis Tests,** and then **Compare Two Independent Proportions.**

b. Enter the data. For **Group 1,** enter **x** as *19* and **n** as *100*. For **Group 2,** enter **x** as *62* and **n** as *200*. Select **OK.**

15–2. The MegaStat commands to create the chi-square goodness-of-fit test on page 547 are:

a. Enter the information from Table 15–2 into a worksheet as shown.

b. Select **MegaStat, Chi-Square/Crosstabs,** and **Goodness of Fit Test** and hit **Enter.**

c. In the dialog box, select *B2:B5* as the **Observed values,** *C2:C5* as the **Expected values,** and enter *0* as the **Number of parameters estimated from the data.** Click **OK.**

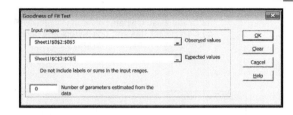

15–3. The MegaStat commands to create the chi-square goodness-of-fit tests on pages 552 and 553 are the same except for the number of items in the observed and expected frequency columns. Only one dialog box is shown.

a. Enter the Levels of Management information shown on page 552.

b. Select **MegaStat, Chi-Square/Crosstabs,** and **Goodness of Fit Test** and hit **Enter.**

c. In the dialog box, select *B1:B7* as the **Observed values,** *C1:C7* as the **Expected values,** and enter *0* as the **Number of parameters estimated from the data.** Click **OK.**

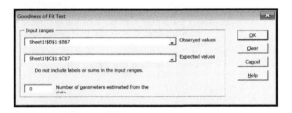

15–4. The MegaStat commands for the contingency table analysis on page 561 are:

a. Enter Table 15–8 on page 559 into cells **A1** through **D3.** Include the row and column labels. DO NOT include the Total column or row.

b. Select **MegaStat** from the **Add-Ins** tab. From the menu select **Chi-square/Crosstab,** then select **Contingency Table.**

c. For the **Input Range,** select cells **A1** through **D3.** Check the **chi-square** and **Expected values** boxes. Select **OK.**

CHAPTER 16

16–1. The MegaStat for Excel commands necessary for the Wilcoxon rank-sum test on page 588 are:

a. Enter the number of no-shows for Atlanta in column A and for Chicago in column B.

b. Select **MegaStat, Nonparametric Tests,** and **Wilcoxon-Mann/Whitney Test,** then hit **Enter.**

c. For **Group 1,** use the data on Atlanta flights (*A1:A9*) and for **Group 2** use the data on Chicago flights (*B1:B8*). Click on **Correct for ties** and **one-tailed,** and *greater than* as the **Alternative,** then click on **OK.**

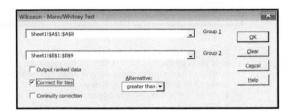

16–2. The MegaStat commands for the Kruskal-Wallis Test on page 592 are:
  a. Enter the data in Table 16–6 into an Excel worksheet including labels into columns A, B, and C starting in row 1.
  b. Select **MegaStat** from the **Add-Ins** tab. From the menu select **Nonparametric Tests,** then select **Kruskal-Wallis Test.**
  c. For the **Input Range,** select cells *A1* through *C9.* Check the **Correct for Ties** box. Select **OK.**

16–3. The Excel commands for the one-way ANOVA on page 593 are:
  a. Enter the data in Table 16–6 into an Excel worksheet including labels into columns A, B, and C starting in row 1.
  b. Select the **Data** tab on the top of the menu. Then, on the far right, select **Data Analysis.** Select **ANOVA: Single Factor,** then click **OK.**
  c. In the dialog box, the **Input Range** is *A1:C9,* click on **Labels in first row,** and enter *E1* as the **Output Range,** then click **OK.**

CHAPTER 18

18–1. The MegaStat commands for creating the seasonal indexes on pages 659 and 660 are:
  a. Enter the coded time period and the value of the time series in two columns. You may also want to include information on the years and quarters.
  b. Select **MegaStat, Time Series/Forecasting,** and **Deseasonalization,** and hit **Enter.**
  c. Input only the range of the sales data, indicate the data are in the first quarter, and click **OK.**

CHAPTER 19

19–1. The Minitab commands for the Pareto chart on page 689 are:
  a. Enter the reasons for water usage in column **C1** and the gallons used in **C2.** Give the columns appropriate names.
  b. Click on **Stat, Quality Tools, Pareto Chart,** and then hit **Enter.**
  c. Indicate **Defects of attribute data** as the variable *Usage* and **Frequencies** as the variable *Gallons.* Click on **Options** and type a chart title, and click **OK.**

19–2. The Minitab commands for the mean and range charts on page 696 are:
  a. Enter the information in Table 19–1 or from the text website, www.mhhe.com/lind16e. The file name is **Table 19–1.**
  b. Click on **Stat, Control Charts, Variables Charts for Subgroups, Xbar-R,** and hit **Enter.**
  c. Select **All observations for a chart are in one column.** Then in the box below, select the variable **Minutes.** For **Subgroup sizes,** enter the variable *Time.*

19–3. The Minitab commands for the p-chart on page 701 are:
  a. Enter the data on the number of defects from page 700.
  b. Click on **Stat, Control Charts, Attribute Charts, P,** and hit **Enter.**
  c. Under **Variables,** select *Defects,* then enter *50* for **Subgroup sizes.** Click on **Labels,** type in the title, and click **OK** twice.

19–4. The Minitab commands for the *c*-bar chart on page 704 are:
  a. Enter the data on the number of misspelled words from page 703 .
  b. Click on **Stat, Control Charts, Attribute Charts, C,** and hit **Enter.**
  c. Select the **Variable** indicating the number of misspelled words, then click on **Labels** and type the title in the space provided, and click **OK** twice.

APPENDIX D: ANSWERS TO ODD-NUMBERED CHAPTER EXERCISES & REVIEW EXERCISES & SOLUTIONS TO PRACTICE TESTS

Answers to Odd-Numbered Chapter Exercises

CHAPTER 1

1. **a.** Interval   **b.** Ratio
    c. Nominal   **d.** Nominal
    e. Ordinal   **f.** Ratio
3. Answers will vary.
5. Qualitative data are not numerical, whereas quantitative data are numerical. Examples will vary by student.
7. A discrete variable may assume only certain values. A continuous variable may assume an infinite number of values within a given range. The number of traffic citations issued each day during February in Garden City Beach, South Carolina, is a discrete variable. The weight of commercial trucks passing the weigh station at milepost 195 on Interstate 95 in North Carolina is a continuous variable.
9. **a.** Ordinal
    b. Ratio
    c. The newer system provides information on the distance between exits.
11. If you were using this store as typical of all Barnes & Noble stores, then it would be sample data. However, if you were considering it as the only store of interest, then the data would be population data.
13.

	Discrete Variable	Continuous Variable
Qualitative	b. Gender d. Soft drink preference g. Student rank in class h. Rating of a finance professor	
Quantitative	c. Sales volume of MP3 players f. SAT scores i. Number of home computers	a. Salary e. Temperature

	Discrete	Continuous
Nominal	b. Gender	
Ordinal	d. Soft drink preference g. Student rank in class h. Rating of a finance professor	
Interval	f. SAT scores	e. Temperature
Ratio	c. Sales volume of MP3 players i. Number of home computers	a. Salary

15. According to the sample information, 120/300 or 40% would accept a job transfer.
17. **a.** Total sales increased by 736,725, found by 1,886,021 − 1,149,296, which is a 64.1% increase.
    b. Market shares through February in 2013 and 2009, respectively, are:

General Motors	22.2%	22.0%
Ford Motor	19.2%	16.2%
Toyota	17.2%	19.7%
Chrysler	13.6%	12.7%
American Honda	10.7%	12.4%
Nissan NA	9.6%	9.4%
Hyundai	5.1%	4.8%
Mazda	2.5%	2.8%

Ford has gained 3.0%, Toyota lost 2.6%, and Honda lost 1.7% of their market share.

c. Percent changes in sales are:

General Motors	165.8%
Ford Motor	197.7%
Toyota	142.9%
Chrysler	175.6%
American Honda	141.4%
Nissan NA	167.0%
Hyundai	174.2%
Mazda	145.4%

Ford had the largest percentage change in sales (197.7%), while Toyota, Honda, and Mazda had the smallest percentage increases (around 142%).
19. Earnings increase about $3 billion per year over the period. However, 2008 sees a very large increase and 2009 sees a large decrease. Perhaps $15 billion of 2008 earnings were somehow "advanced" from the next year or two.
21. **a.** League is a qualitative variable; the others are quantitative.
    b. League is a nominal-level variable; the others are ratio-level variables.

CHAPTER 2

1. 25% market share.
3.

Season	Frequency	Relative Frequency
Winter	100	.10
Spring	300	.30
Summer	400	.40
Fall	200	.20
	1,000	1.00

5. **a.** A frequency table.

Color	Frequency	Relative Frequency
Bright White	130	0.10
Metallic Black	104	0.08
Magnetic Lime	325	0.25
Tangerine Orange	455	0.35
Fusion Red	286	0.22
Total	1,300	1.00

b.

c.

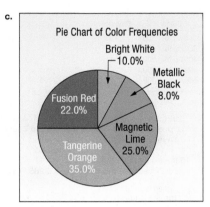

Pie Chart of Color Frequencies

Bright White 10.0%

Metallic Black 8.0%

Fusion Red 22.0%

Magnetic Lime 25.0%

Tangerine Orange 35.0%

d. 350,000 orange, 250,000 lime, 220,000 red, 100,000 white, and 80,000 black, found by multiplying relative frequency by 1,000,000 production.

7. $2^5 = 32$, $2^6 = 64$, therefore, 6 classes

9. $2^7 = 128$, $2^8 = 256$, suggests 8 classes

$i \geq \dfrac{\$567 - \$235}{8} = 41$ Class intervals of 45 or 50 would be acceptable.

11. a. $2^4 = 16$ Suggests 5 classes.

b. $i \geq \dfrac{31 - 25}{5} = 1.2$ Use interval of 1.5.

c. 24

d.

Units	f	Relative Frequency
24.0 up to 25.5	2	0.125
25.5 up to 27.0	4	0.250
27.0 up to 28.5	8	0.500
28.5 up to 30.0	0	0.000
30.0 up to 31.5	2	0.125
Total	16	1.000

e. The largest concentration is in the 27.0 up to 28.5 class (8).

13. a.

Number of Visits	f
0 up to 3	9
3 up to 6	21
6 up to 9	13
9 up to 12	4
12 up to 15	3
15 up to 18	1
Total	51

b. The largest group of shoppers (21) shop at the BiLo Supermarket 3, 4, or 5 times during a month period. Some customers visit the store only 1 time during the month, but others shop as many as 15 times.

c.

Number of Visits	Percent of Total
0 up to 3	17.65
3 up to 6	41.18
6 up to 9	25.49
9 up to 12	7.84
12 up to 15	5.88
15 up to 18	1.96
Total	100.00

15. a. Histogram
b. 100
c. 5
d. 28
e. 0.28
f. 12.5
g. 13

17. a. 50
b. 1.5 thousand miles, or 1,500 miles.
c.

d. $X = 1.5$, $Y = 5$
e.

f. For the 50 employees, about half traveled between 6,000 and 9,000 miles. Five employees traveled less than 3,000 miles, and 2 traveled more than 12,000 miles.

19. a. 40
b. 5
c. 11 or 12
d. About $18/hr
e. About $9/hr
f. About 75%

21. a. 5
b.

Miles	CF
Less than 3	5
Less than 6	17
Less than 9	40
Less than 12	48
Less than 15	50

c.

d. About 8.7 thousand miles

23. a. A qualitative variable uses either the nominal or ordinal scale of measurement. It is usually the result of counts. Quantitative variables are either discrete or continuous. There is a natural order to the results for a quantitative variable. Quantitative variables can use either the interval or ratio scale of measurement.
  b. Both types of variables can be used for samples and populations.
25. a. Frequency table
  b.

  c.

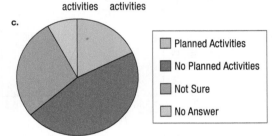

  d. A pie chart would be better because it clearly shows that nearly half of the customers prefer no planned activities.
27. $2^6 = 64$ and $2^7 = 128$, suggest 7 classes
29. a. 5, because $2^4 = 16 < 25$ and $2^5 = 32 > 25$
  b. $i \geq \dfrac{48 - 16}{5} = 6.4$ Use interval of 7.
  c. 15
  d.

Class		Frequency
15 up to 22	|||	3
22 up to 29	₩₩ |||	8
29 up to 36	₩₩ ||	7
36 up to 43	₩₩	5
43 up to 50	||	2
		25

  e. It is fairly symmetric, with most of the values between 22 and 36.
31. a. $2^5 = 32$, $2^6 = 64$, 6 classes recommended.
  b. $i = \dfrac{10 - 1}{6} = 1.5$, use an interval of 2.
  c. 0
  d.

Class	Frequency
0 up to 2	1
2 up to 4	5
4 up to 6	12
6 up to 8	17
8 up to 10	8
10 up to 12	2

  e. The distribution is fairly symmetric or bell-shaped with a large peak in the middle of the two classes of 4 up to 8.

33.

Class	Frequency
0 up to 200	19
200 up to 400	1
400 up to 600	4
600 up to 800	1
800 up to 1,000	2

This distribution is positively skewed with a large "tail" to the right or positive values. Notice that the top 7 tunes account for 4,342 plays out of a total of 5,968, or about 73% of all plays.
35. a. 56   **c.** 55
  b. 10 (found by $60 - 50$)   **d.** 17
37. a. Use $35 because the minimum is ($265 − $82)/6 = $30.5.
  b.

$ 70 up to $105	4
105 up to 140	17
140 up to 175	14
175 up to 210	2
210 up to 245	6
245 up to 280	1

  c. The purchases range from a low of about $70 to a high of about $280. The concentration is in the $105 up to $140 and $140 up to $175 classes.
39. Bar charts are preferred when the goal is to compare the actual amount in each category.

41.

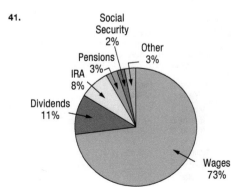

SC Income	Percent	Cumulative
Wages	73	73
Dividends	11	84
IRA	8	92
Pensions	3	95
Social Security	2	97
Other	3	100

By far the largest part of income in South Carolina is wages. Almost three-fourths of the adjusted gross income comes from wages. Dividends and IRAs each contributes roughly another 10%.

43. a. Since $2^6 = 64 < 70 < 128 = 2^7$, 7 classes are recommended. The interval should be at least $(1,002.2 - 3.3)/7 = 142.7$. Use 150 as a convenient value.

b.

45. a. Pie chart
 b. 700, found by 0.7(1,000)
 c. Yes, $0.70 + 0.20 = 0.90$
47. a.

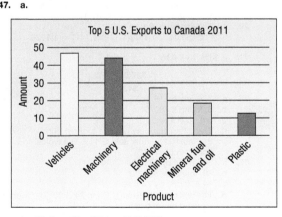

b. 23, found by $(18.4 + 46.9)/281$
 c. 44, found by $(18.4 + 46.9)/(46.9 + 44.2 + 27.1 + 18.4 + 12.6)$
49.

Color	Frequency
Brown	130
Yellow	98
Red	96
Blue	52
Orange	35
Green	33
	444

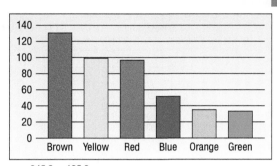

51. $i \geq \dfrac{345.3 - 125.0}{7} = 31.47$ Use interval of 35.

Selling Price	f	CF
110 up to 145	3	3
145 up to 180	19	22
180 up to 215	31	53
215 up to 250	25	78
250 up to 285	14	92
285 up to 320	10	102
320 up to 355	3	105

a. Most homes (53%) are in the 180 up to 250 range.
b. The largest value is near 355; the smallest, near 110.
c.

About 42 homes sold for less than 200.
About 55% of the homes sold for less than 220. So 45% sold for more.
Less than 1% of the homes sold for less than 125.

d.

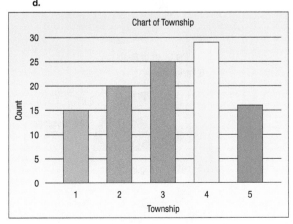

Townships 3 and 4 have more sales than the average and Townships 1 and 5 have somewhat less than the average.

53. Since $2^6 = 64 < 80 < 128 = 2^7$, use 7 classes. The interval should be at least $(1,008 - 741)/7 = 38.14$ miles. Use 40. The resulting frequency distribution is:

Class	f
730 up to 770	5
770 up to 810	17
810 up to 850	37
850 up to 890	18
890 up to 930	1
930 up to 970	0
970 up to 1,010	2

a. The typical amount driven is 830 miles. The range is from 730 up to 1,010 miles.

b. The distribution is "bell shaped" around 830. However, there are two outliers up around 1,000 miles.

c.

Cumulative Frequency of Miles Driven per Month

Forty percent of the buses were driven fewer than 820 miles. Fifty-nine buses were driven less than 850 miles.

d.

Pie Chart of Bus Type

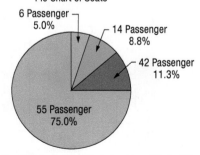

Pie Chart of Seats

The first chart shows that about two-thirds of the buses are diesel. The second diagram shows that nearly three-fourths of the buses have 55 seats.

CHAPTER 3

1. $\mu = 5.4$, found by 27/5

3. a. $\bar{x} = 7.0$, found by 28/4
   b. $(5 - 7) + (9 - 7) + (4 - 7) + (10 - 7) = 0$

5. $\bar{x} = 14.58$, found by 43.74/3

7. a. 15.4, found by 154/10
   b. Population parameter, since it includes all the salespeople at Midtown Ford

9. a. $54.55, found by \$1,091/20
   b. A sample statistic—assuming that the power company serves more than 20 customers

11. $\bar{x} = \dfrac{\Sigma x}{n}$ so
   $\Sigma x = \bar{x} \cdot n = (\$5,430)(30) = \$162,900$

13. a. No mode
   b. The given value would be the mode.
   c. 3 and 4 bimodal

15. a. Mean = 3.583
   b. Median = 5
   c. Mode = 5

17. a. Median = 2.9
   b. Mode = 2.9

19. $\bar{x} = \dfrac{647}{11} = 58.82$
   Median = 58, Mode = 58
   Any of the three measures would be satisfactory.

21. a. $\bar{x} = \dfrac{90.4}{12} = 7.53$
   b. Median = 7.45. There are several modes: 6.5, 7.3, 7.8, and 8.7.
   c. $\bar{x} = \dfrac{33.8}{4} = 8.45$,
   Median = 8.7
   About 1 percentage point higher in winter

23. $22.91, found by $\dfrac{300(\$20) + 400(\$25) + 400(\$23)}{300 + 400 + 400}$

25. $17.75, found by ($400 + \$750 + \$2,400)/200

27. 12.8%, found by $\sqrt[5]{(1.08)(1.12)(1.14)(1.26)(1.05)} = 1.128$

29. 12.28% increase, found by $\sqrt[5]{(1.094)(1.138)(1.117)(1.119)(1.147)} = 1.1228$

31. 2.43%, found by $\sqrt[12]{\dfrac{229.6}{172.2}} - 1$

33. 29.0%, found by $\sqrt[27]{\dfrac{327,577,529}{340,213}} - 1$

35. a. 7, found by $10 - 3$
   b. 6, found by 30/5
   c. 6.8, found by 34/5
   d. The difference between the highest number sold (10) and the smallest number sold (3) is 7. The typical squared deviation from 6 is 6.8.

37. a. 30, found by $54 - 24$
   b. 38, found by 380/10
   c. 74.4, found by 744/10
   d. The difference between 54 and 24 is 30. The average of the squared deviations from 38 is 74.4.

39.

State	Mean	Median	Range
California	33.10	34.0	32
Iowa	24.50	25.0	19

The mean and median ratings were higher, but there was also more variation in California.

41. a. 5
   b. 4.4, found by
   $\dfrac{(8 - 5)^2 + (3 - 5)^2 + (7 - 5)^2 + (3 - 5)^2 + (4 - 5)^2}{5}$

43. a. $2.77

  b. 1.26, found by
$$\frac{(2.68 - 2.77)^2 + (1.03 - 2.77)^2 + (2.26 - 2.77)^2 + (4.30 - 2.77)^2 + (3.58 - 2.77)^2}{5}$$

45. a. Range: 7.3, found by 11.6 − 4.3. Arithmetic mean: 6.94, found by 34.7/5. Variance: 6.5944, found by 32.972/5. Standard deviation: 2.568, found by $\sqrt{6.5944}$.

  b. Dennis has a higher mean return (11.76 > 6.94). However, Dennis has greater spread in its returns on equity (16.89 > 6.59).

47. a. $\bar{x} = 4$
$$s^2 = \frac{(7 - 4)^2 + \cdots + (3 - 4)^2}{5 - 1} = \frac{22}{5 - 1} = 5.5$$

  b. $s = 2.3452$

49. a. $\bar{x} = 38$
$$s^2 = \frac{(28 - 38)^2 + \cdots + (42 - 38)^2}{10 - 1}$$
$$= \frac{744}{10 - 1} = 82.667$$

  b. $s = 9.0921$

51. a. $\bar{x} = \frac{951}{10} = 95.1$
$$s^2 = \frac{(101 - 95.1)^2 + \cdots + (88 - 95.1)^2}{10 - 1}$$
$$= \frac{1,112.9}{9} = 123.66$$

  b. $s = \sqrt{123.66} = 11.12$

53. About 69%, found by $1 - 1/(1.8)^2$

55. a. About 95%

  b. 47.5%, 2.5%

57. Because the exact values in a frequency distribution are not known, the midpoint is used for every member of that class.

59.

Class	f	M	fM	(M − x̄)	f(M − x̄)²
20 up to 30	7	25	175	−22.29	3,477.909
30 up to 40	12	35	420	−12.29	1,812.529
40 up to 50	21	45	945	−2.29	110.126
50 up to 60	18	55	990	7.71	1,069.994
60 up to 70	12	65	780	17.71	3,763.729
	70		3,310		10,234.287

$$\bar{x} = \frac{3,310}{70} = 47.29$$
$$s = \sqrt{\frac{10,234.287}{70 - 1}} = 12.18$$

61.

Number of Clients	f	M	fM	(M − x̄)	f(M − x̄)²
20 up to 30	1	25	25	−19.8	392.04
30 up to 40	15	35	525	−9.8	1,440.60
40 up to 50	22	45	990	0.2	0.88
50 up to 60	8	55	440	10.2	832.32
60 up to 70	4	65	260	20.2	1,632.16
	50		2,240		4,298.00

$$\bar{x} = \frac{2,240}{50} = 44.8$$
$$s = \sqrt{\frac{4,298}{50 - 1}} = 9.37$$

63. a. Mean = 5, found by (6 + 4 + 3 + 7 + 5)/5. Median is 5, found by rearranging the values and selecting the middle value.

  b. Population, because all partners were included

  c. $\Sigma(x - \mu) = (6 - 5) + (4 - 5) + (3 - 5) + (7 - 5) + (5 - 5) = 0$

65. $\bar{x} = \frac{545}{16} = 34.06$

  Median = 37.50

67. The mean is 35.675, found by 1,427/40. The median is 36, found by sorting the data and averaging the 20th and 21st observations.

69. $\bar{x}_w = \frac{\$5.00(270) + \$6.50(300) + \$8.00(100)}{270 + 300 + 100} = \$6.12$

71. $\bar{x}_w = \frac{15,300(4.5) + 10,400(3.0) + 150,600(10.2)}{176,300} = 9.28$

73. $GM = \sqrt[21]{\frac{6,286,800}{5,164,900}} - 1 = 1.0094 - 1.0 = .0094$

75. a. 55, found by 72 − 17

  b. 17.6245, found by the square root of 2795.6/9

77. a. This is a population because it includes all the public universities in Ohio.

  b. The mean is 21,534.

  c. The median is 17,529.

  d. The range is 54,235.

  e. The standard deviation is 13,101.

79. a. There were 13 flights, so all items are considered.

  b. $\mu = \frac{2,259}{13} = 173.77$

  Median = 195

  c. Range = 301 − 7 = 294
$$s = \sqrt{\frac{133,846}{13}} = 101.47$$

81. a. The mean is $717.20, found by $17,930/25. The median is $717.00 and there are two modes, $710 and $722.

  b. The range is $90, found by $771 − $681, and the standard deviation is $24.87, found by the square root of 14,850/24.

  c. From $667.46 up to $766.94, found by $717.20 ± 2($24.87)

83. a. $\bar{x} = \frac{273}{30} = 9.1$, Median = 9

  b. Range = 18 − 4 = 14
$$s = \sqrt{\frac{368.7}{30 - 1}} = 3.57$$

  c. $2^5 = 32$, so suggest 5 classes
$$i = \frac{18 - 4}{5} = 2.8 \quad \text{Use } i = 3$$

Class	M	f	fM	M − x̄	(M − x̄)²	f(M − x̄)²
3.5 up to 6.5	5	10	50	−4	16	160
6.5 up to 9.5	8	6	48	−1	1	6
9.5 up to 12.5	11	9	99	2	4	36
12.5 up to 15.5	14	4	56	5	25	100
15.5 up to 18.5	17	1	17	8	64	64
			270			366

  d. $\bar{x} = \frac{270}{30} = 9.0$
$$s = \sqrt{\frac{366}{30 - 1}} = 3.552$$

  The mean and standard deviation from grouped data are estimates of the mean and standard deviations of the actual values.

85. $\bar{x} = 13 = \frac{910}{70}$

  $s = 5.228 = \sqrt{1807.5/69}$

87. a. The mean team salary is $98,020,000 and the median is $85,750,000. Since the distribution is skewed, the median value of $85,750,000 is more typical.

b. The range is \$142,800,000, found by 198,000,000 − 55,200,000. The standard deviation is \$36,830,000. At least 75% of the team salaries are between \$24,360,000 and \$171,680,000, found by \$98,020,000 plus or minus 2(\$36,830,000).

c. 8.63% per year, found by $\sqrt[23]{\dfrac{3,440,000}{512,930}} - 1$

Mean team payroll is \$104,800,000 and standard deviation is \$44,400,000 in the American League. Mean team payroll is \$92,090,000 and standard deviation is \$28,850,000 in the National League. There is not much difference in the mean payrolls, but there is more dispersion in the American League.

CHAPTER 4

1. In a histogram, observations are grouped so their individual identity is lost. With a dot plot, the identity of each observation is maintained.

3. a. Dot plot **b.** 15
  c. 1, 7 **d.** 2 and 3
5. a. 620 to 629 **b.** 5
  c. 621, 623, 623, 627, 629
7. a. 25 **b.** One
  c. 38,106 **d.** 60, 61, 63, 63, 65, 65, 69
  e. No values **f.** 9
  g. 9 **h.** 76
  i. 16

9.

Stem	Leaves
0	5
1	28
2	
3	0024789
4	12366
5	2

There were a total of 16 calls studied. The number of calls ranged from 5 to 52. Seven of the 16 subscribers made between 30 and 39 calls.

11. Median = 53, found by $(11 + 1)(\frac{1}{2})$ ∴ 6th value in from lowest
  $Q_1 = 49$, found by $(11 + 1)(\frac{1}{4})$ ∴ 3rd value in from lowest
  $Q_3 = 55$, found by $(11 + 1)(\frac{3}{4})$ ∴ 9th value in from lowest
13. a. $Q_1 = 33.25$, $Q_3 = 50.25$
  b. $D_2 = 27.8$, $D_8 = 52.6$
  c. $P_{67} = 47$
15. a. 350
  b. $Q_1 = 175$, $Q_3 = 930$
  c. $930 - 175 = 755$
  d. Less than 0, or more than about 2,060
  e. There are no outliers.
  f. The distribution is positively skewed.

17.

The distribution is somewhat positively skewed. Note that the dashed line above 35 is longer than below 18.

19. a. The mean is 30.8, found by 154/5. The median is 31.0, and the standard deviation is 3.96, found by

$$s = \sqrt{\dfrac{62.8}{4}} = 3.96$$

b. −0.15, found by $\dfrac{3(30.8 - 31.0)}{3.96}$

c.

Salary	$\left(\dfrac{x - \bar{x}}{s}\right)$	$\left(\dfrac{x - \bar{x}}{s}\right)^3$
36	1.313131	2.264250504
26	−1.212121	−1.780894343
33	0.555556	0.171467764
28	−0.707071	−0.353499282
31	0.050505	0.000128826
		0.301453469

0.125, found by $[5/(4 \times 3)] \times 0.301$
21. a. The mean is 21.93, found by 328.9/15. The median is 15.8, and the standard deviation is 21.18, found by

$$s = \sqrt{\dfrac{6,283}{14}} = 21.18$$

b. 0.868, found by [3(21.93 − 15.8)]/21.18
  c. 2.444, found by $[15/(14 \times 13)] \times 29.658$
23.

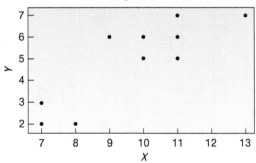

There is a positive relationship between the variables.
25. a. Both variables are nominal scale.
  b. Contingency table
  c. Men are about twice as likely to order a dessert. From the table, 32% of the men ordered dessert, but only 15% of the women.
27. a. Dot plot
  b. 15
  c. 5
29. Stem-and-leaf $N = 23$

3	3	222
5	3	77
11	4	000002
(6)	4	666666
6	5	222222

31. a. $L_{50} = (20 + 1)\frac{50}{100} = 10.50$
  Median $= \dfrac{83.7 + 85.6}{2} = 84.65$

  $L_{25} = (21)(.25) = 5.25$
  $Q_1 = 66.6 + .25(72.9 - 66.6) = 68.175$
  $L_{75} = 21(.75) = 15.75$
  $Q_3 = 87.1 + .75(90.2 - 87.1) = 89.425$

b. $L_{26} = 21(.26) = 5.46$
$P_{26} = 66.6 + .46(72.9 - 66.6) = 69.498$
$L_{83} = 21(.83) = 17.43$
$P_{83} = 93.3 + .43(98.6 - 93.3)$
$= 95.579$

c.

33. **a.** $Q_1 = 26.25$, $Q_3 = 35.75$, Median = 31.50

b. $Q_1 = 33.25$, $Q_3 = 38.75$, Median = 37.50

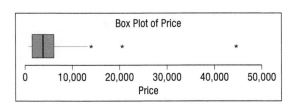

c. The median time for public transportation is about 6 minutes less. There is more variation in public transportation. The difference between Q_1 and Q_3 is 9.5 minutes for public transportation and 5.5 minutes for private transportation.

35. The distribution is positively skewed. The first quartile is about $20 and the third quartile is about $90. There is one outlier located at $255. The median is about $50.

37. **a.**

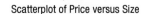
Box Plot of Price

Median is 3,733. First quartile is 1,478. Third quartile is 6,141. So prices over 13,135.5, found by 6,141 + 1.5 × (6,141 − 1,478), are outliers. There are three (13,925; 20,413; and 44,312).

b.

Box Plot of Size

Median is 0.84. First quartile is 0.515. Third quartile is 1.12. So sizes over 2.0275, found by 1.12 + 1.5 (1.12 − 0.515), are outliers. There are three (2.03; 2.35; and 5.03).

c.

Scatterplot of Price versus Size

There is a direct association between them. The first observation is larger on both scales.

d.

Shape/Cut	Average	Good	Ideal	Premium	Ultra Ideal	All
Emerald	0	0	1	0	0	1
Marquise	0	2	0	1	0	3
Oval	0	0	0	1	0	1
Princess	1	0	2	2	0	5
Round	1	3	3	13	3	23
Total	2	5	6	17	3	33

The majority of the diamonds are round (23). Premium cut is most common (17). The Round Premium combination occurs most often (13).

39. $sk = 0.065$ or $sk = \dfrac{3(7.7143 - 8.0)}{3.9036} = -0.22$

41.

Scatterplot of Accidents versus Age

As age increases, the number of accidents decreases.

43. **a.** 139,340,000
b. 5.4% unemployed, found by (7,523/139,340)100
c. Men = 5.64%
Women = 5.12%

45. a.

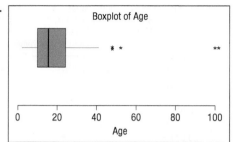

There are five outliers. There is a group of three around 45 years (Angels, Athletics, and Dodgers) and a group of two close to 100 years old (Cubs and Red Sox).

b.

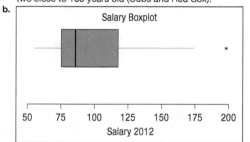

The first quartile is $75,200,000 and the third is $117,720,000. The distribution is positively skewed, with the New York Yankees a definite outlier.

c.

Higher salaries do not necessarily lead to more wins.

d.

The distribution is fairly uniform between 55 and 98.

CHAPTER 5

1.

	Person	
Outcome	1	2
1	A	A
2	A	F
3	F	A
4	F	F

3. a. .176, found by $\frac{6}{34}$ **b.** Empirical

5. a. Empirical
   b. Classical
   c. Classical
   d. Empirical, based on seismological data

7. a. The survey of 40 people about environmental issues
   b. 26 or more respond yes, for example.
   c. $10/40 = .25$
   d. Empirical
   e. The events are not equally likely, but they are mutually exclusive.

9. a. Answers will vary. Here are some possibilities: 123, 124, 125, 999
   b. $(1/10)^3$
   c. Classical

11. $P(A \text{ or } B) = P(A) + P(B) = .30 + .20 = .50$
   $P(\text{neither}) = 1 - .50 = .50.$

13. a. $102/200 = .51$
   b. .49, found by $61/200 + 37/200 = .305 + .185$. Special rule of addition.

15. $P(\text{above } C) = .25 + .50 = .75$

17. $P(A \text{ or } B) = P(A) + P(B) - P(A \text{ and } B) = .20 + .30 - .15 = .35$

19. When two events are mutually exclusive, it means that if one occurs, the other event cannot occur. Therefore, the probability of their joint occurrence is zero.

21. Let A denote the event the fish is green and B be the event the fish is male.
   a. $P(A) = 80/140 = 0.5714$
   b. $P(B) = 60/140 = 0.4286$
   c. $P(A \text{ and } B) = 36/140 = 0.2571$
   d. $P(A \text{ or } B) = P(A) + P(B) - P(A \text{ and } B) = 80/140 + 60/140 - 36/140 = 104/140 = 0.7429$

23. $P(A \text{ and } B) = P(A) \times P(B|A) = .40 \times .30 = .12$

25. .90, found by $(.80 + .60) - .5$.
   .10, found by $(1 - .90)$.

27. a. $P(A_1) = 3/10 = .30$
   b. $P(B_1|A_2) = 1/3 = .33$
   c. $P(B_2 \text{ and } A_3) = 1/10 = .10$

29. a. A contingency table
   b. .27, found by $300/500 \times 135/300$
   c. The tree diagram would appear as:

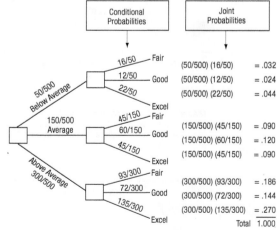

31. a. Out of all 545 students, 171 prefer skiing. So the probability is 171/545, or 0.3138.
   b. Out of all 545 students, 155 are in junior college. Thus, the probability is 155/545, or 0.2844.

c. Out of 210 four-year students, 70 prefer ice skating. So the probability is 70/210, or 0.3333.

d. Out of 211 students who prefer snowboarding, 68 are in junior college. So the probability is 68/211, or 0.3223.

e. Out of 180 graduate students, 74 prefer skiing and 47 prefer ice skating. So the probability is $(74 + 47)/180 = 121/180$, or 0.6722.

33. $$P(A_1|B_1) = \frac{P(A_1) \times P(B_1|A_1)}{P(A_1) \times P(B_1|A_1) + P(A_2) \times P(B_1|A_2)}$$
$$= \frac{.60 \times .05}{(.60 \times .05) + (.40 \times .10)} = .4286$$

35. $$P(\text{night}|\text{win}) = \frac{P(\text{night})P(\text{win}|\text{night})}{P(\text{night})P(\text{win}|\text{night}) + P(\text{day})P(\text{win}|\text{day})}$$
$$= \frac{(.70)(.50)}{[(.70)(.50)] + [(.30)(.90)]} = .5645$$

37. $P(\text{cash} \mid {>}\$50)$
$$= \frac{P(\text{cash})\,P({>}\$50|\text{cash})}{\begin{array}{l}[P(\text{cash})\,P({>}\$50|\text{cash})\\ + P(\text{credit})\,P({>}\$50|\text{credit})\\ + P(\text{debit})\,P({>}\$50|\text{debit})]\end{array}}$$
$$= \frac{(.30)(.20)}{(.30)(.20) + (.30)(.90) + (.40)(.60)} = .1053$$

39. **a.** 78,960,960
  b. 840, found by (7)(6)(5)(4). That is 7!/3!
  c. 10, found by 5!/3!2!
41. 210, found by (10)(9)(8)(7)/(4)(3)(2)
43. 120, found by 5!
45. 10,897,286,400, found by
  $_{15}P_{10} = (15)(14)(13)(12)(11)(10)(9)(8)(7)(6)$
47. **a.** Asking teenagers to compare their reactions to a newly developed soft drink.
  b. Answers will vary. One possibility is more than half of the respondents like it.
49. Subjective
51. **a.** 4/9, found by (2/3) · (2/3)
  b. 3/4, because (3/4) · (2/3) = 0.5
53. **a.** .8145, found by (.95)⁴
  b. Special rule of multiplication
  c. $P(A \text{ and } B \text{ and } C \text{ and } D) = P(A) \times P(B) \times P(C) \times P(D)$
55. **a.** .08, found by .80 × .10
  b. No; 90% of females attended college, 78% of males
  c.

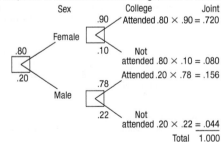

  d. Yes, because all the possible outcomes are shown on the tree diagram.
57. **a.** 0.57, found by 57/100
  b. 0.97, found by (57/100) + (40/100)
  c. Yes, because an employee cannot be both
  d. 0.03, found by 1 − 0.97
59. **a.** 1/2, found by (2/3)(3/4)
  b. 1/12, found by (1/3)(1/4)
  c. 11/12, found by 1 − 1/12
61. **a.** 0.9039, found by (0.98)⁵
  b. 0.0961, found by 1 − 0.9039

63. **a.** 0.0333, found by (4/10)(3/9)(2/8)
  b. 0.1667, found by (6/10)(5/9)(4/8)
  c. 0.8333, found by 1 − 0.1667
  d. Dependent
65. **a.** 0.3818, found by (9/12)(8/11)(7/10)
  b. 0.6182, found by 1 − 0.3818
67. **a.** $P(S) \cdot P(R|S) = .60(.85) = 0.51$
  b. $P(S) \cdot P(PR|S) = .60(1 − .85) = 0.09$
69. **a.** $P(\text{not perfect}) = P(\text{bad sector}) + P(\text{defective})$
  $$= \frac{112}{1,000} + \frac{31}{1,000} = .143$$
  b. $P(\text{defective}|\text{not perfect}) = \dfrac{.031}{.143} = .217$
71. $P(\text{poor}|\text{profit}) = \dfrac{.10(.20)}{.10(.20) + .60(.80) + .30(.60)}$
  $= .0294$
73. **a.** 0.1 + 0.02 = 0.12
  b. 1 − 0.12 = 0.88
  c. (0.88)³ = 0.6815
  d. 1 − .6815 = 0.3185
75. Yes, 256 is found by 2⁸.
77. .9744, found by 1 − (.40)⁴
79. **a.** .185, found by (.15)(.95) + (.05)(.85)
  b. .0075, found by (.15)(.05)
81. **a.** $P(F \text{ and } {>}60) = .25$, found by solving with the general rule of multiplication:
  $P(F) \cdot P({>}60|F) = (.5)(.5)$
  b. 0
  c. .3333, found by 1/3
83. 26⁴ = 456,976
85. 1/3, 628,800
87. **a.** $P(D) = .20(.03) + .30(.04) + .25(.07) + .25(.065)$
  $= .05175$
  b. $P(\text{Tyson}|\text{defective}) = \dfrac{.20(.03)}{[.20(.03) + .30(.04) + .25(.07) + .25(.065)]} = .1159$

Supplier	Joint	Revised
Tyson	.00600	.1159
Fuji	.01200	.2319
Kirkpatricks	.01750	.3382
Parts	.01625	.3140
	.05175	1.0000

89. 0.512, found by (0.8)³
91. .525, found by 1 − (.78)³
93. **a.**

Winning Season	Attendance			
	Low	Moderate	High	Total
No	4	7	2	13
Yes	3	7	7	17
Total	11	10	9	30

  1. 0.5667, found by 17/30
  2. 0.5667, found by 17/30 + 9/30 − 9/30 = 17/30
  3. 0.7778, found by 7/9
  4. 0.1000, found by 3/30
  b.

	Losing Season	Winning Season	Total
New	7	8	15
Old	6	9	15
Total	13	17	30

  1. 0.5667, found by 17/30
  2. 0.2667, found by 8/30
  3. 0.8000, found by 17/30 + 15/30 − 8/30 = 24/30

CHAPTER 6

1. Mean = 1.3, variance = .81, found by:
$$\mu = 0(.20) + 1(.40) + 2(.30) + 3(.10) = 1.3$$
$$\sigma^2 = (0 - 1.3)^2(.2) + (1 - 1.3)^2(.4)$$
$$+ (2 - 1.3)^2(.3) + (3 - 1.3)^2(.1)$$
$$= .81$$

3. Mean = 14.5, variance = 27.25, found by:
$$\mu = 5(.1) + 10(.3) + 15(.2) + 20(.4) = 14.5$$
$$\sigma^2 = (5 - 14.5)^2(.1) + (10 - 14.5)^2(.3)$$
$$+ (15 - 14.5)^2(.2) + (20 - 14.5)^2(.4)$$
$$= 27.25$$

5. a.

Calls, x	Frequency	P(x)	xP(x)	$(x - \mu)^2 P(x)$
0	8	.16	0	.4624
1	10	.20	.20	.0980
2	22	.44	.88	.0396
3	9	.18	.54	.3042
4	1	.02	.08	.1058
	50		1.70	1.0100

b. Discrete distribution, because only certain outcomes are possible.
c. $\mu = \Sigma x \cdot P(x) = 1.70$
d. $\sigma = \sqrt{1.01} = 1.005$

7.

Amount	P(x)	xP(x)	$(x - \mu)^2 P(x)$
10	.50	5	60.50
25	.40	10	6.40
50	.08	4	67.28
100	.02	2	124.82
		21	259.00

a. $\mu = \Sigma x P(x) = 21$
b. $\sigma^2 = \Sigma(x - \mu)^2 P(x) = 259$
$\sigma = \sqrt{259} = 16.093$

9. a. $P(2) = \dfrac{4!}{2!(4 - 2)!}(.25)^2(.75)^{4-2} = .2109$

b. $P(3) = \dfrac{4!}{3!(4 - 3)!}(.25)^3(.75)^{4-3} = .0469$

11. a.

x	P(x)
0	.064
1	.288
2	.432
3	.216

b. $\mu = 1.8$
$\sigma^2 = 0.72$
$\sigma = \sqrt{0.72} = .8485$

13. a. .2668, found by $P(2) = \dfrac{9!}{(9 - 2)!2!}(.3)^2(.7)^7$

b. .1715, found by $P(4) = \dfrac{9!}{(9 - 4)!4!}(.3)^4(.7)^5$

c. .0404, found by $P(0) = \dfrac{9!}{(9 - 0)!0!}(.3)^0(.7)^9$

15. a. .2824, found by $P(0) = \dfrac{12!}{(12 - 0)!0!}(.1)^0(.9)^{12}$

b. .3766, found by $P(1) = \dfrac{12!}{(12 - 1)!1!}(.1)^1(.9)^{11}$

c. .2301, found by $P(2) = \dfrac{12!}{(12 - 2)!2!}(.1)^2(.9)^{10}$

d. $\mu = 1.2$, found by 12(.1)
$\sigma = 1.0392$, found by $\sqrt{1.08}$

17. a. 0.1858, found by $\dfrac{15!}{2!13!}(0.23)^2(0.77)^{13}$

b. 0.1416, found by $\dfrac{15!}{5!10!}(0.23)^5(0.77)^{10}$

c. 3.45, found by (0.23)(15)

19. a. 0.296, found by using Appendix B.1 with n of 8, π of 0.30, and x of 2
b. $P(x \le 2) = 0.058 + 0.198 + 0.296 = 0.552$
c. 0.448, found by $P(x \ge 3) = 1 - P(x \le 2) = 1 - 0.552$

21. a. 0.387, found from Appendix B.1 with n of 9, π of 0.90, and x of 9
b. $P(x < 5) = 0.001$
c. 0.992, found by $1 - 0.008$
d. 0.947, found by $1 - 0.053$

23. a. $\mu = 10.5$, found by 15(0.7) and $\sigma = \sqrt{15(0.7)(0.3)} = 1.7748$

b. 0.2061, found by $\dfrac{15!}{10!5!}(0.7)^{10}(0.3)^5$

c. 0.4247, found by $0.2061 + 0.2186$
d. 0.5154, found by
$0.2186 + 0.1700 + 0.0916 + 0.0305 + 0.0047$

25. $P(2) = \dfrac{[_6C_2][_4C_1]}{_{10}C_3} = \dfrac{15(4)}{120} = .50$

27. N is 10, the number of loans in the population; S is 3, the number of underwater loans in the population; x is 0, the number of selected underwater loans in the sample; and n is 2, the size of the sample. Use formula (6–6) to find
$P(0) = \dfrac{(_7C_2)(_3C_0)}{_{10}C_2} = \dfrac{21(1)}{45} = 0.4667$.

29. $P(2) = \dfrac{[_9C_3][_6C_2]}{[_{15}C_5]} = \dfrac{84(15)}{3003} = .4196$

31. a. .6703
b. .3297

33. a. .0613
b. .0803

35. $\mu = 6$
$P(x \ge 5) = 1 - (.0025 + .0149 + .0446 + .0892 + .1339)$
$= .7149$

37. A random variable is an outcome that results from a chance experiment. A probability distribution also includes the likelihood of each possible outcome.

39. $\mu = \$1,000(.25) + \$2,000(.60) + \$5,000(.15) = \$2,200$
$\sigma^2 = (1,000 - 2,200)^2 .25 + (2,000 - 2,200)^2 .60 +$
$(5,000 - 2,200)^2 .15$
$= 1,560,000$

41. $\mu = 12(.25) + \cdots + 15(.1) = 13.2$
$\sigma^2 = (12 - 13.2)^2 .25 + \cdots + (15 - 13.2)^2 .10 = 0.86$
$\sigma = \sqrt{0.86} = .927$

43. a. $\mu = 10(.35) = 3.5$
b. $P(x = 4) = {}_{10}C_4 (.35)^4 (.65)^6 = 210(.0150)(.0754) = .2375$
c. $P(x \ge 4) = {}_{10}C_x (.35)^x (.65)^{10-x}$
$= .2375 + .1536 + \cdots + .0000 = .4862$

45. a. 6, found by 0.4×15

b. 0.0245, found by $\dfrac{15!}{10!5!}(0.4)^{10}(0.6)^5$

c. 0.0338, found by
$0.0245 + 0.0074 + 0.0016 + 0.0003 + 0.0000$
d. 0.0093, found by $0.0338 - 0.0245$

47. a. $\mu = 20(0.075) = 1.5$
$\sigma = \sqrt{20(0.075)(0.925)} = 1.1779$

b. 0.2103, found by $\dfrac{20!}{0!20!}(0.075)^0(0.925)^{20}$

c. 0.7897, found by $1 - 0.2103$

49. a. 0.1311, found by $\dfrac{16!}{4!12!}(0.15)^4(0.85)^{12}$

b. 2.4, found by (0.15)(16)
c. 0.2100, found by $1 - 0.0743 - 0.2097 - 0.2775 - 0.2285$

51. 0.2784, found by $0.1472 + 0.0811 + 0.0348 + 0.0116 + 0.0030 + 0.0006 + 0.0001 + 0.0000$

53. **a.**

0	0.0002	7	0.2075
1	0.0019	8	0.1405
2	0.0116	9	0.0676
3	0.0418	10	0.0220
4	0.1020	11	0.0043
5	0.1768	12	0.0004
6	0.2234		

b. $\mu = 12(.52) = 6.24$ $\sigma = \sqrt{12(.52)(.48)} = 1.7307$
c. 0.1768
d. 0.3343, found by
   $0.0002 + 0.0019 + 0.0116 + 0.0418 + 0.1020 + 0.1768$

55. **a.** $P(1) = \dfrac{[_7C_2][_3C_1]}{[_{10}C_3]} = \dfrac{(21)(3)}{120} = .5250$

b. $P(0) = \dfrac{[_7C_3][_3C_0]}{[_{10}C_3]} = \dfrac{(35)(1)}{120} = .2917$
   $P(x \geq 1) = 1 - P(0) = 1 - .2917 = .7083$

57. $P(x = 0) = \dfrac{[_8C_4][_4C_0]}{[_{12}C_4]} = \dfrac{70}{495} = .141$

59. **a.** .0498   **b.** .7746, found by $(1 - .0498)^5$
61. $\mu = 4.0$, from Appendix B.2
   a. .0183   **b.** .1954
   c. .6289   **d.** .5665

63. **a.** 0.1733, found by $\dfrac{(3.1)^4 e^{-3.1}}{4!}$

b. 0.0450, found by $\dfrac{(3.1)^0 e^{-3.1}}{0!}$

c. 0.9550, found by $1 - 0.0450$

65. $\mu = n\pi = 23\left(\dfrac{2}{113}\right) = .407$

$P(2) = \dfrac{(.407)^2 e^{-.407}}{2!} = 0.0551$

$P(0) = \dfrac{(.407)^0 e^{-.407}}{0!} = 0.6656$

67. Let $\mu = n\pi = 155(1/3,709) = 0.042$
   $P(4) = \dfrac{0.042^4 e^{-0.042}}{4!} = 0.00000012$
   Very unlikely!

69. **a.** $\mu = n\pi = 15(.67) = 10.05$
   $\sigma = \sqrt{n\pi(1 - \pi)} = \sqrt{15(.67)(.33)} = 1.8211$
   b. $P(8) = {}_{15}C_8(.67)^8(.33)^7 = 6435(.0406)(.000426) = .1114$
   c. $P(x \geq 8) = .1114 + .1759 + \cdots + .0025 = .9163$

71. The mean number of home runs per game is 2.0305, found by
   $4934/[(15)(162)]$.

a. $P(0) = \dfrac{2.0305^0 e^{-2.0305}}{0!} = 0.1313$

b. $P(2) = \dfrac{2.0305^2 e^{-2.0305}}{2!} = 0.2706$

c. $P(x \geq 4) = 0.1484$, found by
   $1 - (0.1313 + 0.2665 + 0.2706 + 0.1832)$

CHAPTER 7

1. **a.** $b = 10, a = 6$

b. $\mu = \dfrac{6 + 10}{2} = 8$

c. $\sigma = \sqrt{\dfrac{(10 - 6)^2}{12}} = 1.1547$

d. Area $= \dfrac{1}{(10 - 6)} \cdot \dfrac{(10 - 6)}{1} = 1$

e. $P(x > 7) = \dfrac{1}{(10 - 6)} \cdot \dfrac{10 - 7}{1} = \dfrac{3}{4} = .75$

f. $P(7 \leq x \leq 9) = \dfrac{1}{(10 - 6)} \cdot \dfrac{(9 - 7)}{1} = \dfrac{2}{4} = .50$

3. **a.** 0.30, found by $(30 - 27)/(30 - 20)$
   b. 0.40, found by $(24 - 20)/(30 - 20)$

5. **a.** $a = 0.5, b = 3.00$

b. $\mu = \dfrac{0.5 + 3.00}{2} = 1.75$

$\sigma = \sqrt{\dfrac{(3.00 - .50)^2}{12}} = .72$

c. $P(x < 1) = \dfrac{1}{(3.0 - 0.5)} \cdot \dfrac{1 - .5}{1} = \dfrac{.5}{2.5} = 0.2$

d. 0, found by $\dfrac{1}{(3.0 - 0.5)} \cdot \dfrac{(1.0 - 1.0)}{1}$

e. $P(x > 1.5) = \dfrac{1}{(3.0 - 0.5)} \cdot \dfrac{3.0 - 1.5}{1} = \dfrac{1.5}{2.5} = 0.6$

7. The actual shape of a normal distribution depends on its mean and standard deviation. Thus, there is a normal distribution, and an accompanying normal curve, for a mean of 7 and a standard deviation of 2. There is another normal curve for a mean of $25,000 and a standard deviation of $1,742, and so on.

9. **a.** 490 and 510, found by $500 \pm 1(10)$
   b. 480 and 520, found by $500 \pm 2(10)$
   c. 470 and 530, found by $500 \pm 3(10)$

11. $z_{Rob} = \dfrac{\$50,000 - \$60,000}{\$5,000} = -2$

$z_{Rachel} = \dfrac{\$50,000 - \$35,000}{\$8,000} = 1.875$

Adjusting for their industries, Rob is well below average and Rachel well above.

13. **a.** 1.25, found by $z = \dfrac{25 - 20}{4.0} = 1.25$

b. 0.3944, found in Appendix B.3

c. 0.3085, found by $z = \dfrac{18 - 20}{2.5} = -0.5$

Find 0.1915 in Appendix B.3 for $z = -0.5$, then $0.5000 - 0.1915 = 0.3085$

15. **a.** 0.3413, found by $z = \dfrac{\$24 - \$20.50}{\$3.50} = 1.00$, then find 0.3413

in Appendix B.3 for $z = 1$

b. 0.1587, found by $0.5000 - 0.3413 = 0.1587$

c. 0.3336, found by $z = \dfrac{\$19.00 - \$20.50}{\$3.50} = -0.43$

Find 0.1664 in Appendix B.3, for $z = -0.43$, then $0.5000 - 0.1664 = 0.3336$

17. **a.** 0.8276: First find $z = -1.5$, found by $(44 - 50)/4$ and $z = 1.25 = (55 - 50)/4$. The area between -1.5 and 0 is 0.4332 and the area between 0 and 1.25 is 0.3944, both from Appendix B.3. Then adding the two areas we find that $0.4332 + 0.3944 = 0.8276$.
   b. 0.1056, found by $0.5000 - .3944$, where $z = 1.25$
   c. 0.2029: Recall that the area for $z = 1.25$ is 0.3944, and the area for $z = 0.5$, found by $(52 - 50)/4$, is 0.1915. Then subtract $0.3944 - 0.1915$ and find 0.2029.

19. **a.** 0.4129: Begin by using formula (7–5) to find the z value for $3,100, which is $(3,100 - 3,000)/450$, or 0.22. Then see Appendix B.3 to find the area between 0 and 0.22, which is 0.0871. Finally, since the area of interest is beyond 0.22, subtract that probability from 0.5000. The result is $0.5000 - 0.0871$, or 0.4129.
   b. 0.1929: Use formula (7–5) to find the z value for $3,500, which is $(3,500 - 3,000)/450$, or 1.11. Then see Appendix B.3 for the area under the standard normal curve. That probability is 0.3665. Since the two points (1.11 and 0.22) are on the same side of the mean, subtract the smaller probability from the larger. The result is $0.3665 - 0.1736 = 0.1929$.
   c. 0.8190: Use formula (7–5) to find the z value for $2,250, which is -1.67, found by $(2,250 - 3,000)/450$. The corresponding area is 0.4525. Since 1.11 and -1.67 are on different sides of the mean, add the corresponding probabilities. Thus, we find $0.4525 + 0.3665 = 0.8190$.

21. a. 0.0764, found by $z = (20 - 15)/3.5 = 1.43$, then $0.5000 - 0.4236 = 0.0764$
  b. 0.9236, found by $0.5000 + 0.4236$, where $z = 1.43$
  c. 0.1185, found by $z = (12 - 15)/3.5 = -0.86$. The area under the curve is 0.3051, then $z = (10 - 15)/3.5 = -1.43$. The area is 0.4236. Finally, $0.4236 - 0.3051 = 0.1185$.
23. $x = 56.60$, found by adding 0.5000 (the area left of the mean) and then finding a z value that forces 45% of the data to fall inside the curve. Solving for x: $1.65 = (x - 50)/4$, so $x = 56.60$.
25. $1,630, found by $2,100 - 1.88($250)
27. a. 214.8 hours: Find a z value where 0.4900 of area is between 0 and z. That value is $z = 2.33$. Then solve for x: $2.33 = (x - 195)/8.5$, so $x = 214.8$ hours.
  b. 270.2 hours: Find a z value where 0.4900 of area is between 0 and $(-z)$. That value is $z = -2.33$. Then solve for x: $-2.33 = (x - 290)/8.5$, so $x = 270.2$ hours.
29. 41.7%, found by $12 + 1.65(18)$
31. a. $\mu = n\pi = 50(0.25) = 12.5$
  $\sigma^2 = n\pi(1 - \pi) = 12.5(1 - 0.25) = 9.375$
  $\sigma = \sqrt{9.375} = 3.0619$
  b. 0.2578, found by $(14.5 - 12.5)/3.0619 = 0.65$. The area is 0.2422. Then $0.5000 - 0.2422 = 0.2578$.
  c. 0.2578, found by $(10.5 - 12.5)/3.0619 = -0.65$. The area is 0.2422. Then $0.5000 - 0.2422 = 0.2578$.
33. a. $\mu = n\pi = 80(0.07) = 5.6$ $\sigma = \sqrt{5.208} = 2.2821$
  0.3483, found from $z = (6.5 - 5.6)/2.2821 = 0.39$ with the corresponding area of 0.1517, then $0.5000 - 0.1517 = 0.3483$
  b. 0.5160, found from $z = (5.5 - 5.6)/2.2821 = -0.04$ with the corresponding area of 0.0160, then $0.5000 + 0.0160 = 0.5160$
  c. .1677, found by $.5160 - 0.3483$.
35. a. Yes. (1) There are two mutually exclusive outcomes: overweight and not overweight. (2) It is the result of counting the number of successes (overweight members). (3) Each trial is independent. (4) The probability of 0.30 remains the same for each trial.
  b. 0.0084, found by
  $\mu = 500(0.30) = 150$
  $\sigma^2 = 500(.30)(.70) = 105$
  $\sigma = \sqrt{105} = 10.24695$
  $z = \dfrac{x - \mu}{\sigma} = \dfrac{174.5 - 150}{10.24695} = 2.39$
  The area under the curve for 2.39 is 0.4916. Then $0.5000 - 0.4916 = 0.0084$.
  c. 0.8461, found by $z = \dfrac{139.5 - 150}{10.24695} = -1.02$
  The area between 139.5 and 150 is 0.3461. Adding $0.3461 + 0.5000 = 0.8461$.
37. a. 0.3935, found by $1 - e^{[(-1/60)\,(30)]}$
  b. 0.1353, found by $e^{[(-1/60)\,(120)]}$
  c. 0.1859, found by $e^{[(-1/60)\,(45)]} - e^{[(-1/60)\,(75)]}$
  d. 41.59 seconds, found by $-60 \ln(0.5)$
39. a. 0.5654, found by $1 - e^{[(-1/18)\,(15)]}$, and 0.2212, found by $1 - e^{[(-1/60)\,(15)]}$
  b. 0.0013, found by $e^{[(-1/18)\,(120)]}$, and 0.1353, found by $e^{[(-1/60)\,(120)]}$
  c. 0.1821, found by $e^{[(-1/60)\,(30)]} - e^{[(-1/18)\,(90)]}$, and 0.3834, found by $e^{[(-1/60)\,(30)]} - e^{[(-1/60)\,(90)]}$
  d. 4 minutes, found by $-18 \ln(0.8)$, and 13.4 minutes, found by $-60 \ln(0.8)$
41. a. $\mu = \dfrac{11.96 + 12.05}{2} = 12.005$
  b. $\sigma = \sqrt{\dfrac{(12.05 - 11.96)^2}{12}} = .0260$
  c. $P(x < 12) = \dfrac{1}{(12.05 - 11.96)} \cdot \dfrac{12.00 - 11.96}{1} = \dfrac{.04}{.09} = .44$
  d. $P(x > 11.98) = \dfrac{1}{(12.05 - 11.96)} \left(\dfrac{12.05 - 11.98}{1}\right)$
  $= \dfrac{.07}{.09} = .78$

e. All cans have more than 11.00 ounces, so the probability is 100%.
43. a. $\mu = \dfrac{4 + 10}{2} = 7$
  b. $\sigma = \sqrt{\dfrac{(10 - 4)^2}{12}} = 1.732$
  c. $P(x < 6) = \dfrac{1}{(10 - 4)} \cdot \left(\dfrac{6 - 4}{1}\right) = \dfrac{2}{6} = .33$
  d. $P(x > 5) = \dfrac{1}{(10 - 4)} \cdot \left(\dfrac{10 - 5}{1}\right) = \dfrac{5}{6} = .83$
45. a. -0.4 for net sales, found by $(170 - 180)/25$. 2.92 for employees, found by $(1,850 - 1,500)/120$.
  b. Net sales are 0.4 standard deviation below the mean. Employees is 2.92 standard deviation above the mean.
  c. 65.54% of the aluminum fabricators have greater net sales compared with Clarion, found by $0.1554 + 0.5000$. Only 0.18% have more employees than Clarion, found by $0.5000 - 0.4982$.
47. a. 0.5000, because $z = \dfrac{30 - 490}{90} = -5.11$
  b. 0.2514, found by $0.5000 - 0.2486$
  c. 0.6374, found by $0.2486 + 0.3888$
  d. 0.3450, found by $0.3888 - 0.0438$
49. a. 0.3015, found by $0.5000 - 0.1985$
  b. 0.2579, found by $0.4564 - 0.1985$
  c. 0.0011, found by $0.5000 - 0.4989$
  d. 1,818, found by $1,280 + 1.28(420)$
51. a. 90.82%: First find $z = 1.33$, found by $(40 - 34)/4.5$. The area between 0 and 1.33 is 0.4082 hours/week for women. Then add 0.5000 and 0.4082 and find 0.9082, or 90.82%.
  b. 78.23%: First find $z = -0.78$, found by $(25 - 29)/5.1$. The area between 0 and (-0.78) is 0.2823. Then add 0.5000 and 0.2823 and find 0.7823, or 78.23%.
  c. Find a z value where 0.4900 of the area is between 0 and z. That value is 2.33. Then solve for x: $2.33 = (x - 34)/4.5$, so $x = 44.5$ hours/week for women.
  40.9 hours/week for men: $2.33 = (x - 29)/5.1$, so $x = 40.9$ hours/week.
53. About 4,099 units, found by solving for x. $1.65 = (x - 4,000)/60$
55. a. 15.39%, found by $(8 - 10.3)/2.25 = -1.02$, then $0.5000 - 0.3461 = 0.1539$.
  b. 17.31%, found by:
  $z = (12 - 10.3)/2.25 = 0.76$. Area is 0.2764.
  $z = (14 - 10.3)/2.25 = 1.64$. Area is 0.4495.
  The area between 12 and 14 is 0.1731, found by $0.4495 - 0.2764$.
  c. On 99.73% of the days, returns are between 3.55 and 17.05, found by $10.3 \pm 3(2.25)$. Thus, the chance of less than 3.55 returns is rather remote.
57. a. 0.9678, found by:
  $\mu = 60(0.64) = 38.4$
  $\sigma^2 = 60(0.64)(0.36) = 13.824$
  $\sigma = \sqrt{13.824} = 3.72$
  Then $(31.5 - 38.4)/3.72 = -1.85$, for which the area is 0.4678. Then $0.5000 + 0.4678 = 0.9678$.
  b. 0.0853, found by $(43.5 - 38.4)/3.72 = 1.37$, for which the area is 0.4147. Then $0.5000 - 0.4147 = .0853$.
  c. 0.8084, found by $0.4441 + 0.3643$
  d. 0.0348, found by $0.4495 - 0.4147$
59. 0.0968, found by:
  $\mu = 50(0.40) = 20$
  $\sigma^2 = 50(0.40)(0.60) = 12$
  $\sigma = \sqrt{12} = 3.46$
  $z = (24.5 - 20)/3.46 = 1.30$.
  The area is 0.4032. Then, for 25 or more, $0.5000 - 0.4032 = 0.0968$.

61. a. $1.65 = (45 - \mu)/5$ $\mu = 36.75$
    b. $1.65 = (45 - \mu)/10$ $\mu = 28.5$
    c. $z = (30 - 28.5)/10 = 0.15$, then $0.5000 + 0.0596 = 0.5596$

63. a. 21.19%, found by $z = (9.00 - 9.20)/0.25 = -0.80$, so $0.5000 - 0.2881 = 0.2119$
    b. Increase the mean. $z = (9.00 - 9.25)/0.25 = -1.00$, $P = 0.5000 - 0.3413 = 0.1587$.
    Reduce the standard deviation. $\sigma = (9.00 - 9.20)/0.15 = -1.33$; $P = 0.5000 - 0.4082 = 0.0918$.
    Reducing the standard deviation is better because a smaller percent of the hams will be below the limit.

65. a. $z = (60 - 52)/5 = 1.60$, so $0.5000 - 0.4452 = 0.0548$
    b. Let $z = 0.67$, so $0.67 = (x - 52)/5$ and $x = 55.35$, set mileage at 55,350
    c. $z = (45 - 52)/5 = -1.40$, so $0.5000 - 0.4192 = 0.0808$

67. $\dfrac{470 - \mu}{\sigma} = 0.25$ $\dfrac{500 - \mu}{\sigma} = 1.28$ $\sigma = 29{,}126$ and $\mu = 462{,}718$

69. $\mu = 150(0.15) = 22.5$ $\sigma = \sqrt{150(0.15)(0.85)} = 4.37$
    $z = (29.5 - 22.5)/4.37 = 1.60$
    $P(z > 1.60) = .05000 - 0.4452 = 0.0548$

71. a. 0.4262, found by $1 - e^{[(-1/27)(15)]}$
    b. 0.1084, found by $e^{[(-1/27)(60)]}$
    c. 0.1403, found by $e^{[(-1/27)(30)]} - e^{[(-1/27)(45)]}$
    d. 2.84 secs, found by $-27 \ln(0.9)$

73. a. 0.2835, found by $1 - e^{[(-1/300{,}000)(100{,}000)]}$
    b. 0.1889, found by $e^{[(-1/300{,}000)(500{,}000)]}$
    c. 0.2020, found by $e^{[(-1/300{,}000)(200{,}000)]} - e^{[(-1/300{,}000)(350{,}000)]}$
    d. Both the mean and standard deviation are 300,000 hours.

75. a. 0.0582, found by $0.5000 - 0.4418$ with $z = (3.500 - 2.495)/0.642 = 1.57$; leads to 1.7 teams, found by $30(0.0582)$. Two teams actually had attendance of more than 3.5 million, so the estimate is accurate.
    b. 0.9032, found by $0.5000 + 0.4032$ with $z = (50 - 98.02)/36.83 = -1.30$; leads to 27.1 teams, found by $30(0.9032)$. All 30 teams actually had salaries of more than \$50 million, so the estimate is not really accurate.

CHAPTER 8

1. a. 303 Louisiana, 5155 S. Main, 3501 Monroe, 2652 W. Central
    b. Answers will vary.
    c. 630 Dixie Hwy, 835 S. McCord Rd, 4624 Woodville Rd
    d. Answers will vary.

3. a. Bob Schmidt Chevrolet
    Great Lakes Ford Nissan
    Grogan Towne Chrysler
    Southside Lincoln Mercury
    Rouen Chrysler Jeep Eagle
    b. Answers will vary.
    c. Yark Automotive
    Thayer Chevrolet Toyota
    Franklin Park Lincoln Mercury
    Mathews Ford Oregon Inc.
    Valiton Chrysler

5. a.

Sample	Values	Sum	Mean
1	12, 12	24	12
2	12, 14	26	13
3	12, 16	28	14
4	12, 14	26	13
5	12, 16	28	14
6	14, 16	30	15

    b. $\mu_{\bar{x}} = (12 + 13 + 14 + 13 + 14 + 15)/6 = 13.5$
    $\mu = (12 + 12 + 14 + 16)/4 = 13.5$
    c. More dispersion with population data compared to the sample means. The sample means vary from 12 to 15, whereas the population varies from 12 to 16.

7. a.

Sample	Values	Sum	Mean
1	12, 12, 14	38	12.66
2	12, 12, 15	39	13.00
3	12, 12, 20	44	14.66
4	14, 15, 20	49	16.33
5	12, 14, 15	41	13.66
6	12, 14, 15	41	13.66
7	12, 15, 20	47	15.66
8	12, 15, 20	47	15.66
9	12, 14, 20	46	15.33
10	12, 14, 20	46	15.33

    b. $\mu_{\bar{x}} = \dfrac{(12.66 + \cdots + 15.33 + 15.33)}{10} = 14.6$
    $\mu = (12 + 12 + 14 + 15 + 20)/5 = 14.6$
    c. The dispersion of the population is greater than that of the sample means. The sample means vary from 12.66 to 16.33, whereas the population varies from 12 to 20.

9. a. 20, found by ${}_6C_3$
    b.

Sample	Cases	Sum	Mean
Ruud, Wu, Sass	3, 6, 3	12	4.00
Ruud, Sass, Flores	3, 3, 3	9	3.00
⋮	⋮	⋮	⋮
Sass, Flores, Schueller	3, 3, 1	7	2.33

    c. $\mu_{\bar{x}} = 2.67$, found by $\dfrac{53.33}{20}$
    $\mu = 2.67$, found by $(3 + 6 + 3 + 3 + 0 + 1)/6$. They are equal.
    d.

Sample Mean	Number of Means	Probability
1.33	3	.1500
2.00	3	.1500
2.33	4	.2000
3.00	4	.2000
3.33	3	.1500
4.00	3	.1500
	20	1.0000

The population has more dispersion than the sample means. The sample means vary from 1.33 to 4.0. The population varies from 0 to 6.

11. a.

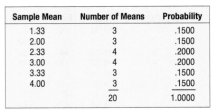

$$\mu = \frac{0 + 1 + \cdots + 9}{10} = 4.5$$

b.

Sample	Sum	$\bar{x}$	Sample	Sum	$\bar{x}$
1	11	2.2	6	20	4.0
2	31	6.2	7	23	4.6
3	21	4.2	8	29	5.8
4	24	4.8	9	35	7.0
5	21	4.2	10	27	5.4

The mean of the 10 sample means is 4.84, which is close to the population mean of 4.5. The sample means range from 2.2 to 7.0, whereas the population values range from 0 to 9. From the above graph, the sample means tend to cluster between 4 and 5.

13. a.–c. Answers will vary depending on the coins in your possession.

15. a. $z = \dfrac{63 - 60}{12/\sqrt{9}} = 0.75$

  $p = .2266$, found by $.5000 - .2734$

b. $z = \dfrac{56 - 60}{12/\sqrt{9}} = -1.00$

  $p = .1587$, found by $.5000 - .3413$

c. $p = .6147$, found by $0.3413 + 0.2734$

17. $z = \dfrac{1,950 - 2,200}{250/\sqrt{50}} = -7.07$ $p = 1$,   or virtually certain

19. a. Formal Man, Summit Stationers, Bootleggers, Leather Ltd., Petries

b. Answers may vary.

c. Elder-Beerman, Frederick's of Hollywood, Summit Stationers, Lion Store, Leather Ltd., Things Remembered, County Seat, Coach House Gifts, Regis Hairstylists

21. a.

Samples	Mean	Deviation from Mean	Square of Deviation
1, 1	1.0	−1.0	1.0
1, 2	1.5	−0.5	0.25
1, 3	2.0	0.0	0.0
2, 1	1.5	−0.5	0.25
2, 2	2.0	0.0	0.0
2, 3	2.5	0.5	0.25
3, 1	2.0	0.0	0.0
3, 2	2.5	0.5	0.25
3, 3	3.0	1.0	1.0

b. Mean of sample means is $(1.0 + 1.5 + 2.0 + \cdots + 3.0)/9 = 18/9 = 2.0$. The population mean is $(1 + 2 + 3)/3 = 6/3 = 2$. They are the same value.

c. Variance of sample means is $(1.0 + 0.25 + 0.0 + \cdots + 3.0)/9 = 3/9 = 1/3$. Variance of the population values is $(1 + 0 + 1)/3 = 2/3$. The variance of the population is twice as large as that of the sample means.

d. Sample means follow a triangular shape peaking at 2. The population is uniform between 1 and 3.

23. Larger samples provide narrower estimates of a population mean. So the company with 200 sampled customers can provide more precise estimates. In addition, they are selected consumers who are familiar with laptop computers and may be better able to evaluate the new computer.

25. a. We selected 60, 104, 75, 72, and 48. Answers will vary.

b. We selected the third observation. So the sample consists of 75, 72, 68, 82, 48. Answers will vary.

c. Number the first 20 motels from 00 to 19. Randomly select three numbers. Then number the last five numbers 20 to 24. Randomly select two numbers from that group.

27. a. 15, found by $_6C_2$

b.

Sample	Value	Sum	Mean
1	79, 64	143	71.5
2	79, 84	163	81.5
⋮	⋮	⋮	⋮
15	92, 77	169	84.5
			1,195.0

c. $\mu_{\bar{x}} = 79.67$, found by $1,195/15$.
  $\mu = 79.67$, found by $478/6$.
  They are equal.

d. No. The student is not graded on all available information. He/she is as likely to get a lower grade based on the sample as a higher grade.

29. a. 10, found by $_5C_2$

b.

Number of Shutdowns	Mean	Number of Shutdowns	Mean
4, 3	3.5	3, 3	3.0
4, 5	4.5	3, 2	2.5
4, 3	3.5	5, 3	4.0
4, 2	3.0	5, 2	3.5
3, 5	4.0	3, 2	2.5

Sample Mean	Frequency	Probability
2.5	2	.20
3.0	2	.20
3.5	3	.30
4.0	2	.20
4.5	1	.10
	10	1.00

c. $\mu_{\bar{x}} = (3.5 + 4.5 + \cdots + 2.5)/10 = 3.4$
$\mu = (4 + 3 + 5 + 3 + 2)/5 = 3.4$
The two means are equal.

d. The population values are relatively uniform in shape. The distribution of sample means tends toward normality.

31. a. The distribution will be normal.

b. $\sigma_{\bar{x}} = \dfrac{5.5}{\sqrt{25}} = 1.1$

c. $z = \dfrac{36 - 35}{5.5/\sqrt{25}} = 0.91$
$p = 0.1814$, found by $0.5000 - 0.3186$

d. $z = \dfrac{34.5 - 35}{5.5/\sqrt{25}} = -0.45$
$p = 0.6736$, found by $0.5000 + 0.1736$

e. 0.4922, found by $0.3186 + 0.1736$

33. $z = \dfrac{\$335 - \$350}{\$45/\sqrt{40}} = -2.11$
$p = 0.9826$, found by $0.5000 + 0.4826$

35. $z = \dfrac{25.1 - 24.8}{2.5/\sqrt{60}} = 0.93$
$p = 0.8238$, found by $0.5000 + 0.3238$

37. Between 5,954 and 6,046, found by $6,000 \pm 1.96\,(150/\sqrt{40})$

39. $z = \dfrac{900 - 947}{205/\sqrt{60}} = -1.78$
$p = 0.0375$, found by $0.5000 - 0.4625$

41. a. Alaska, Connecticut, Georgia, Kansas, Nebraska, South Carolina, Virginia, Utah

b. Arizona, Florida, Iowa, Massachusetts, Nebraska, North Carolina, Rhode Island, Vermont

43. a. $z = \dfrac{600 - 510}{14.28/\sqrt{10}} = 19.9$, $P = 0.00$, or virtually never

b. $z = \dfrac{500 - 510}{14.28/\sqrt{10}} = -2.21$,
$p = 0.4864 + 0.5000 = 0.9864$

c. $z = \dfrac{500 - 510}{14.28/\sqrt{10}} = -2.21$,
$p = 0.5000 - 0.4864 = 0.0136$

45. a. $\sigma_{\bar{x}} = \dfrac{2.1}{\sqrt{81}} = 0.23$

b. $z = \dfrac{7.0 - 6.5}{2.1/\sqrt{81}} = 2.14$, $z = \dfrac{6.0 - 6.5}{2.1/\sqrt{81}} = -2.14$,
$p = .4838 + .4838 = .9676$

c. $z = \dfrac{6.75 - 6.5}{2.1/\sqrt{81}} = 1.07$, $z = \dfrac{6.25 - 6.5}{2.1/\sqrt{81}} = -1.07$,
$p = .3577 + .3577 = .7154$

d. $.0162$, found by $.5000 - .4838$

47. Mean 2012 attendance is 2.495 million. Likelihood of a sample mean this large or larger is 0.0274, found by $0.5000 - 0.4726$, where $z = \dfrac{2.495 - 2.25}{\dfrac{0.70}{\sqrt{30}}} = 1.92$.

CHAPTER 9

1. 51.314 and 58.686, found by $55 \pm 2.58(10/\sqrt{49})$

3. a. 1.581, found by $\sigma_{\bar{x}} = 25/\sqrt{250}$

b. The population is normally distributed and the population variance is known.

c. 16.901 and 23.099, found by 20 ± 3.099

5. a. $20. It is our best estimate of the population mean.

b. $18.60 and $21.40, found by $20 \pm 1.96(\$5/\sqrt{49})$. About 95% of the intervals similarly constructed will include the population mean.

7. a. 8.60 gallons

b. 7.83 and 9.37, found by $8.60 \pm 2.58(2.30/\sqrt{60})$

c. If 100 such intervals were determined, the population mean would be included in about 99 intervals.

9. a. 2.201

b. 1.729

c. 3.499

11. a. The population mean is unknown, but the best estimate is 20, the sample mean.

b. Use the t distribution since the standard deviation is unknown. However, assume the population is normally distributed.

c. 2.093

d. Between 19.06 and 20.94, found by $20 \pm 2.093(2/\sqrt{20})$

e. Neither value is reasonable because they are not inside the interval.

13. Between 95.39 and 101.81, found by $98.6 \pm 1.833(5.54/\sqrt{10})$

15. a. 0.8, found by 80/100

b. Between 0.72 and 0.88, found by
$0.8 \pm 1.96\left(\sqrt{\dfrac{0.8(1 - 0.8)}{100}}\right)$

c. We are reasonably sure the population proportion is between 72 and 88%.

17. a. 0.625, found by 250/400

b. Between 0.563 and 0.687, found by
$0.625 \pm 2.58\left(\sqrt{\dfrac{0.625(1 - 0.625)}{400}}\right)$

c. We are reasonably sure the population proportion is between 56 and 69%.

19. 97, found by $n = \left(\dfrac{1.96 \times 10}{2}\right)^2 = 96.04$

21. 196, found by $n = 0.15(0.85)\left(\dfrac{1.96}{0.05}\right)^2 = 195.9216$

23. 554, found by $n = \left(\dfrac{1.96 \times 3}{0.25}\right)^2 = 553.19$

25. a. 577, found by $n = 0.60(0.40)\left(\dfrac{1.96}{0.04}\right)^2 = 576.24$

b. 601, found by $n = 0.50(0.50)\left(\dfrac{1.96}{0.04}\right)^2 = 600.25$

27. 33.41 and 36.59, found by
$35 \pm 2.030\left(\dfrac{5}{\sqrt{36}}\right)\sqrt{\dfrac{300 - 36}{300 - 1}}$

29. 1.683 and 2.037, found by
$1.86 \pm 2.680\left(\dfrac{0.5}{\sqrt{50}}\right)\sqrt{\dfrac{400 - 50}{400 - 1}}$

31. 6.13 years to 6.87 years, found by $6.5 \pm 1.989(1.7/\sqrt{85})$

33. a. Between $313.41 and $332.59, found by
$323 \pm 2.426\left(\dfrac{25}{\sqrt{40}}\right)$.

b. $350 is not reasonable because it is outside of the confidence interval.

35. a. The population mean is unknown.

b. Between 7.50 and 9.14, found by $8.32 \pm 1.685(3.07/\sqrt{40})$

c. 10 is not reasonable because it is outside the confidence interval.

37. a. 65.49 up to 71.71 hours, found by
$68.6 \pm 2.680(8.2/\sqrt{50})$

b. The value suggested by the NCAA is included in the confidence interval. Therefore, it is reasonable.

c. Changing the confidence interval to 95 would reduce the width of the interval. The value of 2.680 would change to 2.010.

39. 61.47, rounded to 62. Found by solving for n in the equation: $1.96(16/\sqrt{n}) = 4$

41. Between $13,734 up to $15,028, found by $14,381 \pm 1.711\,(1,892/\sqrt{25})$. 15,000 is reasonable because it is inside the confidence interval.

43. a. $62.583, found by $751/12

b. Between $60.54 and $64.63, found by
$62.583 \pm 1.796(3.94/\sqrt{12})$

c. $60 is not reasonable because it is outside the confidence interval.

45. a. 89.4667, found by 1,342/15
   b. Between 84.99 and 93.94, found by
      $89.4667 \pm 2.145(8.08/\sqrt{15})$
   c. Yes, because even the lower limit of the confidence interval is above 80.
47. The confidence interval is between 0.011 and 0.059, found by $0.035 \pm 2.576\left(\sqrt{\dfrac{0.035(1-0.035)}{400}}\right)$. It would not be reasonable to conclude that fewer than 5% of the employees are now failing the test because 0.05 is inside the confidence interval.
49. Between 0.648 and 0.752, found by
   $0.70 \pm 2.576\left(\sqrt{\dfrac{0.70(1-0.70)}{500}}\right)\left(\sqrt{\dfrac{20,000-500}{20,000-1}}\right)$.
   Yes, because even the lower limit of the confidence interval is above 0.500.
51. $52.51 and $55.49, found by
   $\$54.00 \pm 2.032\dfrac{\$4.50}{\sqrt{35}}\sqrt{\dfrac{(500-35)}{500-1}}$
53. 369, found by $n = 0.60(1-0.60)(1.96/0.05)^2$
55. 97, found by $[(1.96 \times 500)/100]^2$
57. a. Between 7,849 and 8,151, found by
      $8,000 \pm 2.756(300/\sqrt{30})$
   b. 554, found by $n = \left(\dfrac{(1.96)(300)}{25}\right)^2$
59. a. Between 75.44 and 80.56, found by
      $78 \pm 2.010(9/\sqrt{50})$
   b. 220, found by $n = \left(\dfrac{(1.645)(9)}{1.0}\right)^2$
61. a. 30, found by $180/\sqrt{36}$
   b. $355.10 and $476.90, found by $\$416 \pm 2.030\left(\dfrac{\$180}{\sqrt{36}}\right)$
   c. About 1,245, found by $\left(\dfrac{1.96(180)}{10}\right)^2$
63. a. 708.13, rounded up to 709, found by
      $0.21(1-0.21)(1.96/0.03)^2$
   b. 1,068, found by $0.50(0.50)(1.96/0.03)^2$
65. a. Between 0.156 and 0.184, found by
      $0.17 \pm 1.96\sqrt{\dfrac{(0.17)(1-0.17)}{2700}}$
   b. Yes, because 18% are inside the confidence interval.
   c. 21,682; found by $0.17(1-0.17)[1.96/0.005]^2$
67. Between 12.69 and 14.11, found by $13.4 \pm 1.96(6.8/\sqrt{352})$
69. a. For selling price: 211.99 up to 230.22, found by
      $221.1 \pm (1.983)(47.11/\sqrt{105}) = 221.1 \pm 9.12$
   b. For distance: 13.685 up to 15.572, found by
      $14.629 \pm (1.983)(4.874/\sqrt{105}) = 14.629 \pm 0.943$
   c. For garage: 0.5867 up to 0.7657, found by $0.6762 \pm$
      $(1.96)\sqrt{\dfrac{0.6762(1-0.6762)}{105}} = 0.6762 \pm 0.0895$
   d. Answers may vary.
71. a. Between $438.34 and $462.24, found by
      $450.29 \pm 1.99\left(\dfrac{53.69}{\sqrt{80}}\right)$
   b. Between 820.72 and 839.50, found by
      $830.11 \pm 1.99\left(\dfrac{42.19}{\sqrt{80}}\right)$
   c. Answers will vary.

CHAPTER 10

1. a. Two-tailed
   b. Reject H_0 when z does not fall in the region between -1.96 and 1.96.
   c. -1.2, found by $z = (49 - 50)/(5/\sqrt{36}) = -1.2$
   d. Fail to reject H_0.

   e. $p = .2302$, found by $2(.5000 - .3849)$. A 23.02% chance of finding a z value this large when H_0 is true.
3. a. One-tailed
   b. Reject H_0 when $z > 1.65$.
   c. 1.2, found by $z = (21 - 20)/(5/\sqrt{36})$
   d. Fail to reject H_0 at the .05 significance level
   e. $p = .1151$, found by $.5000 - .3849$. An 11.51% chance of finding a z value this large or larger.
5. a. $H_0: \mu = 60,000 \quad H_1: \mu \neq 60,000$
   b. Reject H_0 if $z < -1.96$ or $z > 1.96$.
   c. -0.69, found by:
      $$z = \dfrac{59,500 - 60,000}{(5,000/\sqrt{48})}$$
   d. Do not reject H_0.
   e. $p = .4902$, found by $2(.5000 - .2549)$. Crosset's experience is not different from that claimed by the manufacturer. If H_0 is true, the probability of finding a value more extreme than this is .4902.
7. a. $H_0: \mu \geq 6.8 \quad H_1: \mu < 6.8$
   b. Reject H_0 if $z < -1.65$
   c. $z = \dfrac{6.2 - 6.8}{1.8/\sqrt{36}} = -2.0$
   d. H_0 is rejected.
   e. $p = 0.0228$. The mean number of DVDs watched is less than 6.8 per month. If H_0 is true, you will get a statistic this small less than one time out of 40 tests.
9. a. Reject H_0 when $t > 1.833$.
   b. $t = \dfrac{12 - 10}{(3/\sqrt{10})} = 2.108$
   c. Reject H_0. The mean is greater than 10.
11. $H_0: \mu \leq 40 \quad H_1: \mu > 40$
   Reject H_0 if $t > 1.703$.
      $$t = \dfrac{42 - 40}{(2.1/\sqrt{28})} = 5.040$$
   Reject H_0 and conclude that the mean number of calls is greater than 40 per week.
13. $H_0: \mu \leq 40,000 \quad H_1: \mu > 40,000$
   Reject H_0 if $t > 1.833$.
      $$t = \dfrac{50,000 - 40,000}{10,000/\sqrt{10}} = 3.16$$
   Reject H_0 and conclude that the mean income in Wilmington is greater than $40,000.
15. a. Reject H_0 if $t < -3.747$.
   b. $\bar{x} = 17$ and $s = \sqrt{\dfrac{50}{5-1}} = 3.536$
      $$t = \dfrac{17 - 20}{(3.536/\sqrt{5})} = -1.90$$
   c. Do not reject H_0. We cannot conclude the population mean is less than 20.
   d. Between .05 and .10, about .065
17. $H_0: \mu \leq 1.4 \quad H_1: \mu > 1.4$
   Reject H_0 if $t > 2.821$.
      $$t = \dfrac{1.6 - 1.4}{0.216/\sqrt{10}} = 2.93$$
   Reject H_0 and conclude that water consumption has increased. The p-value is between 0.01 and 0.005. There is a slight probability (between one chance in 100 and one chance in 200) this rise could have arisen by chance.
19. $H_0: \mu \leq 50 \quad H_1: \mu > 50$
   Reject H_0 if $t > 1.796$.
      $$t = \dfrac{82.5 - 50}{59.5/\sqrt{12}} = 1.89$$

Reject H_0 and conclude that the mean number of text messages is greater than 50. The p-value is less than 0.05. There is a slight probability (less than one chance in 20) this could happen by chance.

21. 1.05, found by $z = (9{,}992 - 9{,}880)/(400/\sqrt{100})$. Then $0.5000 - 0.3531 = 0.1469$, which is the probability of a Type II error.

23. H_0: $\mu = \$45{,}000$ H_1: $\mu \neq \$45{,}000$
Reject H_0 if $z < -1.65$ or $z > 1.65$.
$$z = \frac{45{,}500 - 45{,}000}{\$3{,}000/\sqrt{120}} = 1.83$$
Reject H_0. We can conclude that the mean salary is not $\$45{,}000$. p-value 0.0672, found by $2(0.5000 - 0.4664)$.

25. H_0: $\mu \geq 10$ H_1: $\mu < 10$
Reject H_0 if $z < -1.65$.
$$z = \frac{9.0 - 10.0}{2.8/\sqrt{50}} = -2.53$$
Reject H_0. The mean weight loss is less than 10 pounds. p-value $= 0.5000 - 0.4943 = 0.0057$

27. H_0: $\mu \geq 7.0$ H_1: $\mu < 7.0$
Assuming a 5% significance level, reject H_0 if $t < -1.677$.
$$t = \frac{6.8 - 7.0}{0.9/\sqrt{50}} = -1.57$$
Do not reject H_0. West Virginia students are not sleeping less than 6 hours. p-value is between .05 and .10.

29. H_0: $\mu \geq 3.13$ H_1: $\mu < 3.13$
Reject H_0 if $t < -1.711$
$$t = \frac{2.86 - 3.13}{1.20/\sqrt{25}} = -1.13$$
We fail to reject H_0 and conclude that the mean number of residents is not necessarily less than 3.13.

31. H_0: $\mu \leq 14$ H_1: $\mu > 14$
Reject H_0 if $t > 2.821$.
$\bar{x} = 15.66$ $s = 1.544$
$$t = \frac{15.66 - 14.00}{1.544/\sqrt{10}} = 3.400$$
Reject H_0. The average rate is greater than 14%.

33. H_0: $\mu = 3.1$ H_1: $\mu \neq 3.1$ Assume a normal population.
Reject H_0 if $t < -2.201$ or $t > 2.201$.
$$\bar{x} = \frac{41.1}{12} = 3.425$$
$$s = \sqrt{\frac{4.0625}{12 - 1}} = .6077$$
$$t = \frac{3.425 - 3.1}{.6077/\sqrt{12}} = 1.853$$
Do not reject H_0. Cannot show a difference between senior citizens and the national average. p-value is about 0.09.

35. H_0: $\mu \geq 6.5$ H_1: $\mu < 6.5$ Assume a normal population.
Reject H_0 if $t < -2.718$.
$\bar{x} = 5.1667$ $s = 3.1575$
$$t = \frac{5.1667 - 6.5}{3.1575/\sqrt{12}} = -1.463$$
Do not reject H_0. The p-value is greater than 0.05.

37. H_0: $\mu = 0$ H_1: $\mu \neq 0$
Reject H_0 if $t < -2.110$ or $t > 2.110$.
$\bar{x} = -0.2322$ $s = 0.3120$
$$t = \frac{-0.2322 - 0}{0.3120/\sqrt{18}} = -3.158$$
Reject H_0. The mean gain or loss does not equal 0. The p-value is less than 0.01, but greater than 0.001.

39. H_0: $\mu \leq 100$ H_1: $\mu > 100$ Assume a normal population.
Reject H_0 if $t > 1.761$.
$$\bar{x} = \frac{1{,}641}{15} = 109.4$$
$$s = \sqrt{\frac{1{,}389.6}{15 - 1}} = 9.9628$$
$$t = \frac{109.4 - 100}{9.9628/\sqrt{15}} = 3.654$$
Reject H_0. The mean number with the scanner is greater than 100. p-value is 0.001.

41. H_0: $\mu = 1.5$ H_1: $\mu \neq 1.5$
Reject H_0 if $t > 3.250$ or $t < -3.250$.
$$t = \frac{1.3 - 1.5}{0.9/\sqrt{10}} = -0.703$$
Fail to reject H_0.

43. H_0: $\mu \geq 10$ H_1: $\mu < 10$
Reject H_0 if $t < -1.895$.
$$\bar{x} = \frac{78.3}{8} = 9.7875 \qquad s = \sqrt{\frac{5.889}{8 - 1}} = 0.9172$$
$$t = \frac{9.7875 - 10}{0.9172/\sqrt{8}} = -0.655 \qquad \text{Do not reject } H_0. \text{ The cost}$$
is not less than $\$10{,}000$.

45. a. $9.00 \pm 1.645(1/\sqrt{36}) = 9.00 \pm 0.274$.
So the limits are 8.726 and 9.274.
b. $z = \dfrac{8.726 - 8.6}{1/\sqrt{36}} = 0.756$.
$P(z < 0.756) = 0.5000 + 0.2764 = .7764$
c. $z = \dfrac{9.274 - 9.6}{1/\sqrt{36}} = -1.956$.
$P(z > -1.96) = 0.4750 + 0.5000 = .9750$

47. $50 + 2.33\dfrac{10}{\sqrt{n}} = 55 - .525\dfrac{10}{\sqrt{n}}$ $n = (5.71)^2 = 32.6$
Let $n = 33$

49. H_0: $\mu \geq 8$ H_1: $\mu < 8$
Reject H_0 if $t < -1.714$.
$$t = \frac{7.5 - 8}{3.2/\sqrt{24}} = -0.77$$
Do not reject the null hypothesis. The time is not less.

51. a. H_0: $\mu = 80$ H_1: $\mu \neq 80$
Reject H_0 if t is not between -2.045 and 2.045.
$$t = \frac{98.02 - 80}{36.83/\sqrt{30}} = 2.68 \qquad \text{Reject the null.}$$
The mean salary is probably not $\$80.0$ million.
b. H_0: $\mu \leq 2{,}000{,}000$ H_1: $\mu > 2{,}000{,}000$
Reject H_0 if $t > 1.699$.
$$t = \frac{2{,}495{,}000 - 2{,}000{,}000}{642{,}000/\sqrt{30}} = 4.22$$
Reject the null. The mean attendance was more than $2{,}000{,}000$.

CHAPTER 11

1. a. Two-tailed test
b. Reject H_0 if $z < -2.05$ or $z > 2.05$
c. $z = \dfrac{102 - 99}{\sqrt{\dfrac{5^2}{40} + \dfrac{6^2}{50}}} = 2.59$
d. Reject H_0
e. p-value $= .0096$, found by $2(.5000 - .4952)$

3. **Step 1** H_0: $\mu_1 \geq \mu_2$ H_1: $\mu_1 < \mu_2$
Step 2 The .05 significance level was chosen.
Step 3 Reject H_0 if $z < -1.65$.
Step 4 -0.94, found by:
$$z = \frac{7.6 - 8.1}{\sqrt{\dfrac{(2.3)^2}{40} + \dfrac{(2.9)^2}{55}}} = -0.94$$

Step 5 Fail to reject H_0.
Step 6 Babies using the Gibbs brand did not gain less weight. p-value = .1736, found by .5000 − .3264.

5. Step 1 $H_0: \mu_1 \leq \mu_2$ $H_1: \mu_1 > \mu_2$
Step 2 The .05 significance level was chosen.
Step 3 If $z > 1.645$, reject H_0.
Step 4
$$z = \frac{61.4 - 60.6}{\sqrt{\frac{(1.2)^2}{45} + \frac{(1.1)^2}{39}}} = 3.187$$
Step 5 Reject the null.
Step 6 It is reasonable to conclude that those who had a Caesarean section are shorter.
The p-value is virtually zero. That much of a difference could almost never be due to sampling error.

7. a. Reject H_0 if $t > 2.120$ or $t < -2.120$. $df = 10 + 8 - 2 = 16$
b. $s_p^2 = \frac{(10-1)(4)^2 + (8-1)(5)^2}{10+8-2} = 19.9375$
c. $t = \frac{23 - 26}{\sqrt{19.9375\left(\frac{1}{10} + \frac{1}{8}\right)}} = -1.416$
d. Do not reject H_0.
e. p-value is greater than .10 and less than .20.

9. Step 1 $H_0: \mu_1 = \mu_2$ $H_1: \mu_1 \neq \mu_2$
Step 2 The .01 significance level was chosen.
Step 3 $df = 12 + 13 - 2 = 23$. Reject H_0 if t is not between −2.807 and 2.807.
Step 4 $s_p^2 = \frac{(12-1)(7,469)^2 + (13-1)(7,474)^2}{12+13-2} = 55,825,000$
$$t = \frac{6,590 - 5,308}{\sqrt{55,825,000\left(\frac{1}{12} + \frac{1}{13}\right)}} = 0.429$$
Step 5 Do not reject H_0.
Step 6 There is no difference in the mean salaries.

11. Step 1 $H_0: \mu_s \leq \mu_a$ $H_1: \mu_s > \mu_a$
Step 2 The .10 significance level was chosen.
Step 3 $df = 6 + 7 - 2 = 11$
Reject H_0 if $t > 1.363$.
Step 4 $s_p^2 = \frac{(6-1)(12.2)^2 + (7-1)(15.8)^2}{6+7-2} = 203.82$
$$t = \frac{142.5 - 130.3}{\sqrt{203.82\left(\frac{1}{6} + \frac{1}{7}\right)}} = 1.536$$
Step 5 Reject H_0.
Step 6 The mean daily expenses are greater for the sales staff. The p-value is between .05 and .10.

13. a. $df = \frac{\left(\frac{25}{15} + \frac{225}{12}\right)^2}{\frac{\left(\frac{25}{15}\right)^2}{15-1} + \frac{\left(\frac{225}{12}\right)^2}{12-1}} = \frac{416.84}{0.1984 + 31.9602}$
$= 12.96 \rightarrow 12df$
b. $H_0: \mu_1 = \mu_2$ $H_1: \mu_1 \neq \mu_2$
Reject H_0 if $t > 2.179$ or $t < -2.179$.
c. $t = \frac{50 - 46}{\sqrt{\frac{25}{15} + \frac{225}{12}}} = 0.8852$
d. Fail to reject the null hypothesis.

15. a. $df = \frac{\left(\frac{697,225}{16} + \frac{2,387,025}{18}\right)^2}{\frac{\left(\frac{697,225}{16}\right)^2}{16-1} + \frac{\left(\frac{2,387,025}{18}\right)^2}{18-1}} = 26.7 \rightarrow 26df$
b. $H_0: \mu_{Private} \leq \mu_{Public}$ $H_1: \mu_{Private} > \mu_{Public}$
Reject H_0 if $t > 1.706$.

c. $t = \frac{12,840 - 11,045}{\sqrt{\frac{2,387,025}{18} + \frac{697,225}{16}}} = 4.276$
d. Reject the null hypothesis. The mean adoption cost from a private agency is greater than the mean adoption cost from a public agency.

17. a. Reject H_0 if $t > 2.353$.
b. $\bar{d} = \frac{12}{4} = 3.00$ $s_d = \sqrt{\frac{2}{3}} = 0.816$
c. $t = \frac{3.00}{0.816/\sqrt{4}} = 7.35$
d. Reject H_0. There are more defective parts produced on the day shift.
e. p-value is less than .005 but greater than .0005.

19. $H_0: \mu_d \leq 0$ $H_1: \mu_d > 0$
$\bar{d} = 25.917$
$s_d = 40.791$
Reject H_0 if $t > 1.796$
$$t = \frac{25.917}{40.791/\sqrt{12}} = 2.20$$
Reject H_0. The incentive plan resulted in an increase in daily income. The p-value is about .025.

21. $H_0: \mu_M = \mu_W$ $H_1: \mu_M \neq \mu_W$
Reject H_0 if $t < -2.645$ or $t > 2.645$ ($df = 35 + 40 - 2$).
$$s_p^2 = \frac{(35-1)(4.48)^2 + (40-1)(3.86)^2}{35+40-2} = 17.3079$$
$$t = \frac{24.51 - 22.69}{\sqrt{17.3079\left(\frac{1}{35} + \frac{1}{40}\right)}} = 1.890$$
Do not reject H_0. There is no difference in the number of times men and women buy take-out dinner in a month. The p-value is between .05 and .10.

23. $H_0: \mu_1 = \mu_2$ $H_1: \mu_1 \neq \mu_2$
Reject H_0 if $z < -1.96$ or $z > 1.96$.
$$z = \frac{4.77 - 5.02}{\sqrt{\frac{(1.05)^2}{40} + \frac{(1.23)^2}{50}}} = -1.04$$
H_0 is not rejected. There is no difference in the mean number of calls. p-value = 2(.5000 − .3508) = .2984.

25. $H_0: \mu_B \leq \mu_A$ $H_1: \mu_B > \mu_A$
Reject H_0 if $t > 1.668$
$$t = \frac{\$61,000 - \$57,000}{\sqrt{\frac{(\$7,100)^2}{30} + \frac{(\$9,200)^2}{40}}} = \frac{\$4,000.00}{\$1,948.42} = 2.05$$
Reject H_0. The mean income is larger for Plan B. The p-value = .5000 − .4798 = .0202.

27. a. $df = \frac{\left(\frac{0.3136}{12} + \frac{0.0900}{12}\right)^2}{\frac{\left(\frac{0.3136}{12}\right)^2}{12-1} + \frac{\left(\frac{0.0900}{12}\right)^2}{12-1}}$
$= \frac{0.0011}{0.000062 + 0.0000051} = 16.37 \rightarrow 16df$
b. $H_0: \mu_a = \mu_w$ $H_1: \mu_a \neq \mu_w$
Reject H_0 if $t > 2.120$ or $t < -2.120$.
c. $t = \frac{1.65 - 2.20}{\sqrt{\frac{0.3136}{12} + \frac{0.0900}{12}}} = -3.00$
d. Reject the null hypothesis. There is a difference.

29. Assume equal population standard deviations.
$H_0: \mu_n = \mu_s$ $H_1: \mu_n \neq \mu_s$
Reject H_0 if $t < -2.086$ or $t > 2.086$.

$$s_p^2 = \frac{(10-1)(10.5)^2 + (12-1)(14.25)^2}{10 + 12 - 2} = 161.2969$$

$$t = \frac{83.55 - 78.8}{\sqrt{161.2969\left(\frac{1}{10} + \frac{1}{12}\right)}} = 0.874$$

p-value $> .10$. Do not reject H_0. There is no difference in the mean number of hamburgers sold at the two locations.

31. Assume equal population standard deviations.
$H_0: \mu_1 = \mu_2$ $H_1: \mu_1 \neq \mu_2$
Reject H_0 if $t > 2.819$ or $t < -2.819$.

$$s_p^2 = \frac{(10-1)(2.33)^2 + (14-1)(2.55)^2}{10 + 14 - 2} = 6.06$$

$$t = \frac{15.87 - 18.29}{\sqrt{6.06\left(\frac{1}{10} + \frac{1}{14}\right)}} = -2.374$$

Do not reject H_0. There is no difference in the mean amount purchased.

33. Assume equal population standard deviations.
$H_0: \mu_1 \leq \mu_2$ $H_1: \mu_1 > \mu_2$ Reject H_0 if $t > 2.567$.

$$s_p^2 = \frac{(8-1)(2.2638)^2 + (11-1)(2.4606)^2}{8 + 11 - 2} = 5.672$$

$$t = \frac{10.375 - 5.636}{\sqrt{5.672\left(\frac{1}{8} + \frac{1}{11}\right)}} = 4.28$$

Reject H_0. The mean number of transactions by the young adults is more than for the senior citizens.

35. $H_0: \mu_1 \leq \mu_2$ $H_1: \mu_1 > \mu_2$ Reject H_0 if $t > 2.650$.
$\bar{x}_1 = 125.125$ $s_1 = 15.094$
$\bar{x}_2 = 117.714$ $s_2 = 19.914$

$$s_p^2 = \frac{(8-1)(15.094)^2 + (7-1)(19.914)^2}{8 + 7 - 2} = 305.708$$

$$t = \frac{125.125 - 117.714}{\sqrt{305.708\left(\frac{1}{8} + \frac{1}{7}\right)}} = 0.819$$

H_0 is not rejected. There is no difference in the mean number sold at the regular price and the mean number sold at the reduced price.

37. $H_0: \mu_d \leq 0$ $H_1: \mu_d > 0$ Reject H_0 if $t > 1.895$.
$\bar{d} = 1.75$ $s_d = 2.9155$

$$t = \frac{1.75}{2.9155/\sqrt{8}} = 1.698$$

Do not reject H_0. There is no difference in the mean number of absences. The p-value is greater than .05 but less than .10.

39. $H_0: \mu_1 = \mu_2$ $H_1: \mu_1 \neq \mu_2$
Reject H_0 if $t < -2.024$ or $t > 2.204$.

$$s_p^2 = \frac{(15-1)(40)^2 + (25-1)(30)^2}{15 + 25 - 2} = 1,157.89$$

$$t = \frac{150 - 180}{\sqrt{1,157.89\left(\frac{1}{15} + \frac{1}{25}\right)}} = -2.699$$

Reject the null hypothesis. The population means are different.

41. $H_0: \mu_d \leq 0$ $H_1: \mu_d > 0$
Reject H_0 if $t > 1.895$.
$\bar{d} = 3.11$ $s_d = 2.91$

$$t = \frac{3.11}{2.91/\sqrt{8}} = 3.02$$

Reject H_0. The mean is lower.

43. $H_0: \mu_O = \mu_R$, $H_1: \mu_O \neq \mu_R$
$df = 25 + 28 - 2 = 51$
Reject H_0 if $t < -2.008$ or $t > 2.008$.
$\bar{x}_O = 86.24$, $s_O = 23.43$
$x_R = 92.04$, $s_R = 24.12$

$$s_p^2 = \frac{(25-1)(23.43)^2 + (28-1)(24.12)^2}{25 + 28 - 2} = 566.335$$

$$t = \frac{86.24 - 92.04}{\sqrt{566.335\left(\frac{1}{25} + \frac{1}{28}\right)}} = -0.886$$

Do not reject H_0. There is no difference in the mean number of cars in the two lots.

45. $H_0: \mu_d \leq 0$ $H_1: \mu_d > 0$ Reject H_0 if $t > 1.711$.
$\bar{d} = 2.8$ $s_d = 6.59$

$$t = \frac{2.8}{6.59/\sqrt{25}} = 2.124$$

Reject H_0. There are on average more cars in the US 17 lot.

47. a. $\mu_1 = $ without pool $\mu_2 = $ with pool
$H_0: \mu_1 = \mu_2$ $H_1: \mu_1 \neq \mu_2$
Reject H_0 if $t > 2.000$ or $t < -2.000$.
$\bar{x}_1 = 202.8$ $s_1 = 33.7$ $n_1 = 38$
$\bar{x}_2 = 231.5$ $s_2 = 50.46$ $n_2 = 67$

$$s_p^2 = \frac{(38-1)(33.7)^2 + (67-1)(50.46)^2}{38 + 67 - 2} = 2,041.05$$

$$t = \frac{202.8 - 231.5}{\sqrt{2,041.05\left(\frac{1}{38} + \frac{1}{67}\right)}} = -3.12$$

Reject H_0. There is a difference in mean selling price for homes with and without a pool.

b. $\mu_1 = $ without attached garage $\mu_2 = $ with garage
$H_0: \mu_1 = \mu_2$ $H_1: \mu_1 \neq \mu_2$
Reject H_0 if $t > 2.000$ or $t < -2.000$.
$\alpha = 0.05$ $df = 34 + 71 - 2 = 103$
$\bar{x}_1 = 185.45$ $s_1 = 28.00$
$\bar{x}_2 = 238.18$ $s_2 = 44.88$

$$s_p^2 = \frac{(34-1)(28.00)^2 + (71-1)(44.88)^2}{103} = 1,620.07$$

$$t = \frac{185.45 - 238.18}{\sqrt{1,620.07\left(\frac{1}{34} + \frac{1}{71}\right)}} = -6.28$$

Reject H_0. There is a difference in mean selling price for homes with and without an attached garage.

c. $H_0: \mu_1 = \mu_2$ $H_1: \mu_1 \neq \mu_2$
Reject H_0 if $t > 2.036$ or $t < -2.036$.
$\bar{x}_1 = 196.91$ $s_1 = 35.78$ $n_1 = 15$
$\bar{x}_2 = 227.45$ $s_2 = 44.19$ $n_2 = 20$

$$s_p^2 = \frac{(15-1)(35.78)^2 + (20-1)(44.19)^2}{15 + 20 - 2} = 1,667.43$$

$$t = \frac{196.91 - 227.45}{\sqrt{1,667.43\left(\frac{1}{15} + \frac{1}{20}\right)}} = -2.19$$

Reject H_0. There is a difference in mean selling price for homes in Township 1 and Township 2.

49. $H_0: \mu_1 = \mu_2$ $H_1: \mu_1 \neq \mu_2$
If t is not between -1.991 and 1.991, reject H_0.

$$s_p^2 = \frac{(53-1)(52.9)^2 + (27-1)(55.1)^2}{53 + 27 - 2} = 2,878$$

$$t = \frac{454.8 - 441.5}{\sqrt{2,878\left(\frac{1}{53} + \frac{1}{27}\right)}} = 1.05$$

Do not reject H_0. There may be no difference in the mean maintenance cost for the two types of buses.

CHAPTER 12

1. 9.01, from Appendix B.6
3. Reject H_0 if $F > 10.5$, where degrees of freedom in the numerator are 7 and 5 in the denominator. Computed $F = 2.04$, found by:

$$F = \frac{s_1^2}{s_2^2} = \frac{(10)^2}{(7)^2} = 2.04$$

Do not reject H_0. There is no difference in the variations of the two populations.

5. $H_0: \sigma_1^2 = \sigma_2^2 \quad H_1: \sigma_1^2 \neq \sigma_2^2$
Reject H_0 where $F > 3.10$. (3.10 is about halfway between 3.14 and 3.07.) Computed $F = 1.44$, found by:

$$F = \frac{(12)^2}{(10)^2} = 1.44$$

Do not reject H_0. There is no difference in the variations of the two populations.

7. **a.** $H_0: \mu_1 = \mu_2 = \mu_3; H_1$: Treatment means are not all the same.
   b. Reject H_0 if $F > 4.26$.
   c & d.

Source	SS	df	MS	F
Treatment	62.17	2	31.08	21.94
Error	12.75	9	1.42	
Total	74.92	11		

   e. Reject H_0. The treatment means are not all the same.

9. $H_0: \mu_1 = \mu_2 = \mu_3; H_1$: Treatment means are not all the same.
   Reject H_0 if $F > 4.26$.

Source	SS	df	MS	F
Treatment	276.50	2	138.25	14.18
Error	87.75	9	9.75	

   Reject H_0. The treatment means are not all the same.

11. **a.** $H_0: \mu_1 = \mu_2 = \mu_3; H_1$: Not all means are the same.
    b. Reject H_0 if $F > 4.26$.
    c. SST = 107.20, SSE = 9.47, SS total = 116.67
    d.

Source	SS	df	MS	F
Treatment	107.20	2	53.600	50.96
Error	9.47	9	1.052	
Total	116.67	11		

    e. Since $50.96 > 4.26$, H_0 is rejected. At least one of the means differs.
    f. $(\bar{x}_1 - \bar{x}_2) \pm t\sqrt{MSE(1/n_1 + 1/n_2)}$
    $= (9.667 - 2.20) \pm 2.262\sqrt{1.052(1/3 + 1/5)}$
    $= 7.467 \pm 1.69$
    $= [5.777, 9.157]$
    Yes, we can conclude that treatments 1 and 2 have different means.

13. $H_0: \mu_1 = \mu_2 = \mu_3 = \mu_4; H_1$: Not all means are equal.
    H_0 is rejected if $F > 3.71$.

Source	SS	df	MS	F
Treatment	32.33	3	10.77	2.36
Error	45.67	10	4.567	
Total	78.00	13		

    Because 2.36 is less than 3.71, H_0 is not rejected. There is no difference in the mean number of weeks.

15. **a.** $H_0: \mu_1 = \mu_2; H_1$: Not all treatment means are equal.
    b. Reject H_0 if $F > 18.5$.

c. $H_0: \mu_1 = \mu_2 = \mu_3; H_1$: Not all block means are equal.
   H_0 is rejected if $F > 19.0$.
d. SS total $= (46.0 - 36.5)^2 + \cdots + (35 - 36.5)^2 = 289.5$
   SST $= 3(42.33 - 36.5)^2 + 3(30.67 - 36.5)^2$
   $= 204.167$
   SSB $= 2(38.5 - 36.5)^2 + 2(31.5 - 36.5)^2 +$
   $2(39.5 - 36.5)^2 = 8 + 50 + 18 = 76$
   SSE $= 289.50 - 204.1667 - 76 = 9.3333$
e.

Source	SS	df	MS	F
Treatment	204.167	1	204.167	43.75
Blocks	76.000	2	38.000	8.14
Error	9.333	2	4.667	
Total	289.5000	5		

f. $43.75 > 18.5$, so reject H_0. There is a difference in the treatments. $8.14 < 19.0$, so do not reject H_0 for blocks. There is no difference among blocks.

17. For treatment:
   $H_0: \mu_1 = \mu_2 = \mu_3$
   H_1: Not all means equal
   Reject if $F > 4.46$.

   For blocks:
   $H_0: \mu_1 = \mu_2 = \mu_3 = \mu_4 = \mu_5$
   H_1: Not all means equal
   Reject if $F > 3.84$.

Source	SS	df	MS	F
Treatment	62.53	2	31.2650	5.75
Blocks	33.73	4	8.4325	1.55
Error	43.47	8	5.4338	
Total	139.73			

There is a difference in shifts, but not by employee.

19.

Source	SS	df	MS	F	P
Size	156.333	2	78.1667	1.98	0.180
Weight	98.000	1	98.000	2.48	0.141
Interaction	36.333	2	18.1667	0.46	0.642
Error	473.333	12	39.444		
Total	764.000	17			

a. Since the p-value (0.18) is greater than 0.05, there is no difference in the Size means.
b. The p-value for Weight (0.141) is also greater than 0.05. Thus, there is no difference in those means.
c. There is no significant interaction because the p-value (0.642) is greater than 0.05.

21. **a.**

Interaction Plot (data means) for Sales

Yes, there appears to be an interaction effect. Sales are different based on machine position, either in the inside or outside position.

b.

Two-way ANOVA: Sales versus Position, Machine				
Source	df	SS	MS	F	P
Position	1	104.167	104.167	9.12	0.007
Machine	2	16.333	8.167	0.72	0.502
Interaction	2	457.333	228.667	20.03	0.000
Error	18	205.500	11.417		
Total	23	783.333			

The position and the interaction of position and machine effects are significant. The effect of machine on sales is not significant.

c.

One-way ANOVA: D-320 Sales versus Position				
Source	df	SS	MS	F	P
Position	1	364.50	364.50	40.88	0.001
Error	6	53.50	8.92		
Total	7	418.00			

One-way ANOVA: J-1000 Sales versus Position				
Source	df	SS	MS	F	P
Position	1	84.5	84.5	5.83	0.052
Error	6	87.0	14.5		
Total	7	171.5			

One-way ANOVA: UV-57 Sales versus Position				
Source	df	SS	MS	F	P
Position	1	112.5	112.5	10.38	0.018
Error	6	65.0	10.8		
Total	7	177.5			

Recommendations using the statistical results and mean sales plotted in part (a): Position the D-320 machine outside. Statistically, the position of the J-1000 does not matter. Position the UV-57 machine inside.

23. $H_0: \sigma_1^2 \le \sigma_2^2$; $H_1: \sigma_1^2 > \sigma_2^2$. $df_1 = 21 - 1 = 20$; $df_2 = 18 - 1 = 17$. H_0 is rejected if $F > 3.16$.

$$F = \frac{(45{,}600)^2}{(21{,}330)^2} = 4.57$$

Reject H_0. There is more variation in the selling price of oceanfront homes.

25. Sharkey: $n = 7$ $s_s = 14.79$
White: $n = 8$ $s_w = 22.95$
$H_0: \sigma_w^2 \le \sigma_s^2$; $H_1: \sigma_w^2 > \sigma_s^2$. $df_s = 7 - 1 = 6$; $df_w = 8 - 1 = 7$. Reject H_0 if $F > 8.26$.

$$F = \frac{(22.95)^2}{(14.79)^2} = 2.41$$

Cannot reject H_0. There is no difference in the variation of the monthly sales.

27. a. $H_0: \mu_1 = \mu_2 = \mu_3 = \mu_4$
H_1: Treatment means are not all equal.
b. $\alpha = .05$ Reject H_0 if $F > 3.10$.
c.

Source	SS	df	MS	F
Treatment	50	$4 - 1 = 3$	50/3	1.67
Error	200	$24 - 4 = 20$	10	
Total	250	$24 - 1 = 23$		

d. Do not reject H_0.

29. $H_0: \mu_1 = \mu_2 = \mu_3$; H_1: Not all treatment means are equal.
H_0 is rejected if $F > 3.89$.

Source	SS	df	MS	F
Treatment	63.33	2	31.667	13.38
Error	28.40	12	2.367	
Total	91.73	14		

H_0 is rejected. There is a difference in the treatment means.

31. $H_0: \mu_1 = \mu_2 = \mu_3 = \mu_4$; H_1: Not all means are equal.
H_0 is rejected if $F > 3.10$.

Source	SS	df	MS	F
Factor	87.79	3	29.26	9.12
Error	64.17	20	3.21	
Total	151.96	23		

Because the computed F of $9.12 > 3.10$, the null hypothesis of no difference is rejected at the .05 level.

33. a. $H_0: \mu_1 = \mu_2$; $H_1: \mu_1 \ne \mu_2$. Critical value of $F = 4.75$.

Source	SS	df	MS	F
Treatment	219.43	1	219.43	23.10
Error	114.00	12	9.5	
Total	333.43	13		

b. $t = \dfrac{19 - 27}{\sqrt{9.5\left(\dfrac{1}{6} + \dfrac{1}{8}\right)}} = -4.806$

Then $t^2 = F$. That is $(-4.806)^2 = 23.10$.
c. H_0 is rejected. There is a difference in the mean scores.

35. The null hypothesis is rejected because the F statistic (8.26) is greater than the critical value (5.61) at the .01 significance level. The p-value (.0019) is also less than the significance level. The mean gasoline mileages are not the same.

37. $H_0: \mu_1 = \mu_2 = \mu_3 = \mu_4$. H_1: At least one mean is different. Reject H_0 if $F > 2.7395$. Since $11.90 > 2.74$, reject H_0. You can also see this from the p-value of $0.000 < 0.05$. Priority mail express is faster than all three of the other classes, and priority mail is faster than either first-class or standard. However, first-class and standard mail may be the same.

39. For color, the critical value of F is 4.76; for size, it is 5.14.

Source	SS	df	MS	F
Treatment	25.0	3	8.3333	5.88
Blocks	21.5	2	10.75	7.59
Error	8.5	6	1.4167	
Total	55.0	11		

H_0s for both treatment and blocks (color and size) are rejected. At least one mean differs for color and at least one mean differs for size.

41. a. Critical value of F is 3.49. Computed F is 0.668. Do not reject H_0.
b. Critical value of F is 3.26. Computed F value is 100.204. Reject H_0 for block means.
There is a difference in homes but not assessors.

43. For gasoline:
H_0: $\mu_1 = \mu_2 = \mu_3$; H_1: Mean mileage is not the same.
Reject H_0 if $F > 3.89$.
For automobile:
H_0: $\mu_1 = \mu_2 = \ldots = \mu_7$; H_1: Mean mileage is not the same.
Reject H_0 if $F > 3.00$.

ANOVA Table				
Source	**SS**	**df**	**MS**	**F**
Gasoline	44.095	2	22.048	26.71
Autos	77.238	6	12.873	15.60
Error	9.905	12	0.825	
Total	131.238	20		

There is a difference in both autos and gasoline.

45. H_0: $\mu_1 = \mu_2 = \mu_3 = \mu_4 = \mu_5 = \mu_6$; H_1: The treatment means are not equal. Reject H_0 if $F > 2.37$.

Source	**SS**	**df**	**MS**	**F**
Treatment	0.03478	5	0.00696	3.86
Error	0.10439	58	0.0018	
Total	0.13917	63		

H_0 is rejected. There is a difference in the mean weight of the colors.

47. a.

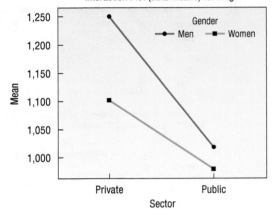

Interaction Plot (data means) for Wage

b. Two-way ANOVA: Wage versus Gender, Sector

Source	DF	SS	MS	F	P
Gender	1	44086	44086	11.44	0.004
Sector	1	156468	156468	40.61	0.000
Interaction	1	14851	14851	3.85	0.067
Error	16	61640	3853		
Total	19	277046			

There is no interaction effect of gender and sector on wages. However, there are significant differences in mean wages based on gender and significant differences in mean wages based on sector.

c. One-way ANOVA: Wage versus Sector

Source	DF	SS	MS	F	P
Sector	1	156468	156468	23.36	0.000
Error	18	120578	6699		
Total	19	277046			

s = 81.85   R-Sq = 56.48%   R-Sq(adj) = 54.06%

One-way ANOVA: Wage versus Gender

Source	DF	SS	MS	F	P
Gender	1	44086	44086	3.41	0.081
Error	18	232960	12942		
Total	19	277046			

s = 113.8 R-Sq = 15.91% R-Sq(adj) = 11.24%

d. The statistical results show that only sector, private or public, has a significant effect on the wages of accountants.

49. a. $H_0: \sigma_{np}^2 = \sigma_p^2 \quad H_1: \sigma_{np}^2 \neq \sigma_p^2$.
Reject H_0 if $F > 2.05$ (estimated).
$df_1 = 67 - 1 = 66; df_2 = 38 - 1 = 37$

$$F = \frac{(50.57)^2}{(33.71)^2} = 2.25$$

Reject H_0. There is a difference in the variance of the two selling prices.

b. $H_0: \sigma_g^2 = \sigma_{ng}^2; H_1: \sigma_g^2 \neq \sigma_{ng}^2$.
Reject H_0 if $F > 2.21$ (estimated).

$$F = \frac{(44.88)^2}{(28.00)^2} = 2.57$$

Reject H_0. There is a difference in the variance of the two selling prices.

c.

Source	SS	df	MS	F
Township	13,263	4	3,316	1.52
Error	217,505	100	2,175	
Total	230,768	104		

$H_0: \mu_1 = \mu_2 = \mu_3 = \mu_4 = \mu_5; H_1$: Not all treatment means are equal. Reject H_0 if $F > 2.46$.
Do not reject H_0. There is no difference in the mean selling prices in the five townships.

51. a. $H_0: \mu_1 = \mu_2 = \mu_3 \quad H_1$: Not all treatment means are equal. Reject H_0 if $F > 4.89$.

Source	SS	df	MS	F
Treatment	28,996	2	14,498	5.62
Error	198,696	77	2,580	
Total	227,692	79		

Reject H_0. The mean maintenance costs are different.

b. $H_0: \mu_1 = \mu_2 = \mu_3 \quad H_1$: Not all treatment means are equal. Reject H_0 if $F > 3.12$.

Source	SS	df	MS	F
Treatment	5,095	2	2,547	1.45
Error	135,513	77	1,760	
Total	140,608	79		

Do not reject H_0. The mean miles traveled are not different.

c. $(441.81 - 506.75) \pm 1.991 \sqrt{2,580\left(\frac{1}{47} + \frac{1}{8}\right)}$

This reduces to -64.94 ± 38.68, so the difference is between -103.62 and -26.26. To put it another way, Bluebird is less costly than Thompson by an amount between $26.26 and $103.62.

CHAPTER 13

1. $\Sigma(x - \bar{x})(y - \bar{y}) = 10.6, s_x = 2.7, s_y = 1.3$

$$r = \frac{10.6}{(5 - 1)(2.709)(1.38)} = 0.75$$

3. a. Sales.
b.

c. $\Sigma(x - \bar{x})(y - \bar{y}) = 36, n = 5, s_x = 1.5811,$
$s_y = 6.1237$

$$r = \frac{36}{(5 - 1)(1.5811)(6.1237)} = 0.9295$$

d. There is a strong positive association between the variables.

5. a. Either variable could be independent. In the scatter plot, police is the independent variable.
b.

c. $n = 8, \Sigma(x - \bar{x})(y - \bar{y}) = -231.75,$
$s_x = 5.8737, s_y = 6.4462$

$$r = \frac{-231.75}{(8 - 1)(5.8737)(6.4462)} = -0.8744$$

d. Strong inverse relationship. As the number of police increases, the crime decreases or, as crime increases the number of police decrease.

7. Reject H_0 if $t > 1.812$.

$$t = \frac{.32\sqrt{12 - 2}}{\sqrt{1 - (.32)^2}} = 1.068$$

Do not reject H_0.

9. $H_0: \rho \leq 0; H_1: \rho > 0$. Reject H_0 if $t > 2.552$. $df = 18$.

$$t = \frac{.78\sqrt{20 - 2}}{\sqrt{1 - (.78)^2}} = 5.288$$

Reject H_0. There is a positive correlation between gallons sold and the pump price.

11. $H_0: \rho \leq 0 \quad H_1: \rho > 0$
Reject H_0 if $t > 2.650$ with df = 13.

$$t = \frac{0.667\sqrt{15 - 2}}{\sqrt{1 - 0.667^2}} = 3.228$$

Reject H_0. There is a positive correlation between the number of passengers and plane weight.

13. a. $\hat{y} = 3.7671 + 0.3630x$

$$b = 0.7522\left(\frac{1.3038}{2.7019}\right) = 0.3630$$
$$a = 5.8 - 0.3630(5.6) = 3.7671$$

b. 6.3081, found by $\hat{y} = 3.7671 + 0.3630(7)$

15. a. $\Sigma(x - \bar{x})(y - \bar{y}) = 44.6$, $s_x = 2.726$, $s_y = 2.011$

$$r = \frac{44.6}{(10 - 1)(2.726)(2.011)} = .904$$

$$b = .904\left(\frac{2.011}{2.726}\right) = 0.667$$

$$a = 7.4 - .677(9.1) = 1.333$$

b. $\hat{Y} = 1.333 + .667(6) = 5.335$

17. a.

b. $\Sigma(x - \bar{x})(y - \bar{y}) = 629.64$, $s_x = 26.17$, $s_y = 3.248$

$$r = \frac{629.64}{(12 - 1)(26.17)(3.248)} = .6734$$

c. $b = .6734\left(\frac{3.248}{26.170}\right) = 0.0836$

$$a = \frac{64.1}{12} - 0.0836\left(\frac{501.10}{12}\right) = 1.8507$$

d. $\hat{y} = 1.8507 + 0.0836(50.0) = 6.0307$ ($ millions)

19. a. $b = -.8744\left(\frac{6.4462}{5.8737}\right) = -0.9596$

$$a = \frac{95}{8} - (-0.9596)\left(\frac{146}{8}\right) = 29.3877$$

b. 10.1957, found by $29.3877 - 0.9596(20)$

c. For each policeman added, crime goes down by almost one.

21. $H_0: \beta \geq 0$ $H_1: \beta < 0$ $df = n - 2 = 8 - 2 = 6$
Reject H_0 if $t < -1.943$.

$$t = -0.96/0.22 = -4.364$$

Reject H_0 and conclude the slope is less than zero.

23. $H_0: \beta = 0$ $H_1: \beta \neq 0$ $df = n - 2 = 12 - 2 = 10$
Reject H_0 if t not between -2.228 and 2.228.

$$t = 0.08/0.03 = 2.667$$

Reject H_0 and conclude the slope is different from zero.

25. The standard error of estimate is 3.378, found by $\sqrt{\frac{68.4814}{8 - 2}}$.

The coefficient of determination is 0.76, found by $(-0.874)^2$. Seventy-six percent of the variation in crimes can be explained by the variation in police.

27. The standard error of estimate is 0.913, found by $\sqrt{\frac{6.667}{10 - 2}}$.

The coefficient of determination is 0.82, found by $29.733/36.4$. Eighty-two percent of the variation in kilowatt hours can be explained by the variation in the number of rooms.

29. a. $r^2 = \frac{1,000}{1,500} = .6667$

b. $r = \sqrt{.6667} = .8165$

c. $s_{y \cdot x} = \sqrt{\frac{500}{13}} = 6.2017$

31. a. $6.308 \pm (3.182)(.993)\sqrt{.2 + \frac{(7 - 5.6)^2}{29.2}}$

$= 6.308 \pm 1.633$
$= [4.675, 7.941]$

b. $6.308 \pm (3.182)(.993)\sqrt{1 + 1/5 + .0671}$
$= [2.751, 9.865]$

33. a. 4.2939, 6.3721

b. 2.9854, 7.6806

35. The correlation between the two variables is 0.298. By squaring x, the correlation increases to .998.

37. $H_0: \rho \leq 0$; $H_1: \rho > 0$. Reject H_0 if $t > 1.714$.

$$t = \frac{.94\sqrt{25 - 2}}{\sqrt{1 - (.94)^2}} = 13.213$$

Reject H_0. There is a positive correlation between passengers and weight of luggage.

39. $H_0: \rho \leq 0$; $H_1: \rho > 0$. Reject H_0 if $t > 2.764$.

$$t = \frac{.47\sqrt{12 - 2}}{\sqrt{1 - (.47)^2}} = 1.684$$

Do not reject H_0. There is not a positive correlation between engine size and performance. p-value is greater than .05 but less than .10.

41. a. The sales volume is inversely related to their market share.

b. $r = \frac{-299.792}{(13 - 1)(3.686)(9.808)} = -0.691$

c. $H_0: \rho \geq 0$ $H_1: \rho < 0$ Reject H_0 if $t < -2.718$ $df = 11$

$$t = \frac{-0.691\sqrt{13 - 2}}{\sqrt{1 - (-0.691)^2}} = -3.17$$ Reject H_0. There is a

negative correlation between cars sold and market share.

d. 47.7%, found by $(-0.691)^2$, of the variation in market share is accounted for by variation in cars sold.

43. a. $r = -0.393$

b. The coefficient of determination is 0.1544, found by squaring (-0.393).

c. $H_0: \rho \geq 0$ $H_1: \rho < 0$ Reject H_0 if $t < -1.697$

$$t = \frac{-0.393\sqrt{32 - 2}}{\sqrt{1 - (-0.393)^2}} = -2.34$$

Reject H_0. There is a negative correlation between points scored and points allowed.

d. For the National conference (NFC): $H_0: \rho \geq 0$ $H_1: \rho < 0$
Reject H_0 if $t < -1.761$.

$$t = \frac{-0.139\sqrt{16 - 2}}{\sqrt{1 - (-0.139)^2}} = -0.53$$

Do not reject H_0. We *cannot* say there is a negative correlation between points scored and points allowed in the NFC. For the American conference (AFC): $H_0: \rho \geq 0$ $H_1: \rho < 0$
Reject H_0 if $t < -1.761$.

$$t = \frac{-0.576\sqrt{16 - 2}}{\sqrt{1 - (-0.576)^2}} = -2.64$$

Reject H_0. We can say there is a negative correlation between points scored and points allowed in the AFC.

45. a.

There is an inverse relationship between the variables. As the months owned increase, the number of hours exercised decreases.

b. $r = -0.827$

c. $H_0: \rho \geq 0$; $H_1: \rho < 0$. Reject H_0 if $t < -2.896$.

$$t = \frac{-0.827\sqrt{10 - 2}}{\sqrt{1 - (-0.827)^2}} = -4.16$$

Reject H_0. There is a negative association between months owned and hours exercised.

47. a. Median age and population are directly related.

b. $r = \dfrac{11.93418}{(10-1)(2.207)(1.330)} = 0.452$

c. The slope of 0.272 indicates that for each increase of 1 million in the population, the median age increases on average by 0.272 year.

d. The median age is 32.08 years, found by $31.4 + 0.272(2.5)$.

e. The p-value (0.190) for the population variable is greater than, say, .05. A test for significance of that coefficient would fail to be rejected. In other words, it is possible the population coefficient is zero.

f. $H_0: \rho = 0$ $H_1: \rho \neq 0$ Reject H_0 if t is not between -1.86 and 1.86.

$df = 8$ $t = \dfrac{0.452\sqrt{10-2}}{\sqrt{1-(0.452)^2}} = 1.433$ Do not reject H_0.

There may be no relationship between age and population.

49. a. $b = -0.4667$, $a = 11.2358$

b. $\hat{y} = 11.2358 - 0.4667(7.0) = 7.9689$

c. $7.9689 \pm (2.160)(1.114)\sqrt{1 + \dfrac{1}{15} + \dfrac{(7 - 7.1333)^2}{73.7333}}$

$= 7.9689 \pm 2.4854$

$= [5.4835, 10.4543]$

d. $R^2 = 0.499$. Nearly 50% of the variation in the amount of the bid is explained by the number of bidders.

51. a.

There appears to be a relationship between the two variables. As the distance increases, so does the shipping time.

b. $r = 0.692$

$H_0: \rho \leq 0$; $H_1: \rho > 0$. Reject H_0 if $t > 1.734$.

$t = \dfrac{0.692\sqrt{20-2}}{\sqrt{1-(0.692)^2}} = 4.067$

H_0 is rejected. There is a positive association between shipping distance and shipping time.

c. $R^2 = 0.479$. Nearly half of the variation in shipping time is explained by shipping distance.

d. $s_{y \cdot x} = 2.004$

53. a. $b = 2.41$

$a = 26.8$

The regression equation is: Price $= 26.8 + 2.41 \times$ Dividend. For each additional dollar of dividend, the price increases by $2.41.

b. To test the significance of the slope, we use $n - 2$, or $30 - 2 = 28$ degrees of freedom. For a 0.05 level of significance, the critical values are -2.048 and 2.048. The t-test statistic is $t = \dfrac{b - 0}{s_b} = \dfrac{2.408}{0.328} = 7.34$. We reject the null hypothesis that the slope is equal zero.

c. $R^2 = \dfrac{5{,}057.6}{7{,}682.7} = 0.658$ Thus, 65.8% of the variation in price is explained by the dividend.

d. $r = \sqrt{.658} = 0.811$ $H_0: \rho \leq 0$ $H_1: \rho > 0$
At the 5% level, reject H_0 when $t > 1.701$.

$t = \dfrac{0.811\sqrt{30-2}}{\sqrt{1-(0.811)^2}} = 7.34$

Thus, H_0 is rejected. The population correlation is positive.

55. a. 35

b. $s_{y \cdot x} = \sqrt{29{,}778{,}406} = 5{,}456.96$

c. $r^2 = \dfrac{13{,}548{,}662{,}082}{14{,}531{,}349{,}474} = 0.932$

d. $r = \sqrt{0.932} = 0.966$

e. $H_0: \rho \leq 0$, $H_1: \rho > 0$; reject H_0 if $t > 1.692$.

$t = \dfrac{.966\sqrt{35-2}}{\sqrt{1-(.966)^2}} = 21.46$

Reject H_0. There is a direct relationship between size of the house and its market value.

57. a. The regression equation is Price $= -773 + 1{,}408$ Speed.

b. The second laptop (1.6, 922) with a residual of -557.60, is priced $557.60 below the predicted price. That is a noticeable "bargain."

c. The correlation of Speed and Price is 0.835.
$H_0: \rho \leq 0$ $H_1: \rho > 0$ Reject H_0 if $t > 1.8125$.

$t = \dfrac{0.835\sqrt{12-2}}{\sqrt{1-(0.835)^2}} = 4.799$

Reject H_0. It is reasonable to say the population correlation is positive.

59. a. $r = .987$, $H_0: \rho \leq 0$, $H_1: \rho > 0$. Reject H_0 if $t > 1.746$.

$t = \dfrac{.987\sqrt{18-2}}{\sqrt{1-(.987)^2}} = 24.564$

b. $\hat{y} = -29.7 + 22.93x$; an additional cup increases the dog's weight by almost 23 pounds.

c. Dog number 4 is an overeater.

61. a.

The relationship is direct. Fares increase for longer flights.

b. The correlation of Distance and Fare is 0.656.
$H_0: \rho \leq 0$ $H_1: \rho > 0$ Reject H_0 if $t > 1.701$. $df = 28$

$t = \dfrac{0.656\sqrt{30-2}}{\sqrt{1-(0.656)^2}} = 4.599$

Reject H_0. There is a significant positive correlation between fares and distances.

c. 43%, found by $(0.656)^2$, of the variation in fares is explained by the variation in distance.

d. The regression equation is Fare $= 147.08 + 0.05265$ Distance. Each additional mile adds $0.05265 to the fare.
A 1,500-mile flight would cost $226.06, found by $147.08 + 0.05265(1{,}500)$.

e. A flight of 4,218 miles is outside the range of the sampled data, so the regression equation may not be useful.

343333

3333

33333333

63. a. There does seem to be a direct relationship between the variables.

2012 Major League Baseball

b. Expected attendance with a salary of 80 million is 2.2529 million, found by $1.17855 + 0.01343(80)$.

c. Increasing the salary by 30 million will increase attendance by 0.4029 million on average, found by $0.01343(30)$. This is also the difference between the expected attendance with a salary of 110 and the expected attendance of 80 million.

d. The regression output from *Excel* is below.

Summary Output

Regression Statistics

Multiple R	0.770317814
R Square	0.593389535
Adjusted R Square	0.578867732
Standard Error	0.416717999
Observations	30

ANOVA

	df	SS	MS	F	Significance F
Regression	1	7.095841062	7.095841062	40.86197572	6.41022E-07
Residual	28	4.862308938	0.173653891		
Total	29	11.95815			

	Coefficients	Standard Error	t Stat	P-value
Intercept	1.178554138	0.21954557	5.368152674	1.01455E-05
Salary 2012	0.013429923	0.002100941	6.392337265	6.41022E-07

$H_0: \beta \le 0$ $H_1: \beta > 0$ $df = n - 2 = 30 - 2 = 28$
Reject H_0 if $t > 1.701$ $t = 0.013429923/0.002100941 = 6.39233$. Reject H_0 and conclude the slope is positive.

e. 0.593389 or 59.3389% of the variation in attendance is explained by variation in salary.

f. The correlation between attendance and batting average is 0.6538.
$H_0: \rho \le 0$ $H_1: \rho > 0$ At the 5% level, reject H_0 if $t > 1.701$.
$$t = \frac{0.6538\sqrt{30-2}}{\sqrt{1-(0.6538)^2}} = 4.573 \quad \text{Reject } H_0.$$
The batting average and attendance is positively correlated. The correlation between attendance and ERA is -0.0548. The correlation between attendance and batting average is stronger than the correlation between attendance and ERA.
$H_0: \rho \ge 0$ $H_1: \rho < 0$ At the 5% level, reject H_0 if $t < -1.701$.
$$t = \frac{-0.0548\sqrt{30-2}}{\sqrt{1-(-0.0548)^2}} = -0.291 \quad \text{Fail to reject } H_0.$$
The ERA and attendance could have no correlation.

CHAPTER 14

1. a. Multiple regression equation
b. The y-intercept
c. $\hat{y} = 64,100 + 0.394(796,000) + 9.6(6,940) - 11,600(6.0) = \$374,748$

3. a. 497.736, found by
$\hat{y} = 16.24 + 0.017(18) + 0.0028(26,500) + 42(3) + 0.0012(156,000) + 0.19(141) + 26.8(2.5)$

b. Two more social activities. Income added only 28 to the index; social activities added 53.6.

5. a. $s_{Y \cdot 12} = \sqrt{\dfrac{SSE}{n-(k+1)}} = \sqrt{\dfrac{583.693}{65-(2+1)}}$
$= \sqrt{9.414} = 3.068$
95% of the residuals will be between ± 6.136, found by $2(3.068)$.

b. $R^2 = \dfrac{SSR}{SS\ total} = \dfrac{77.907}{661.6} = .118$
The independent variables explain 11.8% of the variation.

c. $R^2_{adj} = 1 - \dfrac{\dfrac{SSE}{n-(k+1)}}{\dfrac{SS\ total}{n-1}} = 1 - \dfrac{\dfrac{583.693}{65-(2+1)}}{\dfrac{661.6}{65-1}}$
$= 1 - \dfrac{9.414}{10.3375} = 1 - .911 = .089$

7. a. $\hat{y} = 84.998 + 2.391x_1 - 0.4086x_2$
b. 90.0674, found by $\hat{y} = 84.998 + 2.391(4) - 0.4086(11)$
c. $n = 65$ and $k = 2$
d. $H_0: \beta_1 = \beta_2 = 0$ $H_1:$ Not all βs are 0
Reject H_0 if $F > 3.15$.
$F = 4.14$, reject H_0. Not all net regression coefficients equal zero.
e. For x_1 For x_2
$H_0: \beta_1 = 0$ $H_0: \beta_2 = 0$
$H_1: \beta_1 \ne 0$ $H_1: \beta_2 \ne 0$
$t = 1.99$ $t = -2.38$
Reject H_0 if $t > 2.0$ or $t < -2.0$.
Delete variable 1 and keep 2.
f. The regression analysis should be repeated with only x_2 as the independent variable.

9. a. The regression equation is: Performance = 29.3 + 5.22 Aptitude + 22.1 Union

Predictor	Coef	SE Coef	T	P
Constant	29.28	12.77	2.29	0.041
Aptitude	5.222	1.702	3.07	0.010
Union	22.135	8.852	2.50	0.028

S = 16.9166 R-Sq = 53.3% R-Sq (adj) = 45.5%

Analysis of Variance
Source	DF	SS	MS	F	P
Regression	2	3919.3	1959.6	6.85	0.010
Residual Error	12	3434.0	286.2		
Total	14	7353.3			

b. These variables are effective in predicting performance. They explain 53.3% of the variation in performance. In particular, union membership increases the typical performance by 22.1.
c. $H_0: \beta_2 = 0$ $H_1: \beta_2 \ne 0$
Reject H_0 if $t < -2.179$ or $t > 2.179$.
Since 2.50 is greater than 2.179, we reject the null hypothesis and conclude that union membership is significant and should be included.
d. When you consider the interaction variable, the regression equation is Performance = 38.7 + 3.80 Aptitude − 0.1 Union + 3.61 x_1x_2

Predictor	Coef	SE Coef	T	P
Constant	38.69	15.62	2.48	0.031
Aptitude	3.802	2.179	1.74	0.109
Union	−0.10	23.14	−0.00	0.997
X_1X_2	3.610	3.473	1.04	0.321

The t value corresponding to the interaction term is 1.04. This is not significant. So we conclude there is no interaction between aptitude and union membership when predicting job performance.

11. a. The regression equation is
Price = 3,080 − 54.2 Bidders + 16.3 Age

Predictor	Coef	SE Coef	T	P
Constant	3080.1	343.9	8.96	0.000
Bidders	−54.19	12.28	−4.41	0.000
Age	16.289	3.784	4.30	0.000

The price decreases 54.2 as each additional bidder participates. Meanwhile the price increases 16.3 as the painting gets older. While one would expect older paintings to be worth more, it is unexpected that the price goes down as more bidders participate!

b. The regression equation is
Price $= 3{,}972 - 185$ Bidders $+ 6.35$ Age $+ 1.46\, x_1 x_2$

Predictor	Coef	SE Coef	T	P
Constant	3971.7	850.2	4.67	0.000
Bidders	−185.0	114.9	−1.61	0.122
Age	6.353	9.455	0.67	0.509
$X_1 X_2$	1.462	1.277	1.15	0.265

The t value corresponding to the interaction term is 1.15. This is not significant. So we conclude there is no interaction.

c. In the stepwise procedure, the number of bidders enters the equation first. Then the interaction term enters. The variable age would not be included as it is not significant. Response is Price on 3 predictors, with $N = 25$.

Step	1	2
Constant	4,507	4,540
Bidders	−57	−256
T-Value	−3.53	−5.59
P-Value	0.002	0.000
$X_1 X_2$		2.25
T-Value		4.49
P-Value		0.000
S	295	218
R-Sq	35.11	66.14
R-Sq(adj)	32.29	63.06

13. a. $n = 40$

b. 4

c. $R^2 = \dfrac{750}{1{,}250} = .60$

d. $s_{y \cdot 1234} = \sqrt{500/35} = 3.7796$

e. $H_0: \beta_1 = \beta_2 = \beta_3 = \beta_4 = 0$
H_1: Not all the βs equal zero.
H_0 is rejected if $F > 2.65$.

$$F = \frac{750/4}{500/35} = 13.125$$

H_0 is rejected. At least one β_i does not equal zero.

15. a. $n = 26$

b. $R^2 = 100/140 = .7143$

c. 1.4142, found by $\sqrt{2}$

d. $H_0: \beta_1 = \beta_2 = \beta_3 = \beta_4 = \beta_5 = 0$
H_1: Not all the βs are 0.
H_0 is rejected if $F > 2.71$.
Computed $F = 10.0$. Reject H_0. At least one regression coefficient is not zero.

e. H_0 is rejected in each case if $t < -2.086$ or $t > 2.086$. x_1 and x_5 should be dropped.

17. a. $28,000

b. $R^2 = \dfrac{\text{SSR}}{\text{SS total}} = \dfrac{3{,}050}{5{,}250} = .5809$

c. 9.199, found by $\sqrt{84.62}$

d. H_0 is rejected if $F > 2.97$ (approximately)

$$\text{Computed } F = \frac{1{,}016.67}{84.62} = 12.01$$

H_0 is rejected. At least one regression coefficient is not zero.

e. If computed t is to the left of -2.056 or to the right of 2.056, the null hypothesis in each of these cases is rejected. Computed t for x_2 and x_3 exceed the critical value. Thus, "population" and "advertising expenses" should be retained and "number of competitors," x_1, dropped.

19. a. The strongest correlation is between High School GPA and Paralegal GPA. No problem with multicollinearity.

b. $R^2 = \dfrac{4.3595}{5.0631} = .8610$

c. H_0 is rejected if $F > 5.41$.

$$F = \frac{1.4532}{0.1407} = 10.328$$

At least one coefficient is not zero.

d. Any H_0 is rejected if $t < -2.571$ or $t > 2.571$. It appears that only High School GPA is significant. Verbal and math could be eliminated.

e. $R^2 = \dfrac{4.2061}{5.0631} = .8307$
R^2 has only been reduced .0303.

f. The residuals appear slightly skewed (positive) but acceptable.

g. There does not seem to be a problem with the plot.

21. a. The correlation of Screen and Price is 0.893. So there does appear to be a linear relationship between the two.

b. Price is the "dependent" variable.

c. The regression equation is Price $= -2{,}484 + 101 \times$ Screen. For each inch increase in screen size, the price increases $101 on average.

d. Using "dummy" indicator variables for Sharp and Sony, the regression equation is Price $= -2{,}308 + 94.1$ Screen $+ 15$ Manufacturer Sharp $+ 381$ Manufacturer Sony. Sharp can obtain on average $15 more than Samsung and Sony can collect an additional benefit of $381 more than Samsung.

e. Here is some of the output.

Predictor	Coef	SE Coef	T	P
Constant	-2308.2	492.0	-4.69	0.000
Screen	94.12	10.83	8.69	0.000
Manufacturer_Sharp	15.1	171.6	0.09	0.931
Manufacturer_Sony	381.4	168.8	2.26	0.036

The p-value for Sharp is relatively large. A test of their coefficient would not be rejected. That means they may not have any real advantage over Samsung. On the other hand, the p-value for the Sony coefficient is quite small. That indicates that it did not happen by chance and there is some real advantage to Sony over Samsung.

f. A histogram of the residuals indicates they follow a normal distribution.

g. The residual variation may be increasing for larger fitted values.

23. a.

Scatter Diagram of Sales vs. Advertising, Accounts, Competitors, Potential

Sales seem to fall with the number of competitors and rise with the number of accounts and potential.

b. Pearson correlations

	Sales	Advertising	Accounts	Competitors
Advertising	0.159			
Accounts	0.783	0.173		
Competitors	−0.833	−0.038	−0.324	
Potential	0.407	−0.071	0.468	−0.202

The number of accounts and the market potential are moderately correlated.

c. The regression equation is:
Sales = 178 + 1.81 Advertising + 3.32 Accounts − 21.2 Competitors + 0.325 Potential

Predictor	Coef	SE Coef	T	P
Constant	178.32	12.96	13.76	0.000
Advertising	1.807	1.081	1.67	0.109
Accounts	3.3178	0.1629	20.37	0.000
Competitors	−21.1850	0.7879	−26.89	0.000
Potential	0.3245	0.4678	0.69	0.495

S = 9.60441 R-Sq = 98.9% R-Sq(adj) = 98.7%

Analysis of Variance

Source	DF	SS	MS	F	P
Regression	4	176777	44194	479.10	0.000
Residual Error	21	1937	92		
Total	25	178714			

The computed *F* value is quite large. So we can reject the null hypothesis that all of the regression coefficients are zero. We conclude that some of the independent variables are effective in explaining sales.
d. Market potential and advertising have large *p*-values (0.495 and 0.109, respectively). You would probably drop them.
e. If you omit potential, the regression equation is:
Sales = 180 + 1.68 Advertising + 3.37 Accounts − 21.2 Competitors

Predictor	Coef	SE Coef	T	P
Constant	179.84	12.62	14.25	0.000
Advertising	1.677	1.052	1.59	0.125
Accounts	3.3694	0.1432	23.52	0.000
Competitors	−21.2165	0.7773	−27.30	0.000

Now advertising is not significant. That would also lead you to cut out the advertising variable and report that the polished regression equation is:
Sales = 187 + 3.41 Accounts − 21.2 Competitors

Predictor	Coef	SE Coef	T	P
Constant	186.69	12.26	15.23	0.000
Accounts	3.4081	0.1458	23.37	0.000
Competitors	−21.1930	0.8028	−26.40	0.000

f.

Histogram of the Residuals
(response is Sales)

The histogram looks to be normal. There are no problems shown in this plot.
g. The variance inflation factor for both variables is 1.1. They are less than 10. There are no troubles as this value indicates the independent variables are not strongly correlated with each other.

25. The computer output is:

Predictor	Coef	StDev	t-ratio	p
Constant	651.9	345.3	1.89	0.071
Service	13.422	5.125	2.62	0.015
Age	−6.710	6.349	−1.06	0.301
Gender	205.65	90.27	2.28	0.032
Job	−33.45	89.55	−0.37	0.712

Analysis of Variance

SOURCE	DF	SS	MS	F	p
Regression	4	1066830	266708	4.77	0.005
Error	25	1398651	55946		
Total	29	2465481			

a. $\hat{y} = 651.9 + 13.422x_1 − 6.710x_2 + 205.65x_3 − 33.45x_4$
b. $R^2 = .433$, which is somewhat low for this type of study.
c. $H_0: \beta_1 = \beta_2 = \beta_3 = \beta_4 = 0$; H_1: Not all βs equal zero
Reject H_0 if $F > 2.76$.

$$F = \frac{1,066,830/4}{1,398,651/25} = 4.77$$

H_0 is rejected. Not all the β_is equal 0.
d. Using the .05 significance level, reject the hypothesis that the regression coefficient is 0 if $t < −2.060$ or $t > 2.060$. Service and gender should remain in the analyses; age and job should be dropped.
e. Following is the computer output using the independent variables service and gender.

Predictor	Coef	StDev	t-ratio	p
Constant	784.2	316.8	2.48	0.020
Service	9.021	3.106	2.90	0.007
Gender	224.41	87.35	2.57	0.016

Analysis of Variance

SOURCE	DF	SS	MS	F	p
Regression	2	998779	499389	9.19	0.001
Error	27	1466703	54322		
Total	29	2465481			

A man earns $224 more per month than a woman. The difference between technical and clerical jobs is not significant.
27. a. $\hat{y} = 29.913 − 5.324x_1 + 1.449x_2$
b. EPS is ($t = −3.26$, *p*-value = .005). Yield is not ($t = 0.81$, *p*-value = .431).
c. An increase of 1 in EPS results in a decline of 5.324 in P/E.
d. Stock number 2 is undervalued.
e. Below is a residual plot. It does *not* appear to follow the normal distribution.

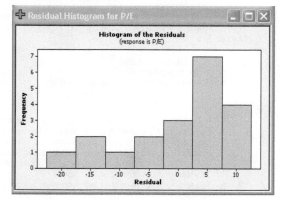

f. There does not seem to be a problem with the plot of the residuals versus the fitted values.

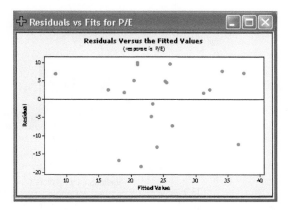

g. The correlation between yield and EPS is not a problem. No problem with multicollinearity.

	P/E	EPS
EPS	−0.602	
Yield	.054	.162

29. a. The regression equation is
Sales (000) = 1.02 + 0.0829 Infomercials

Predictor	Coef	SE Coef	T	P
Constant	1.0188	0.3105	3.28	0.006
Infomercials	0.08291	0.01680	4.94	0.000

Analysis of Variance

Source	DF	SS	MS	F	P
Regression	1	2.3214	2.3214	24.36	0.000
Residual Error	13	1.2386	0.0953		
Total	14	3.5600			

The global test demonstrates there is a relationship between sales and the number of infomercials.

b.

Histogram of RESI1

The residuals appear to follow the normal distribution.

31. a. The regression equation is
Auction Price = −118,929 + 1.63 Loan + 2.1 Monthly Payment + 50 Payments Made

Analysis of Variance

Source	DF	SS	MS	F	P
Regression	3	5966725061	1988908354	39.83	0.000
Residual					
Error	16	798944439	49934027		
Total	19	6765669500			

The computed F is 39.83. It is much larger than the critical value 3.24. The p-value is also quite small. Thus, the null hypothesis that all the regression coefficients are zero can be rejected. At least one of the multiple regression coefficients is different from zero.

b.

Predictor	Coef	SE Coef	T	P
Constant	−118929	19734	−6.03	0.000
Loan	1.6268	0.1809	8.99	0.000
Monthly				
Payment	2.06	14.95	0.14	0.892
Payments				
Made	50.3	134.9	0.37	0.714

The null hypothesis is that the coefficient is zero in the individual test. It would be rejected if t is less than −2.120 or more than 2.120. In this case, the t value for the loan variable is larger than the critical value. Thus, it should not be removed. However, the monthly payment and payments made variables would likely be removed.

c. The revised regression equation is: Auction Price = −119,893 + 1.67 Loan

33. The computer output is as follows:

Predictor	Coef	SE Coef	T	P
Constant	38.71	39.02	.99	.324
Bedrooms	7.118	2.551	2.79	0.006
Size	0.03800	0.01468	2.59	0.011
Pool	18.321	6.999	2.62	0.010
Distance	−0.9295	0.7279	−1.28	0.205
Garage	35.810	7.638	4.69	0.000
Baths	23.315	9.025	2.58	0.011

S = 33.21 R-Sq = 53.2% R-Sq (adj) = 50.3%

Analysis of Variance

SOURCE	DF	SS	MS	F	P
Regression	6	122676	20446	18.54	0.000
Residual Error	98	108092	1103		
Total	104	230768			

a. Each additional bedroom adds about $7,000 to the selling price, each additional square foot adds $38, a pool adds $18,300 to the value, an attached garage increases the value by $35,800, and each mile the home is from the center of the city reduces the selling price by $929.

b. The R-square value is 0.532.

c. The correlation matrix is as follows:

	Price	Bedrooms	Size	Pool	Distance	Garage
Bedrooms	0.467					
Size	0.371	0.383				
Pool	0.294	0.005	0.201			
Distance	−0.347	−0.153	−0.117	−0.139		
Garage	0.526	0.234	0.083	0.114	−0.359	
Baths	0.382	0.329	0.024	0.055	−0.195	0.221

The independent variable *garage* has the strongest correlation with price. Distance is inversely related, as expected, and there does not seem to be a problem with correlation among the independent variables.

d. The results of the global test suggest that some of the independent variables have net regression coefficients different from zero.
e. We can delete *distance*.
f. The new regression output follows.

```
Predictor       Coef    SE Coef       T       P
Constant        17.01     35.24     .48    .630
Bedrooms         7.169     2.559    2.80   0.006
Size             0.03919   0.01470 -2.67   0.009
Pool            19.110     6.994    2.73   0.007
Garage          38.847     7.281    5.34   0.000
Baths           24.624     8.995    2.74   0.007

S = 33.32  R-Sq = 52.4%  R-Sq(adj) = 50.0%

Analysis of Variance
SOURCE            DF      SS     MS      F       P
Regression         5  120877  24175  21.78  0.000
Residual Error    99  109890   1110
Total            104  230768
```

In reviewing the *p*-values for the various regression coefficients, all are less than .05. We leave all the independent variables.

g. & h. Analysis of the residuals, not shown, indicates the normality assumption is reasonable. In addition, there is no pattern to the plots of the residuals and the fitted values of *Y*.

35. a. The regression equation is

Maintenance = 102 + 5.94 Age + 0.374 Miles − 11.8 GasolineIndicator

Each additional year of age adds $5.94 to upkeep cost. Every extra mile adds $0.374 to maintenance total. Gasoline buses are cheaper to maintain than diesel by $11.80 per year.
b. The coefficient of determination is 0.286, found by 65,135/227,692. Twenty-nine percent of the variation in maintenance cost is explained by these variables.
c. The correlation matrix is:

	Maintenance	Age	Miles
Age	0.465		
Miles	0.450	0.522	
GasolineIndicator	−0.118	−0.068	0.025

Age and Miles both have moderately strong correlations with maintenance cost. The highest correlation among the independent variables is 0.522 between Age and Miles. That is smaller than 0.70, so multicollinearity may not be a problem.

d.

```
Analysis of Variance
Source          DF      SS     MS      F       P
Regression       3   65135  21712  10.15  0.000
Residual Error  76  162558   2139
Total           79  227692
```

The *p*-value is zero. Reject the null hypothesis of all coefficients being zero and say at least one is important.

e.

```
Predictor       Coef   SE Coef       T       P
Constant       102.3    112.9     0.91   0.368
Age              5.939    2.227    2.67   0.009
Miles            0.3740   0.1450   2.58   0.012
GasolineIndicator -11.80  10.99   -1.07   0.286
```

The *p*-value of the gasoline indicator is bigger than 0.10. Consider deleting it.

f. The condensed regression equation is

Maintenance = 106 + 6.17 Age + 0.363 Miles

g.

The normality conjecture appears realistic.

h.

This plot appears to be random and to have a constant variance.

CHAPTER 15

1. a. H_0 is rejected if $z > 1.65$.
  b. 1.09, found by $z = (0.75 - 0.70)/\sqrt{(0.70 \times 0.30)/100}$
  c. H_0 is not rejected.
3. a. $H_0: \pi \le 0.52$ $H_1: \pi > 0.52$
  b. H_0 is rejected if $z > 2.33$.
  c. 1.62, found by $z = (.5667 - .52)/\sqrt{(0.52 \times 0.48)/300}$
  d. H_0 is not rejected. We cannot conclude that the proportion of men driving on the Ohio Turnpike is larger than 0.52.
5. a. $H_0: \pi \ge 0.90$ $H_1: \pi < 0.90$
  b. H_0 is rejected if $z < -1.28$.
  c. −2.67, found by $z = (0.82 - 0.90)/\sqrt{(0.90 \times 0.10)/100}$
  d. H_0 is rejected. Fewer than 90% of the customers receive their orders in less than 10 minutes.
7. a. H_0 is rejected if $z > 1.65$.
  b. 0.64, found by $p_c = \dfrac{70 + 90}{100 + 150}$
  c. 1.61, found by
  $$z = \frac{0.70 - 0.60}{\sqrt{[(0.64 \times 0.36)/100] + [(0.64 \times 0.36)/150]}}$$
  d. H_0 is not rejected.
9. a. $H_0: \pi_1 = \pi_2$ $H_1: \pi_1 \ne \pi_2$
  b. H_0 is rejected if $z < -1.96$ or $z > 1.96$.
  c. $p_c = \dfrac{24 + 40}{400 + 400} = 0.08$
  d. −2.09, found by
  $$z = \frac{0.06 - 0.10}{\sqrt{[(0.08 \times 0.92)/400] + [(0.08 \times 0.92)/400]}}$$

e. H_0 is rejected. The proportion infested is not the same in the two fields.

11. $H_0: \pi_d \le \pi_r$ $H_1: \pi_d > \pi_r$
H_0 is rejected if $z > 2.05$.

$$p_c = \frac{168 + 200}{800 + 1,000} = 0.2044$$

$$z = \frac{0.21 - 0.20}{\sqrt{\dfrac{(0.2044)(0.7956)}{800} + \dfrac{(0.2044)(0.7956)}{1,000}}} = 0.52$$

H_0 is not rejected. We cannot conclude that a larger proportion of Democrats favor lowering the standards. p-value = .3015.

13. a. 3
   b. 7.815

15. a. Reject H_0 if $\chi^2 > 5.991$
   b. $\chi^2 = \dfrac{(10-20)^2}{20} + \dfrac{(20-20)^2}{20} + \dfrac{(30-20)^2}{20} = 10.0$
   c. Reject H_0. The proportions are not equal.

17. H_0: The outcomes are the same; H_1: The outcomes are not the same. Reject H_0 if $\chi^2 > 9.236$.

$$\chi^2 = \frac{(3-5)^2}{5} + \cdots + \frac{(7-5)^2}{5} = 7.60$$

Do not reject H_0. Cannot reject H_0 that outcomes are the same.

19. H_0: There is no difference in the proportions.
H_1: There is a difference in the proportions.
Reject H_0 if $\chi^2 > 15.086$.

$$\chi^2 = \frac{(47-40)^2}{40} + \cdots + \frac{(34-40)^2}{40} = 3.400$$

Do not reject H_0. There is no difference in the proportions.

21. a. Reject H_0 if $\chi^2 > 9.210$.
   b. $\chi^2 = \dfrac{(30-24)^2}{24} + \dfrac{(20-24)^2}{24} + \dfrac{(10-12)^2}{12} = 2.50$
   c. Do not reject H_0.

23. H_0: Proportions are as stated; H_1: Proportions are not as stated. Reject H_0 if $\chi^2 > 11.345$.

$$\chi^2 = \frac{(50-25)^2}{25} + \cdots + \frac{(160-275)^2}{275} = 115.22$$

Reject H_0. The proportions are not as stated.

25.

Number of Clients	z-values	Area	Found by	f_e
Under 30	Under −1.58	0.0571	0.5000 − 0.4429	2.855
30 up to 40	−1.58 up to −0.51	0.2479	0.4429 − 0.1950	12.395
40 up to 50	−0.51 up to 0.55	0.4038	0.1950 + 0.2088	20.19
50 up to 60	0.55 up to 1.62	0.2386	0.4474 − 0.2088	11.93
60 or more	1.62 or more	0.0526	0.5000 − 0.4474	2.63

The first and last class both have expected frequencies smaller than 5. They are combined with adjacent classes.
H_0: The population of clients follows a normal distribution.
H_1: The population of clients does not follow a normal distribution.
Reject the null if $\chi^2 > 5.991$.

Number of Clients	Area	f_e	f_o	$f_e - f_o$	$(f_o - f_e)^2$	$[(f_o - f_e)^2]/f_e$
Under 40	0.3050	15.25	16	−0.75	0.5625	0.0369
40 up to 50	0.4038	20.19	22	−1.81	3.2761	0.1623
50 or more	0.2912	14.56	12	2.56	6.5536	0.4501
Total	1.0000	50.00	50	0		0.6493

Since 0.6493 is not greater than 5.991, we fail to reject the null hypothesis. These data could be from a normal distribution.

27. H_0: There is no relationship between community size and section read. H_1: There is a relationship. Reject H_0 if $\chi^2 > 9.488$.

$$\chi^2 = \frac{(170 - 157.50)^2}{157.50} + \cdots + \frac{(88 - 83.62)^2}{83.62} = 7.340$$

Do not reject H_0. There is no relationship between community size and section read.

29. H_0: No relationship between error rates and item type.
H_1: There is a relationship between error rates and item type. Reject H_0 if $\chi^2 > 9.21$.

$$\chi^2 = \frac{(20 - 14.1)^2}{14.1} + \cdots + \frac{(225 - 225.25)^2}{225.25} = 8.033$$

Do not reject H_0. There is not a relationship between error rates and item type.

31. a. This is a binomial situation with both the mean number of successes and failures equal to 23.5, found by 0.5(47).
   b. $H_0: \pi = 0.50$ $H_1: \pi \ne 0.50$
   c.

Distribution Plot
Normal, Mean = 0, StDev = 1

Reject H_0 if z is not between −2.576 and 2.576.

   d. $z = \dfrac{\dfrac{31}{47} - 0.5}{\sqrt{0.5(1 - 0.5)/47}} = 2.19$. We fail to reject the null hypothesis. These data do not prove the coin flip is biased.
   e. The p-value is 0.0286, found by 2(0.5000 − 0.4857). A value this extreme will happen about once out of 35 times with a fair coin.

33. $H_0: \pi \le 0.60$ $H_1: \pi > 0.60$
H_0 is rejected if $z > 2.33$.

$$z = \frac{.70 - .60}{\sqrt{\dfrac{.60(.40)}{200}}} = 2.89$$

H_0 is rejected. Ms. Dennis is correct. More than 60% of the accounts are more than three months old.

35. $H_0: \pi \le 0.44$ $H_1: \pi > 0.44$
H_0 is rejected if $z > 1.65$.

$$z = \frac{0.480 - 0.44}{\sqrt{(0.44 \times 0.56)/1.000}} = 2.55$$

H_0 is rejected. We conclude that there has been an increase in the proportion of people wanting to go to Europe.

37. $H_0: \pi \le 0.20$ $H_1: \pi > 0.20$
H_0 is rejected if $z > 2.33$

$$z = \frac{(56/200) - 0.20}{\sqrt{(0.20 \times 0.80)/200}} = 2.83$$

H_0 is rejected. More than 20% of the owners move during a particular year. p-value = 0.5000 − 0.4977 = 0.0023.

39. $H_0: \pi \geq 0.0008 \qquad H_1: \pi < 0.0008$
H_0 is rejected if $z < -1.645$.

$$z = \frac{0.0006 - 0.0008}{\sqrt{\dfrac{0.0008\,(0.9992)}{10,000}}} = -0.707 \qquad H_0 \text{ is not rejected.}$$

These data do not prove there is a reduced fatality rate.

41. $H_0: \pi_1 \leq \pi_2 \qquad H_1: \pi_1 > \pi_2$
If $z > 2.33$, reject H_0.

$$p_c = \frac{990 + 970}{1,500 + 1,600} = 0.63$$

$$z = \frac{.6600 - .60625}{\sqrt{\dfrac{.63(.37)}{1,500} + \dfrac{.63(.37)}{1,600}}} = 3.10$$

Reject the null hypothesis. We can conclude the proportion of men who believe the division is fair is greater.

43. $H_0: \pi_1 \leq \pi_2 \qquad H_1: \pi_1 > \pi_2 \qquad H_0$ is rejected if $z > 1.65$.

$$p_c = \frac{.091 + .085}{2} = .088$$

$$z = \frac{0.091 - 0.085}{\sqrt{\dfrac{(0.088)(0.912)}{5,000} + \dfrac{(0.088)(0.912)}{5,000}}} = 1.059$$

H_0 is not rejected. There has not been an increase in the proportion calling conditions "good." The p-value is .1446, found by $.5000 - .3554$. The increase in the percentages will happen by chance in one out of every seven cases.

45. $H_0: \pi_1 = \pi_2 \qquad H_1: \pi_1 \neq \pi_2$
H_0 is rejected if z is not between -1.96 and 1.96.

$$p_c = \frac{100 + 36}{300 + 200} = .272$$

$$z = \frac{\dfrac{100}{300} - \dfrac{36}{200}}{\sqrt{\dfrac{(0.272)(0.728)}{300} + \dfrac{(0.272)(0.728)}{200}}} = 3.775$$

H_0 is rejected. There is a difference in the replies of the sexes.

47. $H_0: \pi_s = 0.50, \pi_r = \pi_e = 0.25$
$H_1:$ Distribution is not as given above.
$df = 2$. Reject H_0 if $\chi^2 > 4.605$.

Turn	f_o	f_e	$f_o - f_e$	$(f_o - f_e)^2/f_e$
Straight	112	100	12	1.44
Right	48	50	−2	0.08
Left	40	50	−10	2.00
Total	200	200		3.52

H_0 is not rejected. The proportions are as given in the null hypothesis.

49. $H_0:$ There is no preference with respect to TV stations.
$H_1:$ There is a preference with respect to TV stations.
$df = 3 - 1 = 2$. H_0 is rejected if $\chi^2 > 5.991$.

TV Station	f_o	f_e	$f_o - f_e$	$(f_o - f_e)^2$	$(f_o - f_e)^2/f_e$
WNAE	53	50	3	9	0.18
WRRN	64	50	14	196	3.92
WSPD	33	50	−17	289	5.78
	150	150	0		9.88

H_0 is rejected. There is a preference for TV stations.

51. $H_0: \pi_n = 0.21, \pi_m = 0.24, \pi_s = 0.35, \pi_w = 0.20$
$H_1:$ The distribution is not as given.
Reject H_0 if $\chi^2 > 11.345$.

Region	f_o	f_e	$f_o - f_e$	$(f_o - f_e)^2/f_e$
Northeast	68	84	−16	3.0476
Midwest	104	96	8	0.6667
South	155	140	15	1.6071
West	73	80	−7	0.6125
Total	400	400	0	5.9339

H_0 is not rejected. The distribution of order destinations reflects the population.

53. $H_0:$ The proportions are the same.
$H_1:$ The proportions are not the same.
Reject H_0 if $\chi^2 > 16.919$.

f_o	f_e	$f_o - f_e$	$(f_o - f_e)^2$	$(f_o - f_e)^2/f_e$
44	28	16	256	9.143
32	28	4	16	0.571
23	28	−5	25	0.893
27	28	−1	1	0.036
23	28	−5	25	0.893
24	28	−4	16	0.571
31	28	3	9	0.321
27	28	−1	1	0.036
28	28	0	0	0.000
21	28	−7	49	1.750
				14.214

Do not reject H_0. The digits are evenly distributed.

55.

Hourly Wage	f	M	fM	$M - x$	$(M - x)^2$	$f(M - x)^2$
$5.50 up to 6.50	20	6	120	−2.222	4.938	98.8
6.50 up to 7.50	24	7	168	−1.222	1.494	35.9
7.50 up to 8.50	130	8	1040	−0.222	0.049	6.4
8.50 up to 9.50	68	9	612	0.778	0.605	41.1
9.50 up to 10.50	28	10	280	1.778	3.161	88.5
Total	270		2220			270.7

The sample mean is 8.222, found by $2{,}220/270$. The sample standard deviation is 1.003, found as the square root of $270.7/269$.
$H_0:$ The population of wages follows a normal distribution.
$H_1:$ The population of hourly wages does not follow a normal distribution.
Reject the null if $\chi^2 > 4.605$.

Wage	z-values	Area	Found by	f_e	f_o	$f_o - f_e$	$(f_o - f_e)^2$	$[(f_o - f_e)^2]/f_e$
Under $6.50	Under −1.72	0.0427	0.5000 − 0.4573	11.529	20	−8.471	71.7578	6.2241
6.50 up to 7.50	−1.72 up to −0.72	0.1931	0.4573 − 0.2642	52.137	24	28.137	791.6908	15.1848
7.50 up to 8.50	−0.72 up to 0.28	0.3745	0.2642 + 0.1103	101.115	130	−28.885	834.3432	8.2514
8.50 up to 9.50	0.28 up to 1.27	0.2877	0.3980 − 0.1103	77.679	68	9.679	93.6830	1.2060
9.50 or more	1.27 or more	0.1020	0.5000 − 0.3980	27.54	28	−0.46	0.2116	0.0077
Total		1.0000		270	270	0		30.874

Since 30.874 is greater than 4.605, we reject the null hypothesis not from a normal distribution.

57. H_0: Gender and attitude toward the deficit are not related.
H_1: Gender and attitude toward the deficit are related.
Reject H_0 if $\chi^2 > 5.991$.

$$\chi^2 = \frac{(244 - 292.41)^2}{292.41} + \frac{(194 - 164.05)^2}{164.05}$$
$$+ \frac{(68 - 49.53)^2}{49.53} + \frac{(305 - 256.59)^2}{256.59}$$
$$+ \frac{(114 - 143.95)^2}{143.95} + \frac{(25 - 43.47)^2}{43.47} = 43.578$$

Since $43.578 > 5.991$, you reject H_0. A person's position on the deficit is influenced by his or her gender.

59. H_0: Whether a claim is filed and age are not related.
H_1: Whether a claim is filed and age are related.
Reject H_0 if $\chi^2 > 7.815$.

$$\chi^2 = \frac{(170 - 203.33)^2}{203.33} + \cdots + \frac{(24 - 35.67)^2}{35.67} = 53.639$$

Reject H_0. Age is related to whether a claim is filed.

61. H_0: $\pi_{BL} = \pi_O = .23$, $\pi_Y = \pi_G = .15$, $\pi_{BR} = \pi_R = .12$. H_1: The proportions are not as given. Reject H_0 if $\chi^2 > 15.086$.

Color	f_o	f_e	$(f_o - f_e)^2 / f_e$
Blue	12	16.56	1.256
Brown	14	8.64	3.325
Yellow	13	10.80	0.448
Red	14	8.64	3.325
Orange	7	16.56	5.519
Green	12	10.80	0.133
Total	72		14.006

Do not reject H_0. The color distribution agrees with the manufacturer's information.

63. H_0: Salary and winning are not related H_1: Salary and winning are related   Reject H_0 if $\chi^2 > 3.84$.

	Salary		
Winning	**Lower Half**	**Top Half**	**Total**
No	8	5	13
Yes	7	10	17
Total	15	15	

$$\chi^2 = \frac{(8 - 6.5)^2}{6.5} + \frac{(5 - 6.5)^2}{6.5} + \frac{(7 - 8.5)^2}{8.5} + \frac{(10 - 8.5)^2}{8.5} = 1.22$$

Do not reject H_0. Conclude that salary and winning may not be related.

CHAPTER 16

1. a. If the number of pluses (successes) in the sample is 9 or more, reject H_0.
b. Reject H_0 because the cumulative probability associated with nine or more successes (.073) does not exceed the significance level (.10).

3. a. H_0: $\pi \le .50$; H_1: $\pi > .50$; $n = 10$
b. H_0 is rejected if there are nine or more plus signs. A "+" represents a loss.
c. Reject H_0. It is an effective program because there were nine people who lost weight.

5. a. H_0: $\pi \le .50$ (There is no change in weight.)
H_1: $\pi > .50$ (There is a loss of weight.)
b. Reject H_0 if $z > 1.65$.
c. $z = \dfrac{(32 - .50) - .50(45)}{.50\sqrt{45}} = 2.68$
d. Reject H_0. The weight loss program is effective.

7. H_0: $\pi \le .50$, H_1: $\pi > .50$. H_0 is rejected if $z > 2.05$.

$$z = \frac{42.5 - 40.5}{4.5} = .44$$

Because $.44 < 2.05$, do not reject H_0. No preference.

9. a. H_0: Median $\le \$81,500$; H_1: Median $> \$81,500$
b. H_0 is rejected if $z > 1.65$.
c. $z = \dfrac{170 - .50 - 100}{7.07} = 9.83$
H_0 is rejected. The median income is greater than $81,500.

11.

Couple	Difference	Rank
1	550	7
2	190	5
3	250	6
4	−120	3
5	−70	1
6	130	4
7	90	2

Sums: -4, $+24$. So $T = 4$ (the smaller of the two sums). From Appendix B.8, .05 level, one-tailed test, $n = 7$, the critical value is 3. Since the T of $4 > 3$, do not reject H_0 (one-tailed test). There is no difference in square footage. Professional couples do not live in larger homes.

13. a. H_0: The production is the same for the two systems.
H_1: Production using the Mump method is greater.
b. H_0 is rejected if $T \le 21$, $n = 13$.
c. The calculations for the first three employees are:

Employee	Old	Mump	d	Rank	R^+	R^-
A	60	64	4	6	6	
B	40	52	12	12.5	12.5	
C	59	58	−1	2		2

The sum of the negative ranks is 6.5. Since 6.5 is less than 21, H_0 is rejected. Production using the Mump method is greater.

15. H_0: The distributions are the same. H_1: The distributions are not the same. Reject H_0 if $z < -1.96$ or $z > 1.96$.

A		**B**	
Score	**Rank**	**Score**	**Rank**
38	4	26	1
45	6	31	2
56	9	35	3
57	10.5	42	5
61	12	51	7
69	14	52	8
70	15	57	10.5
79	16	62	13
	86.5		49.5

$$z = \frac{86.5 - \dfrac{8(8 + 8 + 1)}{2}}{\sqrt{\dfrac{8(8)(8 + 8 + 1)}{12}}} = 1.943$$

H_0 is not rejected. There is no difference in the two populations.

17. H_0: The distributions are the same. H_1: The distribution of Campus is to the right. Reject H_0 if $z > 1.65$.

Campus		Online	
Age	**Rank**	**Age**	**Rank**
26	6	28	8
42	16.5	16	1
65	22	42	16.5
38	13	29	9.5
29	9.5	31	11
32	12	22	3
59	21	50	20
42	16.5	42	16.5
27	7	23	4
41	14	25	5
46	19		94.5
18	2		
	158.5		

$$z = \frac{158.5 - \dfrac{12(12 + 10 + 1)}{2}}{\sqrt{\dfrac{12(10)(12 + 10 + 1)}{12}}} = 1.35$$

H_0 is not rejected. There is no difference in the distributions.

19. ANOVA requires that we have two or more populations, the data are interval- or ratio-level, the populations are normally distributed, and the population standard deviations are equal. Kruskal-Wallis requires only ordinal-level data, and no assumptions are made regarding the shape of the populations.

21. a. H_0: The three population distributions are equal. H_1: Not all of the distributions are the same.
b. Reject H_0 if $H > 5.991$.
c.

Sample 1 Rank	Sample 2 Rank	Sample 3 Rank
8	5	1
11	6.5	2
14.5	6.5	3
14.5	10	4
16	12	9
64	13	19
	53	

$$H = \frac{12}{16(16 + 1)}\left[\frac{(64)^2}{5} + \frac{(53)^2}{6} + \frac{(19)^2}{5}\right] - 3(16 + 1)$$
$$= 59.98 - 51 = 8.98$$

d. Reject H_0 because $8.98 > 5.991$. The three distributions are not equal.

23. H_0: The distributions of the lengths of life are the same.
H_1: The distributions of the lengths of life are not the same.
H_0 is rejected if $H > 9.210$.

Salt		Fresh		Others	
Hours	**Rank**	**Hours**	**Rank**	**Hours**	**Rank**
167.3	3	160.6	1	182.7	13
189.6	15	177.6	11	165.4	2
177.2	10	185.3	14	172.9	7
169.4	6	168.6	4	169.2	5
180.3	12	176.6	9	174.7	8
	46		39		35

$$H = \frac{12}{15(16)}\left[\frac{(46)^2}{5} + \frac{(39)^2}{5} + \frac{(35)^2}{5}\right] - 3(16) = 0.62$$

H_0 is not rejected. There is no difference in the three distributions.

25. a.

Scatter Diagram of Female versus Male

b.

Male	Female	d	d^2
4	5	−1	1
6	4	2	4
7	8	−1	1
2	7	−5	25
12	11	1	1
8	6	2	4
5	3	2	4
3	9	−6	36
13	2	11	121
14	10	4	16
1	1	0	0
9	13	−4	16
10	12	−2	4
11	14	−3	9
		Total	242

$$r_s = 1 - \frac{6(242)}{14(14^2 - 1)} = 0.47$$

c. H_0: No correlation among the ranks.
H_1: A positive correlation among the ranks.
Reject H_0 if $t > 1.782$.

$$t = 0.47\sqrt{\frac{14 - 2}{1 - (0.47)^2}} = 1.84$$

H_0 is rejected. We conclude the correlation in population among the ranks is positive. Husbands and wives generally like the same shows.

27.

Representative	Sales	Rank	Training Rank	d	d^2
1	319	8	8	0	0
2	150	1	2	1	1
3	175	2	5	3	9
4	460	10	10	0	0
5	348	9	7	−2	4
6	300	6.5	1	5.5	30.25
7	280	5	6	1	1
8	200	4	9	5	25
9	190	3	4	1	1
10	300	6.5	3	−3.5	12.25
					83.50

a. $r_s = 1 - \dfrac{6(83.5)}{10(10^2 - 1)} = 0.494$
A moderate positive correlation

b. H_0: No correlation among the ranks. H_1: A positive correlation among the ranks. Reject H_0 if $t > 1.860$.

$$t = 0.494\sqrt{\frac{10 - 2}{1 - (0.494)^2}} = 1.607$$

H_0 is not rejected. The correlation in population among the ranks could be 0.

29. H_0: $\pi = .50$. H_1: $\pi \ne .50$. Use a software package to develop the binomial probability distribution for $n = 19$ and $\pi = .50$. H_0 is rejected if there are either 5 or fewer "+" signs, or 14 or more. The total of 12 "+" signs falls in the acceptance region. H_0 is not rejected. There is no preference between the two shows.

31. H_0: $\pi = .50$ H_1: $\pi \ne .50$
H_0 is rejected if there are 12 or more or 3 or fewer plus signs. Because there are only 8 plus signs, H_0 is not rejected. There is no preference with respect to the two brands of components.

33. H_0: $\pi = .50$; H_1: $\pi \ne .50$. Reject H_0 if $z > 1.96$ or $z < -1.96$.
$$z = \frac{159.5 - 100}{7.071} = 8.415$$
Reject H_0. There is a difference in the preference for the two types of orange juice.

35. H_0: Rates are the same; H_1: The rates are not the same.
H_0 is rejected if $H > 5.991$. $H = .082$. Do not reject H_0.

37. H_0: The populations are the same. H_1: The populations differ.
Reject H_0 if $H > 7.815$. $H = 14.30$. Reject H_0.

39. $r_s = 1 - \dfrac{6(78)}{12(12^2 - 1)} = 0.727$
H_0: There is no correlation between the rankings of the coaches and of the sportswriters.
H_1: There is a positive correlation between the rankings of the coaches and of the sportswriters.
Reject H_0 if $t > 1.812$.
$$t = 0.727\sqrt{\frac{12 - 2}{1 - (.727)^2}} = 3.348$$
H_0 is rejected. There is a positive correlation between the sportswriters and the coaches.

41. **a.** H_0: There is no difference in the distributions of the selling prices in the five townships. H_1: There is a difference in the distributions of the selling prices of the five townships. H_0 is rejected if H is greater than 9.488. The computed value of H is 4.70, so the null hypothesis is not rejected. The sample data do not suggest a difference in the distributions of selling prices.
   b. H_0: There is no difference in the distributions of the selling prices depending on the number of bedrooms. H_1: There is a difference in the distributions of the selling prices depending on the number of bedrooms. H_0 is rejected if H is greater than 9.448. The computed value of H is 16.34, so the null hypothesis is rejected. The sample data indicate there is a difference in the distributions of selling prices based on the number of bedrooms. Note: Combine 6 or more into a single group.
   c. H_0: There is no difference in the distributions of the distance from the center of the city depending on whether the home had a pool or not. H_1: There is a difference in the distributions of the distances from the center of the city depending on whether the home has a pool or not. H_0 is rejected if H is greater than 3.84. The computed value of H is 3.37, so the null hypothesis is not rejected. The sample data do not suggest a difference in the distributions of the distances.

43. **a.** H_0: The distributions of the maintenance costs are the same for all manufacturers.
   H_1: The distributions of the costs are not the same.
   H_0 is rejected if $H > 5.991$.
   $$H = \frac{12}{80(81)}\left[\frac{(1765)^2}{47} + \frac{(972)^2}{25} + \frac{(503)^2}{8}\right] - 3(81) = 8.29$$
   H_0 is rejected. There is a difference in the maintenance cost for the three bus manufacturers.
   b. H_0: The distributions of the maintenance costs are the same for bus capacities.
   H_1: The distributions of the costs are not the same.

H_0 is rejected if $H > 7.815$.
$$H = \frac{12}{80(81)}\left[\frac{(96.5)^2}{4} + \frac{(332.5)^2}{7} + \frac{(388.5)^2}{9} + \frac{(2422.5)^2}{60}\right] - 3(81) = 2.74$$
H_0 is not rejected. There is no difference in the maintenance cost for the four different capacities.
   c. H_0: The distributions are the same.
   H_1: The distributions are different.
   Reject H_0 if $z < -1.96$ or $z > 1.96$.
   $$W = \frac{2{,}252 - \dfrac{53(53 + 27 + 1)}{2}}{\sqrt{\dfrac{(53)(27)(53 + 27 + 1)}{12}}} = 1.07$$
   We fail to reject H_0. The distributions could be the same.

CHAPTER 17

1. 114.6, found by ($19,989/$17,446)(100)
   123.1, found by ($21,468/$17,446)(100)
   124.3, found by ($21,685/$17,446)(100)
   91.3, found by ($15,922/$17,446)(100)
   105.3, found by ($18,375/$17,446)(100)
   314.2, found by ($54,818/$17,446)(100)
   475.4, found by ($83,040/$17,446)(100)
3. The mean sales for the earliest three years is $(486.6 + 506.8 + 522.2)/3, or $505.2.
   2011: 90.4, found by (456.6/505.2)(100)
   2012: 85.8, found by (433.3/505.2)(100)
   Net sales decreased by 9.6 and 14.2%, respectively.
5. **a.** $P_t = \dfrac{3.35}{2.49}(100) = 134.54$ $P_s = \dfrac{4.49}{3.29}(100) = 136.47$
   $P_c = \dfrac{4.19}{1.59}(100) = 263.52$ $P_a = \dfrac{2.49}{1.79}(100) = 139.11$
   b. $P = \dfrac{14.52}{9.16}(100) = 158.52$
   c. $P = \dfrac{\$3.35(6) + 4.49(4) + 4.19(2) + 2.49(3)}{\$2.49(6) + 3.29(4) + 1.59(2) + 1.79(3)}(100) = 147.1$
   d. $P = \dfrac{\$3.35(6) + 4.49(5) + 4.19(3) + 2.49(4)}{\$2.49(6) + 3.29(5) + 1.59(3) + 1.79(4)}(100) = 150.2$
   e. $I = \sqrt{(147.1)(150.2)} = 148.64$
7. **a.** $P_W = \dfrac{0.10}{0.07}(100) = 142.9$ $P_C = \dfrac{0.03}{0.04}(100) = 75.0$
   $P_S = \dfrac{0.15}{0.15}(100) = 100$ $P_H = \dfrac{0.10}{0.08}(100) = 125.0$
   b. $P = \dfrac{0.38}{0.34}(100) = 111.8$
   c.
   $$P = \frac{0.10(17{,}000) + 0.03(125{,}000) + 0.15(40{,}000) + 0.10(62{,}000)}{0.07(17{,}000) + 0.04(125{,}000) + 0.15(40{,}000) + 0.08(62{,}000)} \times (100) = 102.92$$
   d.
   $$P = \frac{0.10(20{,}000) + 0.03(130{,}000) + 0.15(42{,}000) + 0.10(65{,}000)}{0.07(20{,}000) + 0.04(130{,}000) + 0.15(42{,}000) + 0.08(65{,}000)} \times (100) = 103.32$$
   e. $I = \sqrt{102.92(103.32)} = 103.12$
9. $V = \dfrac{\$3.8(64) + 7.9(2) + 6.9(10{,}780) + 6.4(220)}{\$1.81(116) + 3.56(2) + 2.32(8{,}967) + 2.72(227)}(100)$
   $= 351.46$
11. **a.** $I = \dfrac{6.8}{5.3}(0.20) + \dfrac{362.26}{265.88}(0.40) + \dfrac{125.0}{109.6}(0.25)$
   $+ \dfrac{622{,}864}{529{,}917}(0.15) = 1.263.$
   Index is 126.3.
   b. Business activity increased 26.3% from 2000 to 2014.

13. $x = (\$89,673)/2.32531 = \$38,564$

"Real" salary increased $\$38,564 - \$19,800 = \$18,764$.

15.

Year	Tinora	Tinora Index	National Index
2000	$28,650	100.0	100
2009	33,972	118.6	122.5
2013	37,382	130.5	136.9

The Tinora teachers received smaller increases than the national average.

17. The index (2000 = 100) for selected years is:

Year	Index	Year	Index	Year	Index	Year	Index
2001	114.5	2004	160.4	2007	187.4	2010	170.0
2002	129.7	2005	163.9	2008	186.6	2011	166.9
2003	146.0	2006	172.0	2009	178.4	2012	172.3

The domestic sales increased almost 90% between 2000 and 2007 and then decreased about 10 percent over the next five years.

19. The index (2000 = 100) for selected years is:

Year	Index	Year	Index	Year	Index	Year	Index
2001	105.4	2004	165.1	2007	241.7	2010	271.0
2002	116.8	2005	186.7	2008	265.2	2011	304.5
2003	139.9	2006	198.6	2009	261.5	2012	315.2

International sales more than tripled between 2000 and 2012.

21. The index (2000 = 100) for selected years is:

Year	Index	Year	Index	Year	Index	Year	Index
2001	100.9	2004	108.9	2007	118.1	2010	113.0
2002	107.3	2005	114.6	2008	117.6	2011	116.8
2003	109.6	2006	121.1	2009	114.5	2012	117.6

The number of employees increased about 15% between 2000 and 2005 and has remained at the same level since 2012.

23. The index (2004 = 100) for selected years is:

Year	2005	2006	2007	2008	2009	2010	2011	2012
Index	113.4	117.2	124.5	132.1	136.6	111.6	109.9	109.9

Revenue increased about 37% until 2009, then returned to almost 2005 levels.

25. The index (2004 = 100) for selected years is:

Year	2005	2006	2007	2008	2009	2010	2011	2012
Index	94.5	97.2	98.2	100.6	99.4	93.5	88.3	92.6

The number of employees decreased around 7% between 2008 and 2012.

27. $P_{ma} = \dfrac{2.00}{0.81}(100) = 246.91$ $P_{sh} = \dfrac{1.88}{0.84}(100) = 223.81$

$P_{mi} = \dfrac{2.89}{1.44}(100) = 200.69$ $P_{po} = \dfrac{3.99}{2.91}(100) = 137.11$

29. $P = \dfrac{\$2.00(18) + 1.88(5) + 2.89(70) + 3.99(27)}{\$0.81(18) + 0.84(5) + 1.44(70) + 2.91(27)}(100) = 179.37$

31. $I = \sqrt{179.37(178.23)} = 178.80$

33. $P_R = \dfrac{0.60}{0.50}(100) = 120$ $P_S = \dfrac{0.90}{1.20}(100) = 75.0$

$P_W = \dfrac{1.00}{0.85}(100) = 117.65$

35. $P = \dfrac{0.60(320) + 0.90(110) + 1.00(230)}{0.50(320) + 1.20(110) + 0.85(230)}(100) = 106.87$

37. $P = \sqrt{(106.87)(106.04)} = 106.45$

39. $P_c = \dfrac{0.05}{0.06}(100) = 83.33$ $P_c = \dfrac{0.12}{0.10}(100) = 120$

$P_P = \dfrac{0.18}{0.20}(100) = 90$ $P_E = \dfrac{.015}{0.15}(100) = 100$

41. $P = \dfrac{0.05(2,000) + 0.12(200) + 0.18(400) + 0.15(100)}{0.06(2,000) + 0.10(200) + 0.20(400) + 0.15(100)}(100)$

$= 89.79$

43. $I = \sqrt{(89.79)(91.25)} = 90.52$

45. $P_A = \dfrac{0.76}{0.287}(100) = 264.81$ $P_N = \dfrac{2.50}{0.17}(100) = 1{,}470.59$

$P_P = \dfrac{26.00}{3.18}(100) = 817.61$ $P_P = \dfrac{490}{133}(100) = 368.42$

47. $P = \dfrac{0.76(1,000) + 2.50(5,000) + 26(60,000) + 490(500)}{0.287(1,000) + 0.17(5,000) + 3.18(60,000) + 133(500)} \times$

$(100) = 703.56$

49. $I = \sqrt{(703.56)(686.58)} = 695.02$

51. $I = 100\left[\dfrac{1,971.0}{1,159.0}(0.20) + \dfrac{91}{87}(0.10) + \dfrac{114.7}{110.6}(0.40)\right.$

$\left. + \dfrac{1,501}{1,214}(0.30)\right] = 123.05$

The economy is up 23.05% from 1996 to 2013.

53. February: $I = 100\left[\dfrac{6.8}{8.0}(0.40) + \dfrac{23}{20}(0.35) + \dfrac{303}{300}(0.25)\right]$

$= 99.50$

March: $I = 100\left[\dfrac{6.4}{8.0}(0.40) + \dfrac{21}{20}(0.35) + \dfrac{297}{300}(0.25)\right]$

$= 93.50$

55. For 1995: $1,876,466, found by $2,400,000/1.279

For 2012: $1,799,486, found by $3,500,000/1.945

CHAPTER 18

1. The weighted moving averages are: 31,584.8, 33,088.9, 34,205.4, 34,899.8, 35,155.0, 34,887.1

3. The regression equation is $\hat{y} = 8,842 - 88.1273t$.

For 2014, $t = 12$ and $\hat{y} = 8,842 - 88.1273(12) = 7,784.47$

5. $\hat{y} = 1.30 + 0.90t$

$\hat{y} = 1.30 + 0.90(7) = 7.6$

7. a. $b = \dfrac{5.274318 - (1.390087)(15)/5}{55 - (15)^2/5}$

$= \dfrac{1.104057}{10} = 0.1104057$

$a = \dfrac{1.390087}{5} - 0.1104057\left(\dfrac{15}{5}\right) = -0.0531997$

b. 28.95%, found by 1.28945 − 1.0

c. $\hat{y} = -0.0531997 + 0.1104057t$ for 2010, $t = 8$

$\hat{y} = -0.0531997 + 0.1104057(8) = 0.8300459$

Antilog of 0.8300459 = 6.76

9.

Quarter	Average SI Component	Seasonal Index
1	0.6859	0.6911
2	1.6557	1.6682
3	1.1616	1.1704
4	0.4732	0.4768

11.

t	Estimated Pairs (millions)	Seasonal Index	Quarterly Forecast (millions)
21	40.05	110.0	44.055
22	41.80	120.0	50.160
23	43.55	80.0	34.840
24	45.30	90.0	40.770

13. $\hat{y} = 5.1658 + .37805t$. The following are the sales estimates.

Estimate	Index	Seasonally Adjusted
10.080	0.6911	6.966
10.458	1.6682	17.446
10.837	1.1704	12.684
11.215	0.4768	5.343

15. a. The ordered residuals are 2.61, 2.83, −48.50, 15.50, −3.72, 17.17, 6.39, 7.72, −0.41, −16.86, 3.81, 7.25, 8.03, −1.08, and −0.75.

b. There are 2 independent variables (k) and the sample size (n) is 15. For a significance level of .05, the upper value is 1.54. Since the computed value of the Durbin-Watson statistic is 2.48, which is above the upper limit, the null hypothesis is not rejected. There is no autocorrelation among these residuals.

17. a. $\hat{y} = 18,000 - 400t$, assuming the line starts at 18,000 in 1995 and goes down to 10,000 in 2010.
b. 400
c. 8,000, found by 18,000 − 400(25)

19. a.

b. $\hat{y} = 1.00455 + 0.04409t$, using t = 1 for 2005
c. For 2007, $\hat{y} = 1.18091$, and for 2012, $\hat{y} = 1.40136$
d. For 2019, $\hat{y} = 1.70999$
e. Each asset turned over 0.044 times.

21. a.

b. $\hat{y} = 49.140 - 2.9829t$
c. For 2011, $\hat{y} = 40.1913$ and for 2014, $\hat{y} = 31.2426$
d. For 2017, $\hat{y} = 22.2939$
e. The number of employees decreases at a rate of 2,983 per year.

23. a. Log $\hat{y} = 0.790231 + .113669t$
b. Log $\hat{y} = 0.9039$, found by 0.790231 + 0.113669(1), antilog is 8.015
Log $\hat{y} = 1.699583$, found by 0.790231 + .113699(8), antilog is 50.071
c. 29.92, which is the antilog of .113669 minus 1
d. Log $\hat{y} = 2.154258$, antilog is 142.65.

25. a.

b. The equations are $\hat{y} = -2.58 + 1.37t$ and/or log $\hat{y} = -0.133 + 0.0831t$.
The equation using the logarithm appears better because R^2 is larger.
c. log $\hat{y} = -0.133 + 0.0831(4) = 0.1994$, antilog is 1.5827.
log $\hat{y} = -0.133 + 0.0831(9) = 0.6149$, antilog is 4.12.
d. log $\hat{y} = -0.133 + 0.0831(26) = 2.0276$, antilog is 106.56. It is reasonable only if the price rises at the historical rate!
e. The annual rate of increase is 21%, found by the antilog of 0.0831 minus 1.

27. a. July 87.5; August 92.9; September 99.3; October 109.1
b.

Month	Total	Mean	Corrected
July	348.9	87.225	86.777
Aug.	368.1	92.025	91.552
Sept.	395.0	98.750	98.242
Oct.	420.4	105.100	104.560
Nov.	496.2	124.050	123.412
Dec.	572.3	143.075	142.340
Jan.	333.5	83.375	82.946
Feb.	297.5	74.375	73.993
March	347.3	86.825	86.379
April	481.3	120.325	119.707
May	396.2	99.050	98.541
June	368.1	92.025	91.552
		1,206.200	

Correction = 1,200/1,206.2 = 0.99486
c. April, November, and December are periods of high sales, while February's sales are lowest.

Note: The solutions to Exercises 29 to 33 may vary due to rounding and the particular software package used.

29. a.

Seasonal Index by Quarter		
Quarter	Average SI Component	Seasonal Index
1	0.5014	0.5027
2	1.0909	1.0936
3	1.7709	1.7753
4	0.6354	0.6370

b. Production is the largest in the third quarter. It is 77.5% above the average quarter. The second quarter is also above average. The first and fourth quarters are well below average, with the first quarter at about 50% of a typical quarter.

31. a. The seasonal indices for package play are shown below. Recall that period 1 is actually July because the data begin with July.

Period	Index	Period	Index
1	0.19792	7	0.26874
2	0.25663	8	0.63189
3	0.87840	9	1.67943
4	2.10481	10	2.73547
5	0.77747	11	1.67903
6	0.18388	12	0.60633

Notice the 4th period (October) and the 10th period (April) are more than twice the average.

b. The seasonal indices for nonpackage play are:

Period	Index	Period	Index
1	1.73270	7	0.23673
2	1.53389	8	0.69732
3	0.94145	9	1.00695
4	1.29183	10	1.13226
5	0.66928	11	0.98282
6	0.52991	12	1.24486

These indices are more constant. Notice the very low values in the 6th (December) and 7th (January) periods.

c. The seasonal indices for total play are:

Period	Index	Period	Index
1	0.63371	7	0.25908
2	0.61870	8	0.65069
3	0.89655	9	1.49028
4	1.86415	10	2.28041
5	0.74353	11	1.48235
6	0.29180	12	0.78876

These indices show both the peaks in October (4th period) and April (10th period) and the valleys in December (6th period) and January (7th period).

d. Package play is relatively highest in April. Nonpackage play is relatively high in July. Since 70% of total play comes from package play, total play is very similar to package play.

33.

Seasonal Index by Quarter		
Quarter	Average SI Component	Seasonal Index
1	1.1962	1.2053
2	1.0135	1.0212
3	0.6253	0.6301
4	1.1371	1.1457

The regression equation is $\hat{y} = 43.611 + 7.21153t$

Period	Visitors	Index	Forecast
29	252.86	1.2053	304.77
30	260.07	1.0212	265.58
31	267.29	0.6301	168.42
32	274.50	1.1457	314.50

In 2013 there were a total of 928 visitors. A 10% increase in 2014 means there will be 1,021 visitors. The quarterly estimates are $1,021/4 = 255.25$ visitors per quarter.

Period	Visitors	Index	Forecast
Winter	255.25	1.2053	307.65
Spring	255.25	1.0212	260.66
Summer	255.25	0.6301	160.83
Fall	255.25	1.1457	292.44

The regression approach is probably superior because the trend is considered.

35. The linear trend line is $\hat{y} = 0.469 + 0.114t$ and the logarithmic trend line is $\log \hat{y} = -0.0854 + 0.0255t$.

The equation using the logarithm appears better because R^2 is larger. The years 2013 and 2014 would be coded $t = 24$ and $t = 25$, respectively.

For 2013: $\log \hat{y} = -0.0854 + 0.0255(24) = 0.5266$, and its antilog is 3.36.

For 2014: $\log \hat{y} = -0.0854 + 0.0255(25) = 0.5521$, and its antilog is 3.57.

37. The linear trend line for the mean amount per transaction (expressed in constant dollars) is $\hat{y} = 41.58 - 0.238528t$.

Customer spending is definitely declining about $0.24 per year. Here is an output for the regression of transactions over time (notice the p-value for time):

The regression equation is CPI = 41.6 − 0.239 Time

```
Predictor      Coef    SE Coef       T       P
Constant     41.583      1.078   38.56   0.000
Time        −0.23853    0.09003   −2.65   0.016
```

39.

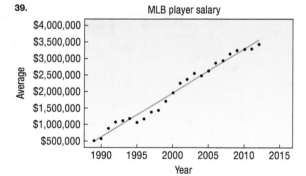

MLB player salary

With 1988 as the base year, the regression equation is:
$\hat{y} = 352,624 + 134,221t$. Salary increased at a rate of $134,221 per year over the period.

CHAPTER 19

1.

Count	38	23	12	10	8
Percent	42	25	13	11	9
Cum %	42	67	80	91	100

About 67% of the complaints concern the problem not being corrected and the price being too high.

3. Chance variation is random in nature; because the cause is a variety of factors, it cannot be entirely eliminated. Assignable variation is not random; it is usually due to a specific cause and can be eliminated.

5. **a.** The A_2 factor is 0.729.
   b. The value for D_3 is 0, and for D_4 it is 2.282.

7. **a.**

Time	$\bar{x}$, Arithmetic Means	R, Range
8:00 a.m.	46	16
8:30 a.m.	40.5	6
9:00 a.m.	44	6
9:30 a.m.	40	2
10:00 a.m.	41.5	9
10:30 a.m.	39.5	1
	251.5	40

$$\bar{\bar{x}} = \frac{251.5}{6} = 41.92 \qquad \bar{R} = \frac{40}{6} = 6.67$$

$$UCL = 41.92 + 0.729(6.67) = 46.78$$

$$LCL = 41.92 - 0.729(6.67) = 37.06$$

   b. Interpreting, the mean reading was 341.92 degrees Fahrenheit. If the oven continues operating as evidenced by the first six hourly readings, about 99.7% of the mean readings will lie between 337.06 degrees and 346.78 degrees.

9. **a.** The fraction defective is 0.0507. The upper control limit is 0.0801 and the lower control limit is 0.0213.
   b. Yes, the 7th and 9th samples indicate the process is out of control.
   c. The process appears to stay the same.

11. $\bar{c} = \dfrac{37}{14} = 2.64$

$2.64 \pm 3 \sqrt{2.64}$

The control limits are 0 and 7.5. The process is out of control on the seventh day.

13. $\bar{c} = \dfrac{6}{11} = 0.545$

$0.545 \pm 3 \sqrt{0.545} = 0.545 \pm 2.215$

The control limits are from 0 to 2.760, so there are no receipts out of control.

15.

Percent Defective	Probability of Accepting Lot
10	.889
20	.558
30	.253
40	.083

17. $P(x \le 1 | n = 10, \pi = .10) = .736$
$P(x \le 1 | n = 10, \pi = .20) = .375$
$P(x \le 1 | n = 10, \pi = .30) = .149$
$P(x \le 1 | n = 10, \pi = .40) = .046$

19.

Reason	Poor wiring	Short coil	Defective plug	Other
Count	80	60	50	10
Percent	40.0	30.0	25.0	5.0
Cum %	40.0	70.0	95.0	100.0

21. **a.** Mean: $UCL = 10.0 + 0.577(0.25) = 10.0 + 0.14425$
$= 10.14425$
$LCL = 10.0 - 0.577(0.25) = 10.0 - 0.14425$
$= 9.85575$
Range: $UCL = 2.115(0.25) = 0.52875$
$LCL = 0(0.25) = 0$
   b. The mean is 10.16, which is above the upper control limit and is out of control. There is too much cola in the soft drinks. The process is in control for variation; an adjustment is needed.

23. **a.** $\bar{\bar{x}} = \dfrac{611.3333}{20} = 30.57$

$\bar{R} = \dfrac{312}{20} = 15.6$

Mean: $UCL = 30.5665 + (1.023)(15.6) = 46.53$
$LCL = 30.5665 - (1.023)(15.6) = 14.61$
Range: $UCL = 2.575(15.6) = 40.17$

   b.

   c. The points all seem to be within the control limits. No adjustments are necessary.

25. $\bar{\bar{x}} = \dfrac{4,183}{10} = 418.3 \qquad \bar{R} = \dfrac{162}{10} = 16.2$

Mean: $UCL = 418.3 + (0.577)(16.2) = 427.65$
$LCL = 418.3 - (0.577)(16.2) = 408.95$
Range: $UCL = 2.115(16.2) = 34.26$
All the points are in control for both the mean and the range.

27. **a.** $p = \dfrac{40}{10(50)} = 0.08$ $3\sqrt{\dfrac{0.08(0.92)}{50}} = 0.115$

$UCL = 0.08 + 0.115 = 0.195$
$LCL = 0.08 - 0.115 = 0$

b.

c. There are no points that exceed the limits.

29.

P Chart for C1

These sample results indicate that the odds are much less than 50-50 for an increase. The percent of stocks that increase is "in control" around 0.25, or 25%. The control limits are 0.06629 and 0.4337.

31. $P(x \le 3 \mid n = 10, \pi = 0.05) = 0.999$
$P(x \le 3 \mid n = 10, \pi = 0.10) = 0.987$
$P(x \le 3 \mid n = 10, \pi = 0.20) = 0.878$
$P(x \le 3 \mid n = 10, \pi = 0.30) = 0.649$
$P(x \le 5 \mid n = 20, \pi = 0.05) = 0.999$
$P(x \le 5 \mid n = 20, \pi = 0.10) = 0.989$
$P(x \le 5 \mid n = 20, \pi = 0.20) = 0.805$
$P(x \le 5 \mid n = 20, \pi = 0.30) = 0.417$

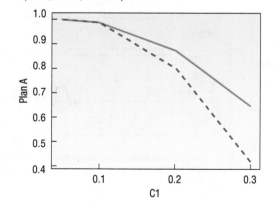

The solid line is the operating characteristic curve for the first plan, and the dashed line, the second. The supplier would prefer the first because the probability of acceptance is higher (above). However, if he is really sure of his quality, the second plan seems higher at the very low range of defect percentages and might be preferred.

33. **a.** $\bar{c} = \dfrac{213}{15} = 14.2;\ 3\sqrt{14.2} = 11.30$

$UCL = 14.2 + 11.3 = 25.5$
$LCL = 14.2 - 11.3 = 2.9$

b.

c. All the points are in control.

35. $\bar{c} = \dfrac{70}{10} = 7.0$

$UCL = 7.0 + 3\sqrt{7} = 14.9$
$LCL = 7.0 - 3\sqrt{7} = 0$

37. $P(x \le 3 \mid n = 20, \pi = .10) = .867$
$P(x \le 3 \mid n = 20, \pi = .20) = .412$
$P(x \le 3 \mid n = 20, \pi = .30) = .108$

APPENDIX D: ANSWERS

Answers to Odd-Numbered Review Exercises

REVIEW OF CHAPTERS 1–4
PROBLEMS
1. **a.** Mean is 147.9. Median is 148.5. Standard deviation is 69.24.
   b. The first quartile is 106. The third quartile is 186.25.
   c.

There are no outliers. The distribution is symmetric. The whiskers and the boxes are about equal on the two sides.
   d. $2^6 = 64$, use 6 classes; $i = \dfrac{299 - 14}{6} = 47.5$, use $i = 50$.

Amount	Frequency
$ 0 up to $ 50	3
50 up to 100	8
100 up to 150	15
150 up to 200	13
200 up to 250	7
250 up to 300	7
Total	50

   e. Answers will vary but include all of the above information.
3. **a.** Mean is $35,768. Median is $34,405. Standard deviation is $5,992.
   b. The first quartile is $32,030. The third quartile is 38,994.
   c.

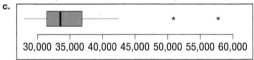

There are two outliers above $50,000. The distribution is positively skewed. The whiskers and the boxes on the right are much larger than the ones on the left.
   d.

Amounts	Frequency
$24,000 up to 30,000	8
30,000 up to 36,000	22
36,000 up to 42,000	15
42,000 up to 48,000	4
48,000 up to 54,000	1
54,000 up to 60,000	1
Total	51

   e. Answers will vary but include all of the above information.
5. **a.** Box plot.
   b. Median is 48, the first quartile is 24, and the third quartile is 84.
   c. Positively skewed with the long tail to the right.
   d. You cannot determine the number of observations.

REVIEW OF CHAPTERS 5–7
PROBLEMS
1. **a.** .035
   b. .018
   c. .648

3. **a.** .0401
   b. .6147
   c. 7,440
5. **a.** $\mu = 1.10$
      $\sigma = 1.18$
   b. About 550
   c. $\mu = 1.833$

REVIEW OF CHAPTERS 8 AND 9
PROBLEMS
1. $z = \dfrac{8.8 - 8.6}{2.0/\sqrt{35}} = 0.59, .5000 - .2224 = .2776$

3. $160 \pm 2.426 \dfrac{20}{\sqrt{40}}, 152.33$ up to 167.67

5. $985.5 \pm 2.571 \dfrac{115.5}{\sqrt{6}}, 864.27$ up to $1,106.73$

7. $240 \pm 2.131 \dfrac{35}{\sqrt{16}}, 221.35$ up to 258.65
   Because 250 is in the interval, the evidence does *not* indicate an increase in production.
9. $n = \left[\dfrac{1.96(25)}{4}\right]^2 = 150$

11. $n = .08(.92)\left(\dfrac{2.33}{0.02}\right)^2 = 999$

13. $n = .4(.6)\left(\dfrac{2.33}{0.03}\right)^2 = 1,448$

REVIEW OF CHAPTERS 10–12
PROBLEMS
1. $H_0: \mu \geq 36; H_1: \mu < 36$. Reject H_0 if $t < -1.683$.
   $$t = \dfrac{35.5 - 36.0}{0.9/\sqrt{42}} = -3.60$$
   Reject H_0. The mean height is less than 36 inches.
3. $H_0: \mu_1 = \mu_2 \quad H_1: \mu_1 \neq \mu_2$
   Reject H_0 if $t < -2.845$ or $t > 2.845$.
   $$s_p^2 = \dfrac{(12 - 1)(5)^2 + (10 - 1)(8)^2}{12 + 10 + 2} = 42.55$$
   $$t = \dfrac{250 - 252}{\sqrt{42.55\left(\dfrac{1}{12} + \dfrac{1}{10}\right)}} = -0.716$$
   H_0 is not rejected. There is no difference in the mean strength of the two glues.
5. $H_0: \mu_1 = \mu_2 = \mu_3 = \mu_4 \quad H_1:$ The means are not all the same
   H_0 rejected if $F > 3.29$.

Source	SS	df	MS	F
Treatments	20.736	3	6.91	1.04
Error	100.00	15	6.67	
Total	120.736	18		

   H_0 is not rejected. There is no difference in the mean sales.
7. **a.** From the graph, marketing salaries may be acting differently.
   b. $H_0: \mu_1 = \mu_2 = \mu_3 = \mu_4$
      $H_1:$ At least one mean is different (for four majors)

H_0: $\mu_1 = \mu_2 = \mu_3$
H_1: At least one mean is different (for three years)
H_0: There is no interaction
H_1: There is interaction

c. The p-value (.482) is high. Do not reject the hypothesis of no interaction.

d. The p-value for majors is small ($.034 < .05$), so there is a difference among mean salaries by major. There is no difference from one year to the next in mean salaries ($.894 > .05$).

REVIEW OF CHAPTERS 13 AND 14 PROBLEMS

1. **a.** Profit

  b. $\hat{y} = a + b_1x_1 + b_2x_2 + b_3x_3 + b_4x_4$

  c. \$163,200

  d. About 86% of the variation in net profit is explained by the four variables.

  e. About 68% of the net profits would be within \$3,000 of the estimates; about 95% would be within 2(\$3,000), or \$6,000, of the estimates; and virtually all would be within 3(\$3,000), or \$9,000, of the estimates.

3. **a.** 0.9261

  b. 2.0469, found by $\sqrt{83.8/20}$

  c. H_0: $\beta_1 = \beta_2 = \beta_3 = \beta_4 = 0$
     H_1: Not all coefficients are zero.
     Reject if $F > 2.87$; computed $F = 62.697$, found by 162.70/4.19.

  d. Could delete x_2 because t-ratio (1.29) is less than the critical t value of 2.086. Otherwise, reject H_0 for x_1, x_3, and x_4 because all of those t-ratios are greater than 2.086.

REVIEW OF CHAPTERS 15 AND 16 PROBLEMS

1. **a.** H_0: Median ≤ 60
     H_1: Median > 60
     $\mu = 20(.5) = 10$
     $\sigma = \sqrt{20(.5)(.5)} = 2.2361$
     H_0 is rejected if $z > 1.65$. There are 16 observations greater than 60.

$$z = \frac{15.5 - 10.0}{2.2361} = 2.46$$

Reject H_0. The median sales per day are greater than 60.

3. H_0: The population lengths are the same.
   H_1: The population lengths are not the same.
   H_0 is rejected if H is > 5.991.

$$H = \frac{12}{24(24 + 1)}\left[\frac{(104.5)^2}{7} + \frac{(125.5)^2}{9} + \frac{(70)^2}{8}\right] - 3(24 + 1)$$
$$= 78.451 - 75 = 3.451$$

Do not reject H_0. The population lengths are the same.

REVIEW OF CHAPTERS 17 AND 18 PROBLEMS

1. **a.** 137.8, found by (14,883/10,799)100

  b. 134.6, found by (14,883/11,056.7)100. Note: 11,056.7 is the average for the period 2008 to 2010.

  c. $8,941 + 1,112t$ and 16,725, found by $8,941 + 1,112(7)$

3. 55.44, found by 1.20[3.5 + (0.7)(61)], and 44.73, found by 0.90[3.5 + (0.7)(66)]

APPENDIX D: ANSWERS

Solutions to Practice Tests

PRACTICE TEST (AFTER CHAPTER 4)
Part 1
1. statistics
2. descriptive statistics
3. population
4. quantitative and qualitative
5. discrete
6. nominal
7. nominal
8. zero
9. seven
10. 50
11. variance
12. never
13. median

Part 2
1. $\sqrt[3]{(1.18)(1.04)(1.02)} = 1.0777$, or 7.77%
2. a. 30 thousands of dollars
   b. 105
   c. 52
   d. 0.19, found by 20/105
   e. 165
   f. 120 and 330
3. a. 70
   b. 71.5
   c. 67.8
   d. 28
   e. 9.34
4. $44.20, found by [(200)$36 + (300)$40 + (500)$50]/1,000
5. a. pie chart
   b. 11.1
   c. three times
   d. 65%

PRACTICE TEST (AFTER CHAPTER 7)
Part 1
1. never
2. experiment
3. event
4. joint
5. a. permutation
   b. combination
6. one
7. three or more outcomes
8. infinite
9. one
10. 0.2764
11. 0.0475
12. independent
13. mutually exclusive
14. only two outcomes
15. bell-shaped

Part 2
1. a. 0.0526, found by (5/20)(4/19)
   b. 0.4474, found by $1 - (15/20)(14/19)$
2. a. 0.2097, found by $16(.15)(.85)^{15}$
   b. 0.9257, found by $1 - (.85)^{16}$
3. 720, found by $6 \cdot 5 \cdot 4 \cdot 3 \cdot 2$

4. a. 2.2, found by .2(1) + .5(2) + .2(3) + .1(4)
   b. 0.76, found by .2(1.44) + .5(0.04) + .2(0.64) + .1(3.24)
5. a. 0.1808. The z value for $2,000 is 0.47, found by (2,000 − 1,600)/850.
   b. 0.4747, found by 0.2939 + 0.1808
   c. 0.0301, found by 0.5000 − 0.4699
6. a. contingency table
   b. 0.625, found by 50/80
   c. 0.75, found by 60/80
   d. 0.40, found by 20/50
   e. 0.125, found by 10/80
7. a. 0.0498, found by $\dfrac{3^0 e^{-3}}{0!}$
   b. 0.2240, found by $= \dfrac{3^3 e^{-3}}{3!}$
   c. 0.1847, found by 1 − [0.0498 + 0.1494 + 0.2240 + 0.2240 + 0.1680]
   d. .0025

PRACTICE TEST (AFTER CHAPTER 9)
Part 1
1. random sample
2. sampling error
3. standard error
4. become smaller
5. point estimate
6. confidence interval
7. population size
8. proportion
9. positively skewed
10. 0.5

Part 2
1. 0.0351, found by 0.5000 − 0.4649. The corresponding
   $z = \dfrac{11 - 12.2}{2.3/\sqrt{12}} = -1.81$
2. a. The population mean is unknown.
   b. 9.3 years, which is the sample mean
   c. 0.3922, found by $2/\sqrt{26}$
   d. The confidence interval is from 8.63 up to 9.97, found by
   $9.3 \pm 1.708\left(\dfrac{2}{\sqrt{26}}\right)$
3. 2,675, found by $.27(1 - .27)\left(\dfrac{2.33}{.02}\right)^2$
4. The confidence interval is from 0.5459 up to 0.7341, found by
   $.64 \pm 1.96\sqrt{\dfrac{.64(1 - .64)}{100}}$

PRACTICE TEST (AFTER CHAPTER 12)
Part 1
1. null hypothesis
2. significance level
3. p-value
4. standard deviation
5. normality
6. test statistic
7. split evenly between the two tails
8. range from negative infinity to positive infinity

9. independent
10. three and 20

Part 2
1. $H_0: \mu \le 90$ $H_1: \mu > 90$ If $t > 2.567$, reject H_0.
$$t = \frac{96 - 90}{12/\sqrt{18}} = 2.12$$
Do not reject the null. The mean time in the park could be 90 minutes.
2. $H_0: \mu_1 = \mu_2$ $H_1: \mu_1 \ne \mu_2$.
$df = 14 + 12 - 2 = 24$
If $t < -2.064$ or $t > 2.064$, then reject H_0.
$$s_p^2 = \frac{(14-1)(30)^2 + (12-1)(40)^2}{14 + 12 - 2} = 1{,}220.83$$
$$t = \frac{837 - 797}{\sqrt{1{,}220.83\left(\frac{1}{14} + \frac{1}{12}\right)}} = \frac{40.0}{13.7455} = 2.910$$
Reject the null hypothesis. There is a difference in the mean miles traveled.
3. **a.** three, because there are 2 df between groups.
   b. 21, found by the total degrees of freedom plus 1.
   c. If the significance level is .05, the critical value is 3.55.
   d. $H_0: \mu_1 = \mu_2 = \mu_3$ H_1: Treatment means are not all the same.
   e. At a 5% significance level, the null hypothesis is rejected.
   f. At a 5% significance level, we can conclude the treatment means differ.

PRACTICE TEST (AFTER CHAPTER 14)
Part 1
1. vertical
2. interval
3. zero
4. -0.77
5. never
6. 7
7. decrease of .5
8. -0.9
9. zero
10. unlimited
11. linear
12. residual
13. two
14. correlation matrix
15. normal distribution

Part 2
1. **a.** 30
   b. The regression equation is $\hat{y} = 90.619X - 0.9401$. If x is zero, the line crosses the vertical axis at -0.9401. As the independent variable increases by one unit, the dependent variable increases by 90.619 units.
   c. 905.2499
   d. 0.3412, found by 129.7275/380.1667. Thirty-four percent of the variation in the dependent variable is explained by the independent variable.
   e. 0.5842, found by $\sqrt{0.3412}$ $H_0: p \ge 0$ $H_1: p < 0$
   Using a significance level of .01, reject H_0 if $t > 2.467$.
$$t = \frac{0.5842\sqrt{30 - 2}}{\sqrt{1 - (0.5842)^2}} = 3.81$$
   Reject H_0. There is a negative correlation between the variables.
2. **a.** 30
   b. 4
   c. 0.5974, found by 227.0928/380.1667
   d. $H_0: \beta_1 = \beta_2 = \beta_3 = \beta_4 = 0$ H_1: Not all βs are 0.
   Reject H_0 if $F > 4.18$ (using a 1% level of significance).

Since the computed value of F is 9.27, reject H_0. Not all of the regression coefficients are zero.
   e. Reject H_0 if $t > 2.787$ or $t < -2.787$ (using a 1% level of significance). Drop variable 2 initially and then rerun. Perhaps you will delete variable(s) 1 and/or 4 also.

PRACTICE TEST (AFTER CHAPTER 16)
Part 1
1. nominal
2. at least 30 observations
3. two
4. 6
5. number of categories
6. dependent
7. binomial
8. comparing two or more independent samples
9. never
10. normal populations, equal standard deviations

Part 2
1. H_0: The proportions are as stated.
   H_1: The proportions are not as stated.
   Using a significance level of .05, reject H_0 if $\chi^2 > 7.815$.
$$\chi^2 = \frac{(120 - 130)^2}{130} + \frac{(40 - 40)^2}{40}$$
$$+ \frac{(30 - 20)^2}{20} + \frac{(10 - 10)^2}{10} = 5.769$$
   Do not reject H_0. Proportions could be as declared.
2. H_0: No relationship between gender and book type.
   H_1: There is a relationship between gender and book type.
   Using a significance level of .01, reject H_0 if $\chi^2 > 9.21$.
$$\chi^2 = \frac{(250 - 197.3)^2}{197.3} + \cdots + \left(\frac{(200 - 187.5)^2}{187.5}\right) = 54.84$$
   Reject H_0. There is a relationship between gender and book type.
3. H_0: The distributions are the same.
   H_1: The distributions are not the same.
   H_0 is rejected if $H > 5.99$.

8:00 a.m.	Ranks	10:00 a.m.	Ranks	1:30 p.m.	Ranks
68	6	59	1.5	67	5
84	20	59	1.5	69	7
75	10.5	63	4	75	10.5
78	15.5	62	3	76	12.5
70	8	78	15.5	79	17
77	14	76	12.5	83	19
88	24	80	18	86	21.5
71	9			86	21.5
				87	23
Sums	107		56		137
Count	8		7		9

$$H = \frac{12}{24(25)}\left[\frac{107^2}{8} + \frac{56^2}{7} + \frac{137^2}{9}\right] - 3(25) = 4.29$$
   H_0 is not rejected. There is no difference in the three distributions.
4. $H_0: \pi \le 1/3$ $H_1: \pi > 1/3$
   At the .01 significance level, the decision rule is to reject H_0 if $z > 2.326$.
$$z = \frac{\left[\frac{210}{500} - \frac{1}{3}\right]}{\sqrt{\frac{\left(\frac{1}{3}\right)\left(1 - \frac{1}{3}\right)}{500}}} = \frac{0.08667}{0.02108} = 4.11$$

Reject the null hypothesis.
The actual proportion of Louisiana children who were obese or overweight is more than one out of three.

PRACTICE TEST (AFTER CHAPTER 18)
Part 1
1. denominator
2. index
3. quantity
4. base period
5. 1982–1984
6. trend
7. moving average
8. autocorrelation
9. residual
10. same

Part 2
1. **a.** 111.54, found by $(145,000/130,000) \times 100$ for 2009
     92.31, found by $(120,000/130,000) \times 100$ for 2010
     130.77, found by $(170,000/130,000) \times 100$ for 2011
     146.15, found by $(190,000/130,000) \times 100$ for 2012
   b. 87.27, found by $(120,000/137,500) \times 100$ for 2010
     126.64, found by $(170,000/137,500) \times 100$ for 2011
     138.18, found by $(190,000/137,500) \times 100$ for 2012
2. **a.** 108.91, found by $(1,100/1,010) \times 100$
   b. 111.18, found by $(4,525/4,070) \times 100$
   c. 110.20, found by $(5,400/4,900) \times 100$
   d. 110.69, found by the square root of $(111.18) \times (110.20)$
3. For January of the fifth year, the seasonally adjusted forecast is 70.0875, found by $1.05 \times [5.50 + 1.25(49)]$.
   For February of the fifth year, the seasonally adjusted forecast is 66.844, found by $0.983 \times [5.50 + 1.25(50)]$.

APPENDIX E: ANSWERS TO SELF-REVIEW

CHAPTER 1

1–1 **a.** On the basis of the sample of 1,960 consumers, we estimate that, if it is marketed, 60% of all consumers will purchase the chicken dinner: $(1,176/1,960) \times 100 = 60\%$.

b. Inferential statistics, because a sample was used to draw a conclusion about how all consumers in the population would react if the chicken dinner were marketed.

1–2 **a.** Age is a ratio-scale variable. A 40-year-old is twice as old as someone 20 years old.

b. Nominal scale. We could arrange the states in any order.

CHAPTER 2

2–1 **a.** Qualitative data, because the customers' response to the taste test is the name of a beverage.

b. Frequency table. It shows the number of people who prefer each beverage.

c.

d.

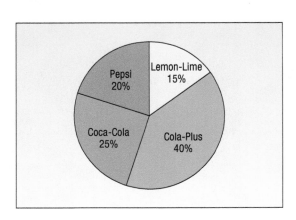

2–2 **a.** The raw data or ungrouped data.

b.

Commission	Number of Salespeople
$1,400 up to $1,500	2
1,500 up to 1,600	5
1,600 up to 1,700	3
1,700 up to 1,800	1
Total	11

c. Class frequencies.

d. The largest concentration of commissions is $1,500 up to $1,600. The smallest commission is about $1,400 and the largest is about $1,800. The typical amount earned is $1,550.

2–3 **a.** $2^6 = 64 < 73 < 128 = 2^7$, so seven classes are recommended.

b. The interval width should be at least $(488 - 320)/7 = 24$. Class intervals of either 25 or 30 are reasonable.

c. Assuming a class interval of 25 and beginning with a lower limit of 300, eight classes are required. If we use an interval of 30 and begin with a lower limit of 300, only 7 classes are required. Seven classes is the better alternative.

Distance Classes	Frequency	Percent
300 up to 330	2	2.7%
330 up to 360	2	2.7
360 up to 390	17	23.3
390 up to 420	27	37.0
420 up to 450	22	30.1
450 up to 480	1	1.4
480 up to 510	2	2.7
Grand Total	73	100.00

d. 17

e. 23.3%, found by 17/73

f. 71.2%, found by $(27 + 22 + 1 + 2)/73$

2–4 **a.**

b.

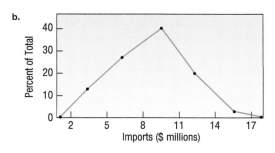

The plots are: (3.5, 12), (6.5, 26), (9.5, 40), (12.5, 20), and (15.5, 2).

c. The smallest annual volume of imports by a supplier is about $2 million, the largest about $17 million. The highest frequency is between $8 million and $11 million.

2–5 a. A frequency distribution.

b.

Hourly Wages	Cumulative Number
Less than $8	0
Less than $10	3
Less than $12	10
Less than $14	14
Less than $16	15

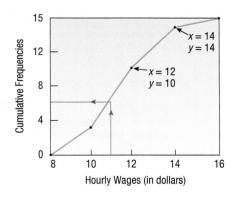

c. About seven employees earn $11.00 or less.

CHAPTER 3

3–1 1. a. $\bar{x} = \dfrac{\Sigma x}{n}$

b. $\bar{x} = \dfrac{\$267,100}{4} = \$66,775$

c. Statistic, because it is a sample value.

d. $66,775. The sample mean is our best estimate of the population mean.

2. a. $\mu = \dfrac{\Sigma x}{N}$

b. $\mu = \dfrac{498}{6} = 83$

c. Parameter, because it was computed using all the population values.

3–2 1. a. $878

b. 3, 3

2. a. 7, found by $(6 + 8)/2 = 7$

b. 3, 3

c. 0

3–3 a.

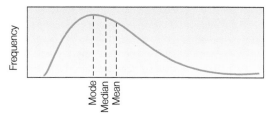

Weekly Sales

b. Positively skewed, because the mean is the largest average and the mode is the smallest.

3–4 a. $237, found by:
$$\dfrac{(95 \times \$400) + (126 \times \$200) + (79 \times \$100)}{95 + 126 + 79} = \$237.00$$

b. The profit per suit is $12, found by $237 − $200 cost − $25 commission. The total profit for the 300 suits is $3,600, found by $300 \times \$12$.

3–5 1. a. About 9.9%, found by $\sqrt[4]{1.458602236}$, then $1.099 − 1.00 = .099$

b. About 10.095%

c. Greater than, because $10.095 > 9.9$

2. 8.63%, found by $\sqrt[20]{\dfrac{120,520}{23,000}} − 1 = 1.0863 − 1$

3–6 a. 22 thousands of pounds, found by $112 − 90$

b. $\bar{x} = \dfrac{824}{8} = 103$ thousands of pounds

c.

x	$(x - \bar{x})$	$(x - \bar{x})^2$
95	−8	64
103	0	0
105	2	4
110	7	49
104	1	2
105	2	4
112	9	81
90	−13	169
	Total	373

Variance $= \dfrac{373}{8} = 46.625$

3–7 a. $\mu = \dfrac{\$16,900}{5} = \$3,380$

b. $\sigma^2 = \dfrac{(3,536 − 3,380)^2 + \cdots + (3,622 − 3,380)^2}{5}$

$= \dfrac{\begin{array}{c}(156)^2 + (−207)^2 + (68)^2 \\ + (−259)^2 + (242)^2\end{array}}{5}$

$= \dfrac{197,454}{5} = 39,490.8$

c. $\sigma = \sqrt{39,490.8} = 198.72$

d. There is more variation in the Pittsburgh office because the standard deviation is larger. The mean is also larger in the Pittsburgh office.

3–8 2.33, found by:
$$\bar{x} = \dfrac{\Sigma x}{n} = \dfrac{28}{7} = 4$$

x	$x - \bar{x}$	$(x - \bar{x})^2$
4	0	0
2	−2	4
5	1	1
4	0	0
5	1	1
2	−2	4
6	2	4
28	0	14

$$s^2 = \frac{\Sigma(x - \bar{x})^2}{n - 1}$$
$$= \frac{14}{7 - 1}$$
$$= 2.33$$
$$s = \sqrt{2.33} = 1.53$$

3–9 a. $k = \dfrac{14.15 - 14.00}{.10} = 1.5$

$k = \dfrac{13.85 - 14.0}{.10} = -1.5$

$1 - \dfrac{1}{(1.5)^2} = 1 - .44 = .56$

b. 13.8 and 14.2

3–10 a. Frequency distribution.

b.

f	M	fM	$(M - \bar{x})$	$f(M - \bar{x})^2$
1	4	4	−8.2	67.24
4	8	32	−4.2	70.56
10	12	120	−0.2	0.40
3	16	48	3.8	43.32
2	20	40	7.8	121.68
20		244		303.20

$$\bar{x} = \frac{\Sigma fM}{M} = \frac{\$244}{20} = \$12.20$$

c. $s = \sqrt{\dfrac{303.20}{20 - 1}} = \$3.99$

CHAPTER 4

4–1 1. a. 79, 105
b. 15
c. From 88 to 97; 75% of the stores are in this range.
2.

7	7
8	0013488
9	1256689
10	1248
11	26

a. 8
b. 10.1, 10.2, 10.4, 10.8
c. 9.5
d. 11.6, 7.7

4–2 a. 7.9
b. $Q_1 = 7.76$, $Q_3 = 8.015$

4–3 The smallest value is 10 and the largest 85; the first quartile is 25 and the third 60. About 50% of the values are between 25 and 60. The median value is 40. The distribution is positively skewed. There are no outliers.

4–4 a. $\bar{x} = \dfrac{407}{5} = 81.4$, Median = 84

$s = \sqrt{\dfrac{923.2}{5 - 1}} = 15.19$

b. $sk = \dfrac{3(81.4 - 84.0)}{15.19} = -0.51$

c.

x	$\dfrac{x - \bar{x}}{s}$	$\left[\dfrac{x - \bar{x}}{s}\right]^3$
73	−0.5530	−0.1691
98	1.0928	1.3051
60	−1.4088	−2.7962
92	0.6978	0.3398
84	0.1712	0.0050
		−1.3154

$$sk = \frac{5}{(4)(3)}[-1.3154]$$
$$= -0.5481$$

d. The distribution is somewhat negatively skewed.

4–5 a. Scatter diagram
b. 16
c. $7,500
d. Strong and direct

CHAPTER 5

5–1 a. Count the number who think the new game is playable.
b. Seventy-three players found the game playable. Many other answers are possible.
c. No. Probability cannot be greater than 1. The probability that the game, if put on the market, will be successful is 65/80, or .8125.
d. Cannot be less than 0. Perhaps a mistake in arithmetic.
e. More than half of the players testing the game liked it. (Of course, other answers are possible.)

5–2 1. $\dfrac{\text{4 queens in deck}}{\text{52 cards total}} = \dfrac{4}{52} = .0769$
Classical.

2. $\dfrac{182}{539} = .338$ Empirical.

3. The probability of the outcome is estimated by applying the subjective approach to estimating a probability. If you think that it is likely that you will save $1 million, then your probability should be between .5 and 1.0.

5–3 a. i. $\dfrac{(50 + 68)}{2,000} = .059$

ii. $1 - \dfrac{302}{2,000} = .849$

b.

c. They are not complementary, but are mutually exclusive.

5–4 **a.** Need for corrective shoes is event A. Need for major dental work is event B.

$$P(A \text{ or } B) = P(A) + P(B) - P(A \text{ and } B)$$
$$= .08 + .15 - .03$$
$$= .20$$

b. One possibility is:

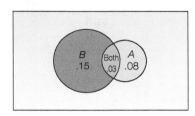

5–5 $(.95)(.95)(.95)(.95) = .8145$

5–6 **a.** .002, found by:

$$\left(\frac{4}{12}\right)\left(\frac{3}{11}\right)\left(\frac{2}{10}\right)\left(\frac{1}{9}\right) = \frac{24}{11,880} = .002$$

b. .14, found by:

$$\left(\frac{8}{12}\right)\left(\frac{7}{11}\right)\left(\frac{6}{10}\right)\left(\frac{5}{9}\right) = \frac{1,680}{11,880} = .1414$$

c. No, because there are other possibilities, such as three women and one man.

5–7 **a.** $P(B_2) = \dfrac{225}{500} = .45$

b. The two events are mutually exclusive, so apply the special rule of addition.

$$P(B_1 \text{ or } B_2) = P(B_1) + P(B_2) = \frac{100}{500} + \frac{225}{500} = .65$$

c. The two events are not mutually exclusive, so apply the general rule of addition.

$$P(B_1 \text{ or } A_1) = P(B_1) + P(A_1) - P(B_1 \text{ and } A_1)$$
$$= \frac{100}{500} + \frac{75}{500} - \frac{15}{500} = .32$$

d. As shown in the example/solution, movies attended per month and age are not independent, so apply the general rule of multiplication.

$$P(B_1 \text{ and } A_1) = P(B_1)P(A_1 \mid B_1)$$
$$= \left(\frac{100}{500}\right)\left(\frac{15}{100}\right) = .03$$

5–8 **a.** $P(\text{visited often}) = \dfrac{80}{195} = .41$

b. $P(\text{visited a store in an enclosed mall}) = \dfrac{90}{195} = .46$

c. The two events are not mutually exclusive, so apply the general rule of addition.

$P(\text{visited often or visited a Sears in an enclosed mall})$
$= P(\text{often}) + P(\text{enclosed mall}) - P(\text{often and enclosed mall})$
$$= \frac{80}{195} + \frac{90}{195} - \frac{60}{195} = .56$$

d. $P(\text{visited often} \mid \text{went to a Sears in an enclosed mall})$
$$= \frac{60}{90} = .67$$

e. Independence requires that $P(A \mid B) = P(A)$. One possibility is: $P(\text{visit often} \mid \text{visited an enclosed mall}) = P(\text{visit often})$. Does $60/90 = 80/195$? No, the two variables are not independent. Therefore, any joint probability in the table must be computed by using the general rule of multiplication.

f. As shown in part (e), visits often and enclosed mall are not independent, so apply the general rule of multiplication.

$$P(\text{often and enclosed mall}) = P(\text{often})P(\text{enclosed} \mid \text{often})$$
$$= \left(\frac{80}{195}\right)\left(\frac{60}{80}\right) = .31$$

g.

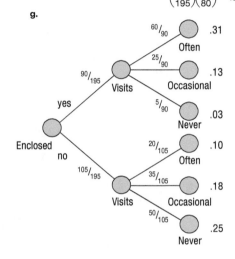

5–9 **a.**
$$P(A_3 \mid B_2) = \frac{P(A_3)P(B_2 \mid A_3)}{P(A_1)P(B_2 \mid A_1) + P(A_2)P(B_2 \mid A_2) + P(A_3)P(B_2 \mid A_3)}$$

b.
$$= \frac{(.50)(.96)}{(.30)(.97) + (.20)(.95) + (.50)(.96)}$$
$$= \frac{.480}{.961} = .499$$

5–10 **1.** $(5)(4) = 20$
2. $(3)(2)(4)(3) = 72$

5–11 **1.** **a.** 60, found by $(5)(4)(3)$.
b. 60, found by:
$$\frac{5!}{(5-3)!} = \frac{5 \cdot 4 \cdot 3 \cdot 2 \cdot 1}{2 \cdot 1}$$
2. 5,040, found by:
$$\frac{10!}{(10-4)!} = \frac{10 \cdot 9 \cdot 8 \cdot 7 \cdot 6 \cdot 5 \cdot 4 \cdot 3 \cdot 2 \cdot 1}{6 \cdot 5 \cdot 4 \cdot 3 \cdot 2 \cdot 1}$$
3. **a.** 35 is correct, found by:
$$_7C_3 = \frac{n!}{r!(n-r)!} = \frac{7!}{3!(7-3)!} = 35$$
b. Yes. There are 21 combinations, found by:
$$_7C_5 = \frac{n!}{r!(n-r)!} = \frac{7!}{5!(7-5)!} = 21$$
4. **a.** $_{50}P_3 = \dfrac{50!}{(50-3)!} = 117,600$

b. $_{50}C_3 = \dfrac{50!}{3!(50-3)!} = 19,600$

CHAPTER 6

6–1 a.

Number of Spots	Probability
1	$\frac{1}{6}$
2	$\frac{1}{6}$
3	$\frac{1}{6}$
4	$\frac{1}{6}$
5	$\frac{1}{6}$
6	$\frac{1}{6}$
Total	$\frac{6}{6} = 1.00$

b.

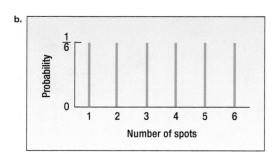

c. $\frac{6}{6}$ or 1.

6–2 a. It is discrete because the values $0.80, $0.90, and $1.20 are clearly separated from each other. Also the sum of the probabilities is 1.00, and the outcomes are mutually exclusive.

b.

x	P(x)	xP(x)
$ .80	.30	0.24
.90	.50	0.45
1.20	.20	0.24
		0.93

The mean is 93 cents.

c.

x	P(x)	$(x - \mu)$	$(x - \mu)^2 P(x)$
$0.80	.30	−0.13	.00507
0.90	.50	−0.03	.00045
1.20	.20	0.27	.01458
			.02010

The variance is .02010, and the standard deviation is 14 cents.

6–3 a. It is reasonable because each employee either uses direct deposit or does not; employees are independent; the probability of using direct deposit is 0.95 for all; and we count the number using the service out of 7.

b. $P(7) = {}_7C_7\,(.95)^7\,(.05)^0 = .6983$

c. $P(4) = {}_7C_4\,(.95)^4\,(.05)^3 = .0036$

d. Answers are in agreement.

6–4 a. $n = 8, \pi = .40$

b. $P(x = 3) = .2787$

c. $P(x > 0) = 1 - P(x = 0) = 1 - .0168 = .9832$

6–5 $P(3) = \dfrac{{}_8C_3\,{}_4C_2}{{}_{12}C_5} = \dfrac{\left(\dfrac{8!}{3!5!}\right)\left(\dfrac{4!}{2!2!}\right)}{\dfrac{12!}{5!7!}}$

$= \dfrac{(56)(6)}{792} = .424$

6–6 $\mu = 4{,}000(.0002) = 0.8$

$P(1) = \dfrac{0.8^1 e^{-0.8}}{1!} = .3595$

CHAPTER 7

7–1 a. $P(x)$

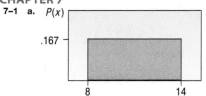

b. $P(x) = (\text{height})(\text{base})$

$= \left(\dfrac{1}{14 - 8}\right)(14 - 8)$

$= \left(\dfrac{1}{6}\right)(6) = 1.00$

c. $\mu = \dfrac{a + b}{2} = \dfrac{14 + 8}{2} = \dfrac{22}{2} = 11$

$\sigma = \sqrt{\dfrac{(b - a)^2}{12}} = \sqrt{\dfrac{(14 - 8)^2}{12}} = \sqrt{\dfrac{36}{12}} = \sqrt{3}$

$= 1.73$

d. $P(10 < x < 14) = (\text{height})(\text{base})$

$= \left(\dfrac{1}{14 - 8}\right)(14 - 10)$

$= \dfrac{1}{6}(4)$

$= .667$

e. $P(x < 9) = (\text{height})(\text{base})$

$= \left(\dfrac{1}{14 - 8}\right)(9 - 8)$

$= 0.167$

7–2 a. $z = (64 - 48)/12.8 = 1.25$. This person's difference of 16 ounces more than average is 1.25 standard deviations above the average.

b. $z = (32 - 48)/12.8 = -1.25$. This person's difference of 16 ounces less than average is 1.25 standard deviations below the average.

7–3 a. $46,400 and $48,000, found by $47,200 ± 1($800).

b. $45,600 and $48,800, found by $47,200 ± 2($800).

c. $44,800 and $49,600, found by $47,200 ± 3($800).

d. $47,200. The mean, median, and mode are equal for a normal distribution.

e. Yes, a normal distribution is symmetrical.

7–4 **a.** Computing z:
$$z = \frac{154 - 150}{5} = 0.80$$

Referring to Appendix B.3, the area is .2881. So $P(150 < \text{temp} < 154) = .2881$.

b. Computing z:
$$z = \frac{164 - 150}{5} = 2.80$$

Referring to Appendix B.3, the area is .4974. So $P(164 > \text{temp}) = .5000 - .4974 = .0026$

7–5 **a.** Computing the z-values:
$$z = \frac{146 - 150}{5} = -0.80 \quad \text{and} \quad z = \frac{156 - 150}{5} = 1.20$$

$$P(146 < \text{temp} < 156) = P(-0.80 < z < 1.20)$$
$$= .2881 + .3849 = .6730$$

b. Computing the z-values:
$$z = \frac{162 - 150}{5} = 2.40 \quad \text{and} \quad z = \frac{156 - 150}{5} = 1.20$$

$$P(156 < \text{temp} < 162) = P(1.20 < z < 2.40)$$
$$= .4918 - .3849 = .1069$$

7–6 85.24 (instructor would no doubt make it 85). The closest area to .4000 is .3997; z is 1.28. Then:
$$1.28 = \frac{x - 75}{8}$$
$$10.24 = x - 75$$
$$x = 85.24$$

7–7 **a.** .0465, found by $\mu = n\pi = 200(.80) = 160$, and $\sigma^2 = n\pi(1 - \pi) = 200(.80)(1 - .80) = 32$. Then,
$$\sigma = \sqrt{32} = 5.66$$
$$z = \frac{169.5 - 160}{5.66} = 1.68$$

Area from Appendix B.3 is .4535. Subtracting from .5000 gives .0465.

b. .9686, found by .4686 + .5000. First calculate z:
$$z = \frac{149.5 - 160}{5.66} = -1.86$$

Area from Appendix B.3 is .4686.

7–8 **a.** .7769, found by:
$$P(\text{Arrival} < 15) = 1 - e^{-\frac{1}{10}(15)}$$
$$= 1 - .2231 = .7769$$

b. .0821, found by:
$$P(\text{Arrival} > 25) = e^{-\frac{1}{10}(25)} = .0821$$

c. .1410, found by
$$P(15 < x < 25) = P(\text{Arrival} < 25) - P(\text{Arrival} < 15)$$
$$= .9179 - .7769 = .1410$$

d. 16.09 minutes, found by:
$$.80 = 1 - e^{-\frac{1}{10}(x)}$$
$$-\ln 0.20 = \frac{1}{10}x$$
$$x = -(-1.609)(10) = 1.609(10) = 16.09$$

CHAPTER 8

8–1 **a.** Students selected are Price, Detley, and Molter.
b. Answers will vary.
c. Skip it and move to the next random number.

8–2 The students selected are Berry, Francis, Kopp, Poteau, and Swetye.

8–3 **a.** 10, found by:
$$_5C_2 = \frac{5!}{2!(5 - 2)!}$$

b.

	Service	Sample Mean
Snow, Tolson	20, 22	21
Snow, Kraft	20, 26	23
Snow, Irwin	20, 24	22
Snow, Jones	20, 28	24
Tolson, Kraft	22, 26	24
Tolson, Irwin	22, 24	23
Tolson, Jones	22, 28	25
Kraft, Irwin	26, 24	25
Kraft, Jones	26, 28	27
Irwin, Jones	24, 28	26

c.

Mean	Number	Probability
21	1	.10
22	1	.10
23	2	.20
24	2	.20
25	2	.20
26	1	.10
27	1	.10
	10	1.00

d. Identical: population mean, μ, is 24, and mean of sample means, $\mu_{\bar{x}}$, is also 24.
e. Sample means range from 21 to 27. Population values go from 20 to 28.
f. No, the population is uniformly distributed.
g. Yes.

8–4 The answers will vary. Here is one solution.

	Sample Number									
	1	2	3	4	5	6	7	8	9	10
	8	2	2	19	3	4	0	4	1	2
	19	1	14	9	2	5	8	2	14	4
	8	3	4	2	4	4	1	14	4	1
	0	3	2	3	1	2	16	1	2	3
	2	1	7	2	19	18	18	16	3	7
Total	37	10	29	35	29	33	43	37	24	17
$\bar{x}$	7.4	2	5.8	7.0	5.8	6.6	8.6	7.4	4.8	3.4

Mean of the 10 sample means is 5.88.

8–5 $$z = \frac{31.08 - 31.20}{0.4/\sqrt{16}} = -1.20$$

The probability that z is greater than -1.20 is .5000 + .3849 = .8849. There is more than an 88% chance the filling operation will produce bottles with at least 31.08 ounces.

CHAPTER 9

9–1 **a.** Unknown. This is the value we wish to estimate.
b. $20,000, point estimate.
c. $20,000 \pm 1.960 \dfrac{\$3,000}{\sqrt{40}} = \$20,000 \pm \$930$

d. The endpoints of the confidence interval are $19,070 and $20,930. About 95% of the intervals similarly constructed would include the population mean.

9–2 a. $\bar{x} = \dfrac{18}{10} = 1.8$ $s = \sqrt{\dfrac{11.6}{10-1}} = 1.1353$

b. The population mean is not known. The best estimate is the sample mean, 1.8 days.

c. $1.80 \pm 2.262 \dfrac{1.1353}{\sqrt{10}} = 1.80 \pm 0.81$

The endpoints are 0.99 and 2.61.

d. t is used because the population standard deviation is unknown.

e. The value of 0 is not in the interval. It is unreasonable to conclude that the mean number of days of work missed is 0 per employee.

9–3 a. $p = \dfrac{420}{1,400} = .30$

b. $.30 \pm 2.576(.0122) = .30 \pm .03$

c. The interval is between .27 and .33. About 99% of the similarly constructed intervals would include the population mean.

9–4 $n = \left(\dfrac{2.576(.279)}{.05}\right)^2 = 206.6$. The sample should be rounded to 207.

9–5 $.375 \pm 1.96 \sqrt{\dfrac{.375(1-.375)}{40}} \sqrt{\dfrac{250-40}{250-1}} =$
$.375 \pm 1.96(.0765)(.9184) = .375 \pm .138$

CHAPTER 10

10–1 a. $H_0: \mu = 16.0; H_1: \mu \neq 16.0$

b. .05

c. $z = \dfrac{\bar{x} - \mu}{\sigma/\sqrt{n}}$

d. Reject H_0 if $z < -1.96$ or $z > 1.96$.

e. $z = \dfrac{16.017 - 16.0}{0.15/\sqrt{50}} = \dfrac{0.0170}{0.0212} = 0.80$

f. Do not reject H_0.

g. We cannot conclude the mean amount dispensed is different from 16.0 ounces.

10–2 a. $H_0: \mu \leq 16.0; H_1: \mu > 16.0$

b. Reject H_0 if $z > 1.645$.

c. $z = \dfrac{16.040 - 16.0}{0.15/\sqrt{50}} = \dfrac{.0400}{.0212} = 1.89$

d. Reject H_0.

e. The mean amount dispensed is more than 16.0 ounces.

f. p-value $= .5000 - .4706 = .0294$. The p-value is less than α (.05), so H_0 is rejected. It is the same conclusion as in part (d).

10–3 a. $H_0: \mu \leq 305; H_1: \mu > 305$

b. $df = n - 1 = 20 - 1 = 19$
The decision rule is to reject H_0 if $t > 1.729$.

c. $t = \dfrac{\bar{x} - \mu}{s/\sqrt{n}} = \dfrac{311 - 305}{12/\sqrt{20}} = 2.236$
Reject H_0 because $2.236 > 1.729$. The modification increased the mean battery life to more than 305 days.

10–4 a. $H_0: \mu \geq 9.0; H_1: \mu < 9.0$

b. 7, found by $n - 1 = 8 - 1 = 7$

c. Reject H_0 if $t < -2.998$.

d. $t = -2.494$, found by:

$$s = \sqrt{\dfrac{0.36}{8-1}} = 0.2268$$

$$\bar{x} = \dfrac{70.4}{8} = 8.8$$

Then

$$t = \dfrac{8.8 - 9.0}{0.2268/\sqrt{8}} = -2.494$$

Since -2.494 lies to the right of -2.998, H_0 is not rejected. We have not shown that the mean is less than 9.0.

e. The p-value is between .025 and .010.

10–5 .0054, found by determining the area under the curve between 10,078 and 10,180.

$$z = \dfrac{\bar{x}_c - \mu_1}{\sigma/\sqrt{n}}$$

$$= \dfrac{10,078 - 10,180}{400/\sqrt{100}} = -2.55$$

The area under the curve for a z of -2.55 is .4946 (Appendix B.3), and $.5000 - .4946 = .0054$.

CHAPTER 11

11–1 a. $H_0: \mu_W \leq \mu_M$ $H_1: \mu_W > \mu_M$
The subscript W refers to the women and M to the men.

b. Reject H_0 if $z > 1.645$.

c. $z = \dfrac{\$1,500 - \$1,400}{\sqrt{\dfrac{(\$250)^2}{50} + \dfrac{(\$200)^2}{40}}} = 2.11$

d. Reject the null hypothesis.

e. p-value $= .5000 - .4826 = .0174$

f. The mean amount sold per day is larger for women.

11–2 a. $H_0: \mu_d = \mu_a$ $H_1: \mu_d \neq \mu_a$

b. $df = 6 + 8 - 2 = 12$
Reject H_0 if $t < -2.179$ or $t > 2.179$.

c. $\bar{x}_1 = \dfrac{42}{6} = 7.00$ $s_1 = \sqrt{\dfrac{10}{6-1}} = 1.4142$

$\bar{x}_2 = \dfrac{80}{8} = 10.00$ $s_2 = \sqrt{\dfrac{36}{8-1}} = 2.2678$

$s_p^2 = \dfrac{(6-1)(1.4142)^2 + (8-1)(2.2678)^2}{6 + 8 - 2}$

$= 3.8333$

$t = \dfrac{7.00 - 10.00}{\sqrt{3.8333\left(\dfrac{1}{6} + \dfrac{1}{8}\right)}} = -2.837$

d. Reject H_0 because -2.837 is less than the critical value.

e. The p-value is less than .02.

f. The mean number of defects is not the same on the two shifts.

g. Independent populations, populations follow the normal distribution, populations have equal standard deviations.

11–3 a. $H_0: \mu_c \geq \mu_a$ $H_1: \mu_c < \mu_a$

b. $df = \dfrac{[(356^2/10) + (857^2/8)]^2}{\dfrac{(356^2/10)^2}{10 - 1} + \dfrac{(857^2/8)^2}{8 - 1}} = 8.93$

so $df = 8$

c. Reject H_0 if $t < -1.860$.

d. $t = \dfrac{\$1{,}568 - \$1{,}967}{\sqrt{\dfrac{356^2}{10} + \dfrac{857^2}{8}}} = \dfrac{-399.00}{323.23} = -1.234$

e. Do not reject H_0.

f. There is no difference in the mean account balance of those who applied for their card or were contacted by a telemarketer.

11–4 a. $H_0: \mu_d \leq 0, H_1: \mu_d > 0$

b. Reject H_0 if $t > 2.998$.

c.

Name	Before	After	d	$(d - \bar{d})$	$(d - \bar{d})^2$
Hunter	155	154	1	−7.875	62.0156
Cashman	228	207	21	12.125	147.0156
Mervine	141	147	−6	−14.875	221.2656
Massa	162	157	5	−3.875	15.0156
Creola	211	196	15	6.125	37.5156
Peterson	164	150	14	5.125	26.2656
Redding	184	170	14	5.125	26.2656
Poust	172	165	7	−1.875	3.5156
			71		538.8750

$$\bar{d} = \frac{71}{8} = 8.875$$

$$s_d = \sqrt{\frac{538.875}{8 - 1}} = 8.774$$

$$t = \frac{8.875}{8.774/\sqrt{8}} = 2.861$$

d. Do not reject H_0. We cannot conclude that the students lost weight. The p-value is less than .025 but larger than .01.

e. The distribution of the differences must be approximately normal.

CHAPTER 12

12–1 Let Mark's assemblies be population 1, then $H_0: \sigma_1^2 \leq \sigma_2^2$; $H_1: \sigma_1^2 > \sigma_2^2$; $df_1 = 10 - 1 = 9$; and df_2 also equals 9. H_0 is rejected if $F > 3.18$.

$$F = \frac{(2.0)^2}{(1.5)^2} = 1.78$$

H_0 is not rejected. The variation is the same for both employees.

12–2 a. $H_0: \mu_1 = \mu_2 = \mu_3$
$H_1:$ At least one treatment mean is different.

b. Reject H_0 if $F > 4.26$.

c. $\bar{x} = \dfrac{240}{12} = 20$

SS total $= (18 - 20)^2 + \cdots + (32 - 20)^2$
$= 578$
SSE $= (18 - 17)^2 + (14 - 17)^2 + \cdots + (32 - 29)^2$
$= 74$
SST $= 578 - 74 = 504$

d.

Source	Sum of Squares	Degrees of Freedom	Mean Square	F
Treatment	504	2	252	30.65
Error	74	9	8.22	
Total	578	11		

e. H_0 is rejected. There is a difference in the mean number of bottles sold at the various locations.

12–3 a. $H_0: \mu_1 = \mu_2 = \mu_3$
$H_1:$ Not all means are equal.

b. H_0 is rejected if $F > 3.98$.

c. $\bar{x}_G = 8.86$, $\bar{x}_1 = 11$, $\bar{x}_2 = 8.75$, $\bar{x}_3 = 6.8$
SS total $= 53.71$
SST $= 44.16$
SSE $= 9.55$

Source	Sum of Squares	df	Mean Square	F
Treatment	44.16	2	22.08	25.43
Error	9.55	11	0.8682	
Total	53.71	13		

d. H_0 is rejected. The treatment means differ.

e. $(11.0 - 6.8) \pm 2.201 \sqrt{0.8682(\frac{1}{5} + \frac{1}{5})} = 4.2 \pm 1.30 = 2.90$ and 5.50
These treatment means differ because both endpoints of the confidence interval are of the same sign—positive in this problem.

12–4 For types:

$H_0: \mu_1 = \mu_2 = \mu_3$
$H_1:$ The treatment means are not equal.

Reject H_0 if $F > 4.46$.
For months:

$H_0: \mu_1 = \mu_2 = \mu_3 = \mu_4 = \mu_5$
$H_1:$ The block means are not equal.

Reject H_0 if $F > 3.84$.
The analysis of variance table is as follows:

Source	df	SS	MS	F
Types	2	3.60	1.80	0.39
Months	4	31.73	7.93	1.71
Error	8	37.07	4.63	
Total	14	72.40		

The null hypotheses cannot be rejected for either types or months. There is no difference in the mean sales among types or months.

12–5 a. There are four levels of Factor A. The p-value is less than .05, so Factor A means differ.

b. There are three levels of Factor B. The p-value is less than .05, so the Factor B means differ.

c. There are three observations in each cell. There is an interaction between Factor A and Factor B means because the p-value is less than .05.

CHAPTER 13

13–1 a. Advertising expense is the independent variable, and sales revenue is the dependent variable.

b.

c.

x	y	$(x - \bar{x})$	$(x - \bar{x})^2$	$(y - \bar{y})$	$(y - \bar{y})^2$	$(x - \bar{x})(y - \bar{y})$
2	7	−0.5	.25	0	0	0
1	3	−1.5	2.25	−4	16	6
3	8	0.5	.25	1	1	0.5
4	10	1.5	2.25	3	9	4.5
10	28		5.00		26	11.0

$$\bar{x} = \frac{10}{4} = 2.5 \qquad \bar{y} = \frac{28}{4} = 7$$

$$s_x = \sqrt{\frac{5}{3}} = 1.2910$$

$$s_y = \sqrt{\frac{26}{3}} = 2.9439$$

$$r = \frac{\Sigma(X - \bar{X})(y - \bar{y})}{(n - 1)s_x s_y} = \frac{11}{(4 - 1)(1.2910)(2.9439)}$$
$$= 0.9648$$

d. There is a strong correlation between the advertising expense and sales.

13–2 $H_0: \rho \le 0, H_1: \rho > 0.$ H_0 is rejected if $t > 1.714$.

$$t = \frac{.43\sqrt{25 - 2}}{\sqrt{1 - (.43)^2}} = 2.284$$

H_0 is rejected. There is a positive correlation between the percent of the vote received and the amount spent on the campaign.

13–3 a. See the calculations in Self-Review 13–1, part (c).

$$b = \frac{rs_y}{s_x} = \frac{(0.9648)(2.9439)}{1.2910} = 2.2$$

$$a = \frac{28}{4} - 2.2\left(\frac{10}{4}\right) = 7 - 5.5 = 1.5$$

b. The slope is 2.2. This indicates that an increase of $1 million in advertising will result in an increase of $2.2 million in sales. The intercept is 1.5. If there was no expenditure for advertising, sales would be $1.5 million.

c. $\hat{Y} = 1.5 + 2.2(3) = 8.1$

13–4 $H_0: \beta_1 \le 0; H_1: \beta > 0.$ Reject H_0 if $t > 3.182$.

$$t = \frac{2.2 - 0}{0.4243} = 5.1850$$

Reject H_0. The slope of the line is greater than 0.

13–5 a.

y	$\hat{y}$	$(y - \hat{y})$	$(y - \hat{y})^2$
7	5.9	1.1	1.21
3	3.7	−0.7	.49
8	8.1	−0.1	.01
10	10.3	−0.3	.09
			1.80

$$s_{y \cdot x} = \sqrt{\frac{\Sigma(y - \hat{y})^2}{n - 2}}$$
$$= \sqrt{\frac{1.80}{4 - 2}} = .9487$$

b. $r^2 = (.9648)^2 = .9308$

c. Ninety-three percent of the variation in sales is accounted for by advertising expense.

13–6 6.58 and 9.62, since $\hat{y}$ for an x of 3 is 8.1, found by $\hat{y} = 1.5 + 2.2(3) = 8.1$, then $\bar{x} = 2.5$ and $\Sigma(x - \bar{x})^2 = 5$. t from Appendix B.5 for $4 - 2 = 2$ degrees of freedom at the .10 level is 2.920.

$$\hat{y} \pm t(s_{y \cdot x})\sqrt{\frac{1}{n} + \frac{(x - \bar{x})^2}{\Sigma(x - \bar{x})^2}}$$

$$= 8.1 \pm 2.920(0.9487)\sqrt{\frac{1}{4} + \frac{(3 - 2.5)^2}{5}}$$

$$= 8.1 \pm 2.920(0.9487)(0.5477)$$

$$= 6.58 \text{ and } 9.62 \text{ (in \$ millions)}$$

CHAPTER 14

14–1 a. $389,500 or 389.5 (in $000); found by
$2.5 + 3(40) + 4(72) - 3(10) + .2(20) + 1(5) = 3,895$

b. The b_2 of 4 shows profit will go up $4,000 for each extra hour the restaurant is open (if none of the other variables change). The b_3 of −3 implies profit will fall $3,000 for each added mile away from the central area (if none of the other variables change).

14–2 a. The total degrees of freedom $(n - 1)$ is 25. So the sample size is 26.

b. There are 5 independent variables.

c. There is only 1 dependent variable (profit).

d. $S_{Y.12345} = 1.414$, found by $\sqrt{2}$. Ninety-five percent of the residuals will be between −2.828 and 2.828, found by $\pm 2(1.414)$.

e. $R^2 = .714$, found by 100/140. 71.4% of the deviation in profit is accounted for by these five variables.

f. $R_{adj}^2 = .643$, found by

$$1 - \left[\frac{40}{(26 - (5 + 1))}\right]\bigg/\left[\frac{140}{(26 - 1)}\right]$$

14–3 a. $H_0: \beta_1 = \beta_2 = \beta_3 = \beta_4 = \beta_5 = 0$
$H_1:$ Not all of the βs are 0.
The decision rule is to reject H_0 if $F > 2.71$. The computed value of F is 10, found by 20/2. So, you reject H_0, which indicates at least one of the regression coefficients is different from zero.

Based on p-values, the decision rule is to reject the null hypothesis if the p-value is less than .05. The computed value of F is 10, found by 20/2, and has a p-value of .000. Thus, we reject the null hypothesis, which indicates that at least one of the regression coefficients is different from zero.

b. For variable 1: $H_0: \beta_1 = 0$ and $H_1: \beta_1 \ne 0$
The decision rule is to reject H_0 if $t < -2.086$ or $t > 2.086$. Since 2.000 does not go beyond either of those limits, we fail to reject the null hypothesis. This regression coefficient could be zero. We can consider dropping this variable. By parallel logic, the null hypothesis is rejected for variables 3 and 4.

For variable 1, the decision rule is to reject $H_0: \beta_1 = 0$ if the p-value is less than .05. Because the p-value is .056, we cannot reject the null hypothesis. This regression coefficient could be zero. Therefore, we can consider dropping this variable. By parallel logic, we reject the null hypothesis for variables 3 and 4.

c. We should consider dropping variables 1, 2, and 5. Variable 5 has the smallest absolute value of t or largest p-value. So delete it first and compute the regression equation again.

14–4 a. $\hat{y} = 15.7625 + 0.4415x_1 + 3.8598x_2$
$\hat{y} = 15.7625 + 0.4415(30) + 3.8598(1)$
$= 32.87$

b. Female agents make $3,860 more than male agents.

c. $H_0: \beta_3 = 0$
$H_1: \beta_3 \ne 0$
$df = 17$; reject H_0 if $t < -2.110$ or $t > 2.110$

$$t = \frac{3.8598 - 0}{1.4724} = 2.621$$

The t statistic exceeds the critical value of 2.110. Also, the p-value = .0179 and is less than .05. Reject H_0. Gender should be included in the regression equation.

CHAPTER 15

15–1 a. Yes, because both $n\pi$ and $n(1-\pi)$ exceed 5:
$n\pi = 200(.40) = 80$, and $n(1-\pi) = 200(.60) = 120$.
   b. $H_0: \pi \geq .40$
$H_1: \pi < .40$
   c. Reject H_0 if $z < -2.326$.

   d. $z = -0.87$, found by:

$$z = \frac{.37 - .40}{\sqrt{\dfrac{.40(1-.40)}{200}}} = \frac{-.03}{\sqrt{.0012}} = -0.87$$

Do not reject H_0.
   e. The p-value is .1922, found by $.5000 - .3078$.
15–2 a. $H_0: \pi_a = \pi_{ch}$
$H_1: \pi_a \neq \pi_{ch}$
   b. .10
   c. Two-tailed
   d. Reject H_0 if $z < -1.645$ or $z > 1.645$.
   e. $p_c = \dfrac{87 + 123}{150 + 200} = \dfrac{210}{350} = .60$

$p_a = \dfrac{87}{150} = .58$ $p_{ch} = \dfrac{123}{200} = .615$

$z = \dfrac{.58 - .615}{\sqrt{\dfrac{.60(.40)}{150} + \dfrac{.60(.40)}{200}}} = -0.66$

   f. Do not reject H_0.
   g. p-value $= 2(.5000 - .2454) = .5092$
There is no difference in the proportion of adults and children that liked the proposed flavor.
15–3 a. Observed frequencies
   b. Six (six days of the week)
   c. 10. Total observed frequencies $\div 6 = 60/6 = 10$.
   d. 5; $k - 1 = 6 - 1 = 5$
   e. 15.086 (from the chi-square table in Appendix B.7).
   f. $\chi^2 = \Sigma\left[\dfrac{(f_o - f_e)^2}{f_e}\right] = \dfrac{(12 - 10)^2}{10} + \cdots + \dfrac{(9 - 10)^2}{10} = 0.8$
   g. Do not reject H_0.
   h. Evidence fails to show a difference in the proportion of absences by day of the week.
15–4 $H_0: P_C = .60, P_L = .30$, and $P_U = .10$.
H_1: Distribution is not as above.
Reject H_0 if $\chi^2 > 5.991$.

Category	f_o	f_e	$\dfrac{(f_o - f_e)^2}{f_e}$
Current	320	300	1.33
Late	120	150	6.00
Uncollectible	60	50	2.00
	500	500	9.33

Reject H_0. The accounts receivable data do not reflect the national average.
15–5 a. Contingency table
   b. H_0: There is no relationship between income and whether the person played the lottery. H_1: There is a relationship between income and whether the person played the lottery.
   c. Reject H_0 if $\chi^2 > 5.991$.
   d. $\chi^2 = \dfrac{(46 - 40.71)^2}{40.71} + \dfrac{(28 - 27.14)^2}{27.14} + \dfrac{(21 - 27.14)^2}{27.14}$
$+ \dfrac{(14 - 19.29)^2}{19.29} + \dfrac{(12 - 12.86)^2}{12.86} + \dfrac{(19 - 12.86)^2}{12.86}$
$= 6.544$
   e. Reject H_0. There is a relationship between income level and playing the lottery.

CHAPTER 16

16–1 a. Two-tailed because H_1 does not state a direction.
   b.

Adding down, $.000 + .003 + .016 = .019$. This is the largest cumulative probability up to but not exceeding .050, which is half the level of significance. The decision rule is to reject H_0 if the number of plus signs is 2 or less or 10 or more.
   c. Reject H_0; accept H_1. There is a preference.
16–2 a. $H_0: \pi = 0.50, H_1: \pi > 0.50$.
   b. Reject H_0 if $z > 1.645$.
   c. Since 80 is more than $n/2 = 100/2 = 50$, we use:

$$z = \frac{(80 - .50) - .50(100)}{.50\sqrt{100}} = \frac{29.5}{5} = 5.9$$

   d. H_0 is rejected.
   e. The screening was effective.
16–3 H_0: The median $\leq \$2,505, H_1$: The median is more than $\$2,505$. The decision rule is to reject H_0 if $z > 1.645$.

$$z = \frac{(42 - .50) - 32}{.50\sqrt{64}} = \frac{9.5}{4} = 2.38$$

Reject H_0 because 2.38 is larger than 1.645. The median amount spent is more than $\$2,505$.
16–4 a. $n = 10$ (because there was no change for A. A.)

b.

Before	After	Difference	Absolute Difference	Rank	R^-	R^+
17	18	−1	1	1.5	1.5	
21	23	−2	2	3.0	3.0	
25	22	3	3	5.0		5.0
15	25	−10	10	8.0	8.0	
10	28	−18	18	10.0	10.0	
16	16	—	—	—	—	—
10	22	−12	12	9.0	9.0	
20	19	1	1	1.5		1.5
17	20	−3	3	5.0	5.0	
24	30	−6	6	7.0	7.0	
23	26	−3	3	5.0	5.0	
					48.5	6.5

H_0: Production is the same.
H_1: Production has increased.
The sum of the positive signed ranks is 6.5; the negative sum is 48.5. From Appendix B.8, one-tailed test, $n = 10$, the critical value is 10. Since 6.5 is less than 10, reject the null hypothesis and accept the alternate. New procedures did increase production.

c. No assumption regarding the shape of the distribution is necessary.

16–5 H_0: There is no difference in the distances traveled by the XL-5000 and by the D2.

H_1: There is a difference in the distances traveled by the XL-5000 and by the D2.

Do not reject H_0 if the computed z is between 1.96 and −1.96 (from Appendix B.3); otherwise, reject H_0 and accept H_1. $n_1 = 8$, the number of observations in the first sample.

XL-5000		D2	
Distance	Rank	Distance	Rank
252	4	262	9
263	10	242	2
279	15	256	5
273	14	260	8
271	13	258	7
265	11.5	243	3
257	6	239	1
280	16	265	11.5
Total	89.5		46.5

$W = 89.5$

$$z = \frac{89.5 - \dfrac{8(8 + 8 + 1)}{2}}{\sqrt{\dfrac{(8)(8)(8 + 8 + 1)}{12}}}$$

$$= \frac{21.5}{9.52} = 2.26$$

Reject H_0; accept H_1. There is evidence of a difference in the distances traveled by the two golf balls.

16–6

Ranks			
Englewood	West Side	Great Northern	Sylvania
17	5	19	7
20	1	9.5	11
16	3	21	15
13	5	22	9.5
5	2	14	8
18			12

$\Sigma R_1 = 89$ $\Sigma R_2 = 16$ $\Sigma R_3 = 85.5$ $\Sigma R_4 = 62.5$
$n_1 = 6$ $n_2 = 5$ $n_3 = 5$ $n_4 = 6$

H_0: The population distributions are identical.
H_1: The population distributions are not identical.

$$H = \frac{12}{22(22 + 1)}\left[\frac{(89)^2}{6} + \frac{(16)^2}{5} + \frac{(85.5)^2}{5} + \frac{(62.5)^2}{6}\right] - 3(22 + 1)$$
$$= 13.635$$

The critical value of chi-square for $k - 1 = 4 - 1 = 3$ degrees of freedom is 11.345. Since the computed value of 13.635 is greater than 11.345, the null hypothesis is rejected. We conclude that the turnover rates are not the same.

16–7 a.

		Rank			
x	y	x	y	d	d^2
805	23	5.5	1	4.5	20.25
777	62	3.0	9	−6.0	36.00
820	60	8.5	8	0.5	0.25
682	40	1.0	4	−3.0	9.00
777	70	3.0	10	−7.0	49.00
810	28	7.0	2	5.0	25.00
805	30	5.5	3	2.5	6.25
840	42	10.0	5	5.0	25.00
777	55	3.0	7	−4.0	16.00
820	51	8.5	6	2.5	6.25
				0	193.00

$$r_s = 1 - \frac{6(193)}{10(99)} = -.170$$

b. H_0: $\rho = 0$; H_1: $\rho \neq 0$. Reject H_0 if $t < -2.306$ or $t > 2.306$.

$$t = -.170\sqrt{\frac{10 - 2}{1 - (-0.170)^2}} = -0.488$$

H_0 is not rejected. We have not shown a relationship between the two tests.

CHAPTER 17

17–1 1.

Country	Amount (millions of tons)	Index
China	716.5	807.8
Japan	107.2	120.9
United States	88.7	100.0
India	77.6	87.5
Russia	70.4	79.4

China produced 707.8% more than the United States.

2.

Year	Average Hourly Earnings	(a) Index	(b) Index
1995	$11.65	100.0	90.8
2000	14.02	120.3	109.2
2005	16.13	138.5	125.7
2013	19.97	171.4	155.6

a. Average hourly earnings increased 71.4% from 1995 until 2013.

b. Averaging the hourly earnings for the years 1995 and 2000 and using this as the base shows earnings increased by 55.6%.

17–2 a. $P_1 = (\$85/\$75)(100) = 113.3$
$P_2 = (\$45/\$40)(100) = 112.5$
$P = (113.3 + 112.5)/2 = 112.9$

b. $P = (\$130/\$115)(100) = 113.0$

c. $P = \dfrac{\$85(500) + \$45(1,200)}{\$75(500) + \$40(1,200)}(100)$

$= \dfrac{\$96,500}{85,500}(100) = 112.9$

d. $P = \dfrac{\$85(520) + \$45(1,300)}{\$75(520) + \$40(1,300)}(100)$

$= \dfrac{\$102,700}{\$91,000}(100) = 112.9$

e. $P = \sqrt{(112.9)(112.9)} = 112.9$

17–3 a. $P = \dfrac{\$4(9,000) + \$5(200) + \$8(5,000)}{\$3(10,000) + \$1(600) + \$10(3,000)}(100)$

$= \dfrac{\$77,000}{60,600}(100) = 127.1$

b. The value of sales has gone up 27.1% from 2001 to 2013.

17–4 a.

For 2009	
Item	**Weight**
Cotton	$(\$0.25/\$0.20)(100)(.10) = 12.50$
Autos	$(1,200/1,000)(100)(.30) = 36.00$
Money turnover	$(90/80)(100)(.60) = 67.50$
Total	116.00

For 2014	
Item	**Weight**
Cotton	$(\$0.50/\$0.20)(100)(.10) = 25.00$
Autos	$(900/1,000)(100)(.30) = 27.00$
Money turnover	$(75/80)(100)(.60) = 56.25$
Total	108.25

b. Business activity increased 16% from 2004 to 2009. It increased 8.25% from 2004 to 2014.

17–5 a. $14,637, found by ($25,000/170.8)(100)

b. $17,944, found by ($41,200/229.6)(100)

c. In terms of the base period, Jon's salary was $14,637 in 2000 and $17,944 in 2013. This indicates that take-home pay increased at a faster rate than the rate price paid for food, transportation, etc.

17–6 $0.51, found by ($1.00/195.4)(100). The purchasing power has declined by $0.49.

17–7 With 2010 as the base period for both series:

Year	IPI	PPI
2007	111.6	89.9
2008	114.3	96.6
2009	99.5	95.7
2010	100.0	100.0
2011	105.3	103.6
2012	109.4	107.9
2013	111.5	109.4

The Industrial Production Index (IPI) increased 11.5% from 2010 until 2013 and the Producer Price Index (PPI) increased 9.4%. The IPI decreased from 2007 to 2010 and by 2013 returned to its 2007 value. The PPI increased steadily from 2007 until 2013.

CHAPTER 18

18–1

Year	Production (thousands)	Three-Year Moving Total	Three-Year Moving Average
2008	2	—	—
2009	6	12	4
2010	4	15	5
2011	5	12	4
2012	3	18	6
2013	10	—	—

18–2 a.

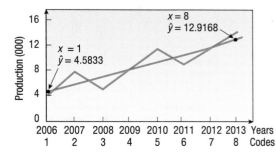

b. $\hat{y} = a + bt = 3.3928 + 1.1905t$ (in thousands)

c. For 2006:

$$\hat{y} = 3.3928 + 1.1905(1) = 4.5833$$

for 2013:

$$\hat{y} = 3.3928 + 1.1905(8) = 12.9168$$

d. For 2016, $t = 11$, so

$$\hat{y} = 3.3928 + 1.1905(11) = 16.4883$$

or 16,488 king-size rockers.

18–3 a.

Year	y	log y	t
2009	2.13	0.3284	1
2010	18.10	1.2577	2
2011	39.80	1.5999	3
2012	81.40	1.9106	4
2013	112.00	2.0492	5

$$b = 0.40945$$
$$a = 0.20081$$

b. About 156.7%. The antilog of 0.40945 is 2.567. Subtracting 1 yields 1.567.

c. About 454.5, found by $\hat{y} = 0.20081 + .40945(6) = 2.65751$. The antilog of 2.65751 is 454.5.

18–4 **a.** The following values are from a software package. Due to rounding, your figures might be slightly different.

	Winter	Spring	Summer	Fall
Mean	119.35	81.66	125.31	74.24
Typical seasonal	119.18	81.55	125.13	74.13

The correction factor is 0.9986.
b. Total sales at Teton Village for the winter season are typically 19.18% above the annual average.

18–5 The forecast value for January of the sixth year is 34.9, found by

$$\hat{y} = 4.4 + 0.5(61) = 34.9$$

Seasonally adjusting the forecast, $34.9(120)/100 = 41.88$. For February, $\hat{y} = 4.4 + 0.5(62) = 35.4$.
Then, $(35.4)95/100 = 33.63$.

CHAPTER 19
19–1

	Poor food	Poor care	Dirty	Nothing to do	No respect	Med. error
Count	84	71	63	45	35	2
Percent	28	24	21	15	12	0
Cum. %	28	52	73	88	100	100

Seventy-three percent of the complaints involve poor food, poor care, or dirty conditions. These are the factors the administrator should address.

19–2 **a.**

Sample Times						
1	2	3	4	Total	Average	Range
1	4	5	2	12	3	4
2	3	2	1	8	2	2
1	7	3	5	16	4	6
					9	12

$$\bar{x} = \frac{9}{3} = 3 \qquad \bar{R} = \frac{12}{3} = 4$$
$$UCL \text{ and } LCL = \bar{x} \pm A_2\bar{R}$$
$$= 3 \pm 0.729(4)$$
$$UCL = 5.916 \qquad LCL = 0.084$$

$$LCL = D_3\bar{R} = 0(4) = 0$$
$$UCL = D_4\bar{R} = 2.282(4) = 9.128$$

b. Yes. Both the mean chart and the range chart indicate that the process is in control.

19–3 $\bar{c} = \frac{25}{12} = 2.083$

$$UCL = 2.083 + 3\sqrt{2.083} = 6.413$$
$$LCL = 2.083 - 3\sqrt{2.083} = -2.247$$

Because LCL is a negative value, we set $LCL = 0$. The shift with seven defects is out of control.
19–4 $P(x \leq 2 | \pi = .30 \text{ and } n = 20) = .036$

CHAPTER 20
20–1

Event	Payoff	Probability of Event	Expected Value
Market rise	$2,200	.60	$1,320
Market decline	1,100	.40	440
			$1,760

20–2 **a.** Suppose the investor purchased Rim Homes stock, and the value of the stock in a bear market dropped to $1,100 as anticipated (Table 20–1). Instead, had the investor purchased Texas Electronics and the market declined, the value of the Texas Electronics stock would be $1,150. The difference of $50, found by $1,150 − $1,100, represents the investor's regret for buying Rim Homes stock.
b. Suppose the investor purchased Texas Electronics stock, and then a bull market developed. The stock rose to $1,900, as anticipated (Table 20–1). However, had the investor bought Kayser Chemicals stock and the market value increased to $2,400 as anticipated, the difference of $500 represents the extra profit the investor could have made by purchasing Kayser Chemicals stock.

20–3

Event	Payoff	Probability of Event	Expected Opportunity Value
Market rise	$500	.60	$300
Market decline	0	.40	0
			$300

20–4 **a.**

Event	Payoff	Probability of Event	Expected Value
Market rise	$1,900	.40	$ 760
Market decline	1,150	.60	690
			$1,450

b.

Event	Payoff	Probability of Event	Expected Value
Market rise	$2,400	.50	$1,200
Market decline	1,000	.50	500
			$1,700

20–5 For probabilities of a market rise (or decline) down to .333, Kayser Chemicals stock would provide the largest expected profit. For probabilities .333 to .143, Rim Homes would be the best buy. For .143 and below, Texas Electronics would give the largest expected profit. Algebraic solutions:

Kayser: $2,400p + (1 - p)1,000$
Rim: $2,200p + (1 - p)1,100$

$$1,400p + 1,000 = 1,100p + 1,100$$
$$p = .333$$

Rim: $2,200p + (1 - p)1,100$
Texas: $1,900p + (1 - p)1,150$

$$1,100p + 1,100 = 750p + 1,150$$
$$p = .143$$

Glossary

Alpha   The probability of a Type I error or the level of significance. Its symbol is the Greek letter α.

Alternate hypothesis   The conclusion we accept when we demonstrate that the null hypothesis is false. It is also called the research hypothesis.

Analysis of variance (ANOVA)   A technique used to test simultaneously whether the means of several populations are equal. It uses the F distribution as the distribution of the test statistic.

Arithmetic mean   The sum of the values divided by the number of values. The symbol for the mean of a sample is $\bar{x}$ and the symbol for a population mean is μ.

Assignable variation   Variation that is not random. It can be eliminated or reduced by investigating the problem and finding the cause.

Autocorrelation   Successive residuals in a time series are correlated.

Bar chart   A graph that shows qualitative classes on the horizontal axis and the class frequencies on the vertical axis. The class frequencies are proportional to the heights of the bars.

Bayes' theorem   Developed by Reverend Bayes in the 1700s, it is designed to find the probability of one event, A, occurring, given that another event, B, has already occurred.

Bias   A possible consequence if certain members of the population are denied the chance to be selected for the sample. As a result, the sample may not be representative of the population.

Binomial probability distribution   A probability distribution based on a discrete random variable. Its major characteristics are:

1. Each outcome can be classified into one of two mutually exclusive categories.
2. The distribution is the result of counting the number of successes.
3. Each trial is independent, meaning that the answer to trial 1 (correct or wrong) in no way affects the answer to trial 2.
4. The probability of a success stays the same from trial to trial.

Block   In a two-way ANOVA, a block effect is a second source of variation, in addition to treatments.

Box plot   A graphic display that shows the general shape of a variable's distribution. It is based on five descriptive statistics: the maximum and minimum values, the first and third quartiles, and the median.

Central limit theorem   As sample size increases, the sampling distribution of the sample mean will approach a normal distribution regardless of the shape of the population.

Chance variation   Variation that is random in nature. This type of variation cannot be completely eliminated unless there is a major change in the techniques, technologies, methods, equipment, or materials used in the process.

Charts   Special graphical formats used to portray a frequency distribution, including histograms, frequency polygons, and cumulative frequency polygons. Other graphical devices used to portray data are bar charts and pie charts.

Chebyshev's theorem   For any set of observations (sample or population), the proportion of the values that lie within k standard deviations of the mean is at least $1 - 1/k^2$, where k is any value greater than 1.

Chi-square distribution   A distribution with these characteristics:

1. Its value can only be positive.
2. There is a family of chi-square distributions, a different one for each different degrees of freedom.
3. The distributions are positively skewed, but as the number of degrees of freedom increases, the distribution approaches the normal distribution.

Chi-square goodness-of-fit test   A test with the objective of determining how well an observed set of frequencies fits an expected set of frequencies. It is concerned with one nominal-scale variable, such as the color of a car.

Class   The interval in which the data are tallied. For example, $4 up to $7 is a class; $7 up to $11 is another class.

Class frequency   The number of observations in each class. If there are 16 observations in the $4 up to $6 class, 16 is the class frequency.

Classical probability   Probability based on the assumption we know the number of possible outcomes and that each of the outcomes is equally likely.

Cluster sampling   A method often used to lower the cost of sampling if the population is dispersed over a wide geographic area. The area is divided into smaller units (counties, precincts, blocks, etc.) called primary units. Then a few primary units are chosen, and a random sample is selected from each primary unit.

Coefficient of determination   The proportion of the total variation in the dependent variable that is explained by the independent variable. It can assume any value between 0 and +1.00 inclusive. This coefficient is computed by squaring the correlation coefficient, r.

Coefficient of multiple determination   The percent of variation in the dependent variable, y, explained by the set of independent variables, $x_1, x_2, x_3, \ldots , x_k$.

Coefficient of skewness   A measure of the lack of symmetry in a distribution. For a symmetric distribution, there is no skewness, so the coefficient of skewness is zero. Otherwise, it is either positive or negative, with the limits of ± 3.0.

Collectively exhaustive   At least one of the events must occur when an experiment is conducted.

GLOSSARY   817

Combination formula A formula to count the number of possible arrangements when the order of the outcomes is not important. For example, the outcome {a, b, c} is considered the same as {c, b, a}.

Conditional probability The likelihood that an event will occur given that another event has occurred.

Confidence interval A range of values constructed from sample data so that the population parameter is likely to occur within that range at a specified probability.

Consumer Price Index An index reported monthly by the U.S. Department of Labor. It describes the change in a market basket of goods and services from the base period of 1982–84 to the present.

Contingency table A table used to classify observations according to two characteristics. If characteristics, such as gender and highest degree earned for a sample of stockbrokers, are cross classified into a table, the result is called a contingency table.

Continuity correction factor Used to improve the accuracy when a continuous distribution is used to estimate a discrete distribution.

Continuous random variable A random variable that may assume an infinite number of values within a given range.

Correlation analysis A group of statistical techniques used to measure the strength of the relationship between two variables.

Correlation coefficient A measure of the strength of association between two variables.

Correlation matrix A listing of all possible simple coefficients of correlation. It consists of the correlations among all the variables.

Critical value A value that is the dividing point between the region where the null hypothesis is not rejected and the region where it is rejected.

Cyclical variation The rise and fall of a time series over periods longer than one year.

Deciles Values of an ordered (minimum to maximum) data set that divide the data into 10 equal parts.

Degrees of freedom The number of items in a sample that are free to vary. Suppose there are two items in a sample, and we know the mean. We are free to specify only one of the two values because the other value is automatically determined (since the two values total twice the mean). Example: If the mean is $6, we are free to choose only one value. Choosing $4 makes the other value $8 because $4 + $8 = 2*($6). So there is 1 degree of freedom in this illustration. We can determine the degrees of freedom by $n - 1 = 2 - 1 = 1$. If n is 4, then there are 3 degrees of freedom, found by $n - 1 = 4 - 1 = 3$.

Dependent samples Dependent samples are characterized by a measurement, then some type of intervention, followed by another measurement. Paired samples are also dependent because the same individual or item is a member of both samples. Example: Ten participants in a marathon were weighed prior to and after competing in the race. We wish to study the mean amount of weight loss.

Dependent variable The variable that is being predicted or estimated.

Descriptive statistics The techniques used to describe the important characteristics of a set of data. This includes organizing the data values into a frequency distribution, computing measures of location, and computing measures of dispersion and skewness.

Discrete random variable A random variable that can assume only certain clearly separated values.

Dot plot A dot plot summarizes the distribution of one variable by stacking dots at points on a number line that shows the values of the variable. A dot plot shows all values.

Dummy variable A qualitative variable. It can assume only one of two possible outcomes.

Empirical probability A concept of probability based on historical information.

Empirical rule For a symmetrical, bell-shaped frequency distribution, approximately 68% of the observations lie within ± 1 standard deviation of the mean; about 95% of the observations lie within ± 2 standard deviations of the mean; and practically all (99.7%) lie within ± 3 standard deviations of the mean.

Episodic variation It is variation that is random in nature, but a cause can be identified.

Event A collection of one or more outcomes of an experiment.

Exhaustive Each observation must fall into one of the categories.

Experiment An activity that is either observed or measured.

Exponential distribution A positively skewed continuous distribution described by the rate parameter, λ.

F distribution It is used as the test statistic for ANOVA problems, as well as others. The major characteristics of the F distribution are:

1. It is never negative.
2. It is a continuous distribution approaching the X-axis but never touching it.
3. It is positively skewed.
4. It is based on two sets of degrees of freedom.
5. Like the t distribution, there is a family of F distributions. There is one distribution for 17 degrees of freedom in the numerator and 9 degrees of freedom in the denominator, there is another F distribution for 7 degrees of freedom in the numerator and 12 degrees of freedom in the denominator, and so on.

Finite-population correction factor (FPC) When sampling without replacement from a finite population, a correction term is used to reduce the standard error of the mean according to the relative size of the sample to the size of the population. The correction factor is used when the sample is more than 5% of a finite population.

Frequency distribution A grouping of data into classes showing the number of observations in each of the mutually exclusive and collectively exhaustive classes.

Frequency table A grouping of qualitative data into mutually exclusive classes showing the number of observations in each class.

General rule of addition Used to find the probabilities of complex events made up of A or B when the events are not mutually exclusive.

General rule of multiplication   Used to find the probabilities of events A and B both happening when the events are not independent.

Geometric mean   The nth root of the product of all the values. It is especially useful for averaging rates of change and index numbers. It minimizes the importance of extreme values. A second use of the geometric mean is to find the mean annual percent change over a period of time.

Global test   A test used to determine if any of the set of independent variables has regression coefficients different from zero.

Histogram   A graphical display of a frequency or relative frequency distribution. The horizontal axis shows the classes. The vertical height of adjacent bars shows the frequency or relative frequency of each class.

Homoscedasticity   The standard error of estimate is the same for all fitted values of the dependent variable.

Hypergeometric distribution   A probability distribution based on a discrete random variable. Its major characteristics are a fixed number of trials, only two possible outcomes, and the probability of success is not the same on each trial.

Hypothesis   A statement or claim about the value of a population parameter. Examples: 40.7% of all persons 65 years old or older live alone. The mean number of people in a car is 1.33.

Hypothesis testing   A statistical procedure, based on sample evidence and probability theory, used to determine whether the statement about the population parameter is reasonable.

Independence   The probability of one event has no effect on the probability of another event.

Independent samples   The samples chosen at random are not related to each other. We wish to study the mean age of the employees at Google and Yahoo. We select a random sample of 28 employees from Google and a sample of 19 employees from Yahoo. A person cannot be an employee in both companies. The samples are independent, that is, unrelated.

Independent variable   A variable that provides the basis for estimation.

Index number   A number that expresses the relative change in price, quantity, or value compared to a base period.

Inferential statistics, also called statistical inference   This facet of statistics deals with estimating a population parameter based on a sample statistic. For example, if a sample of 10 TI-36X solar calculators revealed 2 to be defective, we might infer that 20% of the production is defective.

Interaction   The case in which one independent variable (such as x_2) affects the relationship between another independent variable (x_1) and the dependent variable (y).

Interquartile range   The absolute numerical difference between the first and third quartiles. Fifty percent of a distribution's values occur in this range.

Interval estimate   The interval within which a population parameter probably lies, based on sample information.

Example: According to sample data, the population mean is in the interval between 1.9 and 2.0 pounds.

Interval level of measurement   If one observation is greater than another by a certain amount, and the zero point is arbitrary, the measurement is on an interval scale. For example, the difference between temperatures of 70 degrees and 80 degrees is 10 degrees. Likewise, a temperature of 90 degrees is 10 degrees more than a temperature of 80 degrees, and so on.

Irregular variation   Variation in a time series that is random in nature and does not regularly repeat itself.

Joint probability   A probability that measures the likelihood two or more events will happen concurrently.

Kruskal-Wallis one-way analysis of variance by ranks   A test used when the assumptions for parametric analysis of variance (ANOVA) cannot be met. Its purpose is to test whether several populations are the same. The data must be at least ordinal scale.

Law of large numbers   Over a large number of trials, the empirical probability of an event will approach its true probability.

Least squares method   A technique used to arrive at the regression equation by minimizing the sum of the squares of the vertical distances between the actual y values and the predicted y values.

Level of significance   The probability of rejecting the null hypothesis when it is true.

Linear regression equation   A mathematical equation that defines the relationship between two variables. It has the form $y = a + bx$. It is used to predict y based on a selected x value. y is the dependent variable and x, the independent variable.

Measure of dispersion   A value that shows the spread of a data set. The range, variance, and standard deviation are measures of dispersion.

Measure of location   A single value that is typical of the data. It pinpoints the center of a distribution. The arithmetic mean, weighted mean, median, mode, and geometric mean are measures of location.

Median   The value of the middle observation after all the observations have been arranged from low to high. For example, if observations 6, 9, 4 are rearranged to read 4, 6, 9, the median is 6, the middle value.

Midpoint   The value that divides a class into two equal parts. For the classes $10 up to $20 and $20 up to $30, the midpoints are $15 and $25, respectively.

Mode   The value that appears most frequently in a set of data. For grouped data, it is the midpoint of the class containing the largest number of values.

Multicollinearity   A condition that occurs in multiple regression analysis if the independent variables are themselves correlated.

Multiple regression equation   The relationship in the form of a mathematical equation between several independent variables and a dependent variable. The general form is $\hat{y} = a + b_1x_1 + b_2x_2 + b_3x_3 + \cdots + b_kx_k$. It is used to estimate y given k independent variables, x_i.

Multiplication formula   A formula used to count the number of possible outcomes of an experiment. It states that if there are m ways of doing one thing and n ways of doing another, there are ($m * n$) ways of doing both.

Mutually exclusive   A property of a set of categories such that an individual, object, or measurement is included in only one category.

Nominal level of measurement   The "lowest" level of measurement. Such data can only be classified into categories, and there is no particular order for the categories. For example, it makes no difference whether the categories "male" and "female" are listed in that order, or female first and male second. The categories are mutually exclusive—meaning, in this illustration, that a person cannot be a male and a female at the same time.

Nonparametric or distribution-free tests   Hypothesis tests involving nominal- and ordinal-level data. No assumptions need be made about the shape of the population distribution; that is, we do not assume the population is normally distributed.

Normal probability distribution   A continuous bell-shaped distribution. It is completely described by its mean and standard deviation. Half the observations are less than the mean.

Null hypothesis   A statement about the value of a population parameter that is developed for testing in the face of numerical evidence. It is written as H_0.

One-tailed test   Used when the alternate hypothesis states a direction, such as H_1: $\mu > 40$, read "the population mean is greater than 40." Here the rejection region is only in one tail (the right tail).

Ordinal level of measurement   Data that can be ranked are referred to as ordinal measures. For example, consumer response to the sound of a new speaker might be excellent, very good, fair, or poor.

Outcome   A particular observation or measurement of an experiment.

Outlier   A data point that is unusually far from the others. An accepted rule is to classify an observation as an outlier if it is 1.5 times the interquartile range above the third quartile or below the first quartile.

p-value   The probability of computing a value of the test statistic at least as extreme as the one found in the sample data when the null hypothesis is true.

Parameter   A characteristic of a population.

Percentiles   Values of an ordered (minimum to maximum) data set that divide the data into 100 intervals.

Permutation formula   A formula to count the number of possible arrangements when the order of the outcomes is important. For example, the outcome {a, b, c} is considered different from {c, b, a}.

Pie chart   A chart that shows the proportion or percentage that each class represents of the total number of frequencies.

Point estimate   A single value computed from a sample and used to estimate a population parameter. Example: If the sample mean is 1,020, it is the best estimate of the population mean.

Poisson probability distribution   A discrete probability distribution often used to approximate binomial probabilities when n is large and π is small.

Pooled estimate of the population variance   A weighted average of s_1^2 and s_2^2 used to estimate the common variance σ^2 when using small samples to test the difference between two population means.

Population   The collection, or set, of all individuals, objects, or measurements whose properties are being studied.

Posterior probability   A revised probability based on additional information.

Prior probability   The initial probability based on the present level of information.

Probability   A value between 0 and 1, inclusive, that reports the likelihood that a specific event will occur.

Probability distribution   A listing of all possible outcomes of an experiment and the probability associated with each outcome.

Probability sample   A sample of items or individuals chosen so that each member of the population has a chance of being included in the sample.

Proportion   A fraction or percentage of a sample or a population having a particular trait. If 5 out of 50 in a sample liked a new cereal, the proportion is 5/50, or .10.

Qualitative variables   A nominal-scale variable coded to assume only one nonnumeric outcome or category. For example, a person is considered either employed or unemployed.

Quartiles   Values of an ordered (minimum to maximum) data set that divide the data into four intervals.

Random variable   A variable defined by a probability distribution. It can have different values with their likelihood determined by its probability distribution.

Random variation   The sum of the squared differences between each observation and its treatment mean.

Range   A measure of dispersion found by subtracting the minimum value from the maximum value.

Ratio level of measurement   If the distance between numbers is a constant size, there is a true zero point, and the ratio of two values is meaningful, then the data are ratio scale. For example, the distance between $200 and $300 is $100, and in the case of money there is a true zero point. If you have zero dollars, there is an absence of money (you have none). Also, the ratio between $200 and $300 is meaningful.

Regression equation   An equation that expresses the linear relationship between two variables.

Relative frequency distribution   A frequency distribution that shows the fraction or proportion of the total observations in each class.

Residual   The difference between the actual value of the dependent variable and the estimated value of the dependent variable, that is, $y - \hat{y}$.

Residual variation   It is variation that is random in nature and cannot be identified or predicted.

Sample   A portion, or subset, of the population being studied.

820   GLOSSARY

Sampling distribution of the sample mean   A probability distribution consisting of all possible means of samples of a given size selected from a population.

Sampling error   The difference between a sample statistic and the corresponding population parameter. Example: The sample mean income is $22,100; the population mean is $22,000. The sampling error is $22,100 − $22,000 = $100. This error can be attributed to sampling—that is, chance.

Scatter diagram   Graphical technique used to show the relationship between two variables measured with interval or ratio scales.

Seasonal variation   Patterns of change in a time series within a year. These patterns of change repeat themselves each year.

Secular trend   The smoothed long-term direction of a time series.

Sign test   A test used for dependent samples. The sign test is used to find whether there is a brand preference for two products or to determine whether performance after an experiment is greater than before the experiment. Also, the sign test is used to test a hypothesis about the median.

Significance level   The probability of rejecting the null hypothesis when it is true.

Simple index   The value in the given period divided by the value in the base period. The result is usually multiplied by 100 and reported as a percent.

Simple random sampling   A sampling scheme such that each member of the population has the same chance of being selected as part of the sample.

Spearman's coefficient of rank correlation   A measure of the association between the ranks of two variables. It can range from −1.00 to +1.00. A value of −1.00 indicates a perfect negative association among the ranks and a value of +1.00 means a perfect positive association among the ranks. A value of 0 indicates no association among the ranks.

Special rule of addition   A rule used to find the probabilities of events made up of A or B when the events are mutually exclusive.

Special rule of multiplication   A rule used to find the probability of the joint occurrence of independent events.

Standard deviation   The square root of the variance.

Standard error of estimate   Measures the dispersion of the actual y values about the regression line. It is reported in the same units as the dependent variable.

Statistic   A characteristic of a sample.

Statistics   The science of collecting, organizing, analyzing, and interpreting data for the purpose of making more effective decisions.

Stem-and-leaf display   A method to display a variable's distribution using every value. Values are classified by the data's leading digit. For example, if a data set contains values between 13 and 84, eight classes based on the 10s digit would be used for the stems. The 1s digits would be the leaves.

Stepwise regression   A step-by-step process for finding the regression equation. Only independent variables with non-zero regression coefficients enter the regression equation.

Independent variables are added one at a time to the regression equation.

Stratified random sampling   A population is first divided into subgroups called strata. A sample is then chosen from each stratum. If, for example, the population of interest consisted of all undergraduate students, the sample design might call for sampling 62 freshmen, 51 sophomores, 40 juniors, and 39 seniors.

Subjective concept of probability   The chance of an event happening based on personal estimates such as hunches, opinions, or rumors.

Systematic random sampling   When a population is arranged in some way, such as alphabetically, by height, or in a file drawer, a random starting point is selected, then every kth item becomes a member of the sample. If a sample design called for interviewing every ninth household on Main Street starting with 932 Main, the sample would consist of households at 932 Main, 941 Main, 950 Main, and so on.

t-distribution   Investigated and reported by William S. Gossett in 1908 and published under the pseudonym Student. It is similar to the standard normal distribution presented in Chapter 7. The major characteristics of t are:
1. It is a continuous distribution.
2. It can assume values between minus infinity and plus infinity.
3. It is symmetrical about its mean of zero. However, it is more spread out and flatter at the apex than the standard normal distribution.
4. It approaches the standard normal distribution as n gets larger.
5. There is a family of t distributions. One t distribution exists for a sample of 15 observations, another for 25, and so on.

Test statistic   A value, determined from sample information, used to determine whether to reject the null hypothesis.

Total variation   The sum of the squared differences between each observation and the overall mean.

Treatment   A source of variation. It identifies the several populations being examined.

Treatment variation   The sum of the squared differences between each treatment mean and the grand or overall mean.

Two-tailed test   Used when the alternate hypothesis does not state a direction, such as H_1: $\mu \neq 75$, read "the population mean is not equal to 75." There is a region of rejection in each tail.

Type I error   Occurs when a true H_0 is rejected.

Type II error   Occurs when a false H_0 is not rejected.

Uniform distribution   A continuous distribution that is rectangular in shape. It is completely described by its minimum and maximum values.

Value of perfect information   The difference between the maximum payoff under conditions of certainty and the maximum payoff under uncertainty.

Variance   A measure of dispersion based on the average squared differences from the arithmetic mean.

GLOSSARY

Variance inflation factor   A test used to detect correlation among independent variables.

Weighted index   The prices in the base period and the given period are multiplied by quantities (weights).

Weighted mean   Each value is assigned a relative weight (sometimes a frequency). Each value is multiplied by the weight and then the weighted values are summed. The sum is divided by the sum of the weights.

Wilcoxon rank-sum test   A nonparametric test requiring independent samples. The data must be at least ordinal level.

That is, the data must be capable of being ranked. The test is used when the assumptions for the parametric Student's t test cannot be met. The objective of the test is to find whether two independent samples can be considered as coming from the same population. It is used if the assumptions required for the paired t test cannot be met.

z value   For a random variable that is approximately normally distributed, it is the distance between a selected value and the mean measured in units of the standard deviation.

Index

824   INDEX

INDEX

826   INDEX

INDEX   827

INDEX   829

KEY FORMULAS   Lind, Marchal, and Wathen • *Statistical Techniques in Business & Economics,* 16th edition

CHAPTER 3

• Population mean

$$\mu = \frac{\Sigma x}{N} \qquad \text{[3–1]}$$

• Sample mean, raw data

$$\bar{x} = \frac{\Sigma x}{n} \qquad \text{[3–2]}$$

• Weighted mean

$$\bar{x}_w = \frac{w_1 x_1 + w_2 x_2 + \cdots + w_n x_n}{w_1 + w_2 + \cdots + w_n} \qquad \text{[3–3]}$$

• Geometric mean

$$GM = \sqrt[n]{(x_1)(x_2)(x_3)\cdots(x_n)} \qquad \text{[3–4]}$$

• Geometric mean rate of increase

$$GM = \sqrt[n]{\frac{\text{Value at end of period}}{\text{Value at start of period}}} - 1.0 \qquad \text{[3–5]}$$

• Range

$$\text{Range} = \text{Maximum value} - \text{Minimum value} \qquad \text{[3–6]}$$

• Population variance

$$\sigma^2 = \frac{\Sigma(x - \mu)^2}{N} \qquad \text{[3–7]}$$

• Population standard deviation

$$\sigma = \sqrt{\frac{\Sigma(x - \mu)^2}{N}} \qquad \text{[3–8]}$$

• Sample variance

$$s^2 = \frac{\Sigma(x - \bar{x})^2}{n - 1} \qquad \text{[3–9]}$$

• Sample standard deviation

$$s = \sqrt{\frac{\Sigma(x - \bar{x})^2}{n - 1}} \qquad \text{[3–10]}$$

• Sample mean, grouped data

$$\bar{x} = \frac{\Sigma fM}{n} \qquad \text{[3–11]}$$

• Sample standard deviation, grouped data

$$s = \sqrt{\frac{\Sigma f(M - \bar{x})^2}{n - 1}} \qquad \text{[3–12]}$$

CHAPTER 4

• Location of a percentile

$$L_p = (n + 1)\frac{P}{100} \qquad \text{[4–1]}$$

• Pearson's coefficient of skewness

$$sk = \frac{3(\bar{x} - \text{Median})}{s} \qquad \text{[4–2]}$$

• Software coefficient of skewness

$$sk = \frac{n}{(n - 1)(n - 2)}\left[\Sigma\left(\frac{x - \bar{x}}{s}\right)^3\right] \qquad \text{[4–3]}$$

CHAPTER 5

• Special rule of addition

$$P(A \text{ or } B) = P(A) + P(B) \qquad \text{[5–2]}$$

• Complement rule

$$P(A) = 1 - P(\sim A) \qquad \text{[5–3]}$$

• General rule of addition

$$P(A \text{ or } B) = P(A) + P(B) - P(A \text{ and } B) \qquad \text{[5–4]}$$

• Special rule of multiplication

$$P(A \text{ and } B) = P(A)P(B) \qquad \text{[5–5]}$$

• General rule of multiplication

$$P(A \text{ and } B) = P(A)P(B|A) \qquad \text{[5–6]}$$

• Bayes' Theorem

$$P(A_1|B) = \frac{P(A_1)P(B|A_1)}{P(A_1)P(B|A_1) + P(A_2)P(B|A_2)} \qquad \text{[5–7]}$$

• Multiplication formula

$$\text{Total arrangements} = (m)(n) \qquad \text{[5–8]}$$

• Number of permutations

$$_nP_r = \frac{n!}{(n - r)!} \qquad \text{[5–9]}$$

• Number of combinations

$$_nC_r = \frac{n!}{r!(n - r)!} \qquad \text{[5–10]}$$

CHAPTER 6

• Mean of a probability distribution

$$\mu = \Sigma[xP(x)] \qquad \text{[6–1]}$$

• Variance of a probability distribution

$$\sigma^2 = \Sigma[(x - \mu)^2 P(x)] \qquad \text{[6–2]}$$

• Binomial probability distribution

$$P(x) = {_nC_x}\,\pi^x(1 - \pi)^{n - x} \qquad \text{[6–3]}$$

• Mean of a binomial distribution

$$\mu = n\pi \qquad \text{[6–4]}$$

• Variance of a binomial distribution

$$\sigma^2 = n\pi(1 - \pi) \qquad \text{[6–5]}$$

• Hypergeometric probability distribution

$$P(x) = \frac{(_sC_x)(_{N-s}C_{n-x})}{_NC_n} \qquad \text{[6–6]}$$

• Poisson probability distribution

$$P(x) = \frac{\mu^x e^{-\mu}}{x!} \qquad \text{[6–7]}$$

• Mean of a Poisson distribution

$$\mu = n\pi \qquad \text{[6–8]}$$

CHAPTER 7

• Mean of a uniform distribution

$$\mu = \frac{a + b}{2}$$ **[7–1]**

• Standard deviation of a uniform distribution

$$\sigma = \sqrt{\frac{(b - a)^2}{12}}$$ **[7–2]**

• Uniform probability distribution

$$P(x) = \frac{1}{b - a}$$ **[7–3]**

if $a \le x \le b$ and 0 elsewhere

• Normal probability distribution

$$P(x) = \frac{1}{\sigma \sqrt{2\pi}} e^{-\left[\frac{(x - \mu)^2}{2\sigma^2}\right]}$$ **[7–4]**

• Standard normal value

$$z = \frac{x - \mu}{\sigma}$$ **[7–5]**

• Exponential distribution

$$P(x) = \lambda e^{-\lambda x}$$ **[7–6]**

• Finding a probability using the exponential distribution

$$P(\text{Arrival time} < x) = 1 - e^{-\lambda x}$$ **[7–7]**

CHAPTER 8

• Standard error of mean

$$\sigma_{\bar{x}} = \frac{\sigma}{\sqrt{n}}$$ **[8–1]**

• z-value, μ and σ known

$$z = \frac{\bar{x} - \mu}{\sigma / \sqrt{n}}$$ **[8–2]**

CHAPTER 9

• Confidence interval for μ, with σ known

$$\bar{x} \pm z \frac{\sigma}{\sqrt{n}}$$ **[9–1]**

• Confidence interval for μ, σ unknown

$$\bar{x} \pm t \frac{s}{\sqrt{n}}$$ **[9–2]**

• Sample proportion

$$p = \frac{x}{n}$$ **[9–3]**

• Confidence interval for proportion

$$p \pm z \sqrt{\frac{p(1 - p)}{n}}$$ **[9–4]**

• Sample size for estimating mean

$$n = \left(\frac{z\sigma}{E}\right)^2$$ **[9–5]**

• Sample size for a proportion

$$n = \pi(1 - \pi)\left(\frac{z}{E}\right)^2$$ **[9–6]**

CHAPTER 10

• Testing a mean, σ known

$$z = \frac{\bar{x} - \mu}{\sigma / \sqrt{n}}$$ **[10–1]**

• Testing a mean, σ unknown

$$t = \frac{\bar{x} - \mu}{s / \sqrt{n}}$$ **[10–2]**

• Type II error

$$z = \frac{\bar{x}_c - \mu_1}{\sigma / \sqrt{n}}$$ **[10–3]**

CHAPTER 11

• Variance of the distribution of difference in means

$$\sigma^2_{\bar{x}_1 - \bar{x}_2} = \frac{\sigma^2_1}{n_1} + \frac{\sigma^2_2}{n_2}$$ **[11–1]**

• Two-sample test of means, known σ

$$z = \frac{\bar{x}_1 - \bar{x}_2}{\sqrt{\dfrac{\sigma^2_1}{n_1} + \dfrac{\sigma^2_2}{n_2}}}$$ **[11–2]**

• Pooled variance

$$s^2_p = \frac{(n_1 - 1) s^2_1 + (n_2 - 1) s^2_2}{n_1 + n_2 - 2}$$ **[11–3]**

• Two-sample test of means, unknown but equal σ^2s

$$t = \frac{\bar{x}_1 - \bar{x}_2}{\sqrt{s^2_p\left(\dfrac{1}{n_1} + \dfrac{1}{n_2}\right)}}$$ **[11–4]**

• Two-sample tests of means, unknown and unequal σ^2s

$$t = \frac{\bar{x}_1 - \bar{x}_2}{\sqrt{\dfrac{s^2_1}{n_1} + \dfrac{s^2_2}{n_2}}}$$ **[11–5]**

• Degrees of freedom for unequal variance test

$$df = \frac{[(s^2_1/n_1) + (s^2_2/n_2)]^2}{\dfrac{(s^2_1/n_1)^2}{n_1 - 1} + \dfrac{(s^2_2/n_2)^2}{n_2 - 1}}$$ **[11–6]**

• Paired t test

$$t = \frac{\bar{d}}{s_d / \sqrt{n}}$$ **[11–7]**

CHAPTER 12

• Test for comparing two variances

$$F = \frac{s^2_1}{s^2_2}$$ **[12–1]**

• Sum of squares, total

$$SS\ \text{total} = \Sigma (x - \bar{x}_G)^2$$ **[12–2]**

- Sum of squares, error

$$SSE = \Sigma(x - \bar{x}_c)^2 \qquad \text{[12–3]}$$

- Sum of squares, treatments

$$SST = SS\ total - SSE \qquad \text{[12–4]}$$

- Confidence interval for differences in treatment means

$$(\bar{x}_1 - \bar{x}_2) \pm t\sqrt{MSE\left(\frac{1}{n_1} + \frac{1}{n_2}\right)} \qquad \text{[12–5]}$$

- Sum of squares, blocks

$$SSB = k\Sigma(\bar{x}_b - \bar{x}_G)^2 \qquad \text{[12–6]}$$

- Sum of squares error, two-way ANOVA

$$SSE = SS\ total - SST - SSB \qquad \text{[12–7]}$$

CHAPTER 13

- Correlation coefficient

$$r = \frac{\Sigma(x - \bar{x})(y - \bar{y})}{(n-1)\,s_x s_y} \qquad \text{[13–1]}$$

- Test for significant correlation

$$t = \frac{r\sqrt{n-2}}{\sqrt{1 - r^2}} \qquad \text{[13–2]}$$

- Linear regression equation

$$\hat{y} = a + bx \qquad \text{[13–3]}$$

- Slope of the regression line

$$b = r\frac{s_y}{s_x} \qquad \text{[13–4]}$$

- Intercept of the regression line

$$a = \bar{y} - b\bar{x} \qquad \text{[13–5]}$$

- Test for a zero slope

$$t = \frac{b - 0}{s_b} \qquad \text{[13–6]}$$

- Standard error of estimate

$$s_{y \cdot x} = \sqrt{\frac{\Sigma(y - \hat{y})^2}{n - 2}} \qquad \text{[13–7]}$$

- Coefficient of determination

$$r^2 = \frac{SSR}{SS\ Total} = 1 - \frac{SSE}{SS\ Total} \qquad \text{[13–8]}$$

- Standard error of estimate

$$s_{y \cdot x} = \sqrt{\frac{SSE}{n - 2}} \qquad \text{[13–9]}$$

- Confidence interval

$$\hat{y} \pm t s_{y \cdot x}\sqrt{\frac{1}{n} + \frac{(x - \bar{x})^2}{\Sigma(x - \bar{x})^2}} \qquad \text{[13–10]}$$

- Prediction interval

$$\hat{y} \pm t s_{y \cdot x}\sqrt{1 + \frac{1}{n} + \frac{(x - \bar{x})^2}{\Sigma(x - \bar{x})^2}} \qquad \text{[13–11]}$$

CHAPTER 14

- Multiple regression equation

$$\hat{y} = a + b_1 x_1 + b_2 x_2 + \cdots + b_k x_k \qquad \text{[14–1]}$$

- Multiple standard error of estimate

$$s_{y \cdot 123\ldots k} = \sqrt{\frac{\Sigma(y - \hat{y})^2}{n - (k + 1)}} = \sqrt{\frac{SSE}{n - (k + 1)}} \qquad \text{[14–2]}$$

- Coefficient of multiple determination

$$R^2 = \frac{SSR}{SS\ total} \qquad \text{[14–3]}$$

- Adjusted coefficient of determination

$$R^2_{adj} = 1 - \frac{\dfrac{SSE}{n - (k + 1)}}{\dfrac{SS\ total}{n - 1}} \qquad \text{[14–4]}$$

- Global test of hypothesis

$$F = \frac{SSR/k}{SSE/[n - (k + 1)]} \qquad \text{[14–5]}$$

- Testing for a particular regression coefficient

$$t = \frac{b_i - 0}{s_{b_i}} \qquad \text{[14–6]}$$

- Variance inflation factor

$$VIF = \frac{1}{1 - R_j^2} \qquad \text{[14–7]}$$

CHAPTER 15

- Test of hypothesis, one proportion

$$z = \frac{p - \pi}{\sqrt{\dfrac{\pi(1 - \pi)}{n}}} \qquad \text{[15–1]}$$

- Two-sample test of proportions

$$z = \frac{p_1 - p_2}{\sqrt{\dfrac{p_c(1 - p_c)}{n_1} + \dfrac{p_c(1 - p_c)}{n_2}}} \qquad \text{[15–2]}$$

- Pooled proportion

$$p_c = \frac{x_1 + x_2}{n_1 + n_2} \qquad \text{[15–3]}$$

- Chi-square test statistic

$$\chi^2 = \Sigma\left[\frac{(f_o - f_e)^2}{f_e}\right] \qquad \text{[15–4]}$$

- Expected frequency

$$f_e = \frac{(\text{Row total})(\text{Column total})}{\text{Grand total}} \qquad \text{[15–5]}$$

CHAPTER 16

- Sign test, $n > 10$

$$z = \frac{(x \pm .50) - \mu}{\sigma} \qquad \text{[16–1]}$$

- Wilcoxon rank-sum test

$$z = \frac{W - \dfrac{n_1(n_1 + n_2 + 1)}{2}}{\sqrt{\dfrac{n_1 n_2(n_1 + n_2 + 1)}{12}}}$$ **[16–4]**

- Kruskal-Wallis test

$$H = \frac{12}{n(n + 1)}\left[\frac{(\Sigma R_1)^2}{n_1} + \frac{(\Sigma R_2)^2}{n_2} + \cdots + \frac{(\Sigma R_k)^2}{n_k}\right]$$
$$- 3(n + 1)$$ **[16–5]**

- Spearman coefficient of rank correlation

$$r_s = 1 - \frac{6\Sigma d^2}{n(n^2 - 1)}$$ **[16–6]**

- Hypothesis test, rank correlation

$$t = r_s\sqrt{\frac{n - 2}{1 - r_s^2}}$$ **[16–7]**

CHAPTER 17
- Simple index

$$P = \frac{p_t}{p_0}(100)$$ **[17–1]**

- Simple average of price relatives

$$P = \frac{\Sigma P_i}{n}$$ **[17–2]**

- Simple aggregate index

$$P = \frac{\Sigma p_t}{\Sigma p_0}(100)$$ **[17–3]**

- Laspeyres' price index

$$P = \frac{\Sigma p_t q_0}{\Sigma p_0 q_0}(100)$$ **[17–4]**

- Paasche's price index

$$P = \frac{\Sigma p_t q_t}{\Sigma p_0 q_t}(100)$$ **[17–5]**

- Fisher's ideal index

$$\sqrt{(\text{Laspeyres' price index})(\text{Paasche's price index})}$$ **[17–6]**

- Value index

$$V = \frac{\Sigma p_t q_t}{\Sigma p_0 q_0}(100)$$ **[17–7]**

- Real income

$$\text{Real income} = \frac{\text{Money income}}{\text{CPI}}(100)$$ **[17–8]**

- Using an index as a deflator

$$\text{Deflated sales} = \frac{\text{Actual sales}}{\text{Index}}(100)$$ **[17–9]**

- Purchasing power

$$\text{Purchasing power} = \frac{\$1}{\text{CPI}}(100)$$ **[17–10]**

CHAPTER 18
- Linear trend

$$\hat{y} = a + bt$$ **[18–1]**

- Log trend equation

$$\log \hat{y} = \log a + \log b(t)$$ **[18–2]**

- Correction factor for adjusting quarterly means

$$\text{Correction factor} = \frac{4.00}{\text{Total of four means}}$$ **[18–3]**

- Durbin-Watson statistic

$$d = \frac{\displaystyle\sum_{t=2}^{n}(e_t - e_{t-1})^2}{\displaystyle\sum_{t=1}^{n} e_t^2}$$ **[18–4]**

CHAPTER 19
- Grand mean

$$\bar{\bar{x}} = \frac{\Sigma \bar{x}}{k}$$ **[19–1]**

- Control limits, mean

$$\text{UCL} = \bar{\bar{x}} + A_2\bar{R} \qquad \text{LCL} = \bar{\bar{x}} - A_2\bar{R}$$ **[19–4]**

- Control limits, range

$$\text{UCL} = D_4\bar{R} \qquad \text{LCL} = D_3\bar{R}$$ **[19–5]**

- Mean proportion defective

$$p = \frac{\text{Total number defective}}{\text{Total number of items sampled}}$$ **[19–6]**

- Control limits, proportion

$$\text{UCL and LCL} = p \pm 3\sqrt{\frac{p(1 - p)}{n}}$$ **[19–8]**

- Control limits, c-bar chart

$$\text{UCL and LCL} = \bar{c} \pm 3\sqrt{\bar{c}}$$ **[19–9]**

CHAPTER 20 (ON THE WEBSITE: www.mhhe.com/lind16e)
- Expected monetary value

$$\text{EMV}(A_i) = \Sigma[P(S_j) \cdot V(A_i, S_j)]$$ **[20–1]**

- Expected opportunity loss

$$\text{EOL}(A_i) = \Sigma[P(S_j) \cdot R(A_i, S_j)]$$ **[20–2]**

- Expected value of perfect information

$$\text{EVPI} = \text{Expected value under conditions of certainty}$$
$$- \text{Expected value of optimal decision under}$$
$$\text{conditions of uncertainty}$$ **[20–3]**

Areas under the Normal Curve

Example:
If $z = 1.96$, then
$P(0$ to $z) = 0.4750$.

0.4750

$z \longrightarrow$ 0   1.96

z	0.00	0.01	0.02	0.03	0.04	0.05	0.06	0.07	0.08	0.09
0.0	0.0000	0.0040	0.0080	0.0120	0.0160	0.0199	0.0239	0.0279	0.0319	0.0359
0.1	0.0398	0.0438	0.0478	0.0517	0.0557	0.0596	0.0636	0.0675	0.0714	0.0753
0.2	0.0793	0.0832	0.0871	0.0910	0.0948	0.0987	0.1026	0.1064	0.1103	0.1141
0.3	0.1179	0.1217	0.1255	0.1293	0.1331	0.1368	0.1406	0.1443	0.1480	0.1517
0.4	0.1554	0.1591	0.1628	0.1664	0.1700	0.1736	0.1772	0.1808	0.1844	0.1879
0.5	0.1915	0.1950	0.1985	0.2019	0.2054	0.2088	0.2123	0.2157	0.2190	0.2224
0.6	0.2257	0.2291	0.2324	0.2357	0.2389	0.2422	0.2454	0.2486	0.2517	0.2549
0.7	0.2580	0.2611	0.2642	0.2673	0.2704	0.2734	0.2764	0.2794	0.2823	0.2852
0.8	0.2881	0.2910	0.2939	0.2967	0.2995	0.3023	0.3051	0.3078	0.3106	0.3133
0.9	0.3159	0.3186	0.3212	0.3238	0.3264	0.3289	0.3315	0.3340	0.3365	0.3389
1.0	0.3413	0.3438	0.3461	0.3485	0.3508	0.3531	0.3554	0.3577	0.3599	0.3621
1.1	0.3643	0.3665	0.3686	0.3708	0.3729	0.3749	0.3770	0.3790	0.3810	0.3830
1.2	0.3849	0.3869	0.3888	0.3907	0.3925	0.3944	0.3962	0.3980	0.3997	0.4015
1.3	0.4032	0.4049	0.4066	0.4082	0.4099	0.4115	0.4131	0.4147	0.4162	0.4177
1.4	0.4192	0.4207	0.4222	0.4236	0.4251	0.4265	0.4279	0.4292	0.4306	0.4319
1.5	0.4332	0.4345	0.4357	0.4370	0.4382	0.4394	0.4406	0.4418	0.4429	0.4441
1.6	0.4452	0.4463	0.4474	0.4484	0.4495	0.4505	0.4515	0.4525	0.4535	0.4545
1.7	0.4554	0.4564	0.4573	0.4582	0.4591	0.4599	0.4608	0.4616	0.4625	0.4633
1.8	0.4641	0.4649	0.4656	0.4664	0.4671	0.4678	0.4686	0.4693	0.4699	0.4706
1.9	0.4713	0.4719	0.4726	0.4732	0.4738	0.4744	0.4750	0.4756	0.4761	0.4767
2.0	0.4772	0.4778	0.4783	0.4788	0.4793	0.4798	0.4803	0.4808	0.4812	0.4817
2.1	0.4821	0.4826	0.4830	0.4834	0.4838	0.4842	0.4846	0.4850	0.4854	0.4857
2.2	0.4861	0.4864	0.4868	0.4871	0.4875	0.4878	0.4881	0.4884	0.4887	0.4890
2.3	0.4893	0.4896	0.4898	0.4901	0.4904	0.4906	0.4909	0.4911	0.4913	0.4916
2.4	0.4918	0.4920	0.4922	0.4925	0.4927	0.4929	0.4931	0.4932	0.4934	0.4936
2.5	0.4938	0.4940	0.4941	0.4943	0.4945	0.4946	0.4948	0.4949	0.4951	0.4952
2.6	0.4953	0.4955	0.4956	0.4957	0.4959	0.4960	0.4961	0.4962	0.4963	0.4964
2.7	0.4965	0.4966	0.4967	0.4968	0.4969	0.4970	0.4971	0.4972	0.4973	0.4974
2.8	0.4974	0.4975	0.4976	0.4977	0.4977	0.4978	0.4979	0.4979	0.4980	0.4981
2.9	0.4981	0.4982	0.4982	0.4983	0.4984	0.4984	0.4985	0.4985	0.4986	0.4986
3.0	0.4987	0.4987	0.4987	0.4988	0.4988	0.4989	0.4989	0.4989	0.4990	0.4990

Student's *t* Distribution

Confidence interval

Left-tailed test

Right-tailed test

Two-tailed test

(continued)

	Confidence Intervals, *c*							Confidence Intervals, *c*					
	80%	90%	95%	98%	99%	99.9%		80%	90%	95%	98%	99%	99.9%
df	Level of Significance for One-Tailed Test, α						*df*	Level of Significance for One-Tailed Test, α					
(degrees of freedom)	0.10	0.05	0.025	0.01	0.005	0.0005	(degrees of freedom)	0.10	0.05	0.025	0.01	0.005	0.0005
	Level of Significance for Two-Tailed Test, α							Level of Significance for Two-Tailed Test, α					
	0.20	0.10	0.05	0.02	0.01	0.001		0.20	0.10	0.05	0.02	0.01	0.001
1	3.078	6.314	12.706	31.821	63.657	636.619	36	1.306	1.688	2.028	2.434	2.719	3.582
2	1.886	2.920	4.303	6.965	9.925	31.599	37	1.305	1.687	2.026	2.431	2.715	3.574
3	1.638	2.353	3.182	4.541	5.841	12.924	38	1.304	1.686	2.024	2.429	2.712	3.566
4	1.533	2.132	2.776	3.747	4.604	8.610	39	1.304	1.685	2.023	2.426	2.708	3.558
5	1.476	2.015	2.571	3.365	4.032	6.869	40	1.303	1.684	2.021	2.423	2.704	3.551
6	1.440	1.943	2.447	3.143	3.707	5.959	41	1.303	1.683	2.020	2.421	2.701	3.544
7	1.415	1.895	2.365	2.998	3.499	5.408	42	1.302	1.682	2.018	2.418	2.698	3.538
8	1.397	1.860	2.306	2.896	3.355	5.041	43	1.302	1.681	2.017	2.416	2.695	3.532
9	1.383	1.833	2.262	2.821	3.250	4.781	44	1.301	1.680	2.015	2.414	2.692	3.526
10	1.372	1.812	2.228	2.764	3.169	4.587	45	1.301	1.679	2.014	2.412	2.690	3.520
11	1.363	1.796	2.201	2.718	3.106	4.437	46	1.300	1.679	2.013	2.410	2.687	3.515
12	1.356	1.782	2.179	2.681	3.055	4.318	47	1.300	1.678	2.012	2.408	2.685	3.510
13	1.350	1.771	2.160	2.650	3.012	4.221	48	1.299	1.677	2.011	2.407	2.682	3.505
14	1.345	1.761	2.145	2.624	2.977	4.140	49	1.299	1.677	2.010	2.405	2.680	3.500
15	1.341	1.753	2.131	2.602	2.947	4.073	50	1.299	1.676	2.009	2.403	2.678	3.496
16	1.337	1.746	2.120	2.583	2.921	4.015	51	1.298	1.675	2.008	2.402	2.676	3.492
17	1.333	1.740	2.110	2.567	2.898	3.965	52	1.298	1.675	2.007	2.400	2.674	3.488
18	1.330	1.734	2.101	2.552	2.878	3.922	53	1.298	1.674	2.006	2.399	2.672	3.484
19	1.328	1.729	2.093	2.539	2.861	3.883	54	1.297	1.674	2.005	2.397	2.670	3.480
20	1.325	1.725	2.086	2.528	2.845	3.850	55	1.297	1.673	2.004	2.396	2.668	3.476
21	1.323	1.721	2.080	2.518	2.831	3.819	56	1.297	1.673	2.003	2.395	2.667	3.473
22	1.321	1.717	2.074	2.508	2.819	3.792	57	1.297	1.672	2.002	2.394	2.665	3.470
23	1.319	1.714	2.069	2.500	2.807	3.768	58	1.296	1.672	2.002	2.392	2.663	3.466
24	1.318	1.711	2.064	2.492	2.797	3.745	59	1.296	1.671	2.001	2.391	2.662	3.463
25	1.316	1.708	2.060	2.485	2.787	3.725	60	1.296	1.671	2.000	2.390	2.660	3.460
26	1.315	1.706	2.056	2.479	2.779	3.707	61	1.296	1.670	2.000	2.389	2.659	3.457
27	1.314	1.703	2.052	2.473	2.771	3.690	62	1.295	1.670	1.999	2.388	2.657	3.454
28	1.313	1.701	2.048	2.467	2.763	3.674	63	1.295	1.669	1.998	2.387	2.656	3.452
29	1.311	1.699	2.045	2.462	2.756	3.659	64	1.295	1.669	1.998	2.386	2.655	3.449
30	1.310	1.697	2.042	2.457	2.750	3.646	65	1.295	1.669	1.997	2.385	2.654	3.447
31	1.309	1.696	2.040	2.453	2.744	3.633	66	1.295	1.668	1.997	2.384	2.652	3.444
32	1.309	1.694	2.037	2.449	2.738	3.622	67	1.294	1.668	1.996	2.383	2.651	3.442
33	1.308	1.692	2.035	2.445	2.733	3.611	68	1.294	1.668	1.995	2.382	2.650	3.439
34	1.307	1.691	2.032	2.441	2.728	3.601	69	1.294	1.667	1.995	2.382	2.649	3.437
35	1.306	1.690	2.030	2.438	2.724	3.591	70	1.294	1.667	1.994	2.381	2.648	3.435

(continued-top right)   *(continued)*

Student's *t* Distribution (*concluded*)

(*continued*)

df (degrees of freedom)	Confidence Intervals, c					
	80%	90%	95%	98%	99%	99.9%
	Level of Significance for One-Tailed Test, α					
	0.10	0.05	0.025	0.01	0.005	0.0005
	Level of Significance for Two-Tailed Test, α					
	0.20	0.10	0.05	0.02	0.01	0.001
71	1.294	1.667	1.994	2.380	2.647	3.433
72	1.293	1.666	1.993	2.379	2.646	3.431
73	1.293	1.666	1.993	2.379	2.645	3.429
74	1.293	1.666	1.993	2.378	2.644	3.427
75	1.293	1.665	1.992	2.377	2.643	3.425
76	1.293	1.665	1.992	2.376	2.642	3.423
77	1.293	1.665	1.991	2.376	2.641	3.421
78	1.292	1.665	1.991	2.375	2.640	3.420
79	1.292	1.664	1.990	2.374	2.640	3.418
80	1.292	1.664	1.990	2.374	2.639	3.416
81	1.292	1.664	1.990	2.373	2.638	3.415
82	1.292	1.664	1.989	2.373	2.637	3.413
83	1.292	1.663	1.989	2.372	2.636	3.412
84	1.292	1.663	1.989	2.372	2.636	3.410
85	1.292	1.663	1.988	2.371	2.635	3.409
86	1.291	1.663	1.988	2.370	2.634	3.407
87	1.291	1.663	1.988	2.370	2.634	3.406
88	1.291	1.662	1.987	2.369	2.633	3.405
89	1.291	1.662	1.987	2.369	2.632	3.403
90	1.291	1.662	1.987	2.368	2.632	3.402
91	1.291	1.662	1.986	2.368	2.631	3.401
92	1.291	1.662	1.986	2.368	2.630	3.399
93	1.291	1.661	1.986	2.367	2.630	3.398
94	1.291	1.661	1.986	2.367	2.629	3.397
95	1.291	1.661	1.985	2.366	2.629	3.396
96	1.290	1.661	1.985	2.366	2.628	3.395
97	1.290	1.661	1.985	2.365	2.627	3.394
98	1.290	1.661	1.984	2.365	2.627	3.393
99	1.290	1.660	1.984	2.365	2.626	3.392
100	1.290	1.660	1.984	2.364	2.626	3.390
120	1.289	1.658	1.980	2.358	2.617	3.373
140	1.288	1.656	1.977	2.353	2.611	3.361
160	1.287	1.654	1.975	2.350	2.607	3.352
180	1.286	1.653	1.973	2.347	2.603	3.345
200	1.286	1.653	1.972	2.345	2.601	3.340
∞	1.282	1.645	1.960	2.326	2.576	3.291

connect®
|BUSINESS STATISTICS

The integrated solutions for Lind/Marchal/Wathen's *Statistical Techniques in Business & Economics,16e,* have been specifically designed to help you achieve your course goals of improving student readiness, enhancing student engagement, and increasing their comprehension of content.

Connect® Business Statistics provides a wide array of tools and content to improve instructor productivity and student performance. In fact, the aggregated results of 34 *Connect* adoptions showed an 11% improvement in pass rates, a 16% improvement in retention, two times as many students receiving an A, and 77% reduction in instructor grading time.

FEATURES

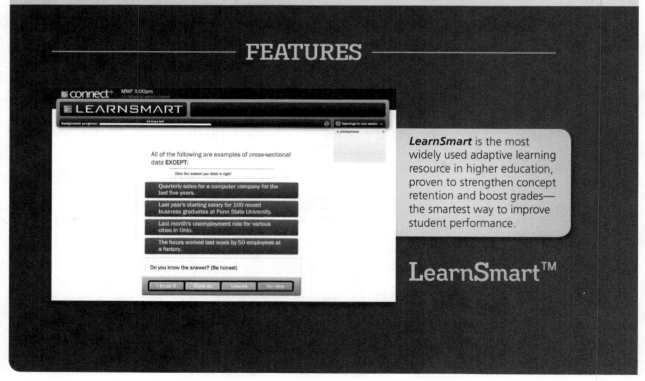

LearnSmart is the most widely used adaptive learning resource in higher education, proven to strengthen concept retention and boost grades—the smartest way to improve student performance.

LearnSmart™

Get Connected.

SmartBook™

An extension of *LearnSmart*, **SmartBook** is an adaptive eBook that helps students focus their study time more effectively. As the student reads, *SmartBook* assesses comprehension and dynamically highlights where they need to study more.

End-of-Chapter and Test Bank Content

Connect Business Statistics includes both static and algorithmic versions of end-of-chapter problems and test bank questions.

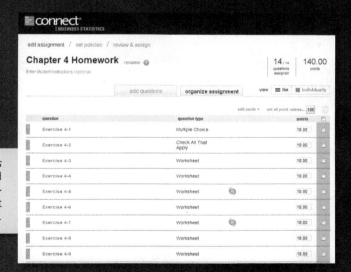

Get Engaged.

Detailed Feedback

Connect Business Statistics helps students learn by providing complete step-by-step solutions for every problem, and you decide when students receive the solutions. These solutions can then be accessed before an exam so students can use them as a study tool for their tests.

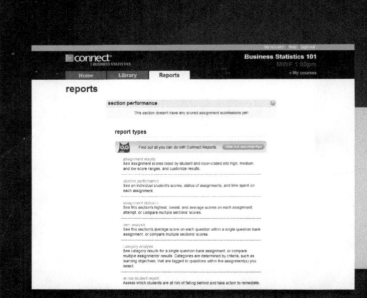

Reporting

Connect Business Statistics generates comprehensive reports and graphs that provide instructors with an instant view of the performance of individual students, a specific section, or multiple sections. Since all content is mapped to learning outcomes, *Connect* reporting is ideal for accreditation or other administrative documentation.